MW00856365

Seismic Attributes for Prospect Identification and Reservoir Characterization

Satinder Chopra

Kurt J. Marfurt

SEG Geophysical Developments Series No. 11

Stephen J. Hill, series editor and volume editor

ISBN 0-931830-41-9 (Series)
ISBN 1-56080-141-7 (Volume)

P.O. Box 702740
Tulsa, OK U.S.A. 74170-2740

Published 2007
Printed in the U.S.A.

Library of Congress Cataloging-in-Publication Data

Chopra, Satinder.

Seismic attributes for prospect identification and reservoir characterization / Satinder Chopra, Kurt J. Marfurt.

p. cm. -- (SEG geophysical developments series ; no. 11)

Includes bibliographical references and index.

ISBN 1-56080-141-7 (volume) -- ISBN 0-931830-41-9 (series)

1. Seismic reflection method. 2. Seismic prospecting. I. Marfurt, K. J. II. Title.

QE539.C52 2007
622'.1592--dc22

2007024043

To our families

Table of Contents

About the Authors

Satinder Chopra is manager of reservoir services at Arcis Corporation, Calgary, Alberta, Canada. He joined the Oil and Natural Gas Corporation Limited (ONGC) of India in 1984 and worked there until 1997. In 1998, he joined CTC Pulsonic in Calgary, which later became Scott Pickford and Core Laboratories Reservoir Technologies. In the last 22 years, Chopra has worked in regular seismic processing, and interactive interpretation but has spent more time in special processing of seismic data involving seismic attributes, including coherence and textures, seismic inversion, AVO, VSP processing, and frequency enhancement of seismic data. His research interests focus on techniques aimed at characterization of reservoirs. He has published five books and more than 100 papers and abstracts and enjoys giving presentations. He is coauthor, with Kurt J. Marfurt, of *Seismic Attribute Mapping of Structure and Stratigraphy* (SEG Distinguished Instructor Series No. 9), which accompanied the 2006 SEG/EAGE Distinguished Instructor Short Course presented by Marfurt.

Chopra received M.S. and M.Phil. degrees in physics from Himachal Pradesh University, Shimla, India. He is chairman of the SEG Publications Committee, is on the editorial board of SEG's THE LEADING EDGE, and is editor of the CSEG *Recorder*. He received several awards at ONGC, and he and his colleagues have received the CSEG Best Poster Awards in successive years from 2002 through 2005. Chopra is a member of SEG, CSEG, EAGE, AAPG, the Association of Professional Engineers, Geologists and Geophysicists of Alberta, and the Texas Board of Professional Geoscientists. He resides in Calgary with his wife and two children.

Kurt J. Marfurt began his geophysical career as an assistant professor teaching mining geophysics at Columbia University's Henry Krumb School of Mines in New York. After five years, he joined Amoco at its Tulsa Research Center. Through successive reorganizations at Amoco, Marfurt obtained diverse experience in seismic modeling, migration, signal analysis, basin analysis, seismic-attribute analysis, reflection tomography, seismic inversion, and multicomponent data analysis. Through Amoco, he won five patents, two in seismic coherence technology. Marfurt joined the University of Houston in 1999 as a professor in the Department of Geosciences and as director of the Center for Applied Geosciences and Energy, where his primary emphasis is on development and calibration of new seismic-attribute technology.

Marfurt is the author of several dozen articles and coeditor of two books published by SEG. He was the instructor for the 2006 SEG/EAGE Distinguished Instructor Short Course and was coauthor, with Satinder Chopra, of *Seismic Attribute Mapping of Structure and Stratigraphy* (SEG Distinguished Instructor Series No. 9), which accompanied the 2006 DISC presentations. Marfurt received the SEG Best Presentation Award for work on seismic modeling (1989) and SEG Best Paper Award for work on seismic coherence (1999). He is a member of GSH, SEG, EAGE, AAPG, and AGU and has served for 17 years as an associate editor or assistant editor of GEOPHYSICS. He resides in Houston with his wife and has two grown daughters.

Acknowledgments

This work began while Satinder Chopra worked for Coherence Technology Company (CTC), which later became part of Core Laboratories. Chopra is particularly indebted to Vasudhaven Sudhakar (Sudha), who first introduced him to coherence-cube technology. Sudhakar's belief in Chopra's abilities sustained him in this work, wherein the intriguing and fascinating aspects of an emerging technology are revealed. Chopra also is indebted to his former CTC/Core Laboratories colleagues Bob Stevens, Laura Evins, and Vladimir Alexeev, who were always willing to help. Thane McKay and Rob Howey have been particularly encouraging and supportive of this writing effort and are gratefully acknowledged. Several examples included in the text have been borrowed from the work of Chopra's other former colleagues, which he and Kurt J. Marfurt gratefully acknowledge.

Chopra thanks his parents, who nurtured in him a thirst for knowledge which continues. He thanks the love of his life, his wife, Amrita, for her love, encouragement, and personal sacrifice, without which he would not have been able to accomplish this work. Special thanks go to his two children. A lot of precious time, which was rightfully theirs, was spent in the writing of this book, he says.

Marfurt, who says his strength is in recognizing if not initiating good ideas, joined this book project after Chopra produced a first draft. Marfurt is particularly indebted to his students and colleagues at Allied Geophysical Labs, University of Houston, who helped to write, debug, calibrate, proofread and, of course, reject many of the concepts that became part of this book. Specifically, he wishes to recognize the contributions of Charlotte Sullivan, Chuck Blumentritt, and Peter Bartok, who kept him honest by grounding him in geology, and Saleh Al-Dossary, Jianlei Liu, Hao Guo, Gabriel Perez, and Cory Hoelting, who helped with algorithm development. Many of the examples come from thesis work by UH students, including Yomi Oyodele, Claudio d'Agosto, Prasad Jyosula, Ivana Lazarevic, Yves Simon, Marija Djordveic, and Joel Famini.

After 32 years of marriage, Marfurt sincerely thanks his wife, Stephanie, for her longtime support and understanding. Although he says he may have rocks in his head, it is Stephanie who is in his heart.

Chopra and Marfurt thank Stephen J. Hill, self-proclaimed "gonzo" editor, for helping to make this book readable for a significantly broader audience than would have been otherwise possible. In his double role as SEG Geophysical Developments Series editor and as volume editor for this book, Hill spent weeks carefully reading and critiquing each chapter of the manuscript. The authors thank Charlotte Sullivan of UH and Susan Nissen of Kansas Geological Survey for reading Chapters 11 through 15 for geologic veracity and Gennady Goloshubin of UH for helping with the mathematics of Chapter 6. Robert E. Sheriff inspired the inclusion of a simple glossary of technical terms and later not only carefully edited it but also made several valuable suggestions. The authors gratefully acknowledge his help.

Chopra and Marfurt thank their coauthors of previously published work from Amoco, Coherence Technology Company, and the University of Houston. Those coauthors will recognize many detailed interpretations, incorporated (without quotes for easier reading) into Chapters 11 through 15.

The authors owe a special acknowledgment to Anne H. Thomas for doing an excellent job of copy editing the text for SEG and to Rowena Mills, SEG manager of GEOPHYSICS and books, for her patience and for ensuring that the final presentation of the text and figures was of good quality. The authors are grateful for their help.

Finally, Chopra and Marfurt thank the following companies for permission to use their data to illustrate this work:

Alberta Energy Company

Amoco Production Company

Anadarko

Arcis

BP

Burlington Resources

CanOxy

CGAS

CGG

ChevronTexaco

ConocoPhillips

Continental Illinois

Core Energy LLC

Core Laboratories

Crestar Energy Development Co. Ltd.

Devon Energy

EnCana Corporation

ExxonMobil

Geco Prakla

Geospectrum

Geotexture

Grand Mesa Petroleum

Kicking Horse Resources

Marathon Oil Co.
Mull Energy Company
Output Exploration LLC
OXY Permian
Paradigm Geophysical
PdVSA
Pemex
Petrovera Resources
Phillips Petroleum
Pohle Oil and Gas
Pure Resources
Saudi Aramco
Seitel
Shell Hibernia Management
Talisman
Texaco
Unocal Resources
WesternGeco

Satinder Chopra
Calgary, Alberta, Canada

Kurt J. Marfurt
Houston, Texas, U.S.A

Chapter 1

Overview of Seismic Attributes

Chapter Objectives

After reading this chapter, you will be able to

- link the historical development of seismic attributes to the development of other technologies
- evaluate the role of seismic attributes in present-day interpretations
- identify several key quantitative workflows that use seismic attributes

Introduction

A seismic attribute is any measure of seismic data that helps us visually enhance or quantify features of interpretation interest. A good seismic attribute is either directly sensitive to the desired geologic feature or reservoir property of interest, or allows us to define the structural or depositional environment and thereby enables us to infer some features or properties of interest. First introduced in the early 1970s, seismic attributes are now used widely for lithological and petrophysical prediction of reservoir properties.

After scanning through the data, a good seismic interpreter develops one or more geologic hypotheses with which to identify leads and build plays. Although science (particularly that based on geologic principles) plays a role, much actual identification of features using seismic data is done intuitively. Many would define seismic interpretation to be a mix of art and science. Once an interpreter has identified a seismic feature or pattern that is associated with successful wells (whether the scientific underpinning is valid or not!), he can rapidly find more of the same. This pattern recognition by experienced interpreters is mind-boggling to younger geophysicists, who often come armed with a larger arsenal of formal mathematics.

One goal of seismic attributes is to capture the interpreter's pattern-recognition expertise by quantifying the amplitude and morphological features seen in the seismic data, using a suite of deterministic calculations performed on a computer. For instance, the coherence attribute developed in the middle 1990s captures the same discontinuities seen in the seismic data and interpreted as faults by Rummerfeld (1954) and others 40 years earlier (Lindseth, 2005).

In the most general sense, seismic attributes encompass all quantities derived from seismic data. Thus, we consider attributes to include such quantities as interval velocity, inversion for acoustic impedance, pore-pressure prediction, reflector terminations, as well as complex-trace attributes and AVO. By assigning the name *attribute* to a quantity that is based on very sophisticated calculations, such as impedance inversion and pore-pressure prediction, we recognize that those estimates somehow are contaminated by errors and thus are amenable to calibration to well data via geostatistics or other data-integration techniques.

Seismic attributes are a powerful aid to seismic interpretation. They allow the geoscientist to interpret faults and channels, recognize the depositional environment, and unravel the structural deformation history more rapidly. By combining information from adjacent seismic samples and traces using a physical model (such as dip and azimuth, waveform similarity, or frequency content), seismic attributes often organize subtle features into displays that provide enhanced images for either a human interpreter or for modern geostatistical or neural-network computer analysis. Although 3D volumetric seismic attributes are used primarily for interpretation, this book is not about 3D seismic interpretation. For an excellent overview of 3D seismic interpretation principles and practices (including excellent sections on attributes), we refer the reader to Brown (2004).

Structure of this Book

Following this introductory chapter, the book is divided into three sections and a glossary of terms.

Section I focuses on the physical and mathematical basis of modern volumetric attributes — dip and azimuth, coherence, curvature, amplitude variability, and spectral decomposition. Section I also addresses issues of seismic-data quality, image enhancement, and multiattribute display. The section concludes with the extension of volumetric attributes to prestack angle- and offset-limited volumes for AVO and fracture analysis.

Section II focuses on the use of attributes in mapping different geologic environments: tectonic deformation, clastic depositional systems, carbonate depositional systems, deep-water deposition, and shallow drilling hazards. We conclude Section II with an overview of the use of geometric attributes in mapping reservoir heterogeneity.

Section III is composed of several published case studies using volumetric attributes. These case studies address mapping faults in a salt withdrawal basin in the Texas-Louisiana salt-dome province, polyphase deformation of Paleozoic rocks in the Central Basin Platform, identifying collapse features and associated fractures in the Fort Worth Basin, mapping channels and faults in the North Sea, and detecting shallow-water flows and hazards in the Gulf of Mexico.

We conclude the volume with a glossary of terms used in the book, to aid interpreters who wish to learn more about seismic processing and image analysis and to help geophysical processors or algorithm developers who wish to learn more about geologic interpretation.

In this introductory chapter, we present a broad-brush overview of seismic attributes and point out where we will go into greater depth. We begin with a summary of the historical development of attributes and conclude with a summary of present-day attribute workflows, interspersed with convincing examples illustrating how attributes aid seismic interpreters in their quest to unravel geology. We believe the historical perspective will allow practicing geoscientists to put in perspective the multitude of attribute and interpretation developments. We hope to show geoscience students how the development of attribute technology was driven not only by business needs, but also by independent developments in color displays, 3D seismic acquisition, and interpretation workstations. Given hard work, tenacity, and intuition sprinkled with a liberal amount of serendipity, students will continue to carry the development of attributes forward at a rapid pace.

Historical Development of Attributes

We provide now a brief account of landmarks in the development of seismic attributes, to help the reader appreciate how different attributes have come into being. For an expanded historical perspective on seismic attributes, readers are referred to Chopra and Marfurt (2005). Figure 1 shows a time line of when specific seismic attributes developed and relates each attribute to key advances in seismic exploration technology.

Digital Recording and Bright-spot Detection

By the late 1960s, a few geophysicists had begun to notice strong isolated reflections and changes in reflection character on seismic sections. In 1975, those reflection phenomena formed the foundation of seismic stratigraphy, based on onlap, offlap, and other morphological patterns (Forrest, 2000). Initially, workers thought some of those reflections were caused by hard streaks, and people were skeptical that such observations were meaningful. Gradually, however, when some of those strong events encountered gas zones on drilling, interpreters started taking them seriously. Such streaks of high amplitudes seen on seismic sections were christened *bright spots*, and they gave birth to bright-spot technology.

A search of worldwide technical literature at the time revealed Russian research papers (e.g., Churlin and Sergeyev, 1963) that already had reported direct detection of hydrocarbons by seismic means. This literature search revealed concerted efforts of studies to correlate bright spots with well data and field studies. It was found that reflections from gas-charged reservoir rocks showed much larger amplitudes than did reflections from adjacent oil or water-saturated zones. Bob Sheriff (R. E. Sheriff, personal communication, 2005) recalled that no one was interested in finding gas during that period — bright spots were sold as a means of finding the associated oil. Only later did we realize that these bright spots were the result of gas, or of gas dissolved in oil, causing a low-impedance anomaly. Even if such phenomena initially were poorly understood, the revelation that anomalously higher-amplitude seismic events in young clastic basins could indicate hydrocarbons gave the seismic exploration method a new level of importance. By 1970, oil companies were using bright-spot phenomena successfully to identify gas-saturated reservoirs (Forrest, 2000).

Digital recording greatly improved the quality of seismic data, and by 1975 nearly all seismic recording was digital. With digital recording came awareness about the importance of preserving relative amplitudes. After its early successes, bright-spot technology evolved rapidly in the early 1970s and included efforts to quantify seismic-amplitude changes and to calculate pay-sand thicknesses. At the time, application of the technology had a major impact on

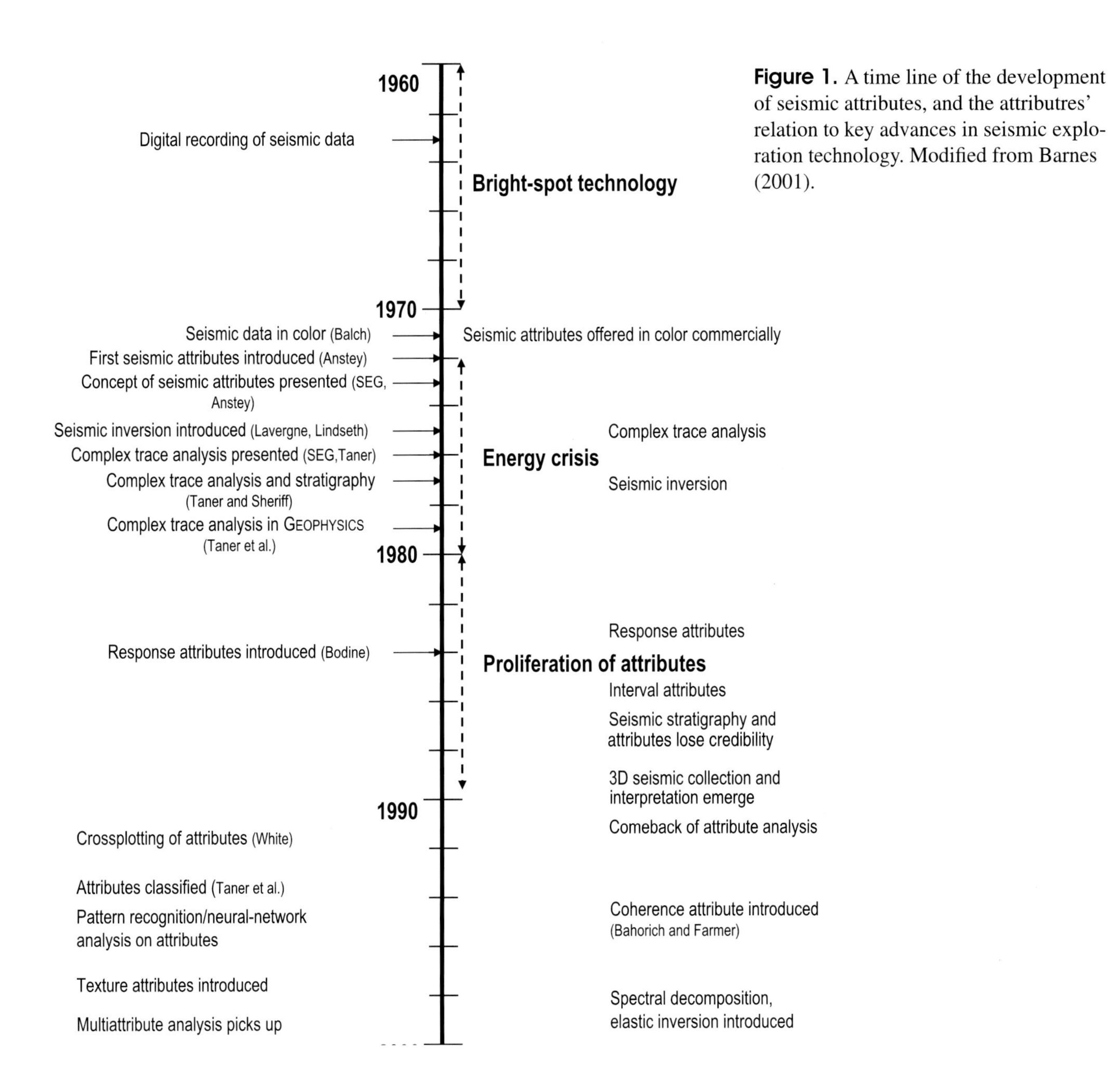

Figure 1. A time line of the development of seismic attributes, and the attributres' relation to key advances in seismic exploration technology. Modified from Barnes (2001).

bidding in the offshore Louisiana shelf and the Gulf of Mexico. Time/structure, velocity, and seismic amplitude remain the most fundamental attributes in use today.

Introduction of color in seismic displays

In 1971, A. H. Balch developed a computer-graphics-photographic system, called the color sonogram, to display the frequency spectra of seismic events simultaneously with their time-varying waveforms (Balch, 1971). In such a display, the waveforms are presented using a conventional variable-area scheme, but with the positive lobe colored to represent the frequency components of the data. The lateral changes in rock attenuation, or the loss of high frequencies because of slight lateral changes in move-out velocity and the like, could show up as color shifts on such displays. Balch's 1971 paper is credited with being the first publication in GEOPHYSICS to display seismic data in color. His work heralded the beginning of an era in which color, with the enhanced dynamic range that it offers, is used for meaningful analysis of seismic data.

At around the same time (1968–69), Nigel Anstey at Seiscom Limited U. K. was working on innovative seismic displays and played a key role in introducing color on seismic sections (N. Anstey, 2005, and personal communication, 2005). Anstey and his team (Ron O'Doherty, Peter Ferrer, Judy Farrell, and later, Lloyd Chapman) installed the first gray-scale laser plotter in their office in London (the plotter had been developed by Southwestern Industrial Electronics, or SIE). In experimenting with that plotter, the team developed color-separation techniques to display two variables on the seismic section: the normal seismic trace to give the structural picture, and an auxiliary modulation in color to show interval velocity, reflection strength, frequency content, or anything else that might prove useful.

The overlay of the color attributes on the black-and-white seismic sections resulted in displays that supplied more information — with the conventional black-and-white seismic display providing structural information, and the seismic attribute providing more-subtle stratigraphic information. Because it occurred during the time of the bright-spot revolution, the most popular such displays were those of reflection strength (the amplitude of the envelope). Figure 2 shows one of Anstey's earliest attribute plots — a reflection-strength attribute (in color) overlaid on a seismic section.

After Anstey's departure from Seiscom Ltd. (Houston) in 1975, his colleagues Turhan Taner and Fulton Koehler followed up on his work and developed a sound mathematical framework for attribute computation (Taner and Sheriff, 1977; Taner et al., 1979). In their approach, the seismic-trace amplitude is treated as the real part of the (complex) analytical signal, whereas the imaginary part of the signal is computed by taking its Hilbert transform. The envelope is computed by taking the square root of the sum of the squares of the real and imaginary components, and the phase is computed by taking the double argument (ATAN2) inverse tangent of the imaginary and real components. Finally, the frequency is computed as the rate of change of the phase. Those computations were carried out at each sample of the seismic trace and have since been dubbed *instantaneous* attributes. By 1975, three principal attributes — instantaneous envelope, phase, and frequency — had been established.

- *Instantaneous envelope* (reflection strength) is sensitive to changes in acoustic impedance and thus to lithology, porosity, hydrocarbons, and thin-bed tuning.
- *Instantaneous phase* is useful for tracking reflector continuity, and therefore, for detecting unconformities, faults, and lateral changes in stratigraphy.
- *Instantaneous frequency* is useful in identifying abnormal attenuation and thin-bed tuning.

Figure 3 shows scanned copies of two slides that Tury Taner used during the middle 1970s and the 1980s in the AAPG-sponsored school on seismic stratigraphy. Figure 3a shows representative reflection characters seen on 2D seismic lines. Figure 3b displays idealized characters used in seismic stratigraphy interpretation. Those early interpretation work-flow concepts motivated later developments in geometric attributes (including volumetric dip and azimuth, reflector parallelism, continuity, and unconformity indicators). In Chapter 2, we present the theory and algorithmic implementation of volumetric estimates of dip and azimuth. In Chapters 12 and 14, we show how seismic stratigraphy has been incorporated into the more-general study of seismic geomorphology.

Color plotting of seismic data

Alongside the theoretical evolution of complex-trace analysis, the hardware and software needed to do efficient color plotting also were developing. Thus, by the late 1970s,

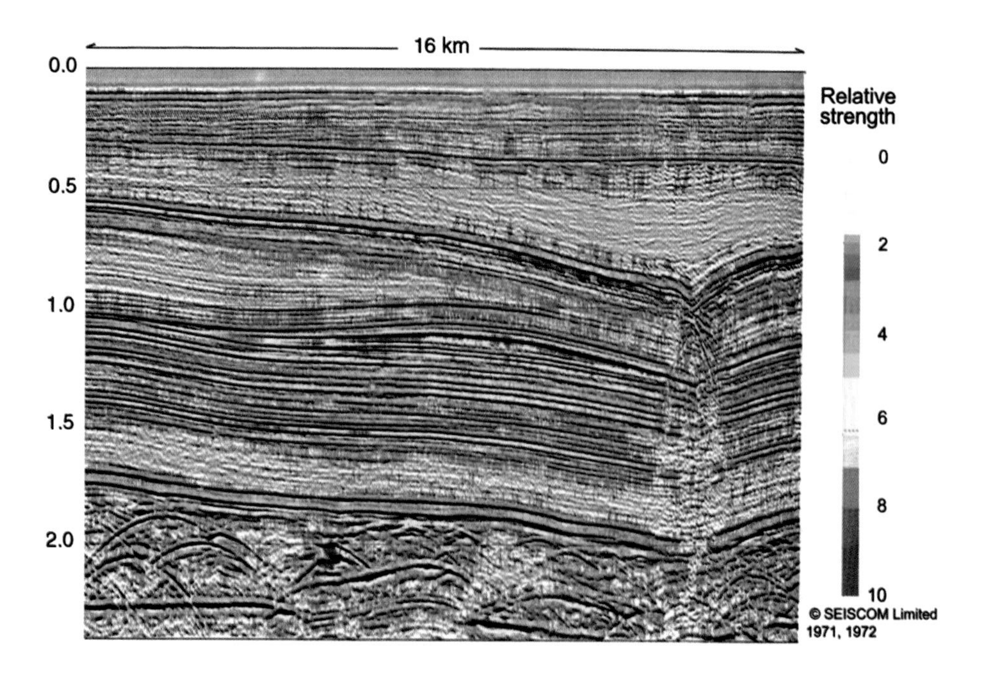

Figure 2. A composite attribute image from the early 1970s, showing reflection strength (in early days, the most popular attribute) superimposed on the structural seismic section. After Anstey (2005).

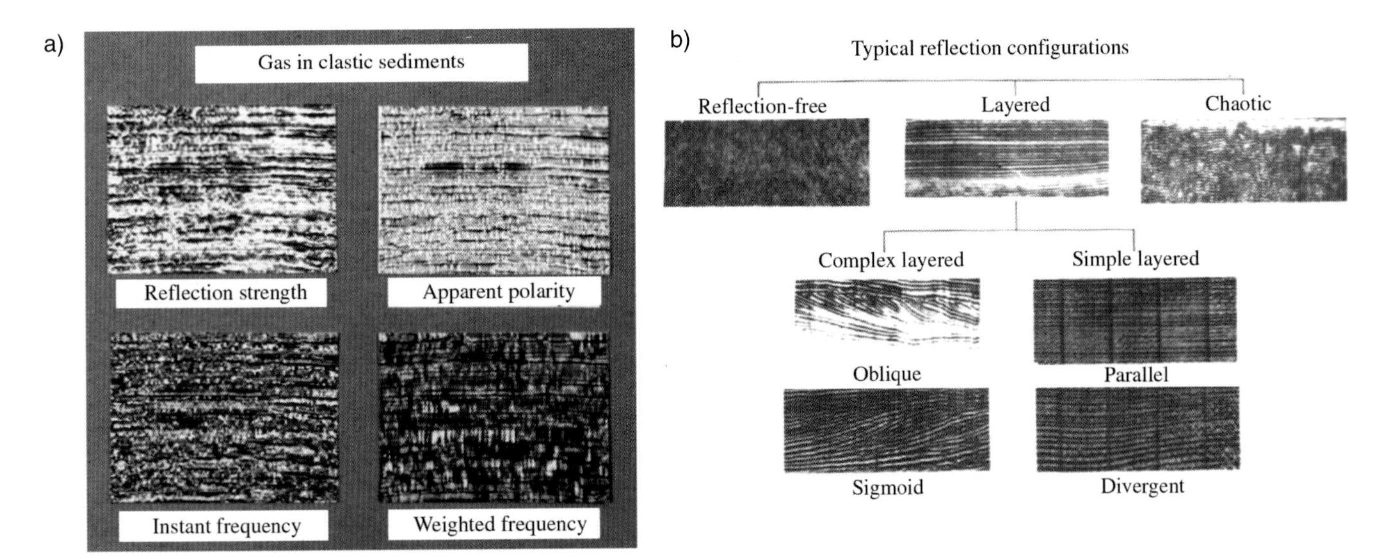

Figure 3. Scanned copies of two slides used by Tury Taner in the middle 1970s and the 1980s in the AAPG-sponsored school on seismic stratigraphy. (a) Complex trace analysis applied to gas-charged reservoirs. (b) Representative reflection characters seen on 2D seismic lines. These early interpretation workflow concepts provided the motivation for later developments in geometric attributes, including volumetric dip and azimuth, reflector parallelism, continuity, and unconformity indicators.

color plotters had invaded the market and the time was right for applying complex-trace analysis to aid seismic interpretation. Color plotting is an important piece of history, because the theoretical development would have had much less impact had there been no good way to display attributes in color. In Chapter 9, we review the basic color models as well as modern methods of using color to display multiple attributes.

Seismic-impedance inversion

During the middle 1970s, another significant contribution from seismic attributes was inversion of poststack seismic amplitudes into acoustic impedance, which is an important physical property of rocks and an aid in studying the subsurface. Inverted impedance sections yielded useful information about lateral changes in lithology and porosity. Conversion of seismic traces into acoustic-impedance and velocity pseudologs was reported first by Lavergne (1975) and Lindseth (1979). Such logs quickly became popular, mainly because of the ease and accuracy of interpreting impedance data and also because of the stratigraphic-interpretation framework that gained popularity at that time. Figure 4 shows an inverted seismic section from the Swan Hills Devonian reef bank that Lindseth used to predict carbonate porosity. Notice that at the time, Lindseth used a transit-time scale rather than a velocity scale. He also used a lithologic color scale to highlight the changes in transit time, which distinguished carbonate sections from clastic sections on the inverted acoustic-impedance sections.

Thus, the 1970s saw the development of important attribute techniques that interpreters still use widely to add value to their data.

Proliferation of attributes in the 1980s

The 1980s brought a proliferation of seismic attributes, including development of the cosine of instantaneous phase, and of dominant frequency, average amplitude, zero-crossing frequency, and many others. The cosine of instantaneous phase was developed because it is a continuous parameter, unlike the phase itself, which has a discontinuity at ±180°. Such a continuous attribute could be interpolated, smoothed, processed, and even migrated. The 1980s also saw the introduction of interval and formation attributes, which measure an average property in a user-defined window centered about a picked horizon, or alternatively, between two picked horizons. Such windowed attributes are used frequently when the seismic reflections associated with a reservoir are sufficiently heterogeneous to preclude tracking a consistent peak or trough on all traces. Interval and formation attributes often are statistically more meaningful, as is the case in well-log correlation, when we combine several thin, discontinuous sand units to generate a net-to-gross sand-ratio map rather than maps specifying individual unit thicknesses.

Robertson and Nogami (1984) made the noteworthy observation that instantaneous frequency at the peak of a zero-phase seismic wavelet is equal to the average frequency of the wavelet's amplitude spectrum. That is to say, on a

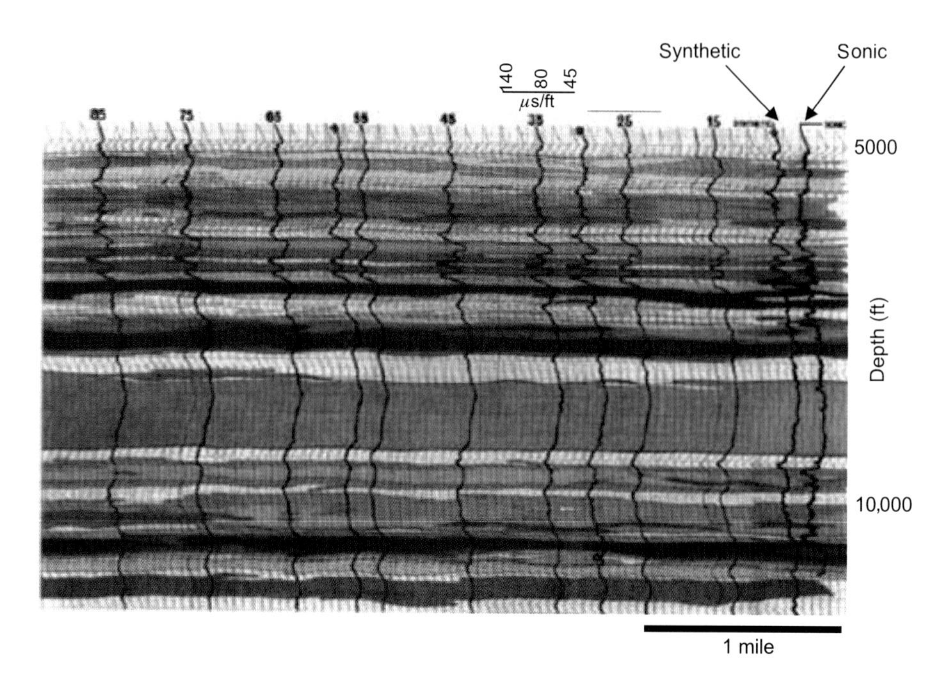

Figure 4. A seislog inverted seismic section from the Swan Hills carbonate formation. After Lindseth (1979).

conventional instantaneous-frequency trace, points exist at which the instantaneous frequency directly measures a property of the Fourier spectrum of the wavelet. For the same reason, the instantaneous phase corresponds to the wavelet's true phase at those points. Such physically meaningful measurements occur at a small number of points. The remaining instantaneous-attribute measures provide little additional information about the seismic wavelet.

However, interpreters were frustrated when they attempted to use such information to quantify reservoir properties. Later, White (1991) showed that Robertson and Nogami's (1984) relationship between instantaneous frequency at the reflector peak and average spectrum does not hold statistically in practice because of noise and waveform interference.

Response attributes

The stablest of the instantaneous attributes was the envelope, which always could be counted on to provided accurate interval thicknesses. Bodine (1984, 1986) examined the instantaneous frequency and phase in terms of the reflection event estimated at the peak of the instantaneous envelope. He argued that because most of the signal energy in a trace is found in the vicinity of envelope peaks, the reflection event's phase and frequency could be described more accurately by assigning them to the value seen at peaks. Whereas Bodine called these response attributes, we prefer Taner's more descriptive term of wavelet attributes. Thus, response (or wavelet) phase is the instantaneous phase at the point at which the envelope is maximal. One value is computed for each maximum and is applied to the width of the energy lobe from trough to trough. This phase is piecewise continuous and measures phase variations, from one energy lobe to the next.

Similarly, response frequency is the value of instantaneous frequency at the point at which the envelope is maximal, and this single value is assigned to the width of the energy lobe between two successive troughs. Because the response frequency is calculated at envelope peaks, it avoids the singularities in the instantaneous phase (the origin of the instantaneous frequency) that we see where seismic events interfere, which is worst at the envelope troughs. Later, Hardage et al. (1998) advocated using these discontinuities in instantaneous frequency for interpretation, and Taner (2000) developed a thin-bed indicator based on the difference between singularity-sensitive instantaneous frequency and the more smoothly varying envelope-weighted instantaneous frequency.

Such singularities form the basis of Liner et al.'s (2004) SPICE (spectral imaging of correlative events) attribute. (We will discuss the SPICE algorithm in Chapter 6 on spectral decomposition). Finally, these peak values also were the ones mapped later by Bahorich and Bridges (1992) in their seismic sequence attribute-mapping effort. Additional discussion of response attributes can be found in Robertson and Fisher (1988).

Interpretive workstations

The 1980s saw the advent of interpretation workstations. Workstation development started in each of the major oil companies — first on mainframes, then on dedicated minicomputers, next on the PCs, and finally on UNIX workstations. Interpretive workstations had two main advantages that beneficially influenced attributes. First, the use of color became pervasive and (unless you wanted a hardcopy!) economical. Second, calculation of a great many attributes became interactive. The benefit of that was more one of personal risk reduction rather than of speed. A daring interpreter could simply try out an idea in the dead of night and show favorable results to his or her boss the next day, if the idea enhanced the map.

Thus, the 1980s brought a rapid expansion in the seismic processing and display capabilities necessary for the explosion of attribute techniques that would occur in the middle 1990s. However, use of attributes actually decreased in the 1980s relative to that in the late 1970s.

Attributes fall out of favor

Complex-trace attributes suffer from waveform interference arising from nearby interfaces that can obscure subtle trends in the data. In particular, instantaneous frequency estimates can fall outside the seismic bandwidth and even can generate negative values. Although a few workers understood that phenomenon and could use it as an indicator of an unconformity or a thin bed, the deleterious consequences of waveform interference were not published. Thus, interpreters who attempted to associate physical meaning with such attributes were frustrated by artifacts. Interpreters also found it difficult to relate those attributes directly to logged reservoir properties such as porosity, so the attributes could not be used to quantify reservoir properties. As the 1980s passed, seismic attributes lost credibility with interpreters. That loss probably was coupled with a loss of faith in seismic stratigraphy as well, because numerous dry holes were drilled on the basis of seismic stratigraphic predictions. Following are three contributing factors suggested by J. D. Robertson (J. D. Robertson, personal communication, 2005) for the industry's disillusionment with attributes and seismic stratigraphy.

Limits to resolution

Given the limited resolution of seismic data available in the 1980s, coupled with the lack of geologic input to interpretation, interpreters lost sight of what seismic data really could resolve, compared with the stratigraphic resolution they were seeking. Numerous interpretations of geologic detail simply were unjustified by the resolution of the seismic data. When geologists attempted interpretations of seismic attributes, they often did not have a sound understanding of the limitations of seismic data, and their geophysicist teammates did not do a good job of educating them in the pitfalls of seismic resolution.

Transition to 3D data

Three-dimensional seismic surveying arose in the early 1970s, and by the middle 1980s it had emerged as a beneficial technique for imaging many onshore and offshore areas around the world. It improved resolution enormously and led to fewer dry wells. Even though it was considered expensive at the time, 3D seismic interpretation proved to be much better at making successful exploration predictions than seismic stratigraphic analysis of 2D seismic data was. That dampened the use of 2D seismic stratigraphic interpretation of attribute sections. Use of attribute techniques resumed only when workstation tools were developed to apply the technology to 3D data.

Careless drilling choices

After the energy crisis of the 1970s and the accompanying rise in oil prices, in the early 1980s oil companies scrambled to drill prospects and were not careful to drill only the good ones. In essence, exploration management allowed too many poor prospects to be drilled, and seismic stratigraphy and attribute analysis took the blame for failures that really should have been blamed on management's poor judgment or overly optimistic predictions of the price of oil.

At that time, other experts also voiced concerns about the limitations of seismic attributes, many of which were summarized by Barnes (2001).

Two-dimensional attributes

By the middle 1980s, considerable improvements in recording and processing techniques had enhanced the information content of seismic data used for stratigraphic interpretation. During that time, several two-dimensional continuity and dip attributes also were developed that were employed in procedures for defining and analyzing seismic facies (Conticini, 1984; Vossler, 1988). Finn (1986) anticipated the need for 3D estimates of dip and azimuth by applying a 2D semblance estimate of apparent dip on surveys of 2D intersecting lines. Although novel and interesting, such procedures did not evoke an enthusiastic response. The results could be subjective, and 2D surveys simply contained too many artifacts from out-of-the-plane reflections.

Horizon and interval attributes

During the middle 1980s and later, horizon attributes (Dalley et al., 1989) and interval attributes (Sonneland et al., 1989) were introduced. Those attributes demonstrated that interpreted horizons exhibited reflector characteristics not easily observed on vertical seismic sections. Areal variations in reflection characteristics could be related to paleogeographic elements (Brown and Robertson, 1985), whereas amplitude extractions of seismic horizons revealed features directly related to stratigraphic events. Amplitude extraction maps were used to interpolate and/or extrapolate reservoir properties from well control (Thadani et al., 1987). The most important reference establishing those workflows was the first edition (in 1986) of Alistair Brown's AAPG Memoir 42.

Industry Adoption of 3D Seismic Technology

The 1990s brought new life to seismic attribute analysis, primarily because the industry had embraced 3D technology — which was by far the most successful new exploration technology of several decades. By its very nature, 3D technology required computer-aided interpretation that led to optimal well locations being presented to the drilling decision teams. Perhaps the single most important contribution in making drilling decisions at that time was the concept of 3D attribute extractions. Finally it was possible to compute attributes for full 3D volumes and examine features of interest in their three-dimensional perspective. Figure 5 shows the seismic data as well as the complex-trace attributes. By animating through those volumes, geoscientists could quickly interpret variations in structural and stratigraphic style from seismic line to seismic line, and they could quickly link subtle variations in seismic lines to their corresponding attributes.

One of the earliest 3D attribute publications is by Dalley et al. (1989). Their colleagues at Shell, Rijks and Jauffred (1991), introduced two concepts that now are commonplace in the interpretation workplace — dip and azimuth maps and amplitude extractions. In Figure 6, we reproduce a suite of images from Rijks and Jauffred (1991), including a vertical section through the seismic data. Figure 6a shows the picked top and bottom of the formation, and Figure 6b shows a dip magnitude map of the upper horizon. Figure 6c is a shaded-relief map of the same horizon, and Figures 6d and 6e are amplitude extractions from the lower and upper horizons, respectively. Such images not only demonstrated the value of 3D seismic data, they also established standard workflows that are accepted as best practices today. We discuss the theory and algorithmic implementation of volumetric estimates of dip and azimuth in Chapter 2. Such estimates will form the reference plane for calculations of seismic coherence discussed in Chapter 3 and amplitude variability in Chapter 5. Dip and azimuth form the basis for the volumetric curvature attributes discussed in Chapter 4.

The association of attributes with 3D seismic data breathed new life into attribute analysis, moving it away from seismic stratigraphy and toward exploitation and reservoir characterization. Contemporaneous developments in rock-physics research provided the quantitative basis of how rock properties affect seismic data, thereby allowing us today to relate attributes directly to rock properties in a much more credible way than was possible in the 1980s (J. D. Robertson, personal communication, 2005).

Seismic sequence attribute mapping

It seems counterintuitive that making maps of attributes generated on 2D surveys did not occur until similar maps were made directly from 3D data. Complex-trace analysis numerically quantified subtle changes in envelope, amplitude, and phase, and those same data attributes could be seen readily by an experienced interpreter from the original seismic data themselves.

However, such human interpretation could not readily be turned into a map. Sonneland et al. (1989) first presented the key concepts, and Bahorich and Bridges (1992) and Bahorich and van Bemmel (1994) followed later by presenting the concept as the seismic sequence attribute map (SSAM). Interestingly, Amoco's involvement in that effort took place out of its Denver exploration office rather than its research center in Tulsa. Because of staff cutbacks resulting from the drop in oil prices, Amoco had outsourced their development of internal workstations in the late 1980s. For that reason, Amoco's research efforts (like those of most other companies) focused on more important technologies, including prestack depth migration and AVO. Bahorich (then at the Denver office) proselytized the value of SSAM so strongly that eventually he was punished and sent to dwell with the technology misfits in Tulsa, thereby solving both problem groups. That fortuitous occurrence soon led to Amoco's development of seismic coherence.

3D seismic exploration comes of age

By the middle 1990s, 3D seismic technology became affordable. Whereas by 1980 only 100 3D seismic surveys had been done, by the middle 1990s an estimated 200 to 300 3D surveys were being conducted annually. Good 3D interpretation workflows on interactive workstations were being perfected. Complex-trace analysis was performed on full 3D seismic volumes and used in the interpretations. However, most 3D interpretation was performed on vertical inlines and crosslines and then projected onto a time slice. Although that worked well, it led to ambiguities in the lateral resolution of faults, especially where faults joined together, crossed, or simply ended as a result of changes in geologic stress.

Seismic coherence

Although in the early 1990s 3D interpretation was used routinely for exploitation, Amoco still used primarily 2D data for exploration. Bahorich was imprisoned with (and accused of being one of) Amoco's researchers and was faced with the problem of making his seismic sequence attribute mapping workflow produce useful results in multiple overlapping 2D surveys. Because the data had radically different amplitudes, phases, and frequencies, little could be done on an interpretative workstation — phase and spectral matching required reprocessing.

Instead, working with programmer Steve Farmer, Bahorich evaluated several alternative attributes that were relatively insensitive to the source wavelet. By computing and mapping a normalized crosscorrelation coefficient between adjacent traces in the same survey, the researchers could eliminate the variability of source wavelet amplitude and phase and could quantify waveform continuity. (Unknown to the Amoco team, this was the subject of Finn's [1986] M.S. thesis, although Finn did not have a ready means of posting his data in map view). Faults were easily seen and could be tracked on the 2D section. Within a week of that development, John Lopez, a structural geologist member of the team working out of Amoco's New Orleans office, applied it to a large 3D data set (Bahorich et al., 1995; Haskell et al., 1995). The results were astounding. Seismic coherence was born. Although it can be stated that the idea of coherence was conceptualized earlier in different ways by different researchers, such as Drecun and Lucas (1985) and Claerbout (1990), the development and application of coherence to 3D seismic data, in the form of coherence cube technology, took the industry by storm.

Bahorich and Farmer (1995, p. 1053) state that their coherence methodology was the "first published method of revealing fault surfaces within a 3D volume for which no fault reflections had been recorded." Their volume of coherence coefficients was computed from the seismic amplitudes on adjacent traces, using a crosscorrelation technique, and it portrayed faults and other stratigraphic anomalies clearly on time slices and horizontal slices. The coherence images distinctly revealed buried deltas, river channels, reefs, and dewatering features. Interpreters loved the remarkable detail with which stratigraphic features appeared on coherence displays, without any interpretation bias, and the fact that some features appeared that previously had been unidentifiable even with close scrutiny. They had a new view of their data.

The Amoco team followed its original three-trace crosscorrelation algorithm with semblance and eigen-decomposition coherence estimates (Marfurt et al., 1998; Marfurt et al., 1999; Gersztenkorn and Marfurt, 1999) that provided improved clarity and lateral resolution (Chopra, 2002). Ac-

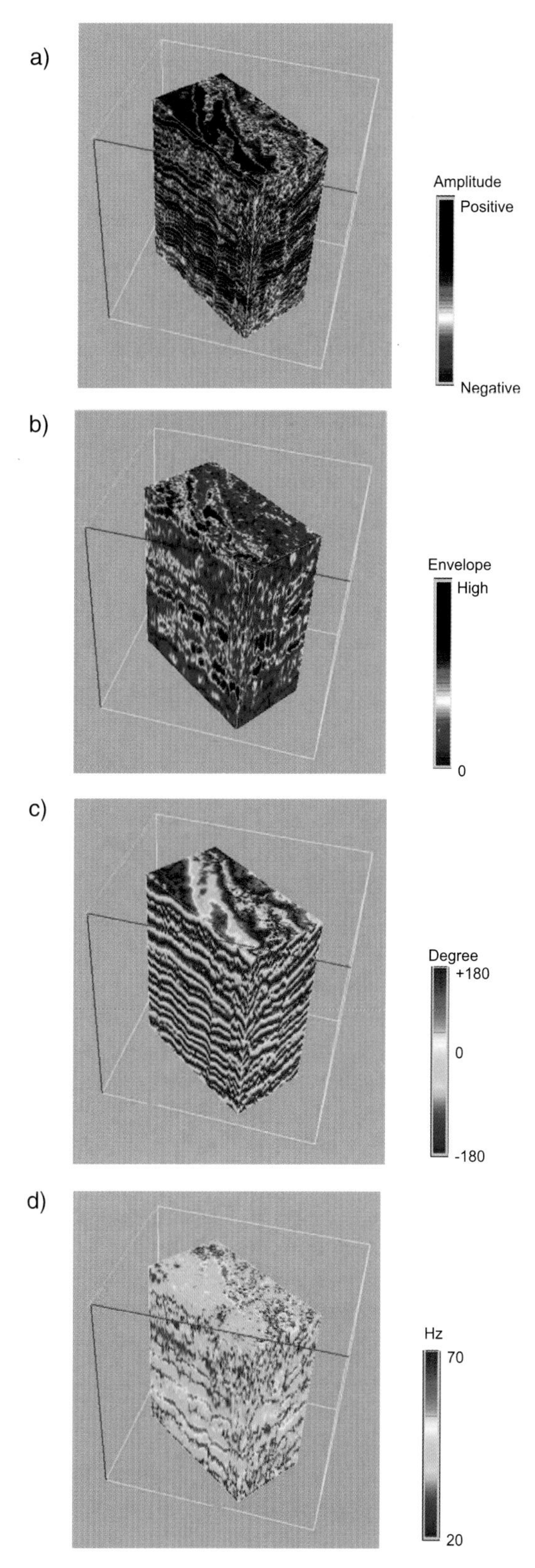

Figure 5. (a) 3D seismic data and (b)–(d) corresponding 3D attribute volumes: (b) reflection envelope, (c) phase, and (d) frequency. The introduction of volumetric attributes made it convenient to interpret seismic signatures on vertical slices, time slices, and horizon slices. Data courtesy of Arcis Corporation, Calgary.

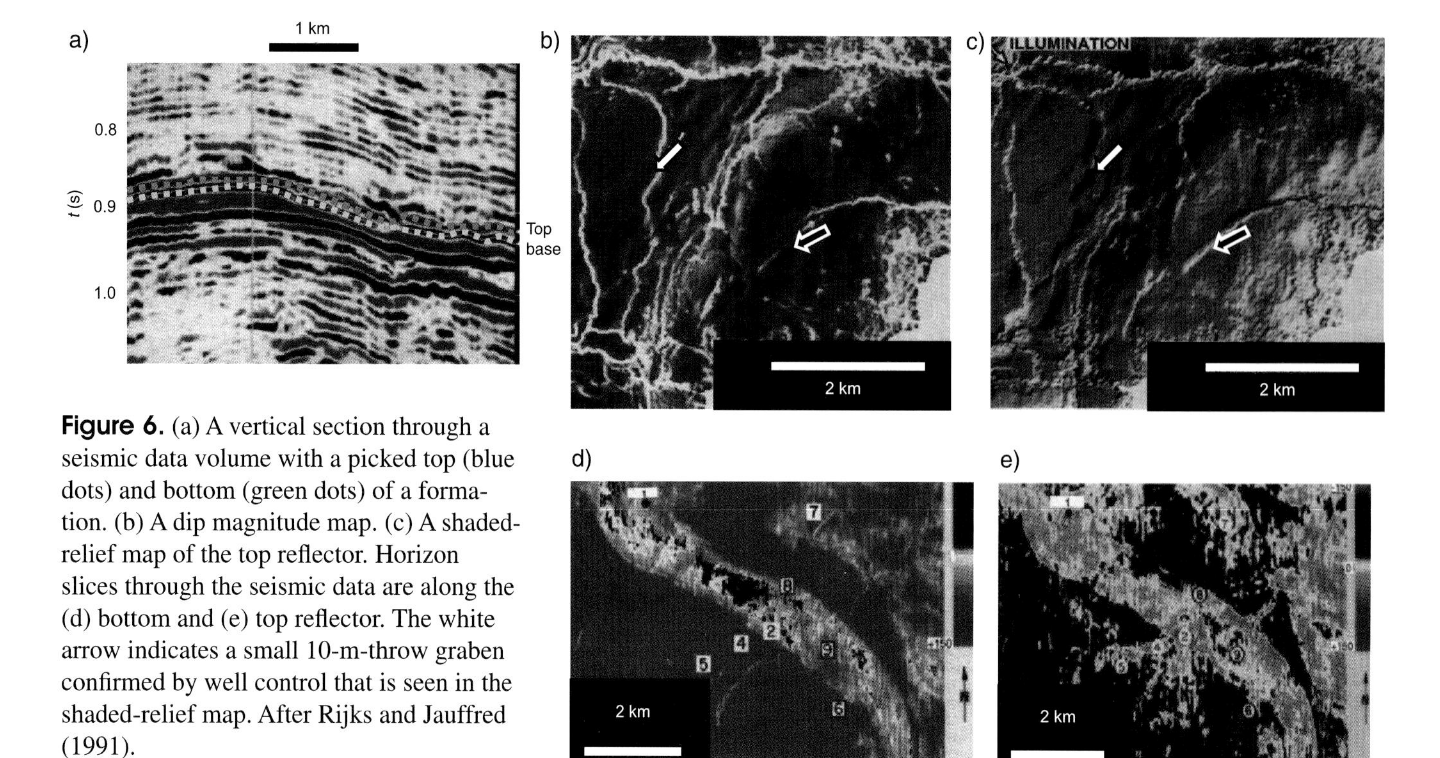

Figure 6. (a) A vertical section through a seismic data volume with a picked top (blue dots) and bottom (green dots) of a formation. (b) A dip magnitude map. (c) A shaded-relief map of the top reflector. Horizon slices through the seismic data are along the (d) bottom and (e) top reflector. The white arrow indicates a small 10-m-throw graben confirmed by well control that is seen in the shaded-relief map. After Rijks and Jauffred (1991).

cording to the SEG's citation recognizing that contribution, "this significantly changed the way geophysicists interpret 3D seismic data and the way oil industry management views geophysicists' contributions to the industry."

Figure 7 exhibits channels on the time slice from a coherence volume and compares that image with the equivalent seismic time slice. Notice the clarity and detail that coherence provides in making the channels stand out.

Figure 8 depicts an example from offshore the east coast of Canada, where northwest-southeast faults and fractures that previously had been difficult to interpret show up clearly on coherence time slices. Overlaying coherence on a seismic time slice enables the interpreter to name the faults and link master and antithetic faults more easily.

Figure 9 shows faults appearing clearly on a coherence volume. Two horizons were interpreted on the seismic volume and are shown here to aid the interpretation.

In Chapter 3, we review the formulation of the full family of coherence attributes, and the best practices in their use. In Chapters 11–15, we use coherence as a tool for mapping structure, stratigraphy, and reservoir heterogeneity.

Spectral decomposition

Seismic processors began using spectral balancing of seismic data in the middle 1970s. In Amoco's implementation, each seismic section was subjected to a suite of 10- to 20-Hz overlapping band-passed filter panels. Those seismic sections were inspected to see which panels contained geologic information (lower-frequency panels typically contained ground roll, whereas higher-frequency panels contained air waves and other noise). Frequency bands containing signal were normalized to have similar amplitudes and then summed back together, whereas bands containing noise were rejected.

In the middle 1990s, Greg Partyka, working out of Amoco's office in Calgary, analyzed similar frequency panels for interpretation. He noticed lateral changes in frequency content resulting from changes in lithology and bed thickness. By limiting his analysis window to approximately 100 ms about the zone of interest, he could quantify the lateral changes by analyzing the amplitude spectra for each frequency. The images were particularly effective in map view. His short-window discrete Fourier transform (SWDFT) analysis became known as spectral decomposition (Partyka et al., 1999).

The same work continues actively today, with many workers preferring the wavelet-transform-based approach introduced by Castagna et al. (2003) over the original SWDFT. In Chapter 6, we review the theoretical basis and algorithmic implementation of both the SWDFT and wavelet-transform implementations of spectral decomposition. We also discuss the closely related SPICE algorithm, which looks for discontinuities in the amplitude spectrum. In Chapters 12 and 13, we show spectral decomposition applied to clastic and carbonate depositional environments.

Seismic inversion revisited

The original recursive or trace-integration seismic inversion technique for acoustic impedance also evolved during the late 1980s and the 1990s, with developments in model-based inversion, sparse-spike inversion, stratigraphic inversion, and geostatistical inversion providing accurate results (Chopra and Kuhn, 2001). Early techniques used a local optimization method that produced good results when provided with an accurate starting model. Local optimization techniques were followed by global optimization methods that gave reasonable results even with sparse well control.

Connolly (1999) introduced elastic impedance, which computes conventional acoustic impedance for finite angles of incidence. That technique was further enhanced by Whitcombe (2002) to reflect different elastic parameters, such as Lamé's parameter λ, bulk modulus K, and shear modulus μ.

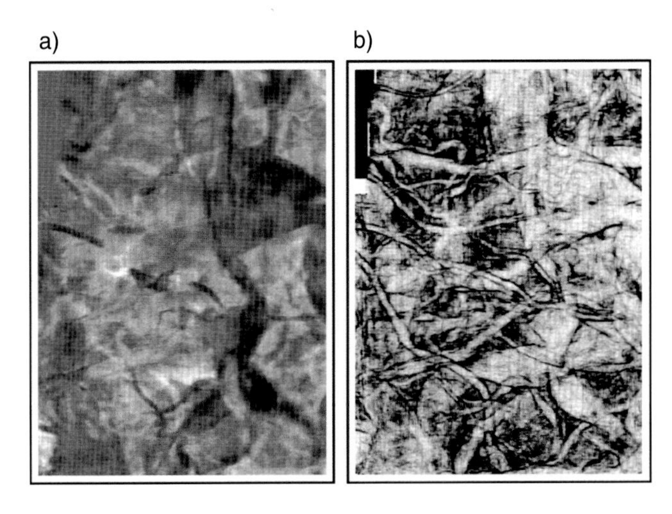

Figure 7. Time slices at 1.184 s through a (a) seismic volume and its corresponding (b) coherence volume. Notice the clarity with which the individual channels show up on the coherence time slice.

Crossplotting of attributes

Crossplotting of attributes was introduced to display the attributes' relationship visually among two or three variables (White, 1991). Verm and Hilterman (1994) used crossplots in AVO analysis, and such crossplots have been used since then as AVO anomaly indicators. When appropriate pairs of attributes are crossplotted, common lithologies and fluid types often cluster together, thereby providing a straightforward interpretation. Also, most rocks in many Tertiary basins are either shales or water-saturated sandstones and lie along an easily recognized trend in the crossplot. Rocks that anomalously plot off of those two trends may indicate the presence of hydrocarbons, thereby meriting further AVO analysis. Extending crossplots to three dimensions is beneficial because data clusters hanging in 3D space are more readily diagnostic and result in more accurate and reliable interpretations.

In Figure 10, we illustrate the use of modern crossplotting software for three attributes that help identify a gas anomaly — λ-ρ on the x-axis, μ-ρ on the y-axis, and fluid stack on the z-axis. In Figure 10a, a blue patch indicates a gas anomaly on a time slice through the λ-ρ volume. We then draw a red polygon on the time slice (outline) to select live data points to be displayed in the crossplot. The red cluster of points in Figure 10b corresponds to the red polygon and five time slices (two above and two below the one shown). The yellow and magenta clusters are the corre-

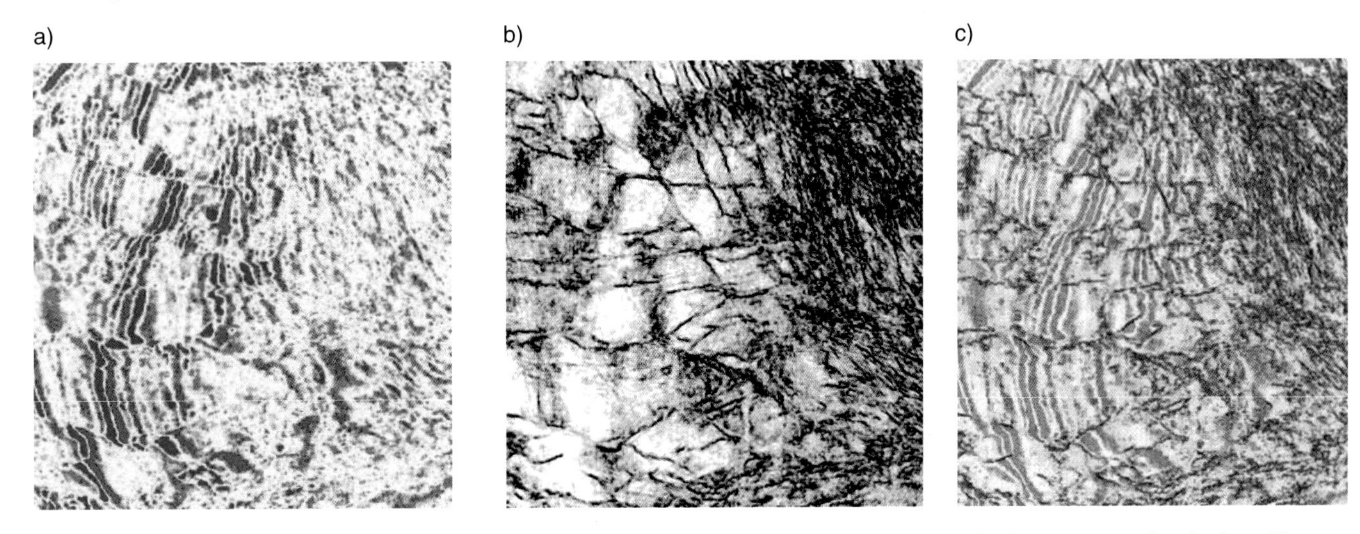

Figure 8. Time slices through (a) a seismic and (b) coherence data volumes. (c) Overlay of coherence on seismic data. Note that the coherence slice not only reveals faults with clarity but also shows the intensively fractured region to the right. After Chopra (2002).

Figure 9. Faults seen clearly on a coherence volume. Two horizons have been interpreted on the seismic volume and are shown here to aid in the interpretation.

sponding contributions from the yellow and magenta polygons in Figure 10a. As the crossplot is rotated toward the left on the vertical axis, the fluid stack shows the expected negative values for the gas sand (Figure 10c). Figure 10d is a 3D crossplot that is seen from the fluid-stack side and that includes only points from the magenta polygon.

Automated pattern recognition on attributes

The proliferation of attributes during the 1980s resulted in an explosion in attribute alternatives available to geophysicists. Besides being overwhelming, the sheer volume of data defied attempts to gauge the information contained within those data using conventional analytical tools, and made the data's meaningful and timely interpretation a challenge. For that reason, one school of geophysicists examined automated pattern-recognition techniques (de Figueiredo, 1982), wherein a computer is trained to see patterns of interest and then made to sift through the available bulk of data seeking those patterns. A second school of geophysi-

a)

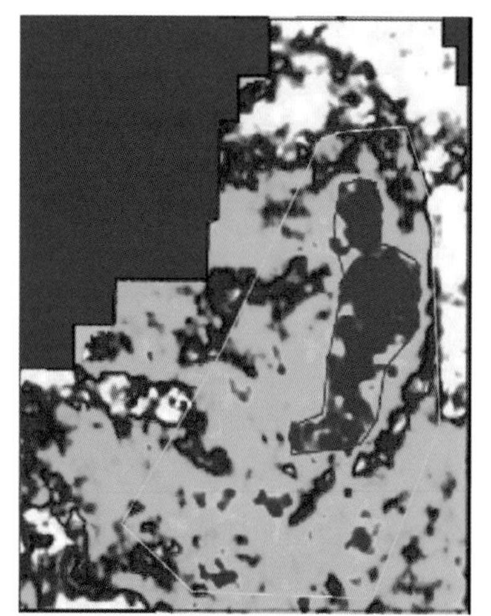

b)

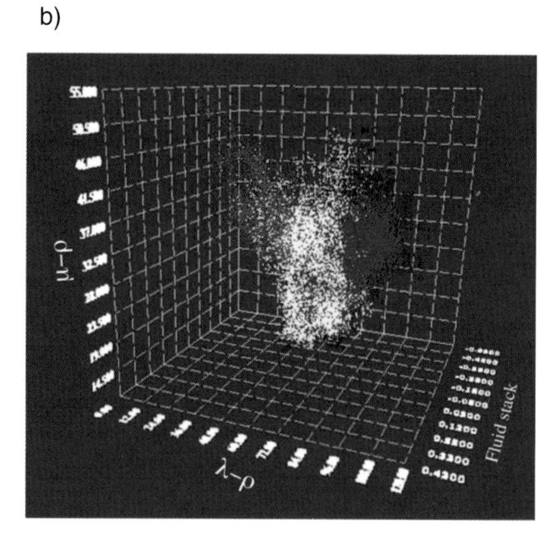

c)

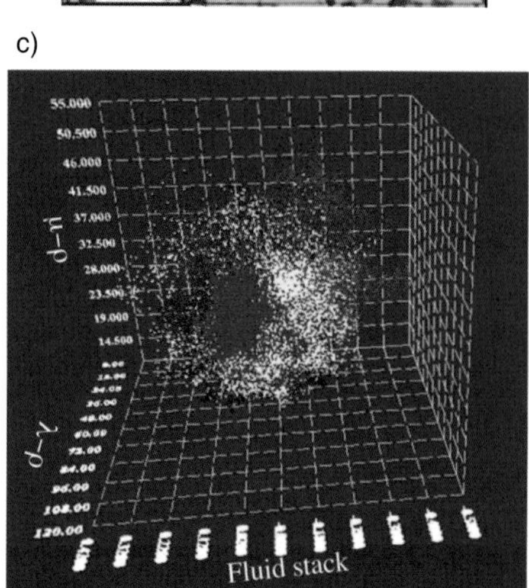

d)

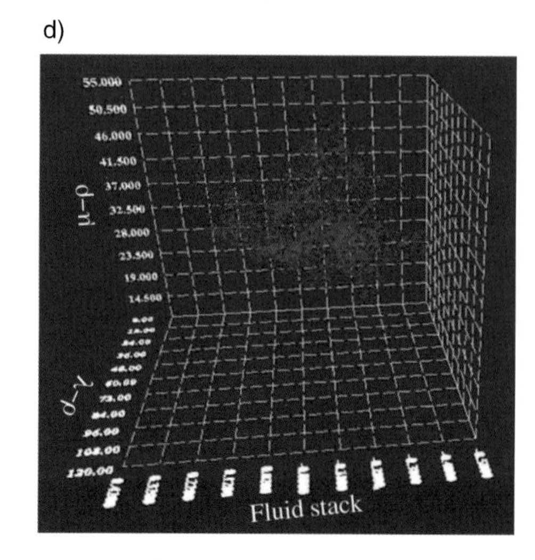

Figure 10. A λ-ρ section (with polygons selected) and corresponding clusters on 3D crossplots. (a) Polygons selected on a time slice from the λ-ρ volume. The red-bordered polygon indicates the area being analyzed. (b) Points within the red, yellow, and magenta polygons show up as different clusters. The gas anomaly (blue on the time slice and enclosed by the magenta polygon) shows up with negative values for the fluid stack. (c) 3D crossplot seen from the fluid stack side, and (d) 3D crossplot seen from the fluid stack side and including only points from the magenta polygon. After Chopra et al. (2003).

cists began combining attributes that are sensitive to relevant geologic features, using multiattribute analysis.

Neural-network application for multiattribute analysis

One attempt at automated pattern recognition took the form of neural networks (Russell et al., 1997), wherein a set of input patterns is related to the output by a transformation that is encoded in the network weights. In Figure 11, we show an example of multivariate statistical analysis being used to determine whether the derived property volumes are related to gas saturation and lithology (Chopra and Pruden, 2003). For the case study from southern Alberta, the gamma-ray logs in the area were diagnostic of sands and there was a fairly even sampling of well data across the field. A nonlinear multiattribute determinant analysis was employed between the derived multiple seismic attribute volumes and the measured gamma-ray values at wells. By training a neural network with a statistically representative population of the targeted log responses (i.e., gamma-ray, sonic, and bulk-density logs) and of the multiple seismic-attribute volumes available at each well, a nonlinear multiattribute transform was computed to produce gamma-ray and bulk-density inversions across the 3D seismic volume.

In Figure 11a and b, we show the λ-ρ and μ-ρ sections, respectively, with the anomaly enclosed in a yellow polygon. The crossplot for these two attributes is shown in Figure 11c. The yellow dots on the crossplots represent the values within the polygons on Figure 11a and b. The magenta polygon on Figure 12a indicates where we would expect to find gas sands in λ-ρ and μ-ρ space in Figure 12b and c. The results of the gamma inversion are shown in Figure 13. The data are scaled to API gamma units in Figure 13a and converted to porosity in Figure 13b using the standard linear density relationship.

From log data, the sand-filled channels are interpreted as having gamma values lower than 50 API units. That cutoff value was used to mask out inverted density values for silts and shales. Analysis of Figure 13a and 13b shows three distinct sand-bearing channels.

We also can use cubic B-spline curves to mathematically represent the relation between pairs of well-log properties, one of which can be estimated from seismic attributes. In this manner, we can generate useful gamma-ray, porosity, or other rock-property volumes (Chopra et al., 2004). In Figure 14 we show spline-curve-inverted porosity.

Enhanced visualization helps attribute interpretation

Once geophysicists realized the benefit of using 3D seismic data in interpreting stratigraphy, interpretation workflows shifted from a simple horizon-based framework to a volume-based one. The goal was to relate diverse geologic units within a given depositional environment over time. In Figure 15, we display strat cubes (subvolumes bounded by two not-necessarily-parallel horizons) generated from the seismic (Figure 15a) and coherence volumes (Figure 15b). The coherence strat cube reveals the north-south channel very clearly, the east-west fault on the right side, and the downthrown side of the north-south fault on the left.

Of course, with all that information also came complex and massive identification work and the need for faster and

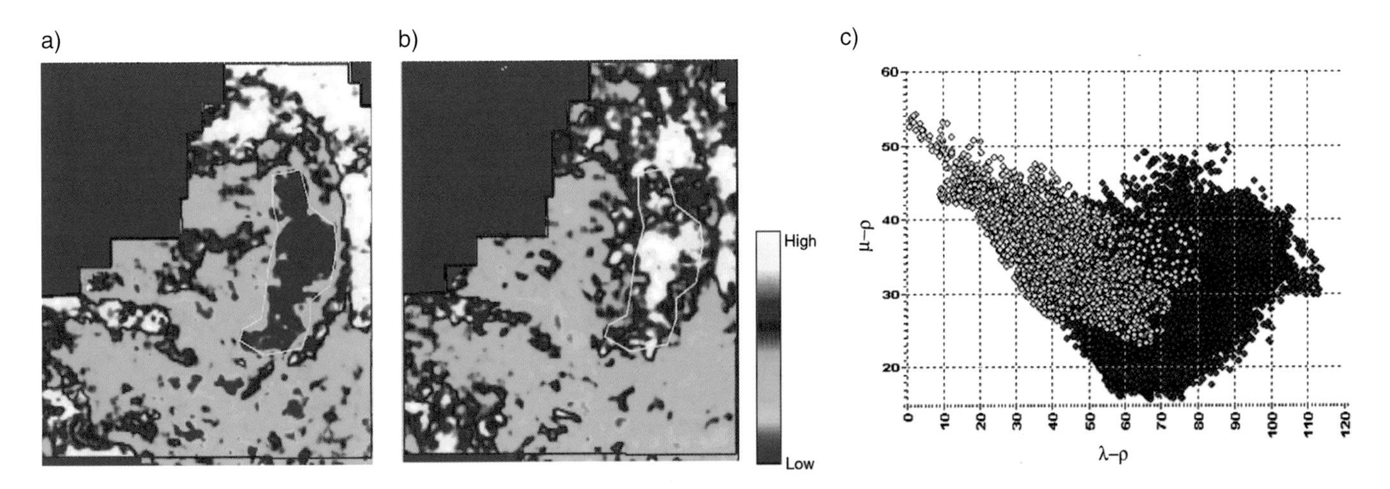

Figure 11. Time slices through (a) λ-ρ and (b) μ-ρ volumes. The suspected gas anomaly is indicated by low (blue) values in the λ-ρ slice and high (yellow) values of μ-ρ in the μ-ρ slice. (c) Crossplot of λ-ρ versus μ-ρ. The red polygon encloses all the live data points on both time slices, and the yellow polygon encloses the suspected anomaly. The crossplot shows the yellow points corresponding to low values of λ-ρ and high values of μ-ρ that are expected for a gas anomaly. After Chopra and Pruden (2003).

more accurate tools. Those needs inspired the significant introduction of techniques for automated identification of seismic objects and stratigraphic features. Keeping pace with such emerging technologies were advancements in visualization, and the results modernized the art of seismic interpretation. Starting at seed voxels, a seed tracker will search for connected voxels that satisfy the user-defined search criteria, thereby generating a 3D geobody within the 3D seismic volume.

Whereas one given attribute will be sensitive to a specific geologic feature of interest, a second attribute may be sensitive to a different kind of feature. Therefore, we can combine multiple attributes to enhance the contrast between features of interest and their surroundings. Different methodologies have been developed to recognize such features.

Meldahl et al. (2001) used neural networks trained on combinations of attributes to recognize features that were identified first in a seed interpretation. The neural network transforms chosen attributes into a new meta-attribute, which indicates the identified feature's probability of occurrence at different seismic positions. In that manner, a human being can train the computer to mimic a human interpreter in associating specific seismic textures, such as reflector dip, amplitude, and waveform, with a given geologic feature.

Trace shape

Although spectral decomposition and wavelet analysis compare seismic waveforms with precomputed waveforms (typically, with windowed tapered sines and cosines), Elf Acquitaine released an important development in the middle 1990s: trace-shape classification. In that approach, the interpreter defines a window of interest pegged to an interpreted horizon and then asks the computer to define a suite

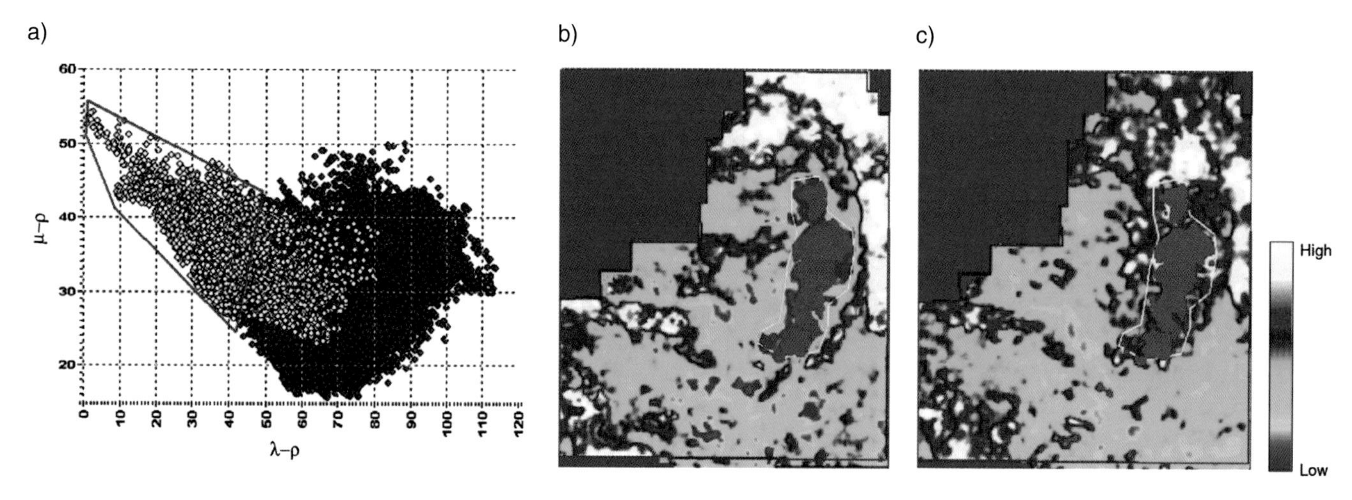

Figure 12. (a) The low values of λ-μ and high values of μ-ρ from Figure 11c enclosed here with the magenta polygon, which highlights their corresponding spatial locations on the (b) λ-ρ and (c) μ-ρ time slices. The job of the interpreter then is to validate his seismic attributes with his interpretation of the depositional and structural setting. After Chopra and Pruden (2003).

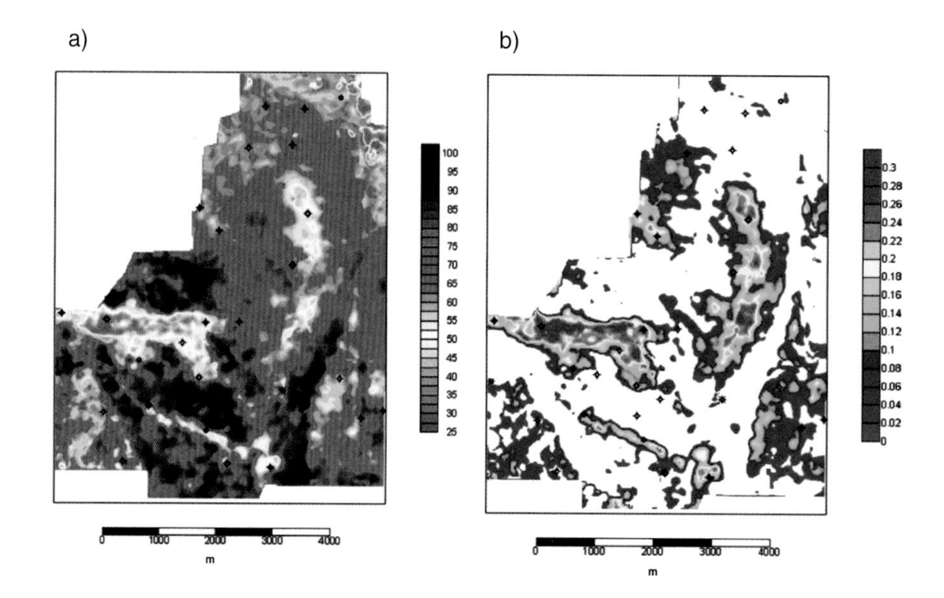

Figure 13. (a) A neural-network inverted gamma-ray response. Note the distinct separation of sand from silt and shale. (b) Neural-network computed porosity from the inverted density response. A mask has been applied to data whose gamma-ray values are representative of silt or shale, thereby producing a density (and subsequent porosity) prediction for the sands. After Chopra and Pruden (2003).

of approximately 10–20 waveforms (classes) that best express the data. The most useful of such classifiers is based on self-organized maps, or SOM (Coleou et al., 2003). Unlike *k*-means and most other classifiers, SOM algorithms order the classes such that similar classes are adjacent to each other on a 1D or 2D topology. By assigning a continuous 1D or 2D color spectrum to those ordered classes, SOM algorithms produce maps whose appearance is relatively insensitive to the number of classes. Although the results can be calibrated to well control through forward modeling, and although actual well classes can be inserted, this technology is particularly well suited to a geomorphology-driven interpretation whereby the interpreter identifies depositional and structural patterns from the images and uses the patterns to infer reservoir properties.

Figure 16a shows a coherence slice from a 3D seismic volume from southern Alberta, depicting the Lower Cretaceous fluvial channels filled with glauconitic sandstone, deposited in an incised valley system discussed earlier in this chapter. The coherence display enhances the channel edges. Figure 16b shows unsupervised classification analysis on the data using a self-organized map algorithm. Each cluster is assigned to a color, with adjacent clusters having adjacent colors along the hue axis. For that reason, clusters within the channel are more gradational, going from cyan to blue, whereas clusters that fall outside the channel have a strong color difference, such as the blue-to-orange boundary indicated by the white arrow in Figure 16b. That boundary also appears on the coherence image in Figure 16a.

Texture attributes

Recently, the study of seismic textures has been revived. Previously, the term texture was applied to seismic sections to pick out zones of common signal character (Love and Simaan, 1984). Now, however, studies are under way that use statistical measures to classify textures using gray-level co-occurrence matrices (Vinther et al., 1995; Vinther, 1997; Whitehead et al., 1999; West et al., 2002; Gao, 2003, 2004; and Chopra and Alexeev, 2005). Some of the statistical measures used are energy (denoting textural uniformity), entropy (measuring predictability from one texel or voxel to another), contrast (emphasizing the difference in amplitude of neighboring voxels), and homogeneity (highlighting the overall smoothness of the amplitude). En-

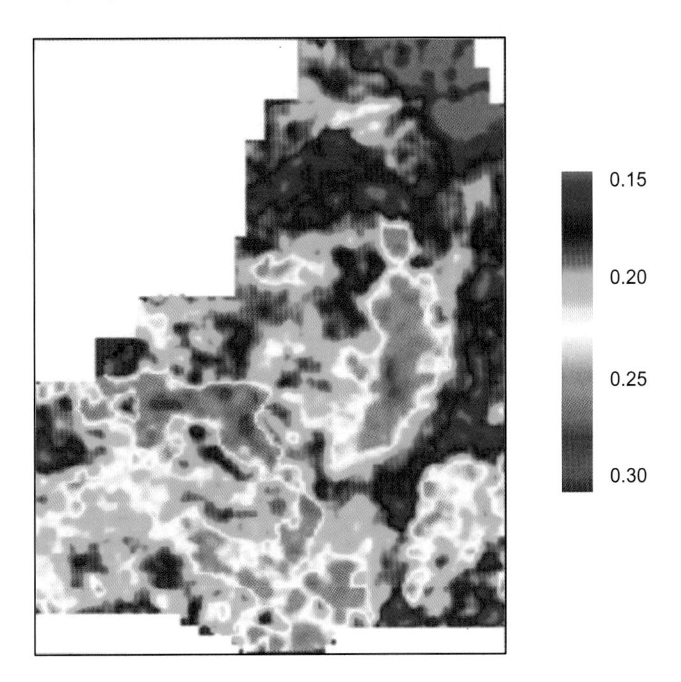

Figure 14. Spline-curve inverted porosity corresponding to the time slices shown in Figures 12 and 13. After Chopra et al. (2004).

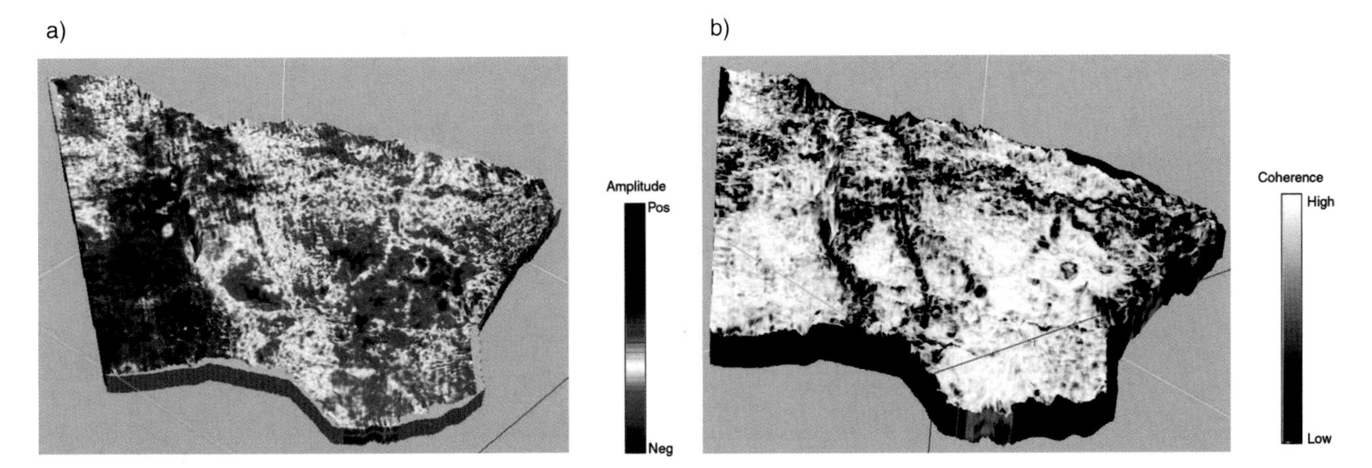

Figure 15. Strat cubes (a subvolume of 60-ms thickness bounded by two not-necessarily-parallel horizons) of the (a) seismic data volume and the (b) coherence volume. Notice the clarity with which the narrow north-south channel is seen on the coherence strat cube, as is the fault (which is seen with the help of relief). An east-west fault trend also appears clearly on the coherence strat cube. Data courtesy of Arcis Corporation, Calgary.

ergy, contrast, and entropy have been found to be the most effective in characterizing seismic data.

Figure 17 shows strat slices from a seismic volume (Figure 17a) compared with an equivalent slice extracted from the energy volume (Figure 17b). The distribution of the producing sandstone at the reservoir level is not seen on the seismic slice, but the signature is seen very clearly on the energy volume.

Figure 18 compares the amplitude (Figure 18a) and energy (Figure 18b) in a horizon slice at the same stratigraphic level. Notice that the channel and levee deposits can be recognized, mapped, and detected more effectively from the energy volume than from the amplitude volume. [Note: The original definition of energy given by Haralick et al. (1973) was redefined as homogeneity by Gao (2003).]

In Chapter 5, we review some of the basic principles of 3D volumetric texture attributes (texels) as well as other measures of amplitude variation along structural dip and azimuth.

Curvature

With the wide availability of 3D seismic data and a renewed interest in fractures, we have seen a rapid acceleration in the use of curvature maps. (We define curvature as a three-dimensional property of a quadratic surface that quantifies the degree to which the surface deviates from being planar.) The structural geology relationship between curva-

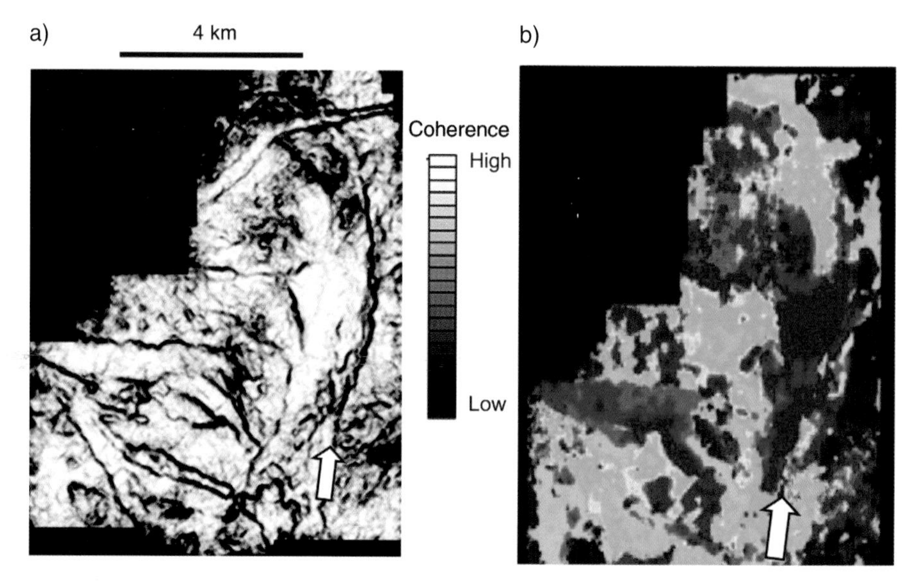

Figure 16. (a) A coherence slice from a 3D seismic volume, and (b) waveform clusters generated using a self-organized map algorithm, both corresponding to the same survey shown in Figures 10 through 14. Large lateral changes in cluster color imply a significant change in waveform, such that those changes also correspond to a coherence edge.

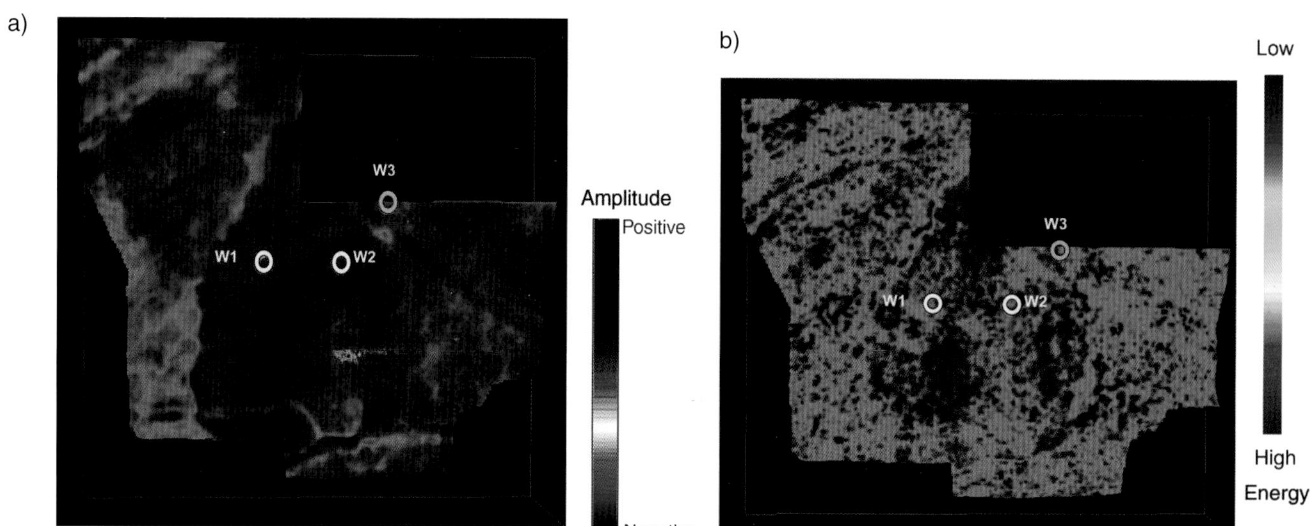

Figure 17. Strat slices from (a) a seismic volume and (b) an energy attribute volume. Notice the distribution of productive sands at the reservoir level, which are seen very clearly on the energy attribute slice but are indistinguishable on the seismic slice. After Chopra and Alexeev (2005).

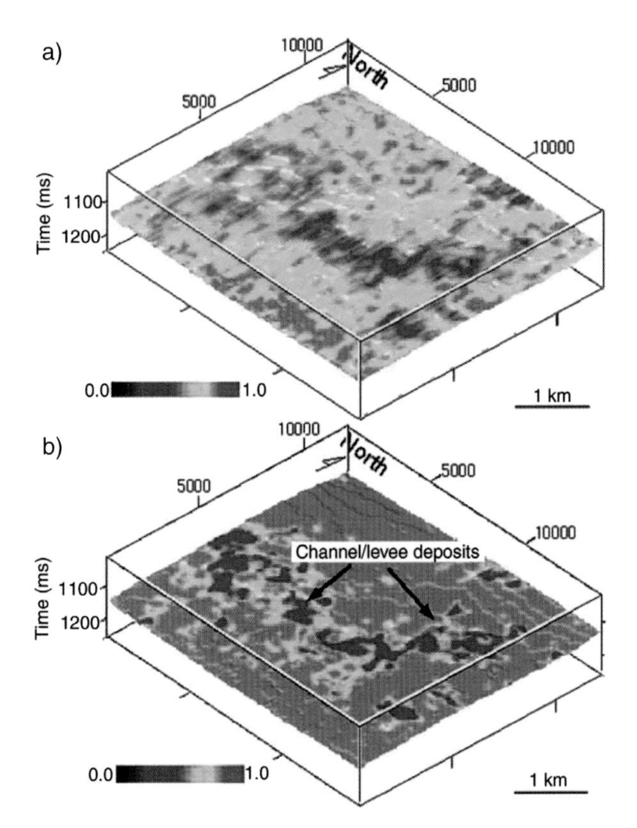

Figure 18. A comparison between (a) average absolute amplitude and (b) homogeneity in a horizon slice at the same stratigraphic level. To avoid a biased comparison, the same processing parameters (texel size and dimension) and a normalized color mapping function are used. Notice that the channel/levee deposits can be recognized, mapped, and detected more effectively from the homogeneity volume than from the amplitude volume. After Gao (2003).

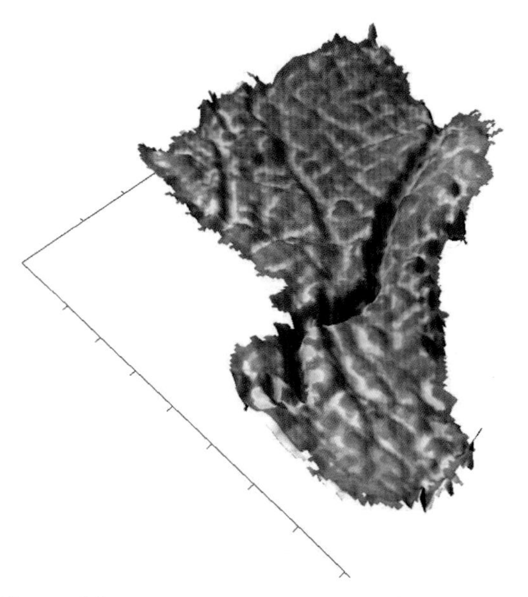

Figure 19. Minimum curvature draped over a near-basement reflection from a survey acquired in the San Juan Basin, New Mexico, U.S.A. A prominent north-south-trending incised valley is apparent, as are some curvilinear faults that strike approximately northwest-southeast. Tick marks are every 1 km. Illumination is from the southwest. Image is courtesy of Bruce Hart, McGill University.

ture and fractures is well established (Lisle, 1994), although the exact relationship between open fractures, paleostructure, and present-day stress is not yet clearly understood. Roberts (2001), Hart et al. (2002), Sigismondi and Soldo (2003), Masaferro et al. (2003), and others have used seismic measures of reflector curvature to map subtle features and predict fractures. Curvature attribute analysis of surfaces helps interpreters remove the effects of regional dip and emphasize small-scale features that might be associated with primary depositional features or small-scale faults. Figure 19 shows minimum curvature draped over a near-basement reflection in part of the San Juan Basin. A prominent north-south-trending incised valley is apparent, as are some faults that strike approximately northwest-southeast.

Figure 20a shows a time-structure map of the top of a Tertiary incised channel-levee complex. Figure 20b shows that complex with the dip component of curvature overlain on a 3D representation of the horizon, and Figure 20c includes shaded relief to enhance features. Note how changing the viewing angle, the zoom, and the surface-illumination angle improves the definition of stratigraphic and structural features, compared with the time-structure map.

In Chapter 4, we present the theoretical basis and algorithmic implementation of volumetric curvature. We apply curvature to mapping structure, stratigraphy, and reservoir heterogeneity in Chapters 11 through 15.

Examples of Present-day Workflows

Attributes used to generate sand probability volumes

When attributes are tied to the available well control, they can be correlated to petrophysical properties, and that helps the interpreter identify and associate high correlations with specific properties. For example, Figure 21 shows how attributes from prestack inversion of a high-resolution seismic data set allowed mapping of sand bodies in a geologically complex area. A key step in the workflow was the petroelastic analysis of well data, which demonstrated that seismic attributes derived from prestack seismic inversion could discriminate between sands and shales.

A multiattribute classification approach, incorporating neural-network training techniques, was used to generate sand-probability volumes derived from P-wave and S-wave impedances estimated using AVO inversion. The study demonstrated that high-resolution seismic data coupled with targeted inversion can increase our confidence and reduce uncertainty.

Crucial to any multiattribute analysis is the selection and the number of seismic attributes to be used. Kalkomey (1997) showed that the probability of observing a spurious correlation increases as the number of control points decreases, and it also increases with an increase in the number of seismic attributes being used. A partial remedy for such a situation is to withhold a percentage of the data during the training step and then later to use those hidden data to validate the predictions (Schuelke and Quirein, 1998). Kalkomey (1997) teaches that to avoid false-positive and false-negative predictions, the interpreter should use only those attributes which have a well-understood physical or geologic reason to correlate to the petrophysical feature of interest. For example,

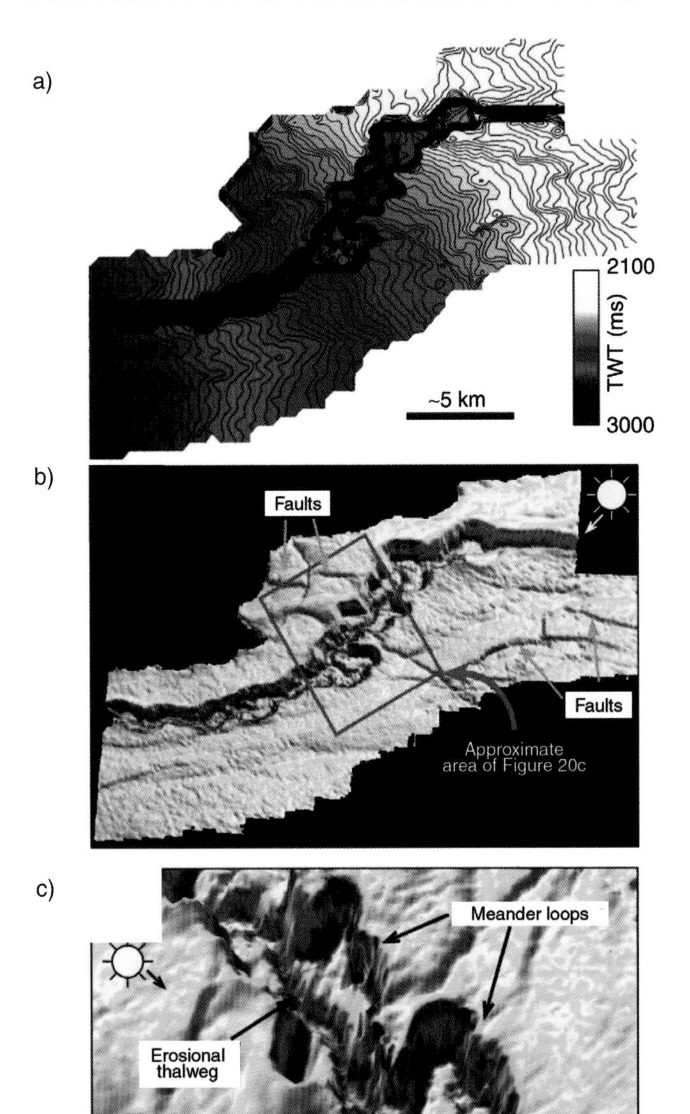

Figure 20. (a) A time-structure map of the top of a Tertiary channel-levee complex. (b) Dip component of curvature and (c) shaded relief overlain on a 3D representation of the horizon, to enhance features. Note the improved definition of stratigraphic and structural features in (b) and (c) compared with the time-structure map. Images courtesy of Bruce Hart, McGill University.

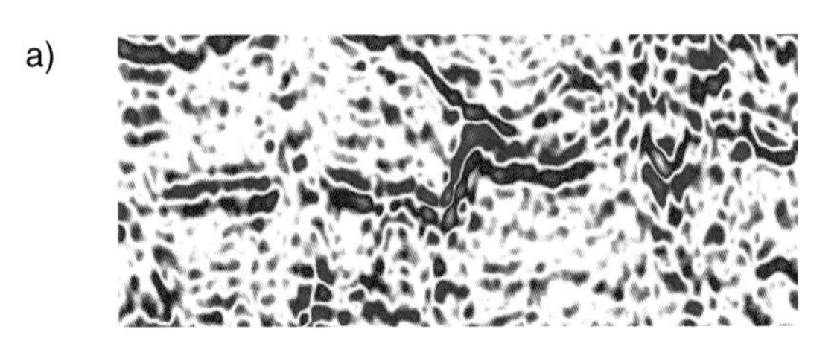

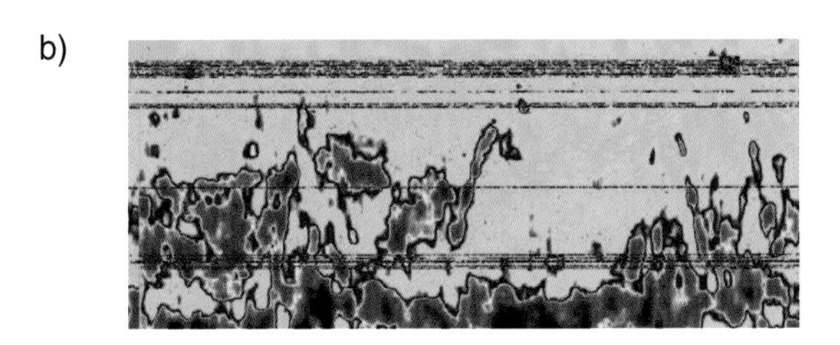

Figure 21. (a) A cross section from the final processed seismic data volume. The dipping event in the center of the panel is interpreted to be a sand injection feature. (b) The same cross section, here from the sand-probability volume derived from multiattribute classification. The classification has predicted that the feature is sand that was injected from the main sand body seen below. (c) The sand-probability volume and amplitude data, displayed using 3D visualization. The figure shows seismic amplitude data in the background; the base reservoir surface is shown in blue, and a possible sand-injection feature is mapped from the inversion results. Note the complexity of the injected sand bodies. Images courtesy of Steve McHugo, WesternGeco.

spectral components and impedance inversion are correlated well to porosity thickness, whereas coherence and curvature generally are not. Therefore, one of our main objectives in writing this book is to define clearly the mathematical formulation, physical basis, and geologic significance of geometric attributes and spectral decomposition.

Time-lapse analysis

Seismic attributes are being used effectively for time-lapse data analysis (4D analysis). Time-lapse data analysis permits us to interpret fluid saturation and pressure changes and helps us understand reservoir dynamics and the performance of existing wells.

Figure 22 shows an example from east of Schiehallion field, West of Shetlands (Parr and Marsh, 2000). (Schiehallion is a producing field off the northern edge of the U. K. and 95 miles west of the Shetlands.) The preproduction surveys in (a) 1993 and (b) 1996 show a high degree of similarity, but the 1999 4D survey (Figure 22c), designed to notice changes in reservoir production, shows large changes around producers and injectors. The poor production rates and low bottom-hole-flowing pressures led to the conclusion that well C was located in a compartment that is poorly connected to injection support. The areal extent of that compartment could be picked by the amplitude increase seen on the 4D image and interpreted from gas liberated from solution. This area is consistent with predictions from material-balance calculations.

Figure 22c from the 1999 survey suggests the possible existence of a connection (marked by an arrow) between producers C and D. Such a connection also was suspected from the material-balance analysis. Figure 23 shows a coherence display at the required level and depicts the expected connection (marked by a circle). Although a plausible explanation for this is not known, we postulate that the attributes on 4D seismic analysis suggest a transmissibility barrier may have been broken between the injector and producer.

Reservoir-based seismic attributes are used to help delineate anomalous areas of a reservoir, where changes from time-lapse data are evident (Galikeev and Davis, 2005). For example, reservoir conditions resulting from CO_2 injection can be detected. Attributes that represent reservoir heterogeneity are generated by computing short-time-window seismic attributes parallel to the reservoir. Such an analysis in short temporal windows ensures that the attribute carries an overprint of geology (Partyka et al., 1999).

Figure 24 illustrates the dynamic changes within the Weyburn reservoir (Canada) that result from increased CO_2 saturation. This image was done by computing the inverted impedance model of the reservoir on the differenced volume of the baseline survey (2000) and the second monitor (2002) survey. Figure 25 is a computed CO_2 saturation map, in which the values represent not absolute CO_2 saturation, but instead an estimate of partial porosity occupied by CO_2 after irreducible water and oil were taken into account.

a)

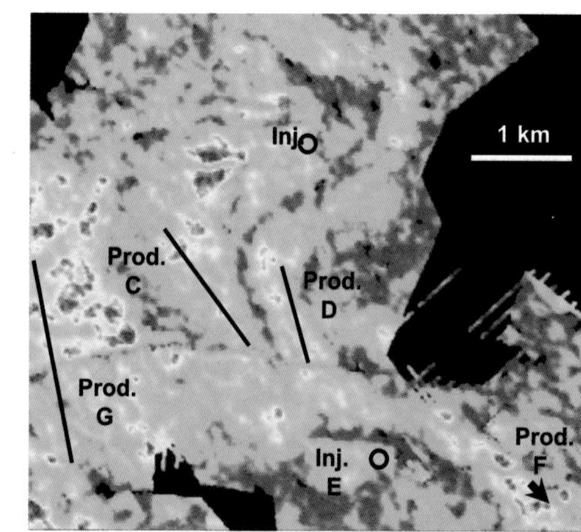

b)

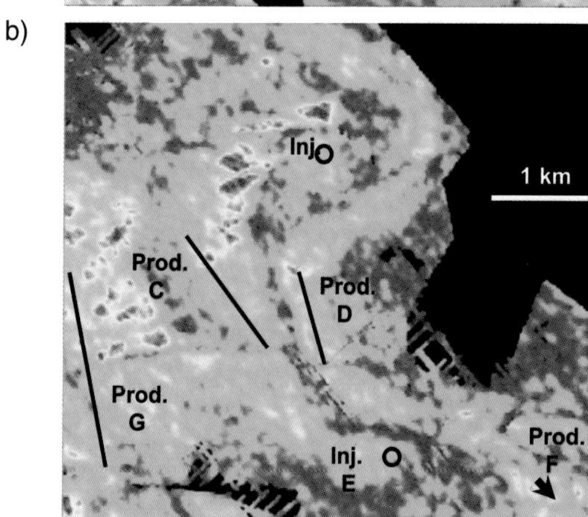

c)

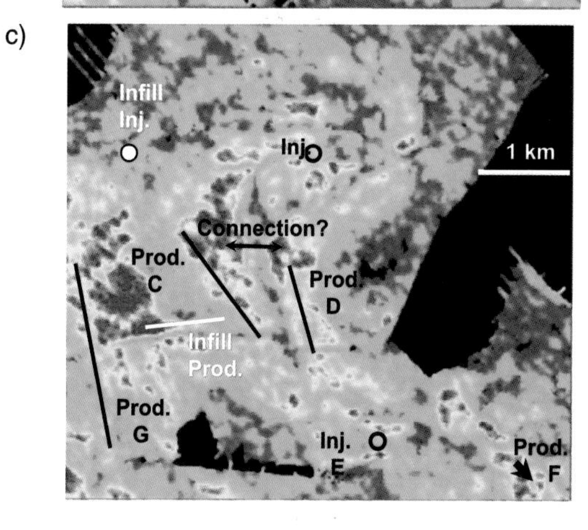

Figure 22. An example from east of Schiehallion. (Schiehallion is a producing field off the northern edge of the U. K. and 95 miles west of the Shetlands.) The net-sand maps based on seismic amplitudes from the preproduction surveys (a) in 1993 and (b) in 1996 show a high degree of similarity. (c) Comparison with the 1999 4D survey, showing large changes around producers and injectors. After Parr and Marsh (2000).

By calibrating 4D seismic attributes with both laboratory rock and fluid analysis and production-engineering information, we can estimate pressure and saturation changes away from the wells. Application of such an analysis to the Cook reservoir of the Gulfaks field, offshore Norway (Lumley et al., 2003), shows that a strong pressure anomaly can be estimated in the vicinity of a horizontal water injector, along with a strong water-saturation anomaly drawing toward a nearby producing well (Figure 26). Those anomalies are in addition to strong evidence of east-west fault-block compartmentalization at the time of the seismic survey.

Attributes for detecting gas zones below regional velocity inversion

Evaluation of gas distribution in the fluid system of the Wind River Basin, where anomalously pressured gas accumulations occur, is a challenge. Using available logs and seismic data, workers have mapped the area's regional velocity inversion surface — that is, the pressure surface separating the anomalously pressured rocks below from the normally pressured rocks above (Surdam et al., 2004b). Seismic attributes have been used successfully to evaluate the distribution of sandstone-rich intervals within the prospective reservoir units.

The Frenchie Draw gas field in the Wind River Basin is an example of an area where detecting and delineating gas zones below the regional velocity inversion surface is difficult. The stratigraphic interval of interest is the Upper Cretaceous–Paleocene Fort Union/Lance lenticular fluvial sandstone formations on a north-plunging structural nose. The gas distribution pattern in the formations is complex, so exploitation has proved to be risky. Surdam et al. (2004a) demonstrated that a good correlation exists between seis-

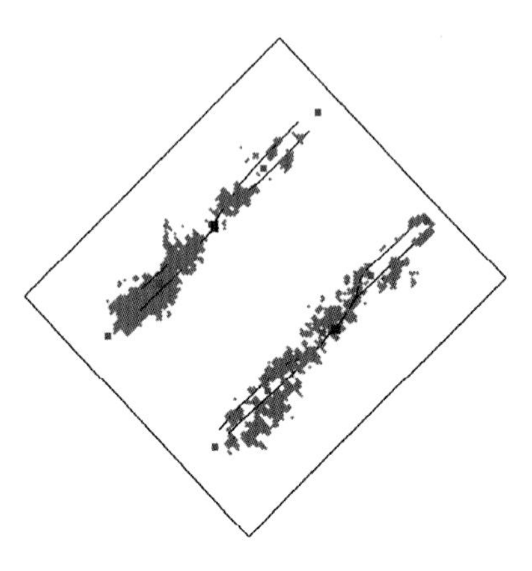

Figure 24. Position of the time-lapse impedance anomalies in depth relative to CO_2 injectors (black) and vertical water injectors (blue). The overall size of the area shown is 9 km^2. After Galikeev and Davis (2005).

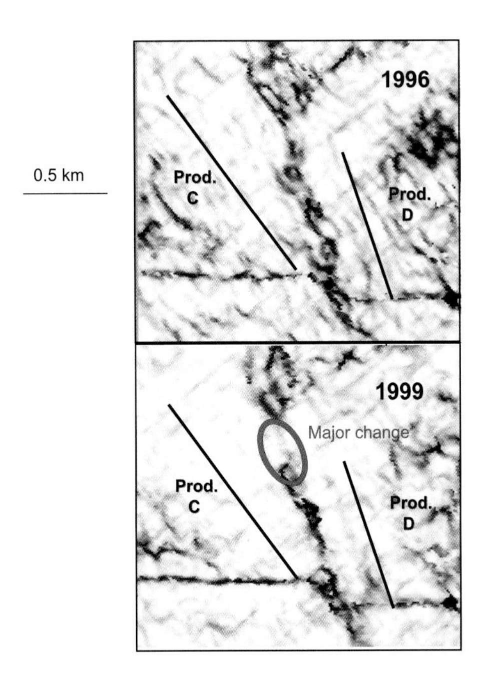

Figure 23. A time slice through a coherence volume corresponding to Figure 22, depicting the expected connection (marked by a circle) between producers C and D. After Parr and Marsh (2000).

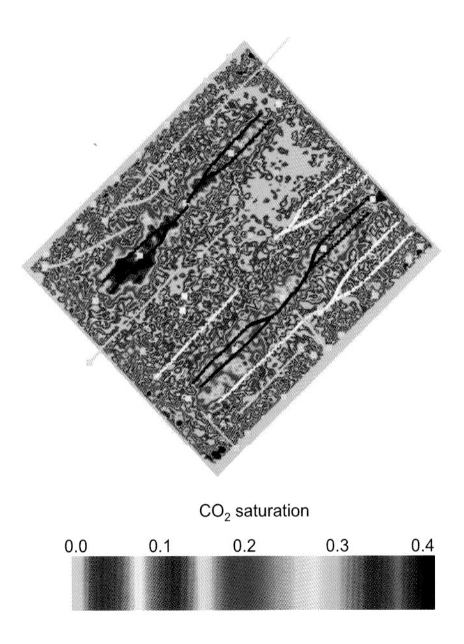

Figure 25. CO_2 saturation map computed from time-lapse (2000–2002 inversion of the difference) impedance values. Shown are areas that responded to CO_2 injection wells (white), to horizontal injectors (black), to areas unresponsive to CO_2 wells (blue), and to vertical water injectors (yellow). The overall size of the area shown is 9 km^2. After Galikeev and Davis (2005).

mic frequency and gamma-ray logs (lithology) in the lower Fort Union/Lance stratigraphic interval. The frequency attribute was used to distinguish sandstone-rich intervals from shale-rich intervals.

Figure 27 shows a frequency-attribute section (with seismic data overlaid) covering the Fort Union/Lance stratigraphic interval that intersects the anomalously slow velocity domains (outlined by white dots). In addition to the north-plunging structural nose seen in the area, a shale-rich sequence (orange) is seen near the upper edge of the gas production. The important thing to note here is the lenticular distribution of the sandstone-rich intervals in blue that stand out against the shale-rich intervals in orange, yellow, and green. This distributional pattern of lithologies corresponds well with the initial interpretations carried out by geoscientists who discovered the field.

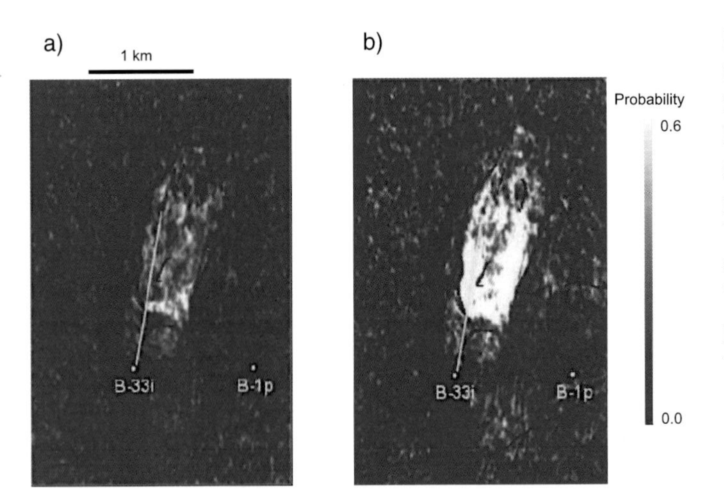

Figure 26. Probability map, on a scale of 0.0 (blue) to 0.6 (white), that (a) water saturation and (b) pore pressure have increased within the Cook reservoir of the Gulfaks field, Norwegian North Sea. Note that a strong pressure anomaly surrounds the B-33 horizontal injector, and implying compartmentalization controlled by an east-west sealing fault. Water saturation change, however, is weak in most of the compartment, because well B-33 injects into the water leg. The saturation change is stronger to the southeast of the compartment, where water is drawn toward nearby producing well B-1. After Lumley et al. (2003).

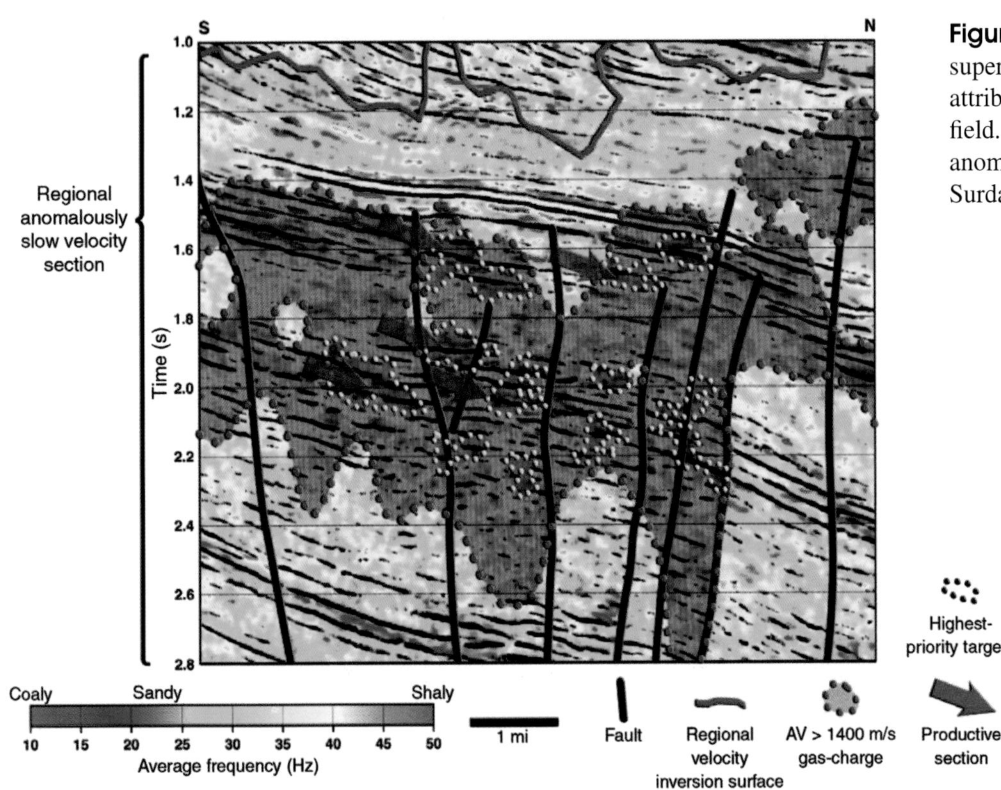

Figure 27. Seismic data display superimposed on a frequency attribute section at Frenchie Draw field. The shaded region shows an anomalous velocity overlap. After Surdam et al. (2004b).

Chapter Summary

A seismic attribute is a quantitative measure of a seismic characteristic of interest. Good seismic attributes and attribute-analysis tools mimic a good interpreter. Over the past decades, we have witnessed attribute developments tracking breakthroughs in seismic acquisition and mapping, fault identification, bright-spot identification, frequency loss, thin-bed tuning, seismic stratigraphy, and geomorphology. Recently, interpreters have used crossplotting to identify clusters of attributes that are associated with either stratigraphic or hydrocarbon anomalies. The attribute community has worked hard, first to duplicate such human-driven clustering through the use of self-organized maps, geostatistics, and neural nets, and then to extend that capability beyond the three dimensions easily visualized by interpreters.

In the following chapters, we will emphasize the theoretical basis, algorithmic implementation, data sensitivity, and interpretational use of modern attributes that measure seismic textures. Volumetric estimates of dip and azimuth, coherence, curvature, and lateral changes in amplitude or energy commonly are called geometric attributes. By including spectral decomposition, texture analysis, and even certain measures of seismic reflectivity within azimuth- and offset-limited volumes, we broaden our scope considerably beyond that of the attributes that clearly map changes in 3D reflector geometry. In contrast, whereas present-day implementation of texture analysis focuses on measures that are averaged over direction, the term texture analysis easily could be generalized to lateral textures measured by dip and azimuth, curvature, and coherence, and to vertical textures measured by spectral decomposition. However, the purpose of this book is to share the science and its application. Therefore, we leave the nomenclature challenge to others and proceed with a discussion of the recently developed volumetric attributes (whatever you wish to call them) that are so useful to interpretation.

References

Anstey, N., 2005, Attributes in color: the early years: CSEG Recorder, **30**, 12–15.

Bahorich, M. S., and S. R. Bridges, 1992, The seismic sequence attribute map (SSAM): 62nd Annual International Meeting, SEG, Expanded Abstracts, 227–230.

Bahorich, M. S., and S. L. Farmer, 1995, 3D seismic discontinuity for faults and stratigraphic features: The coherence cube, The Leading Edge, **14**, 1053–1058.

Bahorich, M. S., and P. van Bemmel, 1994, Stratigraphic interpretation of seismic data on the workstation: 64th Annual International Meeting, SEG, Expanded Abstracts, 481–484.

Bahorich, M. S., J. A. Lopez, N. L. Haskell, S. E. Nissen, and A. Poole, 1995, Stratigraphic and structural interpretation with 3-D coherence: 65th Annual International Meeting, SEG, Expanded Abstracts, 97–100.

Balch, A. H., 1971, Color sonograms: a new dimension in seismic data interpretation: Geophysics, **36**, 1074-1098.

Barnes, A., 2001, Seismic attributes in your facies: CSEG Recorder, **26**, 41–47.

Bodine, J. H., 1984, Waveform analysis with seismic attributes: 54th Annual International Meeting, SEG, Expanded Abstracts, 505–509.

———, 1986, Waveform analysis with seismic attributes: Oil and Gas Journal, **84**, no. 23, 59–63.

Brown, A. R., 1986, Interpretation of three-dimensional seismic data (1st edition), Memoir **42**: AAPG and SEG.

———, 2004, Interpretation of three-dimensional seismic data (6th edition), Memoir **42**: AAPG and SEG.

Brown, A. R., and J. D. Robertson, 1985, Focusing on SEG continuing education — Seismic interpretation for detailed exploration development and production: The Leading Edge, **4**, 60–65.

Castagna, J. P., S. Sun, and R. W. Siegfried, 2003, Instantaneous spectral analysis: Detection of low-frequency shadows associated with hydrocarbons: The Leading Edge, **22**, 120–127.

Chopra, S., 2002, Coherence cube and beyond: First Break, **20,** no. 01, 27–33.

Chopra, S., and V. Alexeev, 2005, Studying seismic textures — A promising interpretation tool: CSEG Recorder, **30**, 28–32.

Chopra, S., V. Alexeev, and Y. Xu, 2003, 3D AVO crossplotting — An effective visualization technique: The Leading Edge, **22,** 1078–1089.

Chopra, S., and O. Kuhn, 2001, Seismic inversion: CSEG Recorder: **26,** no. 1, 10–14.

Chopra, S., and K. J. Marfurt, 2005, Seismic attributes — A historical perspective: Geophysics, **70**, 3SO–28SO.

Chopra, S., and D. Pruden, 2003, Multiattribute seismic analysis on AVO-derived parameters: The Leading Edge, **22,** 998–1002.

Chopra, S., D. Pruden, and V. Alexeev, 2004, Multi-attribute seismic analysis — Tackling non-linearity: First Break, **22**, no. 12, 43–47.

Churlin, V. V., and L. A. Sergeyev, 1963, Application of seismic surveying to recognition of productive part of gas-oil strata: Geolog Nefti I Gaza, **7**, 363.

Claerbout, J. F., 1990, The plane-wave destructor (PWD), Stanford Exploration Project, Report 65.

Coleou, T., M. Poupon, and K. Azbel, 2003, Unsupervised seismic facies classification: A review and comparison of techniques and implementation: The Leading Edge, **22**, 942–953.

Connolly, P., 1999, Elastic impedance: The Leading Edge, **18,** 438–452.

Conticini, F., 1984, Seismic facies quantitative analysis: New tool in stratigraphic interpretation: 54th Annual International Meeting, SEG, Expanded Abstracts, 680–682.

Dalley, R. M., E. C. A. Gevers, G. M. Stampfli, D. J. Davies, C. N. Gastaldi, P. A. Ruijtenberg, and G. J. O. Vermeer, 1989, Dip and azimuth displays for 3D seismic interpretation: First Break, **07**, no. 03, 86–95.

de Figueiredo, R. J. P., 1982, Pattern recognition approach to exploration: *in* R. J. P. de Figueiredo, ed., Concepts and techniques in oil and gas exploration: SEG, 267–286.

Drecun, R., and J. Lucas, 1985, Enhancement of edge patterns on horizontal time slices, 55th Annual International Meeting, SEG, Expanded Abstracts, 579–582.

Finn, C. J., 1986, Estimation of three dimensional dip and curvature from reflection seismic data: M.S. thesis, University of Texas.

Forrest, M., 2000, "Bright" investments paid off: AAPG Explorer, July, 18–21.

Galikeev, T., and T. Davis, 2005, Time-lapse seismic attributes and reservoir volumetric calculation: 67th Annual International Conference and Exhibition, EAGE, Expanded Abstracts, Z99.

Gao, D., 2003, Volume texture extraction for 3D seismic visualization and interpretation: Geophysics, **68,** 1294–1302.

———, 2004, Texture model regression for effective feature discrimination: Application to seismic facies visualization and interpretation: Geophysics, **69,** 958–967.

Gersztenkorn, A., and K. J. Marfurt, 1999, Eigenstructure-based coherence computations as an aid to 3-D structural and stratigraphic mapping: Geophysics, **64,** 1468–1479.

Haralick, R. M., K. Shanmugam, and I. Dinstein, 1973, Textural features for image classification: IEEE Transactions: Systems, Man, and Cybernetics, SMC-**3**, 610–621.

Hardage, B. A., V. M. Pendleton, J. L. Simmons Jr., B. A. Stubbs, and B. J. Uszynski, 1998, 3-D instantaneous frequency used as a coherency/continuity parameter to interpet reservoir compartment boundaries across an area of complex turbidite deposition: Geophysics, **63**, 1520–1531.

Hart, B. S., R. Pearson, R. Pearson, and G. C. Rawling, 2002, 3-D seismic horizon-based approaches to fracture-swarm sweet spot definition in tight-gas reservoirs: The Leading Edge, **21,** 28–35.

Haskell, N. L., S. E. Nissen, J. A. Lopez, and M. S. Bahorich, 1995, 3-D seismic coherency and the imaging of sedimentological features: 65th Annual International Meeting, SEG, Expanded Abstracts, 1532–1534.

Kalkomey, C. T., 1997, Potential risks when using seismic attributes as predictors of reservoir properties: The Leading Edge, **16,** 247–251.

Lavergne, M., 1975, Pseudo diagraphics de vitesse en offshore profond : Geophysical Prospecting, **23**, 695–711.

Lindseth, R. O., 1979, Synthetic sonic logs — A process for stratigraphic interpretation: Geophysics: **44**, 3–26.

———, 2005, Seismic attributes — Some recollections: CSEG Recorder, **30**, 16–17.

Liner, C., C.-F. Li, A. Gersztenkorn, and J. Smythe, 2004, SPICE: A new general seismic attribute: 72nd Annual International Meeting, SEG, Expanded Abstracts, 433–436.

Lisle, R. J., 1994, Detection of zones of abnormal strains in structures using Gaussian curvature analysis: AAPG Bulletin, **78**, 1811–1819.

Love, P. L., and M. Simaan, 1984, Segmentation of stacked seismic data by the classification of image texture: 54th Annual International Meeting, SEG, Expanded Abstracts, 480–482.

Lumley. D., D. Adams, M. Meadows, S. Cole, and E. Ergas, 2003, 4D seismic pressure-saturation inversion at Gulfaks field, Norway: First Break, **21,** 49–56.

Marfurt, K. J., R. L. Kirlin, S. L. Farmer, and M. S. Bahorich, 1998, 3-D seismic attributes using a semblance-based coherency algorithm: Geophysics, **63,** 1150–1165.

Marfurt, K. J., V. Sudhaker, A. Gersztenkorn, K. D. Crawford, and S. E. Nissen, 1999, Coherency calculations in the presence of structural dip: Geophysics, **64,** 104–111.

Masaferro, J. L., M. Bulnes, J. Poblet, and M. Casson, 2003, Kinematic evolution and fracture prediction of the Valle Morado structure inferred from 3D seismic data, Salta Province, northwest Argentina: AAPG Bulletin, **87**, 1083–1104.

Meldahl, P., R. Heggland, B. Bril, and P. de Groot, 2001, Identifying faults and gas chimneys using multiattributes and neural networks: The Leading Edge, **20,** 474–478.

Parr, R. S., and M. Marsh, 2000, Development of 4-D reservoir management West of Shetland: World Oil, **221**, no. 9, 39–47.

Partyka, G., J. Gridley, and J. Lopez, 1999, Interpretational applications of spectral decomposition in reservoir characterization: The Leading Edge, **18**, 353–360.

Rijks, E. J. H., and J. C. E. M. Jauffred, 1991, Attribute extraction: An important application in any detailed 3-D interpretation study: The Leading Edge, **10,** 11–19.

Roberts, A., 2001, Curvature attributes and their application to 3-D interpreted horizons: First Break, **19,** 85–99.

Robertson, J. D., and D. A. Fisher, 1988, Complex seismic trace attributes: The Leading Edge, **7**, 22–26.

Robertson, J. D., and H. H. Nogami, 1984, Complex seismic trace analysis of thin beds: Geophysics, **49**, 344–352.

Rummerfeld, B., 1954, Reflection quality, a fourth dimension: Geophysics, **19**, 684–694.

Russell, B., D. Hampson, J. Schulke, and J. Quirein, 1997, Multiattribute seismic analysis: The Leading Edge, **16**, 1439–1443.

Schuelke, J. S., and J. A. Quirein, 1998, Validation: A technique for selecting seismic attributes and verifying results: 68th Annual International Meeting, SEG, Expanded Abstracts, 936–939.

Sigismondi, M., and J. C. Soldo, 2003, Curvature attributes and seismic interpretation: Case studies from Argentina basins: The Leading Edge, **22,** 1122–1126.

Sonneland, L., O. Barkved, M. Olsen, and G. Snyder, 1989, Application of seismic wave-field attributes in reservoir characterization: 59th Annual International Meeting, SEG, Expanded Abstracts, 813.

Surdam, R. C., Z. S. Jiao, and Y. Ganshin, 2004a, Reducing risk in low-permeability gas formations: Understanding the rock fluid characteristics of Rocky Mountain Laramide Basins: DOE Final Technical Progress Report under contract no. DE-FC26-01NT41325, 39.

Surdam, R. C., Z. S. Jiao, and Y. Ganshin, 2004b, Reducing the risk of exploring for anomalously pressured gas assets: GasTIPS, Winter 2004, 4–8.

Taner, M. T., 2000, Attributes revisited: http://www.rocksolidimages.com/pdf/attrib_revisited.htm, accessed June 22, 2005.

Taner, M. T., F. Koehler, and R. E. Sheriff, 1979, Complex seismic trace analysis: Geophysics, **44**, 1041–1063.

Taner, M. T., and R. E. Sheriff, 1977, Application of amplitude, frequency, and other attributes to stratigraphic and hydrocarbon determination, *in* C. E. Payton, ed., Applications to hydrocarbon exploration: AAPG Memoir 26, 301–327.

Thadani, S. G., F. Aldabert, and A. G. Journel, 1987, An integrated geostatistical/pattern recognition technique for characterization of reservoir spatial variability: 57th Annual International Meeting, SEG, Expanded Abstracts, 372–375.

Verm, R. W., and F. J. Hilterman, 1994, Lithologic color-coded sections by AVO crossplots: 64th Annual International Meeting, SEG, Expanded Abstracts, 1092–1095.

Vinther, R., 1997, Seismic texture classification applied to processed 2-D and 3-D seismic data: 67th Annual International Meeting, SEG, Expanded Abstracts, 721–724.

Vinther, R., K. Mosegaard, K. Kierkegaard, I. Abatzis, C. Andersen, and F. If, 1995, Seismic texture classification: A computer-aided approach to stratigraphic analysis: 65th Annual International Meeting, SEG, Expanded Abstracts, 153–155.

Vossler, D. A., 1988, Automatic whole section seismic reflection mapping: 58th Annual International Meeting, SEG, Expanded Abstracts, 689–691.

West, B., S. May, J. E. Eastwood, and C. Rossen, 2002, Interactive seismic facies classification using textural and neural networks: The Leading Edge, **21**, 1042–1049.

Whitcombe, D. N., 2002, Elastic impedance normalization: Geophysics, **67**, 60–62.

White, R. E., 1991, Properties of instantaneous seismic attributes: The Leading Edge, **10,** 26–32.

Whitehead, P., J. Fairborn, and R. Wentland, 1999, Identifying stratigraphic units by seismic patterns: 69th Annual International Meeting, SEG, Expanded Abstracts, 942–945.

Section I

Geometric Attributes — Their Physical Basis and Sensitivity to Seismic Signal and Noise

Chapter 2

Volumetric Dip and Azimuth

Chapter Objectives

After reading this chapter, you will be able to

- evaluate alternative algorithms for calculating volumetric dip and azimuth in terms of accuracy and lateral resolution
- interpret shaded-relief and apparent-dip images to delineate subtle structural features
- apply composite dip/azimuth/seismic images to determine how a given reflector dips in and out of the plane of view

Introduction

Second to time-structure and amplitude-extraction maps, dip and azimuth maps of interpreted seismic reflectors arguably are the most important product in the interpretation of 3D seismic data. Originally described by Dalley et al. (1989), dip and azimuth maps, along with closely related shaded-relief maps (Barnes, 2003), can highlight subtle faults that have throws of less than 10 ms, as well as stratigraphic features that manifest themselves through differential compaction or through subtle changes in the seismic waveform. As we discussed in Chapter 1, Lisle (1994) and Hart et al. (2002) demonstrated the relationship between reflector curvature and fracture density. Unfortunately, variability in reflector waveform, as well as seismic noise, can cause difficulties with attribute extractions made along picked horizons (Hesthammer and Fossen, 1997).

Because of recent advances in algorithm development, now we can calculate 3D cubes of reflector dip and azimuth without explicitly picking a given horizon. The earliest published work we have found on estimating dip for interpretation purposes, working directly from seismic data, is by Picou and Utzman (1962). They used a 2D unnormalized crosscorrelation scan over candidate dips on 2D seismic lines. Marfurt et al. (1998) generalized a later semblance-based scan by Finn (1986) to a true 3D scan. Barnes (1996, 2000a) presented an alternative approach based on 3D complex-trace analysis that Scheuer and Oldenburg (1988) originally had applied to velocity analysis, whereas Bakker et al. (1999) presented an estimate based on the gradient structure tensor (GST).

Dip and azimuth volumes can be very valuable interpretation tools. Currently, their most important use is to define a local reflector surface upon which we estimate some measure of discontinuity, or conversely, along which we filter the data to extract their continuous component. Examples of the former include the various coherence and edge-detection measures (e.g., Marfurt et al., 1998; Marfurt et al., 1999; Luo et al., 1996, 2001). Examples of the latter include conventional *f-x-y* deconvolution, and structurally ordered filtering (Hoecker and Fehmers, 2002) (which alternatively is called edge-preserving smoothing [Bakker et al., 1999; Luo et al., 2002]).

Because of velocity distortions, estimates of reflector dip and azimuth from time-migrated seismic cubes are only loosely related to true dip and azimuth at depth. Even estimates calculated from prestack depth-migrated data will suffer from errors in the background-velocity model. Nevertheless, because they are differential rather than absolute measures of changes in reflector depth, dip and azimuth maps are less sensitive to long-wavelength errors in the velocity model than are reflector depth measurements. Furthermore, most interpretations of dip and azimuth calculations are done on changes in dip and azimuth — through color display (Marfurt et al., 1998; Lin et al., 2003), through visualization tools such as shaded-relief projections (Barnes, 2003), or through explicit calculation of higher-order derivatives (Marfurt and Kirlin, 2000; Luo et al., 1996; Al-Dossary and Marfurt, 2003) that are sensitive to reflector curvature or rotation. Recently, Barnes (2000b) developed a suite of computer-generated textures similar to those used in traditional interpreter-driven seismic stratigraphy that measure reflector convergence, divergence, parallelism, and disorder, and that are based on an underlying estimate of dip and azimuth.

Definition of Reflector Dip and Azimuth

Mathematically, a planar element of a seismic reflector can be defined uniquely by a point in space, $\mathbf{x} = (x,y,z)$, and a unit normal to the surface, $\mathbf{n} = (n_x,n_y,n_z)$, where n_x , n_y, and n_z denote the components along the x, y, and z axes, respectively, and are chosen such that $n_z \geq 0$ (Figure 1).

Geologically, we define a planar interface such as a formation top or internal bedding surface by means of apparent dips θ_x and θ_y, or more commonly, by the surface's true dip, θ, and its strike, ψ (Figure 1). Apparent dip θ_x is the angle measured in the vertical (x, z) plane from the horizontal x-axis to the interface. Similarly, apparent dip θ_y is the angle measured in the vertical (y,z) plane from the horizontal y-axis to the interface. The strike, ψ, is the angle between north (the y-axis in the SEG-Y trace header convention) and the intersection between the reflector and the horizontal (x,y) plane. The true dip, θ, is always greater than or equal to apparent dips θ_x and θ_y and is the angle measured in a vertical plane perpendicular to the strike between the horizontal plane and the interface. Geologic dips have no sign and always are measured downward from the horizontal plane to the surface. Because the strike defines a line (e.g., northeast-southwest) rather than a vector, we need to state, or more commonly to post on a map, the direction of downward dip (e.g., northwest or southeast).

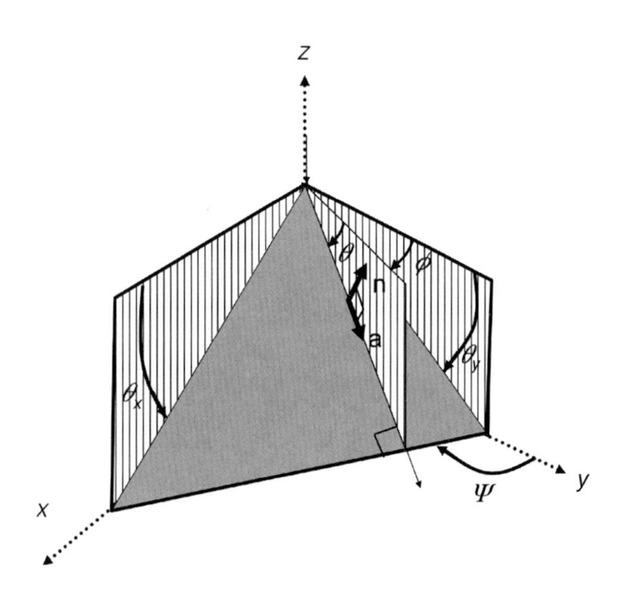

Figure 1. Mathematical, geologic, and seismic nomenclature used in defining reflector dip. By convention, $\mathbf{n}$ = unit vector normal to the reflector; $\mathbf{a}$ = unit vector dip along the reflector; θ = dip magnitude; ϕ = dip azimuth; ψ = strike; θ_x = the apparent dip in the xz plane; and θ_y = the apparent dip in the yz plane.

In seismology, we avoid such mathematical ambiguity and commonly define a reflector by its dip and azimuth. Dip, which is more explicitly called dip magnitude, θ, is identical to that used in the above geologic definition. Azimuth, ϕ, sometimes called dip azimuth, is measured either from the north, or for convenience, from the inline seismic survey axis. Azimuth is perpendicular to the geologic strike and is measured in the direction of maximum downward dip. In this book, we will use the seismic notation of dip and azimuth, as well as apparent dips along the survey axes, θ_x and θ_y, to define the reflector dip unit vector, $\mathbf{a}$, where

$$a_x = \sin\theta \cos\phi, \tag{2.1a}$$

$$a_y = \sin\theta \sin\phi, \tag{2.1b}$$

and

$$a_z = \cos\theta. \tag{2.1c}$$

Although theoretically the different measures of the plane are equivalent, using its normal, $\mathbf{n}$, its dip and strike, θ and ψ, and its apparent dips, θ_x and θ_y, its dip and azimuth, θ and ϕ, respectively, or its vector dip, $\mathbf{a}$, such equivalent measures can differ when stored with finite accuracy in an interpretation workstation. In particular, azimuth and strike are undefined for a horizontal reflector. In contrast, the reflector normal and its components always are defined.

Without knowing the velocity of the earth, we often find it convenient to measure the apparent seismic (two-way) time dips, p and q, where p is the apparent dip measured in s/m (or s/ft) in the inline, or x direction, and q is the apparent dip measured in s/m (or s/ft) in the crossline, or y direction. If the earth can be approximated by a constant velocity, v, the relationships between the apparent time dips p and q, and the apparent angle dips θ_x and θ_y, are

$$p = 2\tan\theta_x/v, \tag{2.2a}$$

and

$$q = 2\tan\theta_y/v. \tag{2.2b}$$

Alternative Means of Computing Volumetric Dip and Azimuth

There are three popular methods of estimating volumetric dip and azimuth from uninterpreted seismic data volumes. These methods require (1) aligning the phase derived from complex-trace analysis, (2) discretely scanning for the most coherent planar reflector, or (3) crosscorrelating the gradient of the data and forming a gradient structure tensor.

Calculation of vector dip using complex-trace analysis

Luo et al. (1996) and Barnes (1996) described a method of estimating vector dip based on a 3D extension of the analytic trace (or complex-trace) attributes described in Chapter 1. They began with Taner et al.'s (1979) instantaneous frequency, ω:

$$\omega(t,x,y)=\frac{\partial\Phi}{\partial t}=\frac{\partial}{\partial t}\text{ATAN2}(u^H,u)=\frac{u\frac{\partial u^H}{\partial t}-u^H\frac{\partial u}{\partial t}}{(u)^2+(u^H)^2}, \quad (2.3)$$

where Φ denotes the instantaneous phase, $u(t,x,y)$ denotes the input seismic data, $u^H(t,x,y)$ denotes its Hilbert transform with respect to time, t, and where ATAN2 denotes the arctangent function whose output varies between $-\pi$ and $+\pi$. The derivatives of u and u^H are obtained either by using finite differences or via a Fourier transform, with the Fourier transform approach being particularly convenient because this is the domain in which the Hilbert transform typically is calculated.

Next, we calculate the instantaneous wavenumbers k_x and k_y:

$$k_x(t,x,y)=\frac{\partial\Phi}{\partial x}=\frac{u\frac{\partial u^H}{\partial x}-u^H\frac{\partial u}{\partial x}}{(u)^2+(u^H)^2}, \quad (2.4a)$$

and

$$k_y(t,x,y)=\frac{\partial\Phi}{\partial y}=\frac{u\frac{\partial u^H}{\partial y}-u^H\frac{\partial u}{\partial y}}{(u)^2+(u^H)^2}. \quad (2.4b)$$

For very large 3D-input seismic data cubes, it is more convenient to estimate the spatial derivatives, $\frac{\partial u}{\partial y}, \frac{\partial u^H}{\partial y}, \frac{\partial u}{\partial y}$, and $\frac{\partial u^H}{\partial y}$, using either central differences or a relatively short Fourier transform, thereby circumventing the need to keep the entire data cube in memory. Alternatively, it is convenient to transpose the cube prior to calculating the derivatives given in equation 2.4. Then, the instantaneous time dip (p,q) is obtained by calculating the ratio of k_x and k_y to ω:

$$p = k_x/\omega, \quad (2.5a)$$

and

$$q = k_y/\omega, \quad (2.5b)$$

and the azimuth ϕ, measured from the y-axis, and true time dip, s, are given by

$$\phi = \text{ATAN2}(q,p), \quad (2.6a)$$

and

$$s = (p^2+q^2)^{1/2}. \quad (2.6b)$$

If the input data are in the depth domain rather than in the time domain, we would calculate k_z rather than ω:

$$k_z(z,x,y)=\frac{\partial\Phi}{\partial z}=\frac{u\frac{\partial u^H}{\partial z}-u^H\frac{\partial u}{\partial z}}{(u)^2+(u^H)^2}, \quad (2.7)$$

where u^H now is the Hilbert transform with respect to depth, z, allowing us to estimate angular dips θ_x and θ_y:

$$\theta_x = \tan^{-1}(k_x/k_z), \quad (2.8a)$$

$$\theta_y = \tan^{-1}(k_y/k_z), \quad (2.8b)$$

$$\theta = \tan^{-1}[(k_x^2+k_y^2)^{1/2}/k_z], \quad (2.8c)$$

and

$$\phi = \text{ATAN2}(k_y, k_x). \quad (2.8d)$$

In Figure 2, we show vertical and horizontal slices through a seismic survey acquired over a salt dome. In Figure 3, we show the instantaneous dip magnitude and azimuth given by equations 2.8c and 2.8d. Taner et al. (1979) warned that the estimate of instantaneous frequency given by equation 2.3 suffers from singularities when reflector events interfere with each other. To remedy this inaccuracy, Taner et al. (1979) suggested replacing equation 2.3 with an envelope-weighted average. Indeed, such singularities form the basis of the recently introduced SPICE (spectral imaging of correlative events) algorithm (Liner et al., 2004), which we will discuss in Chapter 6.

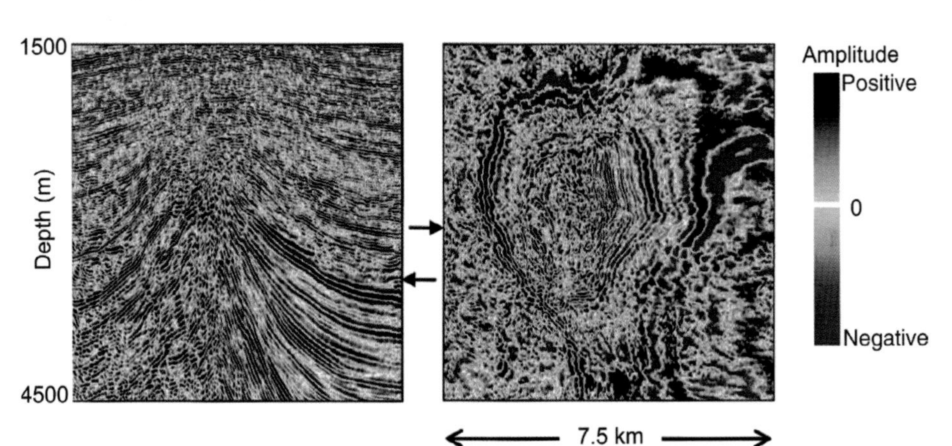

Figure 2. A vertical slice and a horizontal depth slice through a seismic data volume gathered over a salt dome. Note the characteristic "cut-onion" appearance on the depth slice. After Barnes (2000a).

Barnes (2000a) proposed smoothing the calculation of ω, k_x, and k_y over 25 or more adjacent traces prior to estimating dip and azimuth, thereby obtaining improved stability at the expense of some loss of lateral resolution. We show the results of such smoothing in Figure 4. The speckled nature of the instantaneous dip magnitude and azimuth images is diminished, and we obtain a smoother (albeit lower-resolution), more-realistic image.

Calculation of vector dip by discrete scans

Marfurt et al. (1998) generalized Finn's (1986) semblance scanning method to 3D data, to generate a more robust means of estimating reflector dip (Figure 5):

$$c_s(\theta_x,\theta_y) = \frac{\sum_{k=K_S}^{K_E}\left\{\left[\frac{1}{J}\sum_{j=1}^{J}u_j(k\Delta t-p\Delta x_j-q\Delta y_j)\right]^2+\left[\frac{1}{J}\sum_{j=1}^{J}u_j^H(k\Delta t-p\Delta x_j-q\Delta y_j)\right]^2\right\}}{\sum_{k=K_S}^{K_E}\left\{\frac{1}{J}\sum_{j=1}^{J}\left[u_j(k\Delta t-p\Delta x_j-q\Delta y_j)\right]^2+\frac{1}{J}\sum_{j=1}^{J}\left[u_j^H(k\Delta t-p\Delta x_j-q\Delta y_j)\right]^2\right\}} \quad (2.9)$$

where p and q are given by equation 2.2, x_j and y_j denote the local coordinates of the jth trace measured from an origin at the analysis point, J denotes the total number of traces in the analysis window, and K_s and K_e denote the first and last temporal sample, respectively, in the analysis window. Other amplitude-normalized measures include principal-component coherence (Gersztenkorn and Marfurt, 1999), lateral variance normalized by the energy, and a least-squares fit to the data (Bednar, 1998). Details on coherence calculations, including equation 2.9, will be discussed in Chapter 3. A disadvantage of dip scan approaches is that they discretely sample θ_x and θ_y, such that we may miss subtle features that might be discerned by the continuous phase estimated using the complex-trace analysis method given by equation 2.7.

Calculation of vector dip using the gradient structure tensor

The third method of estimating vector dip is based on the gradient structure tensor (GST) and is used by Bakker et al. (1999) and by Hoecker and Fehmers (2002) in their structure-oriented filtering work. The goal of this method is to define, within a small analysis window, the direction in which the seismic data vary the greatest. If our window contains a constant-amplitude planar reflection, that direction will be the normal to the plane. There will be two other axes that are perpendicular to the axis having the most variation. We ad-

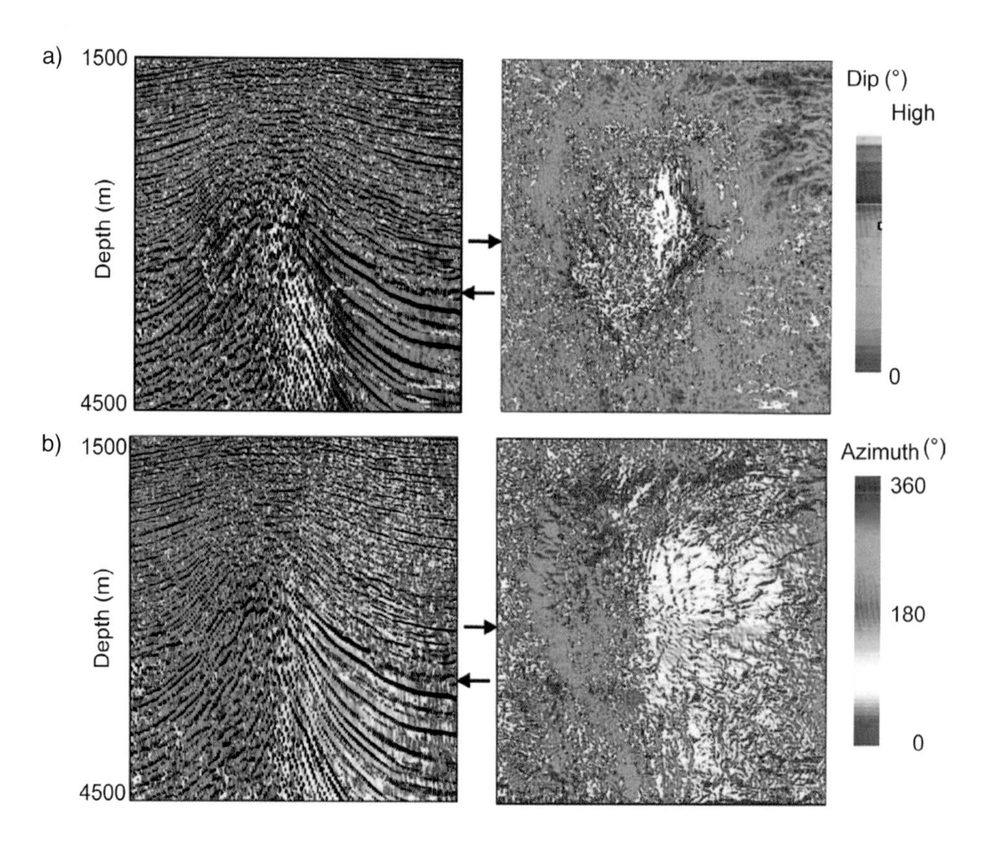

Figure 3. Vertical and horizontal slices corresponding to those shown in Figure 2 through (a) instantaneous dip magnitude, given by equation 2.8c, and (b) instantaneous dip azimuth, given by equation 2.8d. The speckled appearance of adjacent conflicting dip magnitude and dip azimuth are the result of singularities in the complex-trace analysis estimation of k_x, k_y, and ω. After Barnes (2000a).

just one of those two axes to be aligned with the direction of minimum variation. The remaining axis is perpendicular to the other two. Mathematicians would call those three axes the principal axes defining the geometric structure.

To perform the calculation, first we generate a measure of waveform variability along each of three Cartesian axes, $\partial u/\partial x$, $\partial u/\partial y$, and $\partial u/\partial z$. Bakker (1999) recommended calculating these derivatives by convolving the seismic data with the derivatives of a Gaussian filter $\partial G/\partial x$, $\partial G/\partial y$, and $\partial G/\partial z$, where

$$G(x_j, y_j, z_j; \sigma) = \exp[(x_j^2 + y_j^2 + z_j^2)/\sigma^2] \, , \qquad (2.10)$$

and where x_j, y_j, and z_j are the distances along the x-, y-, and z-axes of the jth trace from the point at which the derivative is being analyzed, and σ is the scale parameter. Because we apply this derivative in each of the three directions and convolve it with the original seismic data, we now have three seismic-amplitude-gradient volumes. If the data are sampled optimally, Bakker suggested using a value of σ that is three times the sample, CMP, and line spacing.

Next, we define an analysis window, much as Barnes (2000a) did for his weighted-average estimates of dip and azimuth and Marfurt et al. (1998) did for their discrete semblance search for dip and azimuth. If we had a perfectly flat plane, we would expect the values of $\partial u/\partial z$ at each point in the analysis window to be identical to the ones laterally next to it. The other two gradients would be zero. If we had a vertically planar, constant-amplitude reflector that is perpendicular to the x-axis, we would expect each value of $\partial u/\partial x$ to be identical to the values above and below it. Mathematicians would call each triplet of $\partial u/\partial x$, $\partial u/\partial y$, and $\partial u/\partial z$ a sample vector of the space being analyzed. To extract any consistent trend, we compare each triplet with all other triplets falling within the analysis window. We do this by simple crosscorrelation, resulting in the following covariance matrix:

$$\mathbf{T}_{\mathrm{GS}} = \frac{1}{J(2K+1)} \begin{bmatrix} \sum_{k=-K}^{+K}\sum_{j=1}^{J} \frac{\partial u_{jk}}{\partial x}\frac{\partial u_{jk}}{\partial x} & \sum_{k=-K}^{+K}\sum_{j=1}^{J} \frac{\partial u_{jk}}{\partial y}\frac{\partial u_{jk}}{\partial x} & \sum_{k=-K}^{+K}\sum_{j=1}^{J} \frac{\partial u_{jk}}{\partial z}\frac{\partial u_{jk}}{\partial x} \\ \sum_{k=-K}^{+K}\sum_{j=1}^{J} \frac{\partial u_{jk}}{\partial x}\frac{\partial u_{jk}}{\partial y} & \sum_{k=-K}^{+K}\sum_{j=1}^{J} \frac{\partial u_{jk}}{\partial y}\frac{\partial u_{jk}}{\partial y} & \sum_{k=-K}^{+K}\sum_{j=1}^{J} \frac{\partial u_{jk}}{\partial z}\frac{\partial u_{jk}}{\partial y} \\ \sum_{k=-K}^{+K}\sum_{j=1}^{J} \frac{\partial u_{jk}}{\partial x}\frac{\partial u_{jk}}{\partial z} & \sum_{k=-K}^{+K}\sum_{j=1}^{J} \frac{\partial u_{jk}}{\partial y}\frac{\partial u_{jk}}{\partial z} & \sum_{k=-K}^{+K}\sum_{j=1}^{J} \frac{\partial u_{jk}}{\partial z}\frac{\partial u_{jk}}{\partial z} \end{bmatrix}, \qquad (2.11)$$

where the analysis window includes $\pm K$ samples and J traces. We call this 3×3 covariance matrix, $\mathbf{T}_{\mathrm{GS}}$, the gradient structure tensor. The gradient structure tensor contains information on the waveform variability within the analysis window. Because we have formed the matrix with Cartesian components of amplitude variability, we turn to eigen-

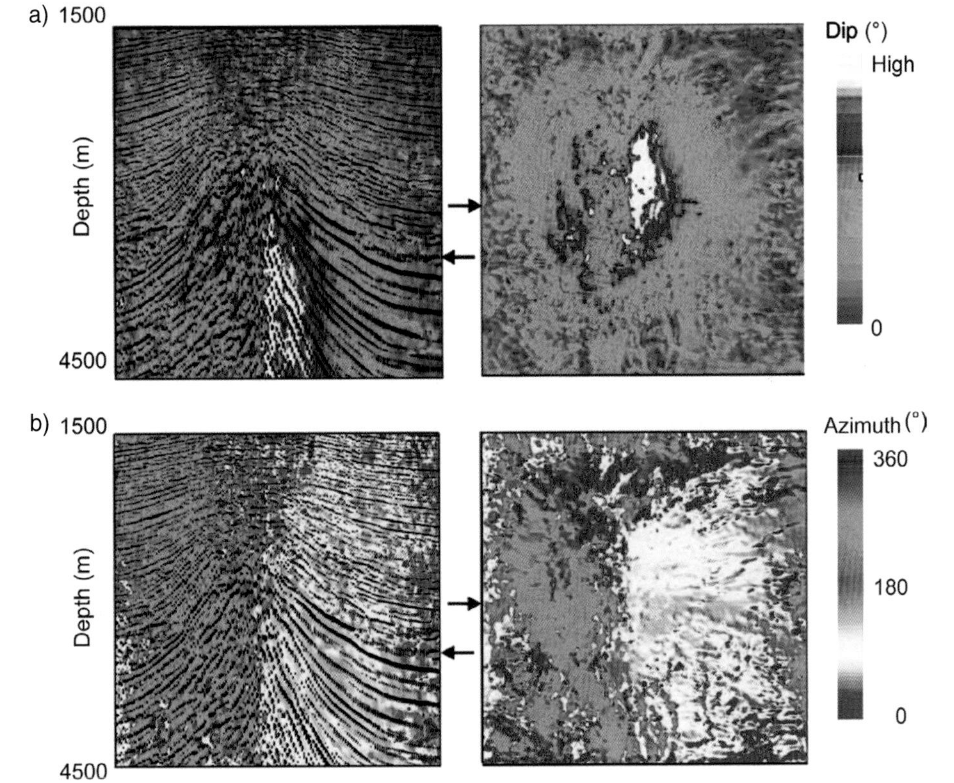

Figure 4. Vertical and horizontal slices corresponding to those shown in Figure 3, here through (a) a smoothed instantaneous dip magnitude and (b) a smoothed instantaneous dip azimuth. Smoothing was performed using an envelope-weighted running mean filter (composed of five inlines, five crosslines, and seven depth samples) on each of the constituent k_x, k_y, and ω components. Note that the singularities seen in Figure 3 are diminished. After Barnes (2000a).

decomposition and write

$$\mathbf{T_{GS}}\,\mathbf{v_m} = \lambda_m\,\mathbf{v}_\mathrm{m} \quad (2.12)$$

where $\mathbf{v_m}$ are the three eigenvectors and λ_m are the corresponding three eigenvalues of the 3 × 3 gradient structure tensor. By convention, the first eigenvector, $\mathbf{v_1}$, defines the direction of maximum variability and thus measures the direction normal to the best plane representing our seismic data-analysis window. For a perfect plane, $\lambda_2 = \lambda_3 = 0$, regardless of the planar orientation. We will discuss eigenvalues and eigenvectors in greater detail in Chapter 3 on coherence. For this chapter, you need to know that its vertical and lateral resolutions are dependent first on the size of the derivative calculation (a function of the value of σ in equation 2.10) and second on the size of the analysis window.

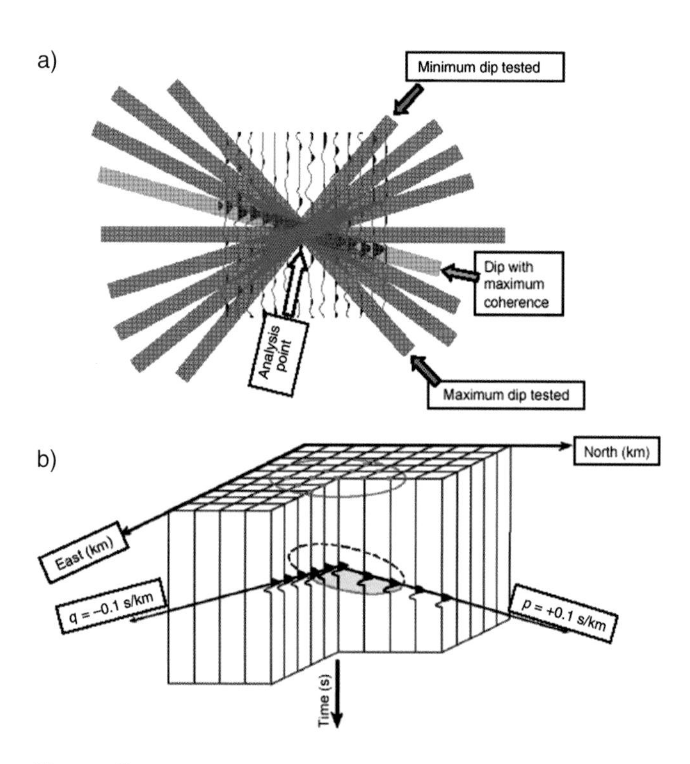

Figure 5. (a) A schematic diagram showing a 2D search-based estimate of coherence. First, the algorithm estimates coherence using semblance, variance, principal component, or some other statistical measure (such as that given by equation 2.9) along a discrete number of candidate dips (shown in magenta and green). In this example, the maximum coherence is calculated along the dip (shown in dark green). Next, the algorithm passes an interpolation curve through the coherence measures estimated by the peak value and two or more neighboring dips (shown here in light green). The peak value of this curve gives an estimate of coherence, whereas the dip value of this peak gives an estimate of instantaneous dip. (b) A schematic diagram showing a 3D search-based estimate of coherence, in which p indicates the inline and q the crossline components of vector time dip. The technique is analogous to that shown in (a). After Marfurt et al. (1998).

Multiwindow Estimates of 3D Vector Dip

Regardless of how such estimates of reflector dip are implemented, they all fail when the analysis window spans a fault. In that situation, they provide at best an estimate of the apparent dip across the fault, rather than of the true reflector dip. Such estimates of apparent dip across faults are excellent edge detectors (e.g., Luo et al., 1996; and shown in Figure 3 in Chapter 5 of this book). We will discuss more details of these aspects in our discussion of computing coherence for highlighting faults and stratigraphic features in 3D seismic data volumes, the topic of Chapter 3. Smoothed estimates of the vector components of dip using mean or median filters can improve estimates of coherence (Marfurt et al., 1999), but they do so at the expense of eliminating details of interest in the reflector dip volumes themselves.

The discrete scan given by equation 2.9 is performed on a regularly sampled grid. Instead of simply assuming that the reflector dip and azimuth correspond to the maximum discretely scanned value, we fit a quadratic surface through the semblance values at the neighboring apparent-dip pairs (θ_x, θ_y), of the form

$$c_s(\theta_x,\theta_y) = \alpha_1\theta_x^{\,2} + \alpha_2\theta_x\theta_y + \alpha_3\theta_y^{\,2} + \alpha_4\theta_x + \alpha_5\theta_y + \alpha_6, \quad (2.13)$$

and solve for the coefficients α_j in a least-squares sense. We then calculate an improved estimate of the vector dip by solving

$$\frac{\partial c_s(\theta_x,\theta_y)}{\partial\theta_x} = 2\alpha_1\hat{\theta}_x + \alpha_2\hat{\theta}_y + \alpha_4 = 0\,,$$

and

$$\frac{\partial c_s(\theta_x,\theta_y)}{\partial\theta_y} = \alpha_2\hat{\theta}_x + 2\alpha_3\hat{\theta}_y + \alpha_5 = 0\,, \quad (2.14)$$

for $(\hat{\theta}_x,\hat{\theta}_y)$, where $(\hat{\theta}_x,\hat{\theta}_y)$ is the apparent-dip pair corresponding to the maximum of the interpolated semblance surface, $c_s(\theta_x,\theta_y)$.

Even if our semblance surface is interpolated, our analysis window may inadvertently span a fault dividing domains having different dips (Figure 6). To obtain an improved estimate of vector dip, we exploit the multiple-analysis-window construct described by Kuwahara et al. (1976) and, to our knowledge, first generalized to seismic amplitudes by Luo et al. (2002) in their edge-preserving smoothing algorithm. In the latter work, Luo et al. (2002) scanned a suite of noncentered, overlapping analysis windows in addition to the centered window, all of which contained the analysis point of interest (Figure 7a). They then calculated the amplitude variance over the J traces that fall within the ith window:

$$\mathrm{var} = \frac{1}{J-1}\sum_{j=1}^{J}(u_{ji} - <u_i>)^2 , \qquad (2.15)$$

where $<u_i>$ denotes the average value of u_{ji} within the ith analysis window. The window having the smallest variance will be assumed to best represent a coherent reflector and will be used in subsequent structure-oriented filtering, which we will discuss in Chapter 8 on seismic image enhancement.

Because we expect amplitudes themselves to change across a discontinuity, we use an energy-normalized coherence estimate (such as the semblance measure given by equation 2.9) rather than the unnormalized variance given by equation 2.15. Although Luo et al. (2002) did not state it explicitly, clearly we also need to search over a suite of candidate dips and choose the window with the maximum coherence using equations 2.9, 2.13, and 2.14. Finally, we generalize the original concept of Luo et al. (2002) by also searching over candidate uncentered-vertical-analysis windows (Figure 7b) that include the analysis point. Figures 8 and 9 display a comparison of the instantaneous dip, the envelope-weighted smoothed dip, and the multiwindow calculations on a vertical slice and a time slice from Vinton Dome, Louisiana, U.S.A. The multiwindow-dip-scan method is less sensitive to aliasing and honors the abrupt changes in dip that are seen along the faults.

Next, we compare our multiwindow estimates of volumetric dip with conventional dip maps made from interpreted horizons. We turn to a survey acquired in the Fort Worth Basin, Texas, U.S.A., and examine two horizons — an easy-to-pick Pennsylvanian-age Caddo Limestone horizon, and a difficult-to-pick, karsted Cambrian-Ordovician-age Ellenburger Group horizon (Figure 10). At the deeper Ellenberger formation, we want to determine whether there is any structural control of the collapse features we see on the vertical section. At the Caddo horizon, we wish to map any differential compaction over these collapse features, which could provide accommodation space for sand sequences above the Caddo. In Figure 11a, we plot the time-structure map of the Caddo Limestone horizon. We also compute and plot the conventional dip-magnitude map (Figure 11b) from the time-structure picks, using a popular commercial software package. The solid white and dotted white rectangular boxes indicate surveys collected in 1995 and 1997, respectively. A larger survey was collected in 1999 (the portion not in these

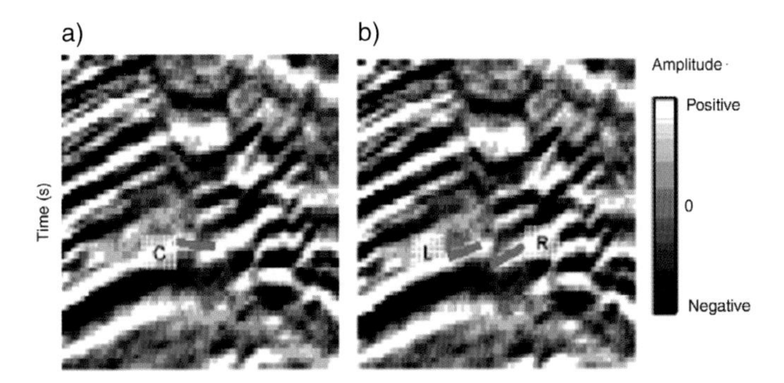

Figure 6. A schematic diagram showing the apparent dip (represented by the magenta lines), estimated using the discrete search algorithm shown in Figure 5, in (a) a window, C, centered about the analysis point, and in (b) windows L and R, shifted to the left and right of the analysis point. Clearly, estimates of apparent dip obtained in either of these two shifted windows are superior to the smoothed apparent dip given by the centered window.

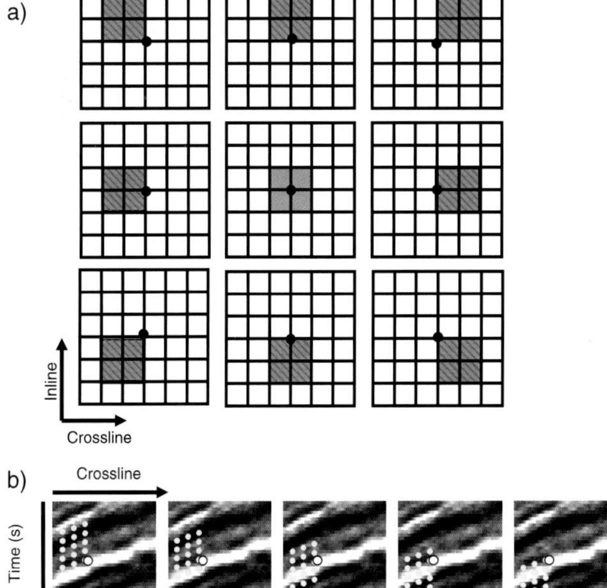

Figure 7. (a) Plan view of a nine-trace, nine-lateral-window search for dip and azimuth. Solid circles indicate the analysis point, and shaded rectangles indicate alternative analysis windows. (b) A vertical view of the first (northwest) window shown in (a), illustrating the search over five vertical windows containing the analysis point indicated by the white dot (only the three crossline traces are displayed). We begin by calculating and then interpolating for the coherence and dip and azimuth within each window, as described in Figure 5. This process is repeated for all 9 × 5 = 45 overlapping analysis windows, each containing the desired analysis point. The dip and azimuth at the analysis point are defined to be the dip and azimuth of the window that encompasses the analysis point that has the maximum coherence. Use of such temporally and laterally shifted analysis windows helps preserve angular unconformities and other features of geologic interest.

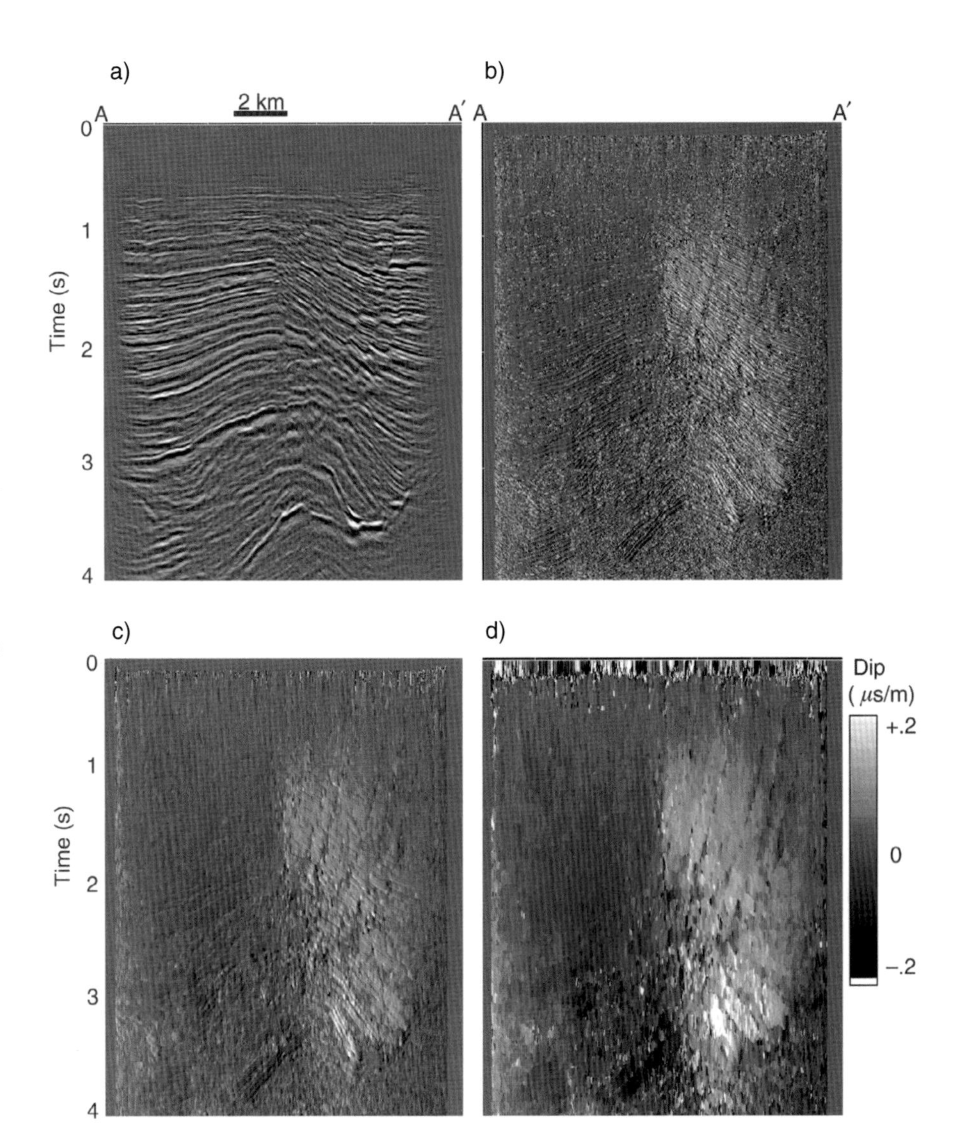

Figure 8. Vertical slices along line AA' from a survey over Vinton Dome, Louisiana, U.S.A., through (a) the original seismic volume, and (b)–(d) through the east-west components of apparent dip, p, calculated (b) using the instantaneous dip estimation given by equations 2.3, 2.4a, and 2.5a; (c) using smoothed values of k_x and ω over a five-trace by five-trace by five-sample window, and (d) using the multiwindow dip scan described in the text. Note the inconsistent estimate of interleaved positive and negative dips in (b), probably resulting from singularities in the frequency and wavenumber calculations (Liner et al., 2004). This inconsistency is averted by smoothing in (c), but at the cost of decreased lateral resolution. The multiwindow dip scan method is less sensitive to aliasing and honors the abrupt changes in dip seen along the faults. Data courtesy of OPEX.

two boxes), after which all three surveys were reprocessed by the same processor using the same processing software. The impact on the time-structure map of the three surveys (Figure 11a) is minimal. In contrast, the dip magnitude shown in Figure 11b is quite sensitive to the three different acquisition programs. Taking the derivative of the time-dip map accentuates the noise. To investigate this sensitivity further, we perform the derivative calculation separately on the time-structure map in the inline and crossline directions and display the results in Figure 12. In Figure 13, we display corresponding results computed using a nine-trace, 20-ms-window, discrete dip scan within a nine-window Kuwahara scheme. The overall shapes are similar except in the area of the two older surveys, where they differ significantly. Even though the Caddo horizon was strong, the time picks were sufficiently contaminated with back-scattered ground roll and other effects to contaminate the derivative calculation. Instead of using only points along the horizon to estimate dip, the multiwindow scan approach uses additional points above and/or below the horizon in the dip estimate, thereby improving the statistics.

Display and Interpretation of Vector Dip

Apparent-dip images

Dip is a vector consisting of dip magnitude and dip azimuth, or their projection on any Cartesian axis. Unfortunately, most commercially available software packages do not allow us to easily display vector volumes. Of course, we can simply plot the components of vector dip. In addition to the two independent east and north components of vector dip, p and q, defined in equation 2.2, Marfurt and Kirlin (2000) suggested plotting the apparent dip at any azimuthal angle ϕ:

$$p_\phi = p\cos\phi + q\sin\phi, \tag{2.16}$$

where ϕ is measured clockwise from north.

In Figure 14, we show apparent-dip images at $\phi = 0°$, 30°, 60°, 90°, 120°, and 150° from north on a time slice at $t = 0.8$ s that cuts the Caddo Limestone horizon displayed earlier in Figures 10 through 13. As we might expect, lineaments are illuminated best by the apparent-dip angle perpendicular to the lineament. Thus, the east-west strike-slip fault cutting across the middle of the image (light gray arrow) is illuminated best when $\phi = 0°$. The northwest-southeast-striking fractures indicated by the dark gray ar-

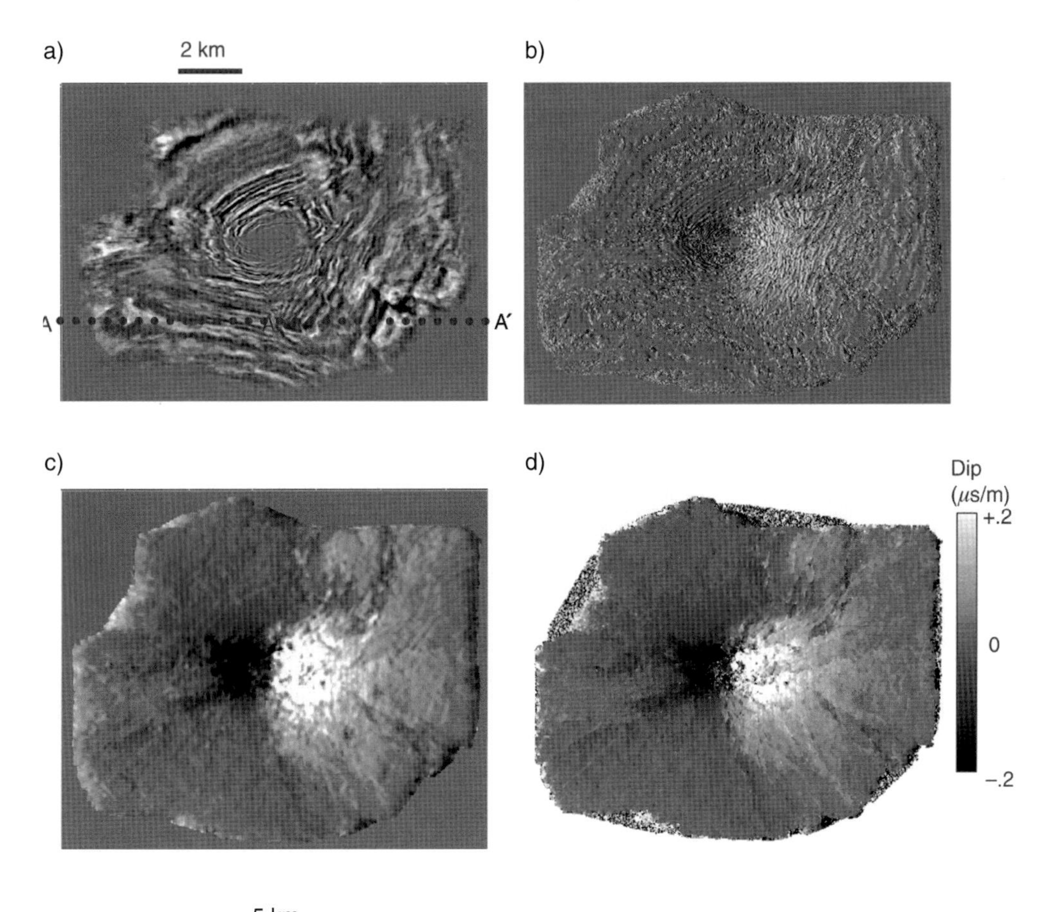

Figure 9. Time slice at $t = 1.000$ s through (a) the original Vinton Dome seismic volume, and (b)–(d) through the inline (east) components of apparent dip calculated using (b) the instantaneous dip estimation given by equations 2.3, 2.4a, and 2.5a, (c) using smoothed values of k_x and ω over a five-trace by five-trace by five-sample window, and (d) using the multiwindow dip scan. Note the aliasing at steep dips in (b). This aliasing is averted by smoothing in (c), but at the cost of decreased lateral resolution. The multiwindow dip scan method is less sensitive to aliasing and honors the abrupt changes in dip seen along the faults. Line AA' indicated on this image is shown in Figure 8.

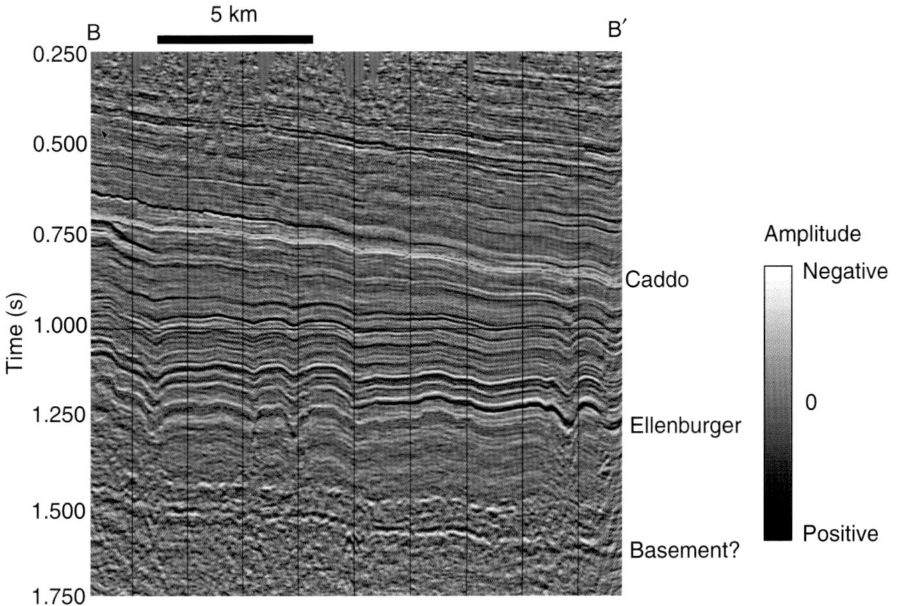

Figure 10. Line BB', through a Fort Worth Basin, Texas, U.S.A., survey. The green Pennsylvanian-age Caddo Limestone horizon is strong, coherent, and easy to pick. In contrast, the red karsted Cambrian-Ordovician Ellenburger Limestone horizon is quite difficult to pick. Seismic data are courtesy of Devon Energy.

rows are best illuminated between $\phi = 30°$ and $\phi = 60°$. The northeast-southwest-trending channel indicated by the black arrow is best illuminated at $\phi = 150°$.

We repeat this process on a time slice at $t = 1.1$ s, which cuts the Ellenburger horizon (Figures 10 and 15). The apparent-dip images allow us to delineate karst-enhanced collapse features clearly. In addition to the short-wavelength holes, we see broader, southwest-northeast-trending lineaments (dark gray arrows) that are associated with the strike-slip fault. We will enhance these images in Chapter 4, where we will discuss spectral estimates of reflector shape.

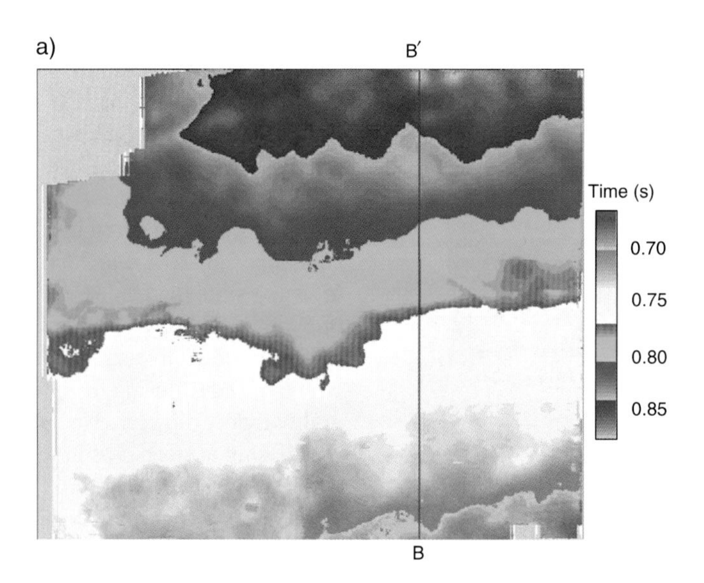

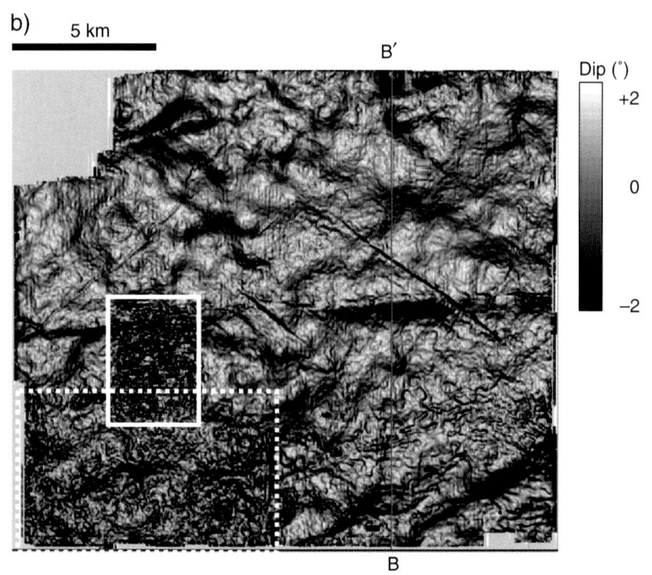

Figure 11. (a) A time-structure map corresponding to the Caddo horizon shown in Figure 10. (b) A conventional dip-magnitude map formed from the inline and crossline components of dip shown in (a). Note the poor quality of the dip-magnitude estimates in the region of the 1995 survey (solid white rectangle) and the 1997 survey (dotted white rectangle). The data outside these two zones were acquired in 1999. The same person reprocessed all surveys using the same software.

Shaded-relief images

We routinely examine the vector component of dip through shaded-relief maps of interpreted horizons (Figure 16a). In this well-established workstation tool, the interpreter chooses an illumination angle (commonly called the angle of the sun) that he then projects against the normal to the interpreted surface. By varying the inclination and azimuth of the sun, the interpreter can nonlinearly enhance or diminish features of interest by alternately illuminating them, casting them in shadows, or steering the reflected

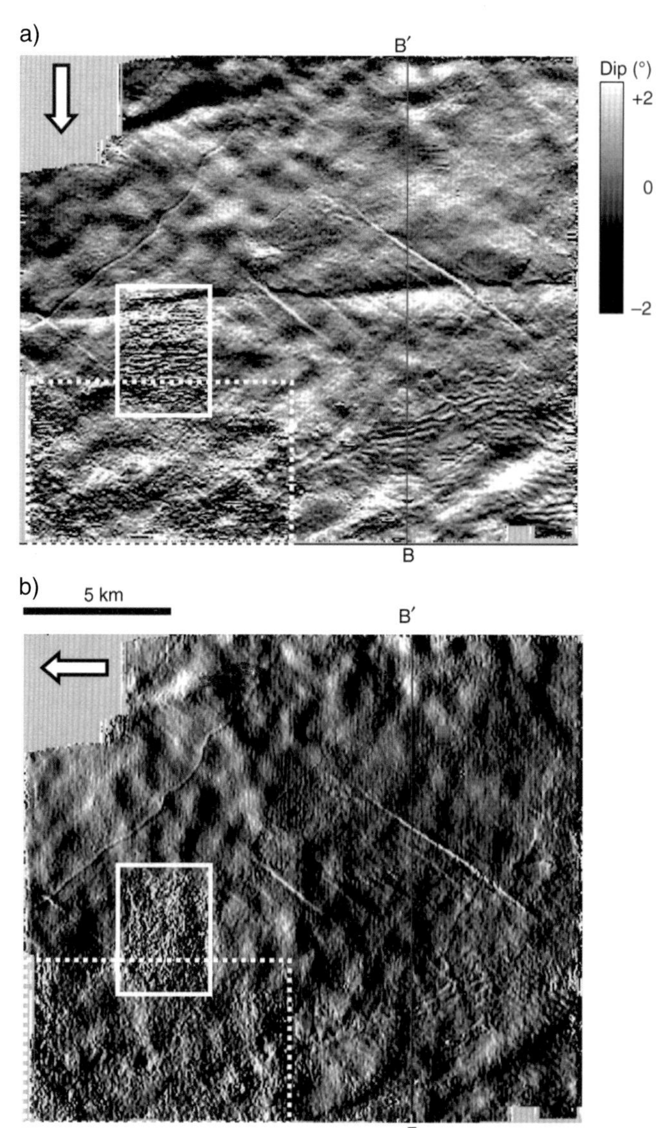

Figure 12. (a) A north-south component of dip, q, and (b) an east-west component of dip, p, computed from the Caddo horizon time-structure map displayed in Figure 11a.

light outside the interpreter's field of view. Barnes (2003) generalized that concept beyond the constraints of a picked surface, to illuminate time slices through a dip and azimuth cube (Figure 16b). He then applied this construct to the data shown in Figure 17. Barnes (2003) stated a preference for his shaded-relief time slice (Figure 17b) over his coherence (discontinuity) time slice (Figure 17c; compare these with the image in Figure 17a, which shows a time slice through the straight seismic data). We wish to caution the reader that although we have the same preference that Barnes had, we believe the difference is the result of geology rather than algorithm. Simply stated, continuity (we will discuss coherence algorithms in Chapter 3) and dip and azimuth measure different properties of the seismic reflection event. To us, the salt dome appears to be folded along the axis defined by the magenta arrow (best seen in the shaded-illumination dip-azimuth image) and faulted along the axis defined by the yellow arrows (best seen in the continuity image). The apparent dip we discussed earlier can be interpreted as a shaded-relief map when the sun is near the horizon.

Composite dip and azimuth seismic images

We conclude this chapter on dip and azimuth with composite images of dip-azimuth and seismic data. Details of the multiattribute color display will be covered in Chapter 9. In a nutshell, here we first follow Rijks and Jauffred (1991) and display dip-azimuth against a 2D color table — in our case, the hue-saturation color table inserted in Figure 18. We also plot the seismic data against a conventional single-gradational gray scale. If the magnitude of the seismic amplitude falls above a user-defined threshold (here, 20% of the maximum clipped value), we plot the seismic data. Otherwise, we plot the dip and azimuth data. In that manner, we maintain the information content of the stronger reflection events and augment that information with dip and azimuth information in areas where the seismic signal-to-noise ratio is lower.

We show two folded sections in Figures 18 and 19. The section in Figure 18 is folded along an east-west vertical line and a time slice at $t = 1.0$ s. The time slice cuts through a carbonate platform in the north and slumping features in the foreground. The image in Figure 19 is folded along a north-south vertical line and a time slice at 1.6 s. Here, we have illuminated a flexure (dipping to the north) that carries throughout most of the section. By referring to the 2D color bar, we see that even though we are looking at 2D slices, we obtain a good indication of whether the reflectors are dipping to the left or right, as well as in and out of the page.

In Figure 20, we display time slices through the same composite volume, at 0.8 s, 1.0 s, 1.2 s, 1.4 s, 1.6 s, and 1.8 s. We note a carbonate platform (low-saturation areas having low dip); the steeply dipping Brushy Canyon slump features (ranging from green in the southwest to yellow in the south to orange in the southeast); and two prominent flexures, one narrow and dipping to the north (indicated by the blue arrow) and the other broader and dipping to the northeast (indicated by the magenta arrow). We enclose areas of organized but perhaps confusing dip with cyan and orange circles.

We turn now to the vertical slices through the composite volume in Figure 21. Here, we are able to confirm that our dip calculation shown on the time slices correctly reflects the structural and depositional features we readily see

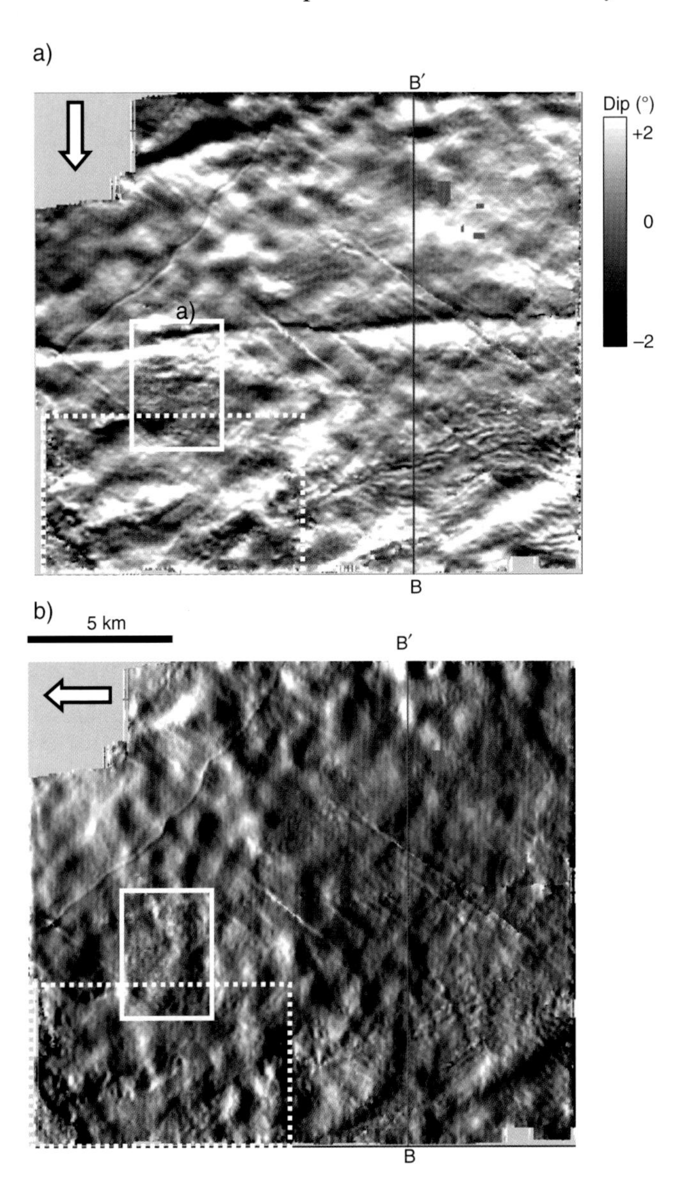

Figure 13. Horizon slices along the Caddo horizon, corresponding to Figure 12, of (a) the north-south component of dip, q, and (b) the east-west component of dip, p, using the multiwindow volumetric dip scan discussed in the text. Note the considerable improvement in the dip estimate seen in the area of the older surveys.

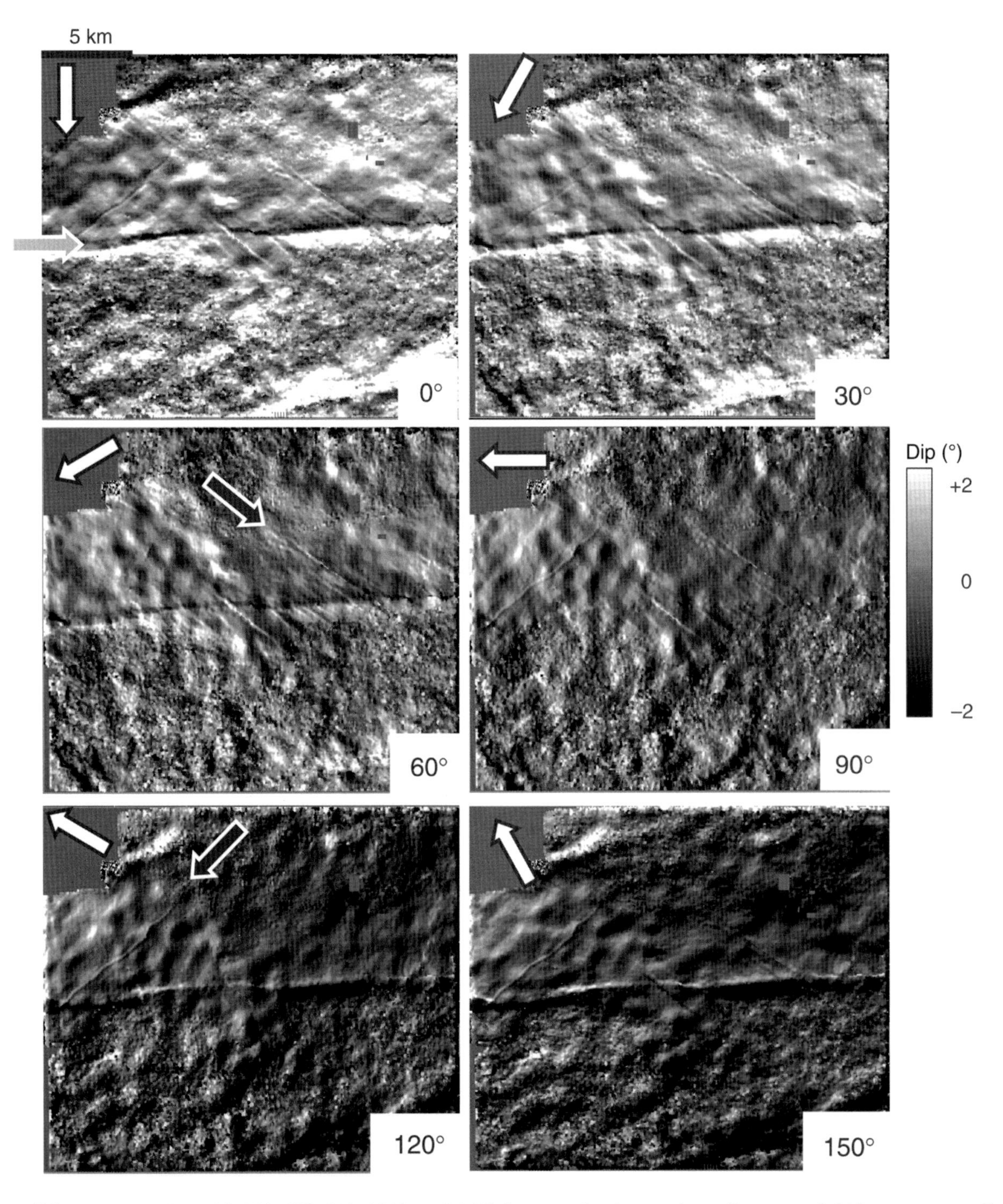

Figure 14. Apparent dip at 0°, 30°, 60°, 90°, 120°, and 150° from north, along a time slice at t = 0.800 s, corresponding approximately to the Caddo horizon shown in Figure 10. The color bar and orientations of the white arrow were chosen to be consistent with commercial horizon-derivative polarity and to interpret the black areas as shadows. The gray and black arrows indicate faults and collapse features that are best illuminated by derivatives perpendicular to strike.

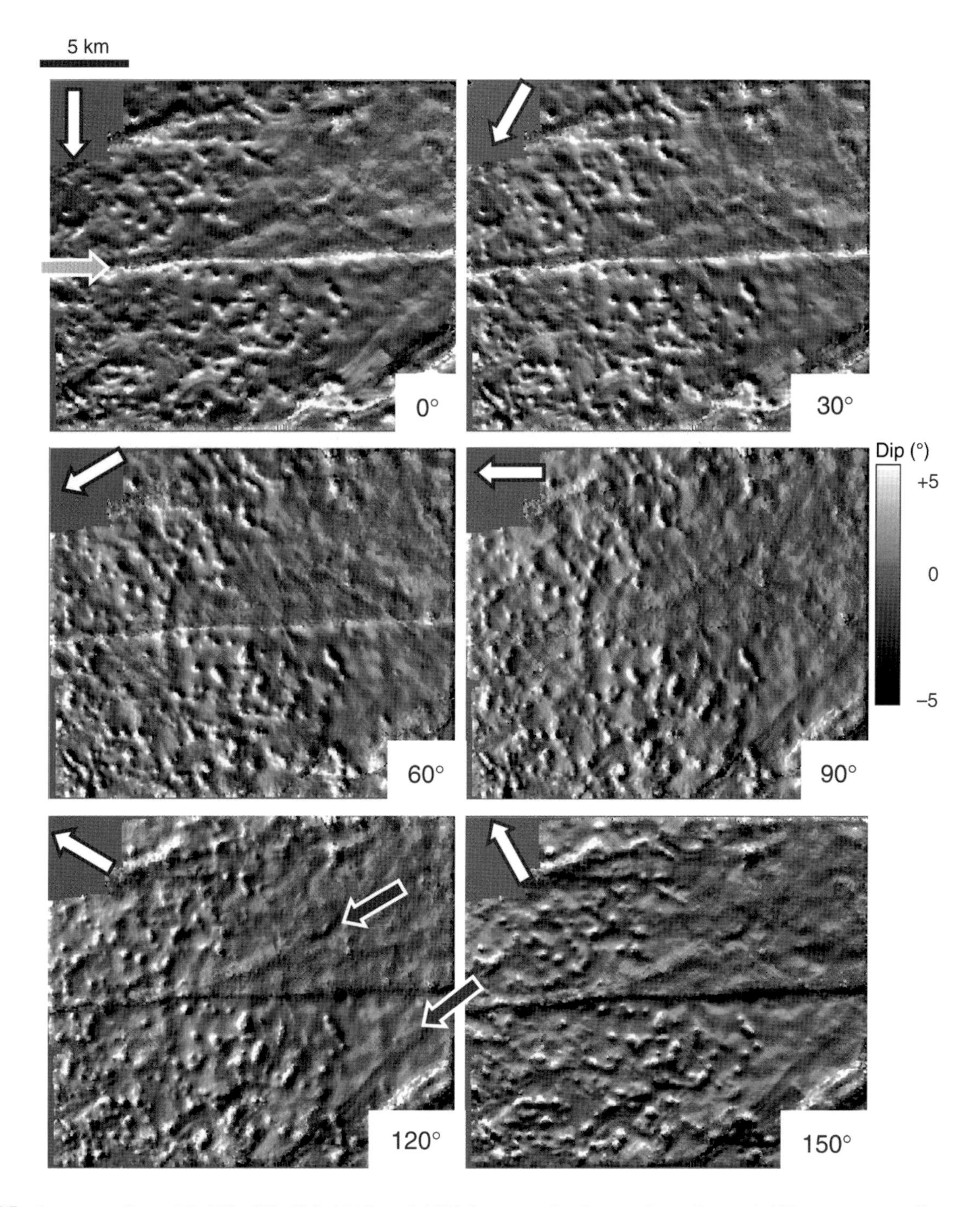

Figure 15. Apparent dip at 0°, 30°, 60°, 90°, 120°, and 150° from north, along a time slice at 1.100 s, corresponding approximately to the Ellenburger level shown in Figure 10. By interpreting the dark areas as shadows, we see that the circular anomalies are collapse features. The gray arrows indicate faults and collapse features that are illuminated best by derivatives perpendicular to strike.

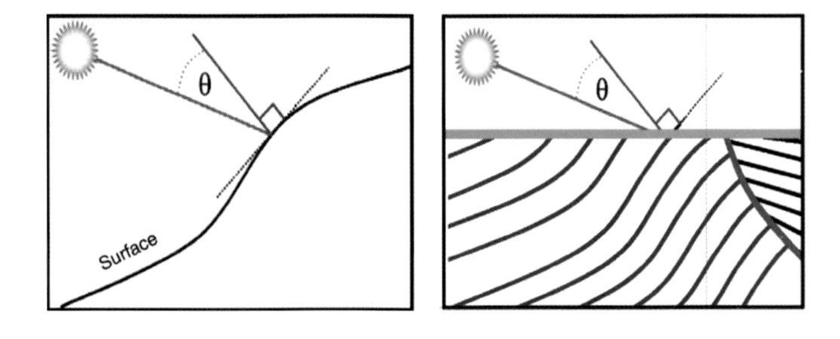

Figure 16. Diagrams illustrating the generation of a shaded-relief map (a) of an interpreted surface and (b) along a time slice cut through a dip and azimuth cube. The intensity of the image is proportional to the angle between the solar illumination and the normal to the dip of the interpreted surface in (a) or to the volumetric dip estimated at the sample along the time slice in (b). (a) After Barnes (2002). AAPG©2002. Reprinted by permission of the AAPG whose permission is required for further use.

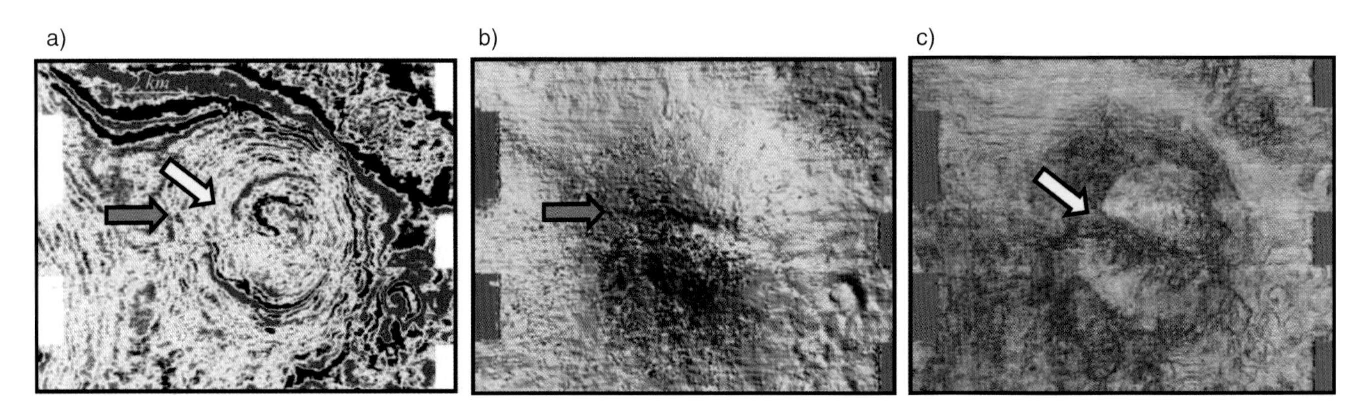

Figure 17. Times slices through (a) a seismic data volume, (b) a shaded-relief image of dip and azimuth, and (c) a continuity volume. The shaded-relief dip and azimuth slice is defined in Figure 16b, and continuity is a measure of waveform similarity or coherence and is described in Chapter 3. Although they are connected through geology, it is important to realize that dip and azimuth, coherence, and seismic amplitude measurements are mathematically independent and therefore illuminate different features. The salt dome appears to be folded along the axis defined by the magenta arrow and faulted along the axis defined by the yellow arrows. After Barnes (2002). AAPG©2002. Reprinted by permission of the AAPG whose permission is required for further use.

Figure 18. A composite image of dip and azimuth and seismic data for a survey from the Delaware Basin, New Mexico, U.S.A. The time slice is at t = 1.000 s and cuts a carbonate platform. The location of WW′ is given in Figure 20. The color display technique is described in Chapter 9, Figure 21. Because the platform is flat, it appears in colors that have a low saturation. Yellow arrows indicate the Brushy Canyon clastic slump deposits in front of the platform, which were deposited at a later time. On the western half of the image, these slumps dip to the south (yellow), and on the eastern half they dip to the southeast (orange). The green arrow indicates a deeper structure dipping to the west-southwest. Data are courtesy of Marathon Oil Co.

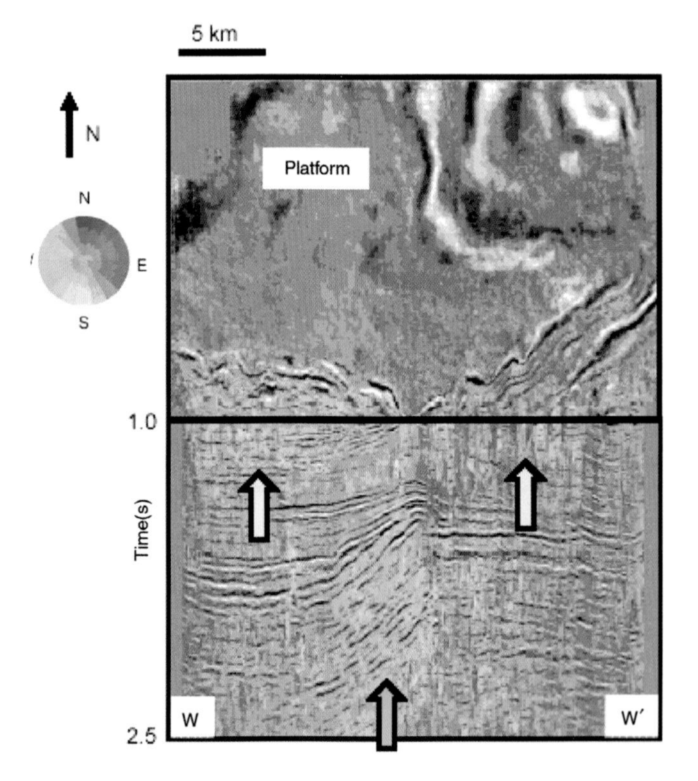

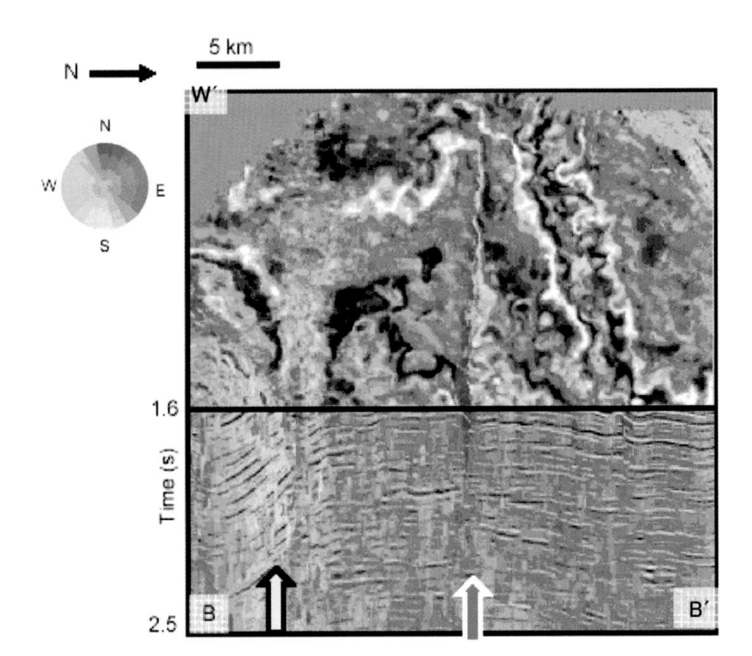

Figure 19. A composite image of dip and azimuth and seismic data for a survey from the Delaware Basin, NM, U.S.A. The time slice, at t = 1.600 s, displays a discrete flexure to the north, shown in blue and indicated by a blue arrow. The location of line BB′ is shown in Figure 20. The Brushy Canyon clastic slumps dip to the south and southwest, appear as yellow through green, and are indicated by a yellow arrow. Data are courtesy of Marathon Oil Co.

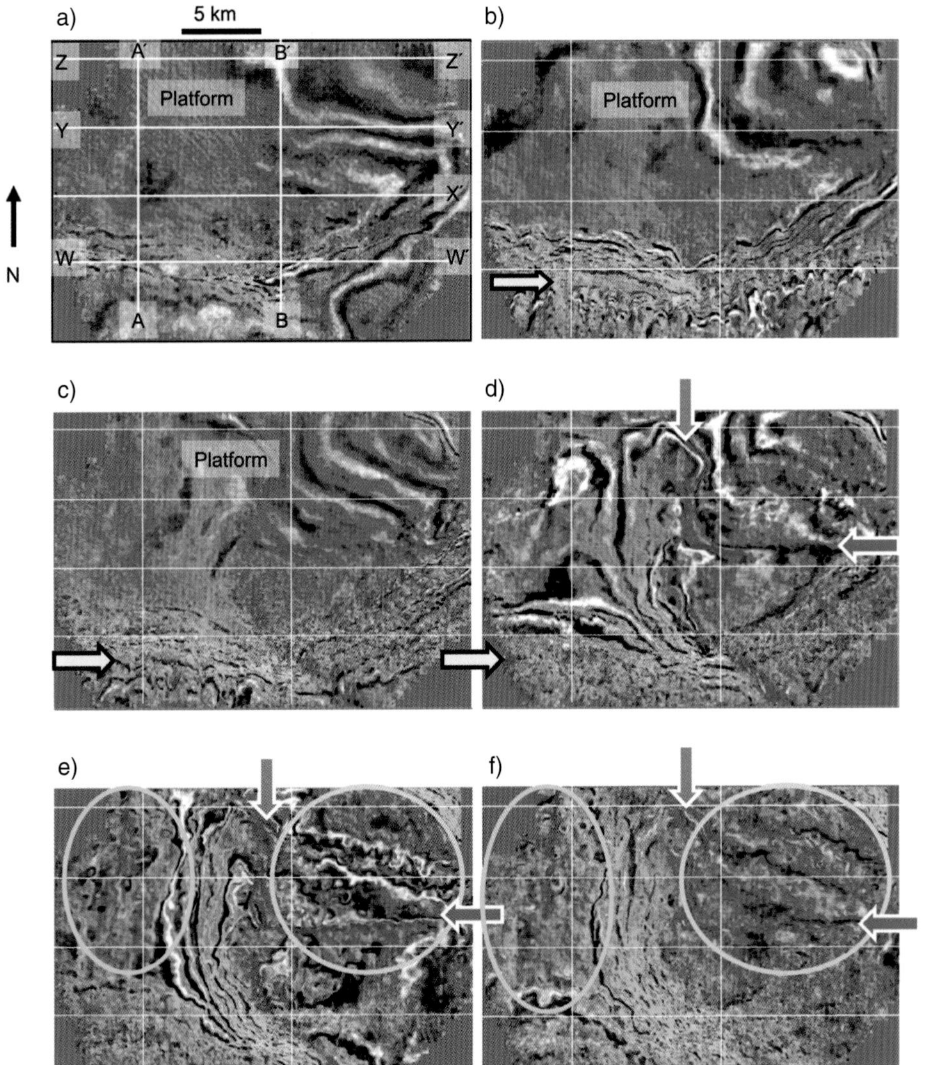

Figure 20. Time slices at t = (a) 0.800, (b) 1.000, (c) 1.200, (d) 1.400, (e) 1.600, and (f) 1.800 s, through the same survey shown in Figures 18 and 19. Yellow arrows indicate the Brushy Canyon clastic slumps, blue arrows point to a discrete flexure toward the north, and the magenta arrow identifies a less pronounced flexure toward the northeast. The cyan ellipse indicates a highly deformed zone of juxtaposed dips. Vertical sections are displayed in Figure 21. Colors are the same as in Figure 18. Compare this figure with Figure 35 in Chapter 3 and Figure 16 in Chapter 5.

in the vertical seismic data. Careful inspection shows that the colors indicate dips in all four cardinal directions, not just the two directions seen in a 2D image. We note the complex yet organized deformation denoted by the cyan and orange circles. These sediments appear to be the result of two orthogonal axes of folding. We will return to these images in Chapter 11, when we discuss attribute expression of tectonic features.

Onlap, Offlap, and Angular Unconformities

We conclude this section with a glimpse into what we perceive is the future of seismic stratigraphy. Given accurate volumetric estimates of dip and azimuth, we should be able to quantitatively estimate onlap, offlap, conformity, angular unconformities, and other components of seismic stratigraphy. Barnes (2000b) was one of the first workers to produce images of reflector parallelism, convergence, and divergence for 3D data. In Figure 22a, we note that converging reflectors appear as blue, whereas diverging reflectors appear as yellow. Using opacity, Barnes displayed these relations in 3D (Figure 22b), providing the interpreter with an image of how the prograding sequence changes parallel to the direction of deposition. Although this example shows only the inline component of divergence and convergence, a vector image could be generated using the HLS color model described in Chapter 9 (where crossline convergence and divergence would appear as red and green, respectively).

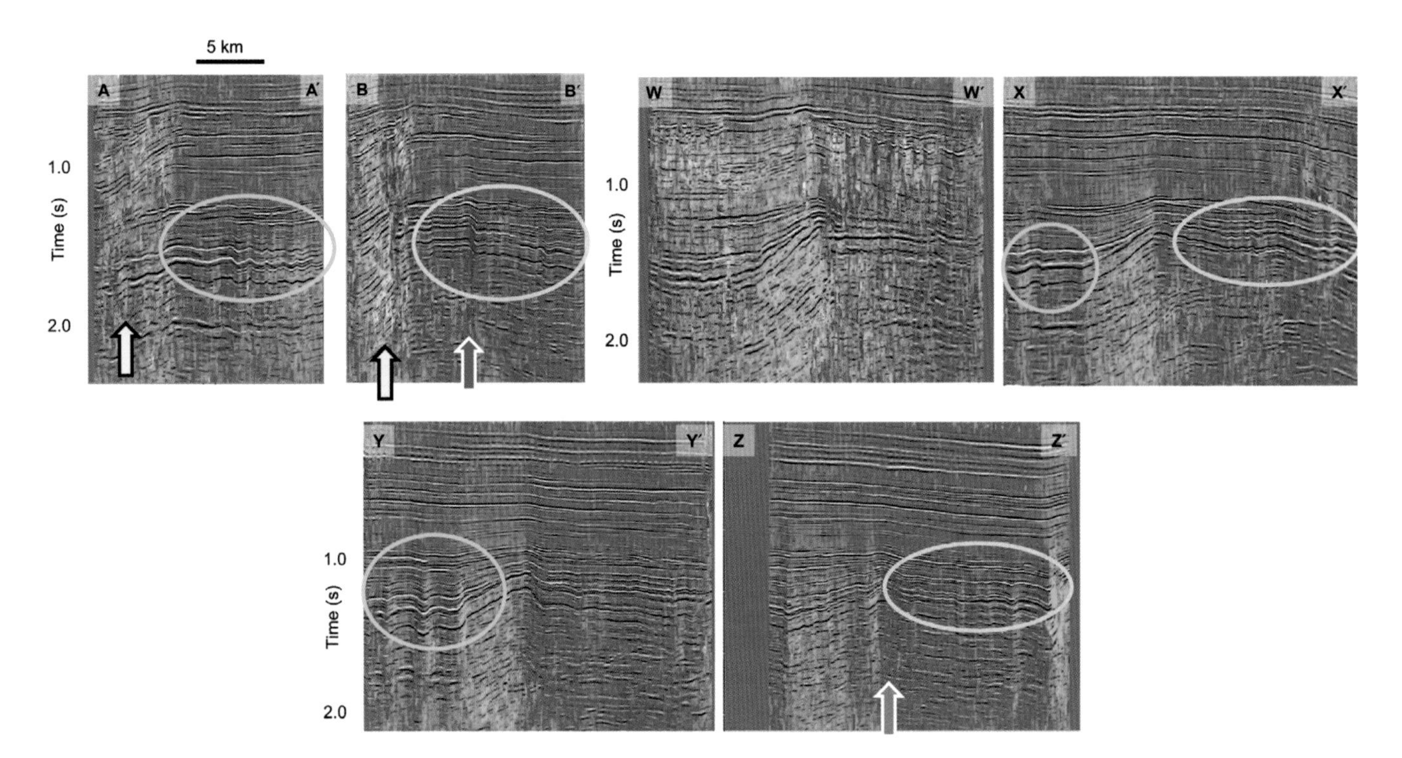

Figure 21. Vertical slices through a composite image of dip and azimuth and seismic data corresponding to the survey shown in Figures18 through 20. Blue and magenta arrows correspond to the north- and northeast-dipping flexures seen in Figure 20. The highly deformed zones bordered by cyan and orange ellipses also are indicated on Figure 20.

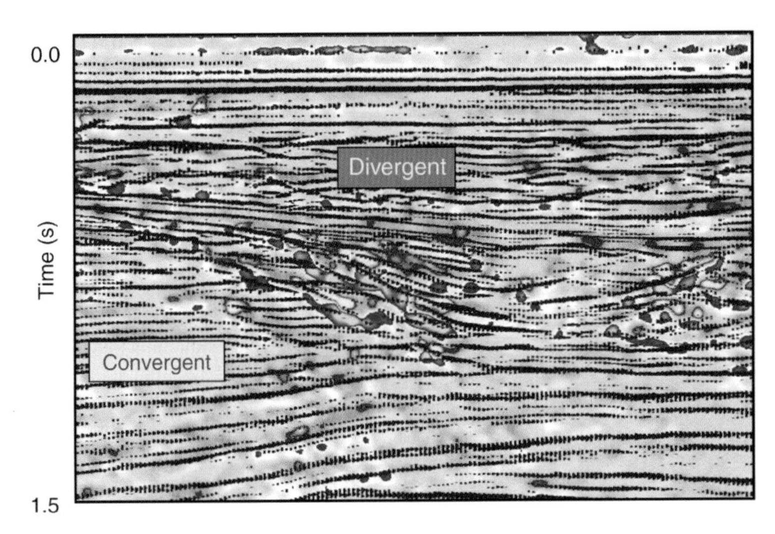

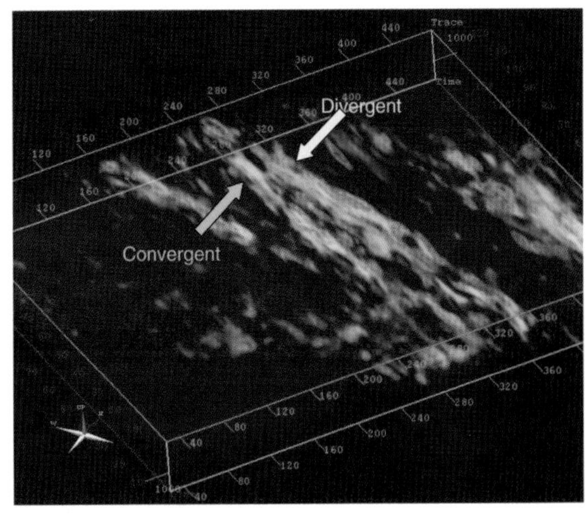

Figure 22. Calculation of reflector convergence and divergence is the first step toward 3D computer-aided seismic stratigraphy. In these images, positive convergence is shown in blue, and negative convergence (divergence) is shown in yellow. Like dip and azimuth, reflector convergence is a vector. Here we display the component of convergence/divergence in the inline direction. After Barnes (2000b).

Chapter Summary

Much of seismic stratigraphy is based on the morphology of seismic textures. Key to mapping these textures are quantitative estimates of dip and azimuth throughout the seismic volume. Identification of reflector terminations and subtle changes in dip and azimuth allow us to infer coherent progradational and transgressive packages, as well as more chaotic slumps, fans, and braided-stream complexes, infill of karsted terrains, gas seeps, and of course, faults and angular unconformities.

We can estimate reflector dip and azimuth by any of three competing methods: (1) by calculating temporal and spatial derivatives of the phase estimated using complex-trace analysis, (2) by an explicit dip scan to find the most coherent reflector, or (3) by calculating the first eigenvector of the gradient structure tensor. By using multiwindow analysis, we can estimate reflector dip and azimuth adjacent to discrete lateral and vertical discontinuities across which the reflector dip and azimuth change.

Accurate estimates of reflector dip and azimuth (or vector dip) are the fundamental building blocks for all geometric attributes as well as for structurally oriented filtering. In Chapter 3, we will show that coherence calculations along accurate estimates of dip have higher lateral resolution and are less sensitive to structural folding and warping overprints than are coherence calculations performed when the vector dip is ignored or somehow smeared. In Chapter 4, we will show that short-wavelength spectral components of reflector curvature (Al-Dossary and Marfurt, 2003), which are derivatives of vector dip, possess improved lateral resolution. Not surprisingly, long-wavelength spectral components of curvature are less sensitive to high-resolution estimates of vector dip.

References

Al-Dossary, S., and K. J. Marfurt, 2003, Improved 3-D seismic edge detection filter applied to Vinton Dome, Louisiana: 73rd Annual International Meeting, SEG, Expanded Abstracts, 2370–2372.

Bakker, P., L. J. van Vliet, and P. W. Verbeek, 1999, Edge-preserving orientation adaptive filtering: Proceedings of the IEEE-CS Conference on Computer Vision and Pattern Recognition, 535–540.

Barnes, A. E., 1996, Theory of two-dimensional complex seismic trace analysis: Geophysics, **61**, 264–272.

———, 2000a, Weighted average seismic attributes: Geophysics, **65**, 275–285.

———, 2000b, Attributes for automated seismic facies analysis: 70th Annual International Meeting, SEG, Expanded Abstracts, 553–556.

———, 2002, What a relief shade can be: AAPG Explorer, **8**. http://www.aapg.org/explorer/geophysical_corner/2002/08gpc.cfm, accessed June 22, 2005.

———, 2003, Shaded relief seismic attribute: Geophysics, **68,** 1281–1285.

Bednar, J. B., 1998, Least-squares dip and coherency attributes: The Leading Edge, **17,** 775–776.

Dalley, R M., E. E. A. Gevers, G. M. Stampli, D. J. Davies, C. N. Gastaldi, P. R. Ruijetnberg, and G. J. D. Vermeer, 1989, Dip and azimuth displays for 3-D seismic interpretation: First Break, **7**, 86–95.

Finn, C. J., 1986, Estimation of three dimensional dip and curvature from reflection seismic data: M.S. thesis, University of Texas, Austin.

Gersztenkorn, A., and K. J. Marfurt, 1999, Eigenstructure based coherence computations as an aid to 3-D structural and stratigraphic mapping: Geophysics, **64**, 1468–1479.

Hart, B. S., R. Pearson, and G. C. Rawling, G. C., 2002, 3-D seismic horizon-based approaches to fracture-swarm sweet spot definition in tight-gas reservoirs: The Leading Edge, **21**, 28–35.

Hesthammer, J., and H. Fossen, 1997, The influence of seismic noise in structural interpretation of seismic attribute maps: First Break, **15**, 209–219.

Hoecker, C., and G. Fehmers, 2002, Fast structural interpretation with structure-oriented filtering: The Leading Edge, **21**, 238–243.

Kuwahara, M., K. Hachimura, S. Eiho, and M. Kinoshita, 1976, Digital processing of biomedical images: Plenum Press, 187–203.

Lin, M. I.-C., K. J. Marfurt, and O. Johnson, 2003, Mapping 3-D multiattribute data into HLS color space — Applications to Vinton Dome, LA: 73rd Annual International Meeting, SEG, Expanded Abstracts, 1728–1731.

Liner, C., C.-F. Li, A. Gerztenkorn, and J. Smythe, 2004, SPICE: A new general seismic attribute: 72nd Annual International Meeting, SEG, Expanded Abstracts, 433–436.

Lisle, R. J., 1994, Detection of zones of abnormal strains in structures using Gaussian curvature analysis: AAPG Bulletin, **79**, 1811–1819.

Luo, Y., S. Al-Dossary, and M. Alfaraj, 2002, Edge-preserving smoothing and applications: The Leading Edge, **21,** 136–158.

Luo, Y., S. Al-Dossary, and M. Marhoon, 2001, Generalized Hilbert transform and its application in Geophysics: 71st Annual Meeting, SEG, Expanded Abstracts, 1835–1838.

Luo, Y., W. G. Higgs, and W. S. Kowalik, 1996, Edge detection and stratigraphic analysis using 3-D seismic data: 66th Annual International Meeting, SEG, Expanded Abstracts, 324–327.

Marfurt, K. J., and R. L. Kirlin, 2000, 3-D broadband estimates of reflector dip and amplitude: Geophysics, **65**, 304–320.

Marfurt, K. J., R. L. Kirlin, S. H. Farmer, and M. S. Bahorich, 1998, 3-D seismic attributes using a running window semblance-based algorithm: Geophysics, **63**, 1150–1165.

Marfurt, K. J., V. Sudhakar, A. Gersztenkorn, K. D. Crawford, and S. E. Nissen, 1999, Coherency calculations in the presence of structural dip: Geophysics, **64**, 104–111.

Picou, C., and R. Utzmann, 1962, La coupe sismique vectorielle: Un pointé semi-automatique: Geophysical Prospecting, **4**, 497–516.

Rijks, E. J. H., and J. C. E. M., Jauffred, 1991, Attribute extraction: An important application in any detailed 3-D interpretation study: The Leading Edge, **10**, 11–19.

Scheuer, T. E., and D. W. Oldenberg, 1988, Local phase velocity from complex seismic data: Geophysics, **53**, 1503–1511.

Taner, M. T., F. Koehler, and R. E. Sheriff, 1979, Complex seismic trace analysis: Geophysics, **44**, 1041–1063.

Chapter 3

Coherence

Chapter Objectives

After reading this chapter, you will be able to

- summarize the physical and mathematical basis of currently available seismic coherence algorithms
- evaluate the impact of spatial and temporal analysis window size on the resolution of geologic features
- recognize artifacts that result from structural leakage and seismic zero crossings
- apply best practices for structural and stratigraphic interpretation

Introduction

Coherence is a measure of similarity between waveforms or traces. When seen on a processed section, the seismic waveform is a response of the seismic wavelet convolved with the geology of the subsurface. That response changes in terms of amplitude, frequency, and phase, depending on the acoustic-impedance contrast and thickness of the layers above and below the reflecting boundary. In turn, acoustic impedance is affected by the lithology, porosity, density, and fluid type of the subsurface layers. Consequently, the seismic waveforms that we see on a processed section differ in lateral character — that is, strong lateral changes in impedance contrasts give rise to strong lateral changes in waveform character.

Figure 1a shows a laterally stable waveform indicating a coherent event. Figure 1b shows a synclinal but laterally invariant waveform. In contrast, Figure 1c and 1d shows variations in waveform that are the result of channels. Geologically, highly coherent seismic waveforms indicate laterally continuous lithologies. Abrupt changes in waveform can indicate faults and fractures in the sediments. In this chapter, we will demonstrate that lateral changes in coherence provide interpretation insights.

Figure 2a shows a segment of a seismic section, and Figure 2b shows its equivalent coherence section. Notice that there are no sharp breaks within the highlighting hexagon; however, a close examination does reveal changes in the seismic waveforms. The coherence section shows these changes as low-coherence features. It is that sensitivity to waveform changes that makes coherence a useful tool for extracting subtle information from seismic data. Similarly, Figure 3b demonstrates the ease with which faults can be seen on the vertical coherence section and easily can be put on a seismic section (Figure 3a).

In Figure 4, we redisplay one of the earliest published applications of coherence: application of the original three-trace crosscorrelation coherence algorithm to a large 3D survey acquired over South Marsh Island, Louisiana, U.S.A. In Figure 4a we see a time slice through seismic data, and in Figure 4b we see the crosscorrelation-based coherence volume. The extremes of the high and low values of coherence were indicated by yellow and red at the time. Unless otherwise stated, other examples in the book use a more consistent black-gray-white color scheme.

3D seismic interpretation

A 3D volume of seismic data allows us to visualize the spatial evolution of structural or stratigraphic features. Such a continuous evolution is basic to our understanding of sedimentary deposition and of the eventual tectonic folding or faulting, and to our study of the configuration and fluid content of a reservoir. The first step toward 3D interpretation is to use time slices along with the vertical sections pulled out of the volume. Whereas vertical seismic sections describe inline dips, the crossline dip can be investigated either by animating through successive inline seismic sections or by taking a perpendicular crossline slice through the seismic data volume. In contrast, time slices show reflector strike. Changes in strike can be tracked by animating through successive time slices.

Depositional systems often show up better on time slices than on vertical sections. For example, river channels usually cut their neighboring geologic strata in characteristically meandering patterns. Such patterns may be obvious on a time slice. The areal disposition of such channels or fault planes is not apparent on one vertical section, so to get a feel for such patterns, several vertical inlines or crosslines must be interpreted. Most of the channels and faults (barring the obvious ones) could go undetected if only vertical sections are interpreted. Time slices are a great help for such an interpretation. Obviously, the interpretation depends on the objective at hand and the quality of the data. Interpretation of subtle details could be a nightmare if the data are of poor quality.

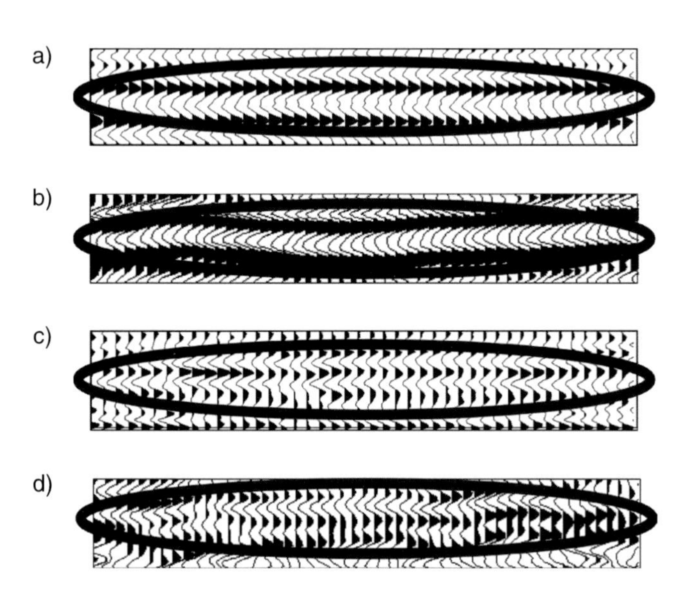

Figure 1. Examples of lateral variations in seismic waveforms: (a) a flat, laterally invariant, or coherent, waveform, (b) a synclinal, but otherwise laterally invariant, or coherent, waveform, (c) a laterally variable waveform indicative of lateral changes in impedance or thickness, and (d) a rapidly varying waveform associated with three channels.

Interactive workstations

Interactive seismic-interpretation workstations are valuable tools for interpreting large volumes of 3D seismic data efficiently. Inlines, crosslines, time slices, and arbitrary profiles can be accessed readily from a single data volume, and that facilitates convenient review and fast editing of the data. Folded displays such as that shown in Figure 5 are a great help in our understanding of subsurface geology. Rapid displays of horizon amplitude maps are possible that inject detail into our understanding of the field. The workstations' increased dynamic range of color displays and color enhancement allows interpreters to readily detect subtle features for stratigraphic interpretation. Because stratigraphy is best studied and displayed with vertical exaggeration, zones of interest can be conveniently zoomed and color can be enhanced interactively.

In areas with high dip or with stratigraphic features that cut through different stratigraphic horizons, flattening consistent stratigraphic horizons or surfaces helps us obtain a greater understanding of the stratigraphy. Investigation of amplitudes along a seismic horizon on which sequences prograde can give the direction of progradation, when the seismic volume is flattened on the horizon and sliced through. We may conduct similar analysis when we study an unconformity surface and the layers subcropping below it, to image a channel system or to determine the areal extent of a reefal buildup. An important shortcoming exists, however — interpretive bias usually enters the data set when we use horizon slices in tracing stratigraphic features, because the

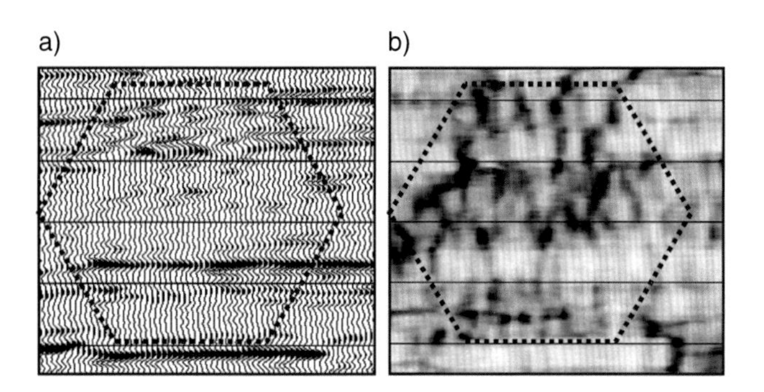

Figure 2. (a) Lateral changes seen on a vertical slice through a seismic data volume. (b) Such lateral changes show up as low-coherence features in the corresponding coherence slice.

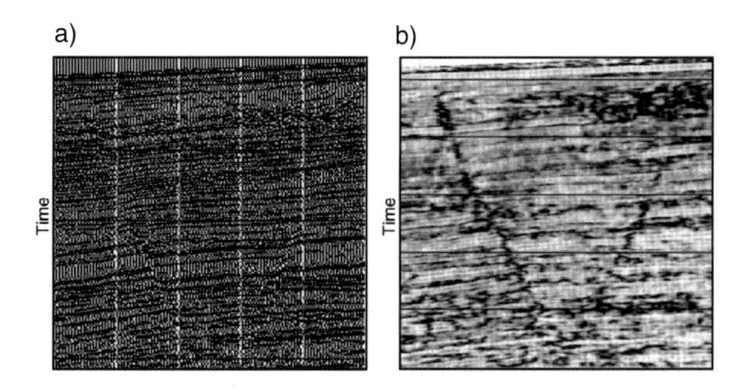

Figure 3. Vertical slices through (a) a seismic data volume and (b) the corresponding coherence volume, indicating the clarity with which the faults appear on coherence displays.

a)

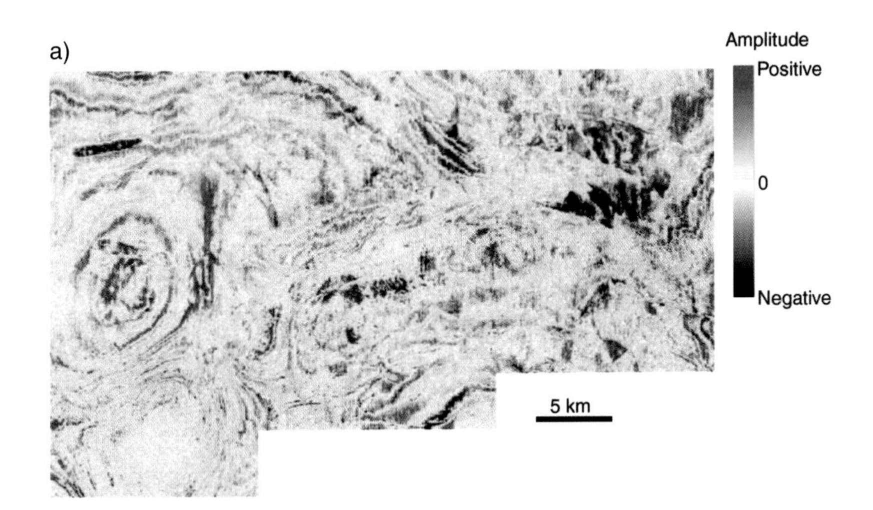

b)

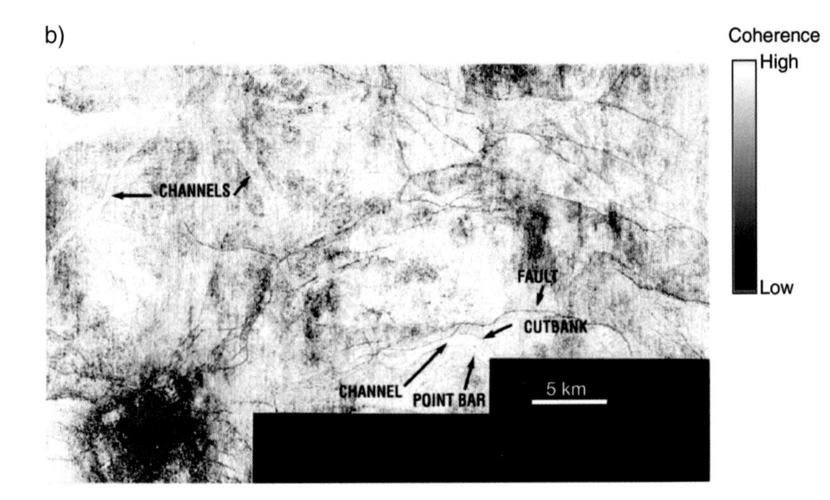

Figure 4. One of the first applications of coherence, showing a time slice at $t = 1.200$ s through (a) the seismic data volume and (b) the crosscorrelation-based coherence volume. The color scale is red (for lowest coherence), black, gray, white, and yellow (for highest coherence). After Bahorich and Farmer (1995).

difficult, time-consuming and subjective process of picking the horizon has to be followed.

3D data for reservoir description

In addition to providing structural and stratigraphic details, 3D seismic surface measurements have come into prominence as an essential element for reservoir description. Their use is particularly widespread in those parts of the world where new reserves are generated by infill and extension drilling that is based on detailed knowledge of the reservoir characteristics.

Reservoirs exhibit a range of physical properties that can be detected as changes in response over appropriate time intervals (e.g., by reservoir monitoring during enhanced oil recovery). Time-lapse seismic analysis is evolving rapidly to identify bypassed hydrocarbons in a producing reservoir. Three-dimensional seismic surveys are carried out over the reservoir area at different times during the life of the field. The first survey generally is done before production is begun, and the second and subsequent surveys are conducted after significant production has started. Changes between preproduction and postproduction surveys are computed and attributed to changes in fluid properties, such as saturation, density, and the like that have taken place between the times of the surveys. Thus, 3D seismic data are used to identify portions of the reservoir that have been depleted and other regions that still have commercially viable hydrocarbon accumulations that could be targeted by an infill-drilling program. Because 3D seismic measurements are being integrated with other information technologies, the potential of reservoir descriptions also is expanding.

Combined with well-log data, 3D seismic information is used routinely to map trends in reservoir heterogeneity. Such mapping was impossible previously with 2D seismic data. With 2D seismic data, reservoir heterogeneity resulting from small-scale faults often was ignored in reservoir-characterization projects because of the difficulty in correlating the faults between coarsely spaced seismic lines. Three-dimensional seismic data now permit us to do detailed geologic modeling, and powerful graphics give us stronger visual evidence. Those advances allow us to define and extend reservoirs and locate development wells optimally for draining off reservoirs effectively and efficiently.

Coherence helps us accurately portray stratigraphic plays and the associated faults. Sometimes, we must use the gauged information to carefully model the structure and stratigraphy and fault blocks so we can visualize the fault planes that intersect, clip, or extend into 3D space. Usually, the results of such exercises provide valuable input to geocellular and reservoir-modeling programs aiming to produce more-accurate volumetric and hydraulic models. Thus, using coherence not only reduces exploration risk but, by giving us a better understanding of the reservoir, ultimately leads to optimum reservoir management.

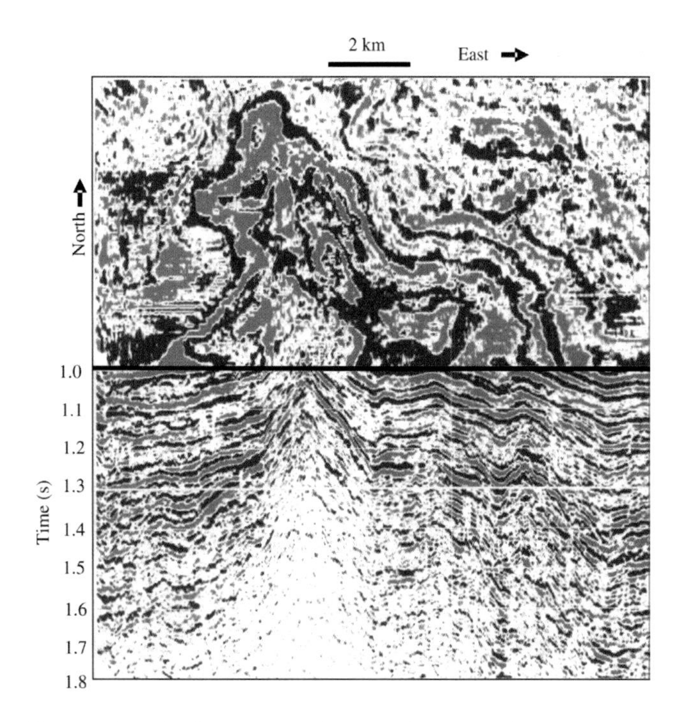

Figure 5. A folded or edge display showing a time slice and vertical section. Courtesy of ONGC, India.

In this chapter, we present the three common methods for calculating coherence (crosscorrelation, semblance, and eigenstructure). Then we present comparative examples that highlight the differences among three coherence methods. Higher-order statistics (Lu et al., 2003) or entropy measures (Cohen and Coifman, 2002) also have been used for computing coherence but are not discussed here.

Crosscorrelation-based Coherence

All coherence measures operate on a spatial window of neighboring traces. The simplest crosscorrelation algorithm operates on three neighboring traces (Figure 6a), whereas more computationally intensive algorithms based on semblance and eigenstructure operate on five, nine, or more neighboring traces (Figure 6b).

Let us begin by examining the crosscorrelation between the magenta master trace (trace 0) and the orange target trace (trace 1) in the inline, or x direction, shown in Figure 6a. We display the crosscorrelation operation graphically in Figure 7. If we slide the target trace by an amount τ_x and define our vertical analysis window to range between $\pm K$ samples above and below our analysis point at time t,

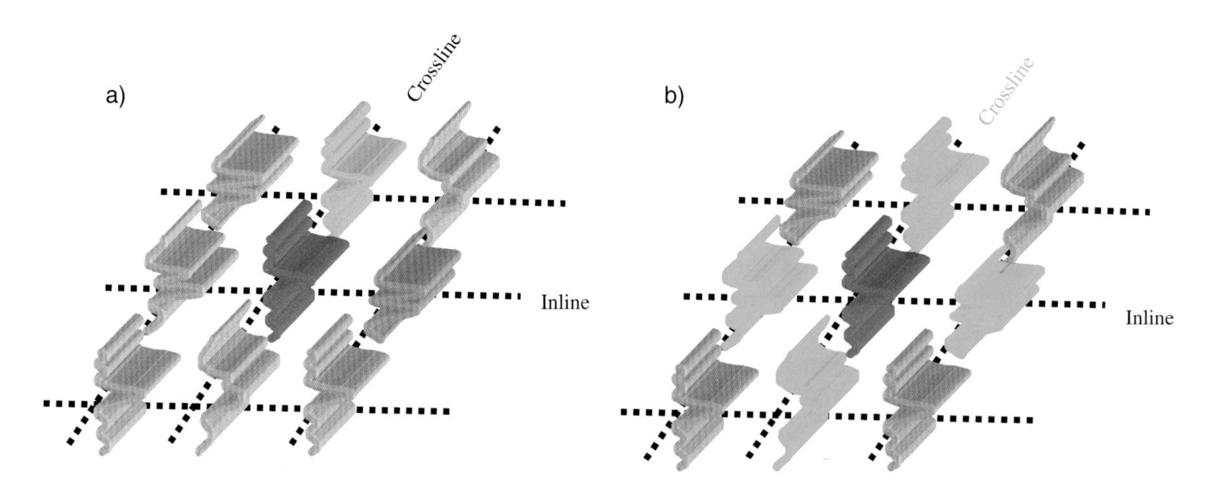

Figure 6. Spatial (or multitrace) analysis windows commonly used in coherence calculations for (a) the crosscorrelation algorithm and (b) the semblance and eigenstructure algorithms. In the crosscorrelation algorithm, we first crosscorrelate the target trace (in magenta) with the inline trace (in orange) over a suite of temporal lags. Then we repeat that process between the target trace and the crossline trace (in cyan). The coherence estimate is obtained using equation 3.4. In the semblance and eigenstructure algorithms, we first estimate dip and azimuth, as discussed in Chapter 2, and then calculate either the semblance (given by equation 3.13) or a covariance matrix (given by equation 3.17) between the target trace (in cyan) and its nearest neighbors. Here we show four nearest neighbors in green and eight nearest neighbors in green and gray. These sets of nearest neighbors give rise to either five- or nine-trace coherence algorithms, respectively.

we can write the normalized crosscorrelation coefficient ρ_x as

$$\rho_x(t,\tau_x) = \frac{\sum_{k=-K}^{+K} \{[u_0(t+k\Delta t) - \mu_0(t)][u_1(t+k\Delta t - \tau_x) - \mu_1(t-\tau_x)]\}}{\sqrt{\left\{\sum_{k=-K}^{+K} [u_0(t+k\Delta t) - \mu_0(t)]^2 \sum_{k=-K}^{+K} [u_1(t+k\Delta t - \tau_x) - \mu_1(t-\tau_x)]^2\right\}}} \quad (3.1)$$

where

$$<u_n> (t) = \frac{1}{2K+1} \sum_{k=-K}^{+K} u_n\,(t+k\Delta t) \quad (3.2)$$

denotes the running-window mean of the nth trace. Because we know that the true mean of properly processed seismic data is 0, we often make the computational simplification that $<u>(t) = 0$ as well. That is a reasonable approximation if the analysis window is greater than a seismic wavelet.

We continue the process for a range of lags, τ_x, and plot the results in Figure 7b. Recalling Chapter 2, we note that the lag τ_x that has the maximum positive-valued normalized crosscorrelation coefficient is a first-order approximation of the inline apparent dip (because the pair of traces displayed in Figure 7 are in the inline direction).

Next, we calculate the normalized crosscorrelation coefficient between the magenta master trace (trace 0) and the neighboring crossline cyan trace (trace 2) shown in Figure 6a, to obtain the crosscorrelation coefficient ρ_y:

$$\rho_y(t,\tau_y) = \frac{\sum_{k=-K}^{+K} \{[u_0(t+k\Delta t) - \mu_0(t)][u_2(t+k\Delta t - \tau_y) - \mu_2(t-\tau_y)]\}}{\sqrt{\left\{\sum_{k=-K}^{+K} [u_0(t+k\Delta t) - \mu_0(t)]^2 \sum_{k=-K}^{+K} [u_2(t+k\Delta t - \tau_y) - \mu_2(t-\tau_y)]^2\right\}}} \quad (3.3)$$

As before, the lag τ_y that has the maximum positive-valued normalized crosscorrelation coefficient is a first-order estimate of crossline apparent dip. Bahorich and Farmer (1995) defined the 3D crosscorrelation coherence estimate, c_{xc}, by combining the inline and the crossline correlation coefficients defined above using the formula

$$c_{xc} \equiv \sqrt{[\max_{\tau_x} \rho_x(t,\tau_x,x_i,y_i)][\max_{\tau_y} \rho_y(t,\tau_y,x_i,y_i)]}\,, \quad (3.4)$$

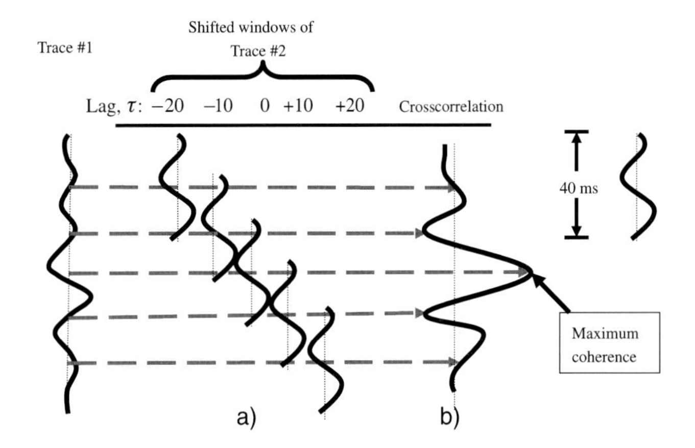

Figure 7. A schematic diagram showing crosscorrelation between two traces. Trace number 1 is held fixed while a window of trace number 2 (here, 40 ms) is slid along at a suite of time lags and is crosscorrelated. The lag having the maximum signed crosscorrelation is a crude measure of inline (or crossline) dip. The crosscorrelation value that corresponds to this peak is then used in equation 3.4 to generate a 3D estimate coherence.

where $\max_{\tau_x} \rho_x(t,\tau_x,x_i,y_i)$ and $\max_{\tau_y} \rho_y(t,\tau_y,x_i,y_i)$ denote crosscorrelation values at lags τ_x and τ_y, respectively, for which ρ_x and ρ_y are maxima. By taking the maximum values of the crosscorrelations with respect to their respective lags, this definition for coherence automatically accommodates for local dip. This analysis is continued for all samples down the master trace and for all the traces in the volume. Thus, a new 3D data volume is generated that contains measurements of the degree of trace-to-trace similarity. Typical window lengths vary from 40 to 100 ms.

Channels often are associated with gas-charged sand in the Gulf of Mexico. In Figure 8a, we show a 40-ms average-absolute-amplitude (AAA) slice and the crosscorrelation coherence through the same volume, showing such a channel (Figure 8b). The AAA is a common measure of reflectivity within an analysis window and is available on almost all commercial workstation systems. We note that the channel edges are difficult to see in the AAA slice but are quite visible in the coherence slice. However, these two attributes are complementary, and when we use them together we interpret the high-amplitude anomaly as a gas-charged sand lying within the channel. (We will discuss defining such complementary displays in Chapter 9).

In Figure 9a, we show a vertical cross section through the seismic data for the same volume as in Figure 8. Although the channels are obvious to an experienced interpreter, we do not know from this lone vertical slice whether we have three channels or a single meandering channel that repeatedly crosses the vertical section. Examination of the coherence slice (Figure 9b) shows clearly that we have three distinct channels, although of course they could be either the same channel occupying different spatial positions at different geologic times, or three simultaneous channels.

Faults may or may not be easy to see on time slices. Faults that cut perpendicularly to reflector strike, such as those indicated by the white arrows in Figure 10b, usually are easy to identify. However, faults that cut parallel to strike, such as those indicated by black arrows in Figure 10b, can be quite difficult to identify. Coherence allows us to identify faults regardless of their orientation (Figure 10a).

Semblance-based Coherence

In the semblance approach to computing coherence, we define a space and a time aperture, or a 3D analysis window, for the data. We also need to define a dip and azimuth for each point in the data volume. This dip and azimuth may be user-defined (implicitly) through flattening, or de-

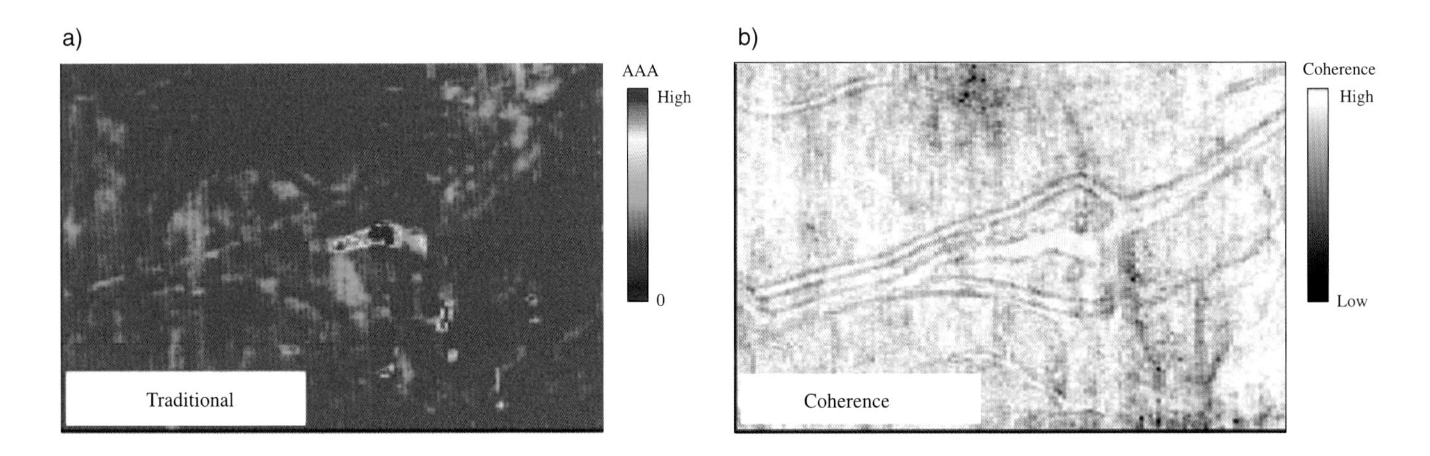

Figure 8. (a) A horizontal time slice of average absolute amplitude (AAA) calculated over a 40-ms vertical analysis window. (b) The corresponding three-trace 40-ms crosscorrelation coherence slice through the same volume. The bright spot seen in (a) corresponds to the highest coherence value displayed in yellow in (b), lying within the channel. Because bright spots generally have a high signal-to-noise ratio, it is common for them to show up with very high coherence. After Bahorich et al. (1995).

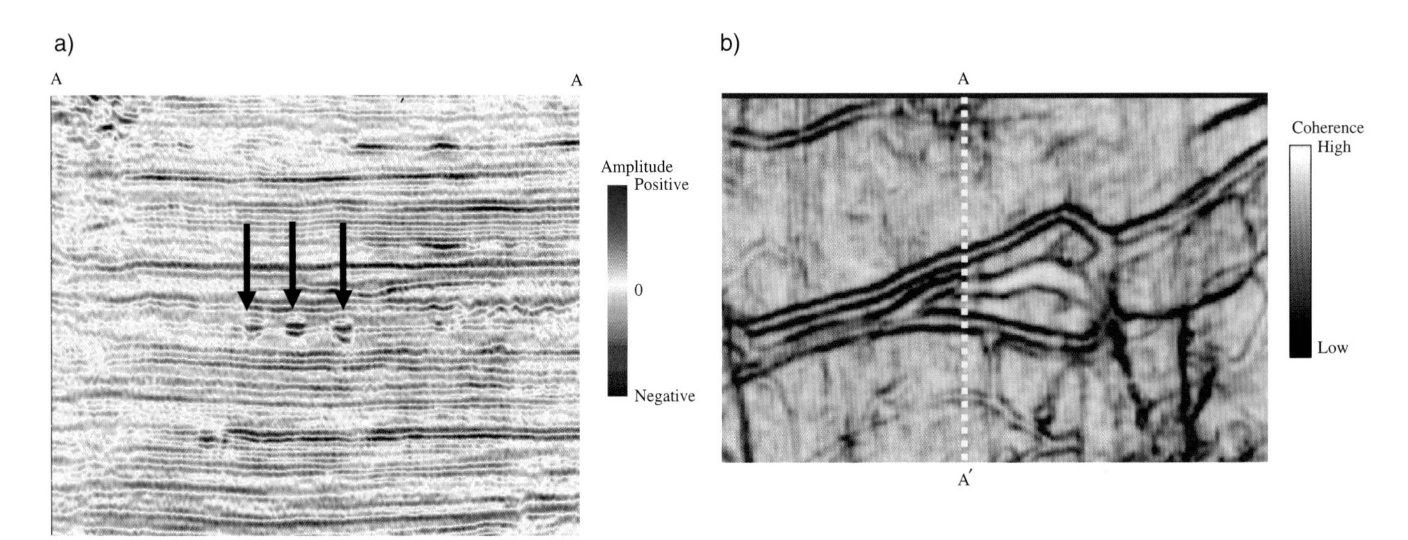

Figure 9. (a) Channels (indicated by arrows) seen on a conventional vertical seismic slice through the same volume as that in the previous figure. (b) Channels in map view generated by an 11-trace 40-ms semblance-based coherence algorithm. Note the higher signal-to-noise ratio of the image here compared with the three-trace crosscorrelation coherence shown in Figure 8b. The map view helps us differentiate between separate channels (perhaps having been formed at different geologic times) and a single meandering channel. After Haskell et al. (1998).

fined explicitly through a separate dip calculation, most typically using the semblance-driven dip scan described by Marfurt et al. (1999) and summarized in Chapter 2.

Let us define an analysis window (either elliptical, as in Figure 11a, or rectangular, as in Figure 11b) containing J traces centered about the analysis point, as shown in Figure 11. We define the semblance $\sigma(t,p,q)$ to be the ratio of the energy of the average trace to the average energy of all the traces along a specified dip:

$$\sigma(t,p,q) \equiv \frac{\left[\frac{1}{J}\sum_{j=1}^{J} u_j(t - px_j - qy_j)\right]^2}{\frac{1}{J}\sum_{j=1}^{J}\left\{\left[u_j(t - px_j - qy_j)\right]^2\right\}} \quad (3.5)$$

where the subscript j denotes the jth trace falling within the analysis window, x_j and y_j are the x and y distances of the jth trace from the center of the analysis window, and the apparent dips p and q are measured in milliseconds per meter or per foot and define a local planar event at time t. This semblance is a measure of the degree of similarity to each other of all of the traces along the selected dip within the selected square or elliptical outline.

The semblance estimate given by equation 3.5 will be contaminated most severely by background noise if we compute the semblance of strong, coherent events near or at their zero crossings. To avoid that problem, we adopt conventional-velocity-analysis semblance scans and calcu-

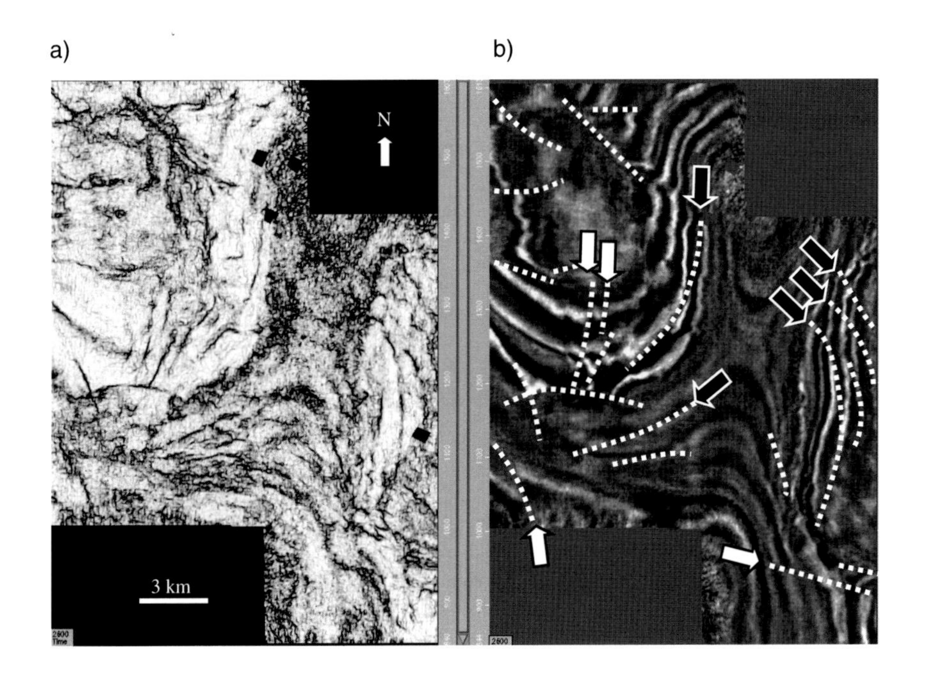

Figure 10. Time slices at t = 2.600 s through (a) the coherence volume and (b) the corresponding seismic volume, for a survey acquired in northwestern Louisiana, U.S.A. White arrows indicate faults that cut perpendicularly to strike and are easy to see on the seismic time slice. Black arrows indicate faults that cut nearly parallel to strike and are difficult to differentiate from normal waveform changes seen on the time slice. Small black rectangles in (a) and corresponding gray rectangles in (b) indicate acreage that was not permitted for exploration. Data are courtesy of Seitel.

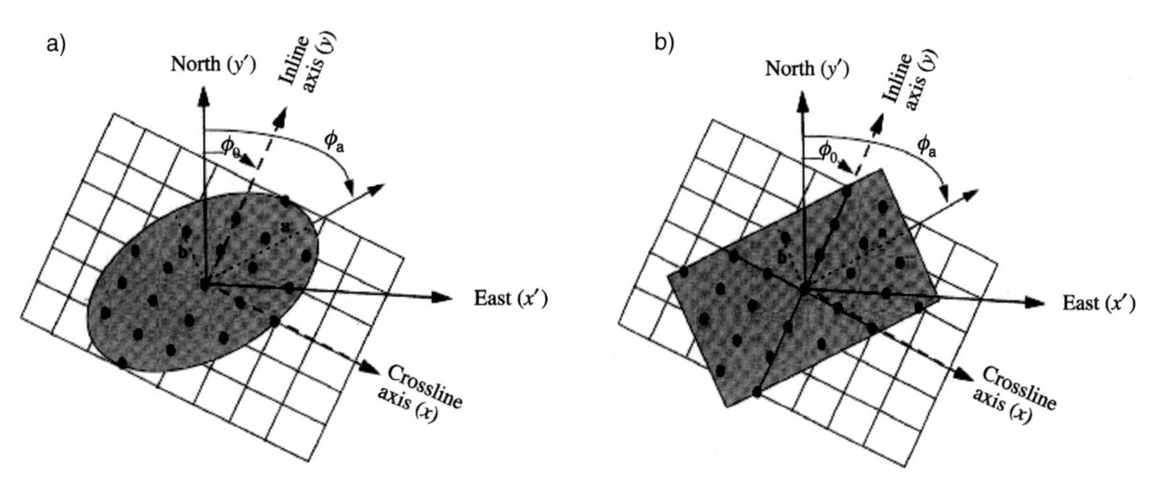

Figure 11. (a) Elliptical analysis window and (b) rectangular analysis window, each centered about an analysis point defined by the length of major axis a, the length of minor axis b, and the azimuth of major axis ϕ_a. The term ϕ_0 indicates the azimuth of the inline seismic axis from north. After Marfurt et al. (1998).

late an average semblance over a vertical analysis window:

$$c_s(t,p,q)=\frac{\sum_{k=-K}^{K}\left[\frac{1}{J}\sum_{j=1}^{J}u_j(t+k\Delta t-px_j-qy_j)\right]^2}{\sum_{k=-K}^{K}\frac{1}{J}\sum_{j=1}^{J}\left[u_j(t+k\Delta t-px_j-qy_j)\right]^2} \tag{3.6}$$

where x_j and y_j denote the x and y distances of the jth trace from the master trace (Figure 6b) and we sum over $(2K + 1)$ samples. Graphically, we display the input to the analysis as the windowed five traces shown in Figure 12a. In Figure 12b, we display the average trace. In Figure 12c, we replace each original trace by the average of all the traces (this extra step will help us compare the semblance algorithm to the eigenstructure algorithm presented later in Figure 17). The semblance is then simply the ratio of the energy of the data shown in Figure 12c to the energy of the data shown in Figure 12a.

Increasing the number of traces in the 11-trace semblance estimate of coherence shown in Figure 9b reduces the random speckles seen in the three-trace crosscorrelation estimate of coherence shown in Figure 8b.

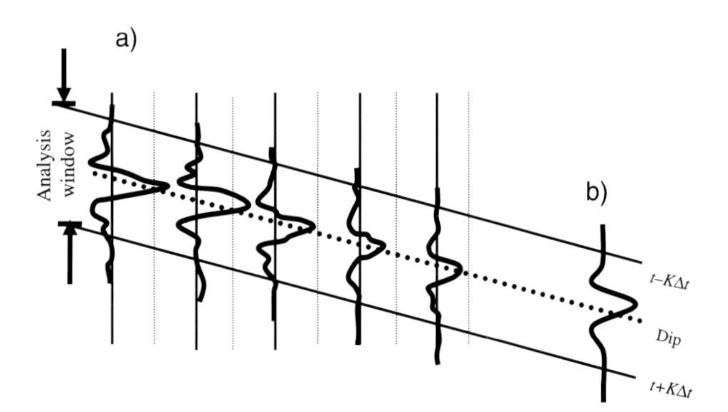

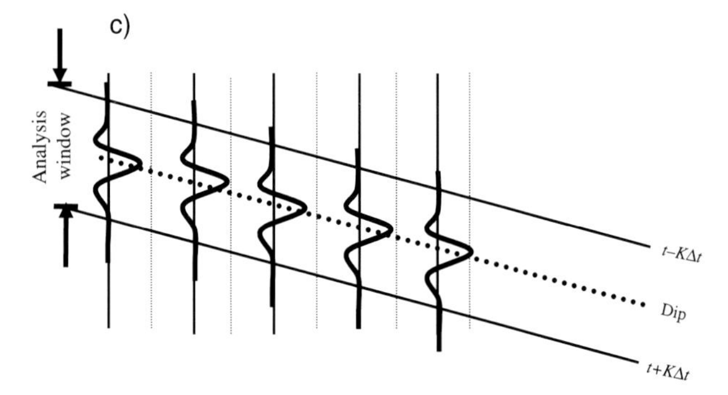

Figure 12. A schematic diagram showing the steps used in semblance estimation of coherence. (a) First, we calculate the energy of the five input traces within an analysis window, (b) then we calculate the average trace, and (c) finally, we replace each trace by the average trace and calculate the energy of the five average traces. The semblance is the ratio of the energy of (c) to the energy of (a). If each windowed trace in (a) has the identical waveform and amplitude, the semblance is 1.0; otherwise, it is less than 1.0.

Variance-based Coherence

Another popular measure of waveform similarity is the variance. As implemented, we will show that the variance estimate of coherence is identical to the semblance estimate discussed above. Modifying the formal definition of variance, var(t,p,q), to be computed along samples lying on a dipping reflector, we write

$$\mathrm{var}(t,p,q)=\frac{1}{J}\sum_{j=1}^{J}\left[u_j(t-px_j-qy_j)-\langle u(t,p,q)\rangle\right]^2, \tag{3.7}$$

where the mean, $\langle u(t,p,q)\rangle$, is defined as

$$\langle u(t,p,q)\rangle\equiv\frac{1}{J}\sum_{j=1}^{J}u_j(t-px_j-qy_j)\,. \tag{3.8}$$

Note here that $\langle u\rangle$ is calculated for each plane parallel to the reflector with the analysis window. Whereas equations 3.7 and 3.8 provide the formal definition of variance, most statisticians use the much more efficient (and mathematically equivalent) computational form

$$\mathrm{var}(t,p,q)=\frac{1}{J}\sum_{j=1}^{J}\left[u(t-px_j-qy_j,x_j,y_j)\right]^2-\left[\frac{1}{J}\sum_{j=1}^{J}u(t-px_j-qy_j,x_j,y_j)\right]^2. \tag{3.9}$$

To estimate coherence, we sum the variance over a vertical analysis window of $2K + 1$ samples and normalize by the energy of all the traces to obtain

$$c_v(t,p,q)\equiv\frac{\sum_{k=-K}^{+K}\frac{1}{J}\sum_{j=1}^{J}\left[u_j(t+k\Delta t-px_j-qy_j)\right]^2-\sum_{k=-K}^{+K}\left[\frac{1}{J}\sum_{j=1}^{J}u_j(t+k\Delta t-px_j-qy_j)\right]^2}{\sum_{k=-K}^{+K}\frac{1}{J}\sum_{j=1}^{J}\left[u_j(t+k\Delta t-px_j-qy_j)\right]^2}, \tag{3.10}$$

or

$$c_v(t,p,q)=1-\frac{\sum_{k=-K}^{+K}\left[\frac{1}{J}\sum_{j=1}^{J}u_j(t+k\Delta t-px_j-qy_j)\right]^2}{\sum_{k=-K}^{+K}\frac{1}{J}\sum_{j=1}^{J}\left[u_j(t+k\Delta t-px_j-qy_j)\right]^2}=1-c_s(t,p,q)\,. \tag{3.11}$$

Thus, the variance estimate of coherence is identical numerically to one minus the semblance estimate of coherence. The variance (and therefore also the semblance) is a measure of how well each trace fits the mean trace. If all traces are equal, the variance estimate of coherence, c_v, is 0.0 (and the semblance estimate of coherence, c_s, is 1.0). However, even if all the traces have the exact same waveform, if their amplitudes are different, c_v is greater than 0.0 and c_s is less than 1.0. In contrast, the crosscorrelation estimate of coherence, c_{xc}, is 1.0 as long as the waveform is the same, regardless of the amplitude of each trace. (We will show later in this chapter that the eigenstructure estimate of coherence has this same desirable sensitivity only to waveform).

Artifacts resulting from ignoring reflector dip and azimuth in coherence calculations

Coherence calculations based on crosscorrelation between the single adjacent trace and the center trace automatically accommodate for local dip through the selection of the maximum value of the crosscorrelation as a function of the time lag, τ. By contrast, because semblance-based coherence calculations typically include many traces about the desired output location, the local dip and azimuth calculation should be completed as a first step. Both semblance and variance estimates of coherence of seismic data currently are provided as an option in a popular interpretive workstation software product. Unfortunately, for computational efficiency, in several implementations no search over dip exists, such that the values of p and q in the preceding equations are set identically to zero. A finite dip will misalign the seismic waveforms, thereby causing a variance or semblance anomaly associated with structure, as seen in Figure 13a-c. Such structure-induced anomalies should not be confused with faults or fractures, although it is not unreasonable to expect fractures where we experience a change in dip.

In general, two good methods exist for calculating coherence volumes in the presence of structural dip. The first workflow, which involves a direct search of volumetric dip and azimuth like that discussed in Chapter 2, prior to or as part of the coherence calculation, is 50–200 times more intensive computationally than a coherence calculation without a dip search. Except for small surveys, such calculations are performed more appropriately on a computer server by a processing center or by an oil company technologist. In such a scenario, the interpreter loads a precomputed coherence volume that includes the advantage of an explicit volumetric dip and azimuth search and then extracts either time slices or horizon slices (Figure 14a and b).

The second workflow is more appropriate to a standalone workstation. The interpreter first flattens a slab of the seismic volume about an interpreted horizon, implicitly defining a dip/azimuth for each trace. The interpreter then

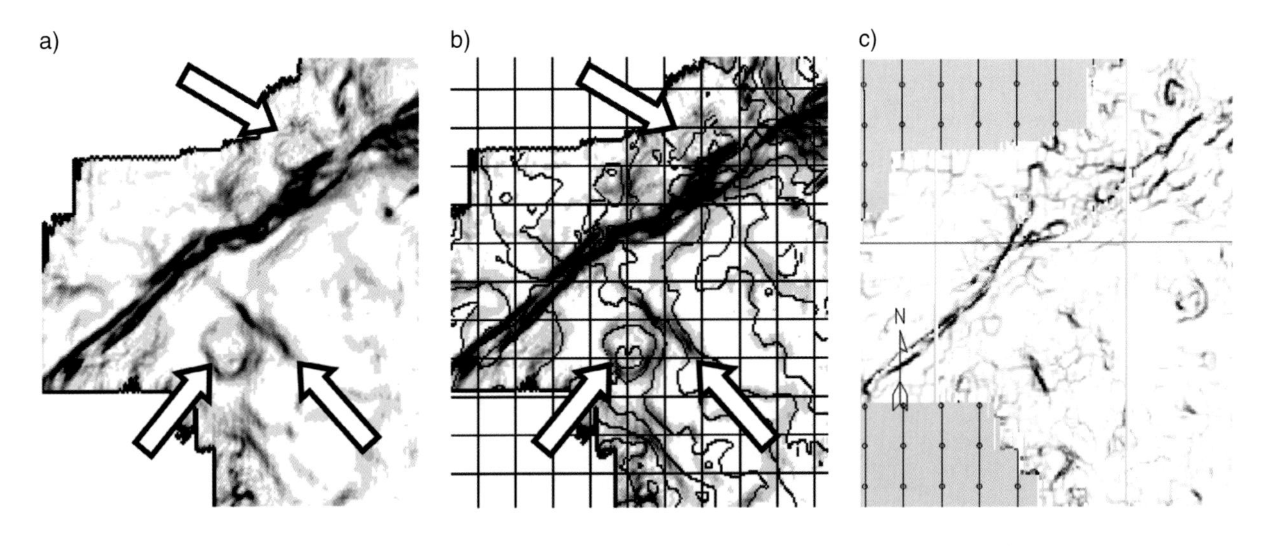

Figure 13. Artifacts generated by not calculating coherence along the dip and azimuth of the reflector: (a) coherence calculated over an entire volume without a dip search and then sliced along a picked horizon; (b) the coherence image shown in (a) overlain by structural contours; and (c) coherence calculated along the dip and azimuth of the reflector. Features seen on the horizon slice in (a) indicated by white arrows initially were thought to show collapse features and fractures of interest. However, when the structural contours were overplotted in (b), it was clear that most of the features were simply the result of structure. After Simon (2005).

calculates coherence without the time-consuming dip search on the flattened slab of data (Figure 14c).

The Manhattan Distance and Other Norms That Measure Waveform Similarity

The semblance estimate given by equation 3.6 is based on notions of similar trace energy, whereas the classical variance estimate given by equation 3.7 is based on notions of squared error about the mean. When they are normalized by the total energy of the data in the analysis window, these two measures become identical. Geophysicists have long used other error measures, in particular when we wish to assign a lower weight to outlier measurements. Equation 3.6 can be generalized to

$$c_r(t,p,q)=\frac{\sum_{k=-K}^{K}\left\|\frac{1}{J}\sum_{j=1}^{J}u_j(t+k\Delta t-px_j-qy_j)\right\|^r}{\sum_{k=-K}^{K}\frac{1}{J}\sum_{j=1}^{J}\left\|u_j(t+k\Delta t-px_j-qy_j)\right\|^r}, \quad (3.12)$$

where the symbol $\|f(x)\|$ indicates the absolute value of the function $f(x)$, and where now we measure what statisticians call the *distance* using the more general r-norm rather than using the Pythagorean squared norm (the sum of the squares, which provides a measure of energy). One major vendor estimates coherence using the Manhattan distance with $r = 1$, rather than the Pythagorean distance with $r = 2$ such as is used in equation 3.6. Although inhabitants of New Jersey and other uncivilized parts of the world west of the Hudson River measure distances as the crow flies, where the shortest distance between two points (x_2,y_2) and (x_1,y_1) is given by a straight line of length $\sqrt{(x_2-x_1)^2+(y_2-y_1)^2}$, the inhabitants of densely built Manhattan measure distances as "so many blocks uptown or downtown, by so many blocks crosstown," giving a distance of $\|x_2 - x_1\| + \|y_2 - y_1\|$. Such an $r = 1$ norm as a measure of error can provide superior results when we are fitting noisy outlier samples. However, we find that by the time most seismic data have been migrated and find their way to a workstation, the strong spikes have been removed, such that equations (3.12) with $r = 1$ and (3.6) with $r = 2$ provide comparable images.

Using Analytic Traces in Coherence Computations

If we use a small vertical-analysis window in equation 3.6, say, $K = 1$, we still may encounter artifacts in our coherence image near zero crossings in the data. In general, we can assume that a constant background level of incoherent seismic noise exists. Once the amplitude of our signal goes below that background level, our coherence algorithm will think the data are incoherent, thereby giving rise to low-coherence artifacts that follow structure, as we see in the example shown in Figure 15. We circumvent such a problem by applying the semblance computation to the an-

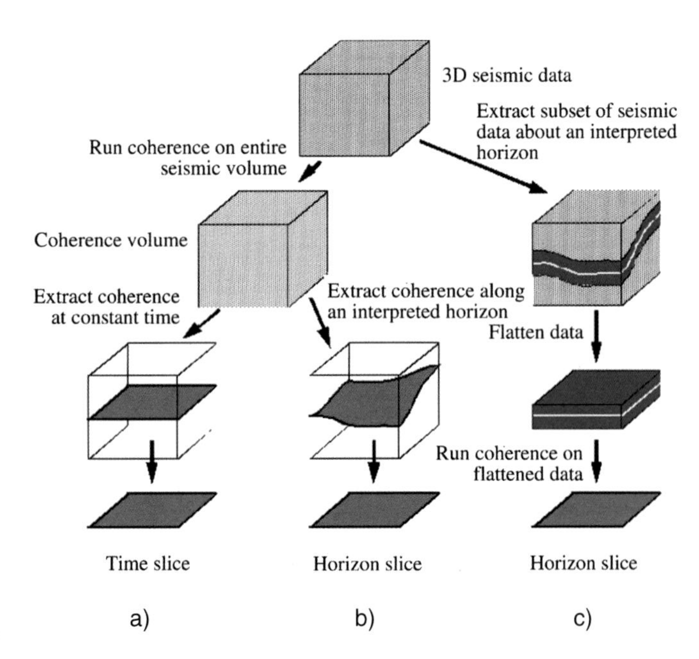

Figure 14. Alternative ways to compute and visualize coherence volumes. Computation of a coherence volume requires a value of dip and azimuth at every input sample. (a)–(b): The simplest but computationally most intensive approach is to calculate coherence for the entire seismic volume, searching for dip and azimuth as part of the calculation. The interpreter then uses a conventional work flow of viewing and interpreting the coherence volume on (a) time slices or (b) horizon slices. (c) A computationally more efficient but in general less accurate approach is first to flatten a window of data along a picked horizon. The dip magnitude of this flattened volume is implicitly equal to zero, such that no dip and azimuth search is needed. The resulting coherence subvolume is a suite of phantom horizons parallel to the original picked horizon. This second approach inherits the interpreter bias and errors made in the original picks. Furthermore, many geologic features, such as diapirs, karst, fluvial deltaic systems, and mass-transport complexes may not be associated with an overlying or underlying horizon that can be picked accurately. Figure courtesy of Sue Nissen.

alytic trace (discussed in Chapter 1), rather than simply to the real trace, as given by

$$c_s(t,p,q) = \frac{\sum_{k=-K}^{K}\left\{\left[\frac{1}{J}\sum_{j=1}^{J}u_j(t+k\Delta t-px_j-qy_j)\right]^2 + \left[\frac{1}{J}\sum_{j=1}^{J}u_j^H(t+k\Delta t-px_j-qy_j)\right]^2\right\}}{\sum_{k=-K}^{K}\frac{1}{J}\sum_{j=1}^{J}\left\{\left[u_j(t+k\Delta t-px_j-qy_j)\right]^2 + \left[u_j^H(t+k\Delta t-px_j-qy_j)\right]^2\right\}}, \quad (3.13)$$

where the superscript H denotes the Hilbert transform (or quadrature, or 90° phase rotation) of the input seismic data. When the original trace goes to zero, the magnitude of the quadrature trace is at a maximum, thus circumventing the previously mentioned problem of accurately calculating the semblance in a small-amplitude portion of a trace in the presence of noise.

Conversely, when the quadrature goes to zero the magnitude of the original trace is at a maximum, again providing a robust semblance-based coherency calculation in the presence of noise. With both real and imaginary parts of the analytic trace included in equation 3.13, the signal-to-noise ratio is good if the envelope (discussed in Chapter 1) of the trace, u, is significantly larger than the level of background noise. Not surprisingly, if the envelope (also known as the reflection strength) falls below the background-noise level, such as we sometimes see in shale-on-shale reflections, we still will see bands of low coherence following structure. We also will see low coherence associated with situations of geologic interest such as turbidites, along angular and erosional unconformities, and within salt and shale diapirs. Figure 16 shows the improved results obtained by estimating the semblance of the analytic trace using equation 3.13 (Figure 16b) versus those obtained by estimating the semblance of the real trace using equation 3.6 (Figure 16a). Note that Figure 16b is significantly whiter, or more coherent, than Figure 16a, with greatly reduced low-coherence artifacts resulting from zero crossings.

Eigenstructure-based Coherence

One drawback of the multitrace semblance- and variance-based estimates of coherence is that they are sensitive not only to waveform but also to lateral changes in seismic amplitude. In contrast, the three-trace crosscorrelation algorithm, although it is more sensitive to noise, is sensitive only to changes in waveform, not in amplitude. Kalkomey (1997), Barnes and Laughlin (2002), and others recommend that when we use multiple seismic attributes for reservoir characterization, those attributes should (1) have a firm basis on physics or geology and (2) be mathematically independent of each other. Our philosophy is that, if possible, each attribute should measure only one property of the seismic response. Then multiple attributes can be combined later either graphically (see Chapter 9) or numerically (using either geostatistics or neural networks). In Chapter 5, we will discuss coherent amplitude gradients, which are a direct measure of lateral changes in reflector amplitude. We will show that although changes in waveform and changes in amplitude often are coupled through the underlying geology, by using eigenstructure analysis, we can separate them into two mathematically independent measures that are amenable to subsequent analysis.

We begin the eigenstructure method with estimates of dip and azimuth, which we discussed in Chapter 2. Not surprisingly, the eigenstructure method can be used as a measure for discretely scanning dip and azimuth. Graphically, the eigenstructure method analyzes a window of traces (Figure 17a) and determines which (yet to be scaled) wavelet best represents the waveform variability (Figure 17b). Then this wavelet is scaled to fit to each input trace, providing what we call the *coherent component* of the data within

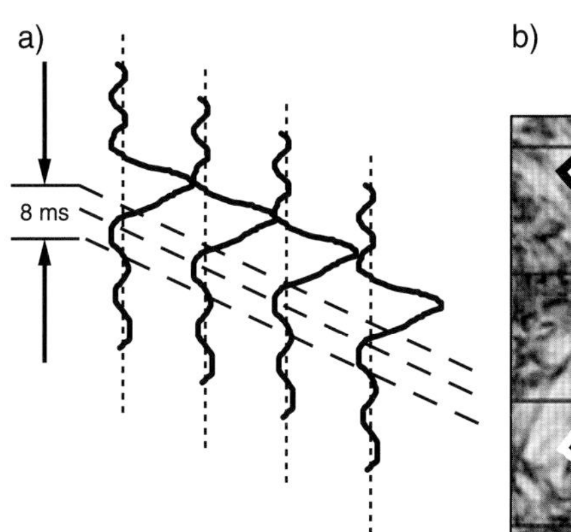

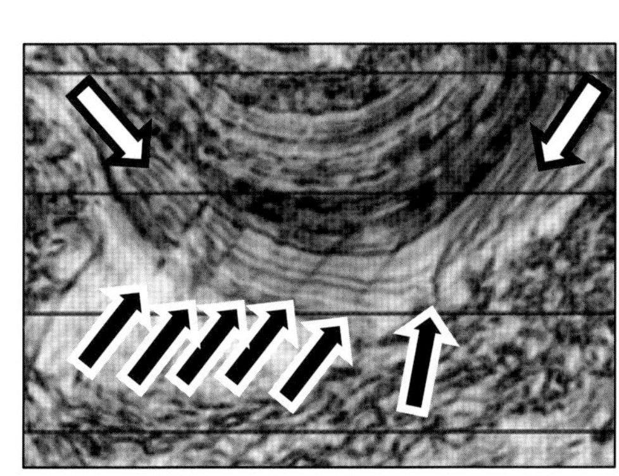

Figure 15. The effect of zero crossings in the signal, using the traditional semblance algorithm given by equation 3.6. (a) The signal-to-noise ratio is low when a short analysis window (here, 8 ms, corresponding to three samples) straddles a zero crossing. (b) The resulting coherence image seen on a time slice at t = 2.164 s. White arrows indicate artifacts associated with low signal-to-noise about zero crossings. Black arrows indicate geologic faults of interest.

the analysis window (Figure 17c). Eigenstructure coherence is simply the ratio of the energy of the coherent component of the data (Figure 17c) to the energy of the original traces (Figure 17a) within the analysis window. For 3D data, the analysis window includes a suite of traces centered around the analysis point (Figure 11).

To help the reader understand the wealth of published information on eigenstructure (also called principal-component) analysis, we will introduce some terminology used by statisticians and show step by step how to calculate the covariance matrix (Figure 18). In step 1, we extract a suite of sample vectors from the data (Figure 12). If our analysis window includes nine traces, the data's sample vector will be of length 9. There will be one sample vector that corresponds to a suite of time-interpolated data samples, for each value of k ranging between $+K$ and $-K$, that falls within our vertical-analysis window and is extracted parallel to a plane defined by apparent dips p and q. Each sample vector forms a row in the data matrix. In step 2, we take each column of the data matrix (which is simply a shifted window of each seismic trace) and crosscorrelate that column with itself and with each other column, forming what we call a *covari-*

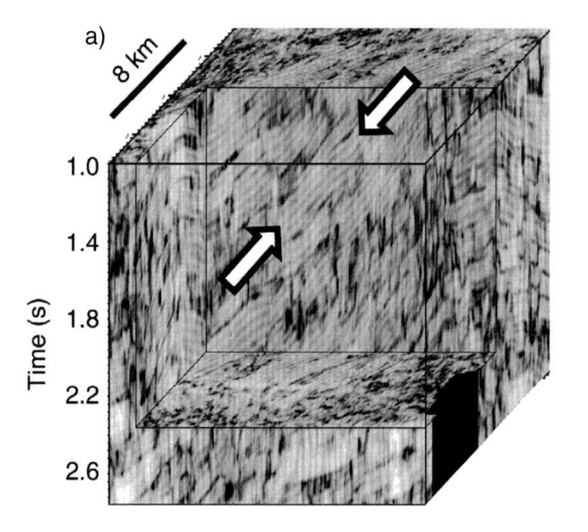

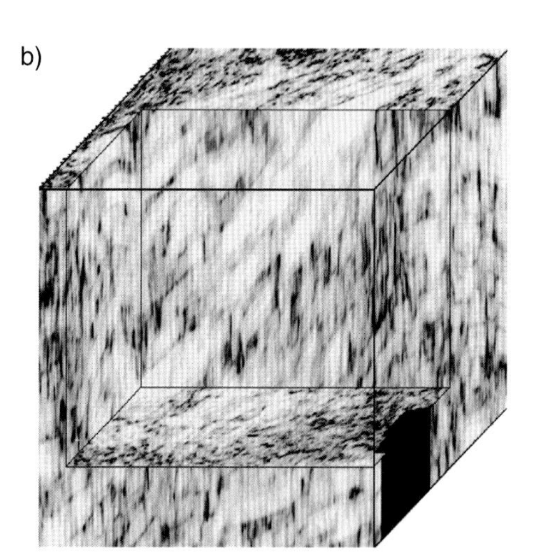

Figure 16. Semblance estimates of coherence generated using (a) the input data trace and (b) the analytic trace. Vertical window length = 20 ms. At a fixed level of noise, the signal-to-noise ratio can become low near reflector zero crossings, thereby resulting in low-coherence artifacts that follow the structure (arrows). Using the analytic trace (equation 3.13) avoids this problem. When the magnitude of the real input trace is low, the magnitude of the quadrature component is high. Likewise, when the magnitude of the quadrature component is low, the magnitude of the real input trace is high, thereby maintaining a good signal-to-noise ratio in the presence of strong reflectors. It still is common to see low-coherence trends following structure when we have low-reflectivity (and hence low signal-to-noise ratio) shale-on-shale events, and for truly incoherent geology such as that encountered with erosional and angular unconformities, or with karst, mass-transport complexes, and turbidites.

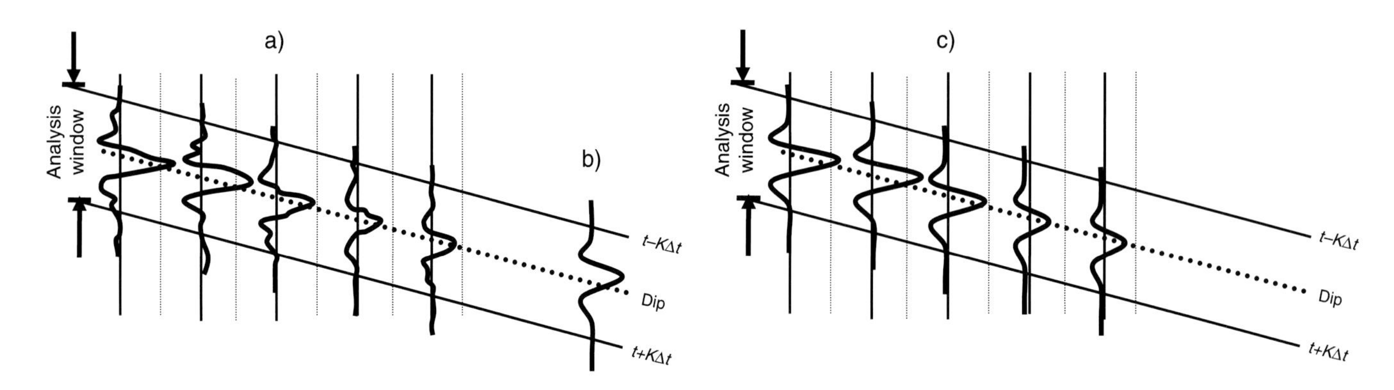

Figure 17. A schematic diagram showing the steps used in eigenstructure estimation of coherence. (a) First, we calculate the energy of the input traces within an analysis window. (b) Next, we calculate the seismic waveform that best approximates the waveform of each input trace, (c) Finally, we replace each trace by a scaled version of (b) that best fits the input trace. The eigenstructure coherence is the ratio of the energy of (c) to the energy of (a). If each windowed trace in (a) has exactly the same waveform (but perhaps a different amplitude), the coherence is 1.0; otherwise, it is less than 1.0.

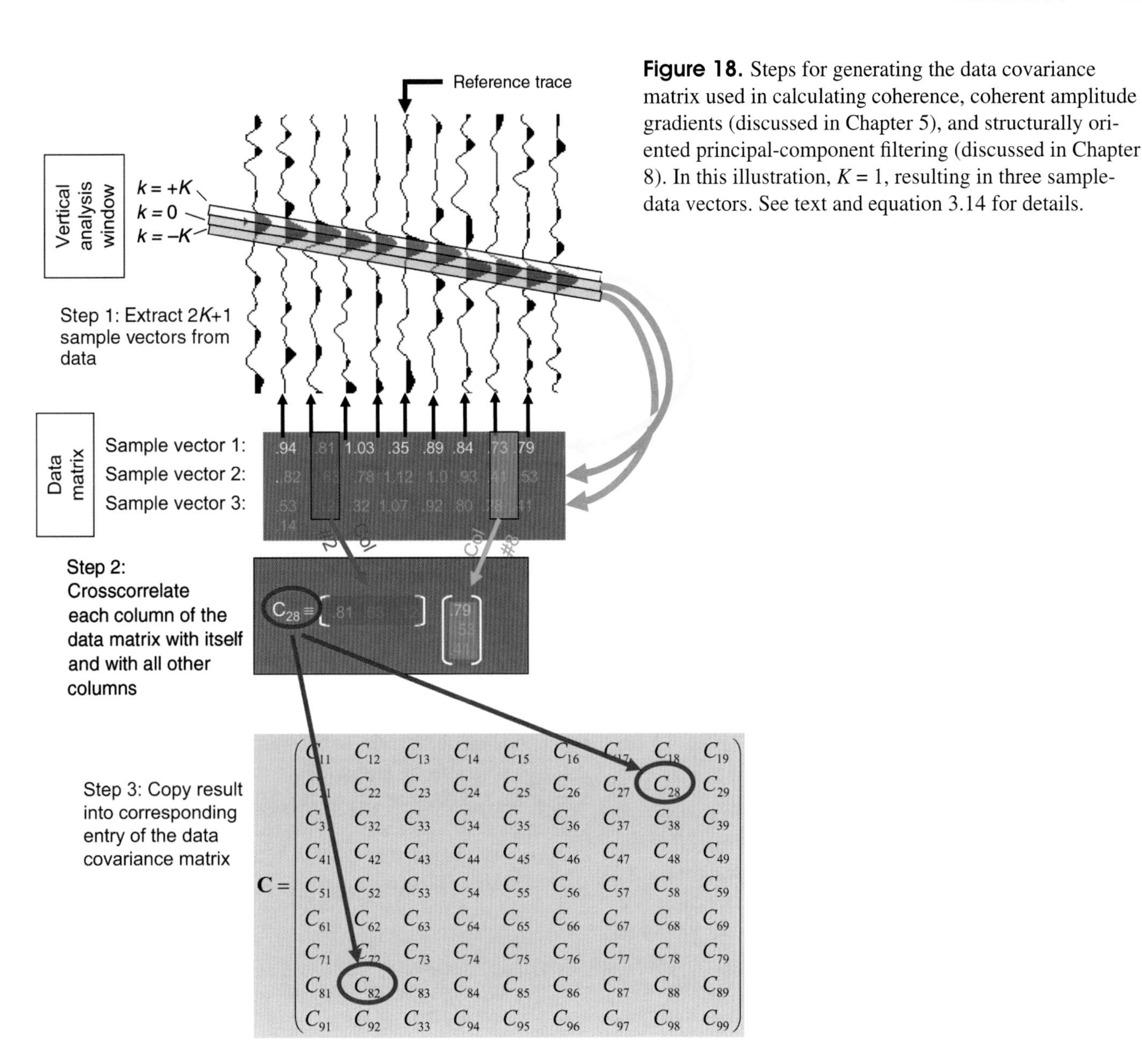

Figure 18. Steps for generating the data covariance matrix used in calculating coherence, coherent amplitude gradients (discussed in Chapter 5), and structurally oriented principal-component filtering (discussed in Chapter 8). In this illustration, $K = 1$, resulting in three sample-data vectors. See text and equation 3.14 for details.

ance matrix. The covariance matrix contains all possible unnormalized crosscorrelations and autocorrelations of all nine windowed traces with each other. Those correlations then are ordered in a systematic fashion, as shown in Figure 18. Specifically, crosscorrelating (without normalization) a window of trace 2 (column 2 of the data matrix) with the corresponding window of trace 8 (column 8 of the data matrix) gives us the C_{28} element of the 9×9 covariance matrix (step 3). Mathematically, the C_{ij} component of the covariance matrix is given as

$$c_{ij}(t,p,q) = \sum_{k=-K}^{+K} [u_i(t + k\Delta t - px_i - qy_i) - <u(t,p,q)>] [u_j(t + k\Delta t - px_j - qy_j) - <u(t,p,q)>] , \quad (3.14)$$

where, unlike in equation 3.8, $<u(t,p,q)>$ is now the mean of each windowed trace. Statisticians often approximate the (unknown) true mean by the sample mean. Fortunately, for properly recorded seismic data, we can assume that the true mean is zero.

When we have computed our covariance matrix, **C**, the next step is to decompose it into eigenvectors, each of which has a corresponding eigenvalue. Interpreters who work with attributes recognize that eigenvectors (also called principal components) and eigenvalues are used routinely in multiattribute analysis for reservoir characterization. If we assume that the mean amplitude value, μ, is zero, then the first eigenvalue, λ_1, tells us what portion of the energy of all the traces in the analysis window can be expressed by a single waveform, with a different scaling parameter for each trace. The corresponding eigenvector, $\mathbf{v}^1$, is a list of those scaling coefficients, one for each trace, that when multiplied by the waveform, best fit the data. We will discuss eigenvectors in Chapter 5 on coherent amplitude gradients and in Chapter 8 on structure-oriented filtering. For now, all we need to know is that any matrix can be decomposed into eigenvectors and eigenvalues. For any diagonally symmetric, real-valued covariance matrix, we can write

$$\mathbf{C}\mathbf{v}^{(m)} = \lambda_m \mathbf{v}^{(m)}, \tag{3.15}$$

where $\mathbf{v}^{(m)}$ indicates the mth eigenvector and λ_m indicates the corresponding mth eigenvalue. In general, for a $J \times J$ covariance matrix, there are J mathematically independent eigenvectors, where J is the number of traces in the spatial analysis window. By convention, the eigenvectors and eigenvalues are ordered, with the one best expressing the energy of data within the analysis window being first, the one best expressing the remaining data variation being second, and so on.

In general, only a few eigenvectors and eigenvalues are needed to represent 95% of the data. Indeed, the eigenstructure coherence estimate (Gersztenkorn and Marfurt, 1999) uses only the first eigenvalue:

$$c_e \equiv \frac{\lambda_1}{\sum_{j=1}^{J} C_{jj}}, \tag{3.16}$$

where J is the number of traces used in the analysis window, the denominator represents the energy of all the traces, and the numerator λ_1 represents the energy that can be represented by the first eigenvector, $\mathbf{v}^1$. Thus, if all the traces in the same analysis window have the exact same shape (but perhaps with different amplitudes, including even traces with reversed polarity), the eigenstructure coherence, c_e, will be 1.0. By contrast, if the waveforms are consistent but the amplitudes are not identical, the semblance coherence, c_s, will not be equal to 1.0 and the variance estimate of coherence, c_e, will not be equal to 0.0. Thus, the eigenstructure coherence has the advantage of being blind to trace-to-trace amplitude scaling differences.

Like the crosscorrelation, semblance, and variance estimates of coherence, the eigenstructure coherence estimate is applied to a window centered on each sample of each trace in the seismic data volume. At each point we extract a data matrix, form the corresponding covariance matrix, calculate the first eigenvalue, calculate the energy of the traces that compose the data matrix, take their ratio, and store the solution as c_e. The analysis cube is moved throughout the 3D seismic volume, and the output is a 3D data set consisting of coherence coefficients defined for each amplitude point of the input 3D data volume.

In Figure 19, we show one of the first applications of the eigenstructure coherence estimate and compare it with the crosscorrelation and semblance estimates of coherence discussed above. In this early application, the eigenstructure algorithm assumed that the apparent dips, p and q, were identically zero, which led to some structural artifacts or leakage such as that discussed earlier in Figure 13. Such artifacts are particularly evident in structurally complex terrains such as those shown next in Figure 20a. By first calculating volumetric dip and azimuth as discussed in Chapter 2 and then performing the calculation using equations (3.14) through (3.16), we obtain the artifact-free result shown in Figure 20b.

In Figure 21, we display a vertical seismic section and a set of seismic time slices at 0.2-s intervals. Note a central syncline bounded by two anticlines. In Figure 22, we display corresponding slices through a coherence volume that was generated using equations 3.14 through 3.16 with the assumption that the dip components p and q were identically zero. Arrows indicate two bands of low coherence that appear on the vertical section exactly where we might anticipate fractures. These features are the result of structural leakage, not fractures, as was verified by a more careful (and more expensive) calculation of coherence along the estimated structural dip and shown in Figure 23.

Typically, dip scans sample the data discretely at finite intervals, such as $\pm 5°$ or ± 0.001ms/m. We can improve our calculations by interpolating the dip as we discussed in Chapter 2. In Figure 24, we display time slices through coherence volumes generated using a three-trace crosscorrelation and a five-trace semblance, an eigenstructure without a dip scan, an eigenstructure with a discrete dip scan, and an eigenstructure with interpolated dips. Each algorithmic approach provides a small but incremental improvement in our image quality.

A final improvement to the eigenstructure calculation is to use the analytic trace rather than the real input trace when we compute the covariance matrix. Marfurt (2006) evaluated two alternatives — forming a complex, symmetric covariance matrix directly with the analytic trace, and using the quadrature component to form additional sample vectors in equation 3.13. The first approach allows for complex eigenvectors and hence some amount of wavelet rotation within the analysis window, which does not fit our preconception of a coherent reflection. In contrast, the second (preferred) method does not. Thus, in the second approach, the equation for our covariance matrix becomes

$$C_{ij}(t,p,q) = \begin{array}{l} \sum_{k=-K}^{+K} \left[u_i(t+k\Delta t - px_i - qy_i) - \mu(t,p,q)\right] \\ \qquad \left[u_j(t+k\Delta t - px_j - qy_j) - \mu(t,p,q)\right] \\ + \sum_{k=-K}^{+K} \left[u_i^H(t+k\Delta t - px_i - qy_i) - \mu^H(t,p,q)\right] \\ \qquad \left[u_j^H(t+k\Delta t - px_j - qy_j) - \mu^H(t,p,q)\right] \end{array} \tag{3.17}$$

where the superscript H denotes the Hilbert transform (or quadrature) of the input data.

In Figure 25, we apply the different generations of coherence algorithms to a data volume from offshore eastern Canada. We can see a progressive improvement in the resolution of discrete faults as we move from the crosscorrelation algorithm, through the five-trace semblance and the five-trace eigenstructure (without dip scan), to the five-trace eigenstructure with the dip scan, using the analytic trace.

Gradient Structure Tensor-based Coherence

Bakker (2003) developed and analyzed a very complete suite of interpretation and data-filtering algorithms based on the gradient structure tensor (GST). The GST was described in Chapter 2 as a robust means of estimating reflector dip and azimuth. In contrast to the $J \times J$ covariance matrix given by equation 3.14, whose size is determined by

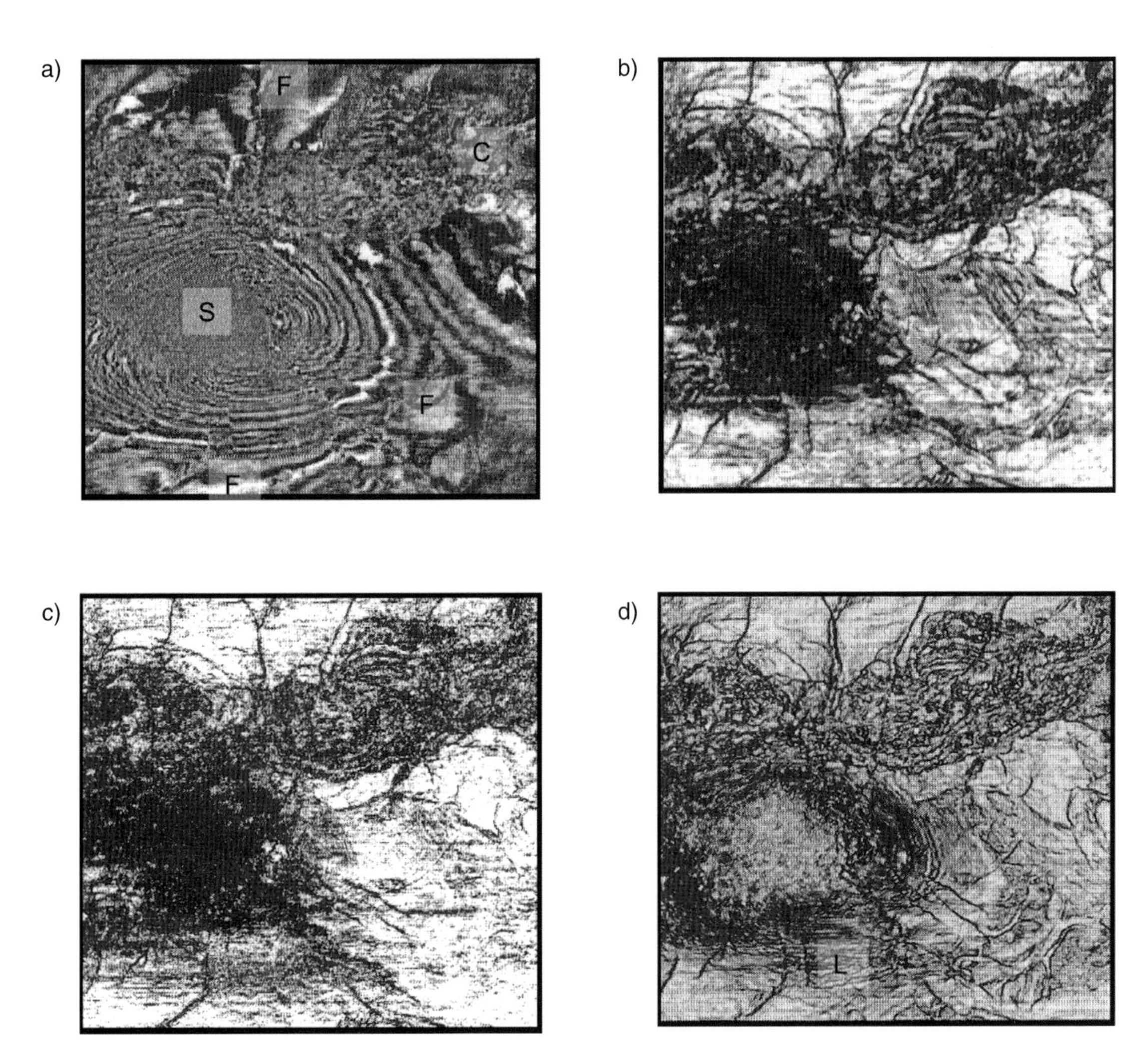

Figure 19. Comparison of alternative coherence algorithms used on data from South Marsh Island, Gulf of Mexico, U.S.A. The volume shown contains both structural and stratigraphic features associated with deposition over a terrane influenced by salt tectonism. (a) A time slice through the time-migrated seismic data at 1.8 s. "S" denotes a salt dome, and "F" indicates several radial faults. Corresponding slices through coherence volumes were generated using the (b) three-trace crosscorrelation algorithm, (c) a five-trace semblance algorithm, and (d) a five-trace eigenstructure algorithm. All coherence computations used the same 80-ms vertical analysis window. The circular rings seen in (a) correspond to sediments that are cut by radial faults (indicated by "F") and that are dipping against a salt dome. The disorganized feature indicated by "C" in the northeast is interpreted to be a canyon. The salt dome and faults appear to be incoherent (black) in (b) through (d). Note that there is considerably less speckle noise in the five-trace semblance algorithm than in the three-trace crosscorrelation algorithm. An even greater improvement in signal to noise and lateral resolution accompanies the five-trace eigenstructure algorithm. The structural artifacts (leakage) about the salt dome indicated by "L" and the overall grayer level of the image in (d) are the result of a failure, in this early work, to search over structural dip. After Gersztenkorn and Marfurt (1996).

the number of traces in the data volume, the covariance matrix given by equation 2.11 is 3 × 3, corresponding to the three-dimensionality of the directional derivative sample vectors. Bakker describes several shape attributes, based on the three eigenvectors and eigenvalues of the GST covariance matrix. The shape attribute that is most similar to the coherence images discussed so far in this chapter is his measure of how planar the features falling within the analysis window are (i.e., his measure of their planarity). For discussion, we will call this calculation the GST-based esti-

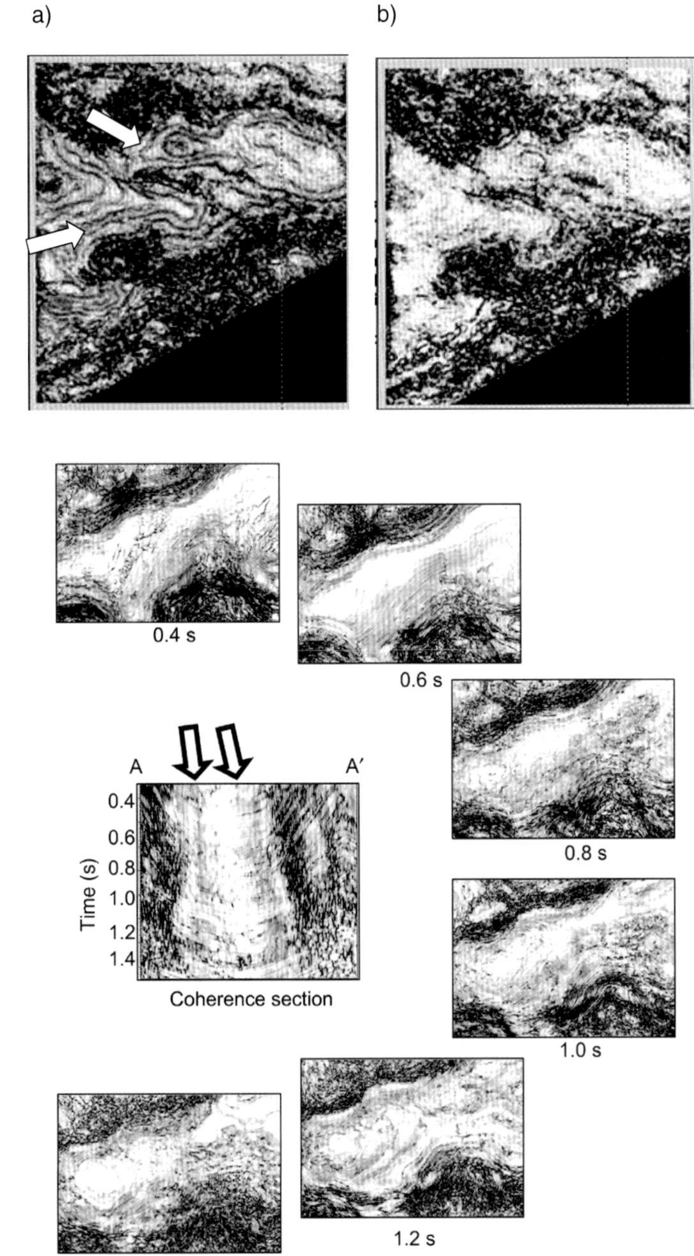

Figure. 20. Comparison of coherence volumes generated (a) without and (b) with a dip search using an identical eigenstructure estimate of coherence. The computational effort needed to generate the coherence volume in (a) is only 10% of that needed to generate the coherence volume in (b). However, failure to estimate waveform similarity along reflector dip results in artifacts that some call *structural leakage*, thereby giving rise to contourlike features indicated by arrows in (a). The low-coherence contours result from the structural dip being such that the lateral analysis window spans events from different geologic horizons, each of which has its own waveform. The contours in this image mask the fault that is seen more clearly in (b). After Chopra (2002).

Figure 21. A vertical seismic slice AA′ and time slices at 0.200-s intervals through a time-migrated seismic volume from the western U.S.A. We note a central syncline bounded by two anticlines.

Figure 22. A vertical slice AA′ and time slices through the eigenstructure coherence volume corresponding to the slices through the seismic volume shown in Figure 21. Coherence was calculated assuming a flat dip. Arrows indicate structural leakage artifacts that might be misinterpreted as low-coherence fracture zones.

mate of coherence:

$$c_{GST} \equiv \frac{\lambda_1 - \lambda_2}{\lambda_1 + \lambda_2} , \quad (3.18)$$

where λ_1, and λ_2 are the first two eigenvalues of the GST. If $\lambda_1 >> \lambda_2$, we have a coherent (and in general, dipping) planar reflector. If $\lambda_1 = \lambda_2 = \lambda_3$, we have totally incoherent energy, and c_{GST} approaches zero. If $\lambda_1 = \lambda_2 >> \lambda_3$, we have a lineament, and c_{GST} again approaches zero. In Figure 26, we display Bakker's (2003) comparison of the GST-based coherence versus the dip-scan-based coherence. The GST-based coherence has lower lateral resolution because it uses a larger analysis window in calculating the derivatives used in equation 2.10. Because the GST matrix is based on derivatives of seismic amplitude, it will join semblance and variance as an attribute that is sensitive both to changes in waveform and to lateral changes in amplitude.

Randen and his colleagues (Randen et al., 2000) have also worked with the GST, defining a measure they call chaos, which we will denote by c_χ :

$$c_\chi = \frac{2\lambda_2}{\lambda_1 + \lambda_3} - 1 . \quad (3.19)$$

Note that if $\lambda_1 >> \lambda_2$, the coherence is high and c_χ goes to –1. If $\lambda_1 \approx \lambda_2 \approx \lambda_3$, c_χ goes to 0. Finally, if $\lambda_1 \approx \lambda_2$, but $\lambda_3 \approx 0$ [Bakker's (2003) lineament attribute], c_χ goes to +1.

At the time of writing this book, we have not found enough published examples to compare quantitatively how the more recently developed GST-based coherence and chaos algorithms compare with the more mature, dip-scan-based coherence algorithms. However, we expect that a similar suite of incremental algorithmic improvements will make these newer techniques competitive and perhaps superior to dip-scan-based coherence.

Least-squares-based Coherence

Our final algorithm, presented by Bednar (1998), is based on a least-squares fit to a plane through a seismic data window. Bednar's paper does not provide explicit details, so we will provide our own interpretation of the method. Clearly, one can fit a plane to a 3D analysis window of seismic data using either a brute-force least-squares fit or a more elegant prediction-error filter. The objective of either approach is to minimize the squared error given by the equation

$$E^2(t,p,q) = \sum_{k=-K}^{+K} \sum_{j=1}^{J} \left\{ \left[\beta_k u_j (k\Delta t - px_j - qy_j) - r_j \right]^2 \right\} , \quad (3.20)$$

with the constraint that

$$\sum_j r_j^2 = 1 . \quad (3.21)$$

In equation 3.20, the unknown coefficients β_k are inversely proportional to the wavelet that best fits the data within the window, and r_j is proportional to the amplitude of the coherent part of the trace. As we did with the eigenstructure algorithm, we solve these equations using an iterative technique, beginning with the mean trace as an estimate of an initial wavelet that best fits the data within the analysis window. Many of the concepts associated with least-squares fitting are closely linked to eigenvector analysis. We present a result of Bednar's (1998) least-squares fit as Figure 27.

Sensitivity of Coherence to Analysis-window Size

One beauty of seismic coherence is that no matter what the implementation, only a limited number of parameters exists — the maximum dip to be searched, a dip-scanning increment, the size of the vertical analysis window, and the

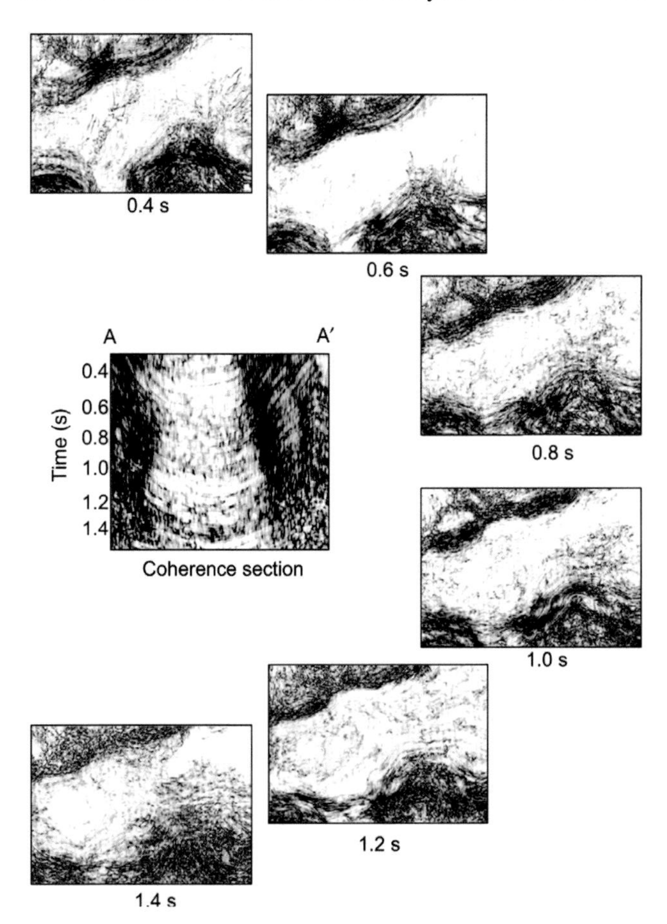

Figure 23. A vertical slice AA′ and time slices through the eigenstructure coherence volume corresponding to those in Figures 21 and 22. Coherence was calculated along reflector dip. Note that the structural leakage has disappeared, although we do see bands of low-coherence shales following structure.

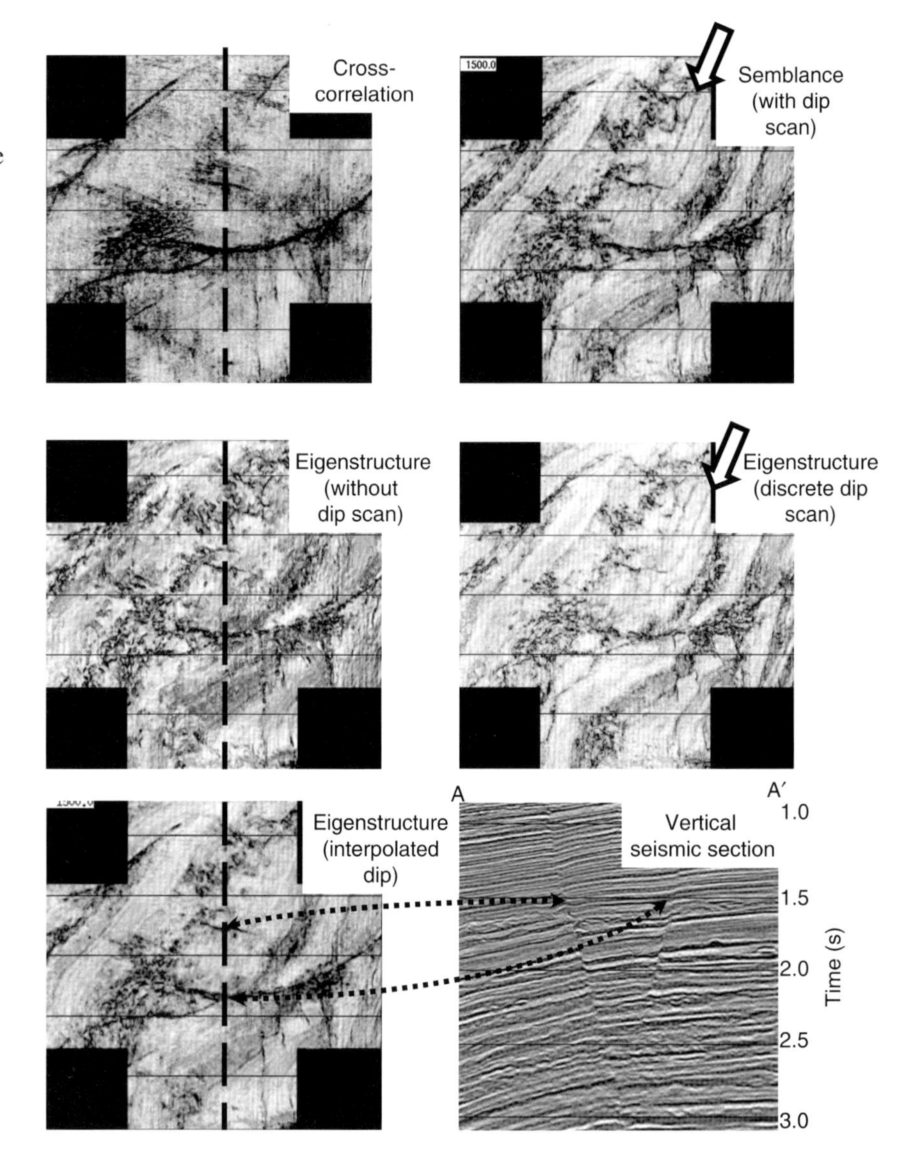

Figure 24. Evolution of seismic coherence algorithms, illustrated by time slices at $t = 1.500$ s through coherence volumes generated by crosscorrelation, semblance with dip search, eigenstructure without dip search, eigenstructure with a discrete dip search, and eigenstructure with an interpolated dip search. Black arrows correlate the discontinuities seen on the coherence slice to the vertical seismic section. Failure to interpolate the semblance-estimated dip results in the structural leakage indicated by the white arrows on the simple dip-scan-coherence calculations.

size of the spatial analysis window. Even though there are only a few parameters to determine, the choice of parameters has a bearing on computation of the final coherence coefficient and hence on the display. We already have noted that an accurate estimate of structural dip is critical. In practice, the interpreter scans through the seismic data and determines the maximum reflector dip by inspection and enters it as an input parameter. Searching for dips that are unreasonably large not only will increase the computation cost, it may also allow the algorithm to misidentify steeply dipping backscattered ground roll as coherent reflectors. In and of itself, the dip-azimuth-scan component of coherence computations is a very powerful filter.

Sensitivity to spatial window size

Increasing the size of our analysis window increases the run time and the angular resolution, and at a fixed depth level it decreases the lateral resolution. Because frequency content decreases with increasing depth, it often makes sense to calculate coherence using a small window for a shallow objective and using a larger window for a deeper objective.

We begin our analysis with coherence computation of a channel system using the following algorithms shown in Figure 28: (b) a three-trace crosscorrelation, (c) a five-trace (r = 12.5-m radius) semblance, and (d) a five-trace (r = 12.5-m radius) eigenstructure. (Figure 28a shows a time slice for the same channel system.) The vertical analysis window is 40 ms for all three algorithm images.

Of the three algorithm images, we prefer the eigenstructure image and will use that for our subsequent analysis. The improvement in lateral resolution in Figure 28d results from the amplitude insensitivity of the eigenstructure algorithm. In Figure 29, we vary the size of the spatial analysis window from r = 12.5 m (shown earlier as Figure 28d)

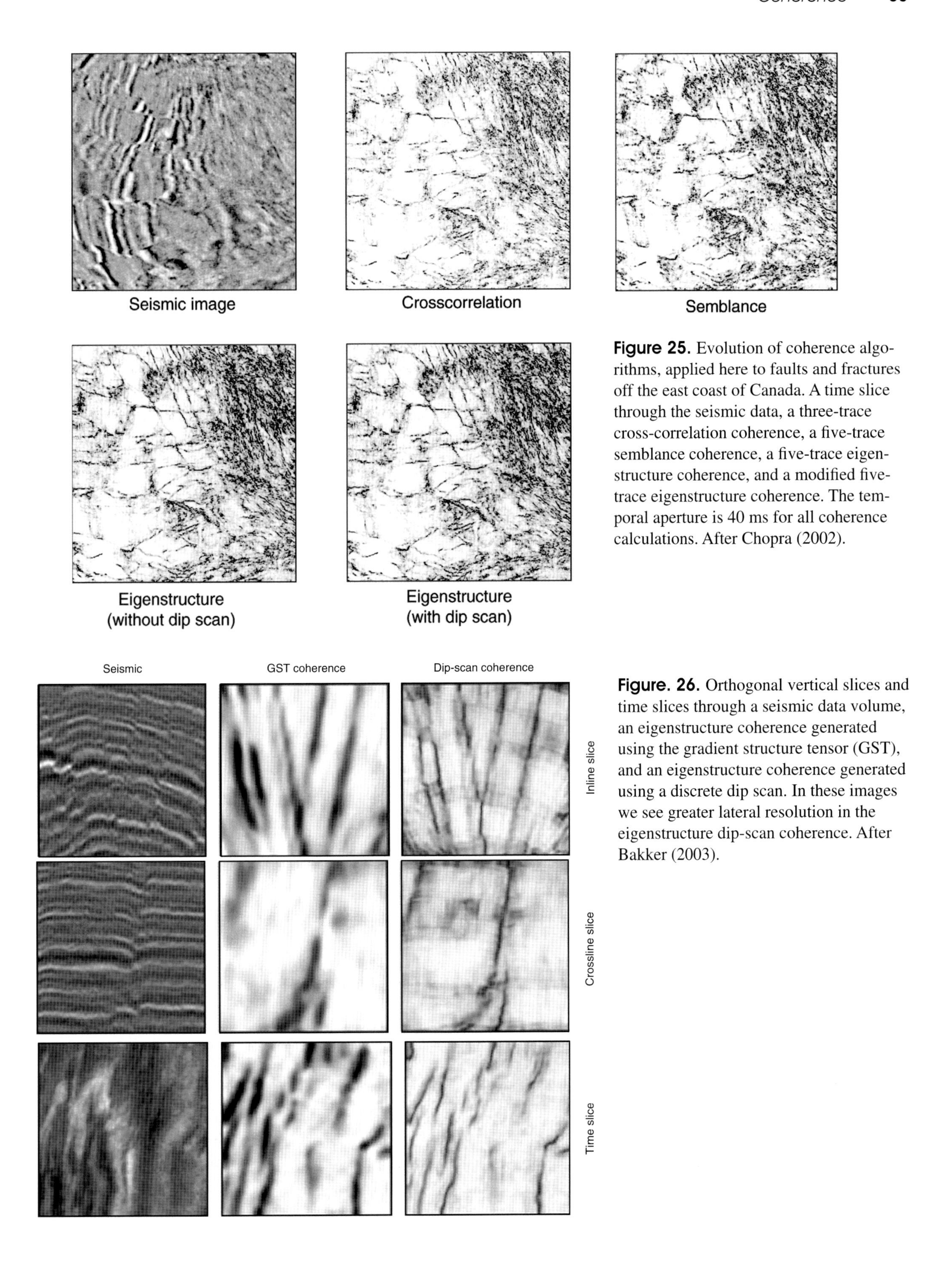

Figure 25. Evolution of coherence algorithms, applied here to faults and fractures off the east coast of Canada. A time slice through the seismic data, a three-trace cross-correlation coherence, a five-trace semblance coherence, a five-trace eigenstructure coherence, and a modified five-trace eigenstructure coherence. The temporal aperture is 40 ms for all coherence calculations. After Chopra (2002).

Figure. 26. Orthogonal vertical slices and time slices through a seismic data volume, an eigenstructure coherence generated using the gradient structure tensor (GST), and an eigenstructure coherence generated using a discrete dip scan. In these images we see greater lateral resolution in the eigenstructure dip-scan coherence. After Bakker (2003).

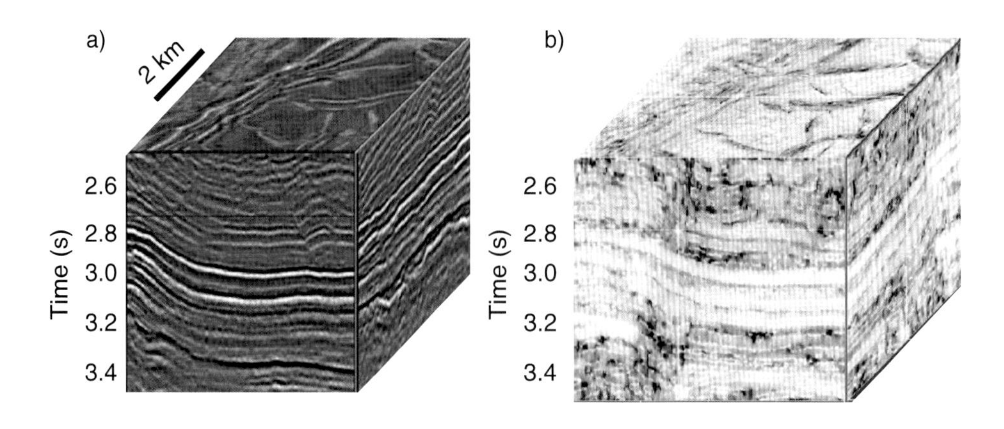

Figure 27. (a) A seismic data volume and the (b) corresponding coherence volume calculated by least-squares fitting of a plane to the seismic data within a data-analysis window using an efficient prediction error filter algorithm. After Bednar (1998).

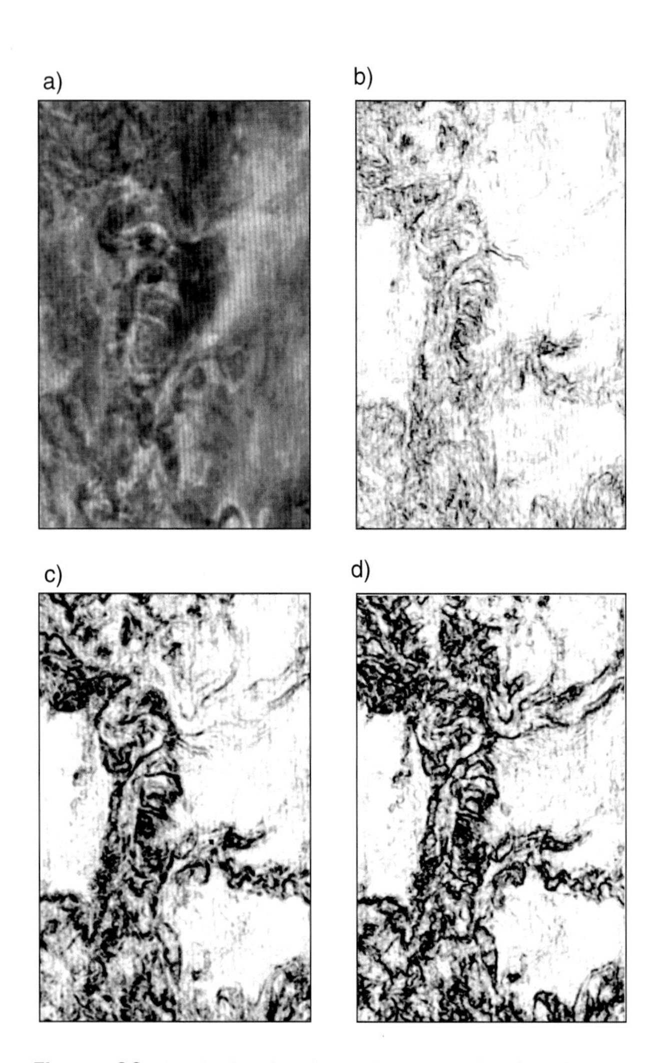

Figure 28. Analysis of a channel system showing the evolution of coherence algorithms. as applied to a channel system. Time slices through (a) a seismic data volume and (b)-(d) through its corresponding (b) three-trace crosscorrelation coherence, (c) five-trace semblance, and (d) five-trace eigenstructure coherence volumes. Note the improvement in lateral resolution as we progress from (b) through (d). The vertical analysis window is 40 ms for all coherence calculations.

through r = 25.0 m, r = 37.5 m, and ending with r = 50 m. The vertical analysis window is fixed at 16 ms. Not surprisingly, a narrow channel indicated by the white arrow is best delineated on the image generated with the smallest lateral window (Figure 29a). Less certain is why the edges of a larger channel indicated by the gray arrow also show up best on this image. The larger-window calculations compute not only coherence but also dip and azimuth using more traces, such that the local estimates of reflector dip and azimuth upon which coherence is calculated may be different. An intermediate-size channel, indicated by the striped arrow, appears only when the aperture is greater than or equal to 25 m (Figure 29b, c, and d). Although most features become progressively more blurred in the 37.5-m- and 50-m-radius images (Figure 29c and d), we can see considerably more detail inside one of the channels in the 37.5-m window, as indicated by the dotted arrow (Figure 29c). We will discuss the impact of larger window analysis of longer wavelength features in Chapters 4 and 5.

Sensitivity to vertical window size

Because the data are of good quality, in Figure 30 we will use our five-trace (r = 12.5 m) eigenstructure image and vary the temporal (vertical) analysis window. The thin channel indicated by the white arrow is best resolved using the 8-ms and 16-ms analysis windows (Figure 30a and 30b, respectively), as is the feature shown by the gray arrow. We expect narrow channels also to be thin. As we increase the vertical analysis window first to 24 ms and then to 32 ms (Figure 30c and 30d, respectively), these two channels bleed away, implying that they are low in amplitude and are confined temporarily. Stacking more (stratigraphically uncorrelated) data into the analysis does not improve the image. In contrast, the channel indicated by the striped arrow appears when we use the larger vertical windows. Most likely, that channel is slightly below the time slice displayed and falls outside the smaller analysis windows. The fact that we are able to detect it using the smaller, 16-ms vertical window and the larger, $r = 25$ m spatial window implies that above this channel, smooth differential compaction may exist that is detected only by the larger spatial window.

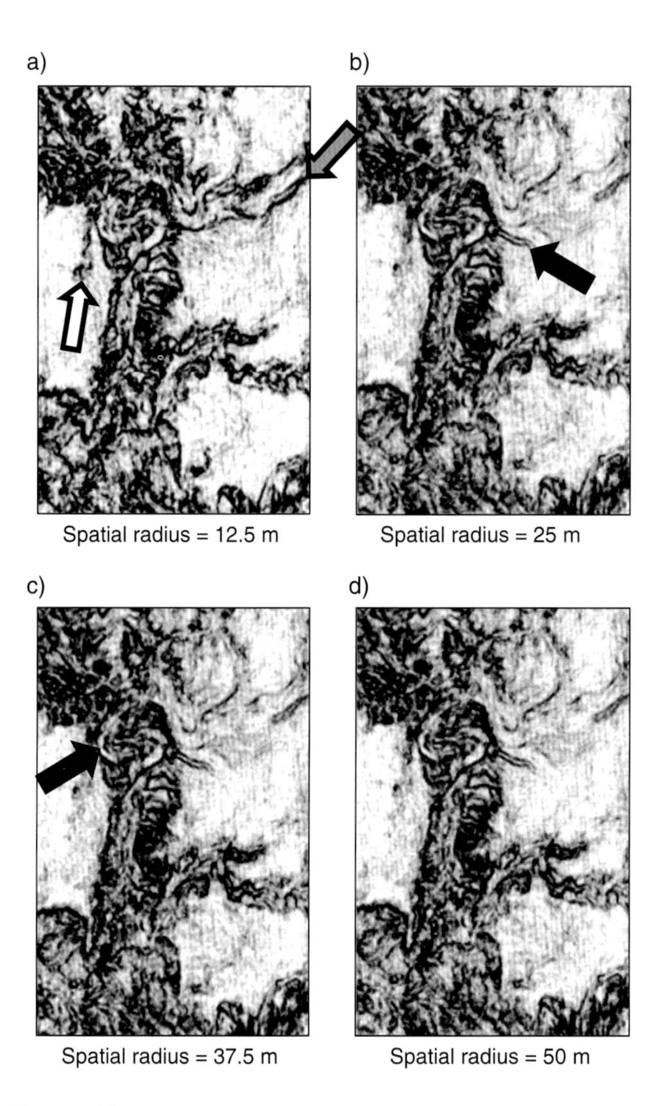

Figure 29. The effect of varying the spatial radius on the channel system shown in Figure 28d, using the eigenstructure algorithm with various spatial windows: (a) $r = 12.5$ m including five traces, (b) $r = 25$ m including 13 traces, (c) $r = 37.5$ m including 25 traces, and (d) $r = 50$ m including 49 traces. The temporal analysis window = 16 ms or 5 samples for all images. Note that the very thin channel feature (white arrow) and the edges of a broad channel (gray arrow) are illuminated by the 12.5-m window but are washed out in the other images from larger analysis windows. In contrast, a somewhat wider channel (vertically striped arrow) is better illuminated when $r > 12.5$ m. Likewise, the horizontally striped arrow indicates greater detail within a meandering-channel complex.

In general, larger temporal (vertical) analysis windows tend to blur stratigraphic features, as Figure 31a and b show. Blumentritt et al. (2003) determined that for thin channels, the optimum vertical analysis window is the reciprocal of the dominant frequency. They noted that shorter windows were more contaminated by noise, whereas longer windows blurred the images and mixed stratigraphic features.

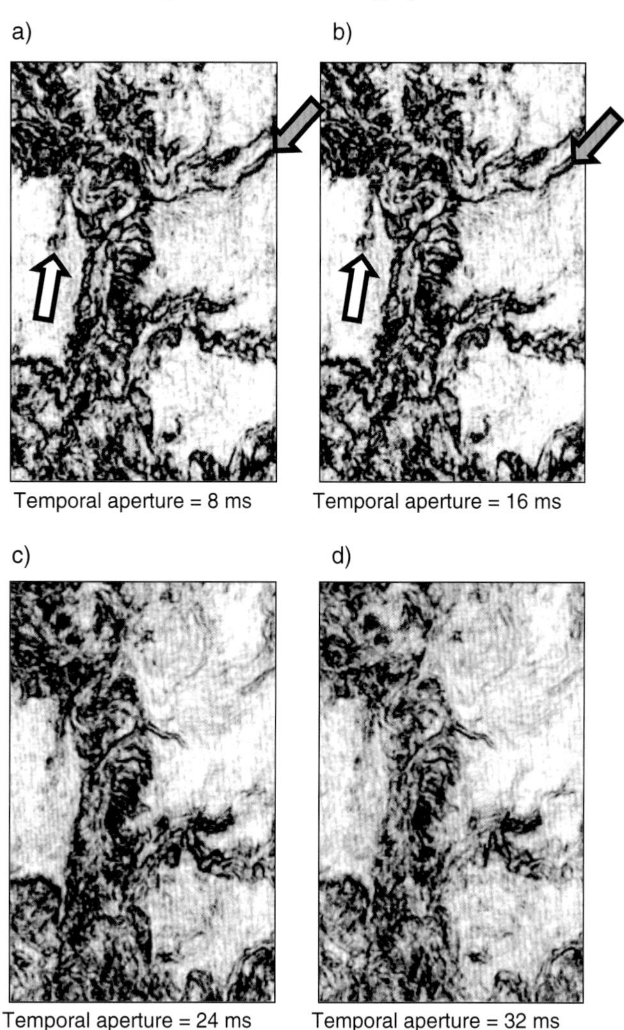

Figure 30. The effect of varying the temporal analysis window on the channel system shown in Figures 28 and 29, here using the eigenstructure algorithm with (a) 8 ms or three samples, (b) 16 ms or five samples, (c) 24 ms or seven samples, and (d) 32 ms or nine samples. The spatial analysis window is $r = 12.5$ m, including five traces. Note that the channel features indicated by the white and gray arrows are resolved better for shorter temporal analysis windows, implying that they are confined to this time slice. In contrast, the channel indicated by the striped arrow is imaged better by the larger temporal analysis windows, indicating that it may lie above or below the time slice displayed. In general, we recommend using small analysis windows for stratigraphic analysis to avoid mixing the information content of different levels.

In contrast, larger temporal (vertical) analysis windows tend to improve vertical faults, as shown in Figure 31c and d. If the fault is vertical, discontinuities align in the stack that is implicit in our crosscorrelation, semblance, and eigenstructure algorithms, and at the same time, noise, including the stratigraphic features of potential interest, is attenuated. Unfortunately, not all faults are vertical. Current implementations of coherence integrate the discontinuities over the vertical axis. Listric faults and other structural features of interest that are not vertical become progressively blurred in coherence displays. When a listric fault cuts a strong reflector and we have a large vertical analysis window, we may even see the fault twice — once when it cuts the reflector above the time slice of interest on the footwall, and a second time when it cuts the reflector below the time slice of interest on the hanging wall. We will point out such artifacts in Chapter 11.

Next, we return to the data volume from South Marsh Island, Louisiana, U.S.A., that we showed initially in Figure 4. In Figure 32, we display time slices at 1.2 s through the original seismic volume (Figure 32a) and a coherence volume (Figure 32b). Although we can see parts of channels and faults on the seismic time slice (indicated by white and gray arrows in Figure 32a), many of the other lineaments, such as the one indicated by the black arrow, are quite ambiguous. Conventional interpretation would require slicing the data vertically at various angles to determine the cause of the feature on the time slice.

The corresponding coherence slice (Figure 32b) clearly shows this lineament to be the edge of a channel. Indeed, many structural and stratigraphic features now appear on the data.

The reader may be somewhat suspicious about such a dramatic difference in image quality. If you are wondering

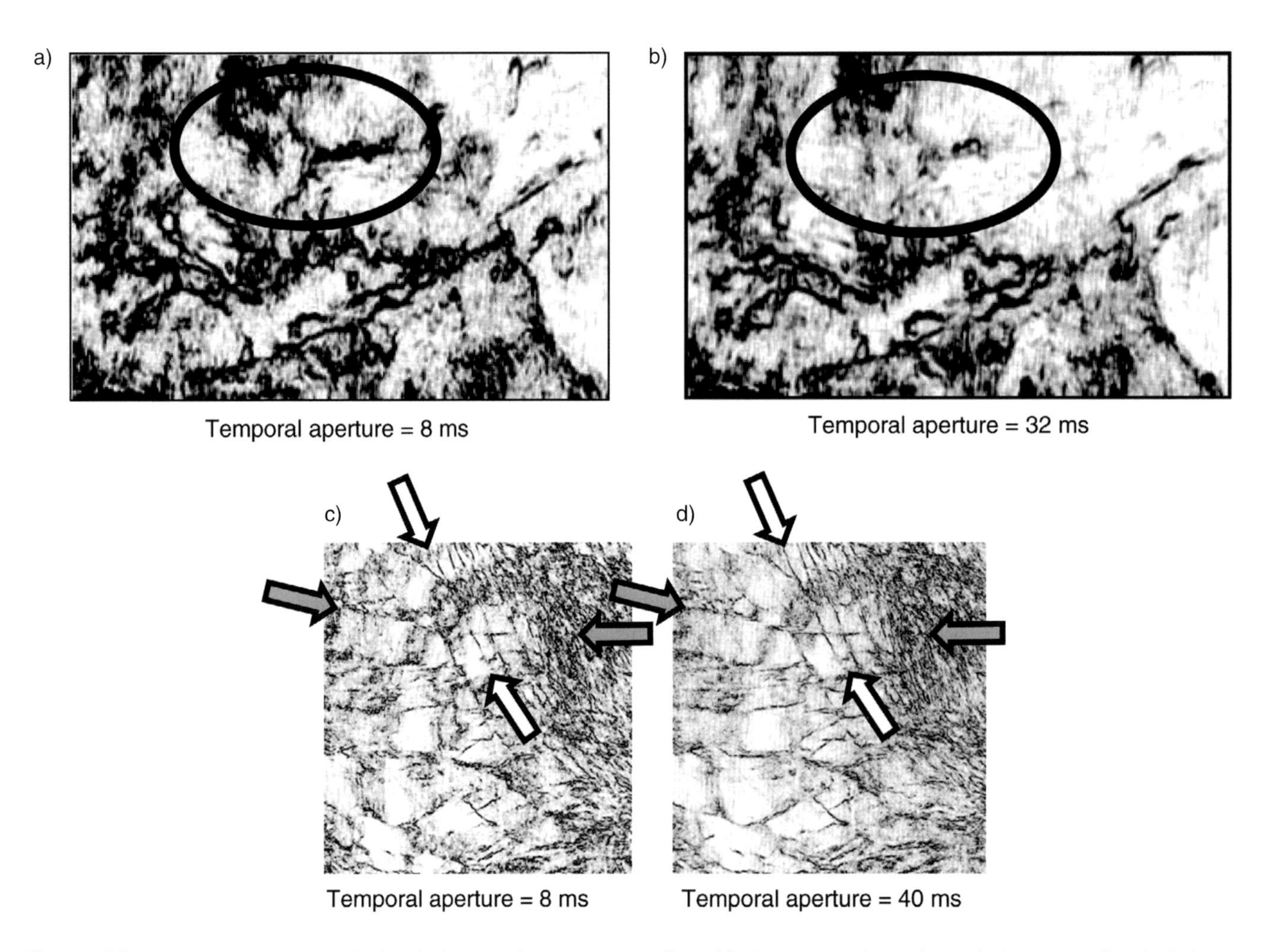

Figure 31. A larger temporal analysis window tends to smear stratigraphic features such as channels [compare the circled features in (a) and (b)] that are confined to a given geologic horizon. In contrast, larger temporal analysis windows improve the appearance of vertical faults [compare the faults in (c) and (d) that are identified by white and gray arrows]. The latter is because the coherence computation stacks similar discontinuities over a larger vertical window.

about the origin of the additional information portrayed in Figure 32b, we remind you that the coherence time slice reveals information that is in the displayed time slice and information in eight additional amplitude time slices that resided in the analysis window. If we were able to animate through these nine time slices and memorize key features, we could convince ourselves that coherence is not creating something out of nothing. To quote Adam Gersztenkorn's concluding remarks in his 1996 SEG presentation (Gersztenkorn and Marfurt, 1996), "Given a sufficiently large salary and sufficient time, a good geoscientist doesn't need coherence to interpret these features."

Benefits of Coherence Extraction along Time Slices versus along Horizon Slices

Now we will compare the appearance of amplitude and coherence data like those we just saw from along a constant time slice, with amplitude and coherence data from the same volumes but taken from along a selected horizon. In Figure 32, we displayed a time slice through the seismic and coherence data volumes at a selected constant time. In Figure 33, we show corresponding horizon slices at approximately the same level; these slices follow a picked horizon of interest.

a)

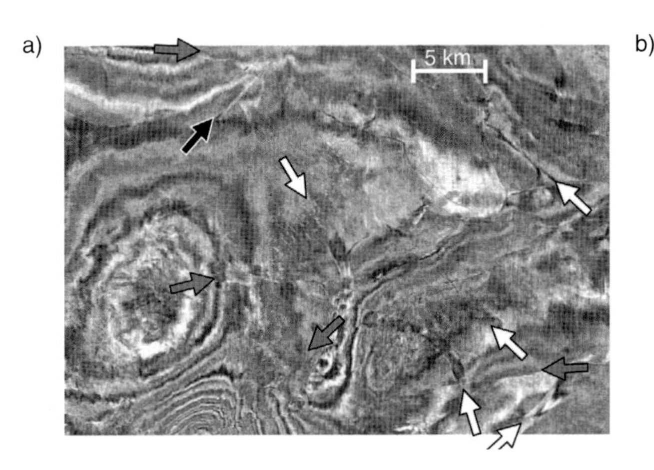

b)

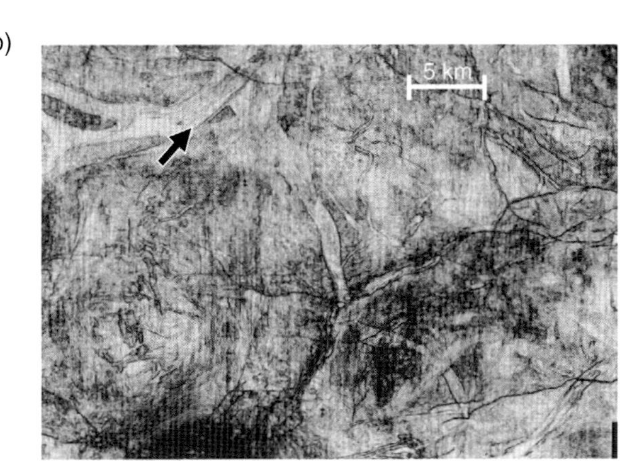

Figure 32. Time slices, at $t = 1.200$ s, through (a) a seismic data volume and (b) the corresponding coherence volume calculated using an 11-trace semblance algorithm. Although channels (white arrows) and faults (gray arrows) can be seen on the seismic time slice, lineaments such as that indicated by the black arrow are more ambiguous. The coherence slice allows us to interpret our data more confidently in the time-slice mode. The black arrow clearly indicates the edge of a channel. Previously unrecognizable faults and channels now appear. After Marfurt et al. (1998).

a)

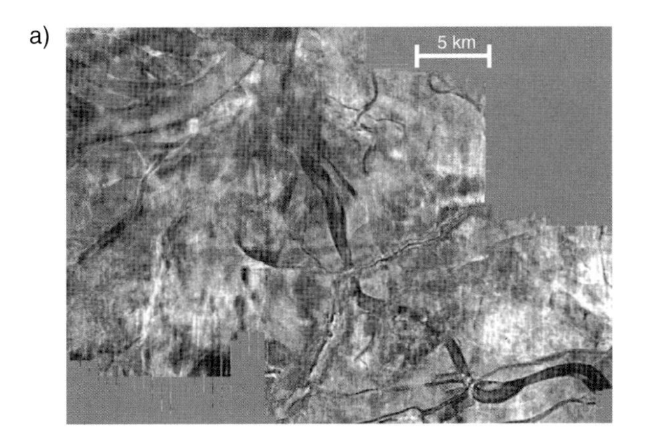

b)

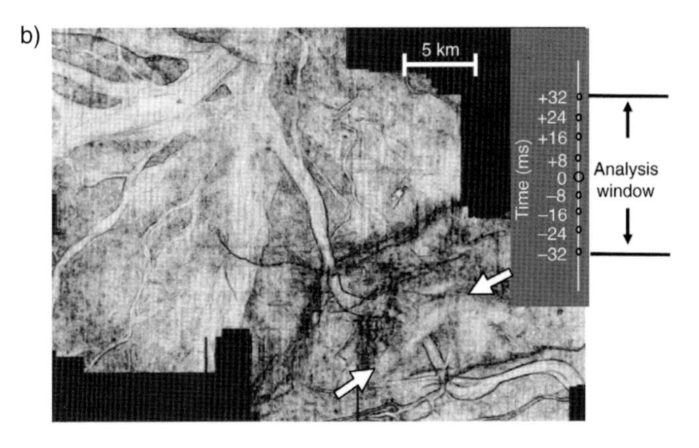

Figure 33. Horizon slices through (a) a seismic data volume and (b) a coherence volume extracted along an interpreted Pleistocene horizon corresponding approximately to the time slice shown in Figure 32. The area displayed is smaller than that seen in Figure 32, because the horizon did not exist over a salt diapir in the southwest and was truncated in the northeast. In general, stratigraphic features are seen best on horizon slices, whereas structural features are seen best on time slices. See text for discussion. Semblance-based coherence was calculated using 11 traces and a 64-ms vertical analysis window. After Marfurt et al. (1998).

The lateral extents of these horizon-based images are not as large as the extent of the previous time slice, because the selected horizon did not exist in the southwest over a salt diapir and had been eroded away in the northeast. Such a limited field of view is one limitation of horizon slices versus time and depth slices. A second limitation is time. It took one of the authors (Marfurt) a full three days to pick the Pleistocene horizon corresponding to Figure 32. (Readers who know this author may have serious doubts also about the quality of his picks, which in polite circles is called *interpreter bias* and which constitutes a third limitation.) Nevertheless, use of horizon slices (whether they are explicitly picked horizons, phantom horizons, or slabs of data flattened about a horizon) is the preferred method for interpreting stratigraphic features. That preference holds in the seismic data directly (Figure 33a) and in the corresponding attribute volume (Figure 33b). In these images, we can see clearly the complex distributary channels, including point and longitudinal bars, of the Pleistocene paleo-Mississippi River. However, the west-southwest- to east-northeast-trending channel indicated by white arrows does not fit with our distributary-channel model and instead cuts the major system at right angles. We suspect that it is part of a later system where the Mississippi River changed its course.

The coherence volume shown in Figure 33b was run with a 64-ms analysis window, to better map faults associated with salt diapirism. To better unravel our channel geometry, we reran the coherence computation using a shorter 16-ms analysis window, and we display the corresponding horizon slice in Figure 34b and a shallower phantom horizon, 24 ms above, in Figure 34a. Because the channel indicated by the white arrows is delineated more clearly along the shallower phantom horizon, we conclude that that channel is a later event that has cut down through the main channel system we see in Figure 34b. Although the images in Figure 34 are less coherent (blacker) in general, they also have better lateral resolution than the image did that used the longer vertical analysis window and was shown in Figure 33b. Longer windows mix stratigraphy, thereby in some sense adding geologic noise to our image. We will discuss such issues in greater detail in Chapter 12, in our discussion of attribute illumination of clastic depositional environments.

We conclude this chapter by examining the coherence expression of the Delaware Basin survey displayed earlier in Chapter 2. Figure 35 shows a suite of time slices at 0.8 s, 1.0 s, 1.2 s, 1.4 s, 1.6 s, and 1.8 s through the coherence volume corresponding to the dip and azimuth seismic overlays shown in Figure 20 of Chapter 2. The carbonate plat-

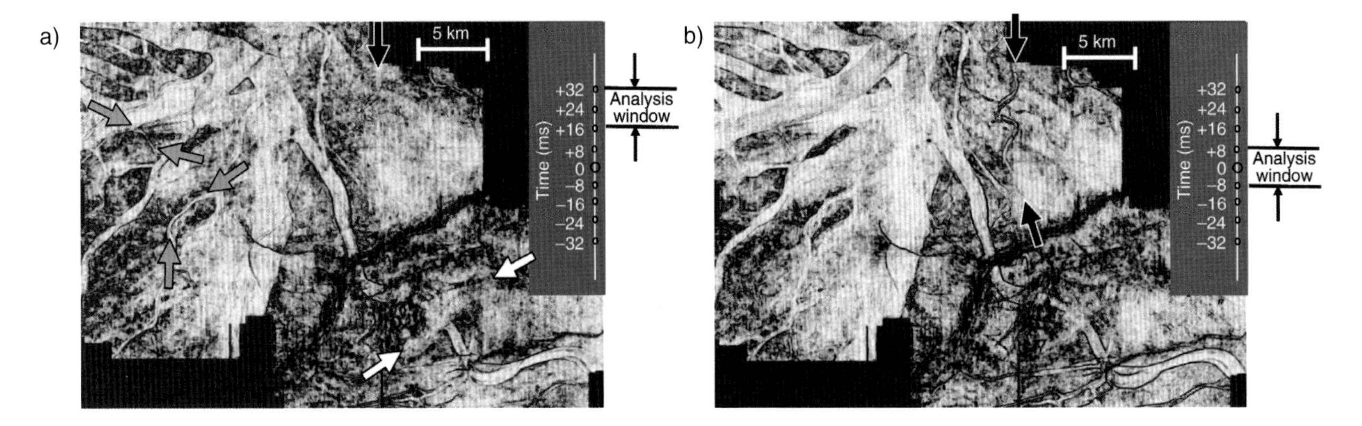

Figure 34. The impact of using a smaller analysis window on resolving stratigraphic features. Both images use a three-sample, 16-ms analysis window that is shifted 24 ms higher in (a) than in the image shown in (b), which is centered about the same horizon shown in Figure 33b. Note the improved lateral resolution that we gain by using a smaller analysis window. Also note that we now see that the narrow (and probably thin) channel features indicated by gray arrows are shallower than those indicated by the black arrows. The broader channel indicated by white arrows has cut down from a shallower horizon. After Marfurt et al. (1998).

form appears to be relatively featureless until we approach its edge. There we encounter the Brushy Canyon sequence dumped into the basin from above (yellow arrows). We do not see the broad fold indicated by the magenta arrow at 1.2 s, but we see it deeper at 1.4 s. We also see the broad fold indicated by the blue arrows and seen earlier on the dip and azimuth slices. The tightly folded strata seen in Figure 20e and 20f of Chapter 2 are quite organized here in Figure 35e and 35f.

Because we know that the reflectors are folded, we attribute these incoherent patterns to thinning of sediments on the anticlinal parts of the folds. We note that such patterns easily could be misinterpreted as channels from the coherence time slice alone. Such misinterpretations can be avoided by testing our hypotheses against conventional vertical slices through the seismic data. These discontinuities appear as vertical discontinuities in Figure 36. Although their appearance is similar to that seen for faults, we interpret these discontinuities to be zones where the rocks have been squeezed tightly and deformed. We will return to these images in subsequent chapters when we discuss curvature and coherent energy gradients.

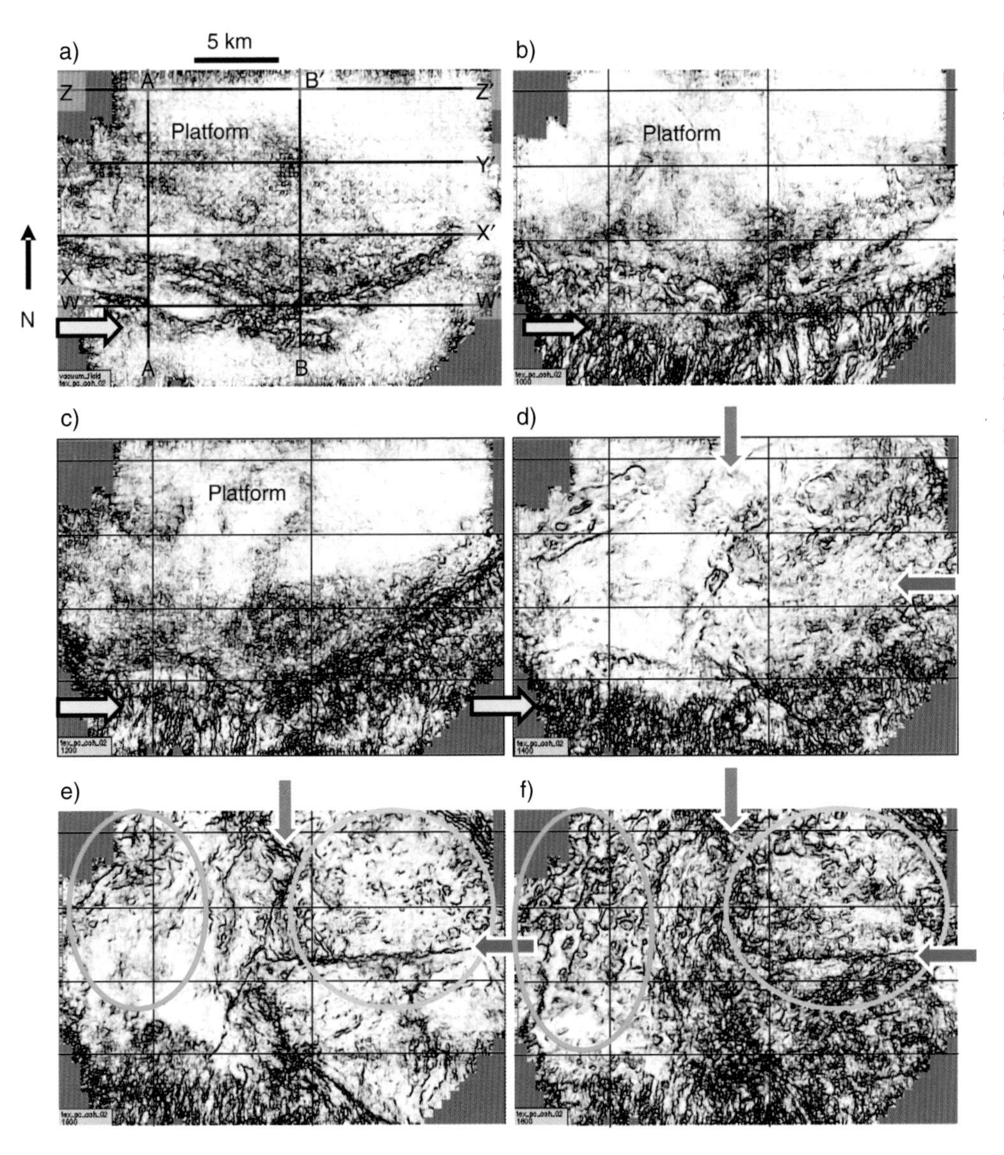

Figure 35. Time slices at t = (a) 0.800 s, (b) 1.000 s, (c) 1.200 s, (d) 1.400 s, (e) 1.600 s, and (f) 1.800 s through the coherence volume corresponding to the dip and azimuth overlays from a survey in the Delaware Basin, New Mexico, U.S.A., and shown in Chapter 2, Figure 20. We have retained the same arrows shown in that figure to aid in the comparison.

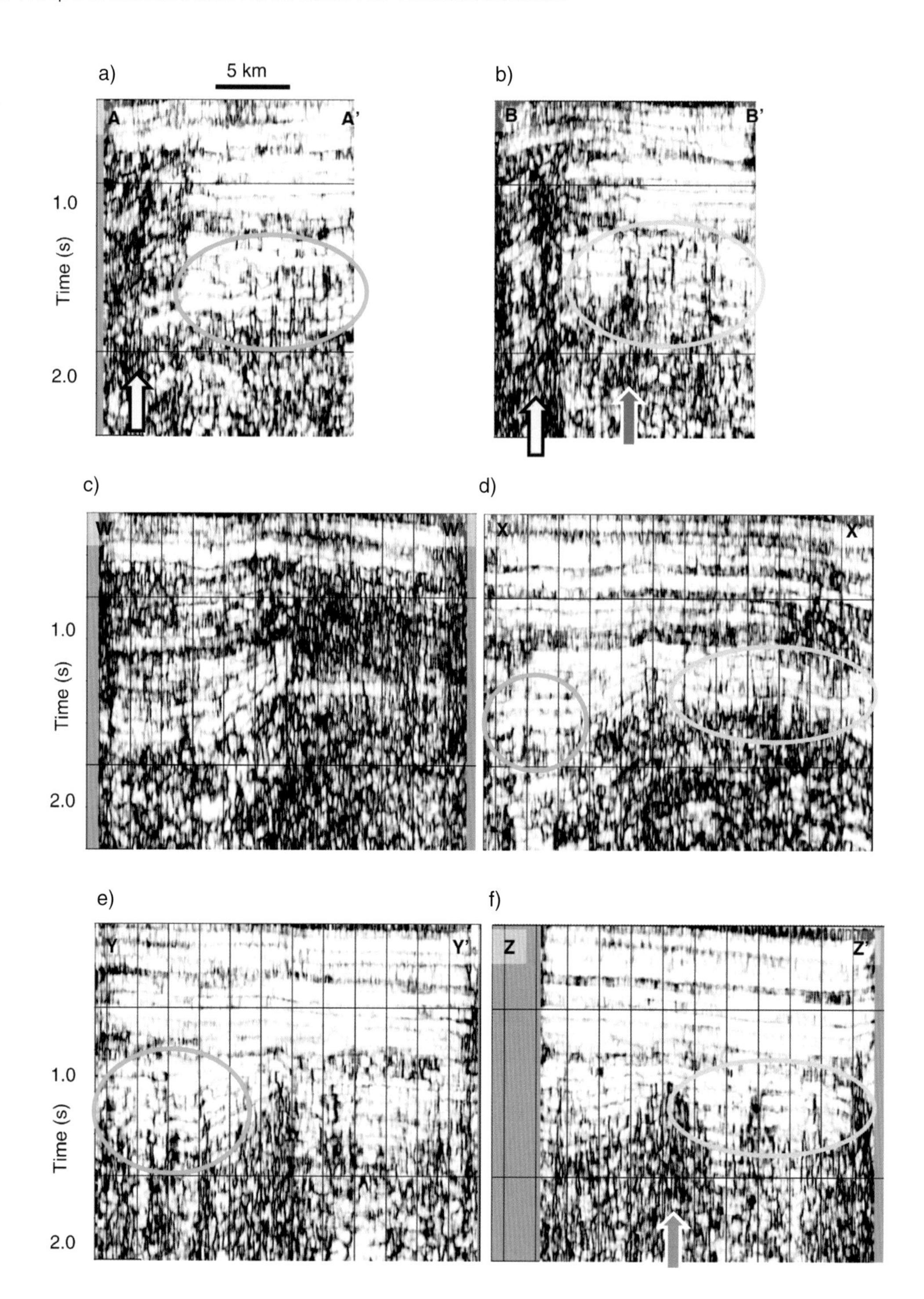

Figure 36. Vertical slices through the coherence volume corresponding to Figure 21 in Chapter 2. Line locations are indicated in Figure 35a.

Chapter Summary

Coherence is a direct measure of waveform similarity. All coherence computations should be performed along the local dip and azimuth of the best reflector at the analysis point. Failure to do so will result in low-coherence artifacts that reflect structures overprinting anomalies of interest that result from discontinuities in the waveform. Crosscorrelation and eigenstructure estimates measure only changes in reflector waveform, whereas semblance, variance, and GST estimates of coherence are sensitive to both waveform and lateral changes of reflector amplitude. Although it is computationally more intensive, the eigenstructure algorithm provides maximum lateral resolution. Furthermore, by using the analytic trace rather than simply the input trace, we can improve the fidelity of coherence images at zero crossings for small vertical analysis windows.

Coherence integrates the information content of adjacent traces and samples in a nonlinear manner that allows us to extract information not seen on any individual time slice. Coherence volumes significantly enhance our ability to see structural and stratigraphic discontinuities on time slices, thereby allowing us to more quickly produce a high-quality 3D interpretation that includes accurate fault and channel geometries. In general, stratigraphic features are shown best on horizon slices using a vertical analysis window that is approximately equal to the period of the dominant frequency. In contrast, structural features that cut across stratigraphy, such as vertical faults, are seen best on constant-time (or depth) slices, which lack the interpreter bias that would be present on horizon-based extractions. Increasing the temporal (or depth) analysis window over vertical faults can improve their clarity by stacking the vertical discontinuities seen in the seismic section. Increasing the spatial (lateral) analysis window increases the cost of computation and decreases lateral resolution, but it can improve the signal-to-noise ratio, particularly in the deeper parts of the seismic volume. In surveys with varying stratigraphic and structural objectives, more than one coherence volume should be generated, with apertures chosen to help visualize the full information content of the seismic data.

References

Bahorich, M. S., and S. L. Farmer, 1995, 3-D seismic coherency for faults and stratigraphic features: The Leading Edge, **14**, 1053–1058.

Bahorich, M.S., J. A. Lopez, N. L. Haskell, S. E. Nissen, and A. Poole, 1995, Stratigraphic and structural interpretation with 3-D coherence: 65th Annual International Meeting, SEG, Expanded Abstracts, 97–100.

Bakker, P., 2003, Image structure analysis for seismic interpretation: Ph.D. thesis, Technische Universiteit Delft.

Barnes, A. E., and K. J. Laughlin, 2002, Comparison of methods for unsupervised classification of seismic data: 64th Conference and Technical Exhibition, EAGE, Extended Abstracts, P–222.

Bednar, J. B., 1998, Least-squares dip and coherency attributes: The Leading Edge, **17**, 775–776.

Blumentritt, C. H., E. C. Sullivan, and K. J. Marfurt, 2003, Channel detection using seismic attributes on the Central Basin Platform, west Texas: 73rd Annual International Meeting, SEG, Expanded Abstracts, 466–469.

Chopra, S., 2002, Coherence cube and beyond: First Break, **20**, 27–33.

Cohen, I., and R. R. Coifman, 2002, Local discontinuity measures for 3-D seismic data: Geophysics, **67**, 1933–1945.

Gersztenkorn, A., and K. J. Marfurt, 1996, Eigenstructure based coherence computations, 66th Annual International Meeting, SEG, Expanded Abstracts, 328–331.

———, 1999, Eigenstructure based coherence computations as an aid to 3-D structural and stratigraphic mapping: Geophysics, **64**, 1468–1479.

Haskell, N. L., and S. E. Nissen, 1998, 3-D seismic coherency and the imaging of sedimentological features, *in* F. M. Gradstein, K. O. Sandvik, and N. J. Milton, eds., Sequence stratigraphy concepts and applications: Elsevier, 197–214.

Haskell, N. L., S. E. Nissen, J. A. Lopez, and M. S. Bahorich, M. S., 1995, 3-D seismic coherency and the imaging of sedimentological features, 65th Annual International Meeting, SEG, Expanded Abstracts, 1532–1534.

Kalkomey, C. T., 1997, Potential risks when using seismic attributes as predictors of reservoir properties: The Leading Edge, **16**, 247–251.

Lu, W., Y. Li, H. Xiao, and S. Zhang, 2003, Higher-order statistics-based coherency estimation algorithm: 73rd Annual International Meeting, SEG, Expanded Abstracts, 1732–1735.

Marfurt, K. J., 2006, Robust estimates of 3D reflector dip and azimuth: Geophysics, **71**, 29–40.

Marfurt, K. J., R. L. Kirlin, S. H. Farmer, and M. S. Bahorich, M. S. 1998, 3-D seismic attributes using a running window semblance-based algorithm: Geophysics, **63**, 1150–1165.

Marfurt, K. J., V. Sudhakar, A. Gersztenkorn, K. D. Crawford, and S. E. Nissen, 1999, Coherency calculations in the presence of structural dip: Geophysics, **64**, 104–111.

Randen, T., E. Monsen, C. Signer, A. Abrahamsen, J. Hansen, T. Saeter, and J. Schlaf, 2000, Three-dimensional texture attributes for seismic data analysis, 70th Annual International Meeting, SEG, Expanded Abstracts, 668–671.

Simon, Y. S., 2005, Stress and fracture characterization in a shale reservoir, north Texas, using correlation between new seismic attributes and well data: M.S. thesis, University of Houston.

Chapter 4

Volumetric Curvature and Reflector Shape

Chapter Objectives

After reading this chapter, you will be able to

- use the most-positive and the most-negative curvatures to map structural lineaments
- choose the appropriate wavelength for examining rapidly varying versus smoothly varying features of interest
- identify domes, bowls, and other features on curvature and shape volumes
- integrate curvature volumes with coherence and other geometric attributes
- choose appropriate curvature volumes for further geostatistical analysis

Introduction

Following Lisle's (1994) correlation of curvature values to fractures measured on an outcrop, curvature has been accepted as a promising means of predicting fractures from surface seismic data. Earlier work by Ericsson et al. (1988), which showed the relationship between production and curvature, is less widely cited. Although images of dip magnitude and dip azimuth of interpreted surfaces first appeared in the published literature soon after the introduction of 3D seismic autopicking software (e.g., Dalley et al., 1989), curvature estimates from seismic data have appeared much more recently. Part of that delay probably is because curvature, being a second-derivative calculation of two-way traveltime surfaces, exacerbates seismic noise, acquisition footprint, and interpreter picking errors in the data. Only after Stewart and Wynn (2000) suggested using spectrally limited estimates of horizon curvature did this technique gain broader acceptance.

We define curvature in two dimensions as the radius of a circle tangent to a curve (Figure 1). We define anticlines as having positive curvature and synclines as having negative curvature. Linear (straight-line) portions of a curve have zero curvature. Thus, portions with a constant dip exhibit zero curvature. Locally, a 2D line can be approximated by a parabolic curve of the form $z(x) = a + bx + kx^2$. The curvature coefficient, k, is inversely proportional to the radius of curvature.

To define curvature in three dimensions, we need to fit two circles tangent to a surface. The circles always reside in orthogonal planes. The centers of these circles lie along an axis that is perpendicular to a plane tangent to the surface. In that manner, curvature measurements are a simple measure of reflector shape and are independent of bulk rotations and translations of the reflector. We adjust the first circle's orientation until we obtain its minimum possible radius. The circle with this minimum radius (i.e., with the tightest curvature) we define as the maximum curvature (k_{max}). The second circle, which is perpendicular to the first circle, always has a radius greater than or equal to the maximum curvature, and for a quadratic surface, is defined as the minimum curvature (k_{min}).

Mathematical Definition of Curvature

Mathematically, the first step in determining the curvature from a grid of measurements is to use least-squares fitting or some other approximation method to fit a quadratic surface, $z(x,y)$, of the form

$$z(x,y) = ax^2 + cxy + by^2 + dx + ey + f, \tag{4.1}$$

to an interpreted horizon. When the coefficient c in equation 4.1 is nonzero, the quadratic surface $z(x,y)$ is said to be rotated with respect to what mathematicians call the principal axes. To find the maximum and minimum curvatures, k_{min} and k_{max}, we need to rotate the coordinate system to another frame. Details can be found in Roberts (2001) as well as in books on solid geometry and 3D computer graphics. We will use the terminology (and equations) presented by Roberts (2001) to calculate the mean curvature, k_{mean}:

$$k_{mean} = [a(1 + e^2) + b(1 + d^2) - cde]/(1 + d^2 + e^2)^{3/2}, \quad (4.2)$$

the Gaussian curvature, k_{Gauss}:

$$k_{Gauss} = (4ab - c^2)/(1 + d^2 + e^2)^2, \quad (4.3)$$

and the principal curvatures:

$$k_1 = k_{mean} + (k_{mean}^2 - k_{Gauss})^{1/2}, \quad (4.4a)$$

$$k_2 = k_{mean} - (k_{mean}^2 - k_{Gauss})^{1/2}. \quad (4.4b)$$

The maximum and minimum curvatures, k_{max} and k_{min}, are related inversely proportionally to the radius of curvature of the two orthogonal circles mentioned above:

$$k_{max} = \begin{cases} k_1 \text{ if } |k_1| \geq |k_2| \\ k_2 \text{ if } |k_1| < |k_2| \end{cases} \quad (4.5a)$$

and

$$k_{min} = \begin{cases} k_2 \text{ if } |k_1| \geq |k_2| \\ k_1 \text{ if } |k_1| < |k_2| \end{cases}. \quad (4.5b)$$

The most-positive curvature, k_{pos}, is

$$k_{pos} = (a + b) + [(a - b)^2 + c^2]^{1/2}, \quad (4.6)$$

and the most-negative curvature, k_{neg}, is

$$k_{neg} = (a + b) - [(a - b)^2 + c^2]^{1/2}. \quad (4.7)$$

Note that the maximum curvature is the principal curvature that has the larger absolute value, whereas the minimum curvature has the smaller absolute value. For this reason, the minimum curvature typically would define the variation in elevation along the long axis of a valley or ridge. Note also that the most-positive curvature can be a negative number and the most-negative curvature can be a positive number (See Figure 2).

We define the dip curvature (the component of curvature projected along the dip direction of a tangent plane to the surface), k_{dip}, as

$$k_{dip} = 2(ad^2 + be^2 + cde)/[(d^2 + e^2)(1 + d^2 + e^2)^{3/2}], \quad (4.8)$$

and the strike curvature (the component of curvature projected along the strike direction of a tangent plane to the surface), k_{strike} as

$$k_{strike} = 2(ae^2 + bd^2 - cde)/[(d^2 + e^2)(1 + d^2 + e^2)^{1/2}], \quad (4.9)$$

the curvedness, c as

$$c = [(k^2_{max} + k^2_{min})/2]^{1/2}, \quad (4.10)$$

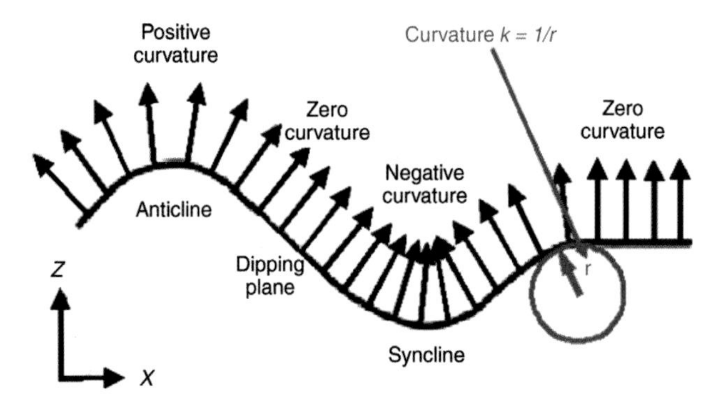

Figure 1. An illustrated definition of 2D curvature. Synclinal features have negative curvature, anticlinal features have positive curvature, and planar features have zero curvature. After Roberts (2001).

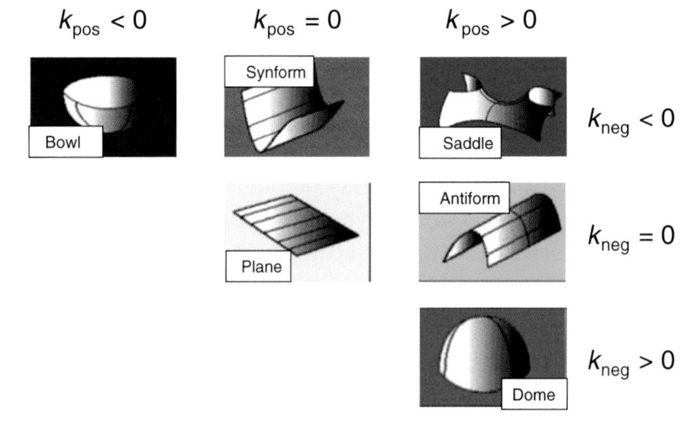

Figure 2. The definition of 3D quadratic shapes expressed as a function of the most-positive curvature, k_{pos}, and the most-negative curvature, k_{neg}. By definition, $k_{neg} \leq k_{pos}$. Thus, if both k_{pos} and k_{neg} are less than zero, we have a bowl, if both are greater than zero we have a dome, and if both are equal to zero, we have a plane. After Bergbauer et al. (2003). AAPG©2003. Reprinted by permission of the AAPG whose permission is required for further use.

the shape index, s, as

$$s = \frac{2}{\pi}\tan^{-1}\left[\frac{k_2 + k_1}{k_2 - k_1}\right], \quad (4.11)$$

and finally, the azimuth of the maximum curvature, ψ, as

$$\psi = \begin{cases} \tan^{-1}[c/(a-b)] \text{if } a \neq b \\ \pi/4 \quad \text{if } a = b \end{cases}. \quad (4.12)$$

The shape index of the dome in Figure 2 is 1.0, that of the antiform is 0.5, that of the saddle, is 0.0, that of the valley is –0.5, and that of the bowl is –1.0. The shape index of a plane is meaningless, as is the azimuth of a flat plane. The principal curvatures k_1 and k_2 measure the maximum and minimum bending of the surface at each point (Lisle, 1994). Note that our sign convention for k_{min} and k_{max} follows that used by Sigismondi and Soldo (2003). Those authors also showed that the maximum curvature allows one to easily determine the relative movement of fault blocks from time slices. In Figure 2, we show reflector shapes as a function of the sign of the most-positive curvature and most-negative curvature.

Relationship between Curvature and Fractures

Clearly, fractures occur when brittle rocks bend. However, the relationship between open fractures and our different curvature measures is quite complicated and depends on lithology, previous faults and fractures, the paleostress regime, pore pressures, and the present-day stress regime. We feel confident that curvature maps (or volumes) derived from seismic data provide an accurate map of the present-day subsurface structure. If deformation was simple and the current stress regime has remained unchanged since the time of structural deformation, we can use such maps to predict open fractures. Much more commonly, however, we need to reconstruct the paleostresses and paleostrains through one or more phases of palinspastic reconstruction. We also may need to consider which faults and fractures have been diagenetically filled or altered. Each stage of deformation adds a fabric or anisotropy to the rock, thereby making its subsequent response to stress more complicated.

Flexures in brittle rock cause fracture swarms (Figure 3). Hart et al. (2002) showed how production can be enhanced by faults and fractures associated with flexures in a tight sandstone (Figure 4a-c). Specifically, they noted that the best-producing wells are correlated to intersections of flexures, such as those seen in yellow in Figure 4c. Inspection of Figure 4b shows that the flexures also would be well represented as zones of high curvature.

Lisle (1994) made one of the earliest correlations of reflector curvature and fractures and predicted that Gaussian curvature, k_{Gauss}, (which is positive for bowls and domes, negative for saddles, and zero for planes, ridges, and valleys), should correlate to open fractures (Figure 5). More recently, Hart (2002) found that strike curvature correlates strongly to open fractures over a producing field in northwestern New Mexico, U.S.A. (Figure 6). In contrast, other workers found that the dip component of curvature correlates to open fractures in the Austin Chalk Formation of central Texas. In each of these cases, variability in lithology and the present-day stress regime determine which fractures are open and which are closed. Such stress regimes can be measured or inferred by borehole breakouts, horizontal image logs, tracers, and production history. We will return to the use of production data to calibrate fracture prediction using curvature in Chapter 15.

Although direct prediction of open fractures using curvature requires a significant amount of geologic unraveling and calibration through production data, curvature images are a powerful aid to conventional structural and strati-

a)
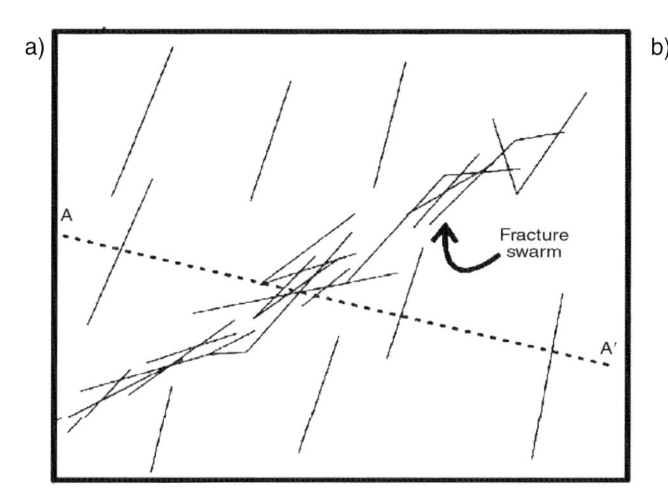

b)
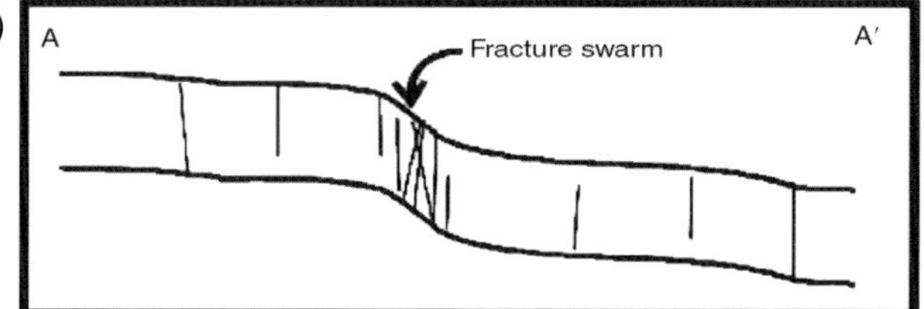

Figure 3. (a) A map view and (b) a cross-section view of an idealized fracture swarm. The fracture swarm is associated with a flexure or fault that may be oriented at some angle to the trend of more pervasive regional fractures. After Hart et al. (2002).

graphic interpretation. Because features that have nonzero curvature in one direction (like valleys or ridges that are not straight but have a constant elevation) tend to have values of k_{min} that fluctuate around zero, Roberts (2001) found that the Gaussian curvature also will be zero and thus is a poor aid in mapping faults.

We have found that the most-positive and most-negative curvatures, k_{pos} and k_{neg}, are the most useful in delineating faults, fractures, flexures, and folds because this pair of measures consistently shows the same polarity for a given geologic feature. That allows us to track it better, either visually or with computer software. Furthermore, a simple dual-gradational color bar (the conventional color bar with either white or black denoting a zero value) allows us to interpret negative values of most-positive curvature as a bowl and positive values of most-negative curvature as a dome (Figure 2).

Other workers have found maximum and minimum curvature to be useful. In Figure 7, we display a vertical section and time-structure map presented by Sigismondi and Soldo (2003). In Figure 8, we display the corresponding dip-magnitude and maximum-curvature maps generated from the picks shown in Figure 7b. Although these two images show essentially the same system of faults, the sign of the maximum curvature (and our knowledge of sediment drag along a fault) allows us to visualize how each block has moved with respect to its neighbors. A cynic might say that such displacement can be discerned readily from the original time-structure map shown in Figure 7b. However, Figure 8 shows the simplest calculation of curvature — one directly applied to the unfiltered interpreted surface. Long-wavelength estimates of reflection curvature extract subtle features that are much less obvious from the original time-structure map.

Figure 9 shows a coherence strat cube intersecting a seismic profile from Alberta, Canada. The profile exhibits prominent faults, some of which are clearly seen on the coherence strat slice. Clearly, on the surface, the coherence exhibits high values and thus the finer detail is not seen.

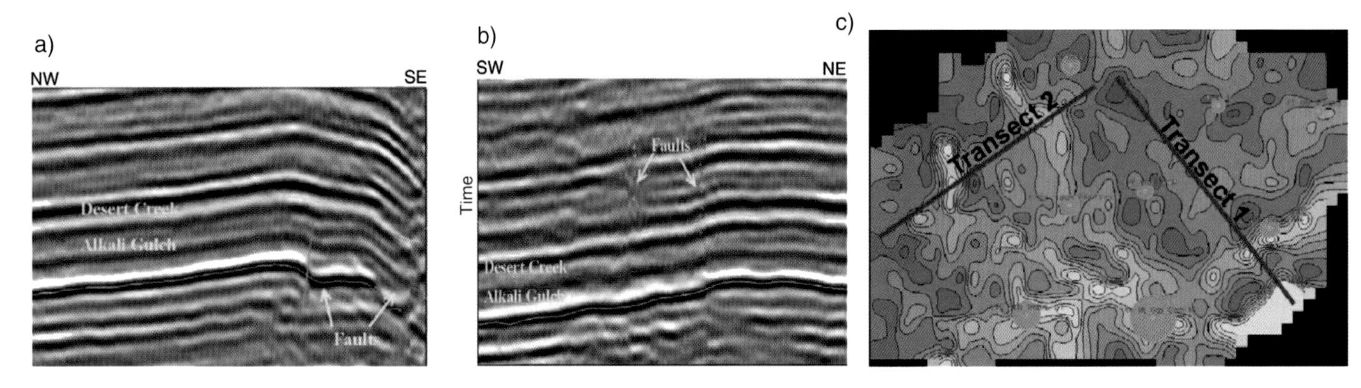

Figure 4. Seismic transects (a) through northeast-striking reverse faults and (b) northwest-striking small-offset normal faults (down to the southwest/left). (c) A dip-magnitude map with high dips shown in yellow. The size of the bubbles is proportional to the best year's production. Note that the larger bubbles fall along intersections of high dip trends, implying that production is enhanced by the presence of fractures. After Hart et al., (2002).

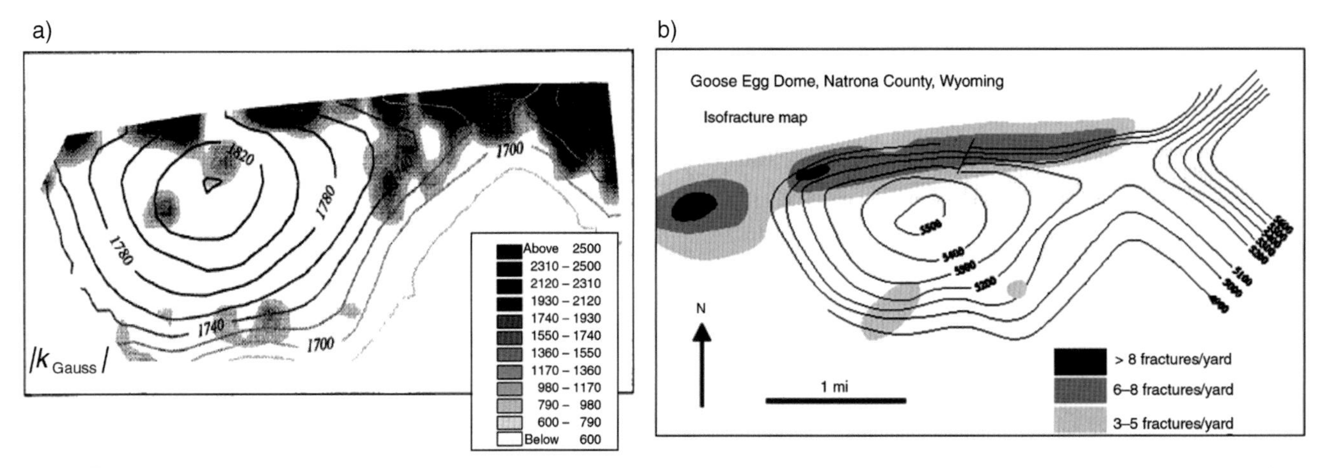

Figure 5. (a) The absolute value of Gaussian curvature calculated from the topographic surface of Goose Egg Dome, Wyoming, U.S.A., and (b) fracture density measured on that outcrop. Note the strong correlation of fracture density and Gaussian curvature. After Lisle (1994). AAPG©1994. Reprinted by permission of the AAPG whose permission is required for further use.

Figure 10a shows the seismic horizon surface and Figure 10b shows the coherence extracted along the surface in 10a. Figure 10c shows the most-positive curvature computed for the horizon in Figure 10a. Figure 10d shows the most-negative curvature computed for the horizon in Figure 10a. Apart from displaying the main faults, the most-positive and the most-negative curvature images in Figures 10c and 10d both clearly display finer details than we see in Figures 10a and 10b. Figure 11 shows those strat cubes at a different angle at which they look more like map views.

Spectral Estimates of Curvature

Several means exist for filtering a seismic horizon to enhance long-wavelength features. The simplest is to smooth the map in an iterative manner. Each pass of smoothing attenuates the shorter-wavelength components and mixes in information from grid points that lie farther and farther from the analysis point. A variation of this process is to fit our quadratic surface (equation 4.1) to more than nine adjacent points. Equally weighting the points in such a fit en-

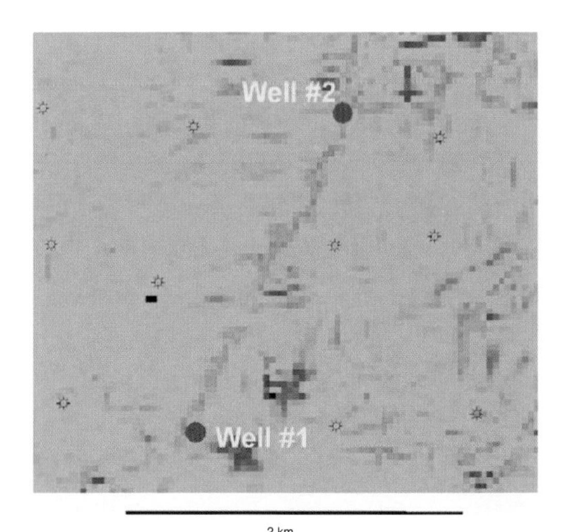

Figure 6. A map of the strike component of curvature calculated from a tight-gas sand from a survey in northwestern New Mexico, U.S.A. Green areas show a northeast- to southwest-trending lineation penetrated by two wells separated by about 2.5 km. These are sweet spot wells that have each produced more than 10 billion cubic feet (bcf) of gas. Analysis of production data shows drainage interference between these wells and not between adjacent wells (open circles). After Hart (2002).

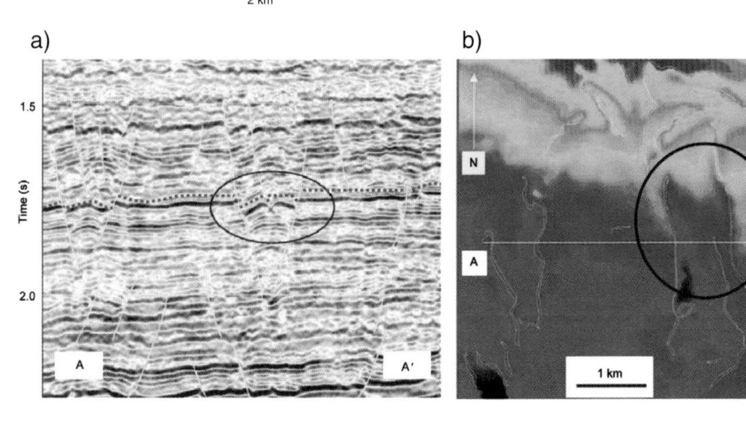

Figure 7. (a) A segment of a seismic section with an interpreted horizon indicated by a red dotted line. The blue circle indicates a graben. (b) The corresponding time-structure map. The blue circle indicates the same graben shown in (a). After Sigismondi and Soldo (2003).

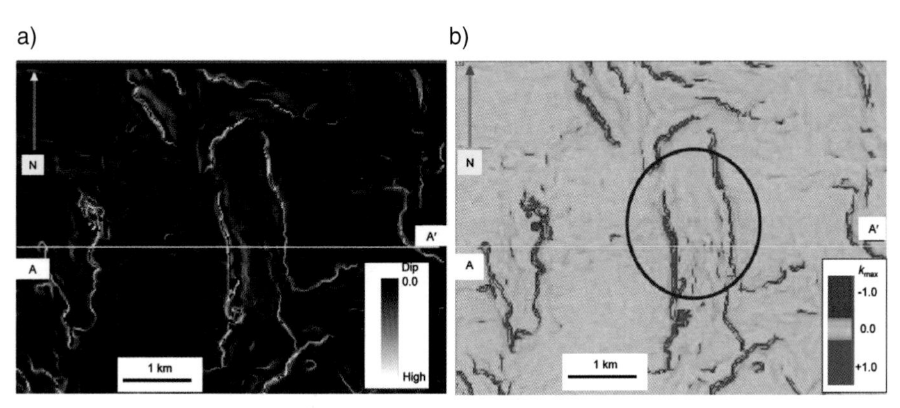

Figure 8. (a) Dip-magnitude and (b) maximum-curvature maps generated from the picks shown in Figure 7b. The maximum curvature represents the smallest circle tangent to the surface. Maximum curvature can have either positive (concave-down) or negative (concave-up) values. Because of drag along the fault, the inside edges of the graben have negative values of maximum curvature, whereas the adjacent footwalls have positive values of maximum curvature. After Sigismondi and Soldo (2003).

hances the long-wavelength components of curvature. In Figure 12, we show the result of calculating curvature using progressively larger analysis windows (3×3, 5×5, 7×7, and 9×9), with the larger analysis windows emphasizing longer wavelengths and clearly showing faulting. Reasons for such differences can be the result either of geology (with the features being flexures rather than sharp faults) or of seismic data quality (with faults being undermigrated or smeared).

A more direct means of calculating spectrally limited estimates of curvature is to transform the picked horizon into the 2D k_x-k_y wavenumber domain (Figure 13). Once the horizon is transformed, we can band-pass those wavenumber components of interest and then perform an inverse transform to generate a filtered horizon from which curvature can be calculated. Bergbauer et al. (2003) demonstrated this process, shown in Figure 14a, and Figure 14b shows the resulting filtered maximum-curvature image. Such longer-wavelength estimates of curvature reduce the impact of short-wavelength artifacts (such as acquisition footprint) and accentuate faults that do not result in a discrete displacement and that could be the result either of geology, or of overmigration or undermigration.

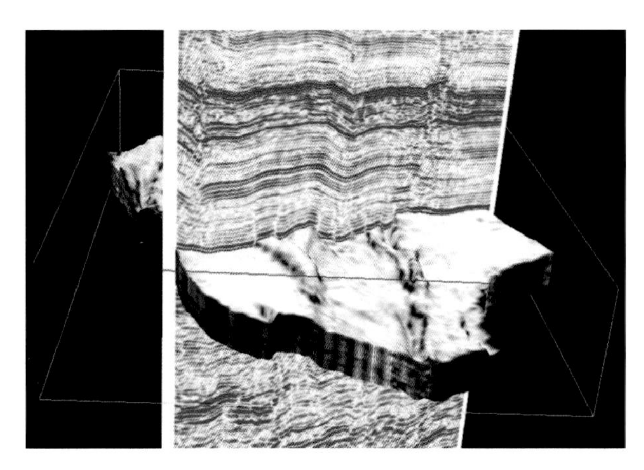

Figure 9. A coherence strat cube intersecting a seismic profile from Alberta, Canada. Data courtesy of Arcis Corporation, Calgary.

Volumetric Curvature: Calculations from Volumetric Estimates of Dip and Azimuth

Because the dip and azimuth volumes we saw in Chapter 2 vary slowly in the vertical direction, we can consider calculating volumetric estimates of curvature, time slice by time slice. Using our input estimates of reflector dip, $p = \frac{\partial z}{\partial x}$ and $q = \frac{\partial z}{\partial y}$, we can evaluate the first and second derivatives of equation 4.1 at $x = y = 0$ in order to calculate the coefficients *a, b, c, d,* and *e*:

$$a = \frac{1}{2}\frac{\partial p}{\partial x}, \tag{4.13a}$$

$$b = \frac{1}{2}\frac{\partial q}{\partial y} \tag{4.13b}$$

$$c = \frac{1}{2}\left(\frac{\partial q}{\partial x} + \frac{\partial p}{\partial y}\right) \tag{4.13c}$$

$$d = p, \tag{4.13d}$$

and

$$e = q. \tag{4.13e}$$

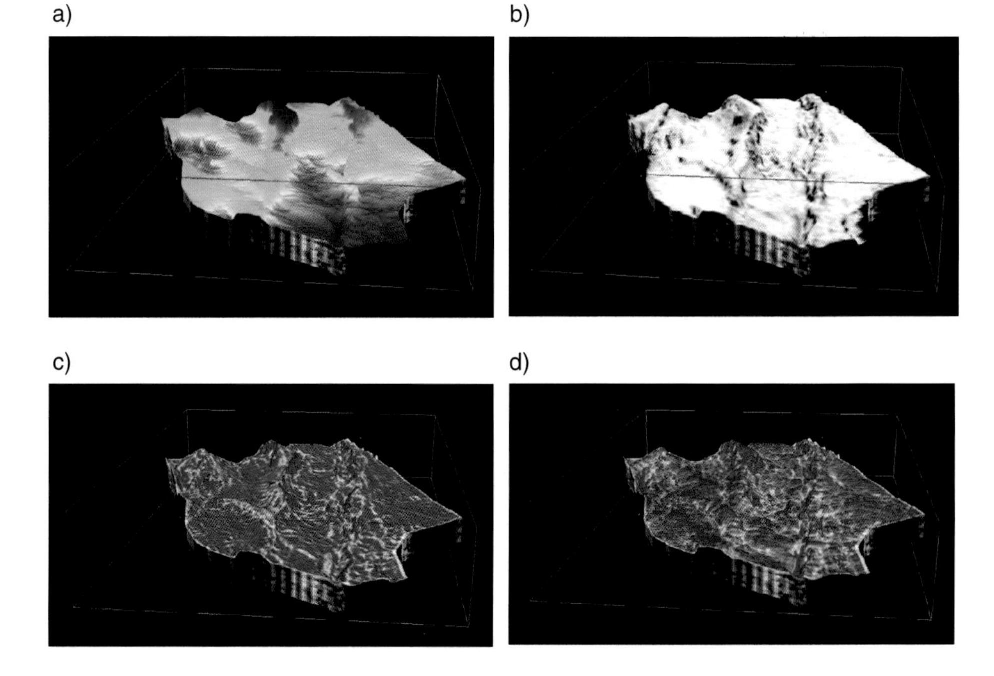

Figure 10. (a) A seismic horizon surface and (b) coherence extracted along the surface in (a). (c) Most-positive curvature computed for the horizon in (a). (d) Most-negative curvature computed for the horizon in (a). Apart from the main faults, finer detail is displayed clearly on both the most-positive-curvature and the most-negative-curvature images. Data courtesy of Arcis Corporation, Calgary.

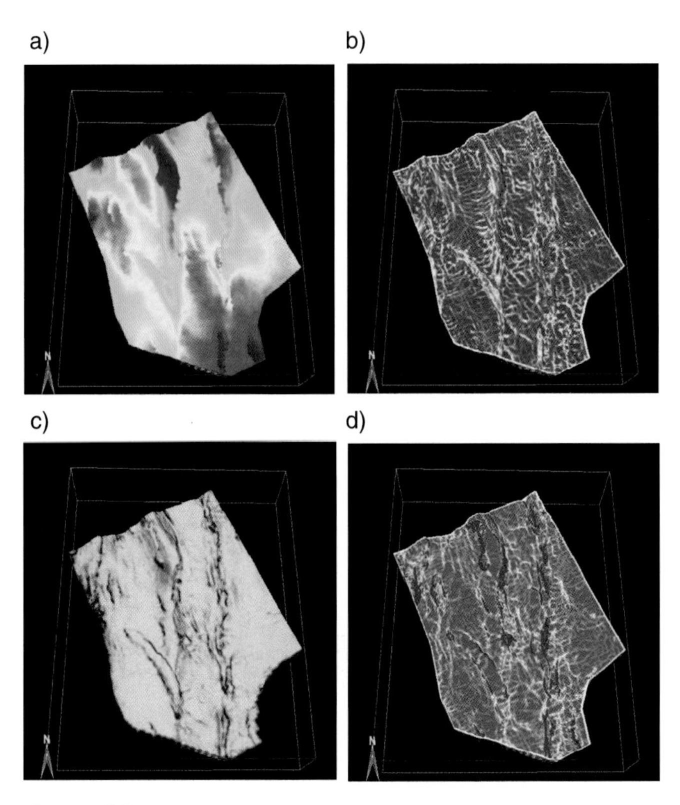

Figure 11. The strat cubes seen in Figure 10, displayed here at a different angle and looking more like map views. Data courtesy of Arcis Corporation, Calgary.

Marfurt and Kirlin (2000) calculated a crude measure of mean curvature (equivalent to equation 4.2 if the tangent to the reflector surface is flat such that $d = e = 0$) using the formula

$$k_{mean} = \frac{1}{2}\left(\frac{\partial p}{\partial x} + \frac{\partial q}{\partial y}\right), \tag{4.14}$$

as well as the rotation given by

$$r_z = \frac{\partial p}{\partial y} - \frac{\partial q}{\partial x}. \tag{4.15}$$

We apply equation 4.14 to the horizon-time-pick estimates of dip shown in Chapter 2, Figure 12a and b, and display the results here in Figure 15a. We note the very poor estimates of mean curvature in the two older portions of the merged surveys indicated by the dotted and solid white rectangles. Next, we apply equation 4.14 to the entire volume of p and q obtained using the multiwindow search technique described in Chapter 2. Results of that estimation process were shown previously as a horizon slice along the Caddo Limestone horizon in Chapter 2, Figure 13a and b. We now plot the horizon slice through the mean-curvature volume in Figure 15b. Note the improved signal-to-noise ratio in the area of the two older surveys indicated by the dotted and solid white rectangles. White arrows indicate faults and fractures that we were able to carry through these areas and that we were unable to interpret in Figure 15a.

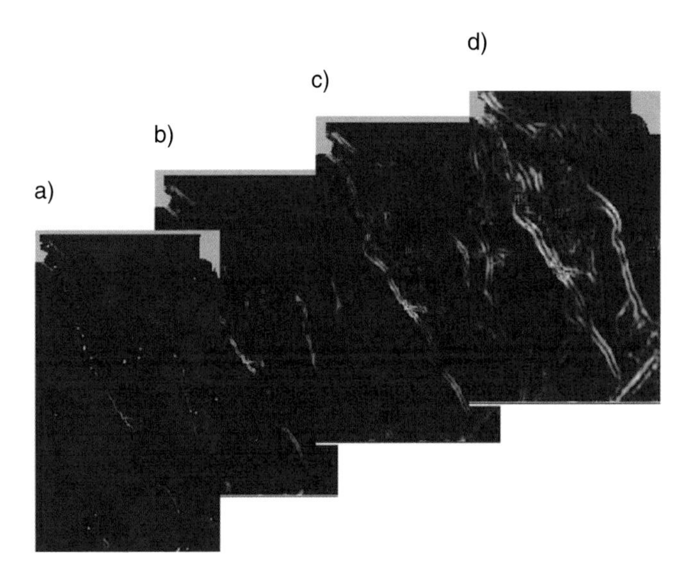

Figure 12. Curvedness calculated at different scales using apertures of (a) 3×3, (b) 5×5, (c) 7×7, and (d) 9×9, respectively. In this example, the longer wavelength (larger aperture) estimates provide a clearer image of the fault-block edges. Recall that the definition of curvedness shows that it is always greater than or equal to zero. After Sigismondi and Soldo (2003).

In general, equations 4.14 and 4.15 provide somewhat noisier images of edges than those provided by the eigenstructure coherence algorithms discussed in Chapter 3. Since Marfurt and Kirlin's (2000) work, more-robust estimates of dip, structurally oriented filtering, and most important, multispectral curvature estimates (or the estimates of curvature at different wavelengths) have provided significantly improved curvature volumes.

Multispectral Estimates of Volumetric Curvature

We begin our discussion of multispectral estimation of curvature by simply showing that geologic structures often have curvature of different wavelengths. In Figure 16, we show a zoomed portion of a vertical line BB′ that was shown previously as Figure 10 in Chapter 2. We have drawn four black circles, each with a different diameter, to approximate the curvature seen on the Marble Falls horizon. These circles have radii of curvature of approximately 500, 250, 100, and 50 m. Depending on our exploration objective, we may wish to generate separate maps that emphasize each of these different wavelengths. Tight, short-wavelength curvature may correspond to intense but highly localized fracture systems. In contrast, broad, long-wavelength curvature may correspond to a wider, more even distribution of fractures. A signal-to-noise issue also must be addressed. Long-wavelength estimates of curvature may incorporate the dip information of 400 or more traces, thereby making their images appear much cleaner than short-wavelength estimates, which may use only 9 to 25 traces.

Saleh Al-Dossary began his work on curvature with a search for edge detectors that could work on volumetric estimates of dip. Image-processing literature led him to evaluate a suite of algorithms that suppressed high-frequency random noise, while at the same time the algorithms sharpened discontinuities between major features. Al-Dossary found that many image-processing algorithms appeared to be evaluated heuristically, at least compared with the much more rigorous signal analysis used by geophysicists pursuing a Ph.D. Therefore, he evaluated not only the results of the operators, but also the spectral properties of the operators themselves. In addition, he evaluated a very different kind of operator that was based on fractional derivatives developed by Cooper and Cowan (2003) to enhance features seen on gravity and magnetic data. Some of this algorithmic work is summarized in Al-Dossary and Marfurt (2006). The results of this work can be applied in either of two ways — either by applying a fractional derivative in place of the operators $\frac{\partial}{\partial x}$ and $\frac{\partial}{\partial y}$ used in equations 4.13, or by applying a conventional first derivative to a k_x-k_y band-passed version of the inline and crossline dip components, p and q.

To show the mathematics behind the fractional derivative, let us assume that we have a function $p(x)$ and its first derivative $\partial p/\partial x$. In the wavenumber domain, the first derivative is given by

$$F(\partial p/\partial x) = -ik_x F(p), \tag{4.16}$$

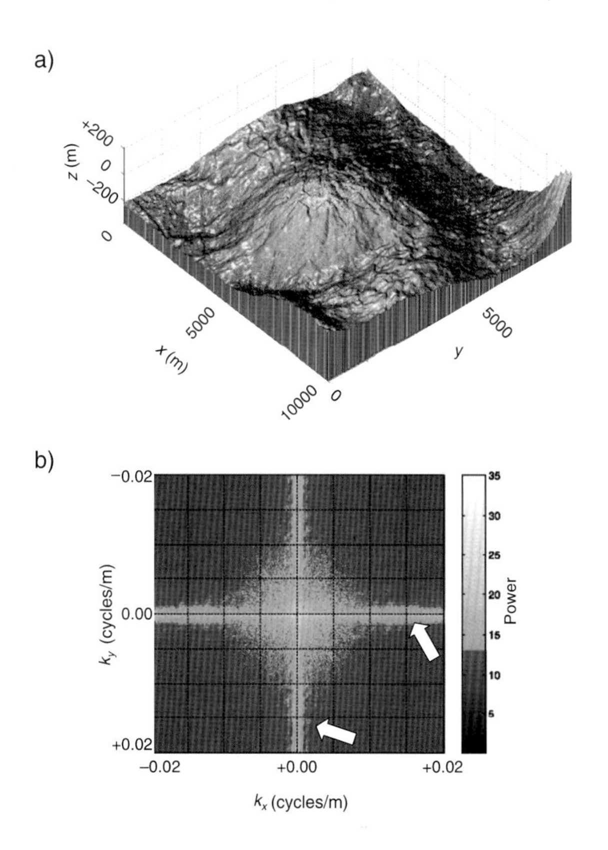

Figure 13. (a) A time-structure map and (b) its 2D Fourier transform. Long-wavelength features are represented by small values of k_x and k_y near the center of (b). The higher-amplitude short-wavelength components (indicated by arrows) that appear along the outer reaches of the k_x and k_y axes correspond to vertical and horizontal striping artifacts seen in (a) as a result of acquisition, processing, or autopickers. After Bergbauer et al. (2003). AAPG©2003. Reprinted by permission of the AAPG whose permission is required for further use.

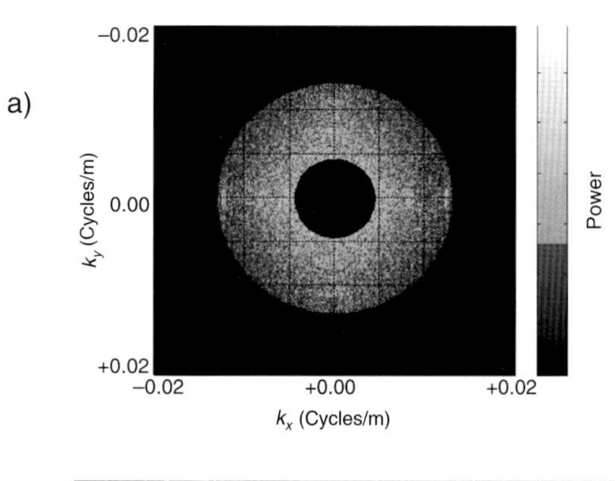

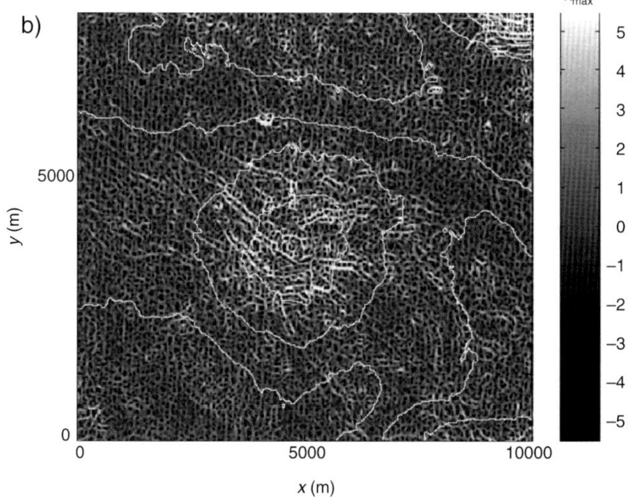

Figure 14. (a) A 2D k_x-k_y band-pass-filtered version of the k_x-k_y plane shown in Figure 10b. Both short and long wavelengths have been eliminated. (b) The resulting band-pass filtered, maximum-curvature image. Structural contours of the surface shown in Figure 13a are displayed in white. Note how the spectrally limited (band-pass-filtered most-negative curvature) enhances faults. After Bergbauer et al. (2003). AAPG©2003. Reprinted by permission of the AAPG whose permission is required for further use.

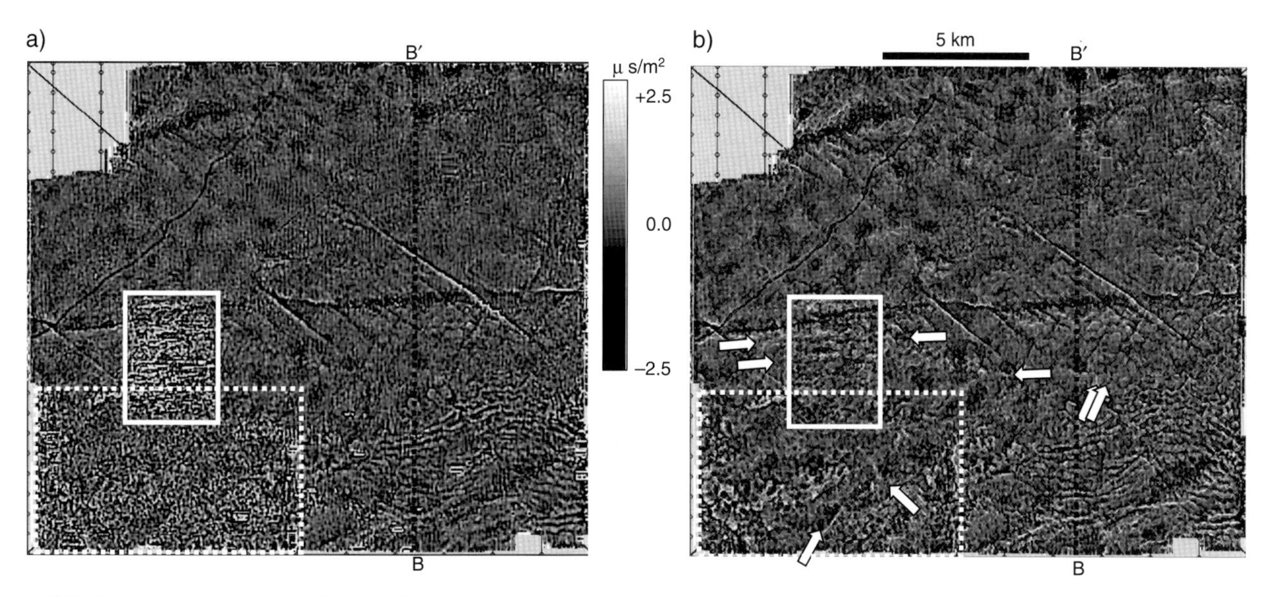

Figure 15. Mean curvature calculated using equation 4.14 (a) from the dip of the picked Caddo horizon shown in Chapter 2, Figure 12, and (b) from the volumetric estimate of dip shown in Chapter 2, Figure 13 and sliced along the Caddo horizon. Note the poor quality of the mean curvature estimates derived from the picked horizon in the region of the older 1995 (in solid white) and 1997 (in dotted white) surveys. Arrows indicate lineaments that are not seen clearly in (a). Data courtesy of Devon Energy.

where $F(u)$ denotes the Fourier transform of a function u, k_x is the wavenumber along the x-axis, and i is the square root of −1. Thus, the effect of a derivative is to increase the high wavenumber content and rotate the phase of each component by 90°. Al-Dossary and Marfurt (2006) defined the fractional derivative as

$$F_{\alpha}(\partial p/\partial x) = -i(k_x)^{\alpha} F(p), \qquad (4.17)$$

where α is a fractional real number greater than or equal to zero.

We display the operators and their spectra for values of α from 0.01 to 1.25 in Figure 17. For computational efficiency, we prefer to convolve the space domain operators plotted in Figure 17a along each time slice with the dip components p and q previously estimated at each seismic bin. In addition, each directional derivative is applied to a circular template rather than to just a linear array of seismic bins along that direction, thereby avoiding a computational bias associated with the acquisition axes. The alternative implementation would be to take the k_x-k_y transform of p and q along each time slice to obtain an image not unlike Figure 13b. Then we simply would multiply the spectrum of each time slice by the k_x (or k_y) operators shown in Figure 17b and transform back to x-y space. However, we consider this approach computationally inefficient because the time to transpose large volumes of seismic data (or attributes) can be significantly greater than the computational time of the convolutional approach.

The value $\alpha = 1.0$ corresponds to the conventional first-derivative operator. As we decrease the value of α, we also decrease the higher wavenumbers, thereby shifting the bandwidth toward the longer wavelengths (lower values of k_x). Seismic processors will note that at $\alpha = 0$, equation 4.17 degenerates into the Hilbert transform (plotted in yellow in Figure 17). Luo et al. (2002) used this space-domain Hilbert transform to detect lateral changes in seismic amplitude; we will review their work in Chapter 5.

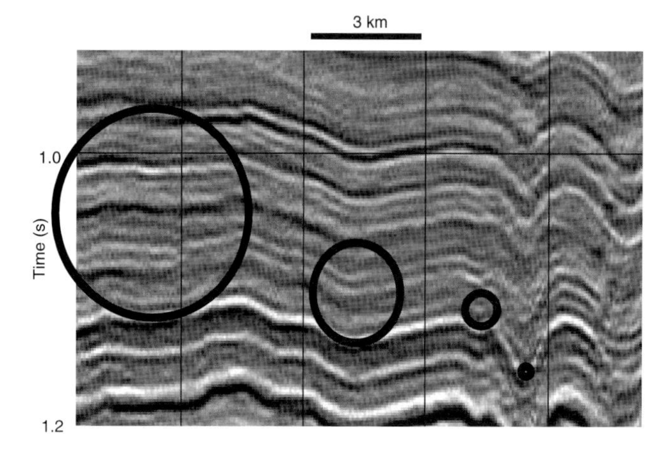

Figure 16. A vertical section through a seismic survey from the Forth Worth Basin, Texas, U.S.A, illustrating radii of curvature of approximately 500, 250, 100, and 50 m along the Marble Falls horizon. Seismic data zoom lies along BB′ indicated in Figure 15. Data courtesy of Devon Energy.

In Figure 18, we display a time slice at $t = 0.8$ s through a coherence volume generated from a seismic survey acquired in the Fort Worth Basin, Texas, U.S.A, corresponding to the same time slice shown in Chapter 2, Figure 14.

Note the incoherent areas to the north and south of the image. The central part of the image cuts through the Caddo Limestone and, with the exception of one or two discrete fractures, is quite coherent.

In Figure 19, we display a vertical slice through the seismic data. White arrows indicate collapse features that appear to be basement controlled. The black arrow indicates a ridge that can be seen in Figure 20b. The gray arrow indicates a dome that can be seen in Figure 20c.

In Figure 20, we display the most-negative curvature, k_{neg}, calculated using equations 4.7, 4.13, and 4.17, for the values α = 2.0, 1.5, 1.0, 0.75, 0.50, and 0.25. Comparing these images with the operator spectra shown in Figure 17b, we note that progressively longer-wavelength features appear as the value of α decreases. These images are complementary, providing the interpreter with different views of the same data volume.

Next, we generate a suite of images at t = 1.2 s, cutting through the Ellenburger limestone from the northerly and easterly dip components at this level and shown previously in Figure 15 of Chapter 2. In Figure 21, we display the principal-component coherence, and in Figure 22, we display

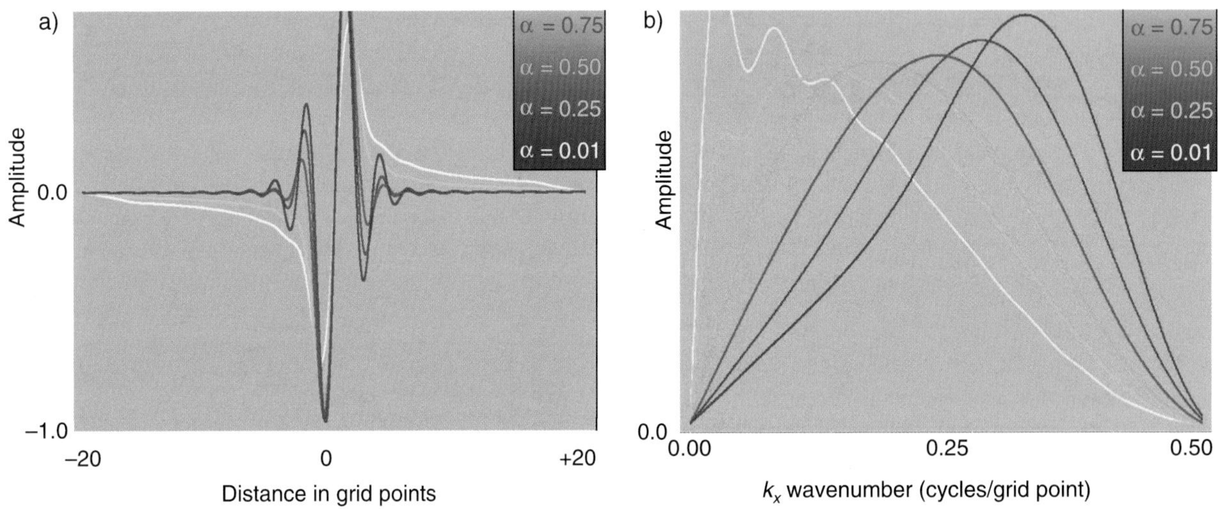

Figure 17. (a) Spatial operators and (b) their corresponding spectra used in the fractional-derivative estimate of curvature given by equation 4.17. The value of α = 1.0 corresponds to the conventional first-derivative operator. As we decrease the value of α, we also decrease the higher frequencies, thereby shifting the bandwidth towards the longer wavelengths (lower values of k_x). Note that in the limit, as α approaches 0.0, the operator shown in yellow in (b) approximates the Hilbert transform. Thus, Luo et al.'s (2002) Hilbert transform edge detector can be interpreted to be an end member of a fractional-derivative edge detector. Modified after Al-Dossary and Marfurt (2006).

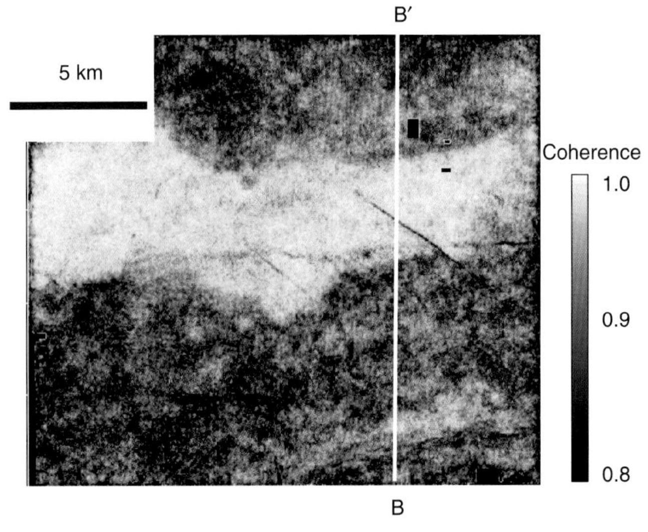

Figure 18. Eigenstructure coherence at t = 0.8 s (approximately the Caddo/Atoka level) through a survey from the Fort Worth Basin, Texas, U.S.A. Data courtesy of Devon Energy.

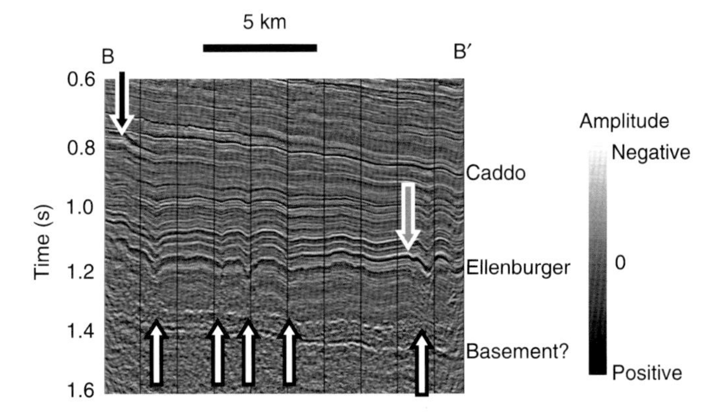

Figure 19. Line BB′ through the seismic data cube from Figure 18. White arrows indicate collapse features that appear to be basement controlled. Black arrow indicates a ridge that can be seen in Figure 20b. Gray arrow indicates a dome that can be seen on Figure 20c.

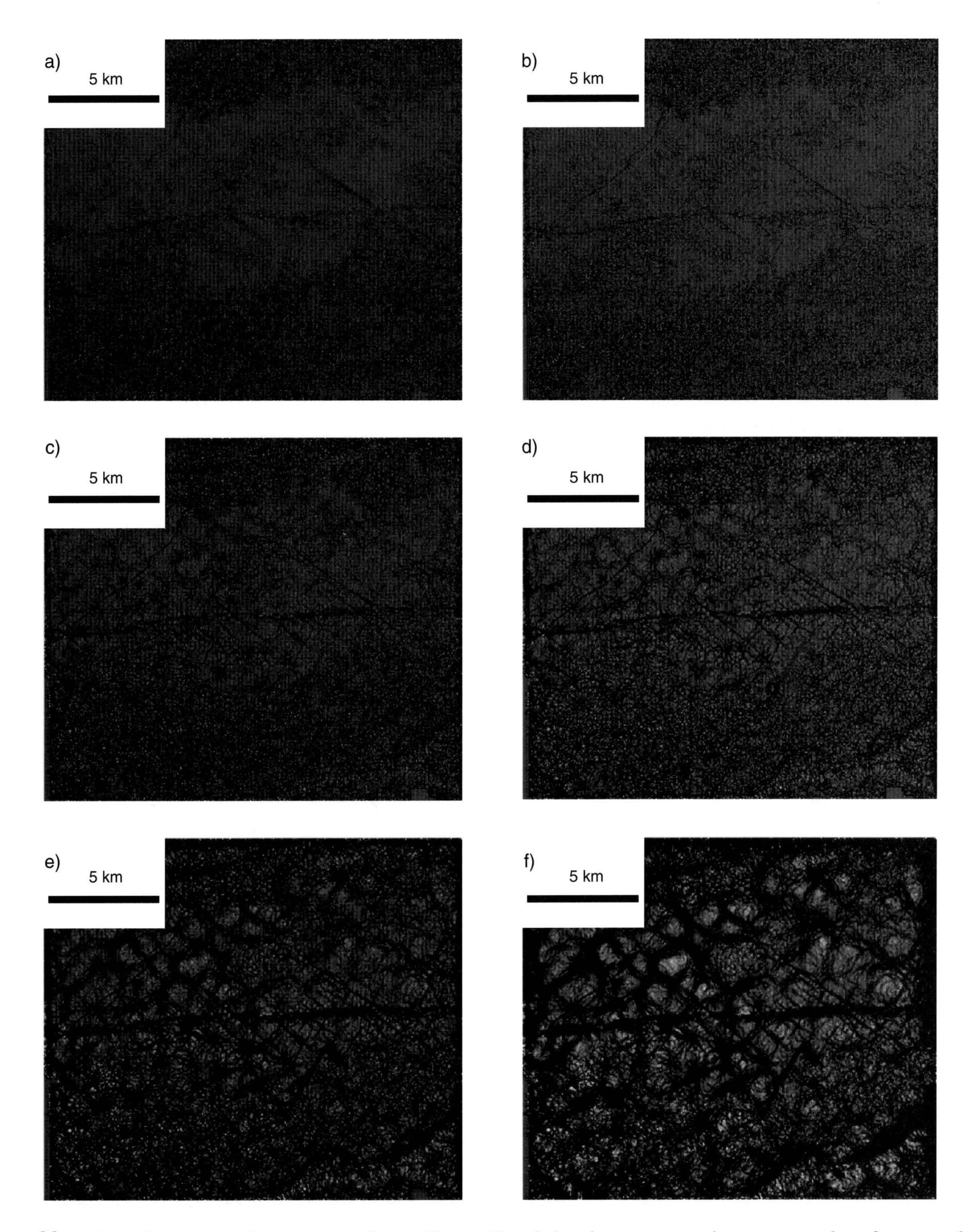

Figure 20. A time slice, at $t = 0.8$ s, corresponding to Figure 18 and showing most-negative curvature, k_{neg}, for spectral components shown in Figure 17b defined by α = (a) 2.00, (b) 1.50, (c) 1.00, (d) 0.75, (e) 0.50, and (f) 0.25. After Al-Dossary and Marfurt (2006).

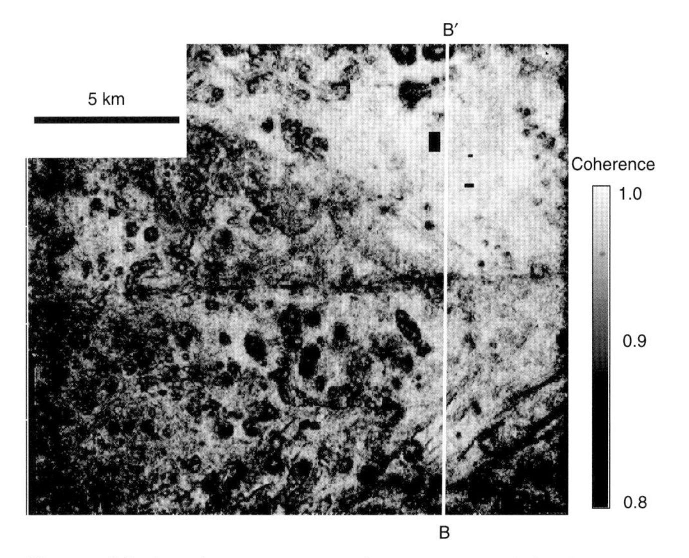

Figure 21. An eigenstructure coherence at $t = 1.2$ s (approximately the Ellenburger level shown in Figure 19) through the same survey shown in Figure 15.

the most-negative curvature, the most-positive curvature, and the Gaussian curvature for $\alpha = 1.00$, which enhances short-wavelength features. In Figure 23, we display the most-negative curvature, the most-positive curvature, and the Gaussian curvature for $\alpha = 0.25$, which enhances long-wavelength features. For completeness, we display the dip curvature and the strike curvature in Figure 24. Although we find the most-negative and most-positive curvatures to be most valuable in conventional structural interpretations, others find these other measures of curvature to be linked more closely to open fractures.

The Shape Index

Although the shape index given by equation 4.11 has been used in topography and terrain mapping (e.g., Mitsova and Hofierka, 1993; Wood, 1996), the bulk of published literature pertains to applications of molecular docking for

Figure 22. Short-wavelength ($\alpha = 1.00$) curvature values at $t = 1.2$ s, corresponding to Figure 19, of (a) most-negative curvature k_{neg}, (b) most-positive curvature, k_{pos}, and (c) Gaussian curvature, k_{Gauss}. Arrows indicate an elongated collapse feature that appears to be structurally controlled. After Al-Dossary and Marfurt (2006).

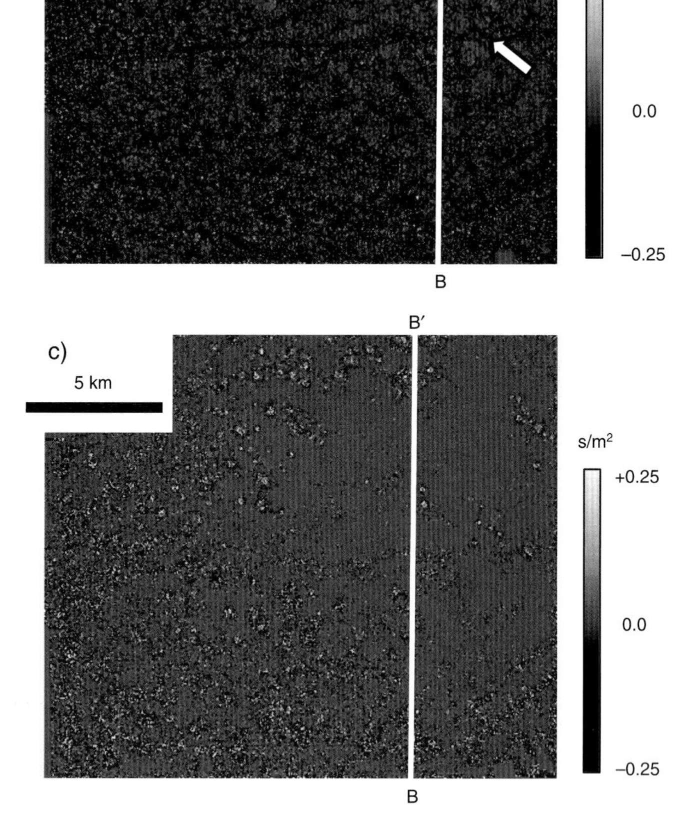

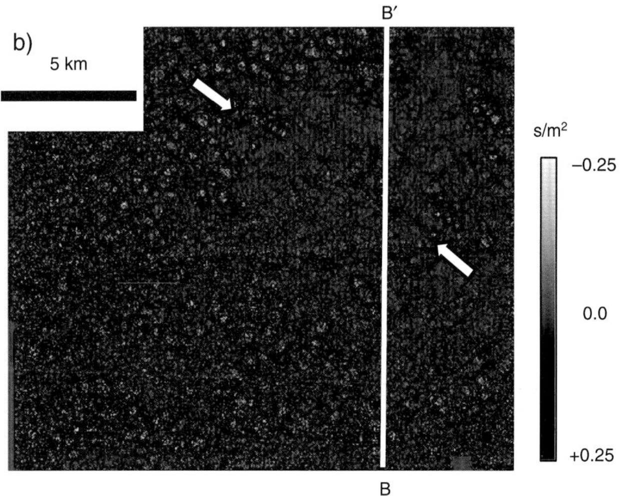

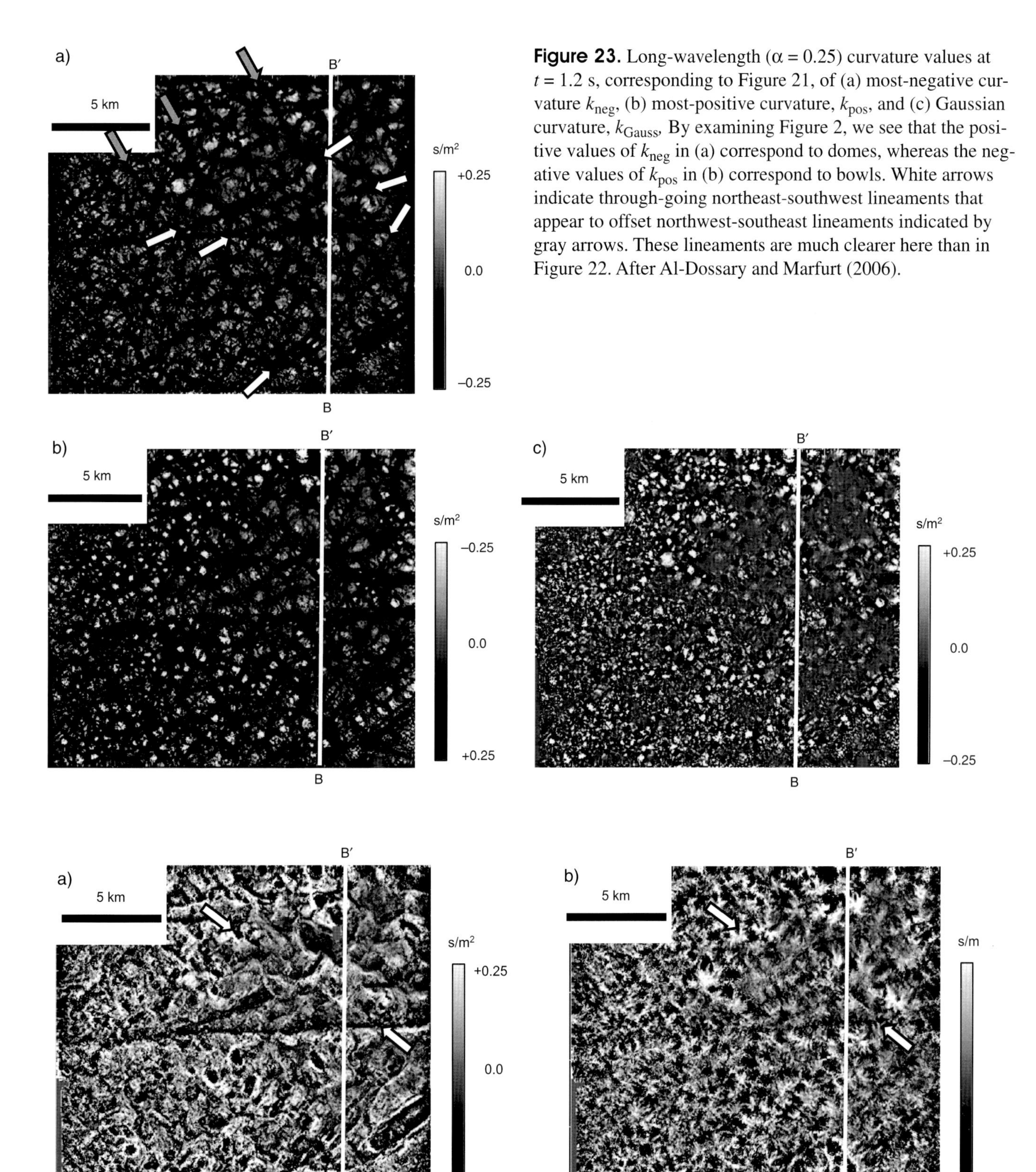

Figure 23. Long-wavelength ($\alpha = 0.25$) curvature values at $t = 1.2$ s, corresponding to Figure 21, of (a) most-negative curvature k_{neg}, (b) most-positive curvature, k_{pos}, and (c) Gaussian curvature, k_{Gauss}. By examining Figure 2, we see that the positive values of k_{neg} in (a) correspond to domes, whereas the negative values of k_{pos} in (b) correspond to bowls. White arrows indicate through-going northeast-southwest lineaments that appear to offset northwest-southeast lineaments indicated by gray arrows. These lineaments are much clearer here than in Figure 22. After Al-Dossary and Marfurt (2006).

Figure 24. (a) Dip curvature, k_{dip}, and (b) strike curvature, k_{strike}, corresponding to the time slices in Figure 21. Although we have found these images less useful than k_{neg} and k_{pos} in interpreting faults and flexures, Hart et al. (2002) and others consider these measures to be more closely correlated to open fractures. After Al-Dossary and Marfurt (2006).

pharmaceutical and genome work, and biometric indicators such as face and fingerprint identification. We show such a biometric identifier in Figure 25, where Woodward and Flynn (2004) scanned 400 human hands using a laser distance-scanning device and were able to identify a specific hand in question with 95% confidence. A close inspection of the authors' hands shows a series of ridges, ruts, and flat spots exacerbated by the worry of typing this manuscript under a tight deadline.

In Figure 26, we display a composite image of the shape index (represented by hue) and curvedness (represented by lightness) using a 2D color bar described in Chapter 9. The value $\alpha = 0.25$ enhances longer-wavelength features. Figure 26b, at $t = 0.8$ s, is at the same level as images displayed in Figures 18 and 20. Figure 23c, at $t = 1.2$ s, is at the same level as images displayed in Figures 21–24. As we saw on the vertical slice shown in Figure 19, the deeper image here has more structural deformation and greater curvedness, and thus is somewhat brighter. Collapse features appear as shades of blue (indicated by the blue arrow) to cyan, and a few isolated domes appear as red (red arrows). The ridge indicated in Figure 19 is indicated here by the yellow arrow.

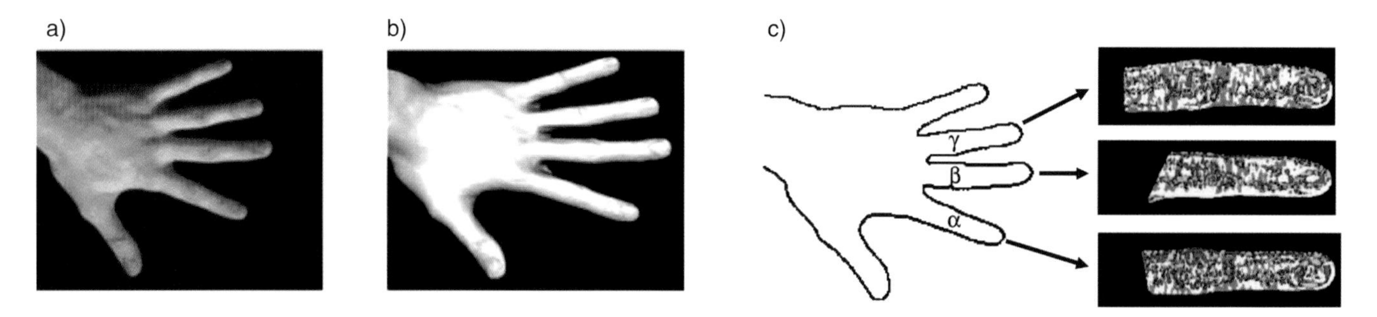

Figure 25. (a) An intensity image and (b) a range (what geoscientists would call a topographic) image of a human hand. (c) Shape indices of the middle three digits, using equation 4.11. Look at your own fingers and try to match the details of ridges and valleys around your knuckles to those in the image. After Woodward and Flynn (2004).

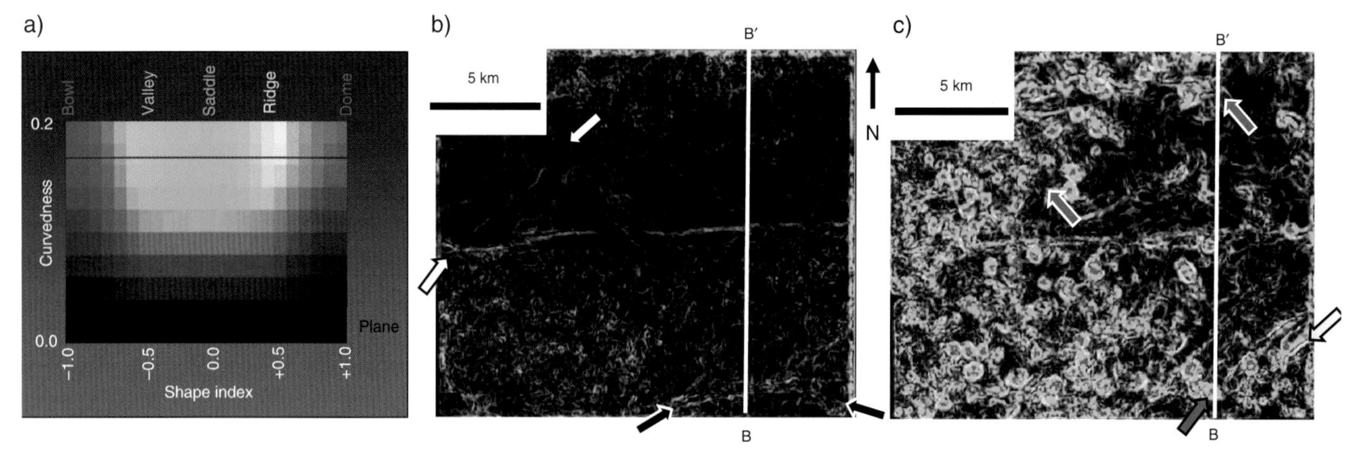

Figure 26. (a) A 2D color table used to display the shape index against curvedness. Planar features will have a curvedness near zero and will be displayed in black. Highly curved features will be plotted as a pure color, thereby allowing us to differentiate between reflector shapes. We plot curvedness, c, and shape index, s, calculated using equations 4. 10 and 4.11 and using this 2D color table, at (b) $t = 0.8$ s, corresponding to Figures 18 and 20, and at (c) $t = 1.2$ s, corresponding to Figures 21 to 23. Note that the shallow section is less contorted and yields a darker image. The cyan valley indicated by white arrows in (b) corresponds to a channel. The yellow ridge indicated by the black arrows corresponds to the ridge seen in Figure 19. Other cyan valley and yellow ridge lineaments correspond to deformation about faults and joints. In contrast, (c) is dominated by collapse features in the Ellenburger Formation. Collapse features appear as blue circles — such as the one indicated by the blue arrow — ringed by yellow ridges and green saddles. Red arrows indicate two domal features, one of which corresponds to the dome indicated by the gray arrow seen in Figure 19. After Al-Dossary and Marfurt (2005).

Shape Components

One goal in seismic attribute analysis is to statistically correlate a given attribute with well logs, production data, or features of interpretational interest. Whereas the human mind can readily identify the shapes displayed in the composite image shown in Figure 26, a computer may lack that ability. Just as dip azimuth has meaning only if the dip magnitude is nonzero, the shape index has interpretational value only when it is used with curvedness or some other measure of the intensity of deformation. In principle, nonlinear neural networks should be able to correlate multiple attributes with validation data. However, other powerful techniques, such as geostatistics, may not. Because we intuitively expect correlations between domes (with four-way closure) and hydrocarbon accumulations, or between bowls and greater accommodation space for sand deposits, or between a particular shape and open fractures, we think it is valuable to generate shape components such as those shown in Figure 27 that correspond to the same time slice as Figure 26. All we have done is multiply the curvedness at every point in the volume by a simple filter (shown in Figure 27f) that passes a shape component of interest.

Lineaments

A human interpreter can readily identify several lineaments in Figure 20f. By using the shape index, curvedness, and azimuth of maximum curvature (perpendicular to the strike of linear features), we can both enhance and count the number of pixels that have a significant lineament component. In Figure 28, we display the filter that is based on the shape index and that will pass features that have a shape best represented as a ridge or valley. In Figure 28b, we display a 2D color table in which the strike of the ridge or valley (perpendicular to the azimuth of maximum curvature given by equation 4.12) is represented by hue, and the curvedness multiplied by the shape index filter is represented by lightness. In Figure 28c, we display the composite image corresponding to the time slice, at t = 0.8 s and α = 0.25,

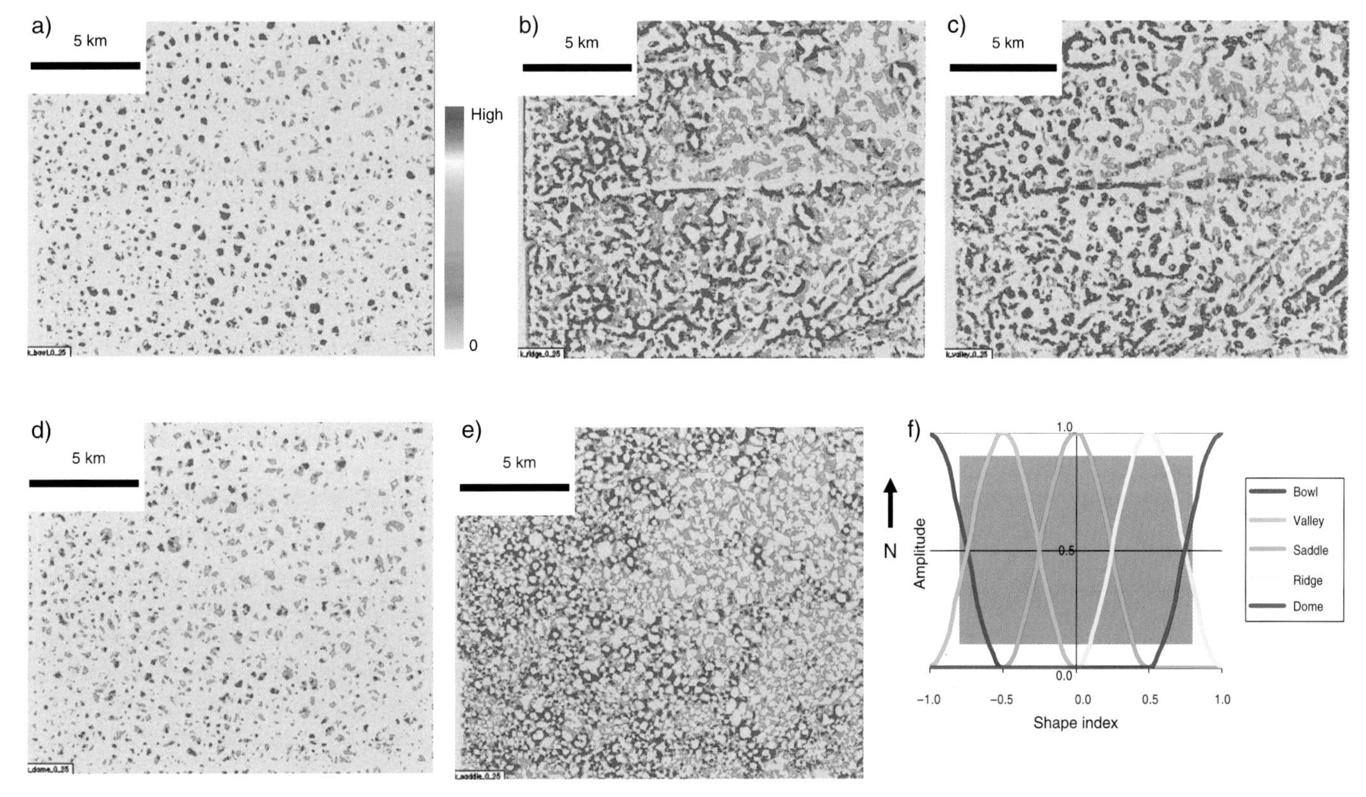

Figure 27. Long-wavelength (α = 0.25) curvature anomalies at t = 1.200 s, decomposed according to shape. First, we calculate the curvedness using equation 4.10. Next, we multiply the curvedness by a filter designed to pass a particular shape: (a) bowl, (b) valley, (c) saddle, (d) ridge, and (e) dome. Corresponding filters are shown in (f). In principle, all the information contained in these five images also is contained in Figure 26c. However, because the sum of a bowl and valley image includes all the features that may correspond to a thicker accommodation space, we expect better performance from statistical transforms that are based on a weighted linear sum of attributes. After Al-Dossary and Marfurt (2006).

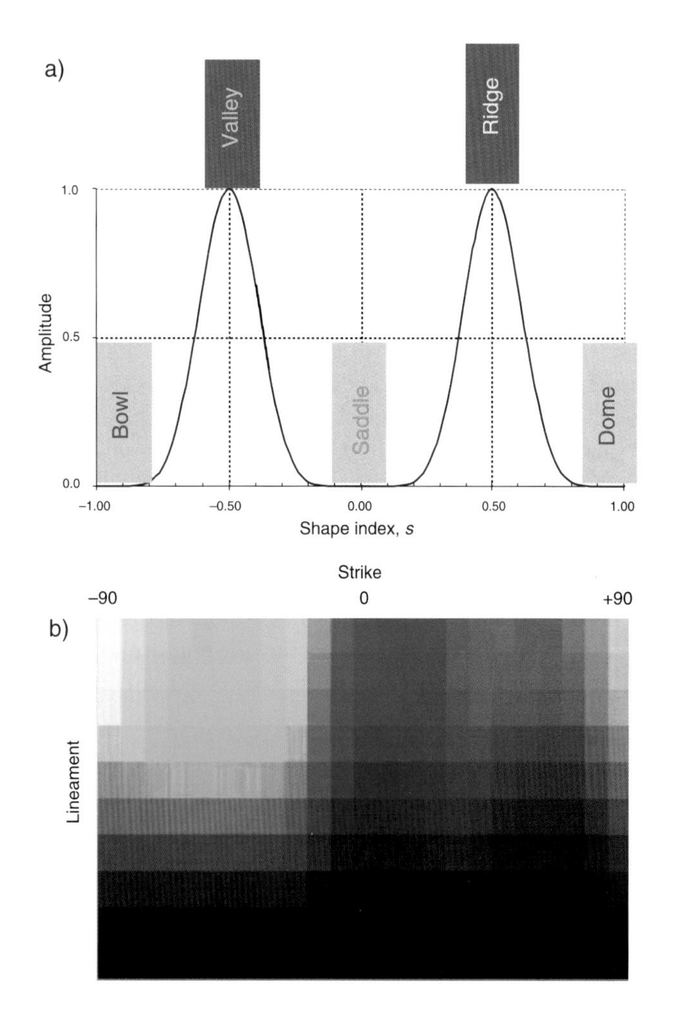

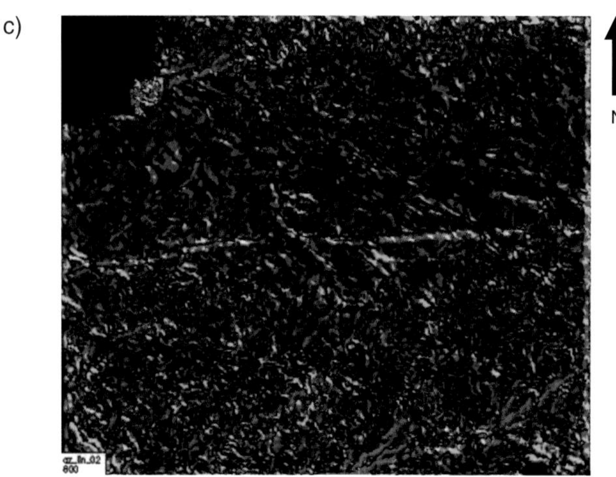

Figure 28. (a) Generation of a lineament attribute, obtained by applying a filter that passes only those values of curvedness that correspond to ridges and valleys. (b) A 2D color bar to display the lineament attribute against curvedness. (c) A time slice at $t = 1.2$ s through the lineament attribute volume. After Al-Dossary and Marfurt (2006).

that was shown in Figure 20f. Note the strong east-west fault (strike of 90° and colored yellow) running through the center of the image. Magenta lineaments strike to the northeast, green lineaments strike to the northwest. We do not see any significant north-south-trending lineaments in blue.

Examples

Central Basin Platform, west Texas, U.S.A.

Our first example is from a survey over the Central Basin Platform of west Texas, U.S.A. The major hydrocarbon production in this area is from the Devonian Thirtyone Formation, which is a chert deposit carried by turbidity flows from the shelf in the north into this deeper part of basin. The reservoir is highly compartmentalized and is enhanced by fractures. (In Chapter 18, we present a case study of the same formation imaged by a neighboring survey.) In Figure 29a, we show an image of the most-positive curvature extracted along the yellow Thirtyone Formation horizon posted on the vertical slice through the seismic data. In Figure 29b, we display an enlarged view of the seismic data corresponding to a producing part of the reservoir indicated by the green box in Figure 29a. Green arrows indicate synclinal and red arrows anticlinal features in this structural high.

In Figure 30, we display the time-structure map of the yellow Thirtyone Formation pick shown in Figure 29a, as well as the corresponding coherence extraction (horizon slice through the coherence volume). In Figure 31, we show corresponding horizon slices through the most-negative-curvature and most-positive-curvature volumes. Green arrows (indicating synclines) and red arrows (indicating anticlines) correspond to those shown in Figure 29b. Note that this subtle warping seen on the vertical seismic image can be carried along the entire horizon, providing constraints on the paleostress environment and on possible fractures.

The coherence extraction is relatively featureless over the zone of interest, whereas the curvature volume is not. This observation reinforces our major point that coherence and curvature volumes are different because they are measuring different attributes of the input seismic volume. In particular, curvature shows subtle (unbroken) flexures not seen by coherence because coherence is sensitive only to lateral discontinuities.

In contrast, we will show images in Chapter 12 (on clastic depositional environments) in which coherence will delineate channels and (in the absence of differential compaction) curvature will not. The curvature computations are volumetric rather than along a surface, which we illustrate

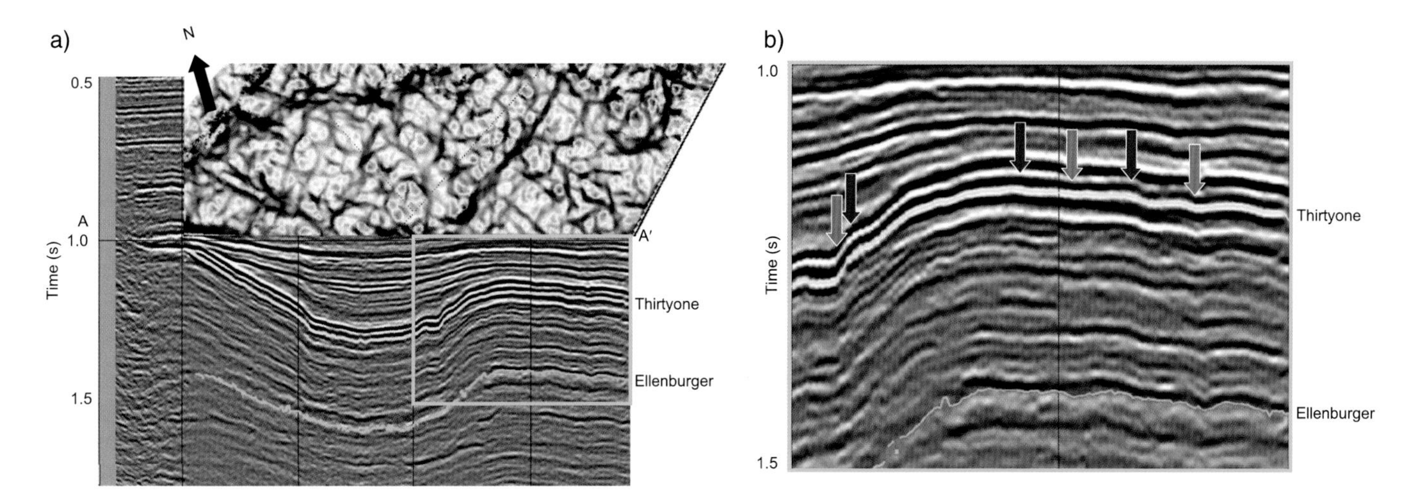

Figure 29. (a) A vertical slice through the seismic data and a horizon slice along the yellow Thirtyone Formation, from the most-positive curvature volume. (b) Enlargement of the seismic data shown in the green box in (a). Green arrows indicate synclinal and red arrows anticlinal features within this structural high. Note how the flexures seen on the seismic can be carried through the volume on the horizon slice through the most-positive curvature volume. Data courtesy of Burlington Resources.

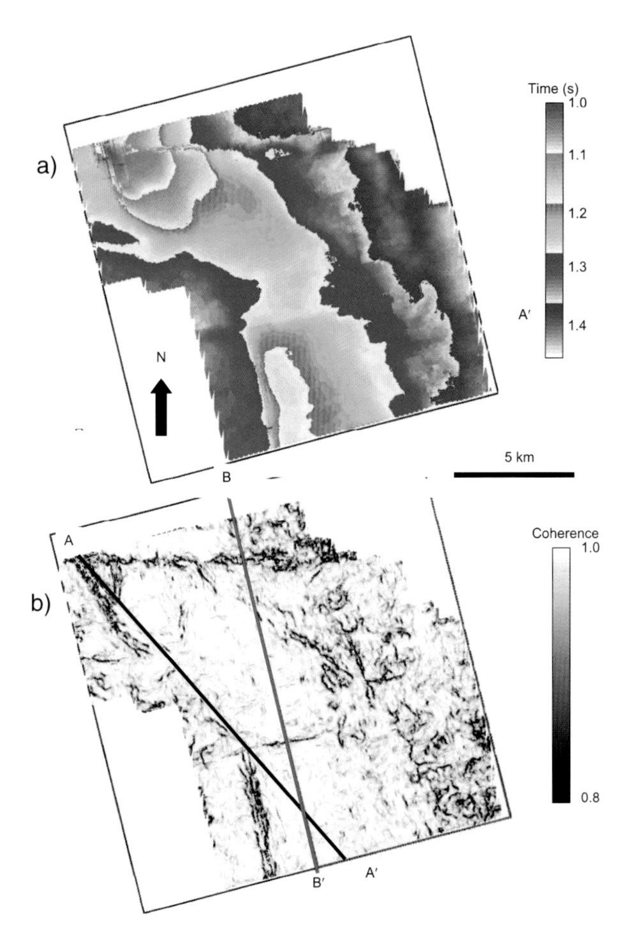

Figure 30. (a) A time-structure map and (b) and a horizon slice through the coherence volume along the yellow Thirtyone Formation pick shown in Figure 29a.

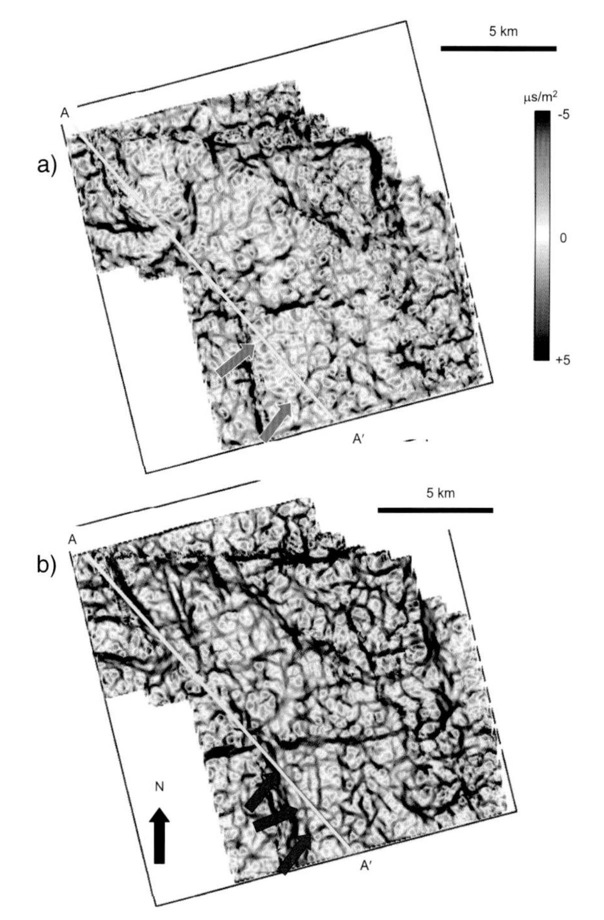

Figure 31. (a) Most-negative-curvature and (b) most-positive-curvature extractions along the yellow Thirtyone Formation pick shown in Figure 29a and corresponding to the images shown in Figure 30. Note the added detail provided by the curvature volumes in areas where the coherence is featureless.

in Figure 32. Figure 32 displays time slices at $t = 1.0$ s through the most-negative-curvature and most-positive-curvature volumes; the posted yellow picks correspond to the intersection with the structurally deformed Thirtyone Formation. To illustrate more explicitly the correlation of these curvature computations to the original seismic data, we display the seismic data, coherence, most-negative curvature, and most-positive curvature in Figures 33 and 34. These curvature images give the interpreter a means of mapping local highs (domes) and lows (bowls) and of carrying subtle flexures across the entire survey.

Vinton Dome, Louisiana, U.S.A.

In Figure 35, we show a time slice through (a) a coherence volume and (b) a vertical slice through the seismic amplitude volume acquired over Vinton Dome, Louisiana, U.S.A. We note that several of the faults easily interpreted on the seismic section in Figure 35b (indicated by arrows) do not show up clearly on the coherence volume. Although these data have been prestack time migrated, the velocity structure is sufficiently complex that the fault edges are blurred (i.e., overmigrated or undermigrated), with residual hyperbolas rendering the faults more continuous and less detectable by coherence measurements. Short-wavelength estimates of curvature see these poorly migrated edges as subtle flexures and provide marginally improved images of the faults (Figure 36). In contrast, long-wavelength estimates of curvature provide strong, continuous fault-plane images, partially compensating for the inaccurate migration (Figure 37). In addition, the long-wavelength estimate of rotation in Figure 37c shows several faults that have a scissorlike rotation about them, thereby defining a nonquadratic surface that was not defined by conventional curvature measures.

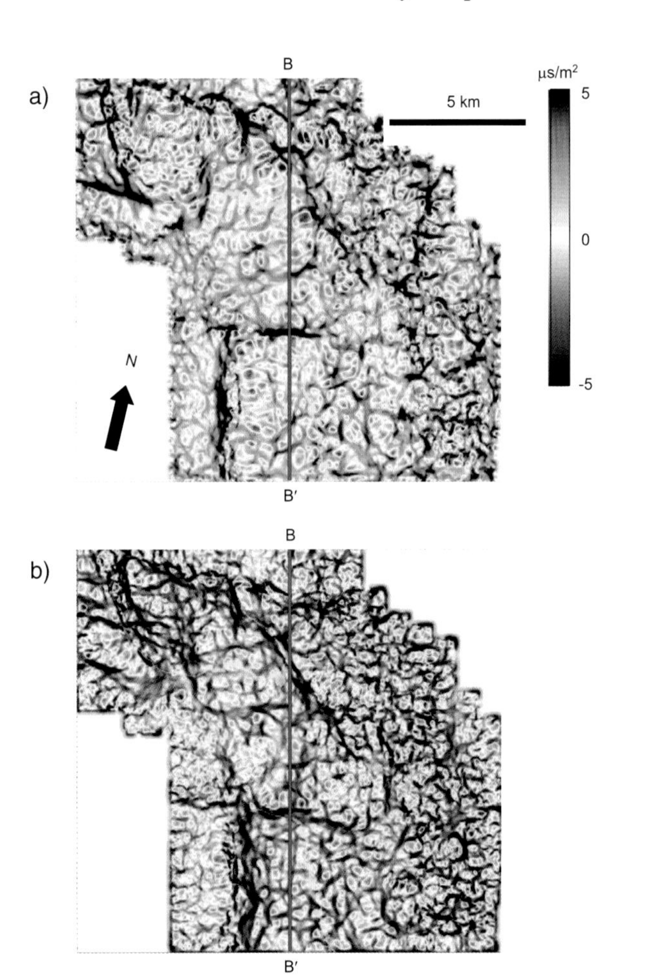

Figure 32. A time slice at 1.0 s through (a) the most-negative-curvature volume and (b) the most-positive-curvature volume from Figure 31. The yellow picks correspond to intersections of the time slice with the Thirtyone Formation pick shown in Figure 29a. Folds and flexures can be interpreted on these time slices prior to picking any horizons.

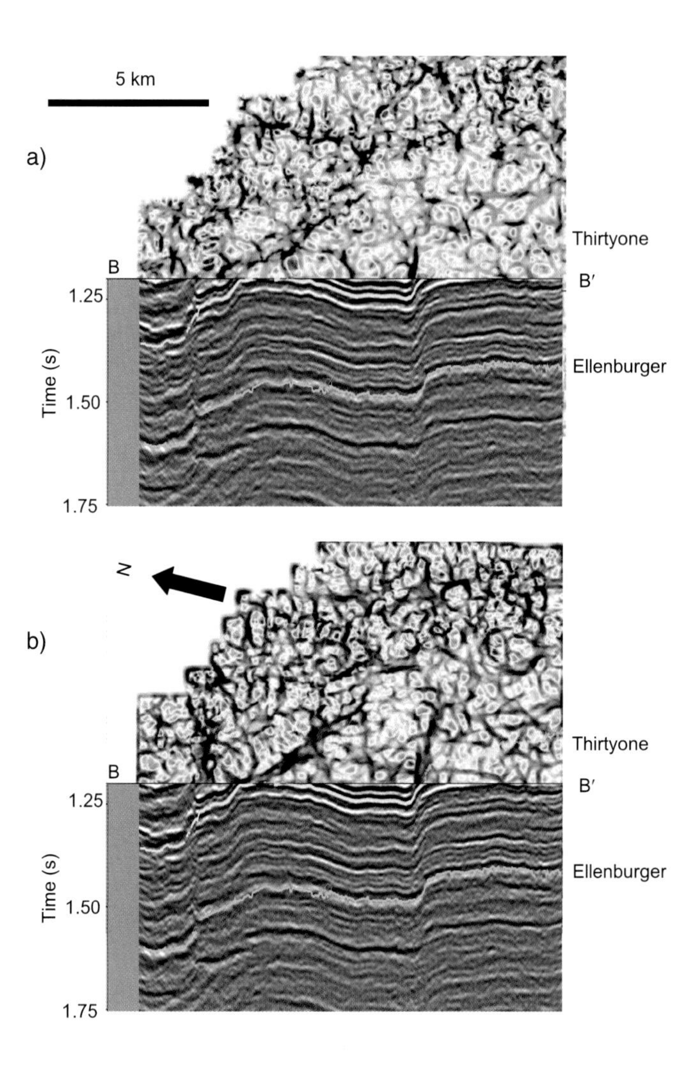

Figure 33. Cube-edge displays folded at 1.0 s along line AA' from Figure 30b, showing seismic data on the vertical section and (a) seismic and (b) coherence data on the time slice. The zone of intersection is relatively featureless on the coherence slice.

Delaware Basin, New Mexico, U.S.A.

As our last example, we return to the survey over the Delaware Basin, New Mexico, U.S.A., that we presented earlier in Chapters 2 and 3. In Figures 38 and 39, we display time slices through the most-negative-curvature volume (Figure 38) and the most-positive-curvature volume (Figure 39), which correspond to images through the volumetric dip and azimuth volume displayed in Chapter 2, Figure 20 and the coherence volume in Chapter 3, Figure 37. These curvature calculations are made directly from information displayed in Figure 20 of Chapter 2. The most-positive-curvature time slice at 0.8 s in Figure 39a shows a flexure that clearly delineates the platform edge (yellow arrow). This platform edge appears to be at a more-northerly position on the 1.0-s time slice. We clearly delineate the platform edge. The east-west flexure indicated by the blue arrow shows up prominently on the deeper most-positive-curvature slices and is somewhat offset to the north on the deeper most-negative-curvature volume. The broader, more-diffuse, north-south flexure indicated by the magenta arrow does not show up as clearly as the east-west flexure, indicating that we need to use a longer-wavelength curvature operator. The complex areas of folding indicated by the cyan and orange circles (and discussed in Chapter 2) appear as a pattern of spatially periodic flexures.

Figure 40 displays vertical slices through a composite image of the most-negative-curvature volume and the seismic data volume, and Figure 41 shows vertical slices through a composite image of the most-positive-curvature volume

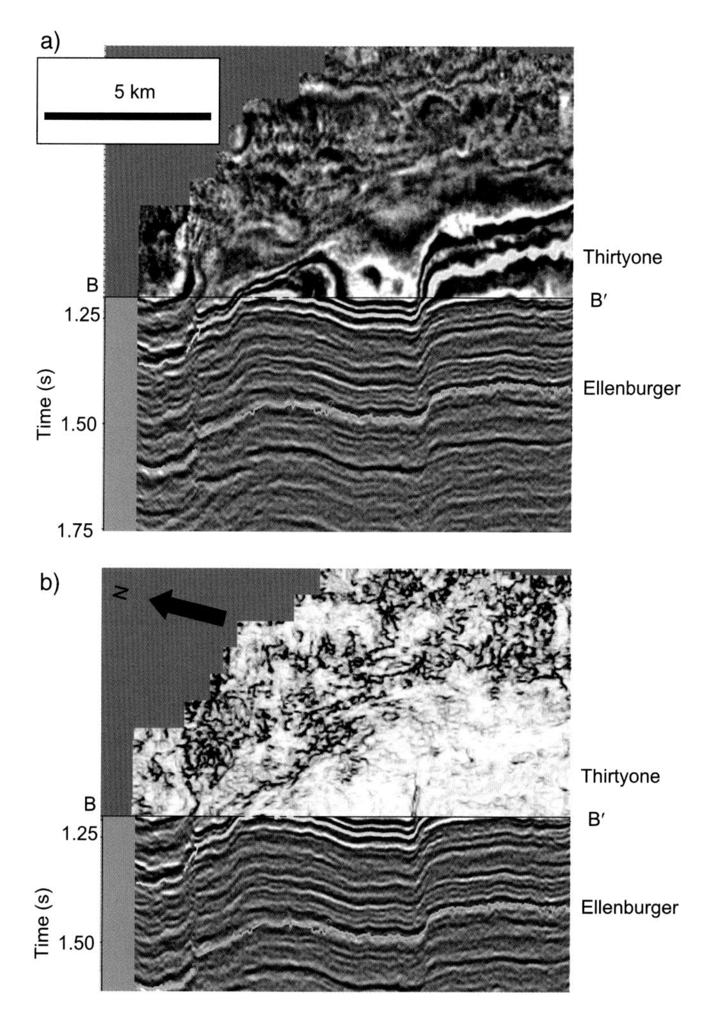

Figure 34. Cube-edge displays folded at 1.0 s along line AA′ from Figure 30b, showing seismic data on the vertical section and (a) most-negative curvature and (b) most-positive curvature on the time slice. We can easily track folds and flexures seen on the seismic image into the survey along the curvature slices.

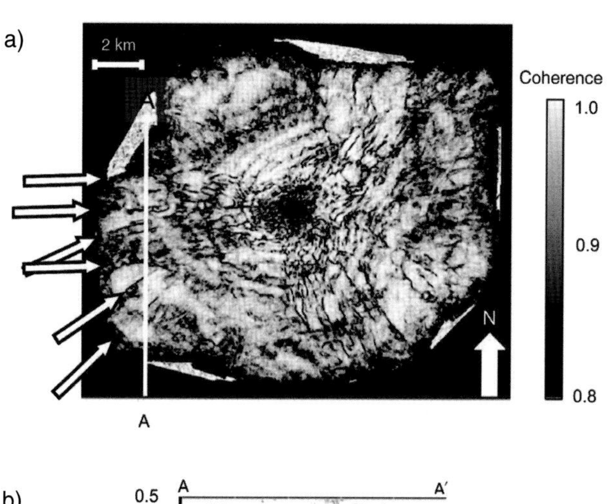

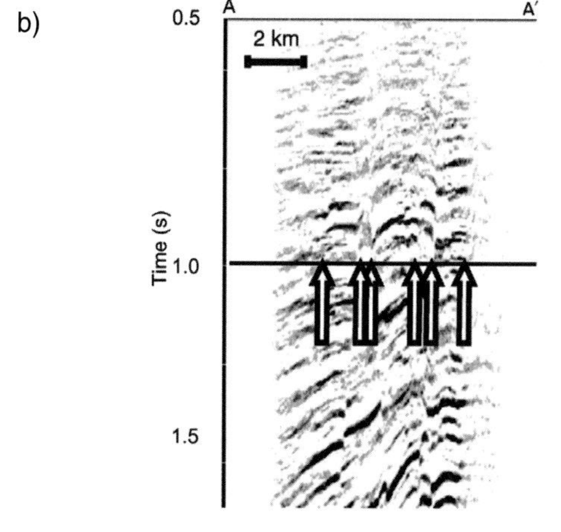

Figure 35. (a) A time slice at 1.0 s through a coherence volume and (b) vertical slice through the seismic data from a survey acquired over Vinton Dome, Louisiana, U.S.A. The arrows correspond to the same faults shown in Figures 36 and 37. Note that some of these faults appear to be discrete discontinuities, but others appear to be folds, either resulting from drag along the fault, or from inaccurate migration. Faults having a folded appearance show up more clearly in the curvature image than in the coherence volumes. After Al-Dossary and Marfurt (2006).

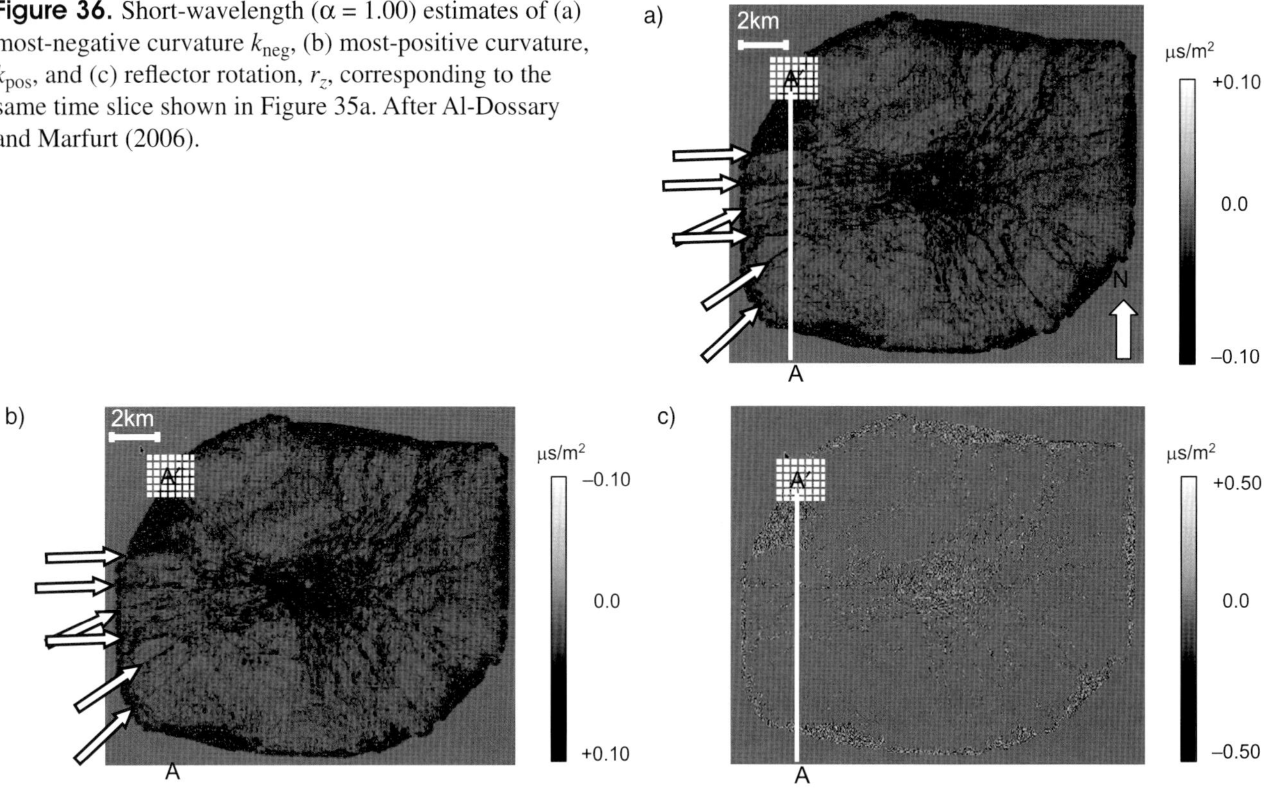

Figure 36. Short-wavelength ($\alpha = 1.00$) estimates of (a) most-negative curvature k_{neg}, (b) most-positive curvature, k_{pos}, and (c) reflector rotation, r_z, corresponding to the same time slice shown in Figure 35a. After Al-Dossary and Marfurt (2006).

Figure 37. Long-wavelength ($\alpha = 0.25$) estimates of (a) most-negative curvature, k_{neg}, (b) most-postive curvature, k_{pos}, and (c) reflector rotation, r_z, corresponding to the same time slice shown in Figures 35a and 36. White arrows depict faults that are not seen as clearly on the coherence time slice shown in Figure 35b. Gray arrows correspond to faults where reflectors have significant rotation about the fault plane. Such rotations are not represented by the quadratic surface used in curvature calculations. The black arrow indicates noisy, low-fold areas of the data. After Al-Dossary and Marfurt (2006).

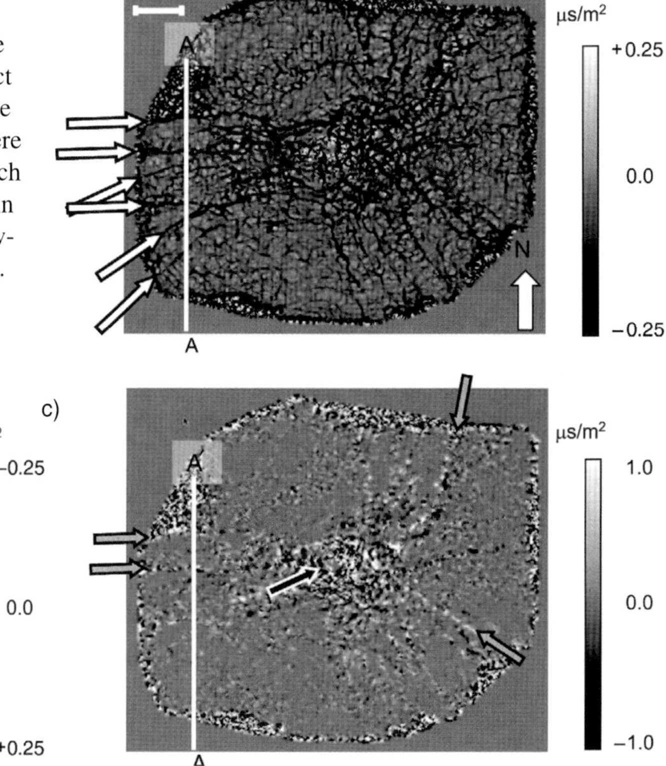

b) 2 km A′ A μs/m² –0.25 0.0 +0.25

and the seismic data volume. Here, we note that the folded structures have sharper crests and broader valleys, resulting in the spatially periodic, most-positive-curvature image seen in Figure 39e and f. In contrast, the gentler and longer-wavelength synclines appear to be more diffuse on the corresponding most-negative-curvature slices.

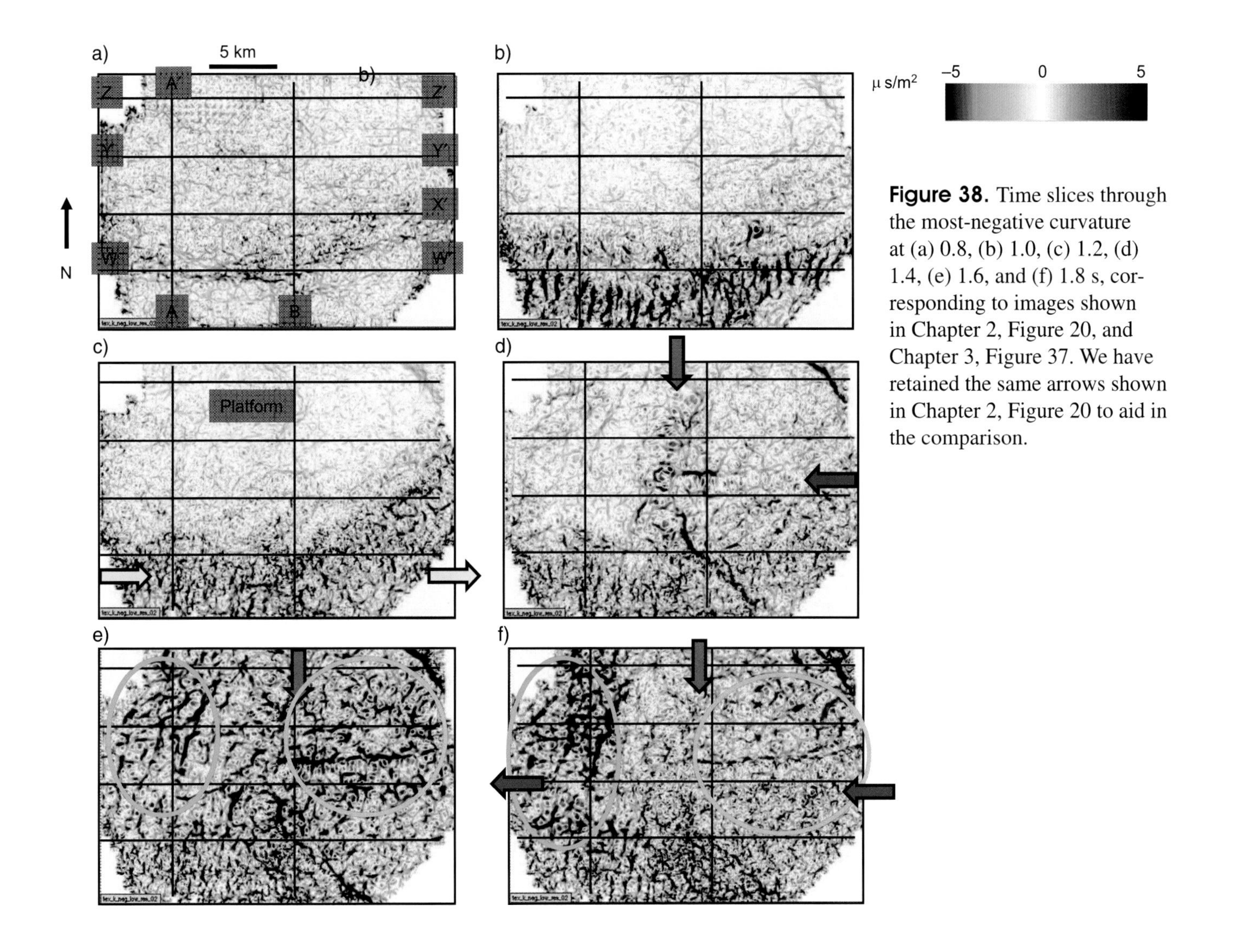

Figure 38. Time slices through the most-negative curvature at (a) 0.8, (b) 1.0, (c) 1.2, (d) 1.4, (e) 1.6, and (f) 1.8 s, corresponding to images shown in Chapter 2, Figure 20, and Chapter 3, Figure 37. We have retained the same arrows shown in Chapter 2, Figure 20 to aid in the comparison.

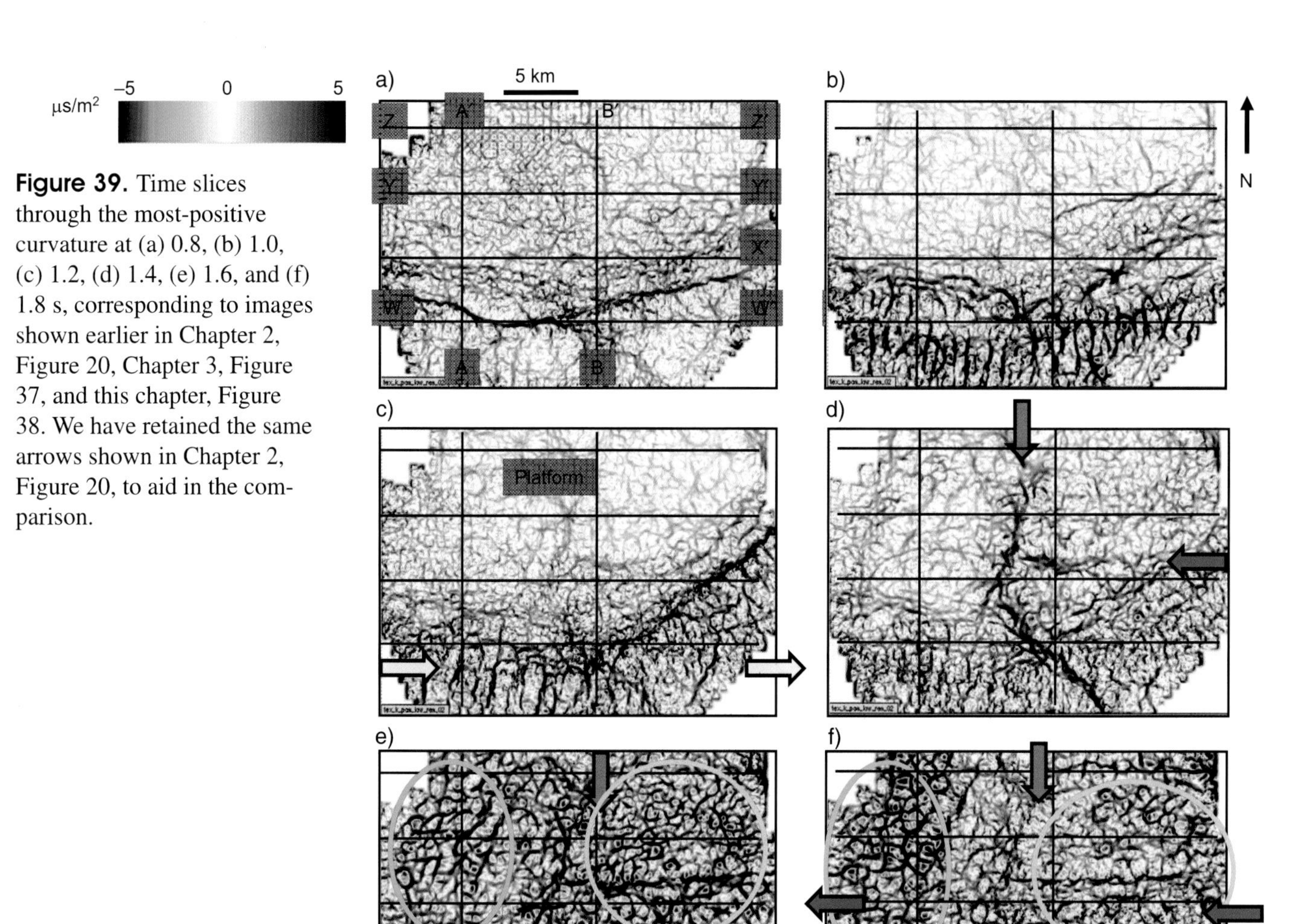

Figure 39. Time slices through the most-positive curvature at (a) 0.8, (b) 1.0, (c) 1.2, (d) 1.4, (e) 1.6, and (f) 1.8 s, corresponding to images shown earlier in Chapter 2, Figure 20, Chapter 3, Figure 37, and this chapter, Figure 38. We have retained the same arrows shown in Chapter 2, Figure 20, to aid in the comparison.

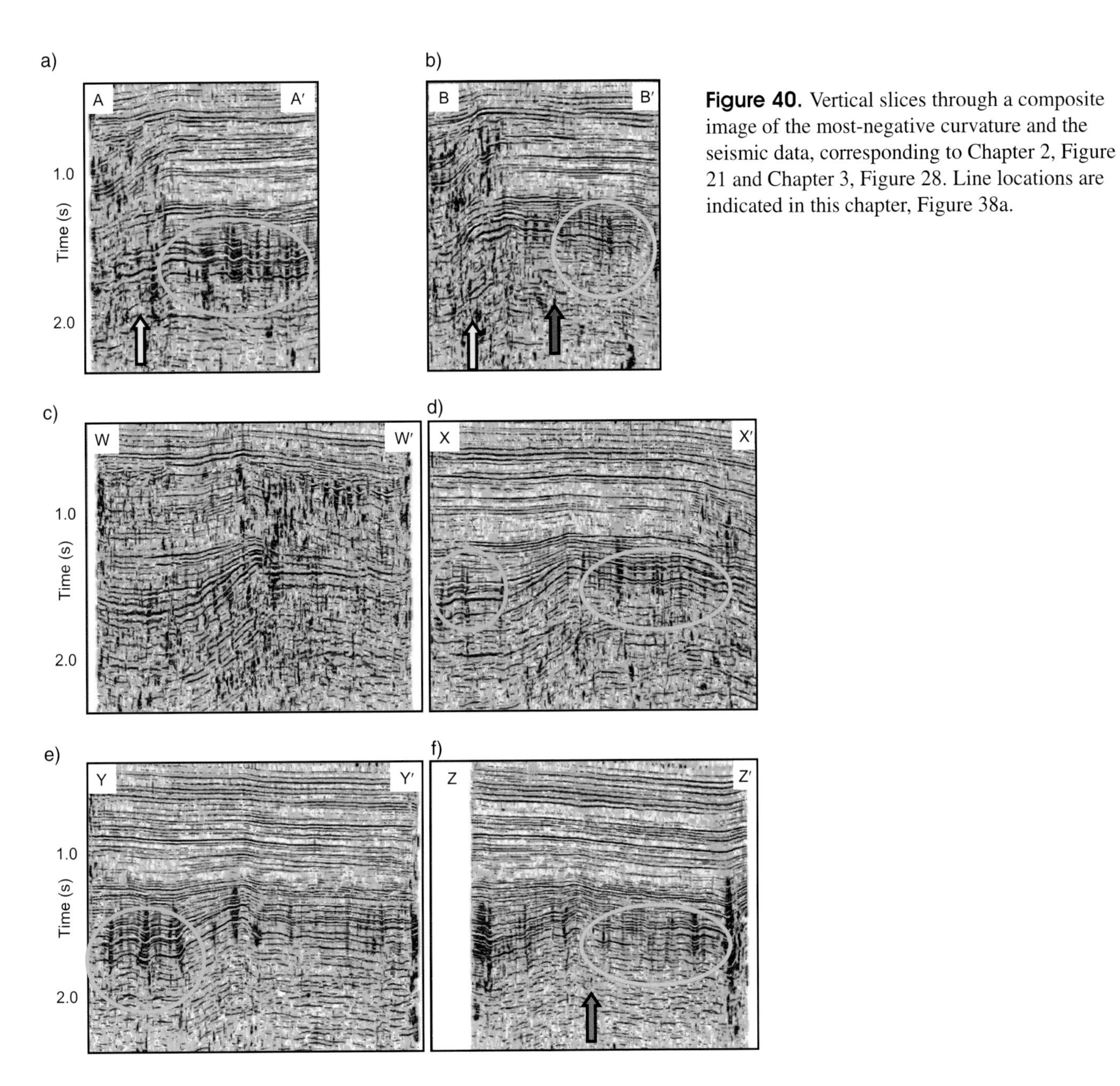

Figure 40. Vertical slices through a composite image of the most-negative curvature and the seismic data, corresponding to Chapter 2, Figure 21 and Chapter 3, Figure 28. Line locations are indicated in this chapter, Figure 38a.

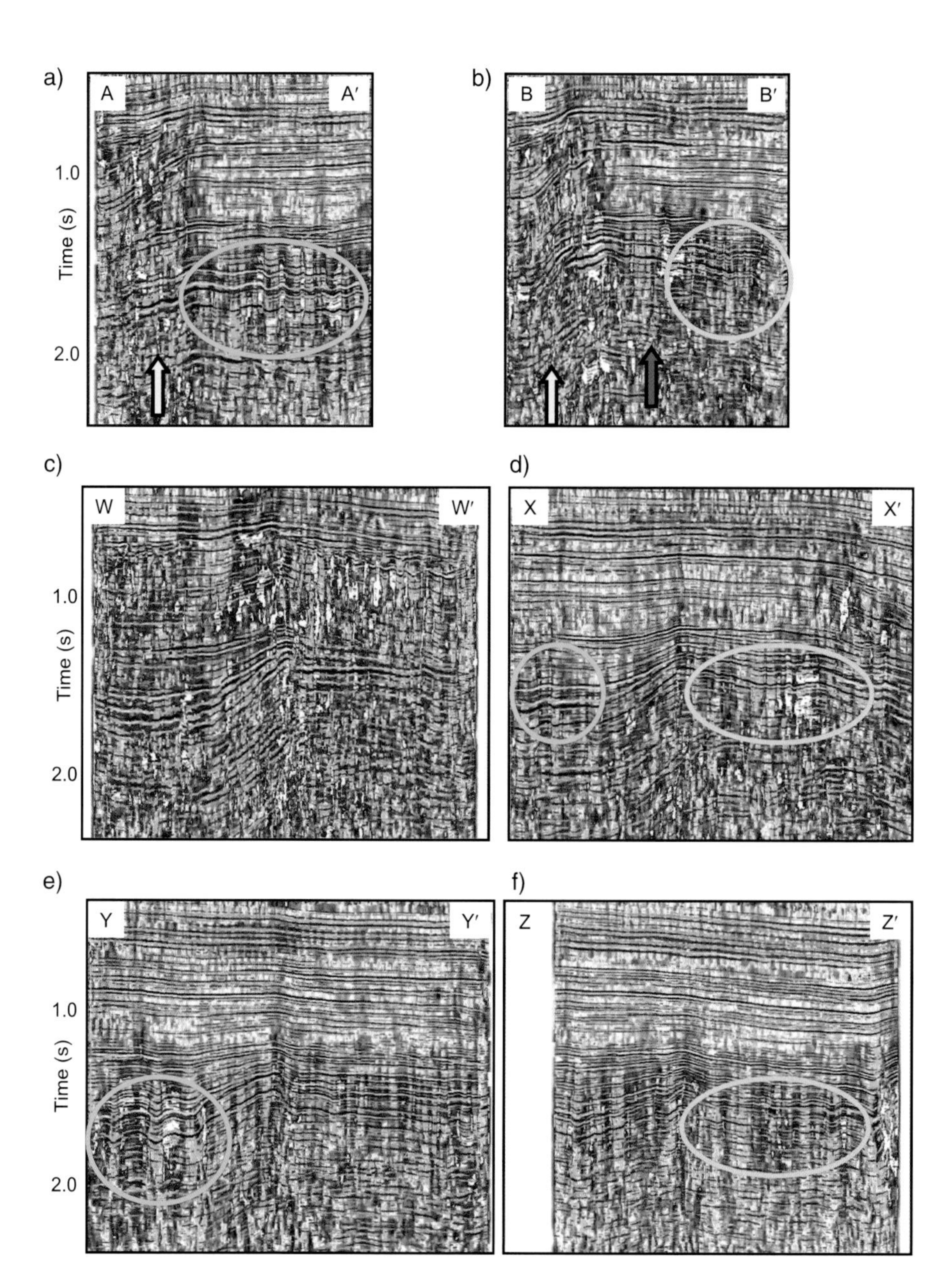

Figure 41. Vertical slices through a composite image of the most-positive curvature and the seismic data, corresponding to Chapter 2, Figure 21 and Chapter 3, Figure 28. Line locations are indicated in Figure 39a.

Chapter Summary

This chapter shows well-established methods for generating curvature measurements from interpreted horizons applied to volumetric estimates of dip and azimuth. Curvature calculations performed directly on the dip and azimuth cubes provide good edge-detection images for high-quality data. However, the true power of this technique is achieved by calculating curvature of broader features by altering the wavelength of the calculation. Longer-wavelength estimates of curvature can be obtained by successively smoothing maps or dip and azimuth volumes, by explicitly filtering the data in the k_x-k_y wavenumber domain, or by explicitly filtering the curvature operators. These latter two approaches are more general than simple smoothing, thereby allowing the interpreter to explicitly define wavelengths of interest. In addition to enhancing longer-wavelength flexures, folds, and compaction features, long-wavelength estimates of curvature can improve our ability to map poorly focused faults that are contaminated by residual diffraction hyperbolae.

Volumetric estimates of reflector curvature and rotation are based on, and are only as good as, the volumetric estimates of reflector dip and azimuth discussed in Chapter 2. In contrast, volumetric estimates of curvature and rotation are independent of the coherence measures discussed in Chapter 3. The different images seen by curvature and coherence are equally dependent on geology and on mathematics. Certain features, such as well-focused normal faults, show up equally well on coherence and curvature volumes. However, in the absence of differential compaction, curvature attributes provide poor images of channels. In contrast, curvature provides excellent images of subtle flexures, folds, and collapse features that are not commonly seen on coherence volumes. Reflector rotation can be a good indicator of data quality as well as of scissor movement along a fault.

The most-negative and most-positive curvatures are the most unambiguous of the curvature images in highlighting faults and folds. Several authors have shown a strong correlation between Gaussian curvature, dip curvature, and strike curvature, and the presence of open fractures. Currently, such calibration work using image logs, production history, tracer data in conjunction with physical and numerical models, geostatistics, and neural nets is an active area of research, with Fischer and Wilkerson (2000) relating the orientation of fractures to fold shape and Stewart and Wynn (2003) predicting strain from spectral estimates of curvature.

The shape index, when it is corendered with curvedness, allows us to visualize 3D reflector morphology on simple time slices. Shape indices have proven to be a valuable tool in facial recognition and other biomarker technology, as well as with molecular docking analysis. We fully expect shape indices or a successor based on curvature measures to form a key component in future computer-assisted seismic-stratigraphy analysis.

If volumetric estimates of curvature have a major limitation, it is in the restrictions applied to the calculations themselves. The vector dip is a true 3D calculation centered on the analysis point that would follow the best reflector as it ascended and descended in time or depth. However, because we wish to calculate curvature even when only piecewise-continuous reflectors are available, we calculate the derivatives of dip on constant-time time slices (or constant-depth depth slices). For steeply dipping horizons and/or long-wavelength estimates, we expect that these measures undesirably mix geology of different formations. Under such conditions, predictions of fracture intensity are linked not to thin-plate theory, but rather to some more-complicated composite-plate deformation. Although we anticipate there will be near-term improvements in our estimates that will better follow the local dip, we know that such improvements will not be trivial to implement.

References

Al-Dossary, S., and K. J. Marfurt, 2006, 3-D volumetric multispectral estimates of reflector curvature and rotation: Geophysics, **71**, 41–51.

Bergbauer, S., T. Mukerji, and P. Hennings, 2003, Improving curvature analyses of deformed horizons using scale-dependent filtering techniques: AAPG Bulletin, **87**, 1255–1272.

Cooper, G. R., and D. R. Cowan, 2003, Sunshading geophysical data using fractional order horizontal gradients: The Leading Edge, **22**, 204–205.

Dalley, R M., E. E. A. Gevers, G. M. Stampli, D. J. Davies, C. N. Gastaldi, P. R. Ruijetnberg, and G. J. D.Vermeer, 1989, Dip and azimuth displays for 3-D seismic interpretation: First Break, **7**, 86–95.

Ericsson, J. B., H. C. McKeon, and R. J. Hooper, 1988, Facies and curvature controlled 3-D fracture models in a Cretaceous carbonate reservoir, Arabian Gulf, *in* G. Jones, Q. J. Fisher, and R. J. Knoipe, eds., Faulting, fault sealing and fluid flow in hydrocarbon reservoirs: Geological Society of London Special Publication 147, 299–312.

Fischer, M. P., and M. S. Wilkerson, 2000, Predicting the orientation of joints from fold shape: Results of pseudo-three-dimensional modeling and curvature analysis, Geology, **28**, 15–18.

Hart, B. S., 2002, Validating seismic attributes: Beyond statistics, The Leading Edge, **21**, 1016–1021.

Hart, B. S., R. A. Pearson, and G. C. Rawling, 2002, 3-D seismic horizon-based approaches to fracture-swarm sweet spot definition in tight-gas reservoirs: The Leading Edge, **21**, 28-35.

Lisle, R. J., 1994, Detection of zones of abnormal strains in structures using Gaussian curvature analysis: AAPG Bulletin, **78**, 1811–1819.

Luo, Y., S. Al-Dossary, M. Marhoon, and M. Alfaraj, 2003, Generalized Hilbert transform and its application in geophysics: The Leading Edge, **22,** 198–202.

Marfurt, K, J, and R. L. Kirlin, 2000, 3-D broadband estimates of reflector dip and amplitude: Geophysics, **65**, 304–320.

Mitsova, H., and J. Hofierka, 1993, Interpolation by regionalized spline with tension II: Application to terrain modeling and surface geometry analysis: Mathematical geology, **25**, 657–669.

Roberts, A., 2001, Curvature attributes and their application to 3D interpreted horizons. First Break, **19**, 85–99.

Sigismondi, E. M., and C. J. Soldo, 2003, Curvature attributes and seismic interpretation: Case studies from Argentina basins: The Leading Edge, **22**, 1122–1126.

Stewart, S. A., and T. J. Wynn, 2000, Mapping spatial variation in rock properties in relationship to scale-dependent structure using spectral curvature, Geology, **28**, 691–694.

Wood, J. D., 1996, The geomorphological characterization of digital elevation models: Ph.D. thesis, University of Leicester.

Woodward, D. L., and P. J. Flynn, 2004, Finger surface as a biometric identifier: Biometric Consortium Conference, Arlington, VA.

Wynn, T. J., and S. A. Stewart, 2003, The role of spectral curvature mapping characterizing subsurface strain distributions, *in* M. Ameen, ed., Fractures and in-situ stress characterization of hydrocarbon reservoirs: Geological Society of London Special Publication **209**, 127–143.

Chapter 5

Lateral Changes in Amplitude and Pattern Recognition

Chapter Objectives

After reading this chapter, you will be able to

- interpret lateral changes in amplitude that occur because of thin-bed tuning
- identify channels and other thin stratigraphic features on amplitude-gradient images
- predict which geologic features can be seen best by amplitude gradients, curvature, and coherence attributes
- use gray-level co-occurrence matrices to quantify seismic textures for visual and computer-assisted interpretation
- apply best practices for stratigraphic interpretation

Introduction

In Chapter 2, we examined how dip and azimuth can quantify lateral changes in reflector time (or depth). In Chapter 3, we examined how coherence can quantify lateral changes in reflector waveform. In the first section of this chapter, we will examine the third family of geometric attributes that measure trace-to-trace variation — those attributes that are sensitive to lateral changes in amplitude.

A primary goal of this book is to clearly define the physical and mathematical basis of the seismic attributes commonly used in interpretation, so that we can relate them better to geologic lithology and fluid properties via geostatistics.

We also will show that many of the mathematically independent attributes, some of which we have discussed already and some that we introduce in this chapter, may be linked through the underlying geology. Whereas any one of these three families of attributes may be sensitive to thick channels and faults, their responses to subtler features vary. In particular, many thin, lithologically heterogeneous gas-charged reservoirs can be characterized by strong reflection events that have a constant waveform. Such heterogeneities are not seen by crosscorrelation or eigenstructure estimates of coherence, but they are expressed through subtle changes in waveform amplitude. Likewise, subtle changes in thin-bed thickness also cause variations in waveform amplitude.

Geometric attributes that estimate dip, azimuth, curvature, and energy-weighted coherent-amplitude gradients (discussed in this chapter) provide valuable information about coherent reflectors. Coherence attributes provide excellent images of discrete discontinuities, but do not discriminate between high-energy low-coherence zones [such as a mass-transport complex (MTC) or a slump] and low-energy low-coherence zones (such as often occur with shale-on-shale reflections).

We address these others kinds of textures in the second section of this chapter. This latter type of analysis leads us into the area of statistical pattern recognition, which, along with the morphological pattern recognition discussed in Chapters 2 through 4 (angular unconformities detected using dip and azimuth, meandering-channel edges using coherence, etc.), provides the building blocks for computer-assisted interpretation.

Seismic Resolution and Thin-bed Tuning

To better understand the effect of bed thickness on seismic amplitude, we examine the simple wedge model shown in Figure 1. In this figure, we assume a simple low-impedance layer encased in a higher-impedance material such as one we might encounter in a sand channel that cuts through and is later buried by shale. The impedance changes in Figure 1a generate a negative reflection coefficient at the top and an equal but opposite reflection coefficient at the bottom of the wedge (Figure 1b). We generate the synthetic seismogram in Figure 1c by convolving these two reflection coefficients with a band-limited wavelet. As the wedge thins toward the left, the positive side lobe of the negative reflection from the top constructively interferes with the positive main lobe of the reflection from the bottom. Similarly, the negative side lobe from the positive reflection from the bottom constructively interferes with the negative main lobe of the reflection from the top. The maximum constructive interference occurs when the wedge thickness is one-quarter of the effective source wavelength, or, when measured in two-way traveltime, the wedge thickness is one-half the thickness of the dominant period (indicated by arrows in Figures 1c and 1d). For thicknesses smaller than this, the waveform's shape stabilizes (Figure 2a) and only the seismic amplitude changes with thickness. Widess (1973) showed that when we are well below the one-quarter-wavelength (tuning) thickness, amplitude changes linearly with thickness, as indicated by Figure 2b and as defined by

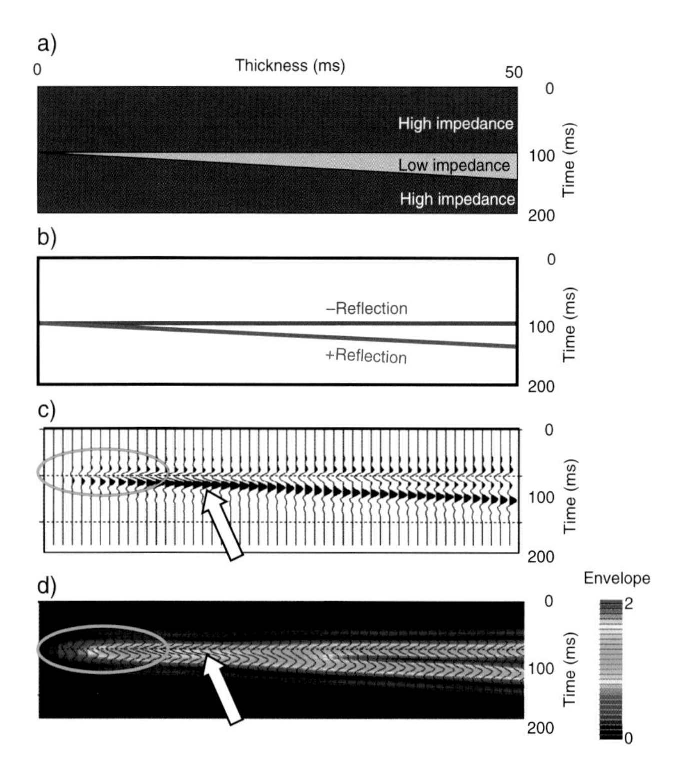

Figure 1. (a) Thin-bed resolution and the classic wedge model of a low-impedance layer encased in a higher-impedance matrix. (b) Reflectivity and thickness: the wedge increases in thickness from 0 to 50 ms from left to right, with a negative reflection on the top and a positive reflection on the bottom. (c) Seismic synthetic data generated by convolving (b) with an 8-10-40-50-Hz Ormsby filter. (d) Instantaneous envelope (also called reflection strength) computed from the seismic data in (c). The peak energy occurs at the one-quarter-wavelength (one-half-period two-way traveltime) tuning thickness indicated by the white arrow. Below the tuning thickness (which is indicated by the green ellipse), only the amplitude changes,whereas the phase and frequency remain fixed. Such subtle changes in amplitude allow us to map lateral changes in bed thickness using lateral changes in amplitude variability (and as we discuss in a later section in this book, using spectral decomposition). After Partyka (2001).

$$R\delta(t+T/2)w(t)-R\delta(t-T/2)w(t)\cong RT\frac{\partial w}{\partial t}, \quad (5.1)$$

where R is the reflection coefficient, $w(t)$ is the seismic wavelet, and $\delta\ (t+T/2)$ and $\delta\ (t-T/2)$ represent spikes at the top and bottom of the thin layer of two-way traveltime thickness, T. Many readers may recognize equation 5.1 as the finite difference approximation to the first derivative. One well-known property of Fourier transforms is that if

$$w(t) \Leftrightarrow W(\omega) \quad (5.2)$$

denotes the Fourier transform pair, where ω is the temporal frequency, then

$$\frac{\partial w}{\partial t} \Leftrightarrow i\omega W(\omega). \quad (5.3)$$

From equation 5.1, we see that for thin beds, amplitude changes linearly with thickness T. In addition, the low frequencies are attenuated and the high frequencies are amplified (determined by the ω term in equation 5.3), whereas the phase is rotated by 90° (the i term in equation 5.3).

Below the tuning thickness, we do not expect to detect any significant changes in coherence using algorithms sensitive only to waveform (and not to amplitude), such as the crosscorrelation algorithm given by equation 3.4 and the eigenstructure algorithm given by equations 3.15 and 3.16. Because these particular coherence algorithms are insensitive to amplitude changes, they will not detect lateral changes that occur in lithology within a thin bed below the tuning thickness and that do not cause a polarity reversal, such as may occur in a sand-filled thin channel cutting through a shale matrix. In contrast, we do expect such subtle features to be detectable by attributes sensitive to lateral changes in amplitude. That motivates us to consider attributes that will be sensitive to such changes.

The Sobel Filter

The simplest amplitude-sensitive multitrace attribute is the Sobel filter, or spatial first-derivative operator, which on a seismic time slice would have the form

$$e=\left\{\left[\frac{\partial u(t)}{\partial x}\right]^2+\left[\frac{\partial u(t)}{\partial y}\right]^2\right\}^{1/2}=$$

$$\left\{\left[\frac{u(t,x+\Delta x,y)-u(t,x-\Delta x,y}{2\Delta x}\right]^2\right.$$

$$\left.+\left[\frac{u(t,x,y+\Delta y)-u(t,x,y-\Delta y)}{2\Delta y}\right]^2\right\}^{1/2}. \qquad (5.4)$$

Equation 5.4 is used routinely in photographic digital image processing.

By adding three steps, Luo et al. (1996) modified the Sobel filter to make it applicable to seismic data. First, they took the derivatives along a plane defined by reflector dip and azimuth. Second, they stacked those derivatives along a vertical analysis window to improve the signal-to-noise ratio. Third, they normalized the result by dividing the differences by the energy of the input traces, such that they measure relative changes in amplitude rather than absolute changes. Using the notation used in equations 3.1 and 3.3, in which the analysis trace is u_0, the next adjacent inline trace is u_1, and the next adjacent crossline trace is u_2, we obtain Luo et al.'s (1996) original edge-detection algorithm

$$e(t,\tau_x,\tau_y)=$$

$$\frac{\left(\sum_{k=-K}^{+K}\left\{[u_0(t+k\Delta t)-u_1(t+k\Delta t-\tau_x)]^2+[u_0(t+k\Delta t)-u_2(t+k\Delta t-\tau_y)]^2\right\}\right)^{1/2}}{\left(\sum_{k=-K}^{+K}\left\{2[u_0(t+k\Delta t)]^2+[u_1(t+k\Delta t-\tau_x)]^2+[u_2(t+k\Delta t-\tau_y)]^2\right\}\right)^{1/2}} \qquad (5.5)$$

where τ_x and τ_y are the delays associated with the reflector dip in the inline direction, x, and the crossline direction, y. As with the crosscorrelation algorithm discussed in Chapter 3, the edge computation given here by equation 5.5 is offset from the target trace in the analysis. In Figures 3a and b we display one of Luo et al.'s (1996) first published results using equation 5.5 and note that Figure 3b looks remarkably like the semblance-based and variance-based coherence algorithms.

Although we suspect that Chevron has improved on this algorithm, we have not seen any details in the published literature. However, we display the results of the present-day implementation as Figure 4. In Figure 4a, we show a dip-magnitude map generated from the water-bottom pick for a survey acquired over the western Niger Delta slope at water depths of about 1300–1500 m. The seafloor is ruptured by faulting related to gravity-driven extension and diapirism, and has mud diapirs and mud volcanoes (Adeogba et al., 2005). Two mud diapirs are seen. One is on the west central part of the image, which also has a concentration of mud volcanoes at its crest and a few more on its eastern flank. An eastern mud diapir is barely visible because most of it falls outside the study area.

Figure 4b is a horizon slice 250 ms below the water bottom through an attribute cube generated using a modern implementation of the Sobel filter defined by equation 5.5. In this image, we are able to observe fault patterns, channel forms, fan geometries, mud mounds, and gas-escape craters on diapirs, channel knickpoints, mudflows, slumps, bypass incisions, and large-scale scours. These features were not nearly as well defined on conventional displays such as inlines, crosslines, and time slices from the seismic volume.

Sensitivity of Variance and Semblance Measures to Amplitude Variability

Semblance and variance definitions of coherence depend on lateral amplitude changes, whereas the eigenstructure and crosscorrelation definitions of coherence do not. If

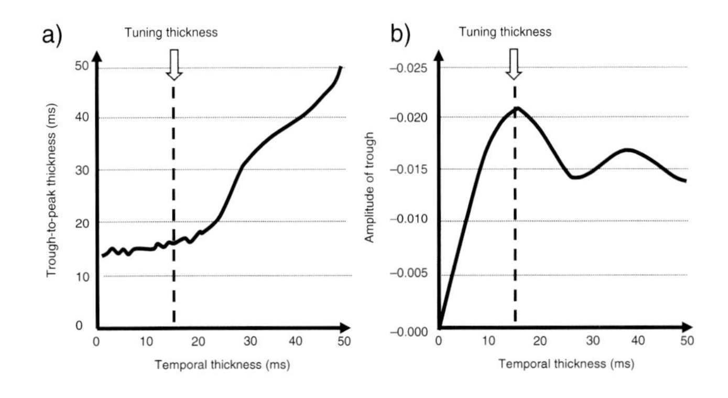

Figure 2. The sensitivity of (a) reflector trough-to-peak thickness and (b) the trough amplitude for the simple wedge model shown in Figure 1. Note the nearly linear variation of trough amplitude with thickness for small values of thickness (≤10 ms). After Partyka (2001); in turn after Widess (1973).

we substitute the classical definition of variance for the computational definition of variance given by equation 3.7 in Chapter 3, we obtain

$$c_v(t,p,q) = \frac{\sum_{k=-K}^{+K} \frac{1}{J} \sum_{j=1}^{J} \left[u_j(t+k\Delta t - px_j - qy_j) - \mu(t,p,q) \right]^2}{\sum_{k=-K}^{+K} \frac{1}{J} \sum_{j=1}^{J} \left[u_j(t+k\Delta t - px_j - qy_j) \right]^2}, \tag{5.6}$$

where $\mu(t,p,q)$ is the mean trace along the reflector dip and azimuth defined by the apparent dip pair, (p,q). Clearly, if each trace is identical along the reflector dip and azimuth, then each of those traces is also equal to their mean, such that the variance estimate of coherence, c_V, given by equation 5.6, is zero. In contrast, if the waveform of each trace is identical but the amplitude of that waveform for each trace varies (e.g., if one trace can be represented by a 30-Hz Ricker wavelet of peak amplitude 1.0 and an adjacent trace can be represented by a 30-Hz Ricker wavelet of peak amplitude 1.1), then the variance estimate of coherence is nonzero. Because by equation 3.10 we showed that the semblance and variance estimates of coherence are directly related to each other (with $c_S = 1 - c_V$), we could state that the semblance estimate of coherence also is sensitive to amplitude. In contrast, the crosscorrelation and eigenstructure estimates of coherence given by equations 3.4 and 3.15 are sensitive only to changes in waveform, not to changes in amplitude.

Hilbert Transform Estimates of Amplitude Variability

Implementation of the Sobel filter given by equation 5.4 uses only the adjacent traces and produces what we called a short-wavelength derivative estimate in Chapter 4. Our processed seismic data have been binned into a regular grid of inlines and crosslines separated by distances Δx and Δy. Clearly, we could have binned our data at some coarser or finer grid and applied the Sobel filter defined by equation 5.4. In Figure 5, we display four such possible difference operators, where the grid operator spacing corresponds to 25 m, 75 m, 125 m, and 175 m. Note that because we

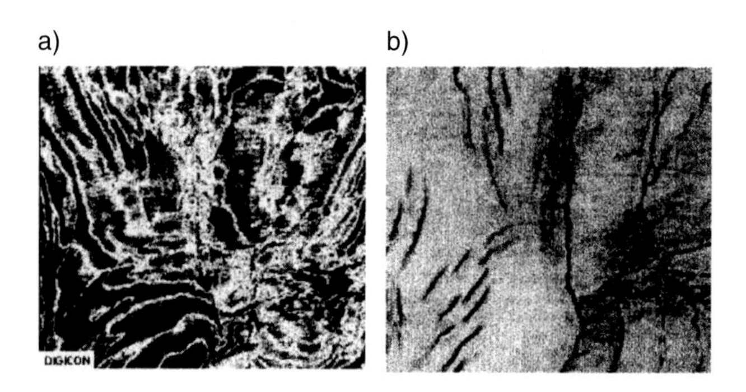

Figure 3. (a) A seismic time slice and (b) a corresponding edge-detection attribute obtained on the basis of the Sobel filter, using equation 5.5. Amplitude derivatives were calculated along reflector dip and azimuth. After Luo et al. (1996).

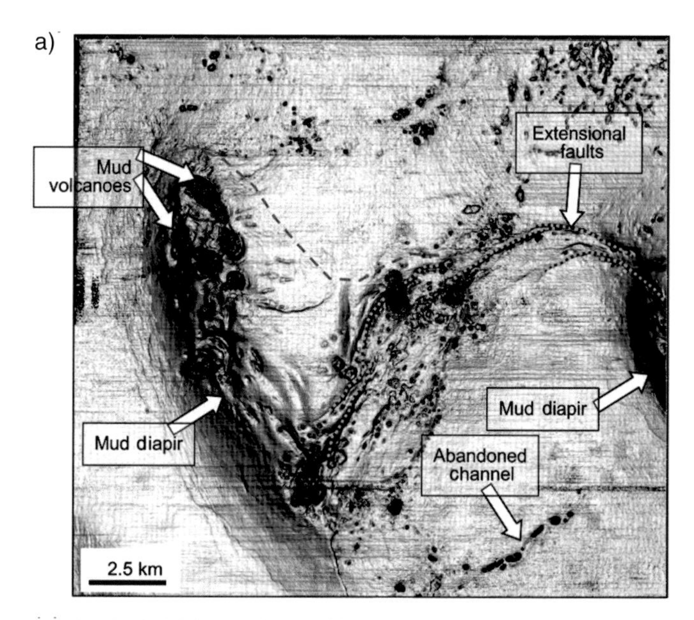

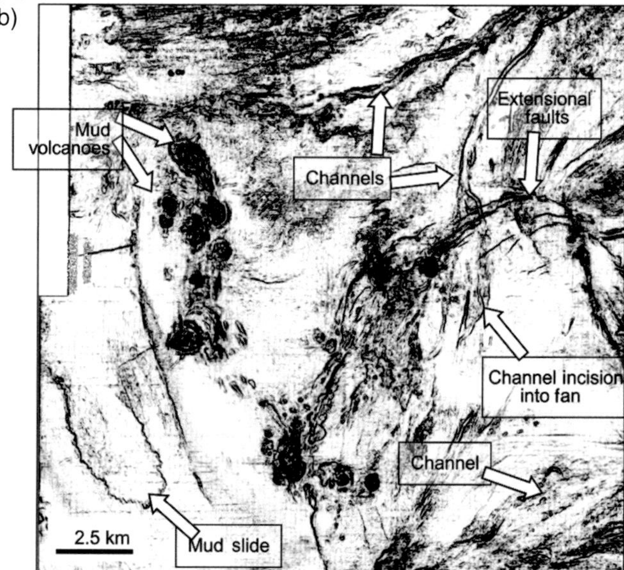

Figure 4. (a) A conventional dip-magnitude map generated from water-bottom picks. (b) A horizon slice, 250 ms below the water bottom through an edge cube generated using a variation of equation 5.2. After Adeogba et al. (2005). AAPG©2005. Reprinted by permission of the AAPG whose permission is required for further use.

divide by $m\Delta x$ in equation 5.4, the magnitude of the operator decreases in each image.

In Figure 6, we display graphically what such operators do. Many readers will recall fondly their pleasant days in calculus class, where a derivative was defined as the limit, as Δx approaches zero, of the chord (i.e., the secant) joining two points on a curve, which we plot in Figure 6a. As Δx becomes smaller and smaller, the slope of the chord more and more accurately represents the slope of the curve being analyzed. If the curve being analyzed has a wavelength that is much longer than any of the distances used in the difference operators, such as in the case displayed in Figure 6b, all of the derivative estimates will be identical. If our horizontal wavelengths are long and our data are noisy, we may consider stacking the results of all these derivative estimates to obtain a more robust estimate.

Mathematically, the derivative operator given by equation 5.6 is a linear operation, which means we obtain the same result if we stack the operator before applying it to the data or if we stack the results of each operator after ap-

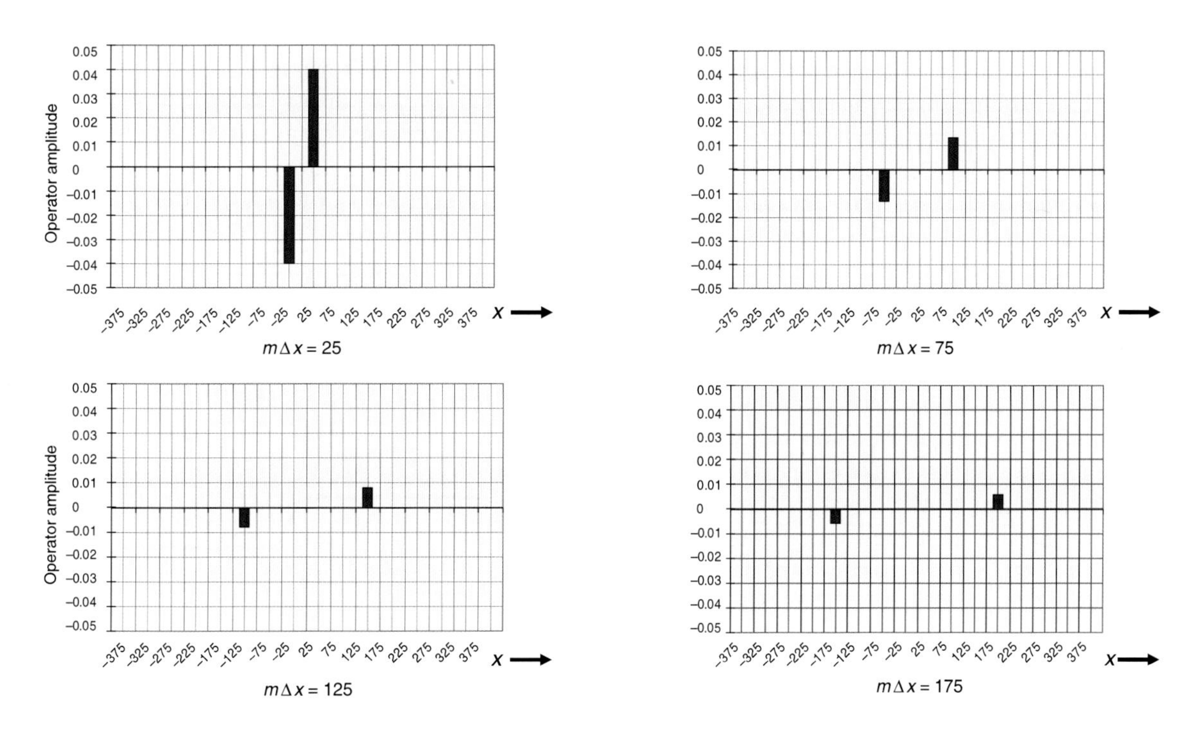

Figure 5. Alternative finite-difference approximations to the first derivative defined as $\frac{\partial u}{\partial x} \approx \frac{u(x + m\Delta x) - u(x - m\Delta x)}{2m\Delta x}$, where Δx is the seismic bin size and m is the number of bins away from the center analysis point.

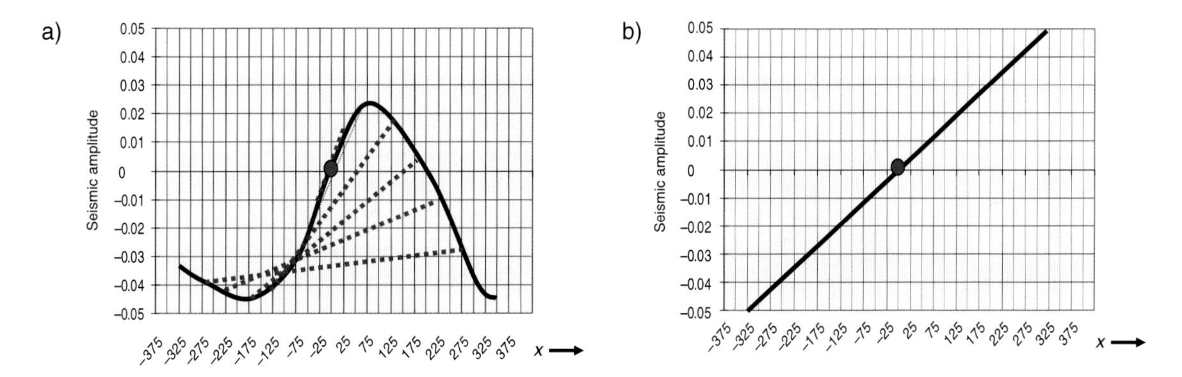

Figure 6. Graphical display of the approximations made to the first derivative (or slope) using the operators shown in Figure 5 for (a) an amplitude variation that has as moderate wavelength, on the order of 10 seismic bins, and (b) an amplitude variation that has a very long wavelength compared with the seismic bin size Δx. For very long wavelengths, each of the alternative finite-difference approximations provides the same estimate of the first derivative.

plying it to the data. Stacking the operator gives us

$$\frac{\partial u}{\partial x} = \sum_{m=1}^{M} \left[\frac{u(t, x+m\Delta x, y)}{m\Delta x} - \frac{u(t, x-m\Delta x, y)}{m\Delta x} \right], \quad (5.7)$$

which we display in Figure 7.

By now, the astute reader may recognize that we have built up a Hilbert transform operator from a suite of finite-difference operators. Unlike the Hilbert transform operator used in conventional complex-trace analysis, we wish to apply the operator in Figure 7 along the horizontal axis (across traces) rather than along the vertical axis (across samples).

Luo et al. (2003) recognized that many stratigraphic features do not have abrupt edges, but instead are represented by changes that have a finite wavelength, such as the amplitude variation over the idealized channel shown in Figure 8. The conventional Sobel filter produces a good image of the cutbank channel edge to the right of Figure 8b, but a poor image of the point bar channel edge to the left. In contrast to this, in Figure 8c we show how the Hilbert transform filter images both sides of the channel equally well, although the steep cutbank looks overly smeared. Application of the derivative operator given by equation 5.7 enhances the long-wavelength variation and diminishes the short-wavelength variations, as we observed in Figure 6. Luo et al. (2003) added an additional twist. Instead of adding each term equally, first they raised the absolute value of each term to the power r, summed the results, and then normalized by taking the rth root. The reader will recall these kinds of *r-norm* measurements when we discussed the Manhattan distance estimate of coherence in Chapter 3.

The result of this weighting is similar to the fractional derivatives presented in the discussion of curvature in Chapter 4 — the seismic interpreter can now view his or her lateral variation (of amplitude in this chapter, of vector dip in Chapter 4) in a manner that enhances short-wavelength, moderate-wavelength, or long-wavelength variation. Indeed, the Hilbert transform displayed in Figure 7 is

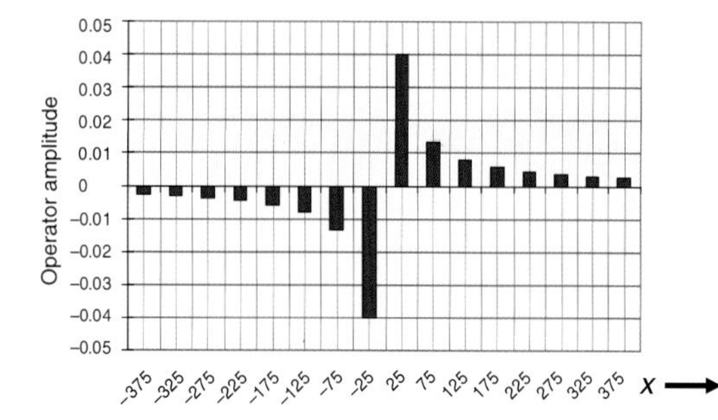

Figure 7. The Hilbert transform displayed as a linear combination of the difference operators displayed in Figure 5.

nearly identical to the very-long-wavelength ($\alpha = 0.01$) fractional-derivative operator plotted in yellow in Figure 14a of Chapter 4.

Luo et al. (2003) call this variation of the Sobel filter the generalized Hilbert transform, or GHT. For readers not enamored with the mathematical beauty of the Hilbert transform, we suggest simply interpreting this method as a suite of weighted-difference operators, each of which operates at a different length and thereby enhances edges that have different wavelengths. The result of Luo et al.'s (2003) weighting is to push the sensitivity of their generalized Hilbert transform to intermediate wavelengths, thereby providing a good balance between the cutbank and point-bar amplitude edges, as shown in Figure 8d.

In Figure 9c, we display the results of the generalized Hilbert transform applied to seismic data shown in Figure 9a. The channel images are superior to those obtained using the eigenstructure-coherence algorithm shown in Figure 9b. The differences result from three causes. First, the GHT edge-detector is a long-wavelength operator and is able to extract subtle, long-wavelength changes in amplitude gradients unseen within the smaller (typically five- to nine-trace) eigenstructure coherence-analysis window. Second,

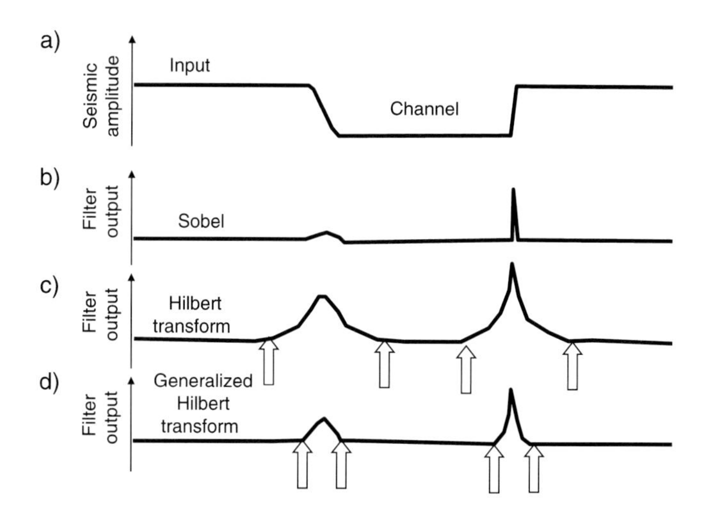

Figure 8. The sensitivity of alternative edge detectors to abrupt changes and togradational lateral changes in amplitude. (a) A cross section of a thin channel, with the inner bank on the left and the outer (or cut) bank on the right. Following Widess (1974), the amplitude response is linearly proportional to the channel thickness. (b) The response of a three-point Sobel (or first-derivative) filter. The steep cutbank shows up well, but the gradational inner bank shows up poorly. (c) The response of a 61-point Hilbert transform filter. Both sides of the channel are imaged equally well, but we feel that the steep cutbank is overly smeared. (d) The response of a 21-point generalized $r = 2$ Hilbert transform filter. Both sides of the channel are well imaged. After Luo et al. (2003).

larger operators use more traces and will do a better job of stacking out errors caused by the difficult near-surface conditions. Third, the eigenstructure- (and crosscorrelation-) coherence operators are insensitive to lateral changes in amplitude of a fixed waveform. If such channels are well below the tuning thickness, their waveform will not change (Figure 1) but their amplitude will. Ideally, calculations of lateral changes in reflectivity operate along the dip and azimuth of the seismic reflector at each point in the seismic volume. Usually, for small analysis windows containing five to 25 traces, we can approximate reflector dip by a local plane as described in Figure 1 of Chapter 2. However, for larger windows containing 100 or more traces (such as the generalized Hilbert transform shown in Figure 9c), this approximation may break down except in regions that do not have a high degree of structural deformation. In areas with structural deformation, before we apply long-wavelength amplitude edge detectors we recommend first flattening a volume about the zone of interest to remove most of the impact of regional curvature.

Energy-weighted Coherent-amplitude Gradients

Although the previous algorithms have measured amplitude variability of the total seismic data regardless of the waveform, an alternative approach is to measure amplitude variability of just the coherent component of the seismic data. We discussed eigenvalues and eigenvectors in Chapter 3 as part of our coherence estimate. We review that process now by redisplaying here, as Figure 10a-d, the graphic explanation of the eigenstructure calculation shown in Figure 17 of Chapter 3. In Figure 10d, we plot the amplitude of

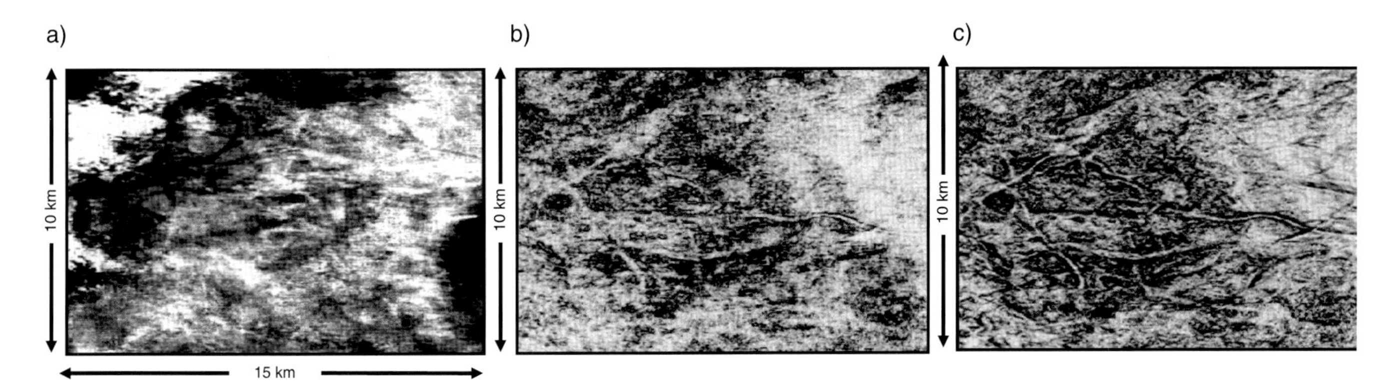

Figure 9. (a) A time slice through (a) a seismic data volume and (b) the corresponding eigenstructure coherence volume and (c) the amplitude-variability volume generated using the generalized $r = 2$ norm Hilbert transform from a survey on the Arabian Peninsula. Amplitude anomalies associated with channel fill and changes in thickness are clearly present but are somewhat diffuse and difficult to delineate on the seismic amplitude time slice shown in (a). The eigenstructure estimate of coherence in (b) is insensitive to these changes in amplitude. In contrast, the generalized Hilbert transform in (c) is a direct measure of amplitude variability and delineates the channels clearly. After Luo et al. (2003).

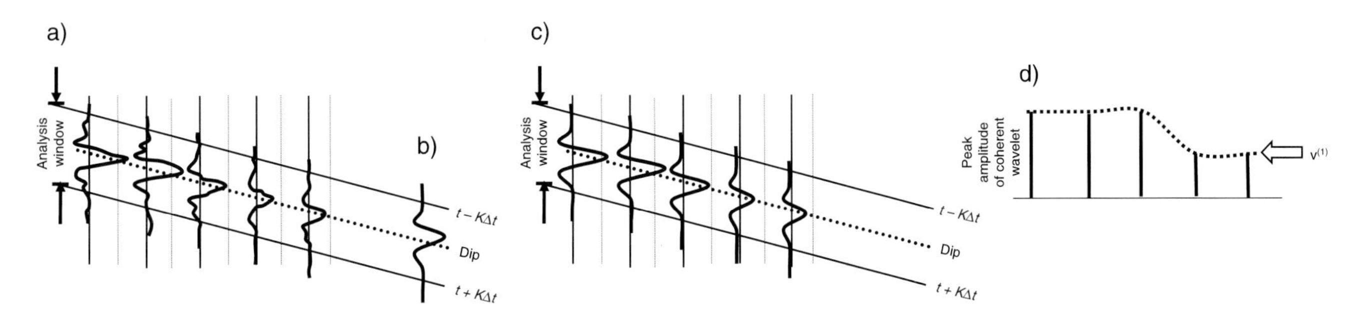

Figure 10. A schematic diagram summarizing the steps in the eigenstructure estimate of coherence shown earlier in Chapter 3, Figure 17. The steps are to (a) calculate the energy of the input traces within an analysis window, (b) calculate the seismic waveform that best approximates the waveform of each input trace, and (c) replace each trace with a scaled version of (b) that best fits the input trace. The amplitudes of the five wavelets in (c) define the components of the five-element-long principal-component eigenvector, $\mathbf{v}^{(1)}$. To calculate energy-weighted coherent-amplitude gradients, we take the derivative of the curve shown by the dotted line in (d) and weight it by the sum of the coherent energy within the analysis window shown in (c).

the coherent wavelet that fits each trace best within the analysis window. These five data points form the five elements of the principal-component (or first) eigenvector $\mathbf{v}^{(1)}$, given in Chapter 3 by equation 3.15. To analyze the lateral variation in these values, we fit a curve through them, as shown by the dotted line in Figure 10d.

This concept is readily generalized to 3D data. Here, we can think of the mathematical eigenvector, $\mathbf{v}^{(1)}$, as being a discretely sampled map, $v(x,y)$, that represents the lateral variation of the coherent energy within the analysis along the structural dip and azimuth of the reflector (Figure 11).

Two variants of the amplitude-gradient calculation exist. The simplest estimate is to take the derivative of the unit-length principal-component eigenvectors themselves, $\mathbf{v}^{(1)}$. We will call those derivatives *eigenvector gradients*. Unfortunately, such gradients are overly sensitive to noise in low-energy areas of the seismic volume.

We have found that a more useful estimate is to weight these derivatives by the principal-component eigenvalue, λ_1. First, for simplicity, we assume that each trace in the analysis window has the exact same waveform (but possibly different amplitudes), such as we see in Figure 10c. Given that waveform, we can express all the traces shown in Figure 10c with the single eigenvector shown in Figure 10d. Next, we recognize that each element of the diagonal of $\mathbf{C}$ given by equation 3.17 is a measure of energy based on the real and quadrature components of the seismic traces. It is a well-established mathematical fact that the sum of the diagonal elements of the covariance matrix $\mathbf{C}$ is equal

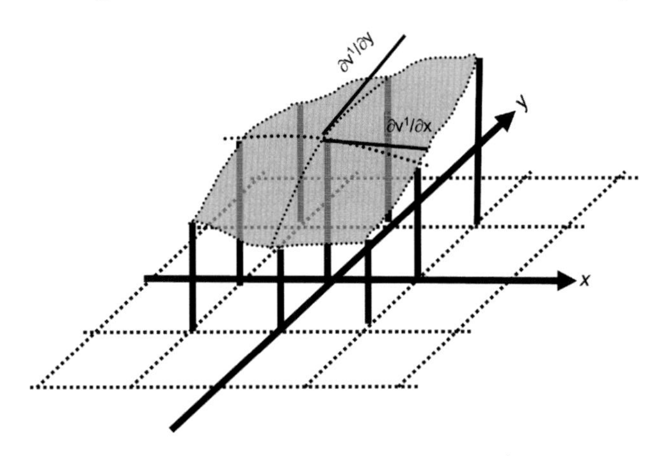

Figure 11. Interpretation of the eigenvector, $\mathbf{v}^1$, corresponding to a nine-trace analysis window, as the representation of a map of coherent amplitude, $v(x,y)$. From this map, we can calculate gradients, $\frac{\partial v}{\partial x}(x,y)$, and $\frac{\partial v}{\partial y}(x,y)$, which will indicate lateral changes in the coherent amplitude. These gradients are particularly useful in mapping lateral changes in layer thickness when the layer thickness is less than one-quarter-wavelength. For such thin layers, the amplitude variation is proportional to thickness and the waveform remains nearly constant. After Marfurt (2006).

to sum of the eigenvalues. Thus, if all of the energy is represented by just one eigenvalue-eigenvector pair, and if the eigenvector has been normalized to be of unit length, then λ_1 is equal to the energy of the traces in the analysis window. If the traces in the analysis window have different waveforms, the argument is somewhat more complicated and requires first that the data be decomposed into principal components (which we will do in Chapter 8) such that the condition of waveform similarity holds and reproduces the argument made earlier.

In summary, λ_1 is a measure of the energy within the analysis window, whereas $\mathbf{v}^1$ is a measure of the lateral variation of amplitude across the analysis window. Therefore, we will call the spatial derivatives of $\lambda_1\mathbf{v}^1$ energy-weighted coherent-amplitude gradients. The energy-weighted coherent-amplitude gradients are large when there is rapidly varying, high-amplitude coherent energy, and the gradients are small when the reflectivity is either smoothly varying, low energy, or incoherent. We have found the images from energy-weighted coherent-amplitude gradients to be quite complementary to coherence images and to provide needed detail in reservoirs represented by a strong, consistent waveform.

To minimize the impact of acquisition footprint (acquisition footprint will be discussed later in Chapter 8), Marfurt (2006) avoids using simple derivatives calculated along the x- and y-axes (the inline and crossline directions) by using a more general derivative operator of the form

$$\frac{\partial v}{\partial x}(x,y) \approx \frac{2}{J-1}\sum_{j=2}^{J}\frac{x_j}{2r_j^2}v_j, \tag{5.8a}$$

and

$$\frac{\partial v}{\partial y}(x,y) \approx \frac{2}{J-1}\sum_{j=2}^{J}\frac{y_j}{2r_j^2}v_j, \tag{5.8b}$$

where

$$r_j = (x_j^2 + y_j^2)^{1/2} \tag{5.8c}$$

and where x and y are measured from an origin at the analysis point in a centered J-trace analysis window. Note that the center trace ($j = 1$) is not included in the calculation. Inspection of equations 5.8a–c shows that they can be interpreted to be an unweighted average of x- and y-components of directional derivatives obtained by pairs of points straddling the analysis point in the analysis window.

Although gradients of coherent energy can be quite effective in mapping faults and fractures, we have found them to be most useful in delineating thin channels for which they emphasize subtle lateral changes in tuning. Stratigraphic features such as channels are examined best by using horizon slices that better represent a fixed point in geologic time. In Figure 12, we reexamine the Vinton Dome data volume shown previously in Chapter 2, Figures 8 and 9 and in Chapter 4, Figures 36 and 37. Here, we display extractions, along the Hackberry horizon, of amplitude, coherence, and the east-west and north-south components of the energy-weighted coherent-amplitude gradient. Because of the complex lateral variation in velocity and our use of prestack time instead of a more appropriate prestack depth migration, resolution of the coherence image is poor. However, we still are able to clearly delineate meandering channels that formed before and during salt diapirism. Identification of such channels in a structural setting can offer interesting exploration opportunities.

In Figure 13, we display horizon slices of east-west (Figure 13b) and north-south (Figure 13a) components of the energy-weighted coherent-amplitude gradient corresponding to the coherence slice shown in Chapter 3, Figure 33b. Overall, the two images express the same geology. However, subtle differences do occur, which we indicate with arrows in Figure 13. Yellow arrows indicate narrow channels, which we also interpret to be thin — well below the tuning thickness and thus having no lateral change in waveform. The two channels indicated by magenta arrows

a)

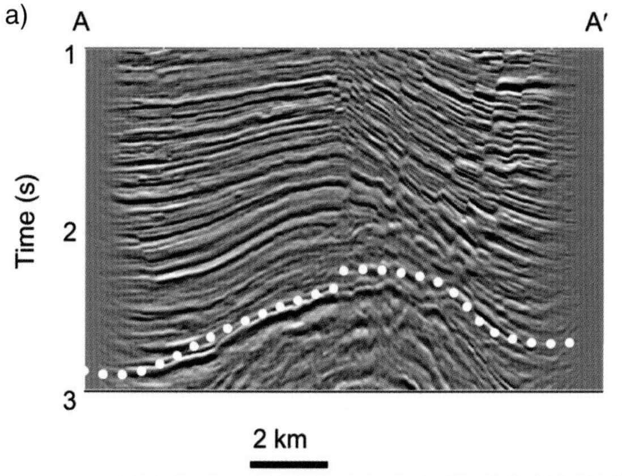

Figure 12. (a) A vertical slice through the seismic amplitude volume along line AA′. The dotted line indicates the Hackberry horizon. Horizon slices along the Hackberry horizon through (b) the seismic amplitude (c) the coherence, (d) the east-west energy-weighed coherent-amplitude gradient, and (e) the north-south energy-weighted coherent-amplitude gradient. Faults have a wormy appearance because the data have been migrated poorly, resulting in interfingering of reflectors. In contrast, the components of the energy-weighted amplitude gradient away from the faults give accurate images of channels (indicated by arrows) and other stratigraphic features, including areas where the coherence is very high (white). Seismic data courtesy of OPEX. After Marfurt (2006).

b)

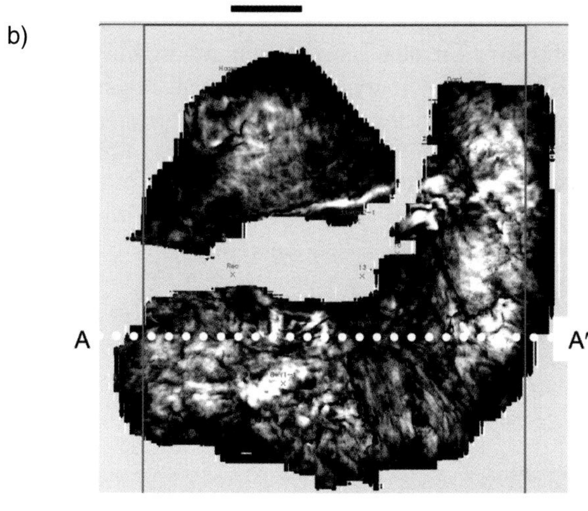

c)

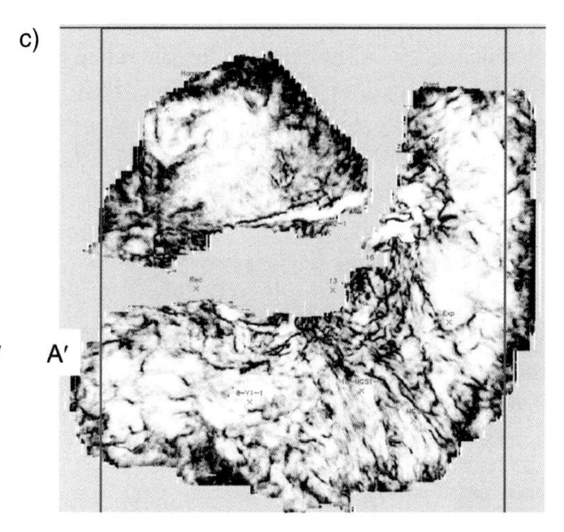

d)

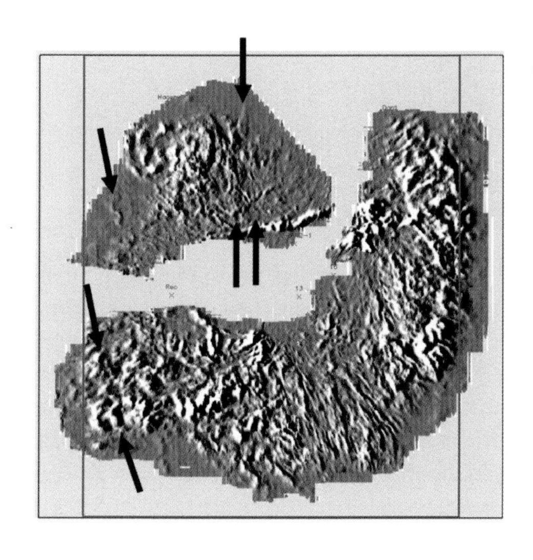

e)

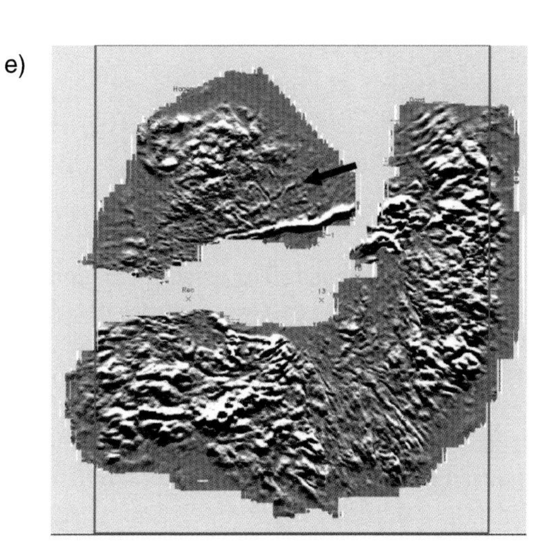

in Figure 13a are wider but have a much gentler lateral change in amplitude. Although our eye can see them easily in Figure 13a, the local nine-trace coherence algorithm used to compute Figure 33b in Chapter 3 cannot. Such slowly varying, long-wavelength changes in amplitude would be a good candidate for Luo et al.'s (2003) generalized Hilbert transform, which we discussed in the previous section.

In Figure 14, we show a similar comparison but in a carbonate terrain. Both the eigenstructure coherence and the energy-weighted coherent-amplitude gradients were computed using a nine-trace, ±10-ms-analysis window. The images are horizon slices of a chert reservoir through the respective attribute cubes of the Devonian Thirtyone Formation from the Central Basin Platform, Texas, U.S.A. The

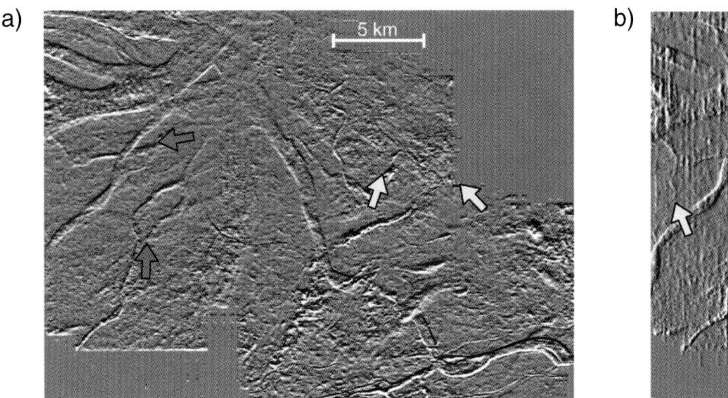

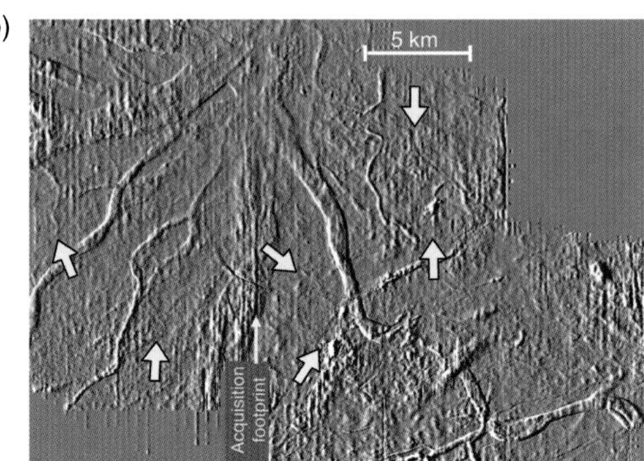

Figure 13. Horizon extractions corresponding to Chapter 3, Figure 33b: (a) north-south and (b) east-west components of the energy-weighted coherent-amplitude gradients described in Figure 11. The vertical analysis window was ± 32 ms. Yellow arrows indicate narrow channels not readily seen on the coherence images shown in Chapter 3, Figure 33b. Statistically, narrow channels also are thin. If they are thinner than the tuning thickness, they will be expressed only as a lateral change in amplitude, not in waveform. Magenta arrows indicate a wider channel that is not seen in the coherence horizon slice in Chapter 3, Figure 33b. We interpret these channels to have a longer-wavelength gradational change in amplitude such as that shown in Figure 8, so they are not well illuminated by our nine-point coherence algorithm. After Marfurt and Kirlin (2000).

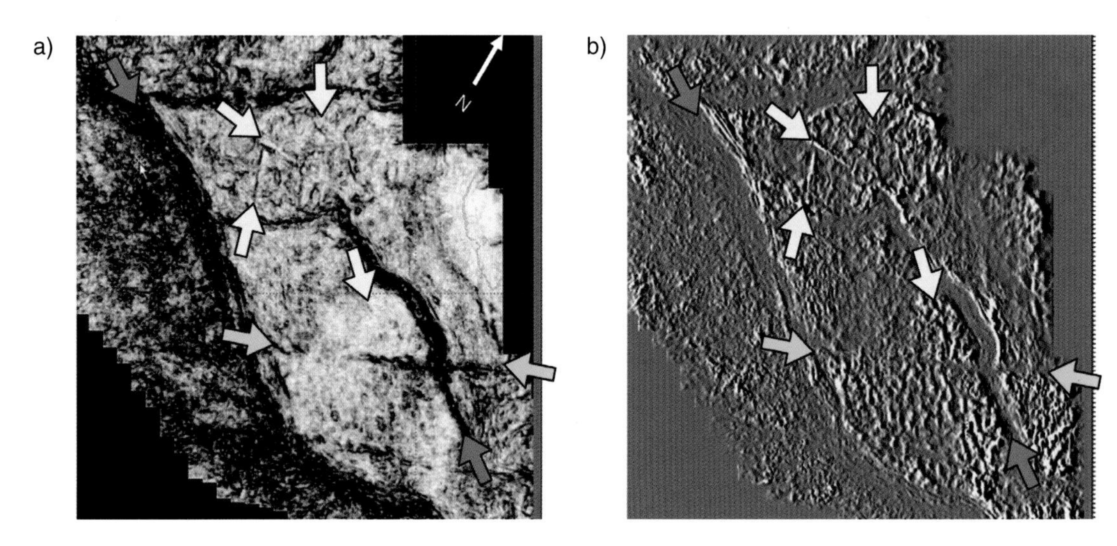

Figure 14. Horizon slice along the Devonian Thirtyone Formation from a survey in the Central Basin Platform, Texas, U.S.A., of (a) eigenstructure coherence, and (b) the east-west component of the energy-weighted coherent-amplitude gradient. Note that the reverse faults indicated by yellow arrows show up as low-coherence black zones in the coherence image. Because they are almost totally incoherent, they appear as blank gray zones in the energy-weighted coherent-amplitude gradient image. We can see channels in the northern third of both images. Although the southern one-third of the coherence image is relatively featureless, we still see channel-like features in the southern one-third of the amplitude gradient image. These channels cross an east-west fault indicated by green arrows on the horizon extraction, further suggesting that they are sedimentary features. After Blumentritt et al. (2003).

chert was deposited as turbidite flows of sponge spicules that grew on the platform to the north; these flows gave rise to a highly productive but highly compartmentalized reservoir. We can see hints of these channels on the coherence horizon extraction in the northern one-third of the image shown in Figure 14a, but there is little hint of the reservoir heterogeneity in the southern one-third of the image. The two magenta arrows indicate broad zones corresponding to major reverse faults cutting the survey area. Because the data in those zones is highly incoherent, they appear as black bands in Figure 14a.

In contrast to the amplitude-gradient work developed by Luo et al. (1996, 2003) and applied to the complete seismic volume, the east-west energy-weighted coherent-amplitude gradient shown in Figure 14b is applied only to the coherent component of the data. For that reason, the reverse faults indicated by magenta arrows appear as blank zones (pure gray on a black-gray-white single-gradational-color bar). In the northern one-third, we see the same channels on the amplitude gradient that we see on the coherence, but in slightly more detail. In the southern one-third, the energy-weighted coherent-amplitude gradient is superior to the coherence image and provides strong evidence of reservoir heterogeneity. The east-west gradient preferentially highlights north-south-trending features that we interpret to be turbidite deposits from the north. Indeed, these features are quite continuous across the east-west fault indicated by the green arrows, which has several hundred milliseconds of throw. The continuity of the north-south-trending features suggests that they are stratigraphic rather than structural.

We see a similar algorithmic behavior in Figure 15, which exhibits channels of approximately Pennsylvanian age seen on a time slice from a survey acquired in the Midcontinent area (Oklahoma) of the U.S.A. Again, the images resemble each other, but we can trace the path of the channels considerably farther using the energy-weighted coherent-amplitude gradients.

In Figure 16, we display time slices at (a) 0.800, (b) 1.000, (c) 1.200, (d) 1.400, (e) 1.600, and (f) 1.800 s. These images correspond to the dip and azimuth images shown in Figure 20 of Chapter 2, the coherence image in Figure 35 of Chapter 3, and the most-negative-curvature and most-positive-curvature images from Figures 38 and 39 of Chapter 4. To facilitate the comparison of these images in Figure 16, we have retained the arrows from Figure 20 of Chapter 2. A significant acquisition footprint in the shallow time slices creates the subtle crosshatching appearance that is especially evident in the upper, right-hand portion of the cross section. This acquisition footprint arises from the varying fold and azimuth distribution in the CMP bins. The edges of the slump features in the southern part of the survey are indicated by the yellow arrows in Figures 16a–d, but we conclude that the coherence images shown in Figure 35 of Chapter 3 provide better resolution. Once again, however, the energy-weighted coherent-amplitude gradients show better delineation of channels, which are indicated by the red arrows in Figure 16d. Note that the channels are only partially resolved by the coherence. Also, because no differential compaction overlies these channels, they are not resolved at all by the curvature images in Figures 38 and 39 of Chapter 4. Finally, the north-south-trending channel indicated by the magenta arrow in Figure 16d appears to be structurally controlled.

The time slice images at 1.600 and 1.800 s are somewhat less clear to interpret. First, at this level, we know from Figures 38 and 39 of Chapter 4 that we have consider-

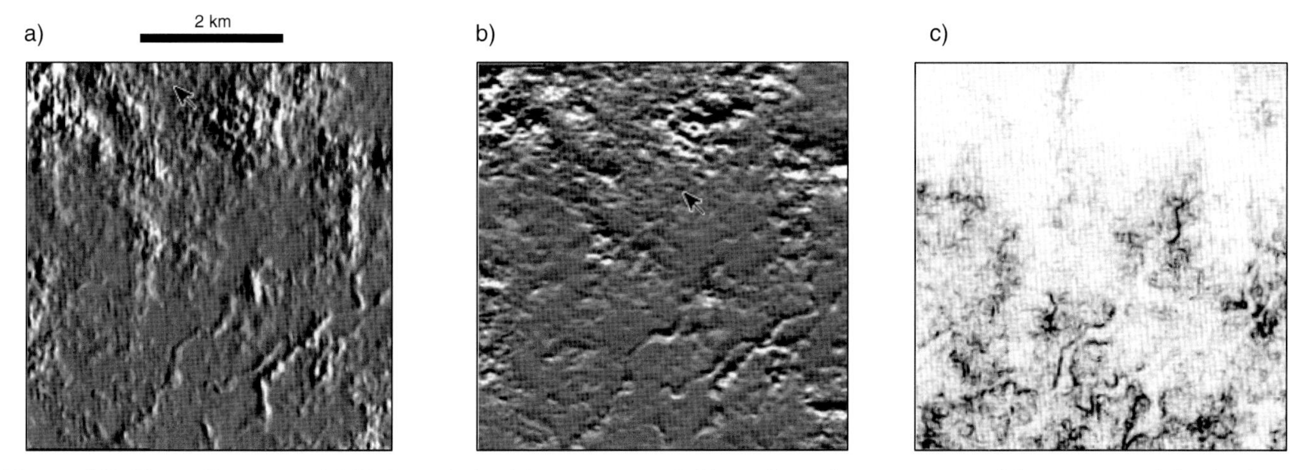

Figure 15. Time slices at $t = 0.832$ through the (a) east-west and (b) north-south components of the energy-weighted coherent-amplitude gradients, and (c) a coherence time slice through a survey at approximately Pennsylvanian level from the midcontinent, U.S.A. Although the channels can be seen on the coherence time slice, they can be traced farther using the amplitude gradient images.

able folding, so we do not expect to see clearly defined stratigraphic features on a time slice. In Figures 16e and 16f, we do see lineaments that follow the crests of the folds seen in Figure 39 of Chapter 4 and that we interpret to be changes in amplitude that result either from deposition on paleotopography or from differential compaction. The red and blue arrows in Figures 16d–f indicate strong fold axes seen in the dip and azimuth, coherence, and curvature images. These fold axes do not appear on the energy-weighted coherent-amplitude gradient images, which implies that any thinning or thickening about these axes is insignificant.

Second Derivatives of Amplitude: Amplitude Curvature

If we think of structural curvature, which we discussed in Chapter 4, as being lateral second derivatives of the time-structure (or phase) component of seismic data, it seems reasonable to expect information also to be contained in the lateral second derivative of the amplitude behavior of seismic data. In Figure 17a, we provide an idealized cross section across a lateral change in amplitude. In Figure 17b, we calculate the first derivative in x of the amplitude shown in

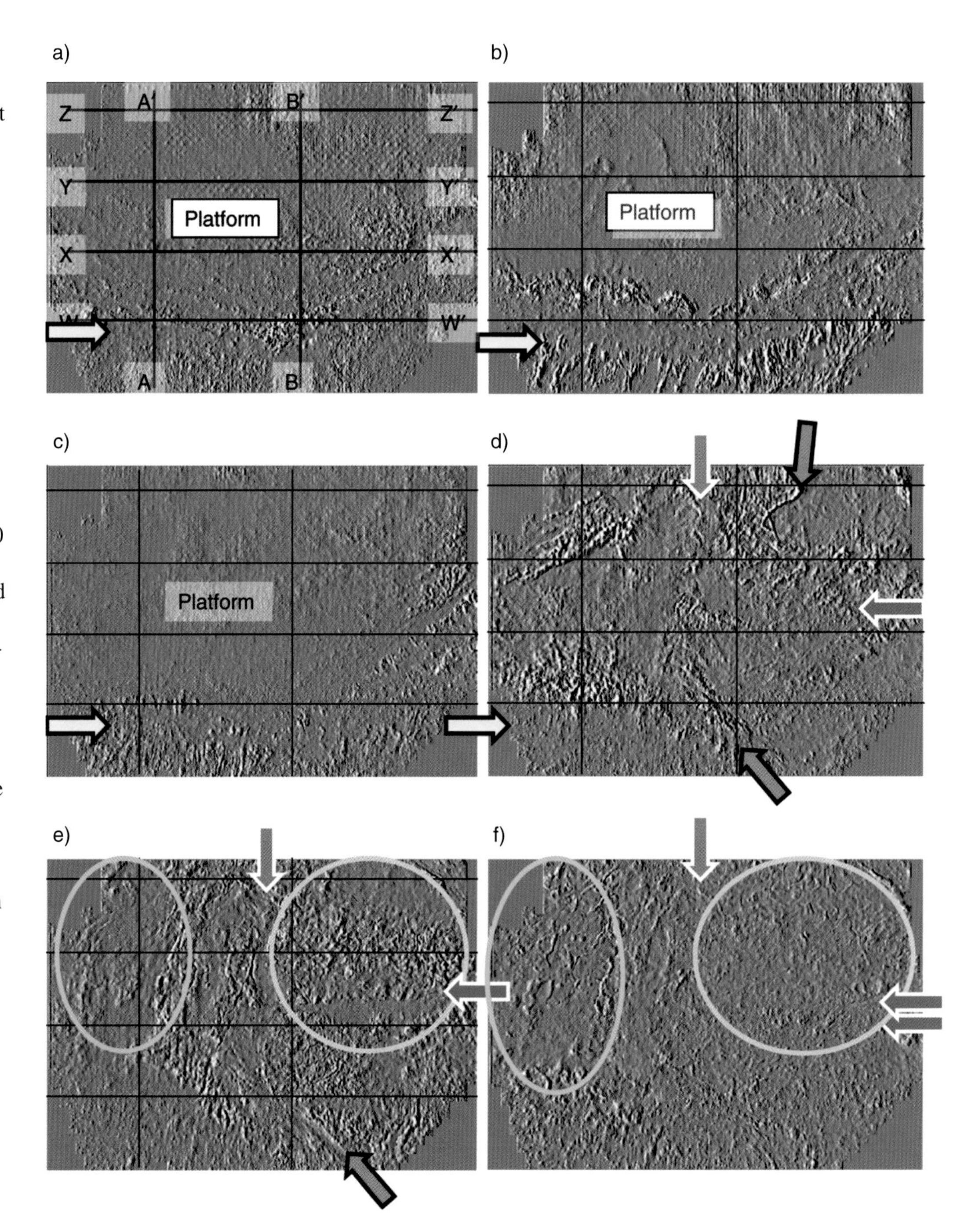

Figure 16. Time slices through the east-west component of the coherent energy-weighted amplitude gradient at (a) 0.800, (b) 1.000, (c) 1.200, (d) 1.400, (e) 1.600, and (f) 1.800 s corresponding to images shown in earlier in Chapter 2, Figure 20, Chapter 3, Figure 35, and Chapter 4, Figures 38 and 39. We have retained the same arrows shown in Chapter 2, Figure 20 to aid in the comparison. Here, we indicate channels at t = 1.400 and 1.600 s with red arrows. The structural feature indicated by the magenta arrows appears to control a north-south-trending channel. We also note strong lineaments within the circles on the 1.600 and 1.800 s images. These features are deeper than our well control and are more ambiguous to interpret. We interpret them to be changes in amplitude that result from deposition on paleotopography or from differential compaction.

Figure 17a. In Figure 17c, we display the amplitude's second derivative in x. In three dimensions, we fit a quadratic surface to the amplitudes and calculate the curvature measures discussed in Chapter 4. Computationally, all the equations presented in Chapter 4 that were applied to the inline and crossline components of reflector dip and azimuth also can be applied to the inline and crossline components of the energy-weighted coherent-amplitude gradients (or to other directional measures of amplitude variability).

As was the case with structural curvature, we have found that long-wavelength estimates of amplitude curvature provide additional information. Figure 18 is a time-thickness map of the area between the top and base of a carbonate reef, generated from a survey acquired in southeastern Saskatchewan. The figure includes a representative vertical seismic slice through the reef. We note that there are considerable lateral changes in amplitude that result from changes in thickness and (possibly) changes in lithology, such as dolomitization. Amplitude is weakest where the reef is thickest.

In Figure 19a, we display the amplitude extraction along the top of the picked reef from Figure 18. The weakest amplitudes are light blue. In Figures 19b and 19c, we display the most-negative and most-positive amplitude curvatures. The most-negative-curvature anomalies in dark green track primarily what we identified as low-amplitude (light blue) anomalies in Figure 19a. In contrast, the most-positive curvature in Figure 19c tracks the edges of the reef. Quantitative analysis of such second-derivative maps awaits calibration with geostatistics. For now, we recognize such images as another means of measuring subtle changes in seismic character.

Pattern Recognition of Seismic Data: Texture Mapping

Interpretation of seismic data for the ultimate objective of finding hydrocarbons has always been driven by pattern recognition. Interpretation of seismic wiggles and wavelets is done in terms of their patterns, which yield information about subsurface geology. Recognition of the patterns of amplitude on a horizon extraction, for example, has been used for a long time, but it is not enough. The human mind is highly skilled at recognizing patterns — ask any parent looking for their child in a crowd. Imitating this skill with computers requires two steps: (1) extracting distinguishing features in our seismic data and (2) assigning subvolumes of seismic data to classes or clusters. Step two is the subject of human interpretation and ongoing developments in geostatistics and neural networks, neither of which will be addressed in this book. The first step falls cleanly into the domain of attributes. A good attribute or texture should be robust and insensitive to local distortions. In this section, we address three types of pattern recognition used in seismic interpretation: waveform classification, seismic geomorphology, and texture mapping. We touch only briefly on the first two.

A photographic or computer image consists of a spatial arrangement of colors and their intensities. The repeating pattern of local variations (in the small neighborhood considered) in image intensity is called *texture*. It is a feature used to partition images into regions of interest and to classify those regions. So in that sense, texture is an important defining characteristic of an image.

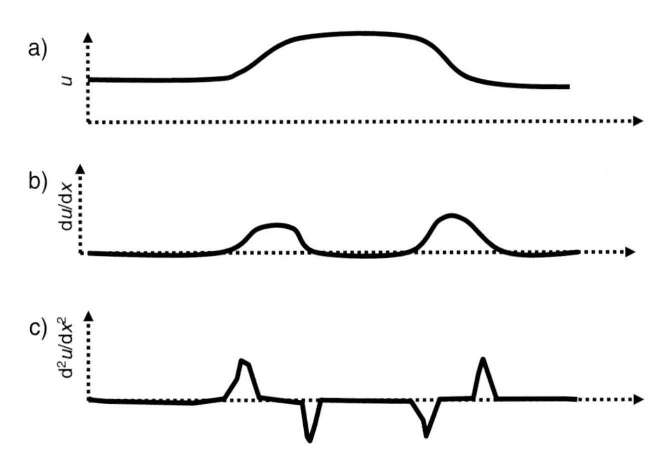

Figure 17. A schematic diagram of (a) an amplitude anomaly, (b) its first spatial derivative, and (c) its second spatial derivative. The extrema of (c) demarcate the limits of the anomaly.

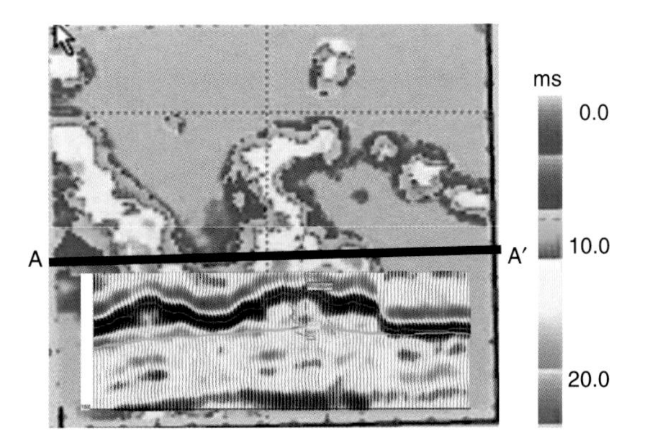

Figure 18. A time thickness map and a vertical slice through a Winnepegosas reef from southeastern Saskatchewan, Canada. The thickness is calculated between the blue pick (top) and the green pick (base). Note that here, the maximum amplitude corresponds to the thinnest part of the reef complex. Data courtesy of Talisman.

Textures consist of texture *primitives,* or *elements*, which sometimes also are referred to as *texels*. Textures usually are described as fine-grained, coarse-grained, smooth, and the like. These features can be found in the *tone* and *structure* of a texture. Whereas tone refers to the pixel intensity properties in the texel, structure represents the spatial relationship among texels. Thus, if texels are small but tonal differences between them are large, we talk of a fine texture. Likewise, if texels are large and consist of several pixels, a coarse texture results.

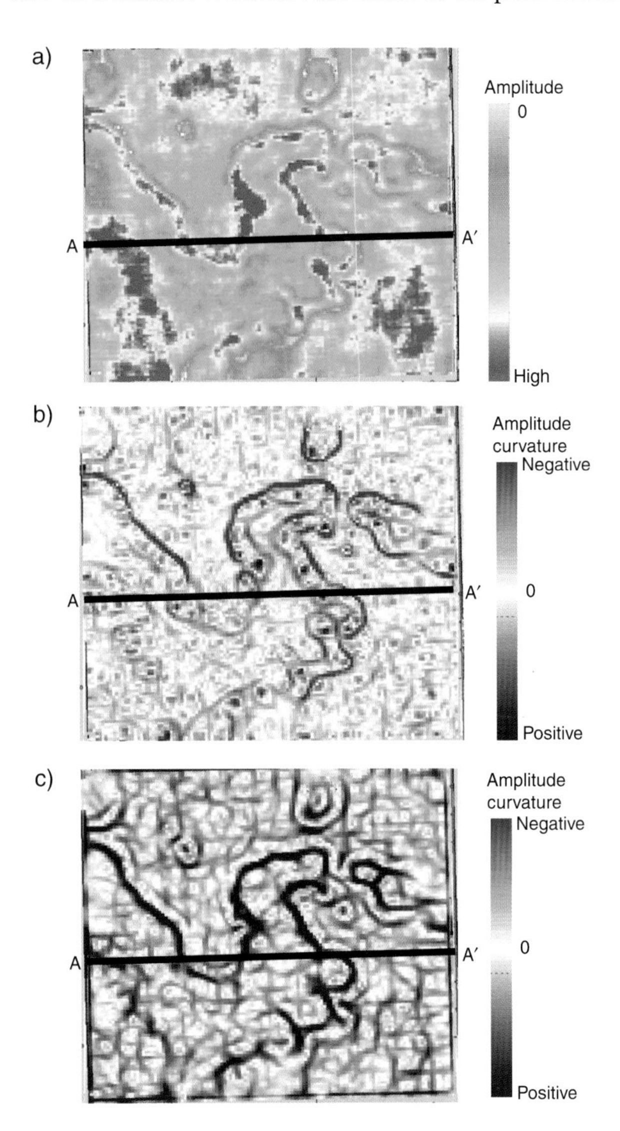

Figure 19. (a) Amplitude, (b) long-wavelength most-negative-amplitude curvature, and (c) long-wavelength most-positive-amplitude curvature, along the top of the reef (blue pick) shown in Figure 18. Here, the strong negative values of the most-negative-curvature, seen as dark green, track the low-amplitude light-blue trends in the amplitude horizon slice. In contrast, the strong positive values of the most-positive-curvature, seen as dark red, track the high-amplitude red trends in the amplitude horizon slice. These latter anomalies delineate the edges of the reef. The rectilinear features seen in both (b) and (c) are the result of acquisition footprint. Two hundred traces were used in the curvature calculations. Data courtesy of Talisman.

An example of natural textures is rock texture. Rock textures usually are nonhomogeneous and strongly directional. In addition, the grain size and color of the texture can vary significantly in some rock texture types, so their analysis and classification can be difficult.

Visual textures contain variations of intensities, which form certain repeated patterns. These patterns may be caused by physical-surface properties such as roughness or reflectance differences. Because of their stochastic nature, rock textures can be characterized into different orders of statistics. First-order probability distribution of the amplitude of the quantized image can be used to extract the statistical distribution. These statistics are easy to compute and include the mean, standard deviation, skewness, and kurtosis.

Instead of distinguishing the variation in intensity, it is possible to distinguish features via their shape or their structural characteristics. These help us in extracting features that in turn help describe textural properties of classes. Co-occurrence matrices have been used quite successfully in many pattern-recognition applications, including remote sensing. Three measurements are used commonly for analyzing textures: spectral, structural, and statistical measures.

Spectral measures of texture

Light reflected from a rock surface forms part of the visible spectrum. Thus, characterization of the rock essentially becomes characterization of its reflected light. Achromatic light has only one attribute — its intensity. The scalar measure of reflectance is gray-level. All colors can be seen as variable combinations of the three primary colors: red (R), green (G), and blue (B). Although these colors and their combinations are used in measurement of the visible spectrum, another scheme, called the HLS model, is implemented to extract spectral information from the textural image. In this model, hue (H) describes a pure color, and saturation (S) gives a measure of the degree to which the pure color is diluted by white light. Lightness (L) is decoupled from the color information of the image.

Structural measures of texture

Brick-wall-type regular textures are composed of similar patterns that are repeated structurally. By defining texture primitives, whereby each primitive is described by a tonal value, we can use two displacement vectors, along which primitives are formed, to determine the spatial distribution of those primitives in a neighborhood. For example, we may assume a texture primitive to be a parallelogram and the primitives to be arranged along the periodicity angles of the parallelogram.

Statistical measures of texture

Textures can be regular, or they can be random but with consistent properties. Thus, a logical way to describe such textures is through their statistical properties.

Co-occurrence matrices are calculated locally within a small window that glides across the image. The choice of window size is a judicious one: The window should be small enough that the low-pass-filtering effects from masking remain tolerable, yet large enough that the extracted information exhibits statistical significance.

A co-occurrence matrix (COM) is a square matrix whose elements correspond to the relative frequency of occurrence of pairs of gray levels of pixels that are separated by a certain distance and lie in a given direction. The immediate neighbors of any pixel can lie on one of four possible directions: 0°, 45°, 90°, and 135°. The COM is constructed for observing pairs of gray-level values at distance d from each other in the direction considered. Thus, four matrices can be derived for each distance, with P representing a COM: $P(0,d)$, $P(45,d)$, $P(90,d)$, and $P(135,d)$. Thus, the spatial relationship is derived in terms of distance d and angle θ.

Let us consider an image that has the elements shown in Figure 20. We will refer to this image as a test image. This test image has four gray levels (1, 2, 3, and 4). If we fix the spatial relationship (or the position operator) as the element to the right, then the gray-level co-occurrence matrix (GLCM) becomes

$$\mathbf{GLCM} = \begin{bmatrix} 2 & 2 & 1 & 0 \\ 0 & 2 & 0 & 0 \\ 0 & 0 & 3 & 1 \\ 0 & 0 & 0 & 1 \end{bmatrix}. \quad (5.9)$$

The element in the first row, second column of the matrix given in equation 5.9 indicates how many times in Figure 20 the number 2 occurs to the right of number 1. This happens exactly two times, so GLCM(1,2) = 2. Similarly, the number of times that the value 4 occurs to the right of value 4 is only one time, so GLCM(4,4) = 1. There are no occurrences of 4 appearing to the right of 1, so CGLM(1,4) = 0.

The matrix in equation 5.9 is not symmetrical (e.g., the value of the cell 1,2 is not the same as the value of 2,1). This matrix can be made symmetrical by counting each pixel pair twice — that is, once to the right and once to the left.

An alternative and easier way to make the matrix symmetrical is to add the matrix to its transpose (interchanging the rows and columns of the original matrix). The transpose of the GLCM matrix given by equation 5.9 is

$$\mathbf{GLCM}^{\mathrm{T}} = \begin{bmatrix} 2 & 0 & 0 & 0 \\ 2 & 2 & 0 & 0 \\ 1 & 0 & 3 & 0 \\ 0 & 0 & 1 & 1 \end{bmatrix}. \quad (5.10)$$

Thus, adding the transpose to its GLCM gives the symmetrical matrix

$$\mathbf{GLCM}_{\mathbf{Sym}} = \begin{bmatrix} 4 & 2 & 1 & 0 \\ 2 & 4 & 0 & 0 \\ 1 & 0 & 6 & 1 \\ 0 & 0 & 1 & 2 \end{bmatrix}. \quad (5.11)$$

In general, as Figure 21 shows, we will use four different axes, each of which will generate its own COM for an intersample distance, d, that is equal to 1.

The four matrices in Figure 21b can be combined into an averaged co-occurrence matrix because no directional variations in texture are expected.

$$\mathbf{GLCM}_{\mathbf{Sum}} = \begin{bmatrix} 16 & 4 & 6 & 0 \\ 4 & 12 & 5 & 0 \\ 6 & 5 & 12 & 6 \\ 0 & 0 & 6 & 2 \end{bmatrix}. \quad (5.12)$$

The next step is to scale the GLCM such that it looks like a probability table. It is an approximation, because a true probability would need continuous values, whereas the gray

1	1	2	2
1	1	2	2
1	3	3	3
3	3	4	4

Figure 20. A test image that will be used to form a co-occurrence matrix, taking into account the relationship between the different co-occurrence pairs and the distance between the adjacent elements. This schematic shows a 4 × 4 window of seismic amplitudes that have been scaled to fall within four bins. A value of 1 indicates the lowest (typically negative) amplitude, whereas a value of 4 indicates the highest amplitude. Typically, scaling units will be a fraction of the rms amplitude of the seismic data volume.

levels are integer values and so are discrete. This process is referred to as normalizing the matrix and consists of dividing the elements by the sum of values. Thus, the co-occurrence matrix represents the joint probability occurrence of gray levels i and j for two pixels with a defined spatial relationship in an image. That normalization results in

$$\mathbf{P} = \begin{bmatrix} 0.19 & 0.05 & 0.07 & 0.00 \\ 0.05 & 0.14 & 0.06 & 0.00 \\ 0.07 & 0.06 & 0.14 & 0.07 \\ 0.00 & 0.00 & 0.07 & 0.02 \end{bmatrix}. \quad (5.13)$$

where we now use the symbol P to denote that our GCLM is an estimate of probability. Each element of equation 5.13 represents the probability of going from gray level i to gray level j, when the intersample spacing is d and the direction is θ.

In practice, instead of computing a simple average, usually we perform a weighted average — that is, each value in the matrix is multiplied by a factor (weight) before summing and dividing by the number of values. This allows us to account for the relative importance of each value.

GLCMs for seismic data

The GLCM has dimensions $n \times n$, where n is the number of gray levels. For application to seismic data, the gray levels refer to the dynamic range of the data. For example, 8-bit data will have 256 gray levels. A GLCM computed for those data would have 256 rows and 256 columns (or 65 536 elements). Similarly, 16-bit data would have a matrix of size 65 536 × 65 536 = 429 496 720 elements, which could be overwhelming even for a computer (Haralick et al., 1973; Reed and Hussong, 1989; Gao, 2003). Usually, the seismic data are rescaled to be 4-bit data (resulting in a 16 × 16 matrix) or five-bit data (resulting in a 32 × 32 matrix). In practice, this does not result in any significant differences in the computed properties.

The structure of GLCMs as applied to seismic data can be understood easily. Figure 22b shows the region segments 1, 2, and 3 selected for GLCM computation, and the computed GLCMs are shown to the right. For strong continuous reflections, the GLCM exhibits a tight distribution along the diagonal. The matrix size chosen is 32 and the parameters chosen are 4, 3, and 1, respectively, in the x, y, and z directions. Window 2 has lower amplitudes as well as incoherent reflections, so the GLCM shows a scatter about the diagonal. Discontinuous or incoherent reflections have more occurrences farther away from the diagonal (window 3).

For a matrix size 16, we see a smaller number of elements in the GLCM (Figure 22a), whereas for a matrix size 64, there is a higher population of points (Figure 22c).

Although GLCMs give us all this information, they are not suitable for direct interpretation by a human being. Haralick et al. (1973) demonstrated the derivation of 14 different measures of textural features from the input GLCMs. Each of those features represents specific image properties, such as coarseness, contrast, or textural complexity. The four such measures used most commonly are energy, entropy, contrast, and homogeneity.

Energy

Energy is a measure of textural uniformity of an image. Mathematically, it is given as

$$\sum_i \sum_i P_{i,j}^2 \quad (5.14)$$

where P_{ij} denotes the ith row and the jth column of the GCLM matrix $\mathbf{P}$, such as the one in equation 5.13. Energy is low when all elements in the GLCM are equal, and it is useful for highlighting geometry and continuity.

Entropy

Entropy is a measure of disorder or complexity of the image.

$$\text{Entropy} = \sum_i \sum_i P_{i,j} \log P_{i,j}. \quad (5.15)$$

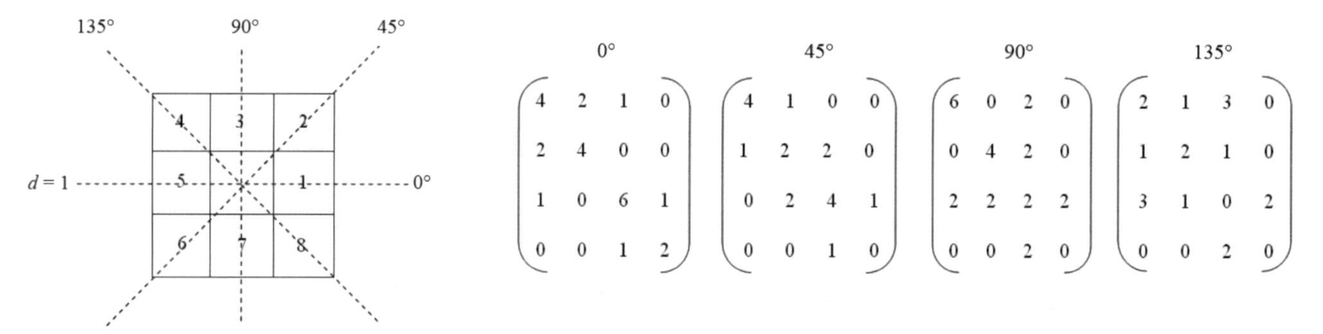

Figure 21. Computation of a gray-level co-occurrence matrix (GLCM) by comparing each element shown in Figure 20 with its eight neighbors. In this manner, we will compute preliminary GLCM matrices at 0°, 45°, 90°, and 135° from the vertical. The final GLCM matrix will be an average of these four preliminary GLCM matrices.

Entropy is large for images that are not uniform texturally. In such a case, many GLCM elements have low values. Entropy measures the organization of pixels. It is large when the values of GLCM are uniform, which is possible in the case of an equiprobable scenario.

Contrast

Contrast is a measure of the image's contrast or of the amount of local variation present in an image.

$$\text{Contrast} = \sum_i \sum_i (i-j)^2 P_{i,j} \quad (5.16)$$

Contrast, or inertia, is high for contrasted pixels, and its homogeneity (defined below) is low. When used together, both inertia and homogeneity provide discriminating information.

Homogeneity

Homogeneity is a measure of the overall smoothness of an image.

$$\text{Homogeneity} = \sum_i \sum_i \frac{1}{1+(i-j)^2} P_{i,j} \quad (5.17)$$

Homogeneity achieves its maximum value when most of the occurrences in the GLCM are concentrated near the main diagonal. Highly contrasting pixels result in low-homogeneity values, so homogeneity is inversely proportional to contrast. Homogeneity is useful for quantifying reflection continuity.

For 3D seismic volumes, computing GLCM texture attributes at one location yields the localized features at that point. If we repeat the computation of those attributes in a sequential manner throughout the volume, we transform the input seismic volume into at least four texture attributes, which we discuss below. For seismic data with significant dips, it is advisable to dip-steer a GLCM calculation using techniques discussed in Chapter 2. West et al. (2002) adopted a gradient-based dip-steering method, wherein the horizontal (dx) and vertical (dy) gradients of pixel values are computed in two orthogonal directions and then used to estimate the true dip and azimuth for dip and directional

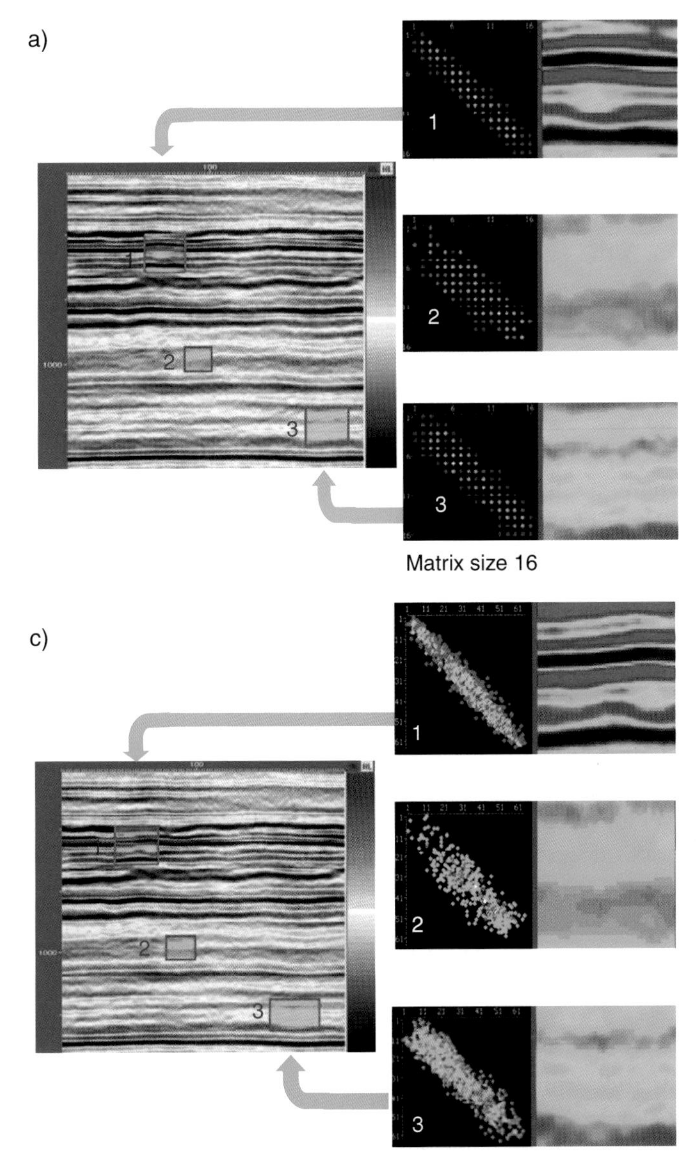

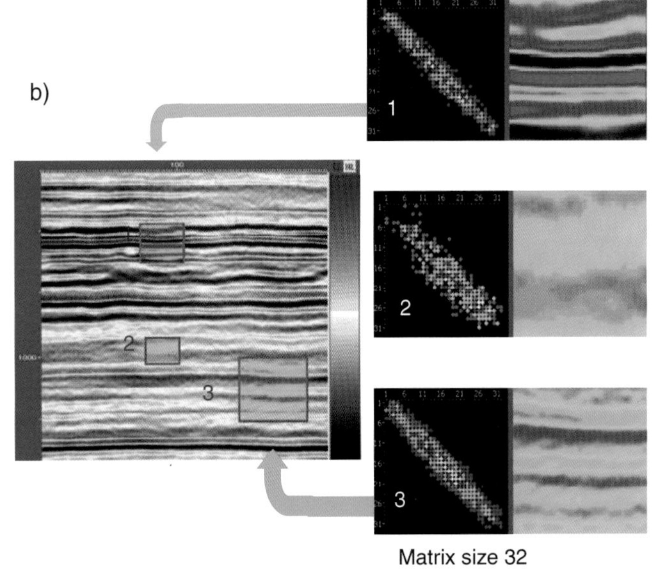

Figure 22. (a) Computation of GLCMs for different reflection characteristics selected by polygons marked 1, 2, and 3. The size of the matrix used for computation is (a) 16 × 16 (b) 32 × 32. and (c) 64 × 64. Notice that with a matrix size of 16, fewer elements are seen populating the GLCM, compared with the 32-element GLCM. The highest density of elements occurs with a 64-element GLCM.

steering of the GLCM calculations. This method is the basis for the gradient structure tensor estimate of dip and azimuth, also discussed in Chapter 2.

High-amplitude continuous reflections, which generally are associated with marine shale deposits, have relatively low energy, high contrast, and low entropy (Gao, 2003). Low-amplitude discontinuous reflections, which generally are associated with massive sand or turbidite deposits, have high energy, low contrast, and high homogeneity. Low-frequency high-amplitude anomalies, which generally indicate hydrocarbon accumulation, generally exhibit high energy, low contrast, and low entropy, relative to nonhydrocarbon sediments.

Case study 1

Our first case study focuses on a 3D surface-seismic survey in southern Alberta, Canada. The target zone was Lower Cretaceous glauconitic fluvial deposits that have been productive in the area. The 3D seismic survey was acquired to create a stratigraphic model that would be consistent with the available well control and would match the production history. Our ultimate goal was to locate the remaining undeveloped potential in the known fluvial deposits and to find additional drilling targets in untested fluvial sandstones and in the area in general. The model we developed was based on a comprehensive geophysical and geological interpretation wherein the geological data were integrated closely into the geophysical model. That integration was required because the Lower Cretaceous system in the study area has exhibited a very complex fluvial environment through time. That complex environment makes single single-discipline interpretations very difficult in terms of new drilling locations, compared with those that could be decided on the basis of the present analysis.

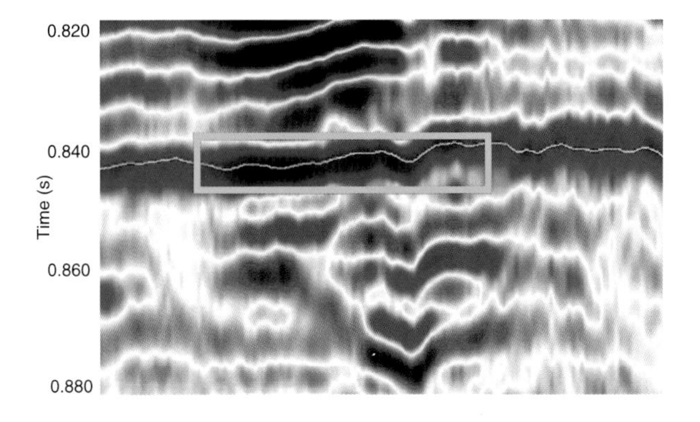

Figure 23. A segment of a seismic section showing Lower Cretaceous glauconitic fluvial deposits, seen tracked in the highlighted zone.

Because our objective was stratigraphic, we processed the seismic data to preserve relative amplitudes. Prestack time migration improves our ability to resolve stratigraphic objectives and extract high-quality seismic attributes, so we ran it on the data. That migration improved the stack image in terms of frequency and lateral definition of features by better energy focusing and improved image positioning prior to stack (Reilly, 2002). Figure 23 is a segment of the seismic section showing the level of production from the glauconitic sandstone.

Stratal volumes allow seismic interpreters to study objects in a 3D perspective, which in turn sheds light on those objects' origin and spatial relationships. Stratal cubes are subvolumes of seismic data (or their attributes) bounded by two horizons that may or may not be parallel. Figure 24a is a stratal volume display from the original seismic data, here covering the zone of interest at the level of the reservoir (just below the horizon shown in Figure 23). Figure 24b shows a stratal slice through a coherence volume, processed using a semblance algorithm. Although a better definition of some of the subsurface features can be interpreted here versus in the migrated stack, this display does not yield much information about the areal extent of the productive sands.

Texture-attribute analysis was run on the subvolume covering the broad zone of interest, and Figure 24c-f depicts the energy, entropy, homogeneity, and contrast-attributes, respectively. Figure 24c shows high values of energy associated with the fluvial deposits, and the areal distribution is depicted as we would expect it to be. However, this inference needs corroboration from the other texture attributes. We see that corroboration in Figure 24d-e. The high energy in Figure 24c is associated with low entropy and high homogeneity. Another observation is interesting here. Well W3 (to the northeast of W2) has a different pressure and apparently does not share the same producing formation with well W2. The low coherence (Figure 24b) indicates an islandlike feature surrounding well W3, and the texture attributes confirm that observation.

Although it is possible to interpret the productive sands on gamma-ray logs for wells W1 and W2 (which have values lower than approximately 50 API units), the texture-attribute displays provide a more intuitive presentation of the geology and show the areal spread of these productive sands. Figure 25 shows the 3D view of the stratal cube extracted from the energy attribute.

Case study 2

Case study 2 is from south-central Alberta, Canada. This 3D survey was acquired to explore the possibility of deciding on reservoir pockets that could be drilled. The field has been producing for about a year. Of the seven

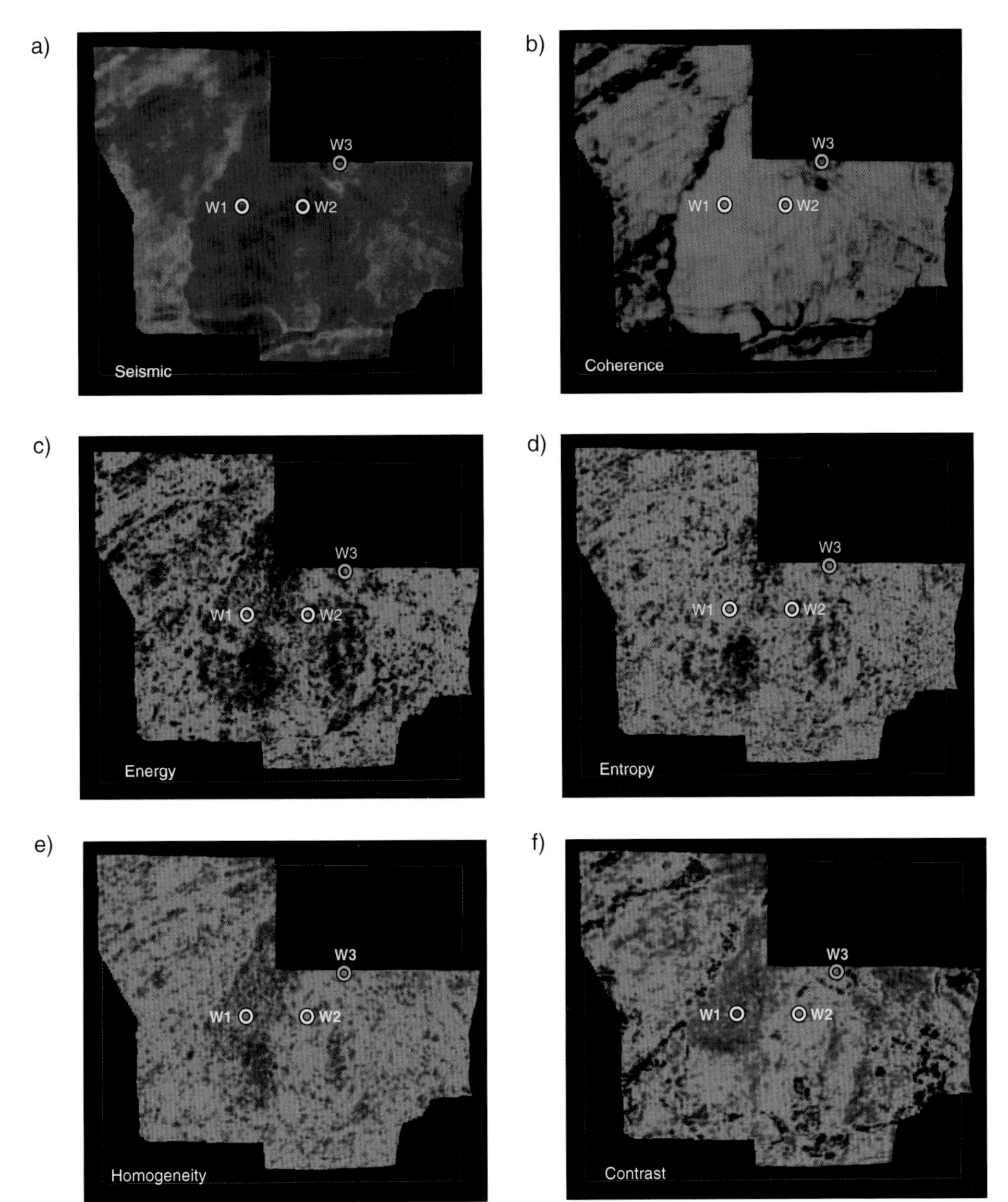

Figure 24. Stratal slices through (a) a seismic amplitude volume and (b) a corresponding coherence volume at the level of a producing sandstone. The seismic amplitudes indicate the sandstone distribution. The coherence slice indicates the channel edges clearly, and there are indications of channel sands in the top left section. However, no indication on the images corresponds to the productive sands. (c)-(f) Stratal slices are shown from (c) energy, (d) entropy, (e) homogeneity, and (f) contrast attributes at the same zone of interest. The energy attribute indicates high values that are interpreted to be associated with the same productive sands seen in wells W1 and W2. Corresponding to these high values of energy, low values of entropy and high values of homogeneity are seen, which we would expect of fluvial deposits. The low-contrast feature seen around well W3 indicates a separate block that is confirmed by a different observed pressure in this well.

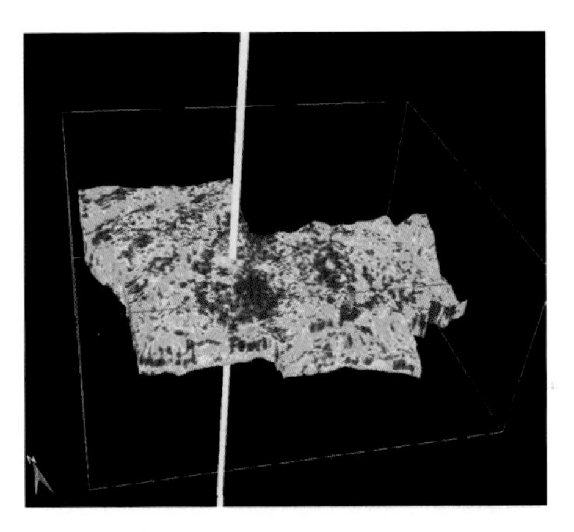

Figure 25. A 3D view of the stratal cube extracted from the energy attribute in Figure 24c. The top surface indicates high values of energy that are interpreted to be associated with productive sandstone deposits at this level.

wells in the area (Figures 26 and 27), four are oil wells, two are gas wells, and one is abandoned. The 3D seismic amplitudes were expected to indicate signatures that consistently characterized the two subsurface gas formations, whereas the oil formations could not be detected solely on the basis of amplitudes. Also, the pressure data in the wells indicated that wells Gas-1 and Oil-1 should drain different pools. The seismic data in their native form do not help in this diagnosis (Figure 26a).

The coherence display in Figure 26b indicates several discontinuities at the reservoir level of interest, thereby showing that the reservoir's producing formations do not form a uniform blanket, although no distinct faults or channel edges are obvious.

The texture attributes (Figure 27) indicate areas that calibrate nicely for the gas wells. The gas-bearing formations indicate high energy, low entropy, and high homogeneity. All four oil-bearing formations show moderate values of energy and homogeneity, and low entropy.

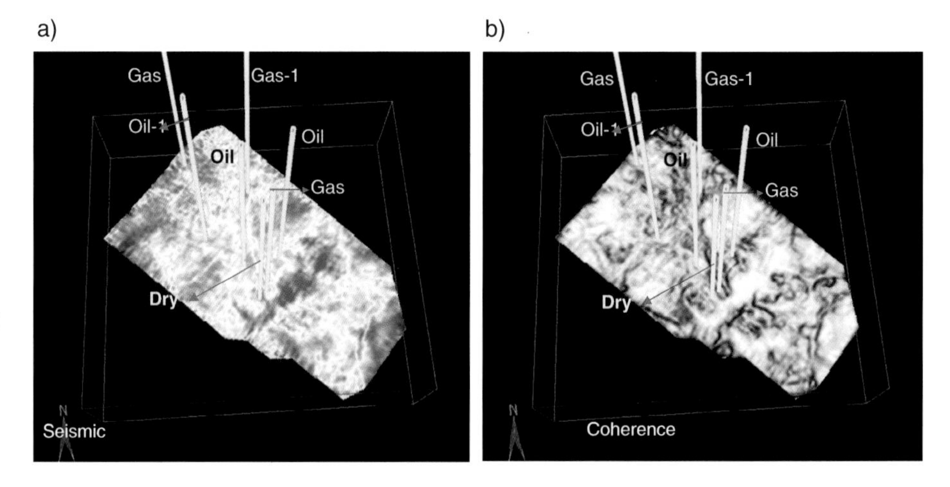

Figure 26. A stratal slice at the reservoir level from (a) the seismic amplitude volume and (b) the corresponding coherence volume shown in Figures 24a and 24b. The stratal slice does not show signatures that would characterize the two gas formations or the four oil-bearing formations. The coherence stratal slice shows discontinuities at this level, indicating a fragmented formation and explaining the different production pressures observed in Gas-1 and Oil-1 wells.

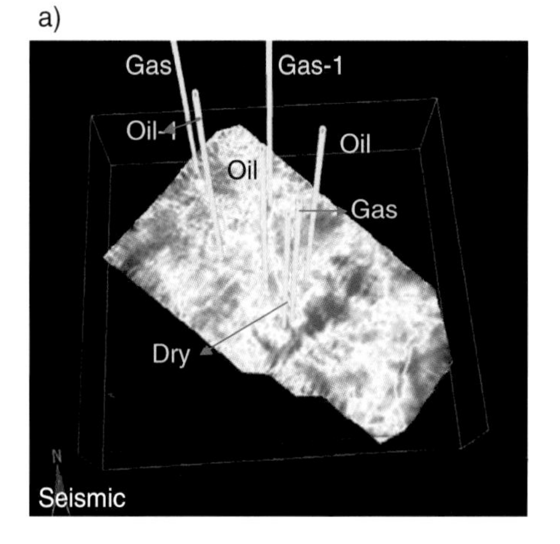

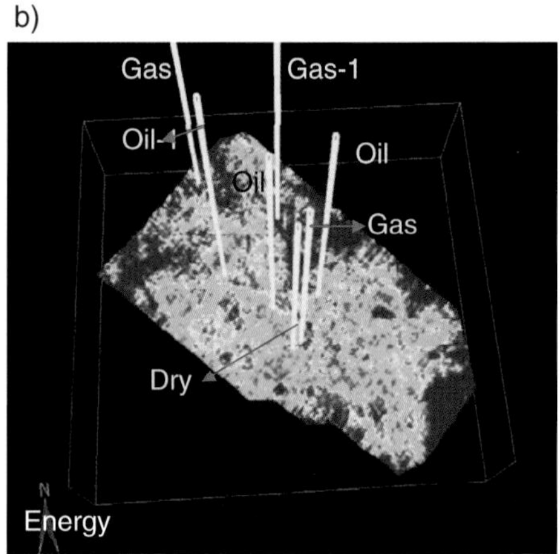

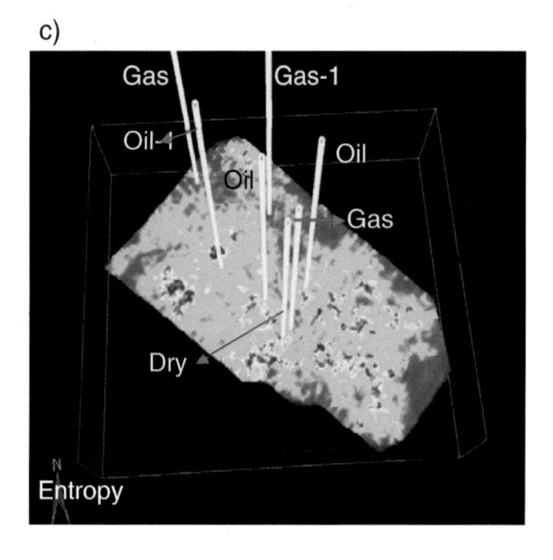

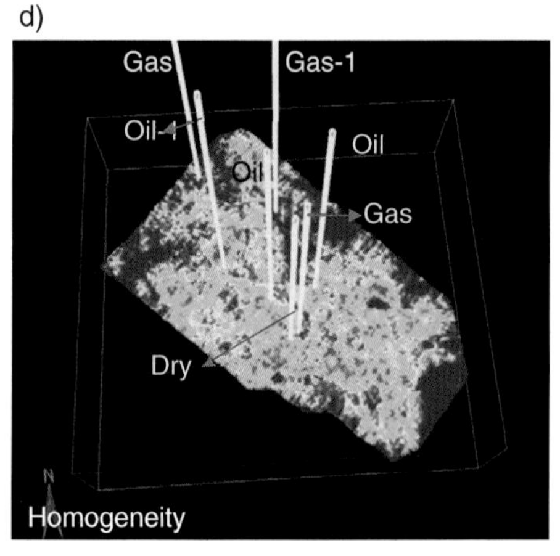

Figure 27. A stratal slice from (a) seismic, (b) energy, (c) entropy, and (d) homogeneity attributes. Notice that the two gas wells penetrate high-energy pockets, the four oil wells penetrate moderate-energy pockets, and the dry well penetrates low-energy pockets. High- to moderate-energy pockets are associated with low entropy and high homogeneity, as we would expect for fluvial deposits.

Other examples

Figure 28 shows a salt canopy detected from a seed in a texture energy cube. The texture energy of salt is significantly higher than that in surrounding areas, so the whole salt body can be detected, isolated, and mapped effectively by propagating the seed within the salt. Because amplitude samples within the salt body are similar to and connected with those in the surrounding areas, seed-based propagation may cause bleeding across the salt boundary and is not effective for automatic salt detection.

Figure 29 shows (a) an original amplitude section and (b) a texture energy section. An energy cube with opacity applied (Figure 29c) isolates the high-energy feature (red) along a channel system by rendering transparent the low-homogeneity features. It is difficult to isolate the same feature using the original amplitude volume because the amplitude is limited in discriminating channels from other geologic features.

Figure 30 compares the horizon slices of amplitude and energy at the same stratigraphic level. Notice that the channel and levee deposits can be recognized, mapped, and detected more effectively from the energy volume than from the amplitude volume.

Seismic facies application of texture attributes

Seismic facies can be defined as stratigraphic units or regions with characteristic reflection patterns that are distinguishable from those of other areas on the basis of reflection amplitudes, continuity, geometry and/or internal configuration of reflectors bounded by stratigraphic horizons (Mitchum, 1977). Attempts to analyze seismic facies usually involve two steps. First, seismic facies patterns are defined in terms of their lateral and vertical extents. Second, those defined seismic facies are interpreted in terms of their lateral and vertical associations and their calibration with wells, all of which give insight into the geological and depositional settings. This step is significant because the relationship between seismic data, seismic facies, and depositional environment is not unique.

Conventionally, an interpreter delineates seismic facies between mapped horizons. This entails examining the dominant seismic facies on vertical sections through the seismic volume and posting that information on a map. Usually, a 2D map is produced that generalizes the distribution of seismic facies vertically within a mapped interval. Besides being laborious, it may be difficult to map different seismic facies consistently in large and complex areas, especially if multiple mapping units are involved.

West et al. (2002) have demonstrated a probabilistic neural-network approach to mapping seismic facies quantitatively in 3D surface seismic data. In West et al.'s approach, interactive training of neural networks begins with definition of analysis parameters such as calculation volume, window size, analysis distance, and the like. The interpreter selects polygons on key seismic lines extracted out of 3D seismic volumes that exhibit different seismic facies. The computer then computes the associated GLCMs, and in this way several examples of each class of facies are specified. After the training procedure, several quality controls are run. The result of this exercise is a seismic facies classification volume in which each trace and sample has a seismic facies classification.

Figure 31 shows the definition of training polygons on a seismic section. The interpreter has selected the polygons on the basis of their reflection character. The classification scheme used is ASC (amplitude semicontinuous), HAC (high-amplitude continuous), LAC (low-amplitude continuous), LASC (low-amplitude semicontinuous), MASC (moderate-amplitude semicontinuous), MAC (moderate-amplitude continuous), and HASC (high-amplitude semicontinuous). The result of the textural analysis is a seismic classification volume, which is examined and calibrated with the available well and core information. Figure 32b is an example from a

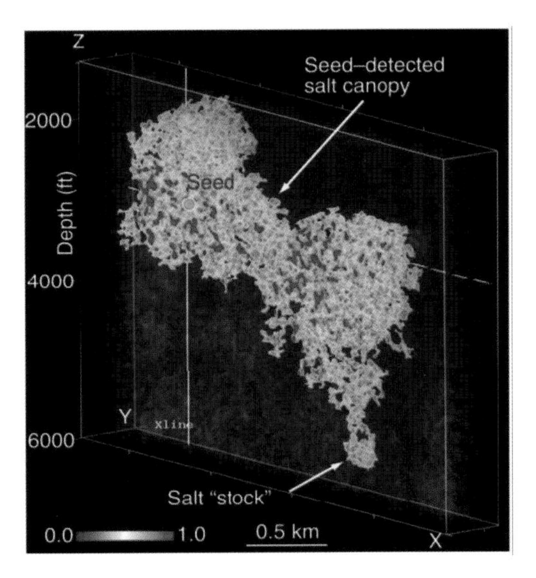

Figure 28. A salt canopy detected by using a seed in a texture energy volume. The energy values corresponding to the salt are higher than the surrounding areas, and the salt body can be detected more effectively from the energy volume than by using a seismic volume. Use of a seismic volume would result in bleeding across the boundaries and would prevent a crisper definition of the salt canopy. After Gao (2003).

channelized deepwater reservoir, where a slice from the seismic facies classification volume is seen being compared with an equivalent slice from the coherence volume (Figure 32a). The coherence slice (Figure 32a) highlights the lateral edges of the channel (red lines), a broad, older sinuous element (1), and a narrower, younger sinuous element (2). The seismic facies slice (Figure 32b) shows that sinuous element (1) is composed of HAC to MASC seismic facies, whereas sinuous element 2 is composed primarily of HAC seismic facies. An interesting fact is that because the textural analysis seismic facies classification yields a volume, this type of analysis can be applied at different stratigraphic levels in an interval of interest, regardless of whether those intervals are bounded by mapped horizons. Calibration of different features with the well data results in an interpretation map of the environment of deposition (Figure 32c).

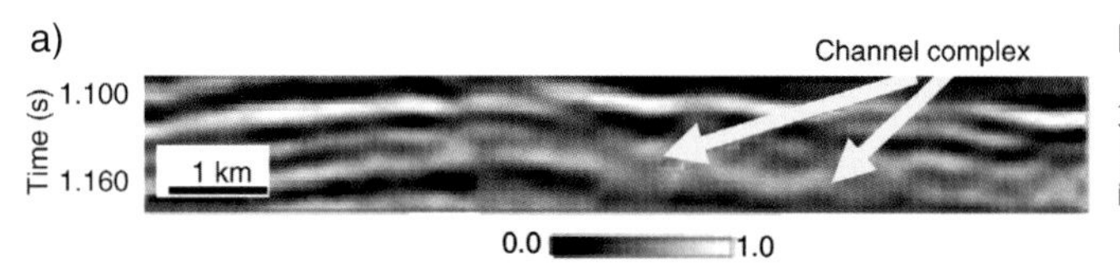

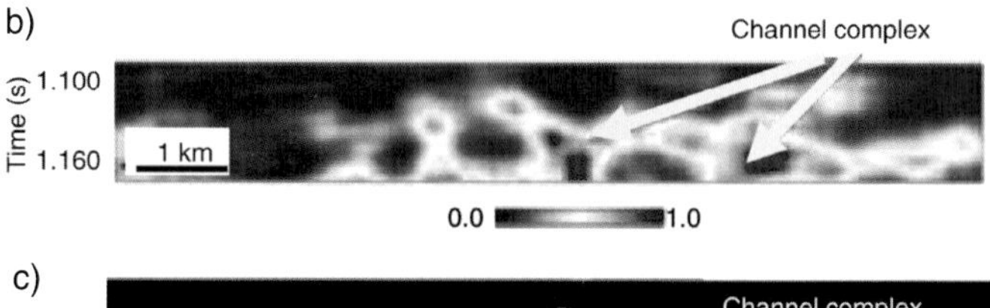

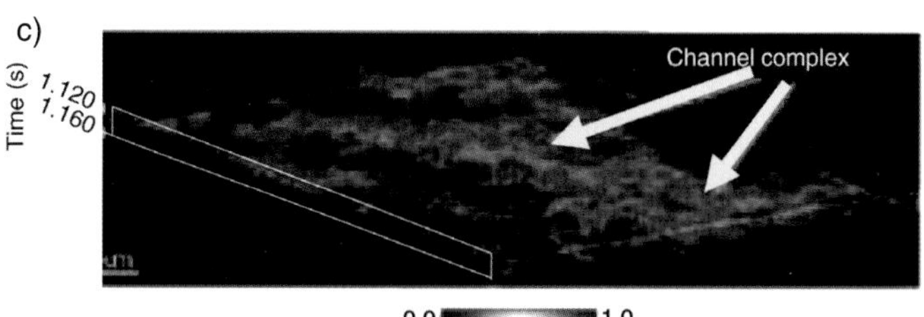

Figure 29. (a) A segment of the original seismic section from Figure 28. (b) The corresponding texture energy section. (c) The texture energy subcube, with an opacity filter applied. The high-energy feature (red) along a channel system is revealed clearly by rendering the low-energy amplitudes as transparent. The same would be difficult to visualize and isolate from the original amplitude volume. After Gao (2003).

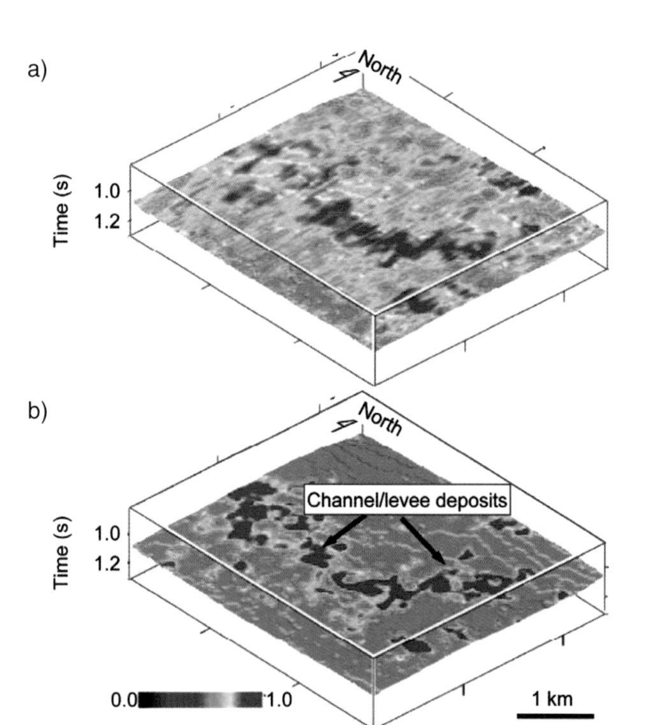

Figure 30. A horizon slice comparison at the same stratigraphic level from (a) a texture energy volume and (b) a seismic amplitude volume. Notice how the channel and levee deposits can be recognized, mapped, and detected more effectively from the texture energy volume than from the seismic amplitude volume. After Gao (2003).

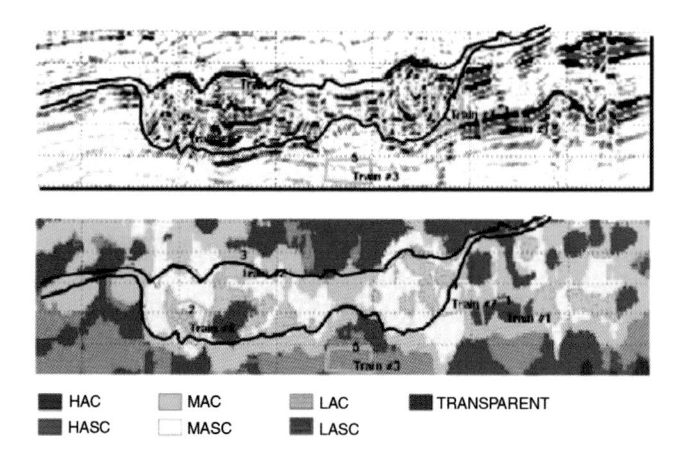

Figure 31. A typical seismic facies classification using an interpreter-trained probabilistic neural network, in which multiple facies classes have been identified. The seismic classification scheme on the right consists of high amplitude (HA), moderate amplitude (MA), low amplitude (LA), continuous (C), and semicontinuous (SC) seismic facies. After West et al. (2002).

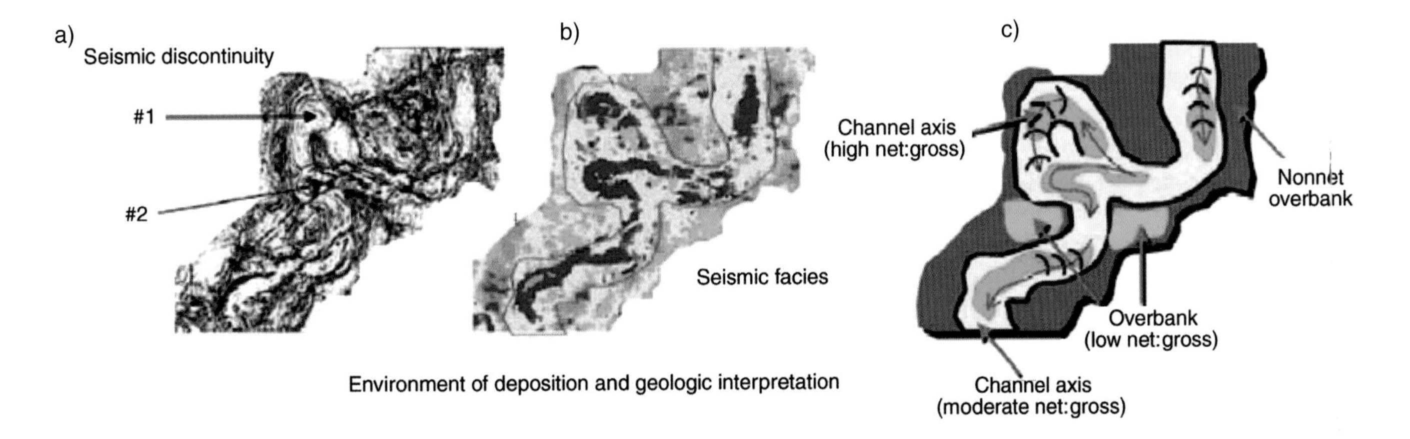

Figure 32. (a) A coherence slice highlighting the lateral edges of a channel (red lines), a broad, older sinuous element (1), and a narrower, younger sinuous element (2). (b) A seismic facies slice showing that sinuous element (1) is composed of HAC to MASC seismic facies, whereas sinuous element 2 is composed primarily of HAC seismic facies. Because the textural-analysis seismic-facies classification is a volume, this type of analysis can be applied at different stratigraphic levels within an interval of interest, whether or not the interval is bounded by mapped horizons. (c) Considering the conceptual relationships between seismic facies and their potential associated geologic fill, the net-to-gross environment can be understood and 3D regions can delineate differing depositional and geologic properties. After West et al. (2002).

Chapter Summary

Because of the oscillatory nature of the seismic wavelet, and hence of the seismic trace, all good measures of changes in reflector amplitude should be calculated along the dip and azimuth of an assumed reflector.

Lateral changes in bed thickness, lithology, and porosity result in lateral changes in thin-bed tuning. Eigenstructure and crosscorrelation coherence algorithms are designed to be sensitive only to reflector waveforms and will not see coherent lateral changes in reflector amplitude. Other coherence algorithms, including semblance, variance, and Manhattan-distance estimates of reflector similarity, are sensitive to both amplitude and waveform. In a similar manner, algorithms designed to measure changes in reflector amplitude — such as Luo et al.'s (1996) derivative algorithm — generally also are sensitive to reflector waveform. Unfortunately, all such algorithms commonly are referred to as coherence or edge detectors, which further obscures their differences.

Whenever possible, we recommend using algorithms that are as mathematically decoupled from each other as possible, thereby providing the interpreter with orthogonal (independent) views of his or her data. Obvious end members exist that we could separate. For instance, a lateral change in porosity of a thin reservoir may give rise only to a subtle amplitude variation, with the waveform remaining constant. In contrast, a continuous reflector may be crosscut by backscattered ground roll. The amplitude of the coherent part of the reflector would remain constant, whereas the waveform and coherence measure would not. Simpler edge-detection algorithms would see both of these features as edges or discontinuities.

In contrast, energy-weighted coherent-amplitude gradients are sensitive to lateral changes in amplitude for a fixed waveform. Such gradients are particularly effective in detecting thin channels that are not seen by eigenstructure and principal-component coherence algorithms, and the gradients provide insight into reservoir heterogeneity. Because they work only on the coherent component of the data, energy-weighted coherent-amplitude gradients highlight channels that have stronger reflectivity and deemphasize incoherent fault zones that may confuse our stratigraphic interpretation.

Long-wavelength estimates of amplitude variability, such as Luo et al.'s (2003) generalized Hilbert transform, can enhance lateral changes in reservoir thickness and porosity that are more gradational and that have scales larger than the typical five- or nine-trace coherence algorithm. Long-wavelength second-derivative estimates of amplitude variability, achieved by applying the most-positive-curvature and most-negative-curvature algorithms to amplitude gradients, also can enhance such subtle changes in reflectivity.

At present, long-wavelength estimates of changes in amplitude should be applied with care. Reflector dip varies slowly in the vertical direction (except near unconformities), thereby allowing long-wavelength estimates of structural curvature on time slices. In contrast, seismic amplitude varies rapidly in the vertical direction and renders long-wavelength estimates of amplitude changes challenging in structurally complex terrains. Although long-wavelength derivative calculations can be applied readily to dipping planes, such calculations produce artifacts if the reflector has any structural curvature falling within the (rather large) analysis window. For that reason, we recommend that long-wavelength estimates of amplitude gradients be restricted to subvolumes of data that have been flattened to remove most of the structural curvature.

Texture-attribute studies usually are not associated with seismic attribute studies. We consider texture analysis in its most general form to be a superset of the geometric attributes that comprise the major focus this book. Texture analysis uses second-order statistics to extract attributes that in turn help describe the textural properties of classes. Textures based on GLCMs work well so long as the granularity of textures being examined is of the order of the pixel size, which commonly occurs on seismic data. On the basis of our analysis, we conclude that

1) texture attributes enhance our understanding of the reservoir by providing a clearer picture of the distribution, volume, and connectivity of the hydrocarbon-bearing facies of the reservoir,
2) texture attributes are a quantitative suite that aids the visual process an interpreter goes through in using the conventional attributes,
3) the simultaneous and exhaustive analysis that generates texture attributes gives insights into the linkages of the reservoir's geology and geophysics, and in some cases of its engineering properties, and
4) application of texture analysis for seismic facies classification, using neural networks, holds promise in that it can provide seismic facies information that is not provided by any conventional seismic approach.

References

Adeogba, A. A., T. R. McHargue, S. A. Graham, 2005, Transient fan architecture and depositional controls from near-surface 3-D seismic data, Niger Delta continental slope: AAPG Bulletin, **89**, 627–643.

Blumentritt, C. H., E. C. Sullivan, and K. J. Marfurt, 2003, Channel detection using seismic attributes on the Central Basin Platform, west Texas: 73rd Annual International Meeting, SEG, Expanded Abstracts, 466–469.

Chopra, S., and V. Alexeev, 2005, Applications of texture attributes to 3D seismic data: CSEG Recorder, **30**, 28–32.

Gao, D., 2003, Volume texture extraction for 3-D seismic visualization and interpretation: Geophysics, **68,** 1294–1302.

Haralick, R. M., K. Shanmugam, and I. Dinstein, 1973, Textural features for image classification: IEEE Transactions: Systems, Man, and Cybernetics, SMC-**3**, 610–621.

Luo, Y., S. al-Dossary, M. Marhoon, and M. Alfaraj, 2003, Generalized Hilbert transform and its application in geophysics: The Leading Edge, **22,** 198–202.

Luo, Y., W. G. Higgs, and W. S. Kowalik, 1996, Edge detection and stratigraphic analysis using 3-D seismic data: 66th Annual International Meeting, SEG, Expanded Abstracts, 324–327.

Marfurt, K. J., 2006, Robust estimates of 3D reflector dip and azimuth: Geophysics, **71**, 29–40.

Marfurt, K. J., and R. L. Kirlin, 2000, 3-D broadband estimates of reflector dip and amplitude: Geophysics, **65**, 304–320.

Mitchum, R. M., 1977, Seismic stratigraphy and global changes of sea level, Part I: Glossary of terms used in seismic stratigraphy, *in* C. E. Payton, ed., Seismic stratigraphy: Applications to hydrocarbon exploration: AAPG Memoir 26, 205–212.

Partyka, G., 2001, Seismic thickness estimation: three approaches, pros and cons: 71st Annual International Meeting, SEG, Expanded Abstracts, 503–506.

Reed, T. B., and D. Hussong, 1989, Digital image processing techniques for enhancement and classification of SeaMARCII side-scan sonar imagery: Journal of Geophysical Research, **94**, 7469–7490.

Reilly, J., 2002, 3-D prestack data mining to meet emerging challenges: 72nd Annual International Meeting, SEG, Expanded Abstracts, 476–479.

West, B., S. May, J. E. Eastwood, and C. Rossen, 2002, Interactive seismic facies classification using textural and neural networks: The Leading Edge, **21**, 1042–1049.

Widess, M. B., 1973, How thin is a thin bed?: Geophysics, **38**, 1176–1254.

Chapter 6

Spectral Decomposition and Wavelet Transforms

Chapter Objectives

After reading this chapter, you will be able to

- identify the geologic features highlighted by spectral decomposition and wavelet transforms
- interpret spectral anomalies in the context of thin-bed tuning
- analyze singularities of seismic data for structural and stratigraphic details
- evaluate the use of spectral information as a direct hydrocarbon indicator

Introduction

Since the beginning of digital recording, geophysical data processors have decomposed the measured seismic signal into its Fourier (or spectral) components to attenuate low-frequency ground roll, 50- or 60-Hz cultural noise, and high-frequency random noise. Also, data processors have routinely balanced the source spectrum through seismic-deconvolution and wavelet-shaping techniques to account for the input source signature, spectral changes resulting from ghost-period multiples, and attenuation of the overburden.

Any time series can be represented in terms of a summation of other time series. For example, in Fourier analysis, we can represent any time series by a weighted summation of selected sinusoidal functions. In this example, the set of the selected sinusoidal time series is termed *basis functions* because they are the units from which we can recreate the original time series.

If one of those sinusoidal functions is crosscorrelated with another one of a different selected frequency, the crosscorrelation will be zero. Mathematicians would state that such selected sinusoidal functions are orthogonal (perpendicular) to each other. Thus, such a set of sinusoidal functions is not internally redundant. In recreating the original time series, no particular sinusoidal function can replace another one in the summation. In our context, a spectral or wavelet component is simply the crosscorrelation coefficient of a given basis function with seismic data.

If we choose to amplify or mute a given component and reconstruct the data from new weighted sums, we obtain an altered (filtered) version of the original data. In our example of Fourier analysis, because the basis functions or the selected sinusoidal functions are orthogonal to each other, mathematicians would term the orthogonal Fourier transform to be an orthogonal transform. Such orthogonal transforms provide a minimum number of computed components that represent the measured seismic data. Orthogonal implementations of wavelet transforms in particular are effective at data compression. Because many of the wavelet components are very small, often we can represent a trace consisting of a thousand or more seismic samples with only one-tenth as many wavelet components.

Running-window spectral-filtering and spectral-balancing techniques have been applied to seismic data at least since the latter half of the 1970s. In those applications, each seismic trace is broken into a suite of shorter, overlapping traces centered about the output sample. Longer windows provide more-robust statistics, with typical windows being 1000 or 500 ms in length, and with shorter windows of 250 ms providing poorer results. In part, the poor results are because of an assumption that the underlying reflectivity has a white spectrum. If the underlying reflectivity is not white, it would be distorted during the spectral-balancing step. Because of this focus on spectral balancing, spectral *analysis* of shorter windows was overlooked until the middle 1990s. The impetus for using spectral analysis of shorter windows ultimately came from seismic interpretation rather than from seismic processing. In general, seismic interpreters are quite content with *relative* spectral measurements, such as the frequency at which tuning occurs, and do not require the absolute value of each frequency component desired by processors, which are needed to reconstruct original data.

Because we only wish to interpret spectral components rather than to filter components and (efficiently) reconstruct the data, we no longer are bound by orthogonal transforms. As an example, if we wish to analyze seismic data within a 100-ms window, Nyquist's sampling criterion states that we only need to decompose the data at 10-Hz increments — say, at 10, 20, 30, 40, 50, and 60 Hz for band-limited seismic data with a highest-frequency contribution between 60 and 70 Hz and no amplitude at 0 Hz. Knowledge of the spectral components at these seven frequencies completely and uniquely describes this time series. Fast Fourier transforms (FFT) provide a particularly effective means of generating such components.

Unfortunately, the efficiency of FFT is so ingrained in processors' heads, they forget that instead they could use a simple slow Fourier transform — that is, they could simply crosscorrelate any sine and cosine with the data. In that manner, we will use slow Fourier transforms (more properly called discrete Fourier transforms) to decompose the data into sinusoidal components separated by 1 or 2 Hz, thereby allowing the interpreter to inspect a more finely sampled spectrum for features of interest. Because the 10-Hz frequency interval will do the job, the use of the finer frequency sampling (1 or 2 Hz) is extra work that provides no additional information.

Although in theory we could reconstruct any given spectral component at the desired 1-Hz interval from the minimal number of components defined by Nyquist's criterion (at 10-Hz intervals), it is simpler computationally to calculate them directly at the desired (1-Hz) sampling. Likewise, orthogonal wavelet-transform components used in data compression also can be oversampled, allowing an interpreter to inspect a more finely sampled spectrum for features of interest.

We begin this chapter by reviewing basic concepts of seismic resolution and thin-bed tuning. Then we briefly review the properties of Fourier transforms, emphasizing the impact of the shape and size of the seismic analysis window. That will give us a quantitative understanding of the similarities and differences between two different methods: short-window discrete Fourier transforms (commonly called spectral decomposition) and wavelet transforms (called instantaneous spectral analysis). After defining the terms and establishing the theoretical basis, we provide a suite of examples that exhibit these types of analysis in terms of both workflow and the features that are amenable to the analysis. We close the chapter with a brief overview of the recently introduced SPICE (spectral imaging of correlative events) algorithm, showing its relationship to both instantaneous-attribute analysis and wavelet-decomposition analysis.

Seismic Resolution and Thin-bed Tuning

To better understand the effect of bed thickness on thin-bed resolution, we return to the simple wedge model shown in Chapter 5, Figure 1. Generally, the top and bottom reflections from a thin bed do not have the equal and opposite values routinely used in seismic modeling of a thin-bed response. Castagna (2005) recently demonstrated that this overly simplified model, in which reflection coefficients have equal magnitude but opposite signs, is pathological and that for the more general case the limits to vertical resolution are less severe. Accounting for attenuation also may allow us to increase the resolution (Goloshubin et al., 2002; Korneev et al., 2004).

Nevertheless, we will follow Widess (1973), Kallweit and Wood (1982), and Robertson and Nogami (1984) and use this wedge model to understand why we can detect thin-bed anomalies even for this worst-case model. The maximum constructive interference occurs when the wedge thickness is one-quarter of the effective-source wavelength or, when measured in two-way traveltime, it is one-half the thickness of the dominant period (indicated by arrows in Figures 1c and 1d of Chapter 5). For thicknesses smaller than that, the waveform stabilizes first and then remains constant, and only the seismic amplitude changes with thickness. Thus, below tuning, the frequency spectrum's shape does not change with changes in thickness because the waveform does not change shape. For this (worst-case) model (which may not be valid in actual practice), Widess (1973) showed that when we are well below the one-quarter-wavelength tuning thickness, the amplitude changes linearly with thickness (Chapter 5, Figure 2).

Kallweit and Wood (1982) examined this problem of resolution with a model consisting of two reflectors that have equal reflection coefficients of the same sign. The authors showed that when the thickness falls below that given by Rayleigh's criteria (Figure 1), it cannot be estimated from seismic data alone. Kallweit and Wood's (1982) paper had a profound impact on the seismic processing community. Although the authors took care to point out the difference between detection of relative changes in thickness and resolution (determination) of a given thickness, a whole generation of seismic processors (including the second author of this book) apparently confused the issue and felt that spectral mapping of reservoirs thinner than one-quarter wavelength would be fruitless. Not until the 1990s did Partyka and his colleagues revisit Widess's observations and show that amplitude variation with frequency, or more appropriately, amplitude variation across strata of varying thickness for a fixed frequency, could be used as a powerful interpretation tool.

Relevant Concepts of Fourier Analysis

Fourier analysis is simply crosscorrelation of the seismic data with a suite of sines and cosines at predetermined frequencies. Each crosscorrelation coefficient between a given sine and cosine pair and the data is called a frequency component. Commonly, we use Euler's theorem:

$$e^{i\omega t} = \cos(\omega t) + i\sin(\omega t), \qquad (6.1)$$

where $\omega = 2\pi f$ and is the radial frequency measured in radians per second, f is the temporal frequency measured in Hertz, and $i = \sqrt{-1}$. We then express the crosscorrelation coefficients of sines and cosines with the data as a complex number, $A(\omega)$:

$$A(\omega) = \sum_k e^{i\omega k\Delta t} d(k\Delta t) = \sum_k \cos(\omega k\Delta t) d(k\Delta t) + i\sum_k \sin(\omega k\Delta t) d(k\Delta t) \qquad (6.2)$$

where k is the sample index, Δt is the time-sample increment, and $d(k\Delta t)$ is the seismic data at time $t = k\Delta t$. It also is common to define $A(\omega)$ in terms of its amplitude, $a(\omega)$, and its phase, $\phi(\omega)$:

$$A(\omega) = a(\omega)e^{i\phi(\omega)}. \qquad (6.3)$$

Until now, research efforts have focused more on the amplitude component of the spectrum, $a(\omega)$. However, we expect that changes with respect to frequency of the phase, $\phi(\omega)$, may allow us to differentiate between upward-fining and upward-coarsening sequences, both of which have the same amplitude spectrum.

Although sines and cosines are used for spectral decomposition, other transforms also can be used to decompose waveforms for interpretation. One major software vendor decomposes seismic data using orthogonal Tchebychev polynomials as a basis function, and another vendor derives (nonorthogonal) basis functions defined by the data themselves using self-organized maps, or alternatively, using (orthogonal) principal-component analysis. Regardless of the basis functions used, the transform coefficients are obtained by simply crosscorrelating each basis function with a window of the data in a fashion analogous to obtaining the Fourier coefficients through equation 6.2.

In this chapter, we limit ourselves to basis functions that are windowed sines and cosines and we use either the short-window discrete Fourier transform (SWDFT) or the wavelet-transform basis functions.

For both the SWDFT and the wavelet transforms, the basis functions are tapered sines and cosines. They differ from each other in the application of their respective tapers. For the SWDFT, the tapers are independent of frequency and are the same for all sines and cosines. For wavelet transforms, the tapering windows are proportional to the frequency of the sines and cosines and are shorter for higher frequencies.

It should come as no surprise that the unwindowed Fourier transform of a $\sin(\omega_0 t)$ or $\cos(\omega_0 t)$ function has a single nonzero value at $\omega = \omega_0$. However, with the use of these new, tapered-windowed basis functions, we will observe nonzero amplitudes over a range of frequencies. This smearing in the frequency domain occurs because the basis functions are tapered. Thus, we need to understand the spectrum of the tapered window itself.

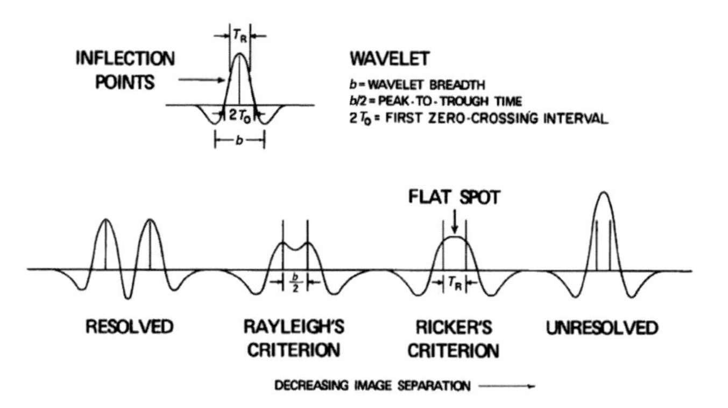

Figure 1. The definition of resolution between two reflectors with the same reflection coefficient that also has the same sign (indicated by the vertical lines). The effective frequency of the source wavelet is defined as $1/b$, where b is the wavelet breadth. We can interpret the separation as being either in time (for this chapter on thin-bed resolution) or in space (for later chapters on lateral resolution). Rayleigh's limit of resolution occurs when images are separated by the peak-to-trough time interval, whereas Ricker's limit occurs when images are separated by a time interval equal to the separation between inflection points. After Kallweit and Wood (1982).

For the SWDFT, we choose a tapered analysis window, $w(t)$, with length b, of the form

$$w(k\Delta t) \equiv w_k = \begin{cases} \frac{1}{2}\left[1+\cos(\pi \frac{|k\Delta t| - b + \xi}{\xi})\right] & if\ b-\xi \le |k\Delta t| \le b \\ 1 & if\ \ |k\Delta t| \le b-\xi \\ 0 & if\ \ |k\Delta t| > b \end{cases}, \tag{6.4}$$

where the window function $w(t - \tau) = w(k\Delta t)$ will be centered about each analysis point at time τ. By tapering the sharp corners of the analysis window, we minimize undesired side lobes in the frequency spectrum (Figure 2b). Typically, in the case of a tapered-windowed DFT, the length of the window, b, will be a fixed 50 or 100 ms for all frequencies, and the length of the taper, ξ, will be 20% of the window length. The same slab of data (of fixed length 50 or 100 ms) will be analyzed by each frequency. We display a suite of SWDFT wavelets and their corresponding spectra in Figure 2. Note that both the temporal window and the spectral width are of fixed size for all frequencies. The result of higher or lower frequencies is simply to shift the analyzed spectra up or down.

In contrast, the window functions $w(t)$ that are used in wavelet-transform decomposition are typically Gaussian and have the form

$$w(k\Delta t) \equiv w_k = \frac{1}{\sqrt{\sigma}} \exp\left[\frac{-(k\Delta t)^2}{2\sigma^2}\right], \tag{6.5}$$

where σ defines the width of the wavelet. For the popular Morlet wavelet transform, $\sigma = 1/f_C$, where f_C is the central frequency to be analyzed and is measured in Hertz.

We plot representative Morlet wavelets and their corresponding spectra in Figure 3. Note that in contrast to the SWDFT, the higher-frequency Morlet wavelets have shorter temporal extent but broader frequency spectra than the

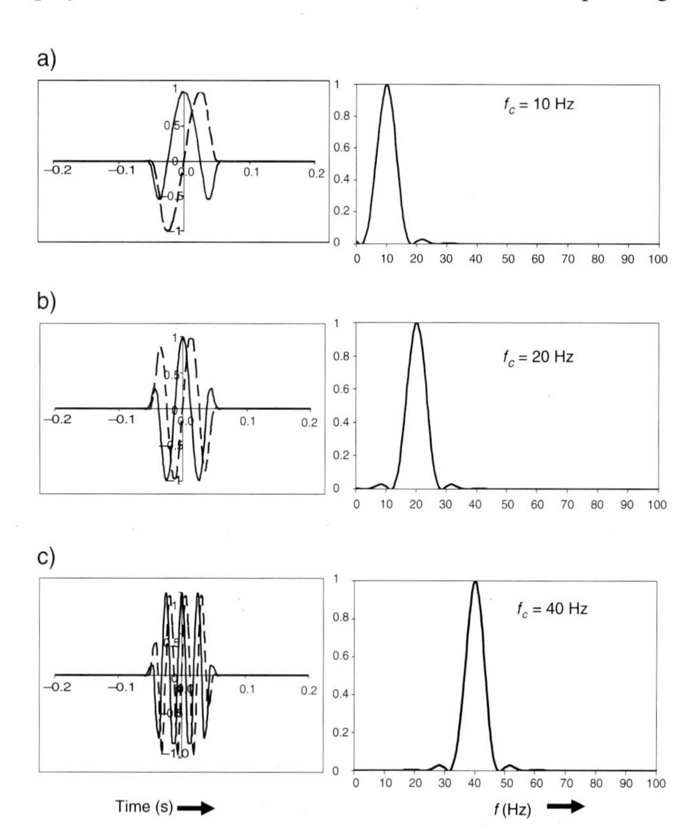

Figure 2. Seismic wavelets and their Fourier spectra at (a) 10, (b) 20, and (c) 40 Hz, representative of those used in short-window discrete Fourier transform (SWDFT) spectral decomposition analysis. Window width is a constant 0.100 s; window taper is 0.020 s. Solid and dashed lines indicate the cosine and sine wavelets, respectively. Note the side lobes of the spectra. Also note that the spectrum of the 10-Hz wavelet extends into negative frequencies.

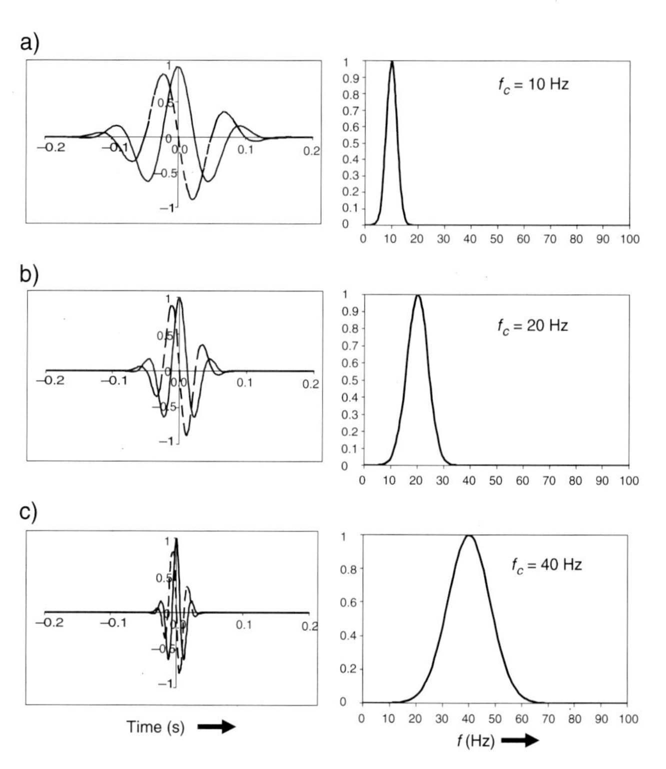

Figure 3. Seismic wavelets and their Fourier spectra that have center frequencies at (a) 10, (b) 20, and (c) 40 Hz, representative of those used in the continuous-wavelet transform (CWT). Morlet wavelets commonly are used in wavelet compression and in instantaneous spectral analysis, using the window defined by $w(k\Delta t) \equiv w_k = \frac{1}{\sqrt{\sigma}} \exp\left[\frac{-(k\Delta t)^2}{2\sigma^2}\right]$, where k is the sample number, Δt is the sample increment, and $\sigma = 1/f_C$. Solid and dashed lines indicate the cosine and sine wavelets, respectively. Note that the bandwidth increases with center frequency.

corresponding SWDFT wavelets displayed in Figure 2. Equally important, two Morlet wavelets of different frequency at the same analysis point will analyze different windows of seismic data. Thus, if an interpreter wishes to explicitly analyze the frequency content of a specific fixed-temporal-window geologic interval across multiple frequencies, the SWDFT is more appropriate for the job.

Looking ahead to the end of this chapter, we note that the recently introduced SPICE algorithm (spectral imaging of correlative events) uses a similar but significantly longer analysis window, $\sigma = 3/f_c$, to provide greater frequency resolution at the expense of reduced temporal resolution (Liner et al., 2004). We display the SPICE wavelets and their corresponding spectra in Figure 4. Note that although the wavelets are longer in time, the spectra are narrower than those of the Morlet wavelet displayed in Figure 3. Although the window function, $w(t)$, is different for each of the SWDFT, Morlet, and SPICE algorithms, they all are implemented by crosscorrelating the data, $u(t)$, with windowed sines and cosines, $w(t-\tau)\exp[i\omega(t-\tau)]$, or equivalently, by crosscorrelating sines and cosines, $\exp[i\omega(t-\tau)]$, with the windowed data, $w(t-\tau)u(t)$:

$$S(\omega,\tau = j\Delta t) = \sum_{n=0}^{N} e^{i\omega(n-j)\Delta t} w[(n-j)\Delta t]u(n\Delta t) \, , \quad (6.6)$$

where $S(\omega,\tau)$ are the transform coefficients for each frequency, ω, for an analysis centered about time τ at the jth sample, $w(t)$ is the analysis window given by equations 6.4 and 6.5, and the seismic data are $(N+1)$ samples long.

Examining Figures 2 and 3, we observe the following. First, as defined, the effective data analysis window for the SWDFT is fixed whereas that for the wavelet transform is variable — shorter for higher frequencies and longer for lower frequencies. Second, the spectra of both basis functions are centered about the center frequency, f_c. Third, the bandwidths of the tapered SWDFT basis functions are independent of frequency, whereas those of the wavelet transform are narrower at low-center frequencies and broader at high-center frequencies. Most important, all spectral components, whether we are using the short-window DFT or the variable-window CWT (continuous-wavelet transform), have contributions from neighboring frequencies. Because most interpreters are not experienced seismic data processors, we emphasize that although we may see geologic features of interest at a 2-Hz component, rarely do we actually record such low-frequency data. Instead, we display the information content from higher frequencies (say, 8–10 Hz) that fall within the tails of the frequency spectra displayed in Figures 2b, 3b, and 4b. Such a pitfall is particularly prevalent when we use an insufficiently tapered SWDFT, in which side lobes in the frequency spectrum can mix in even more frequencies.

To further clarify the SWDFT, we display Partyka et al.'s (1999) images comparing SWDFT to the spectral balancing routinely used in seismic processing. In Figure 5, we show a reflectivity sequence. For simplicity, we assume that the spectra of the earth's reflectivity are white, implying that there is an equal probability of a given amplitude reflection coefficient anywhere within the time series.

In general, we do not know the source wavelet. Instead, we process our data to look as though they have been acquired using a band-limited white source wavelet. We do this by spectrally balancing the measured seismic data, $u(t)$. One way of achieving such a balance is to crosscorrelate the seismic data, $u(t)$, with sines and cosines, thereby generating Fourier components. Often, we compute an average spectrum that is representative of all the traces in the survey. We calculate the peak spectral amplitude, a_{max}, of that

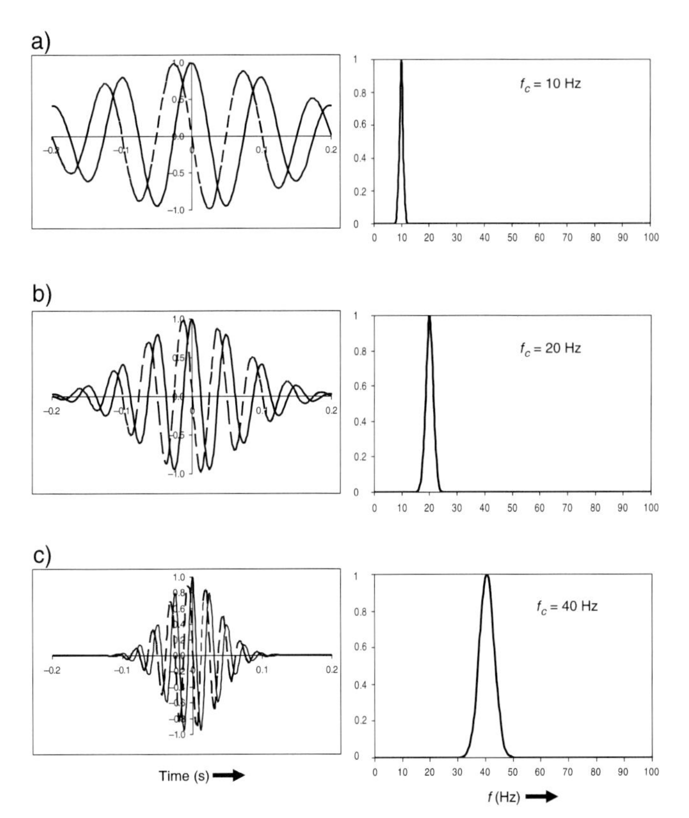

Figure 4. Seismic wavelets and their Fourier spectra at (a) 10, (b) 20, and (c) 40 Hz, representative of those used in the CWT for the SPICE algorithm, using the window defined by $w(k\Delta t) \equiv w_k = \frac{1}{\sqrt{\sigma}}\exp\left[\frac{-(k\Delta t)^2}{2\sigma^2}\right]$,

$w(k\Delta t) \equiv w_k = \frac{1}{\sqrt{\sigma}}\exp\left[\frac{-(k\Delta t)^2}{2\sigma^2}\right]$, where k is the sample number, Δt is the sample increment, and $\sigma = 3/f_c$. Solid and dashed lines indicate the cosine and sine wavelets, respectively. The seismic wavelet for 10 Hz goes beyond the scale of this plot.

average spectrum and define a noise threshold, ε, as a fraction of that peak amplitude (Figure 6a). Next, we scale each spectral component by the value $1./[a(f) + \varepsilon a_{max}]$, so that the new spectral peak is 1.0, the noise threshold is scaled to 0.5, and the spectral components below the noise threshold are scaled down toward zero (Figure 6b). This new scaled spectrum is equivalent to the spectrum of the idealized source wavelet shown in Figure 5. Deconvolution algorithms are designed to achieve a similar result — to generate a band-limited processed-data spectrum by eliminating multiples and reverberations that otherwise would color it.

The SWDFT shown in Figure 7 differs somewhat from conventional spectral analysis of the entire seismic trace. Although we may still wish to assume that the reflectivity is white, the fact that we have only 26–51 samples in our 100-ms analysis window implies that we have only a specific realization drawn from a white spectrum. In general, the spectrum of that windowed reflectivity series is not white, it is colored. When the resulting data window, $u(t)$, is multiplied by the white spectrum of the source wavelet, it also has a colored spectrum. We address how to obtain a white source-wavelet spectrum from windowed data in the next section. But if we can, we want the spectrum of the seismic data to be a band-limited version of the spectrum of the reflectivity series within the analysis window.

Spectral Decomposition Using the Short-window Discrete Fourier Transform

The workflow for carrying out spectral decomposition using the SWDFT consists of the following steps, which are illustrated in Figure 8.

1) We select the zone of interest, which typically follows an interpreted horizon. We select the horizon and define a constant-thickness slab of data that lie a given number of milliseconds above and below the selected horizon in the seismic data volume (Figure 8a).
2) Next, we (or our software) extract and then flatten this slab of data (Figure 8b).
3) We (or our software) apply a DFT to the slab of data, frequency by frequency, generating a sequence of constant-frequency spectral-component maps (Figure 8c).
4) We calculate an average or median spectrum representative of the entire slab of data.
5) Next, we assume that the geology and therefore reflectivity are sufficiently random across the entire zone of interest for the average reflectivity spectrum to be white.

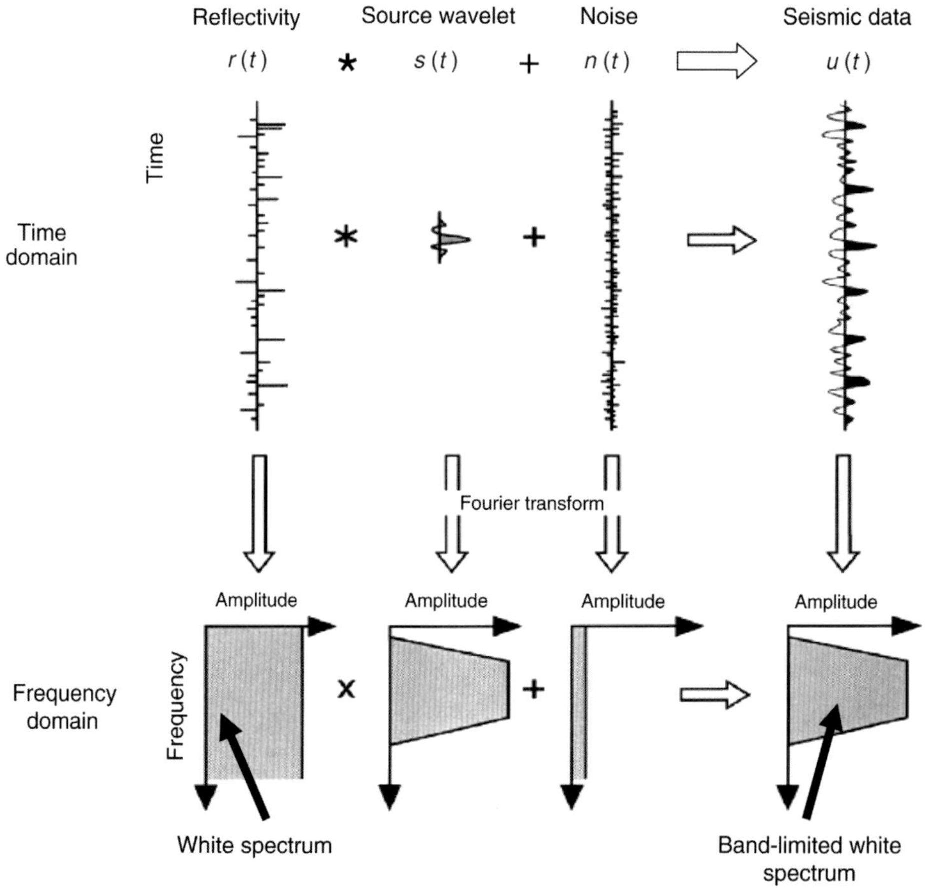

Figure 5. Long-window spectral decomposition and the convolutional model. Typically, we assume that the multiple-free reflectivity spectrum has very little structure (in this case, we display a white spectrum). Next, we calculate the Fourier spectrum of the entire (unwindowed) trace. Finally, we explicitly flatten its spectrum, which, under the assumption of white additive noise, will flatten the spectrum of the source wavelet. Similar assumptions are made in the deconvolution algorithms routinely used in seismic processing. After Partyka et al. (1999).

6) We then calculate a spectral compensation factor 1./[$<a(f)> + \varepsilon<a>_{max}$], where $<a(f)>$ denotes the average (or median) spectral component at frequency, f, and where $<a>_{max}$ denotes the peak amplitude of this average (or median) spectrum. If this compensation factor is applied to the average (or median) spectra, it generates a result comparable to that displayed in Figure 6b. When this compensation factor is applied to the spectra of the individual windowed traces, it statistically removes the effect of the unknown source wavelet, thereby resulting in a colored spectrum that is representative of the colored reflectivity within the analysis window.

7) Finally, we (or our software) reload the spectrally balanced frequency slices into the interpretation workstation for analysis (Figure 8d).

The spectral decomposition (SWDFT) frequency slices allow the interpreter to visualize interference patterns, such as thin-bed tuning associated with channels and deltas in plan view. This is not a magical process creating information out of nothing. The SWDFT has taken 25–50 time slices and combined them with variable weights (the sines and cosines used in crosscorrelation) to form 50–100 frequency slices. The interpreter animates through these images and chooses the images that fit his or her geologic model. Because the basis functions are not orthogonal, many of the images are redundant, with much similarity between images created at neighboring frequencies. Other images contain only noise. That is the case for images at frequencies at the low and high ends of the seismic source's frequency spectrum. As the following examples show, identification of textures and patterns that are indicative of geologic processes is proportional to the interpreter's skills and understanding of the depositional environment.

The SWDFT can be applied to a series of overlapping windows that encompass the reservoir, or even to the entire seismic volume (Marfurt and Kirlin, 2001), thereby generating a 4D cube (x, y, frequency, and time/depth of window center) from a 3D cube. If he lacks 4D interpretation software, the interpreter simply loads these volumes into the workstation in multiplexed form. The interpreter can then either roll through the resulting slices one at a time for spectral analysis of one horizon, or N_f at a time (where N_f is the number of frequencies) for common frequency analysis of multiple, flattened horizons.

Examples

Our first example comes from Partyka et al. (1999), who introduced spectral decomposition to the industry at large. In Figure 9 we display a conventional amplitude extraction (Figure 9a) and an instantaneous envelope extraction (Figure 9b) along a Pleistocene-age horizon from

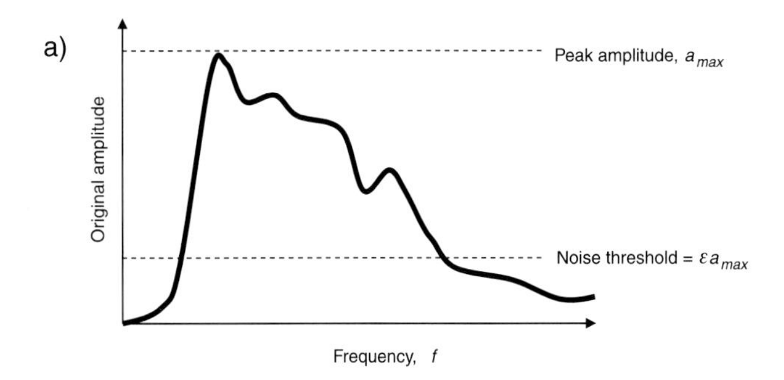

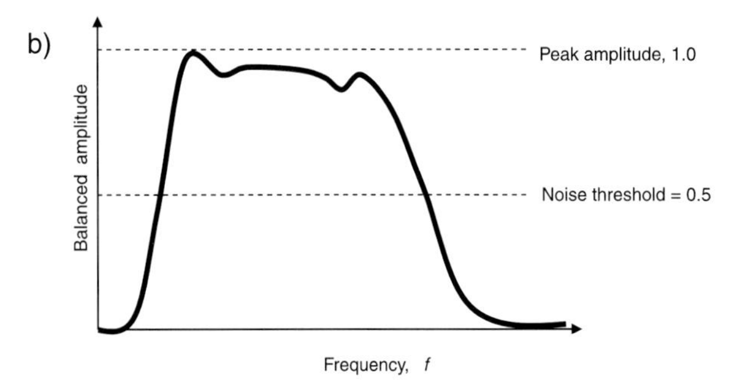

Figure 6. The concept of spectral balancing to achieve a band-limited white spectrum in the presence of noise. (a) First, we calculate each spectral component, $a(f)$, and its maximum, a_{max}. Next, we estimate a noise level as a fraction, ε, of the peak spectral amplitude. (b) Finally, we rescale each spectral component by 1./[$a(f) + \varepsilon a_{max}$] so that the new peak spectrum is 1.0.

South Marsh Island, on the continental shelf in the Gulf of Mexico. These images are of the paleo-Mississippi River, approximately 150 km west of the river's current position. We see a complex distributary system, including bifurcating channels, point bars, and longitudinal bars that are controlled by faults in the southeastern portion of the image.

In Figure 10 we display images of SWDFT spectral components at 16 and 26 Hz, corresponding to the images in Figure 9. The narrow channel, A, is poorly imaged in Figure 9 but is clearly visible on the 26-Hz spectral component in Figure 10b. The same channel appears fainter on the 16-Hz image in Figure 10a, implying that 26 Hz is closer to the tuning frequency than 16 Hz is. In contrast, although channel B appears in all four images in Figures 9 and 10, it has maximum lateral resolution in the 16-Hz spectral component (Figure 10a), in which we see discrete meander loops indicated by the white arrow.

The wider channel, B, is better imaged (tuned) in the lower-frequency, 16-Hz image, whereas the narrow channel, A, is better imaged (tuned) at the higher, 26-Hz frequency. That finding is consistent with the well-established correlation between channel width and thickness.

Laughlin et al. (2002) constructed a cartoon to describe this phenomenon (Figure 11), in which they note that the

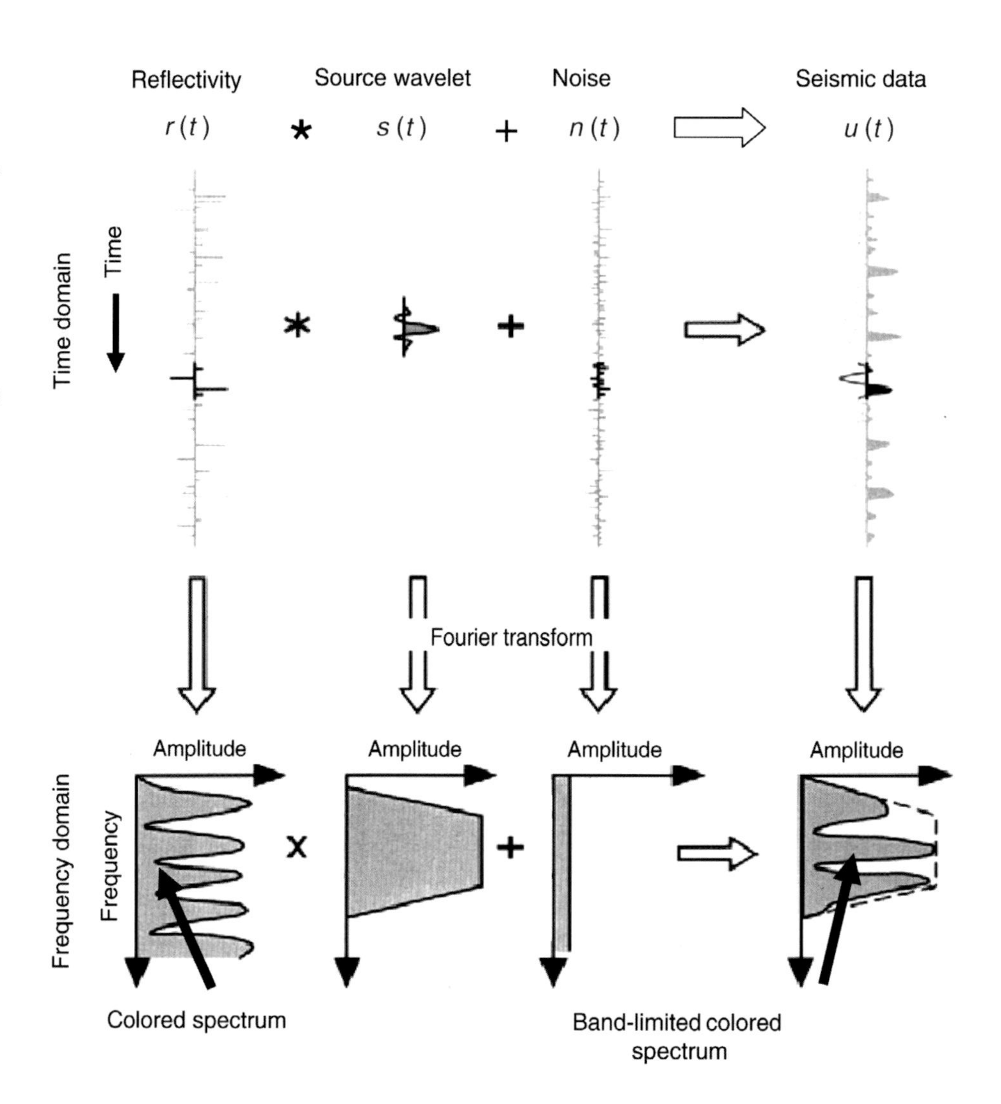

Figure 7. Short-window spectral decomposition and the convolutional model. Although we may wish to assume that the reflectivity has a more or less white spectrum, any short-windowed realization of this white distribution will have only a few discrete reflection spikes and thus invariably will have a colored spectrum. If we process the data to provide a band-limited white source spectrum and assume we have white noise, the colored spectrum of the windowed seismic data will be a band-limited representation of the colored spectrum of the reflectivity within the window. After Partyka et al. (1999).

thalweg of deeper channels is imaged by low frequencies, whereas the shallower flanks (and longitudinal and point bars) of the channel are imaged by high frequencies.

The above-described model is illustrated clearly in our second example, taken from a 3D onshore data volume over a real channel (Figure 12) (Bahorich et al., 2002). Although an amplitude map showed reasonable detail about the shape of the reservoir, the spectral-decomposition images clearly illuminated the thickest and thinnest sequences in the reservoir. Amplitude maps of certain frequencies showed the thinning of levies — information that helped the interpreter map the detailed geometry of the reservoir. That geometry was confirmed subsequently by well control.

Our third example comes from Peyton et al. (1998), who applied spectral decomposition and coherence to successfully image deep (~3500 m) Pennsylvanian stratigraphic features in the Anadarko Basin, Oklahoma, U.S.A. The authors merged three different 3D surveys into a single survey covering the area of study (Figure 13). Their objective was to map multiple stages of incised valleys into three coarsening-upward marine parasequences (the lower, middle, and upper Red Fork sandstone) bounded by the regionally extensive Pink limestone above and the Inola Limestone Member of the Boggy Shale and the Novi limestone below (Figure 14). Variable sediment fill in the incised channels results in a complex internal architecture that is difficult to interpret on conventional horizon slices through the seismic data. This study focuses on the upper Red Fork incised-valley system, which is the largest such system and which images most clearly on 3D seismic and also contains the best reservoir rocks in the area.

Before acquisition of the 3D surveys, it was believed that the valley fills in this region occurred in four stages, with stage III being the most abundant hydrocarbon producer. Of the several wells drilled, some were believed to have penetrated the edge of stage III valley fill; however, those wells did not produce. Wells producing from stage III sands indicate a gap in the production (shown in yellow in Figures 14b and 15b). The fairly large width (0.75 to 1.5 km) of the Red Fork valley fill, coupled with the extensive well control defining the infill, make the valley fill an attractive exploration target. Thus, the area was covered with 3D seismic surveys in an attempt to reduce risk and to explore undrilled potential in stage III sands. The seismic data acquired have good quality, with a dominant frequency of 50 Hz and the bandwidth extending to 80 Hz.

The seismic cross section AA′ in Figure 14 shows the lower Skinner Shale marker directly above the Novi limestone bounding the Red Fork interval. In between these two markers, the incised valleys are characterized by discontinuous reflections of varying amplitudes. Obviously, interpreters will find it difficult to use traditional interpretation techniques (e.g., autopicking horizons, amplitude mapping, isochron mapping, etc.) to interpret the Red Fork incised valley fill. Furthermore, it is difficult to identify the individual stages of fill. As was eventually learned, cross section AA′ shown in Figures 12–15 begins in the regional Red Fork marine parasequences in the south, cuts through three stages of valley fill, and ends in the regional Red Fork deposits at the north (Figure 16).

Unlike the simple amplitude extraction shown in our earlier Gulf of Mexico example in Figure 9a, reflectivity over the Red Fork incised valley changes significantly with the valley fill, making horizon slices through the seismic data difficult to interpret. For that reason, Peyton et al. (1998) used spectral decomposition and coherence to image the edges of the channels and interpret the internal features therein. Because the Red Fork interval was 50-ms thick (Figure 14), spectral components ranging from 20 Hz to 50 Hz were computed at 1-Hz intervals within a 50-ms window parallel to, but not including, the Novi limestone. In Figure 15a, we show the 36-Hz amplitude slice from the

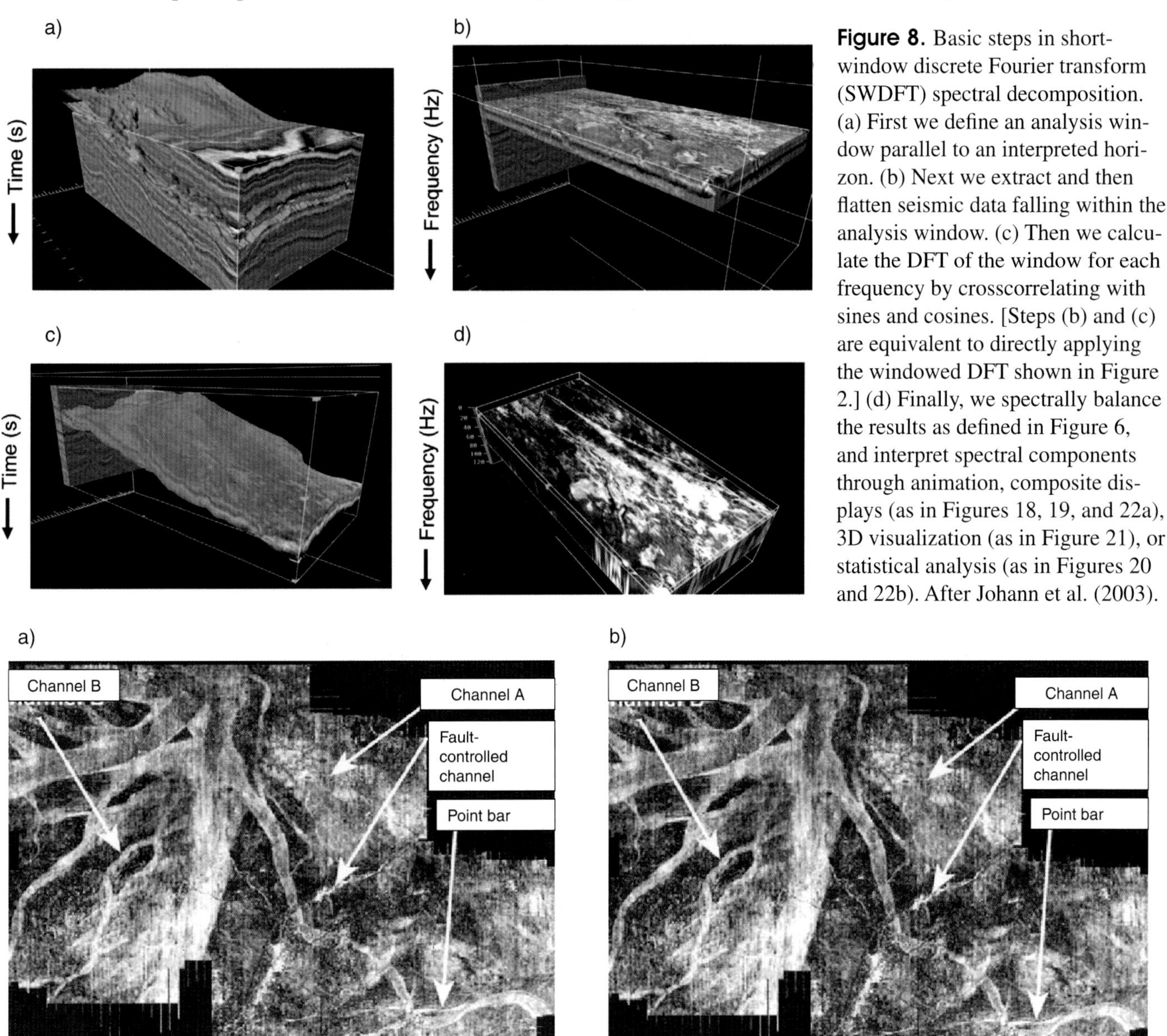

Figure 8. Basic steps in short-window discrete Fourier transform (SWDFT) spectral decomposition. (a) First we define an analysis window parallel to an interpreted horizon. (b) Next we extract and then flatten seismic data falling within the analysis window. (c) Then we calculate the DFT of the window for each frequency by crosscorrelating with sines and cosines. [Steps (b) and (c) are equivalent to directly applying the windowed DFT shown in Figure 2.] (d) Finally, we spectrally balance the results as defined in Figure 6, and interpret spectral components through animation, composite displays (as in Figures 18, 19, and 22a), 3D visualization (as in Figure 21), or statistical analysis (as in Figures 20 and 22b). After Johann et al. (2003).

Figure 9. (a) An amplitude extraction and (b) a full-bandwidth instantaneous envelope along a horizon from offshore Louisiana, U.S.A. After Partyka et al. (1999).

Red Fork spectral decomposition. That slice shows not only the valley edges but the internal features, which, according to extensive well control, have been interpreted to be different stages of valley fill (Figure 15b).

Figure 15c is a corresponding horizon slice through the coherence volume. Note that here we can see the edges of the channels and different stages of the valley fill, although the internal details are more pronounced on the spectral decomposition image (Figure 15b). We saw in Chapter 3 that coherence maps lateral variation in waveform and is relatively insensitive to amplitude. In contrast, spectral decomposition is a direct measure of relative amplitude within a given frequency band. We interpret the differences in these images to mean that although the amplitudes differ between stage V and stage III, the waveform is quite similar.

Images from coherence and spectral decomposition show that stage III valley fill crossing the 1996 survey (Figure 13) connects the producing wells in the western half of the study area with the producing well to the east, as interpreted before the 3D acquisition. Closer examination of the spectral decomposition and coherence images led to interpretation of an apparently younger valley that trends northwesterly in the eastern part of the 1996 survey and cuts out the stage III fill, but then bends to the southwest and diverges from stage III valley fill. This interesting observation led workers to reinterpret the well logs for the area (Figure 16), and their new interpretation included a younger valley fill stage V (Figure 15). In summary, integration of well-log interpretation and the shapes and patterns of features of interest on spectral decomposition and coherence images led to a more accurate final interpretation.

In our fourth example, from Bahorich et al. (2002), preliminary analysis of the 3D seismic data volume yielded the amplitude map shown in Figure 17a. The anomaly

a)

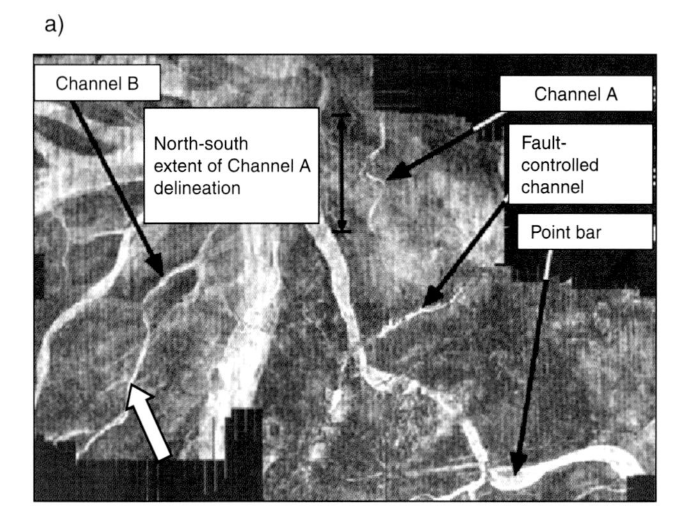

b)

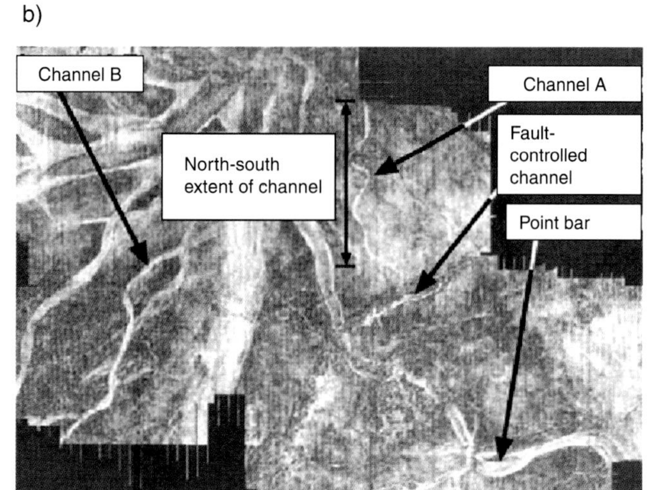

Figure 10. SWDFT spectral components at (a) 16 Hz and (b) 26 Hz along a horizon from offshore Louisiana, U.S.A., corresponding to the images in Figure 9. After Partyka et al. (1999).

a)

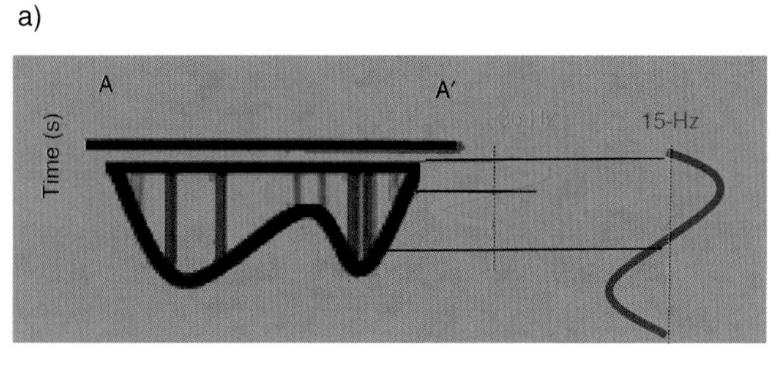

b)

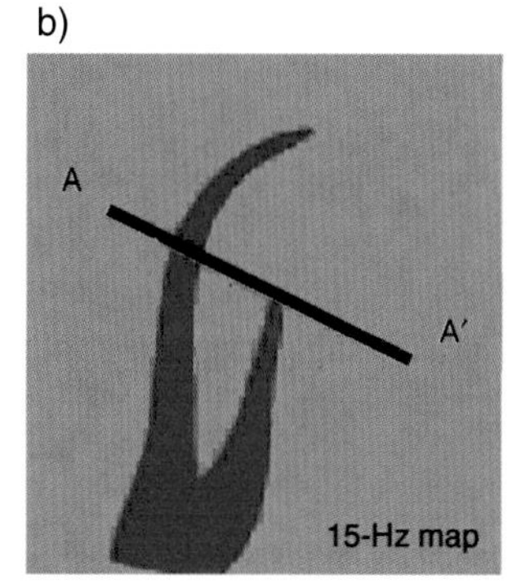

c)

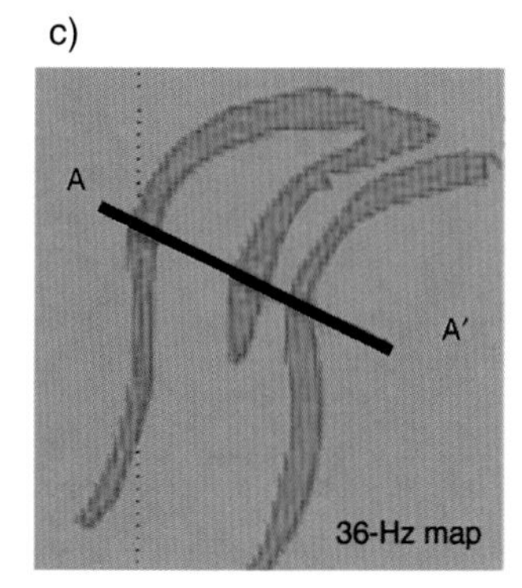

Figure 11. A schematic diagram showing the interrelationship between thin-bed tuning and the amplitude of spectral components through an idealized channel. (a) A vertical cross section, and (b) spectral components at a higher frequency and (c) at a low frequency, shown in map view. On the thinner flanks, thin-bed tuning occurs at the higher-frequency components (in green). In the thalweg or center of the channel, thin-bed tuning occurs at the lower frequencies (in red). After Laughlin et al. (2002).

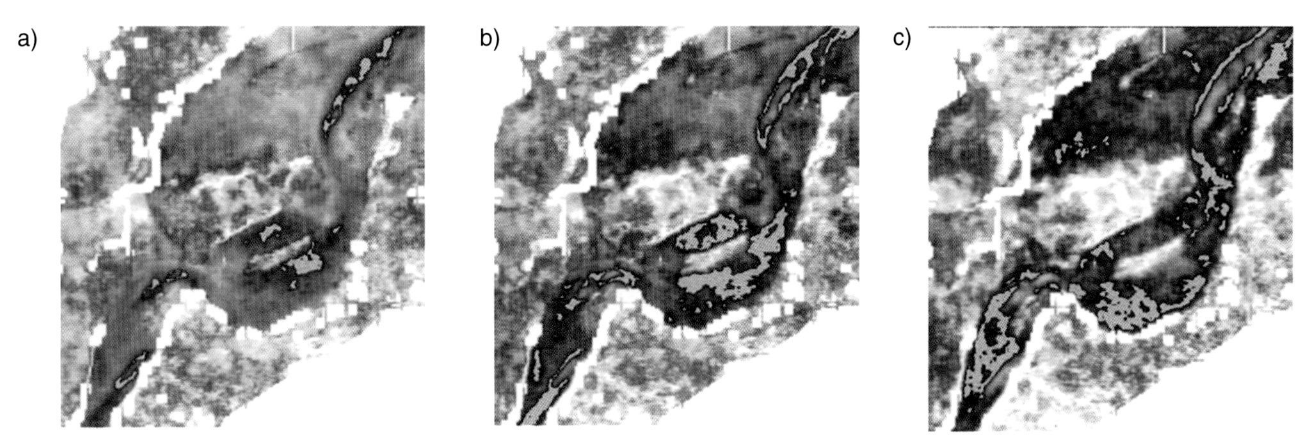

Figure 12. Three spectral components, increasing in frequency from (a) through (c), with the highest spectral amplitude plotted in yellow. Each spectral component responds uniquely to variations in reservoir thickness. The thickest part of the channel is seen in (a), thinner parts of the channel appear in (b), and the thinnest parts, including the flanks of the channel, appear in (c). Data are courtesy of Apache Corp. After Bahorich et al. (2002). Reprinted by permission of Hart's E&P.

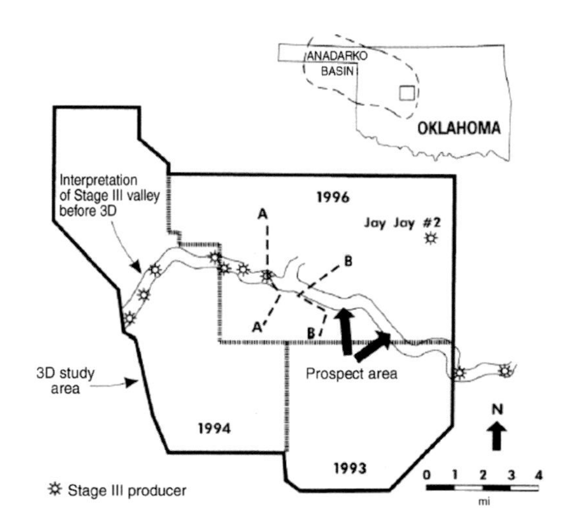

Figure 13. A location map showing 3D survey outlines, lines of cross section, wells producing from upper Red Fork stage III valley fill, and an interpreted outline of the stage III valley before acquisition of 3D seismic data. After Peyton et al. (1998).

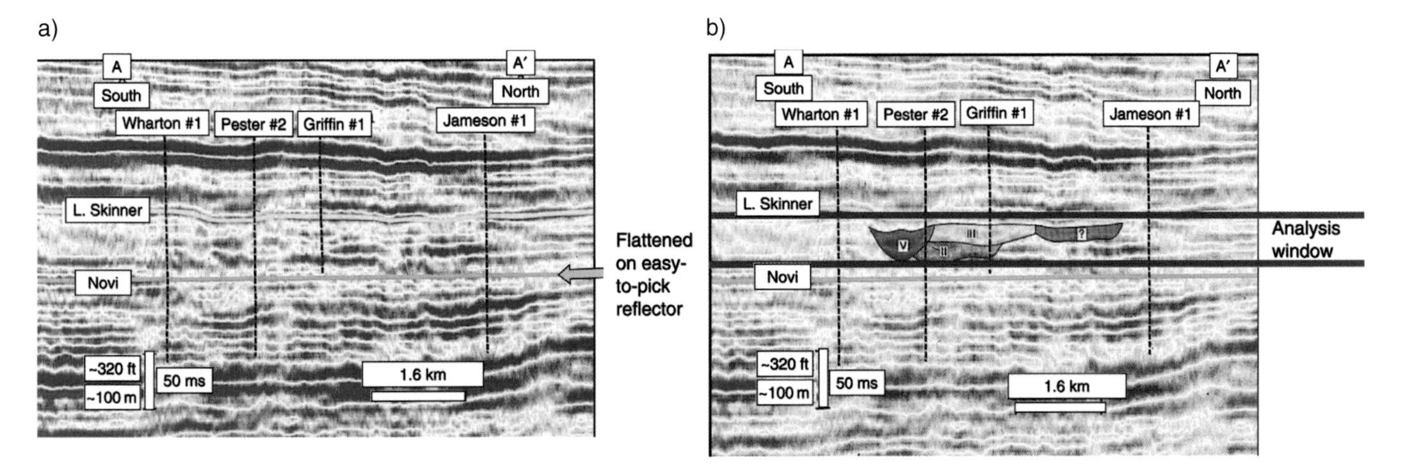

Figure 14. Seismic cross section AA′ flattened on the Novi horizon (a) without and (b) with channel interpretation. After Peyton et al. (1998).

marked with a black arrow seemed promising, but conventional displays generated during interpretation did not clarify depositional controls and trapping mechanisms and thereby left the prospect's potential in doubt. Spectral decomposition images not only confirmed the existence of the amplitude anomaly but also illuminated an inferred, subtle stratigraphic trapping sequence running northeast-southwest (Figure 17b). That sequence was not readily seen on

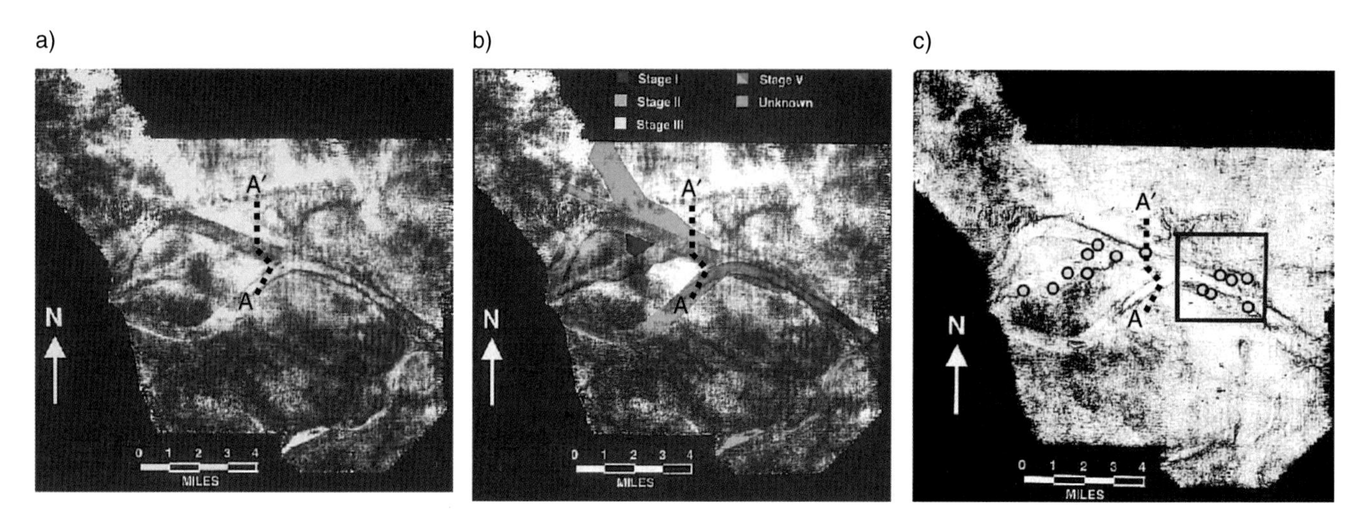

Figure 15. A 36-Hz amplitude slice from spectral decomposition of Red Fork deposits (a) without and (b) with current interpretation. (c) A coherence slice 36 ms below the lower Skinner horizon, showing wells with faults in the Red Fork and Inola intervals. After Peyton et al. (1998).

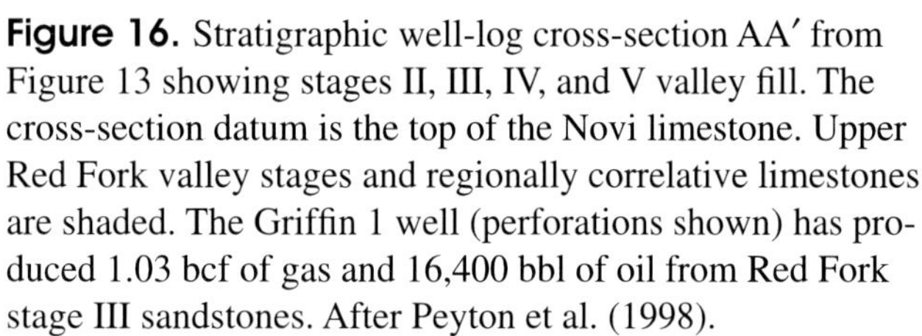

Figure 16. Stratigraphic well-log cross-section AA′ from Figure 13 showing stages II, III, IV, and V valley fill. The cross-section datum is the top of the Novi limestone. Upper Red Fork valley stages and regionally correlative limestones are shaded. The Griffin 1 well (perforations shown) has produced 1.03 bcf of gas and 16,400 bbl of oil from Red Fork stage III sandstones. After Peyton et al. (1998).

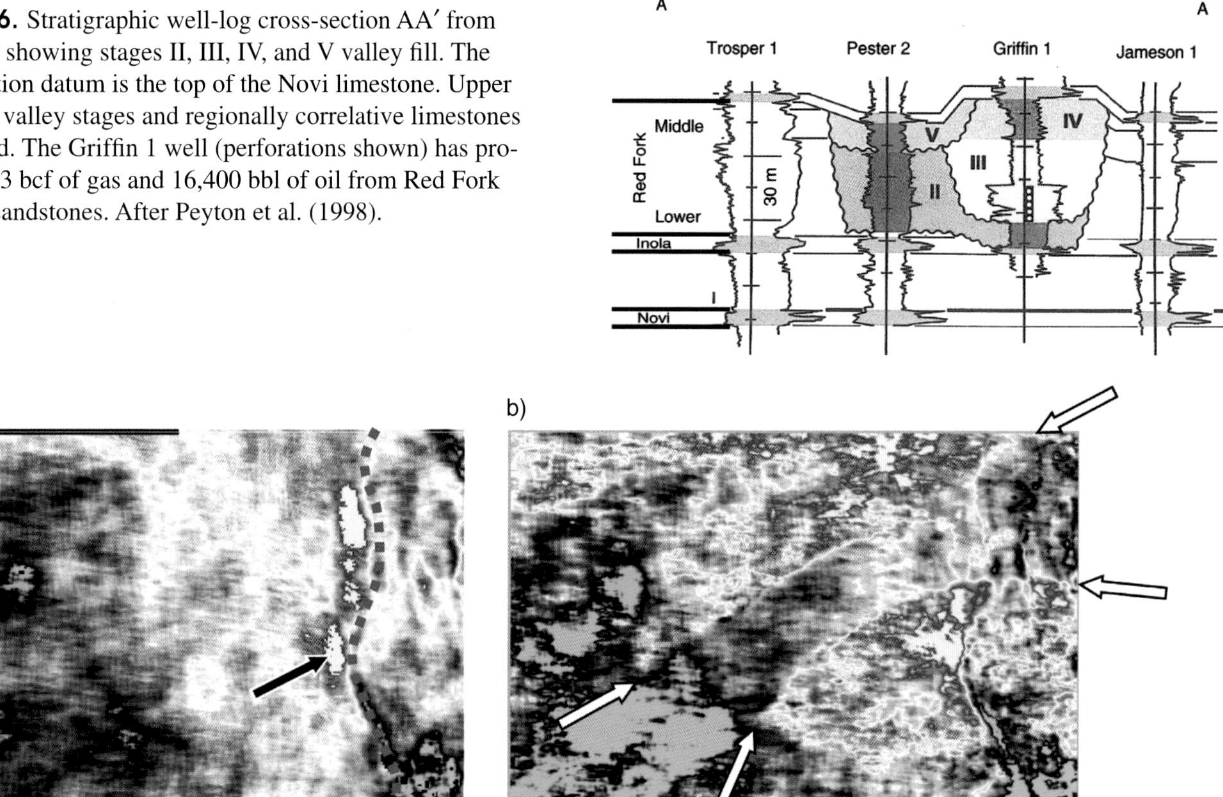

Figure 17. (a) A conventional broadband amplitude map showing an anomaly. The black arrow indicates an amplitude anomaly. The dashed blue line indicates a fault. (b) Spectral decomposition imaging, which clearly shows a stratigraphic feature as the trapping mechanism to the north, indicated by arrows. After Bahorich et al. (2002). Reprinted by permission of Hart's E&P.

the conventional map. Animation through discrete spectral decomposition images helped interpreters understand the stratigraphic setup of this potential reservoir and prepare to exploit the area.

Visualizing a suite of spectral components

Multispectral seismic images of reservoirs using spectral decomposition strongly resemble multispectral optical images obtained by remote sensing or satellite imagery techniques. One of the most common false-color image techniques (which will be described in Chapter 9) is to plot three discrete frequencies against red, green, and blue (RGB). Figure 18, from Bahorich et al. (2002), is a time slice combining three spectral frequencies over several channel sequences, offshore West Africa. Such an image can help in reservoir characterization and well placement. Features that are tuned at a higher frequency and that are interpreted to correspond to levee complexes appear here to be blue, whereas those tuned at an intermediate frequency are green. The thickest channels appear as orange and yellow. Low reflectivity shows up as dark colors.

Hall and Trouillot (2004) also plotted spectral components at 30 Hz, 40 Hz, and 50 Hz against RGB, where a bright response is represented as white (Figures 19a–d). Yellow hues in Figure 19d indicate that the red (30-Hz) map and the green (40-Hz) map have coincident high-amplitude responses. In Figure 19e, we see a redisplay of the authors' data using the HLS (hue, lightness, and saturation)

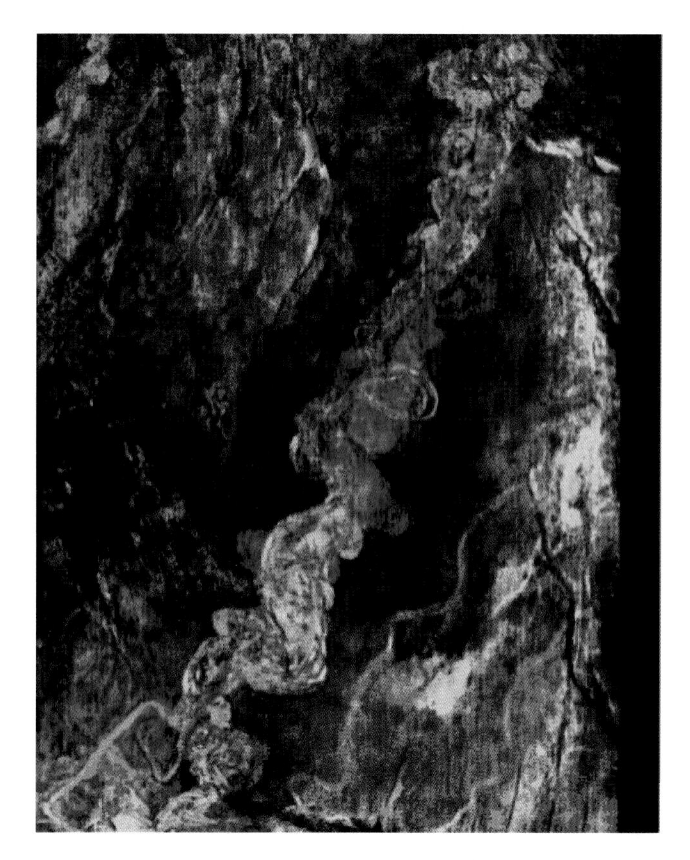

Figure 18. High-resolution spectral decomposition, showing details of a complex reservoir image from offshore West Africa. After Bahorich et al. (2002). Reprinted by permission of Hart's E&P.

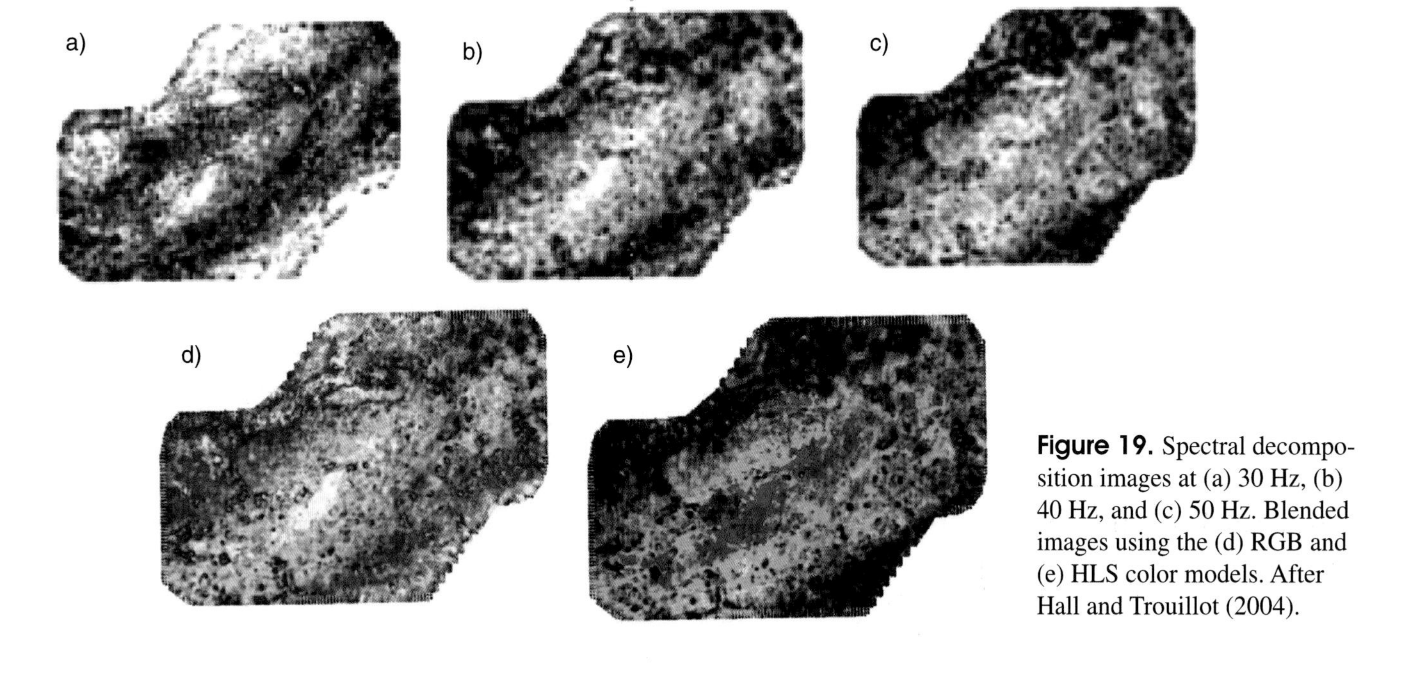

Figure 19. Spectral decomposition images at (a) 30 Hz, (b) 40 Hz, and (c) 50 Hz. Blended images using the (d) RGB and (e) HLS color models. After Hall and Trouillot (2004).

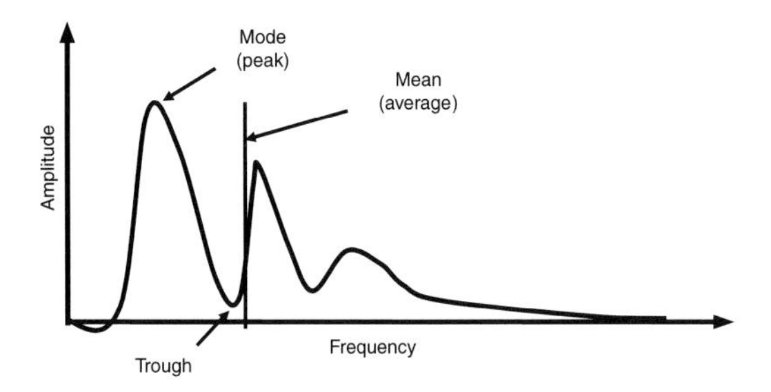

Figure 20. A schematic diagram showing a typical spectrum resulting from spectral decomposition. In general, the mode of the spectrum changes strongly and the mean frequency changes only moderately with changes in thin-bed tuning.

color model discussed in Chapter 9. Using the HLS color model, the same three amplitude slices are represented by hue (the wavelength of the color), lightness (the brightness of the color), and saturation (the amount of color tinting added), respectively. Then the images are combined to give the final map, in which a bright, saturated red color indicates that all three frequencies are bright in that area.

Because a typical seismic spectrum might look like the schematic shown in Figure 20, three components may not show sufficient detail. To address this problem, Johann et al. (2003) used optical stacking of a complete suite of 16 frequency components ranging from 5 Hz to 80 Hz (Figure 21).

Alternatively, we can calculate statistical measures such as the mean, standard deviation, skewness, and kurtosis of the spectrum. Marfurt and Kirlin (2001) found that the mode or peak of the spectrum is more sensitive to thin-bed tuning than the mean is. In Figure 22a, we plot an RGB image of the 16-Hz, 26-Hz, and 36-Hz spectral components corresponding to the same horizon shown in Figures 9 and 10. In Figure 22b, we plot the peak frequency (mode of the spectrum) against hue and α-blend it with an image of coherence plotted against gray scale (α = 0.50; we discuss α-blending in Chapter 9). Low frequencies (blue) correspond to thicker parts of the channel, and higher frequencies (yellow to yellow-green) correspond to thinner channels (white arrow), a point bar (gray arrow), and a longitudinal bar (black arrow). The combination of coherence and spectral decomposition is particularly effective, with coherence delineating channel edges, and the mode of the spectrum indicating channel thickness.

The Continuous Wavelet Transform and Instantaneous Spectral Analysis

Although the short-window discrete Fourier transform has been employed frequently with seismic data to provide lateral localization of the frequency content, the nonnegligible-length window limits the technique's temporal resolution (Xia, 1999; Sun et al., 2002; Sinha et al., 2003). In contrast, the length of the continuous-wavelet transform's (CWT) wavelet is proportional to the center frequency, f_c, as shown in Figure 3. Thus, both narrow-band ringing and broad-band impulsive reflections can be analyzed and positioned better in time.

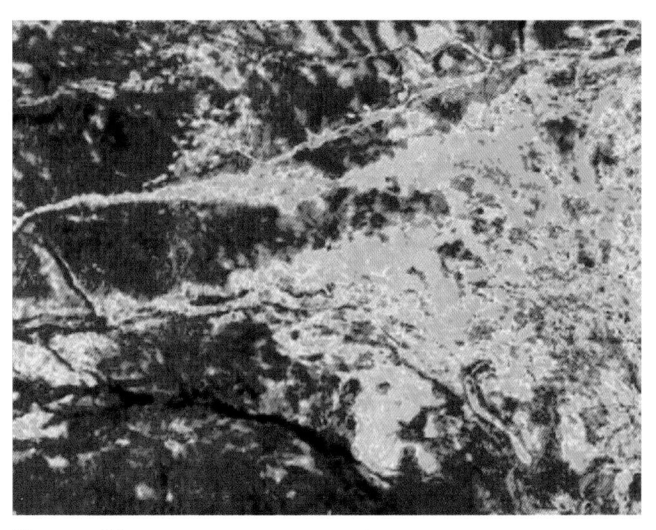

Figure 21. A composite image of spectral components ranging between 5 and 80 Hz, obtained with optical stacking. Each slice is assigned the same opacity. After Johann et al. (2003).

Among CWT workers, σ in equation 6.5 is called the scale, and τ in equation 6.6 is called the translation along the time axis; together they produce a 2D time-scale image for each trace. Liner et al. (2004) used this time-scale map directly in their SPICE algorithm, which we will discuss later in this chapter. However, Sinha et al. (2003) and their colleagues improved the interpretability of the time-scale map by converting it to a time-frequency map. The CWT approach involves the following steps:

1) Decompose the seismogram into wavelet components, $S(\omega,\tau)$, as a function of the scale, σ, and the translation shift, τ, using equation 6.6.
2) Multiply the complex spectrum of each wavelet used in the basis function by its CWT coefficient and sum the result to generate instantaneous frequency gathers.
3) Sort these frequency gathers to produce constant frequency cubes, time slices, horizon slices, or vertical sections.

As with the SWDFT, commercial CWT visualization packages can be adapted to help us interpret the results.

Matched-pursuit technique

Although the CWT discussed above forms a set of oversampled, nonorthogonal basis functions, we still can adjust the coefficients to reconstruct the original data. Whereas an orthogonal CWT provides the most efficient means of representing seismic data with the fewest number of wavelet components, the matched-pursuit technique is designed to provide wavelet components of greater interest to the interpreter.

Liu and Marfurt (2005) offered details of such an algorithm based on Ricker and Morlet wavelets using the flow shown in Figure 23. They began by precomputing a table of complex wavelets for a finely sampled suite of frequencies. The real and imaginary components of those wavelets are simply the cosine and sine wavelets shown in Figure 3a. Next, they generated a complex trace using Hilbert transforms, from which they calculated the instantaneous envelope and frequency of each trace. They then searched for the largest values of the envelope and its corresponding instantaneous frequency. Next, they least-squares-fitted that suite of wavelets to the complex trace, solving for complex coefficients that correspond to the amplitude and phase of the complex wavelet that best fits the data. Finally, they subtracted that amplitude and phase-rotated complex wavelet from the current version of the data, thereby generating a new residual trace. They repeated the process on the residual until the energy of the residual trace fell below a user-defined threshold.

Liu and Marfurt (2005) illustrate this process through the example shown in Figure 24. The result after the first iteration is shown in the left column, the result after the fourth iteration is in the center column, and the result after the sixteenth iteration is in the right column. The location and magnitude of the wavelet envelope are shown in Figure 24d. Each wavelet envelope, frequency, and phase is extracted from the precomputed complex wavelet table and added in to generate the modeled seismic data (Figure 24a). These modeled seismic data are subtracted from the original seismic data to generate residual seismic data (Figure 24b). As described in Figure 23, iterations cease once the residual is sufficiently small (in this case, after 16 iterations). Each complex wavelet has its own precomputed complex spectrum. Like the modeled seismic data, these modeled complex spectra accumulate as the iterations progress, resulting in a spectral decomposition from the wavelet decomposition. The magnitude of the 40-Hz component is shown in Figure 24c.

To our knowledge, Castagna et al. (2003) were the first to develop such a matched-pursuit wavelet-decomposition technique for interpretation. To illustrate the improved resolution of their instantaneous spectral analysis (ISA) over the well-established discrete Fourier transform method, Castagna et al. (2003) applied both techniques to the synthetic trace we show in Figure 25a. The ISA time-frequency plot (Figure 25c) shows the amplitude spectra for each time sample. The first event on the synthetic seismogram (Figure 25a) comes from an isolated reflector and is a single

a)

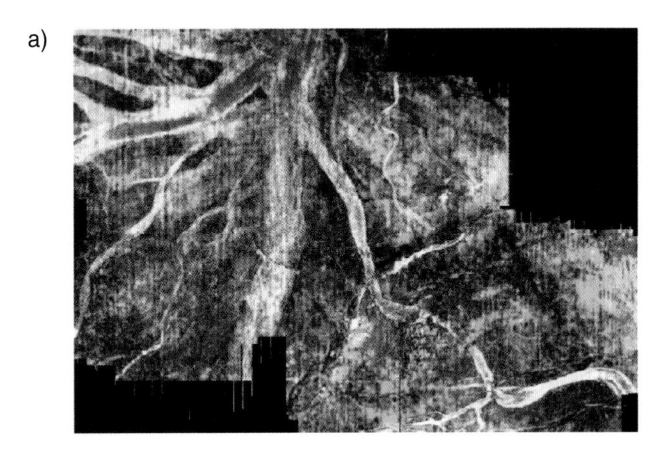

b)

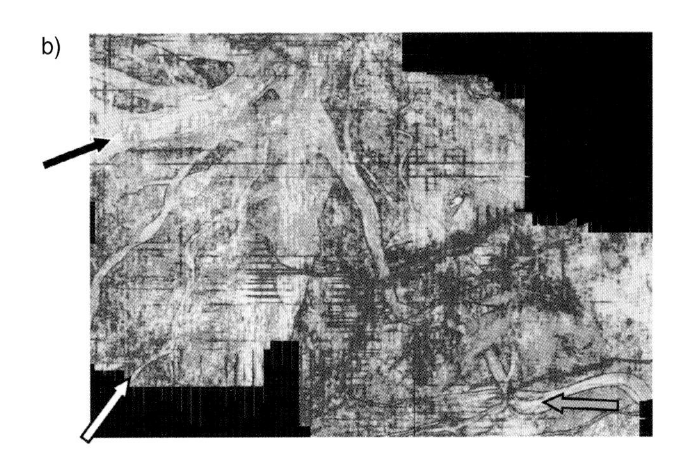

Figure 22. Alternative means of plotting multiple spectral information corresponding to the images shown in Figures 9 and 10. (a) A blended image using the RGB color model. R corresponds to 16 Hz, G to 26 Hz, and B to 36 Hz (after Wessels et al., 1996). (b) A blended image of the mode of the spectrum (plotted against hue) and coherence (plotted as a gray scale, with low coherence being black). The low-frequency (blue) areas correspond to a thicker channel, whereas the high-frequency (yellow) areas correspond to a thinner channel (white arrow), a point bar (gray arrow), and a longitudinal bar (black arrow). After Marfurt and Kirlin (2001).

wavelet (40 Hz). On the frequency spectrum shown in Figure 25c, notice that the duration of the wavelet is identical to the duration of the arrival in the time domain. Compare this with the SWDFT (spectral decomposition) image in Figure 25d, in which the time duration is equal to the window length of 100 ms.

The second event is a composite event generated by adding separate 10-Hz and 40-Hz events arriving at the same time. The ISA image (Figure 25c) shows a low-frequency arrival spread over time and a high-frequency arrival that has a short time duration. The SWDFT result (Figure 25d) shows almost no frequency discrimination between the two events. The side lobes may result from using a less than optimal taper in an insufficiently long window in the SWDFT analysis.

The third event is generated by two interfering arrivals of the same frequency (30 Hz). We can just barely resolve the temporal separation.

The fourth event is a composite of four events (at 20 Hz and 30 Hz) arriving at two different but distinct times. Although the time separation is acceptable, we interpret the results to be two (25-Hz) events instead of the four events that were input.

The fifth and final event is a composite of three 20-Hz events that are very closely spaced in time. Although the energy is concentrated around 20 Hz, the events appear to be somewhat resolved at frequencies greater than 30 Hz. In contrast, the SWDFT image shows a broader, smeared image, ranging from 10 to 50 Hz. In summary, this example shows that the ISA algorithm has not only greater temporal resolution but also better frequency resolution than does the SWDFT algorithm.

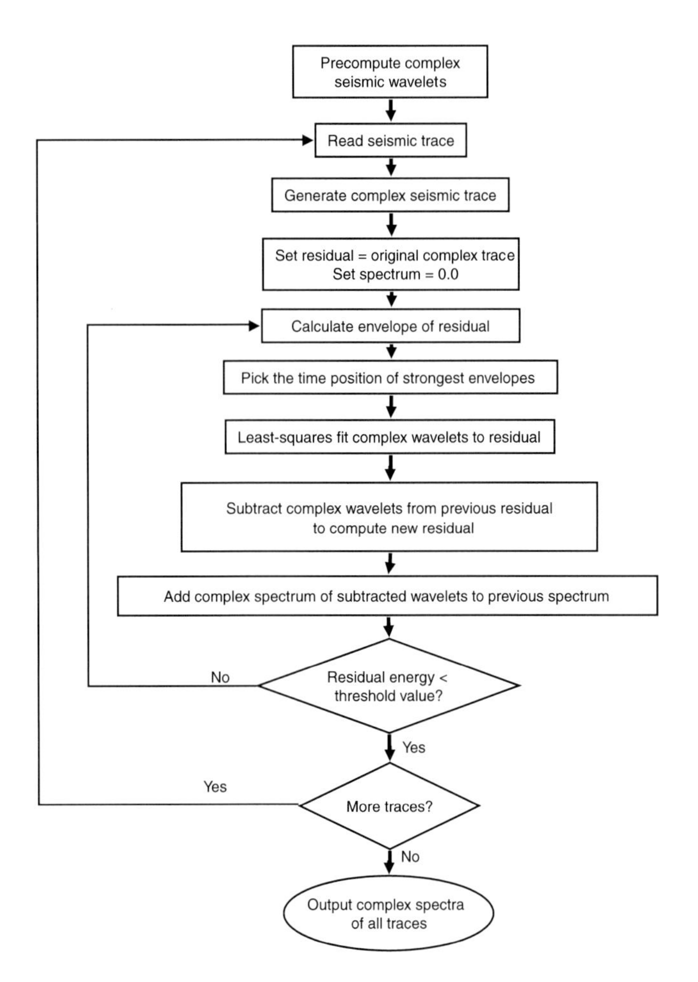

Figure 23. A flow-chart for a Morlet wavelet decomposition algorithm using a matched-pursuit technique. After Liu and Marfurt (2005).

Each input seismic trace originally displayed amplitudes as a function of time, but ultimately each trace displays amplitudes as a function of time and frequency. Similarly, each 2D seismic line becomes a time, frequency, and CDP-number cube. We show two slices through such an output cube in Figure 26. The first, Figure 26a, is a time-frequency slice for a fixed CDP number like those shown in Figure 25. The second, Figure 26b, is a time versus CDP-number cube for a selected frequency. We can interpret such common frequency gathers to be the amplitude at a given time for a given frequency.

Mapping stratigraphic features

As we do with spectral decomposition, we can use the CWT to identify thin-bed tuning. The displays shown in Figure 27 come from a Waha-Lockridge 3D seismic volume from west Texas, U.S.A. (Sinha et al., 2003). The time slice in Figure 27a indicates a channel feature in blue. A significant objective here was to try to determine the disposition and/or extension of the channel in the 3D volume, because that information is crucial for reservoir characterization. Application of the continuous-wavelet transform yielded a time-frequency-CDP volume. Figure 27b is a 20-Hz slice that does not show the channel at all; this may be because the channel is not thick enough to tune. The same time slice for 40 Hz (Figure 27c) shows the channel and is similar to the image in Figure 27a. A higher frequency (95 Hz, in Figure 27d) greatly enhances the definition of the channel feature and reveals a thin meandering channel at the bottom center. Continuous-wavelet transform spectral decomposition helps us analyze the data better and extract information that could be crucial for reservoir characterization.

Frequency-dependent Behavior of Hydrocarbon Reservoirs

Anomalous behavior of gas sands

Our first example of frequency-dependent behavior is from Alondra field in the Burgos Basin, Mexico (Burnett et al., 2003). Production comes from clean Midway-age low-impedance sands that are approximately 20 m thick, have porosities between 13% and 18%, and lie at a depth of approximately 2000 m. In Figure 28, we display the seismic data and corresponding ISA frequency components at 20 Hz and 40 Hz. At 20 Hz, the reservoir looks similar to other deeper reflectors. However, at 40 Hz, the reservoir is significantly brighter than the other nearby reflections. This anomalous amplitude is the result of both thin-bed tuning and gas charge. The gas charge makes the reservoir reflection coefficients larger than those in the adjacent brine-filled areas, and the thin-bed tuning effect of those large reflection coefficients preferentially reflects higher frequencies, thus making the 40-Hz image brighter than the 20-Hz image.

Our second example comes from the Macuspana Basin in Mexico (Burnett et al., 2003). Production here comes from thin, Pliocene-Pleistocene sands believed to be fluvial in origin. Reservoir pressures and water levels indicate that those sands can be quite discontinuous and can have complex reservoir geometry. Wavelet transforms were used to generate two frequency panels depicting the reservoir — one at 25 Hz (Figure 29a) and one at 35 Hz (Figure 29b). The reservoir appears to be continuous on the 25-Hz panel

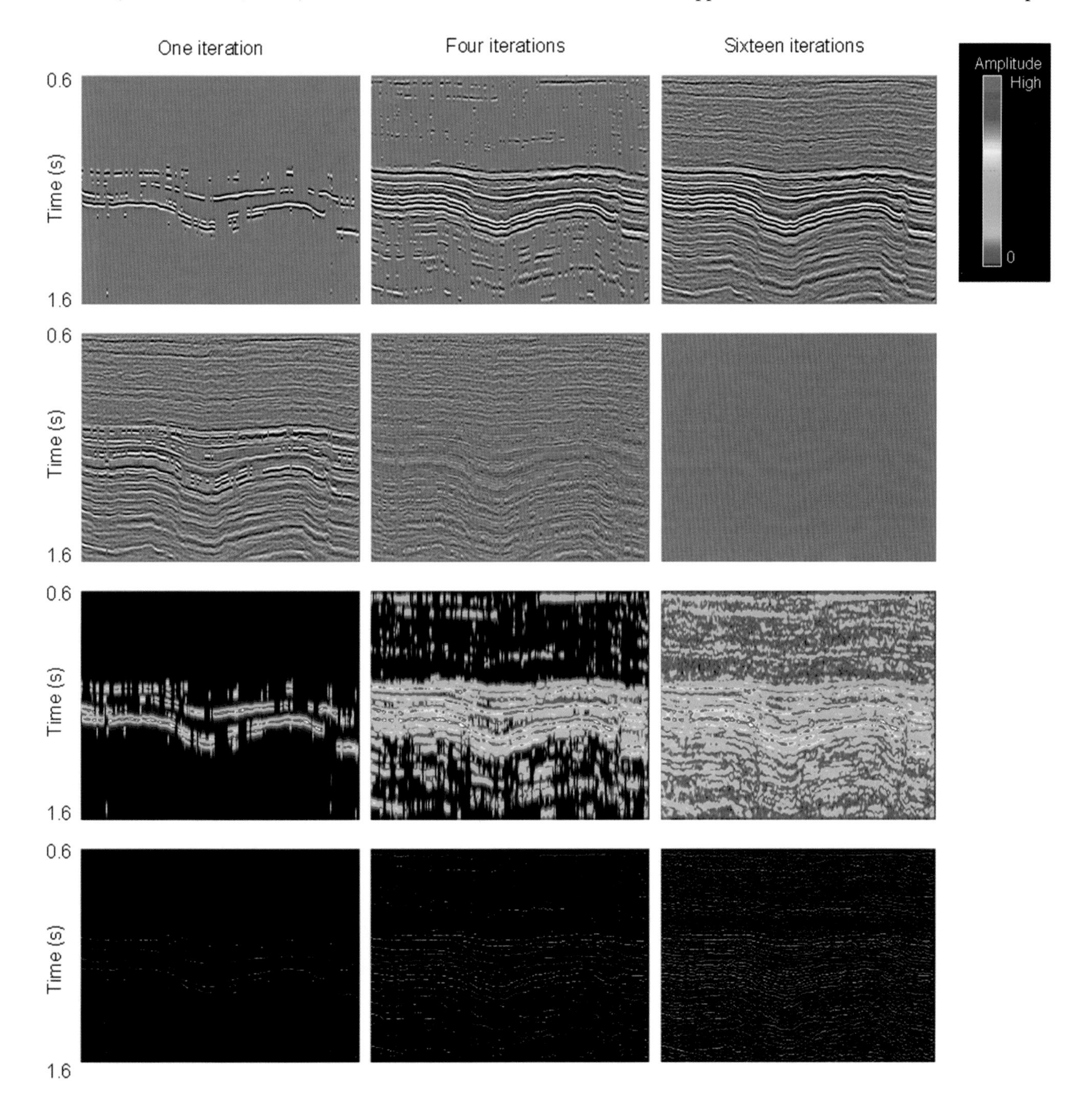

Figure 24. Example showing matched-pursuit wavelet decomposition of a seismic line from a survey acquired over the Central Basin Platform, west Texas, U.S.A. Columns represent algorithm results after the first, fourth, and sixteenth iterations of (a) modeled data, (b) residual (unmodeled) data, (c) 40-Hz component of the modeled data, and (d) wavelet location and envelope of the modeled data. The frequency and phase of the modeled wavelets are not displayed. After Liu and Marfurt (2005); data courtesy of Burlington Resources.

but is discontinuous on the 35-Hz panel — which is indeed the case, because the two wells have different pressures. Well Bitzal 11 is now plugged, but well Bitzal 9 is still producing. The extension of the reservoir amplitude to the left on the 35-Hz panel suggests that the reservoir is thinning in the direction of Bitzal 9 (Figure 29b). As occurred in the previous example, the gas in this reservoir shifts the resonant frequency to the higher side, and it can be detected easily when illuminated at this resonant frequency. The ability of the wavelet-transform technique to resolve individual reflections in the frequency domain helps us achieve such objectives.

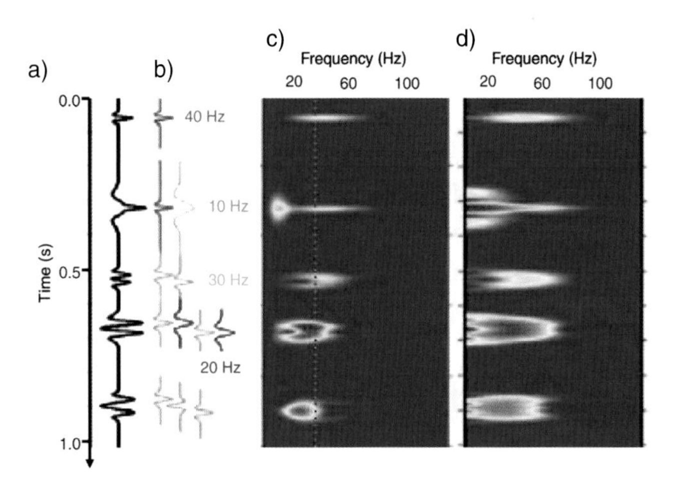

Figure 25. (a) A synthetic waveform with (b) transient arrivals (black) and constituent wavelets (color-coded by center frequency). Comparison of (c) instantaneous spectral analysis (ISA or wavelet-transform analysis) with (d) short-time-window discrete Fourier transform analysis. Although the short-window DFT has excellent vertical resolution, the frequency spectrum has been smoothed by convolution with the spectrum of the window and false events are associated with side lobes of transient arrivals. After Castagna et al. (2003).

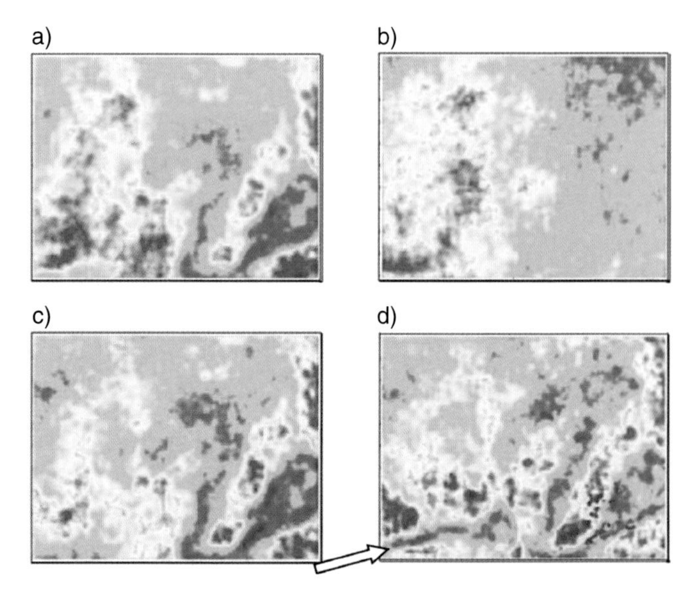

Figure 27. (a) A time slice from Waha-Lockridge 3D data volume in west Texas, showing a channel feature in blue. (b)-(d). Spectral amplitudes at (b) 20 Hz, (c) 40 Hz, and (d) 95 Hz. The channel feature is not thick enough to be seen on the 20-Hz slice but shows up well on the 40-Hz slice. At 95 Hz, we see that the channel extends to the bottom left, indicated by the white arrow. After Sinha et al. (2003).

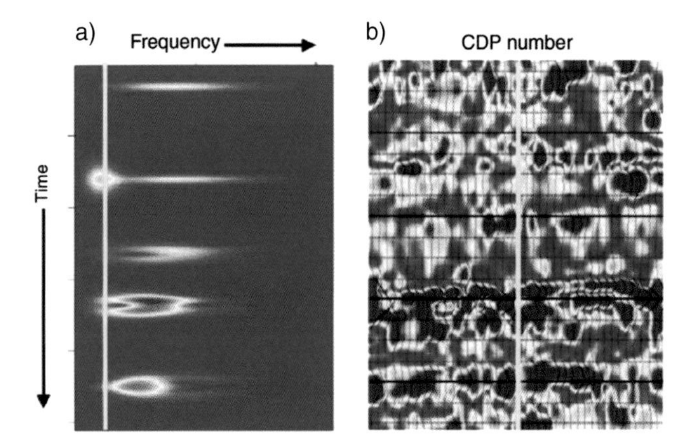

Figure 26. (a) A frequency gather and (b) a common frequency section obtained by sorting many frequency gathers according to frequency. The common frequency gathers can be thought of as instantaneous amplitude at a given frequency. After Castagna et al. (2003)

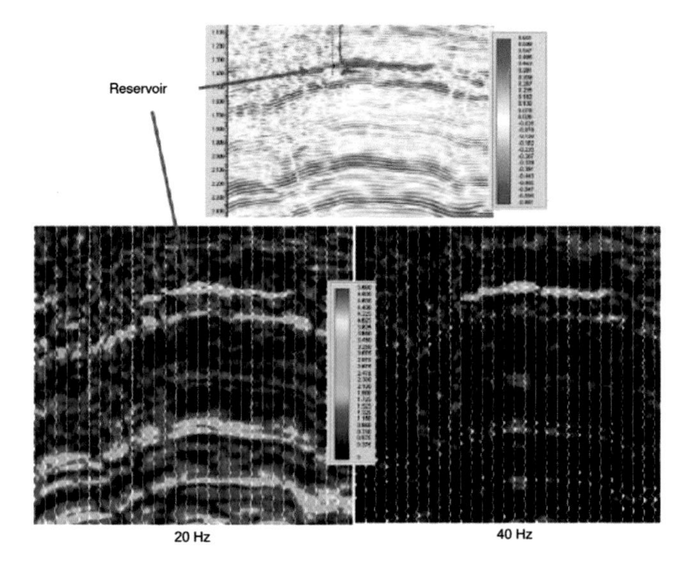

Figure 28. Seismic data and ISA components of a Midway-age gas reservoir, Burgos Basin, Mexico, showing differential reflectivity. The reservoir is not anomalous at 20 Hz but exhibits anomalous reflectivity at 40 Hz. After Burnett et al. (2003).

Our third example comes from Sun et al. (2002) and is a fractured-carbonate gas reservoir. Figure 30a is a seismic line, for which we show corresponding frequency panels generated using wavelet transforms at 40 Hz (Figure 30b) and at 60 Hz (Figure 30c). Note that the spectral amplitude below the formation at around 1.250 s is severely attenuated on the 60-Hz panel relative to the 40-Hz panel. This attenuation anomaly shows clearly on the difference section between the 40-Hz and 60-Hz panels (Figure 30d), where the amplitudes cancel above the reservoir formation and attenuation starts at the reservoir top. Sun et al. (2002) attributed this attenuation to the thick overlying gas formation.

Sun et al. (2002) made a similar observation that we show in our fourth example, which compares spectral amplitudes computed using wavelet transforms at 20 Hz (Figure 31a) and at 30 Hz (Figure 31b) for a thick reservoir in a different data set. In this example, attenuation at the higher frequency (30 Hz) again suggests a thick reservoir.

Having seen two examples of attenuation resulting from an overlying thick gas reservoir, Sun et al. (2002) provide our fifth example, which examines a thin gas reservoir. Here we show a seismic line (Figure 32a) and corresponding spectral components obtained using wavelet transforms at 30 Hz (Figure 32b) and at 70 Hz (Figure 32c). The target is at 1.650 s, between the white arrows. In contrast to the previous examples, no attenuation anomaly can be seen here because of the thinness of the reservoir.

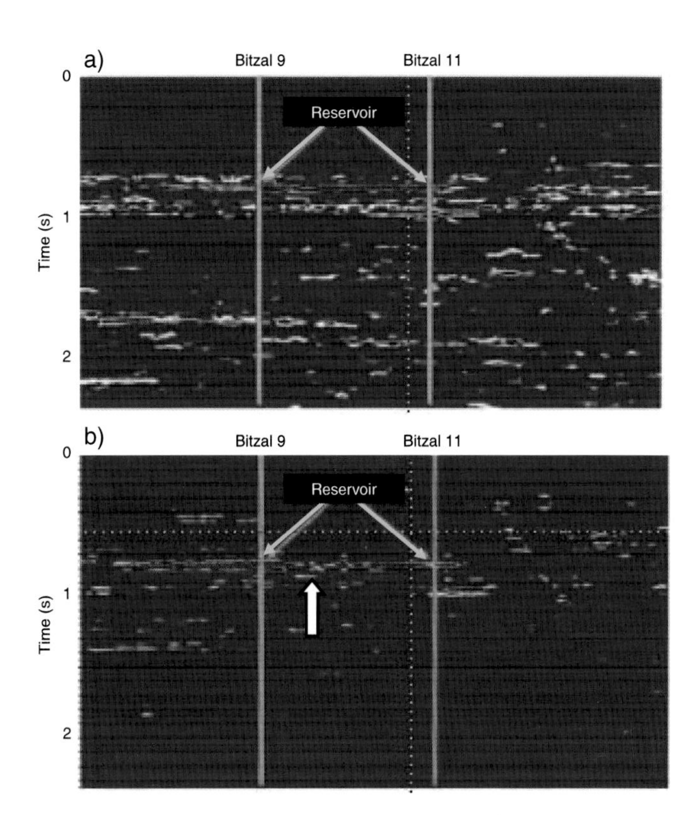

Figure 29. Isofrequency panels showing a reservoir that is more anomalous and resolved better at (b) 35 Hz than at (a) 25 Hz. The reservoir pressures in the two wells are different, implying that there are two separate reservoirs, as indicated by the white arrow on the 35-Hz component. Notice in particular how much farther to the left the reservoir extends on the 35-Hz section. After Burnett et al. (2003).

Low-frequency shadows

Low-frequency shadows often have been observed beneath amplitude anomalies associated with gas reservoirs. The term *shadow* refers to a lowering of seismic frequencies seen beneath gas reservoirs. Such low-frequency shadows are caused by abnormally high attenuation of high-frequency energy in the gas reservoir itself. In relatively thick gas reservoirs that offer a sufficient travel path, energy absorption shifts the spectral energy from high to low frequencies. Consequently, reflections from just below such reservoirs exhibit anomalously low frequencies and have been used as substantiating indicators of hydrocarbons.

To distinguish such low-frequency shadows in seismic data, traditionally we look for spectral differences in the data from above and below the zone. Thus, we determine an average spectrum above the zone, which we then compare with an average spectrum below the zone. We ascribe the difference to attenuation within the zone. Conventional transforms have shortcomings, as we explained earlier, so wavelet transforms are a good choice.

Figure 33a shows a segment of a seismic section from the Gulf of Mexico (Castagna et al., 2003). The characteristic blue trough corresponds to a reservoir. Wavelet-transform-generated frequency sections for 10 Hz and 30 Hz are shown in Figures 33b and 33c, respectively. At 10 Hz, the reservoir appears nice and bright, but interestingly, a zone of abnormally strong low-frequency energy beneath the reservoir also appears. At 30 Hz, the reservoir still shows up clearly, but the energy below the reservoir is no longer visible.

Figure 34 shows another example, here exhibiting two distinct reservoirs, from the North West Shelf of Australia. Figures 34a through c show the frequency sections for 10, 20, and 30 Hz, respectively. At 10 Hz, the brightest event on the section is the one below the deeper gas pay, which is believed to be a low-frequency shadow. At 20 Hz, the gas reservoirs show up brighter than the shadow, which still persists. At 30 Hz, the shadow disappears.

Two other examples of low-frequency shadows in images from the Gulf of Mexico are shown in Figures 35 and 36.

The diffusive-Q model

Goloshubin et al. (2002) and Korneev et al. (2004) attributed such low-frequency anomalies to a diffusive-Q model, with attenuation depending on reservoir-fluid mobility. To verify this hypothesis, they proposed separate, careful seismic processing to enhance the low-frequency component of the data, with careful attention paid to reflections that have an abnormally slow interval velocity. Their attenuation model predicts hydrocarbon mobility, m, to be proportional to the following function of spectral amplitudes, $a(\omega)$:

$$m \sim \left(\frac{\partial a}{\partial \omega}\right)^2 \omega . \qquad (6.7)$$

To validate their model, the researchers examined the data shown in Figure 36a. They then performed spectral analysis on those data and plotted the results of equation 6.7 (Figure 36b). Next, they were given production from four wells as a blind test (Figure 37a). They calibrated their theoretical relationship between their mobility attribute and production (Figure 37b) to each of the training wells. Finally, they predicted production using the map shown in Figure 38, which correlates very well with the production

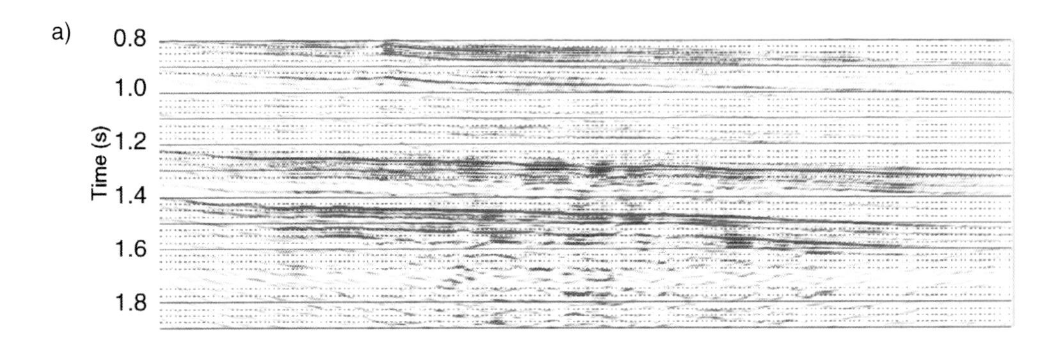

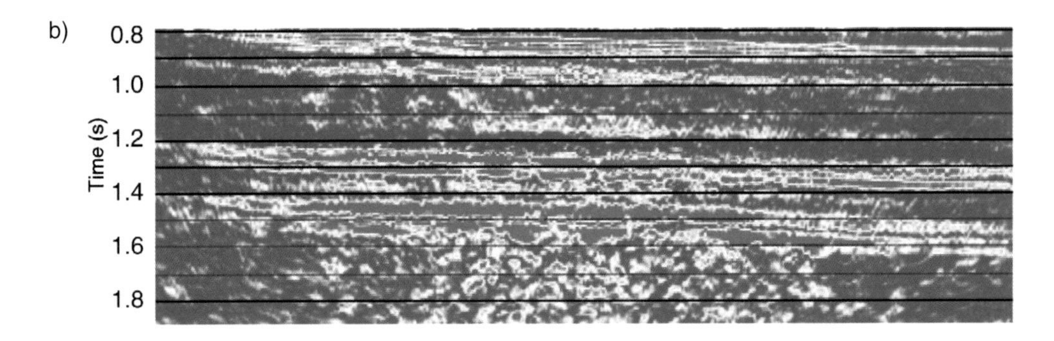

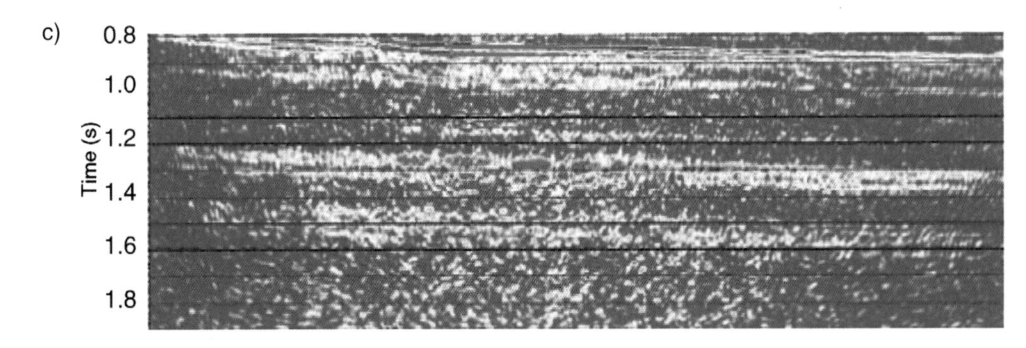

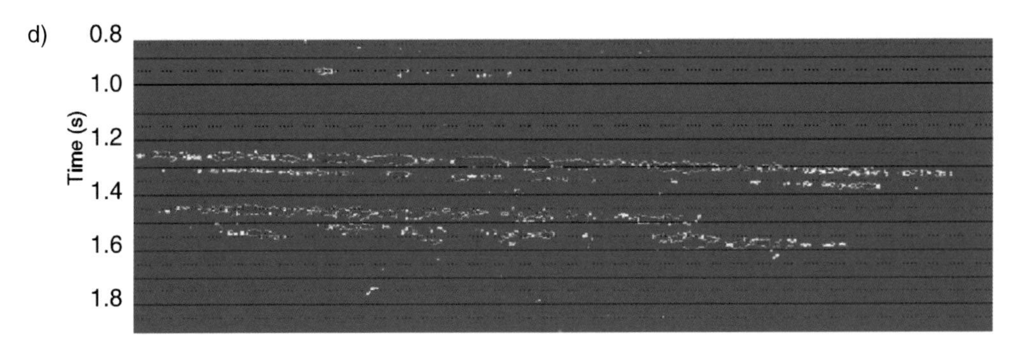

Figure 30. (a) A seismic section from a fractured carbonate reservoir. (b)-(c). Spectral amplitudes at (b) 40 Hz and (c) 60 Hz. (d) The difference between (b) and (c). After Sun et al. (2002).

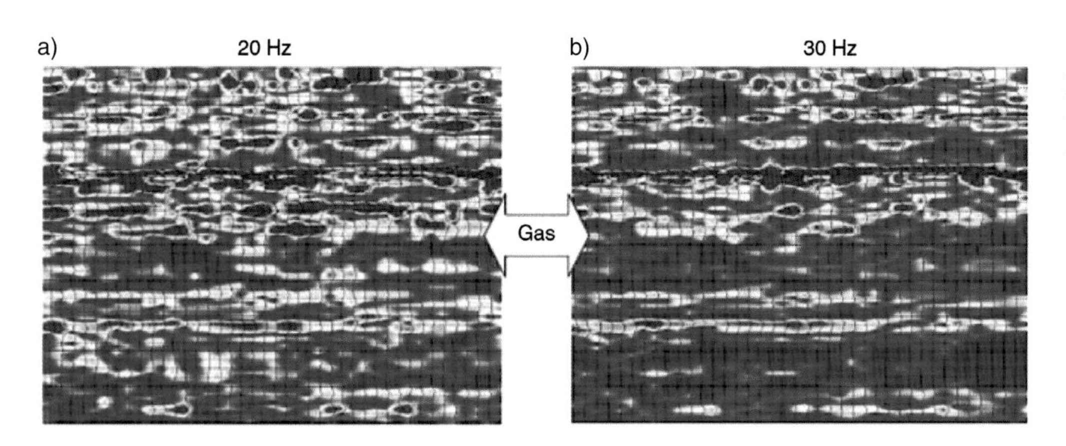

Figure 31. A spectral comparison of a thick reservoir at (a) 20 Hz and (b) 30 Hz. After Sun et al. (2002).

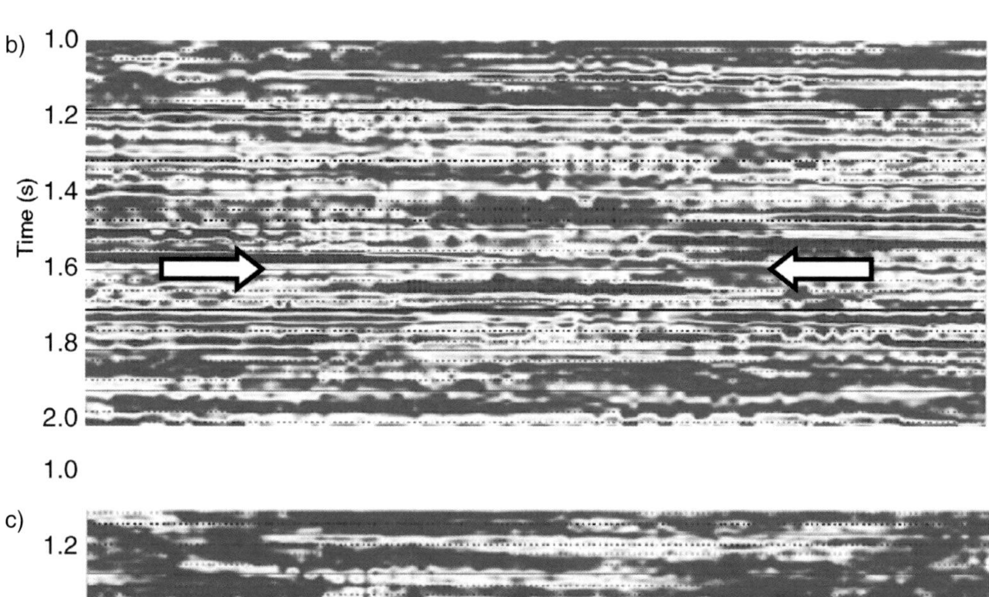

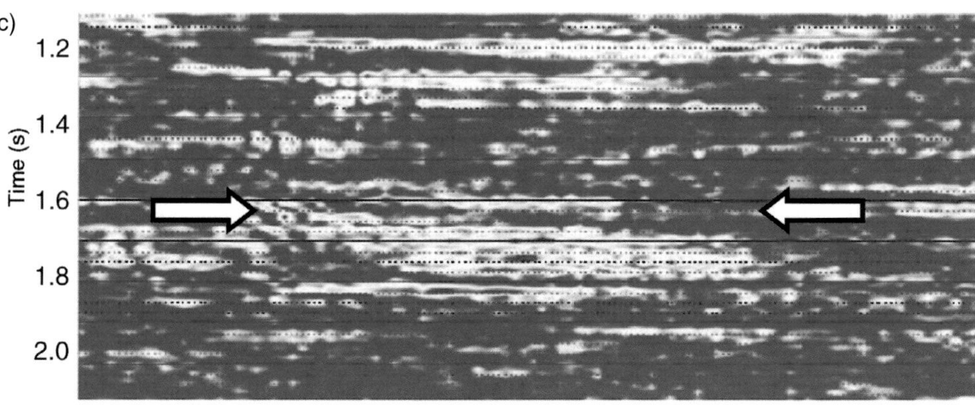

Figure 32. (a) A seismic section from a thin gas reservoir. (b)-(c). Spectral amplitudes at (b) 30 Hz and (c) 70 Hz. After Sun et al. (2002).

data not used in the training. If their approach can be applied successfully to other reservoirs, it will help differentiate fluid product and also may be the first seismic measurement that is sensitive to permeability.

a)

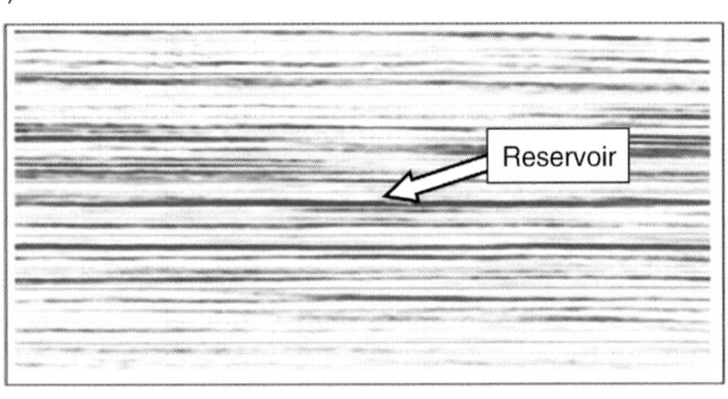

b)

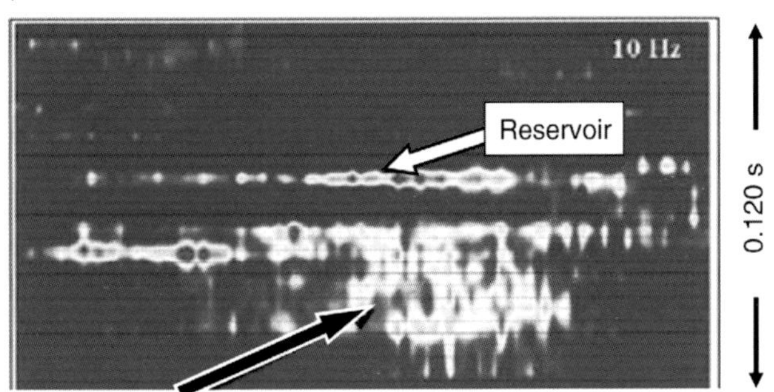

c)

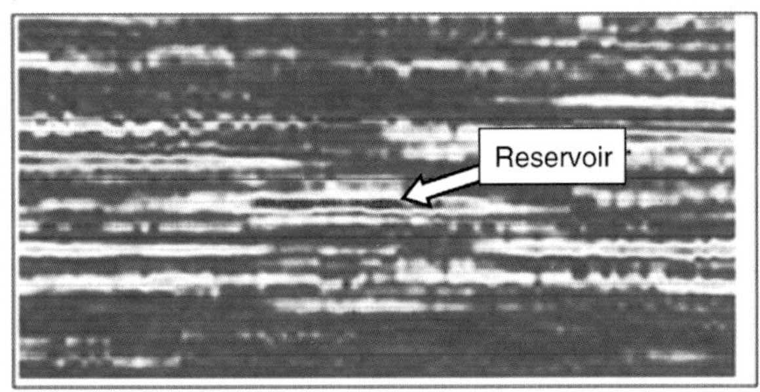

Figure 33. (a) Broadband migrated stacked section for an offshore Tertiary clastic section. Troughs are blue, and peaks are red. The reservoir (arrow) is a classic bright spot (low-impedance gas sands with a characteristic leading trough) of 15- to 20-m thickness. No shadowing is apparent beneath the reservoir. (b)-(c) Spectral amplitude images at (b) 10 Hz and (c) 30 Hz. The black arrow indicates where significant low-frequency energy occurs beneath the reservoir; that energy is absent elsewhere. The low-frequency shadow disappears in the 30-Hz image, where events immediately below the reservoir appear somewhat attenuated. After Castagna et al. (2003).

Spectral Imaging of Correlative Events (SPICE)

Until now, we have examined our multiplicity of spectral attributes in four ways: (1) through sequential examination of frequency slices; (2) through 3D visualization or optically stacking the images, such as is illustrated in Figure 8d; (3) through simple statistical analysis such as calculation of mode, bandwidth, and kurtosis; and (4) as in Goloshubin et al.'s (2002) effort, through fitting a model response to each of the spectral amplitudes. Liner et al. (2004) recently presented a novel way of combining that information, and it promises to become a very powerful interpretation tool. Their method also uses the part of the seismic waveform that traditionally has been problematic in calculations of instantaneous frequency and instantaneous dip.

Li and Liner (2004) began by using a continuous-wavelet transform. However, for spectral resolution reasons we can see (by comparing Figure 4 with Figure 3) that they used a somewhat longer analysis window ($\sigma = 3/f_c$), such as that shown in Figure 4. Unlike Castagna (2003), they did not use a matched-pursuit technique to least-squares-fit the data, nor did they minimally sample the data using orthogonal transforms, as is done routinely in data compression. Instead, they oversampled their analysis (in scale space) by a factor of 3 or 4 to obtain a more densely sampled time-scale spectrum.

Li and Liner calculated the coefficients of these wavelet transforms applied against the data $u(t)$ for each value of t and s and call the result $W(t,s)$. Next they used the concept of the Holder exponent, h, which is defined implicitly by

$$|W\{u\}(t,s)| \leq Cs^h, \tag{6.8}$$

where s is the scale, t is time, and C is a constant. The Holder exponent is the smallest possible value of h for which equation 6.8 holds true. To solve equation 6.8, we take the logarithm of both sides to obtain

$$\log|W\{u\}(t,s)| \leq \log(C) + h\log(s), \tag{6.9}$$

which Li and Liner (2004) solved using well-established curve-fitting techniques (Figure 39b).

The Holder exponent is a measure of mathematical singularities of a function. Smooth functions without singularities, such as a smoothly varying seismic source wavelet, are deficient in very high frequencies, such that h is a large positive number (Figure 40). The differential operator, $-i\omega \sim is^{-1}$, which is involved when we convert an acoustic-impedance log to a reflection-coefficient log, has a large negative Holder exponent, h. A discrete jump in the time domain has a Holder exponent of 0, and a singularity in the time domain (a delta function, commonly called a *spike* by geophysicists) has a Holder exponent of –1.

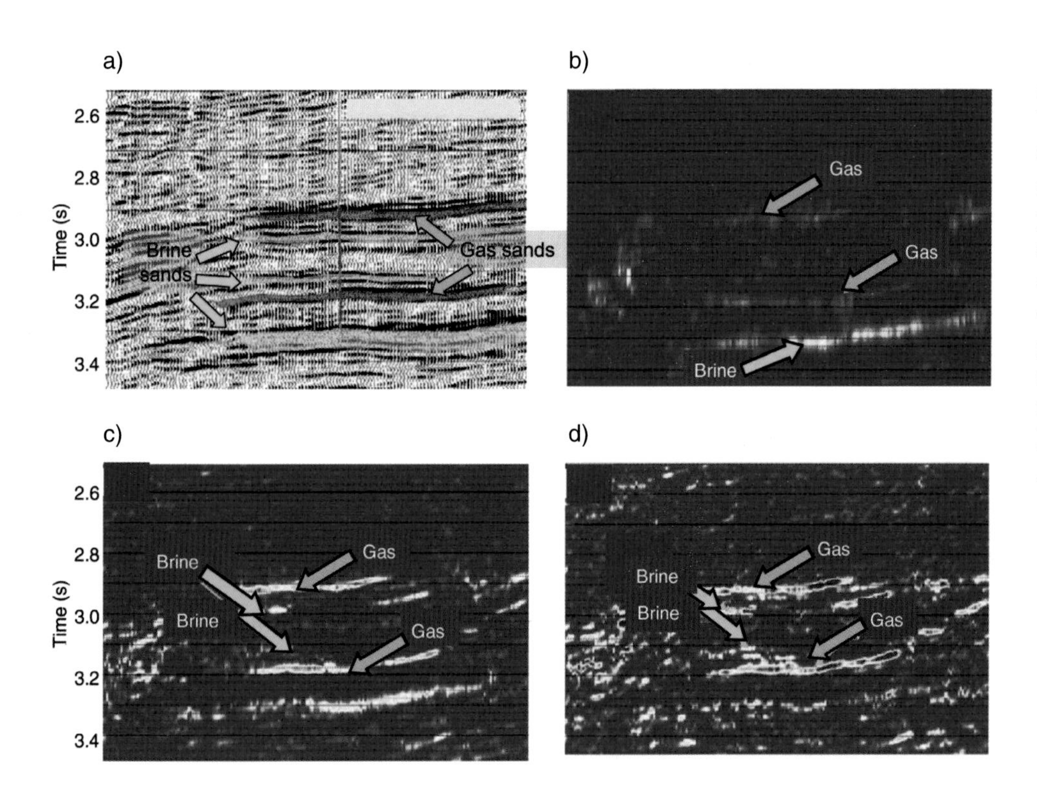

Figure 34. (a) A broadband seismic section from the North West Shelf of Australia. Gas sands are pink and brine sands are blue. (b)-(d). Spectral components at (b) 10 Hz, (c) 20 Hz, and (d) 30 Hz. The low-frequency shadow indicated by the cyan arrow beneath the lower gas sand is the strongest event at 10 Hz, but it is weaker than the overlying gas sands at 20 Hz, and it fades away at 30 Hz. After Castagna et al. (2003).

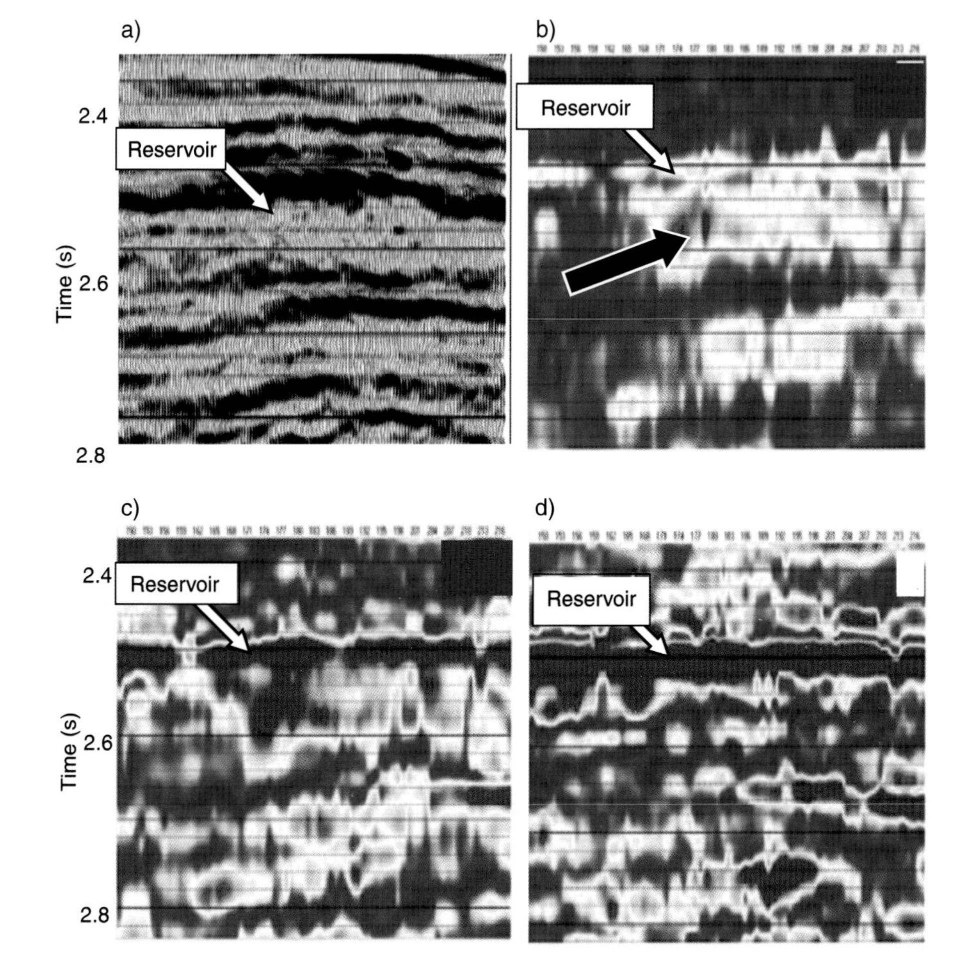

Figure 35. (a) Seismic data and (b)-(d) spectral components at (b) 8 Hz, (c) 12 Hz, and (d) 20 Hz. Shadowing is not particularly apparent on the broadband data. The low-frequency shadow beneath the reservoir indicated by the black arrow is the strongest event on the 8-Hz section, is comparable in amplitude to the reservoir at 12 Hz, and is completely attenuated at 20 Hz. After Castagna et al. (2003).

The SPICE attribute is a simple function of the Holder exponent. In Figure 41, Smythe et al. (2004) computed the SPICE attribute first from an acoustic-impedance log, next from the corresponding reflection-coefficient log, then from the corresponding synthetic seismic trace, and finally from the real seismic trace. At each stage, the time-dependent appearance of the SPICE attribute changes only slightly, because transformation from impedance log to reflection-coefficient log to synthetic does not introduce any new discontinuities. For that reason, a SPICE attribute applied to seismic data is close to what we would expect if we were to apply the SPICE attribute to an acoustic-impedance cross section — that is, to the geology.

Figure 42 shows the value of Liner et al.'s (2004) SPICE technique. Here, we see a very subtle onlap or pinch-out on the seismic data (Figure 42a). Whereas an experienced interpreter can see these geometries, today's autopickers cannot. Because the SPICE attribute accentuates discontinuities, the image in Figure 42b clearly shows the pinch-out, and in a manner by which it could be tracked by an autopicker.

Next we display a vertical slice through the seismic data (Figure 43c) and two horizon slices through the corresponding eigenstructure-coherence volume (Figure 43a) and SPICE volume (Figure 43b) from a survey from West Cameron, Gulf of Mexico, U.S.A. Here we can clearly see channels and faults on both the SPICE and the coherence images. The visibility of channels should not surprise us, because we know they often cause discontinuities in impedance, which in turn give rise to a mathematical singularity, as shown by the wavelet transform. But the appearance of faults at first is somewhat puzzling. If the faults were perfectly vertical, we suspect we would not see them using the trace-by-trace SPICE analysis technique. However, rarely are faults so nearly vertical that vertical traces do not cross them and experience singularities. Thus, the SPICE algorithm is quite complementary to coherence, in that it enhances the appearance of horizontal discontinuities instead of vertical discontinuities.

We end this chapter by reviewing some earlier work on waveform singularities. Early on, Taner et al. (1979) realized that interference of wavelets from adjacent reflectors often caused erratic estimates of instantaneous frequency. They addressed this problem by generating a smoothed, envelope-weighted version of the instantaneous frequency, which they called the *weighted-average frequency* (Figure 44). Later, Taner and coworkers developed what they termed a thin-bed indicator. The thin-bed indicator is the difference between the instantaneous frequency (Figure 45a) and the (smoother) weighted-average frequency (Figure 45b), and we display it in Figure 45c. Instantaneous acceleration (the time derivative of instantaneous frequency) also is quite sensitive to this waveform interference. Although the SPICE algorithm clearly provides more-robust images, the idea of waveform singularities has been recognized for more than 25 years.

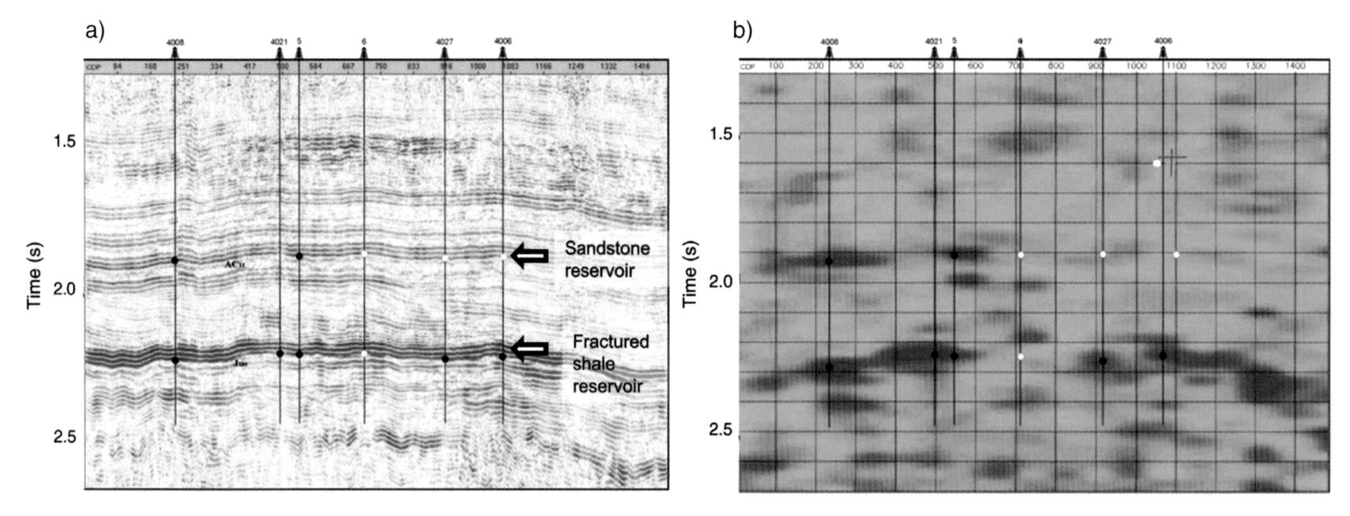

Figure 36. (a) A 2D seismic line from western Siberia and (b) a corresponding attribute proportional to fluid mobility, *m*, given by equation 6.8. Black circles indicate high oil saturation. White circles indicate no oil saturation. Some of these wells will be used to predict hydrocarbons, as shown in Figure 37. After Goloshubin et al. (2002).

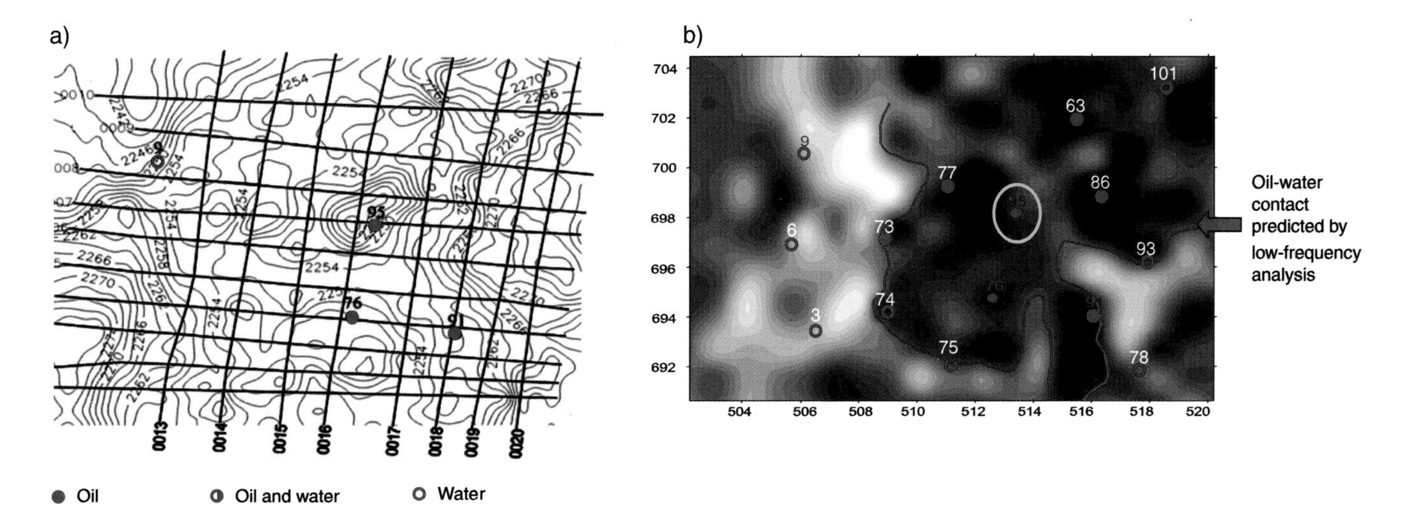

Figure 37. (a) A time-structure map corresponding to the 2D survey shown in Figure 36a. A blind test based on four calibration wells (three oil wells and one water well) was used to calibrate the hydrocarbon-imaging attribute shown in Figure 34b to the theoretical curve shown here in (b), which is a map of the fluid mobility attribute. The orange circled well is used in the calibration shown in Figure 38.

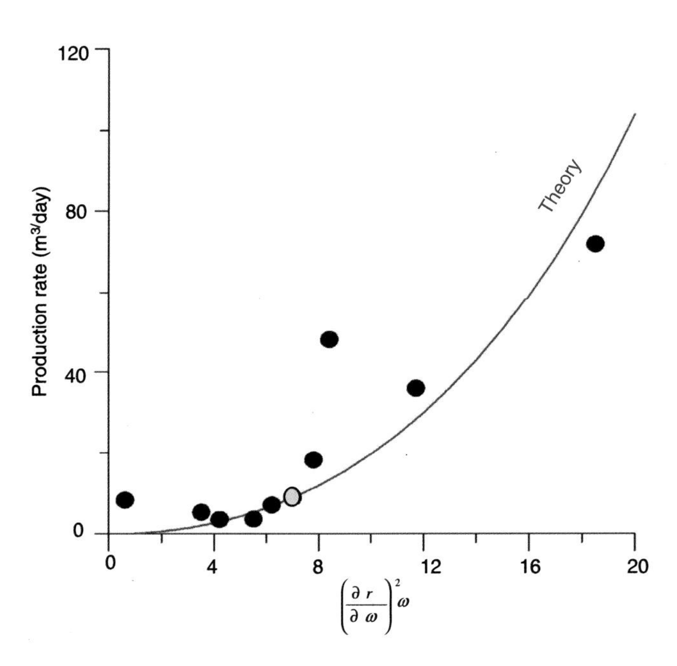

Figure 38. Production versus the mobility attribute given by equation 6.7 for the wells shown in Figure 37b. The predicted hydrocarbon production (the blue curve) as a function of the mobility factor is calibrated to fit the production data seen at the orange circled well, which corresponds to the orange data point in Figure 37b. Note how closely the production at the other wells follows this theoretical curve. After Goloshubin et al. (2002).

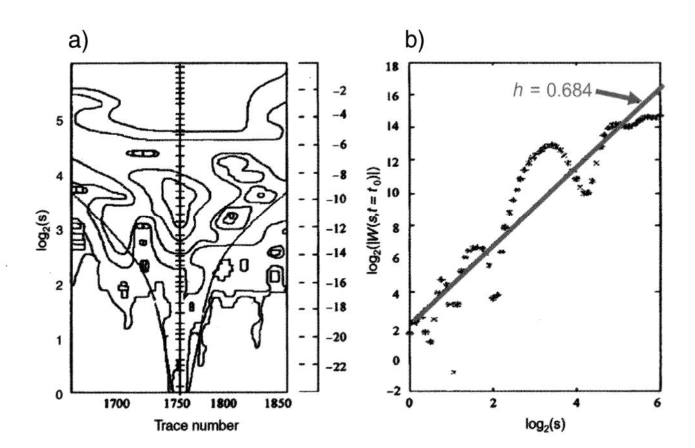

Figure 39. (a) A scalogram contour plot of wavelet spectral coefficients at a given time and for a suite of seismic traces. (b) Fitting of the power of the Holder exponent to wavelet coefficients. Each wavelet has its own spectrum (as shown in Figure 4) and does not correspond to a single carrier frequency, f_c. After Li and Liner (2004).

Figure 40. The Holder exponent h measures the strength of a singularity. The higher the value of h, the more regular the function (distribution) is.

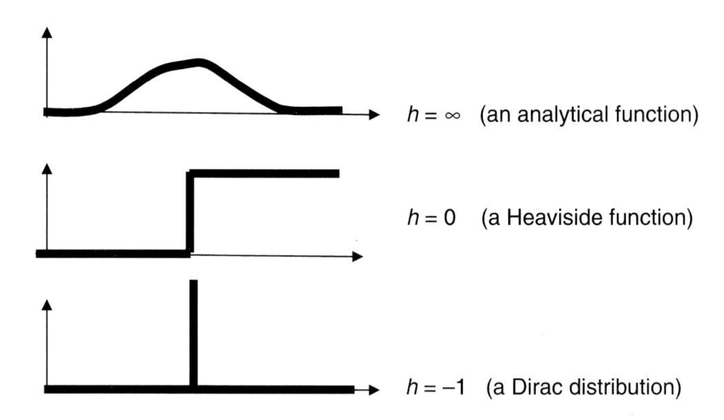

Figure 41. Singularities measured by the Holder exponent in the underlying acoustic impedance retain the same form if we convolve the data with smooth analytical functions. In this case, we begin with a discontinuity in the acoustic impedance, indicated between the yellow and blue lithologies. Because the derivative operator in the frequency (and scale) domain, $-iw$, is continuous, we do not change the singular nature of our acoustic-impedance profile. Likewise, because the source wavelet used in generating a synthetic trace also is continuous, the singularity on the synthetic trace is nearly identical to that of the acoustic impedance. Because the synthetic trace was designed to match the real seismic trace, we can show that the singularity on the seismic data is very close to the singularity seen on the acoustic-impedance log. Thus, the SPICE algorithm represents changes in the acoustic-impedance log. After Smythe et al. (2004).

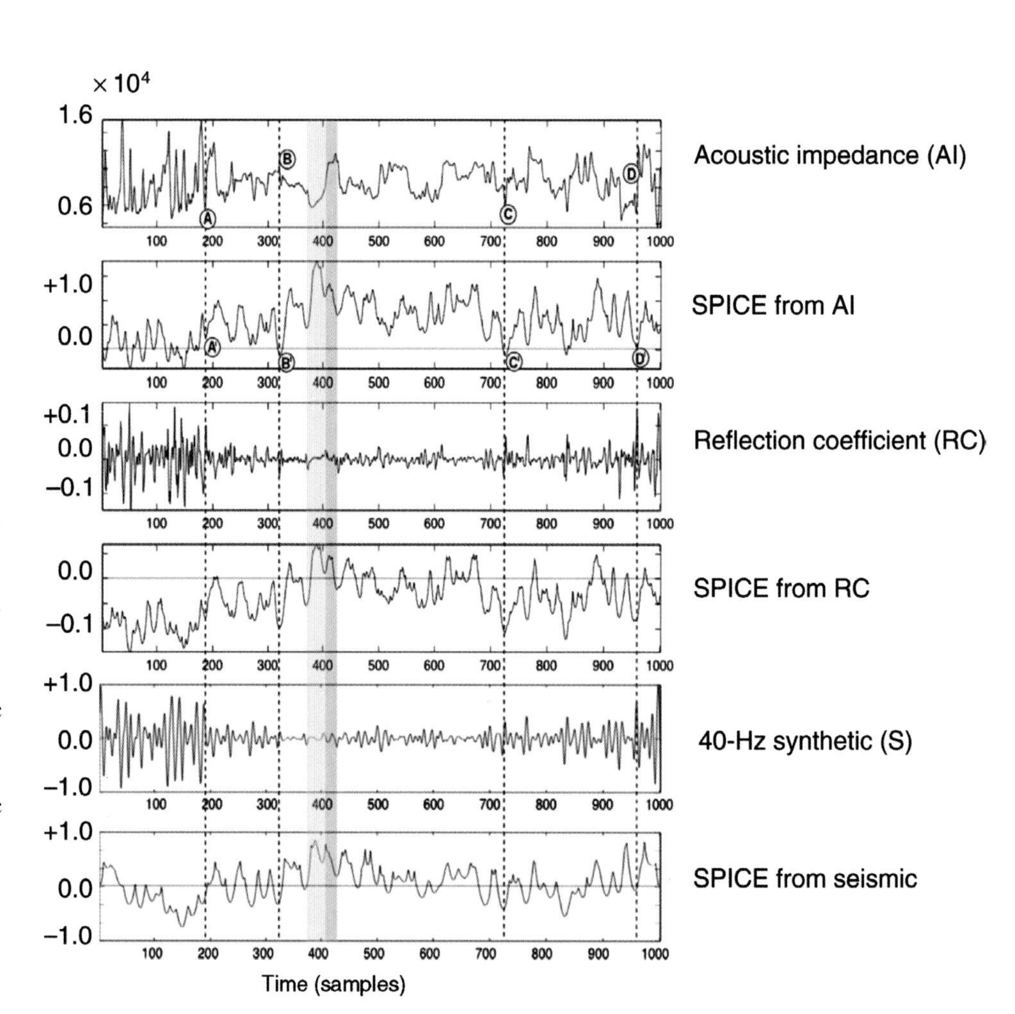

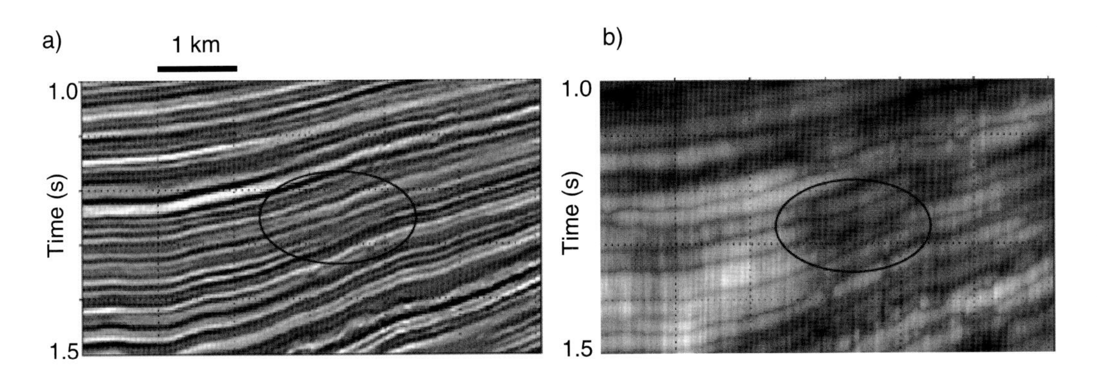

Figure 42. Vertical slices through (a) a seismic data volume and (b) a SPICE volume. The SPICE algorithm enhances singularities between waveforms, such as the subtle pinch-out circled. After Liner et al. (2004).

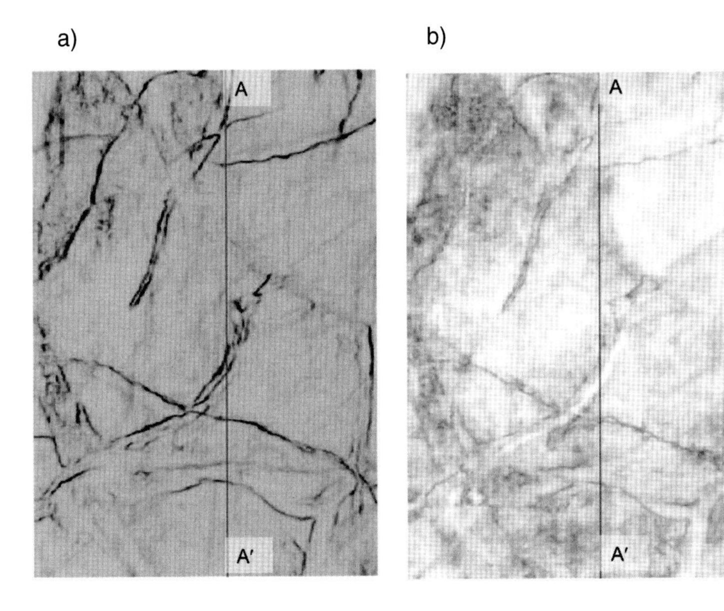

Figure 43. Miocene horizon slices from a West Cameron, Gulf of Mexico, U.S.A., survey through (a) an eigenstructure coherence volume and (b) a SPICE volume. (c) A vertical section showing a known Miocene channel. After Liner et al. (2004).

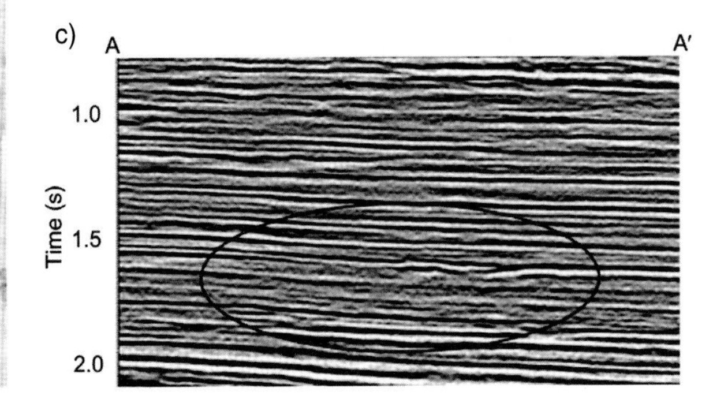

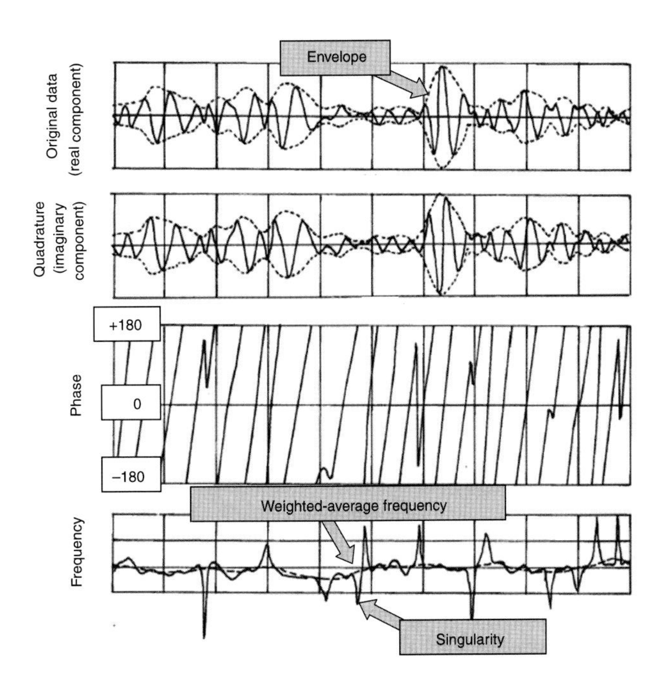

Figure 44. Complex trace attributes, including the real trace, its quadrature, its envelope, and its instantaneous phase and instantaneous frequency. Waveform interference results in singularities in the instantaneous frequency, such as the negative excursion indicated by the lowermost gray arrow. Such singularities can be suppressed by calculating a weighted-average frequency obtained by weighting the instantaneous frequency by the envelope and smoothing over a short time window. After Taner et al. (1979).

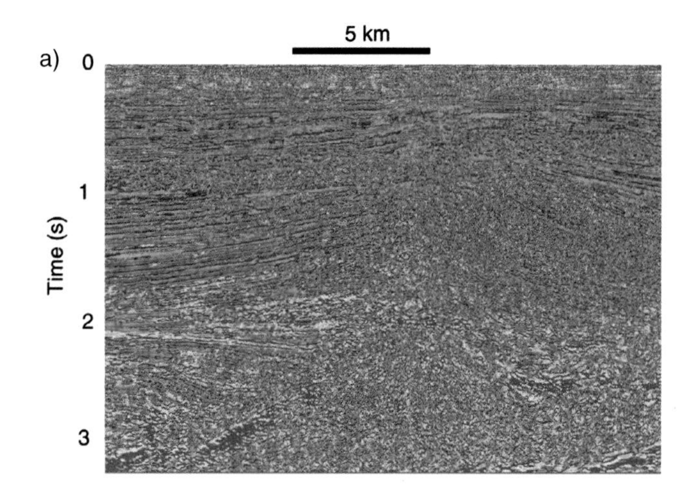

Figure 45. (a) An instantaneous frequency, (b) a weighted-average frequency, and (c) the difference between (a) and (b), giving a thin-bed indicator attribute. The image in (c) is plotted using a color bar that highlights the extreme values. This thin-bed indicator is based on the same physical phenomena as the SPICE algorithm displayed in Figure 41. After Taner (2000).

Chapter Summary

In this chapter, we have reviewed the spectral-analysis techniques used by interpreters. The SWDFT and wavelet transforms differ from each other through the choice of their analysis window. Spectral decomposition uses a fixed-length analysis window for all frequencies, allowing us to compare which frequency component is dominant within a geologic formation. In contrast, continuous-wavelet transforms use windows that are inversely proportional to the frequency being analyzed, thereby providing maximum temporal resolution at the expense of analyzing different regions of a geologic formation. The SWDFT and wavelet components are sensitive to thin-bed tuning, to attenuation resulting from overlying scatterers and hydrocarbons, and to the gas-oil ratio. Moreover, spectral components are able to detect lateral changes in thin-bed tuning well below the classical one-quarter-wavelength limits of resolution.

Because spectral decomposition operates on a fixed, user-defined, temporal window, within which the spectral content is balanced, we conclude that SWDFT is the method of choice when formation-based attributes are appropriate — such as when we are estimating tuning thickness or mapping stratigraphic variability for examination on maps. In contrast, because the (matched-pursuit) CWT decomposition reconstructs the data and has minimal mixing of temporally separate events, we feel that CWT decomposition is the method of choice for direct hydrocarbon indicators, seismic-attenuation studies, and enhancement of seismic bandwidth.

Several reasons exist for low-frequency anomalies in properly processed seismic data, including waveform healing below an overlying gas reservoir, fault whispers, and most intriguing, reservoir permeability and the viscous response of oil.

The CWT forms the basis of the recently introduced SPICE algorithm, which maps discontinuities between reflector wavelets and promises to be a powerful tool in mapping unconformities and subtle sequence boundaries. By construction, the SPICE algorithm is very sensitive to changes in the underlying acoustic impedance of interest and is relatively insensitive to the (temporally smooth) seismic source wavelet. Although we may not expect the SPICE algorithm to see vertical faults because it operates on individual traces one at a time, faults rarely are perfectly vertical. Thus, the SPICE algorithm can map not only singularities resulting from stratigraphy but also singularities resulting from faulting.

References

Bahorich, M., A. Motsch, K. Laughlin, and G. Partyka, 2002, Amplitude responses image reservoir: Hart's E & P, January, 59–61.

Burnett, M. D., and J. P. Castagna, 2003, Application of spectral decomposition to gas basins in Mexico: The Leading Edge, **22**, 1130–1141.

Castagna, J. P., 2005., Spectral decomposition and high resolution reflectivity inversion: Oral presentation, Oklahoma City Geophysical Society, January 17.

Castagna, J. P., S. Sun, and R. W. Siegfried, 2003, Instantaneous spectral analysis: Detection of low-frequency shadows associated with hydrocarbons: The Leading Edge, **22**, 120–127.

del Valle-García, R., and L. Ramirez-Cruz, 2002, Spectral attributes for attenuation analysis in a fractured carbonate reservoir: The Leading Edge, **21**, 1038–1041.

Goloshubin, G., V. Korneev, and V. Vingalov, 2002, Seismic low-frequency effects from oil-saturated reservoir zones: 72nd Annual International Meeting, SEG, Expanded Abstracts, 1813–1816.

Hall, M., and E. Trouillot, 2004, Predicting stratigraphy with spectral decomposition: 2004 CSEG National Convention.

Johann, P., G. Ragignin, and M. Spinola, 2003, Spectral decomposition reveals geological hidden features in the amplitude maps from a deep-water reservoir in the Campos Basin: 73rd Annual International Meeting, SEG, Expanded Abstracts, 1740–1743.

Kallweit, R. S., and L. C. Wood, 1982, The limits of resolution of zero-phase wavelets: Geophysics, **47**, 1035–1046.

Korneev, V. A., G. M. Goloshubin, T. M. Daley, and D. B. Silin, 2004, Seismic low-frequency effects in monitoring fluid-saturated reservoirs: Geophysics, **69**, 522–532.

Laughlin, K., P. Garossino, and G. Partyka, 2002, Spectral decomp applied to 3-D: AAPG Explorer, May, http://www.aapg.org/explorer/geophysica_corner/2002/05gpc.cfm, accessed April 9, 2005.

Li, C.-F., and C. L. Liner, 2004, Wavelet-based analysis of singularities in seismic data: US Patent 6,745,129.

Liner, C., C.-F. Li, A. Gersztenkorn, and J. Smythe, 2004, SPICE: A new general seismic attribute: 72nd Annual International Meeting, SEG, Expanded Abstracts, 433–436.

Liu, J., and K. J. Marfurt, 2005, Matching-pursuit decomposition using Morlet wavelets: 75th Annual International Meeting, SEG, Expanded Abstracts.

Marfurt, K. J., and R. L. Kirlin, 2001, Narrow-band spectral analysis and thin-bed tuning: Geophysics, **66**, 1274–1283.

Partyka, G., 2001, Seismic thickness estimation: Three approaches, pros and cons, 71st Annual International Meeting, SEG, Expanded Abstracts, 503–506.

Partyka, G., J. Gridley, and J. A. Lopez, 1999, Interpretational applications of spectral decomposition in reservoir characterization: The Leading Edge, **18**, 353–360.

Partyka, G., J. Thomas, K. Turco, and D. Hartmann, 2000, Upscaling petrophysical properties to the seismic scale: 70th Annual International Meeting, SEG, Expanded Abstracts, 1636–1638.

Peyton, L., R. Bottjer, and G. Partyka, 1998, Interpretation of incised valleys using new 3-D seismic techniques: A case history using spectral decomposition and coherency: The Leading Edge, **17**, 1294–1298.

Robertson, J. D., and H. H. Nogami, 1984, Complex seismic trace analysis of thin beds: The Leading Edge, **49**, 344–352.

Sinha, S., P. Routh, P. Anno, and J. Castagna, 2003, Time-frequency attribute of seismic data using continuous wavelet transform: 73rd Annual International Meeting, SEG, Expanded Abstracts, 1481–1484.

Smythe, J., A. Gersztenkorn, B. Radovich, C.-F. Li, and, C. Liner, 2004, SPICE: Layered Gulf of Mexico shelf framework from spectral imaging: The Leading Edge, **23**, 921–926.

Sun, S., R. Siegfried, and J. Castagna, 2002, Examples of wavelet transform time-frequency analysis in direct hydrocarbon detection: 72nd Annual International Meeting, SEG, Expanded Abstracts, 457–460.

Taner, M. T, 2000, Attributes revisited: http://www.rocksolidimages.com/pdf/attrib_revisited.htm

Taner, M. T., F. Koehler, and R. E. Sheriff, 1979, Complex seismic trace analysis: Geophysics, **44**, 1041–1063.

Widess, M. B., 1973, How thin is a thin bed?: Geophysics, **38,** 1176–1254.

Xia, L., 1999, Spectral analysis of seismic data using wavelet transforms: M.S. thesis, University of Oklahoma.

Chapter 7

Influence of Data Acquisition and Processing on Geometric Attributes

Chapter Objectives

After reading this chapter, you will be able to

- use coherence and other attributes to control the quality of the choice of processing parameters
- recognize an acquisition footprint on seismic attribute time and horizon slices
- identify the limits to vertical and lateral resolution
- choose an appropriate migration algorithm
- evaluate the use of impedance inversion and vertical seismic profiles to improve vertical resolution

Introduction

Because the quality of seismic data acquisition and processing directly determines our ability to manually interpret a seismic section, it is no surprise that seismic data quality also directly influences our results when we calculate geometric attributes. Indeed, subtle acquisition-footprint artifacts, which are common in most seismic data volumes, generally do not impede an experienced interpreter from constructing a time-structure map (although autotrackers fail to track horizons). However, the same acquisition footprint can contaminate geometric-attribute images considerably. Significant data-quality issues, such as poorly migrated subsalt seismic images that require much interpreter care and judgment, can render attribute images almost useless.

Geometric attributes are not alone in being sensitive to data quality. Although we do not address them in this text, AVO and impedance inversion are equally sensitive to data quality. More important, modern reservoir characterization workflows based on geostatistics or neural networks are even more sensitive to seismic noise than are the attributes mentioned.

The quality of seismic data is determined (1) by processes the analyst can control, such as the choice of algorithmic parameters; (2) by processes controlled by others, such as limitations on seismic aperture and fold by a fixed budget; and (3) by processes controlled by geology, such as a complex overburden above the target. Henry (2004) revisited Sheriff's (1975) analysis of factors that determine seismic data and amplitude, which we summarize in Figure 1. Each of these problems (except for poor illumination) can be ameliorated partially through careful processing or can be accounted for through careful interpretation.

The sensitivity of geometric attributes to seismic data quality is a double-edged sword. We can accept attribute artifacts and attempt to interpret through them, or alternatively, we can use this sensitivity as an evaluation tool to help us choose improved processing parameters and flows.

We begin this chapter by evaluating the sensitivity of geometric-attribute images to the most basic processing parameters — in particular to statics and velocities. Then we examine the cause and appearance of acquisition footprint. Next, we review the limits to lateral resolution and demonstrate the value of prestack migration. We end the chapter with a discussion on improving vertical resolution through impedance inversion (which uses well control) and through waveform estimation and deconvolution using vertical seismic profiles.

Importance of Quality Control in Seismic Processing

Seismic processing involves multiple steps, and the quality of every step's output is a function of the input data and the parameters used in processing those data. Selection of the processing steps and of the parameters themselves is vulnerable to human error, be it biased or unintentional. Consequently, we perform procedural checks to evaluate the results at different steps. Quality control is recognized as an essential and highly cost-effective step in exploration programs.

To perform effective quality control, the seismic analyst must make sure that with each processing step the selected process or algorithm adds value to the resulting data. Added value may be measured in terms of better definition of the events or features of interest, in terms of overall improvement in the signal-to-noise ratio, or in terms of some processing product such as an autocorrelogram that reveals the data's periodicity. If a given process does not add value, the analyst should eliminate it from the flow. If a process diminishes the quality of the image, the analyst must isolate or understand the reason for loss of quality and then remove that problem before proceeding further.

With today's continually swelling volumes of 3D seismic data and increasing sophistication of geophysical algorithms, prompt and quick quality-control measures need to be adopted and executed. After each key step of the processing sequence, the analyst extracts time slices from the 3D seismic volume to ensure that either the signal quality is maintained or the image is focused better and that no undesired effects have been introduced.

Discontinuities, tears, or striations observed on time slices in the inline or crossline directions usually indicate problems such as improper source and receiver indexing during data preparation, or disharmonization of statics between swaths. The analyst must identify such discontinuities to avoid introducing artifacts and corrupting the reliability of the results for subsequent interpretation.

Because data volumes have grown exponentially in size and processing algorithms have grown increasingly more sophisticated, oil-company geophysicists have become more involved in interpretation, data integration, and reservoir characterization and frequently outsource the acquisition and processing tasks to specialists in service companies.

How can a young geophysicist (or more likely still, a young geologist or engineer) who lacks hands-on processing experience judge whether the correct processing parameters were chosen? One approach is to evaluate alternative-processing choices (and their corresponding intermediate seismic images) in the context of geology, and particularly, in the context of the structural and stratigraphic features that make sense for the basin in question.

Interpretation-driven processing has long been used in seismic processing. In the middle 1980s, interpreters commonly unfurled long rolls of paper down the hall, showing a suite of vertical slices through 3D migrated volumes, with multiple panels that had been generated using a different multiplicative factor of the stacking velocity. The interpreter doing quality control then chose the sections that showed the best reflector terminations against faults. In contrast, migration velocities that were too fast or too slow resulted in fault terminations being contaminated by residual diffraction smiles or frowns. In the next section we show how this same process is easily extended to modern 3D processing techniques using geometric attributes.

Coherence as a Quality-control Indicator

Time slices usually cut across structural dip, thereby sampling both positive and negative lobes of the seismic waveform. Because subtle changes in geology are easily masked by the waveform on seismic time slices, these slices are not ideal for interpretation. In previous chapters, we have shown how coherence, and other attributes, such as

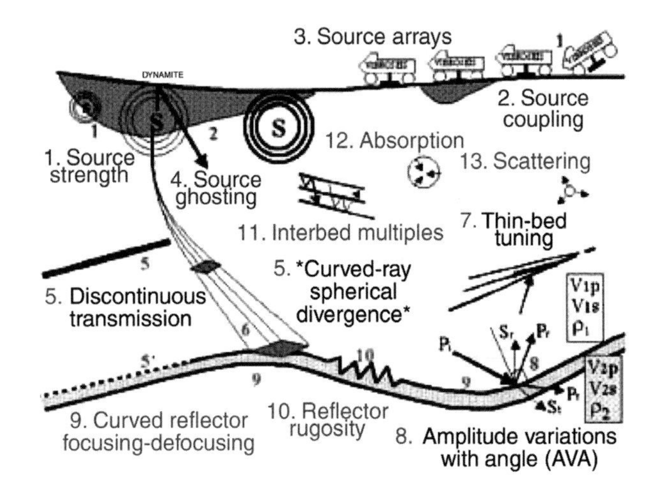

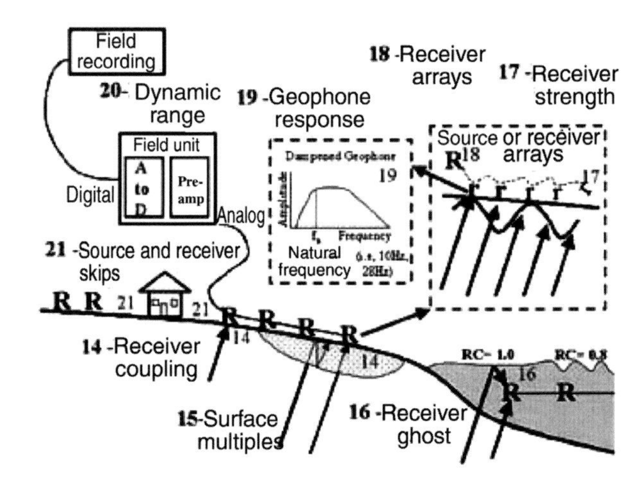

Figure 1. Factors that affect seismic amplitudes. After Henry (2004) and in turn after Sheriff (1975).

spectral decomposition, can aid the interpreter by enhancing subtle structural and stratigraphic features.

Here we show how coherence can help the seismic processor. Shortcomings in data acquisition, trace indexing, and processing introduce similar (although undesirable) temporal and spatial waveform changes. For that reason, coherence provides an excellent quality-control tool in the processing shop and an excellent means of communicating that quality control to the nonprocessing oil-company geophysicist.

In an attribute-driven workflow, the seismic analyst performs a series of key processing steps, thereby generating either a coherence volume or coarsely spaced coherence time slices, and then examines the images interactively on a workstation (Figure 2). Coherence volumes may be generated at the brute stack stage, after application of residual statics, after application of DMO, and finally, after migration.

In Figure 3, we show a comparison of amplitude and coherence time slices at different stages of the processing sequence. Notice that the time slice at the brute-stack stage (Figures 3a and 3d) shows crisscrossing channels with poorly defined edges, as well as some poorly focused faults. After residual statics (Figures 3b and 3e), the edges of the channels are better defined and the faults are clearer. After the final migration (Figures 3c and 3f), the time slice reveals sharp channel edges and fault discontinuities. In this sequence, value is added at each step of the processing flow. Using coherence provides the analyst with a quantitative quality-control measure at each stage in the flow and ensures that an optimal product is being readied.

Often instances occur wherein the early part of the processing sequence proceeds as planned, but inspection of the final product reveals a previously unseen feature of interest, and that feature appears to be focused suboptimally. In Figure 4 we show an example in which coherence was run on such a final product, but the quality-control step, in which the channels were identified, revealed blurred channel edges (Figure 4a). In such cases, we must revert to an earlier processing step that precedes deterioration of the results. In this example, we needed to reanalyze the migration velocities, which then yielded the image shown in Figure 4b.

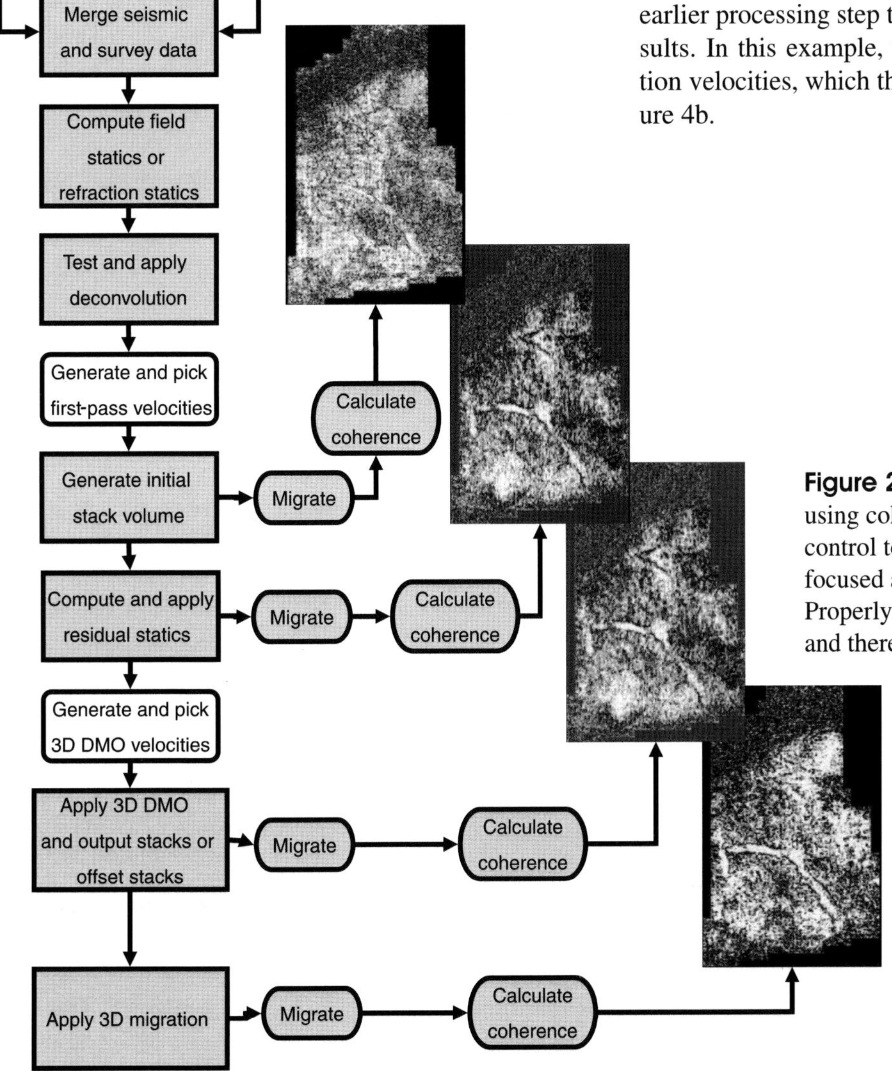

Figure 2. A typical processing sequence, using coherence as a processing quality-control tool. Poorly imaged volumes are less focused and therefore are more coherent. Properly imaged volumes are more focused and therefore are less coherent.

Junior-level seismic analysts without a strong geology background are comfortable choosing processing parameters and workflows that enhance reflector continuity and fault terminations. However, identification of subtler stratigraphic features such as channels, slumps, dewatering features, reefs, and karst on vertical and horizontal slices through the seismic data requires significant experience and a great deal of time. By transforming intermediate seismic data into images that look more geologic, the processing specialist can choose appropriate parameters and thereby provide the interpreter with an improved product.

The obvious extension is target-oriented processing. Here, coherence images guide a choice of parameters that is driven more by the improvement of details within the reservoir and less by processing protocols that work well for the data volume as a whole.

In addition to aiding interpreters in their choice of processing parameters, coherence can help workers decide whether one particular algorithm is better than another in, say, reducing backscattered noise. In Figure 5, we compare the performance of two different algorithms for random noise attenuation: *f-x-y* deconvolution in Figure 5a, and τ-*p-q* filtering in Figure 5b. In this case, *f-x-y* deconvolution provides a sharper image.

Besides the above uses for coherence, we can use it to evaluate the performance of a process or an algorithm more

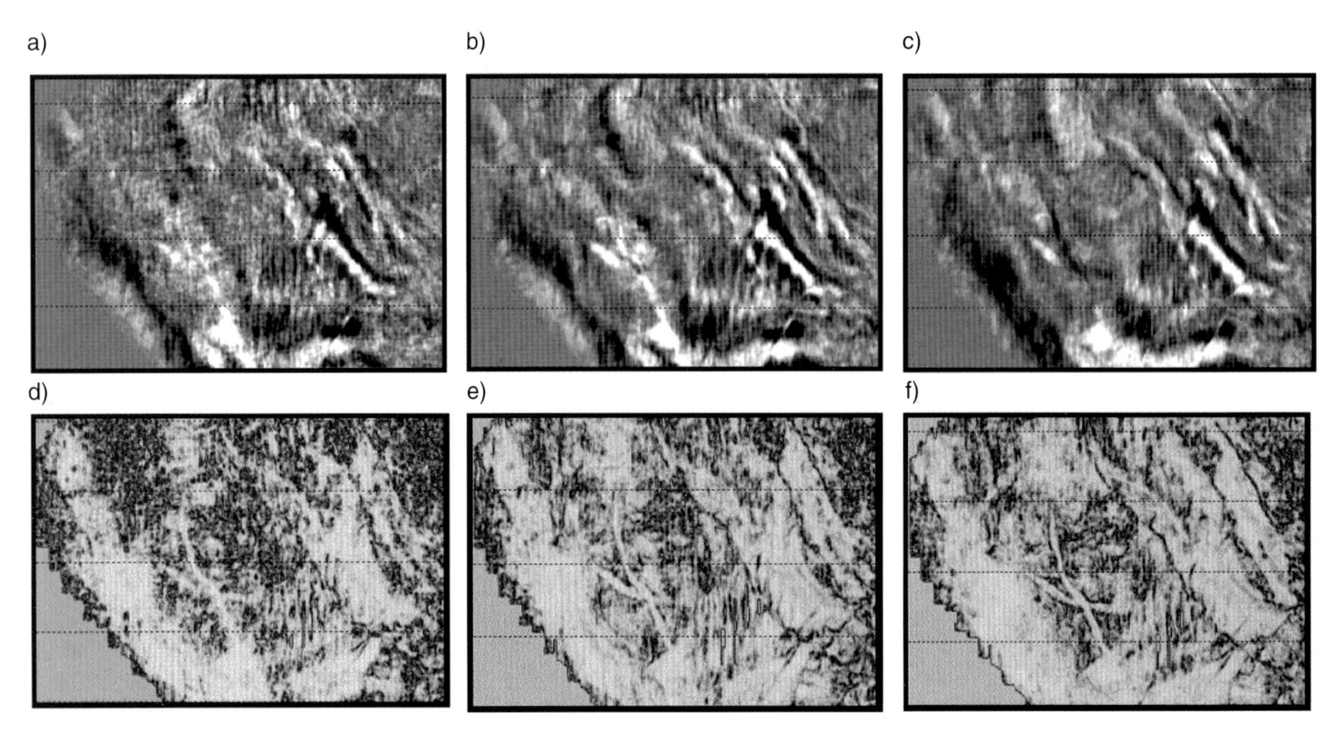

Figure 3. Time slices through the seismic data generated at different stages in processing: (a) a brute stack followed by migration, (b) residual statics followed by stack and migration, and (c) an image after final migration with an improved velocity model, and (d)-(e) slices through the three corresponding coherence volumes.

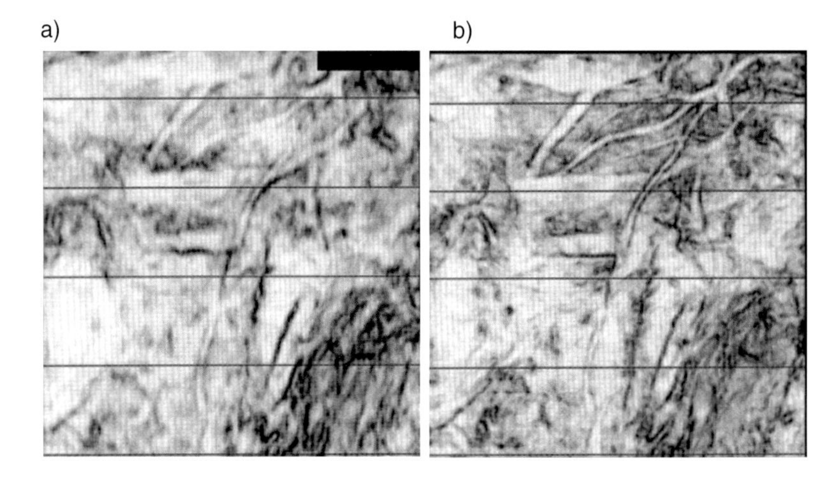

Figure 4. An example showing coherence after (a) an initial velocity model and (b) the final 3D velocity model for the same data. Note the marked improvement in lateral resolution provided by more careful velocity analysis.

effectively by slicing through coherence volumes before and after the algorithm and comparing the results. Azimuth moveout (AMO) is a wave-equation-based regridding algorithm that rotates the azimuth and modifies the offset of 3D prestack data (Biondi et al., 1998). The effectiveness of AMO application on a 3D volume from central Alberta and the advantages that accrue in doing so are illustrated in Figure 6. Figure 6 shows a pair of coherence time slices (at t = 320 ms), before (Figure 6a) and after (Figure 6b) AMO processing. Notice the missing data along the receiver lines before AMO application. At least two fault trends can now be seen starting from the left, one running downward and the other going to the right. Figure 6c-d and Figure 6e-f show similar pre- and post-AMO comparisons at 1324 ms and 1760 ms. Notice the improved focusing of the north-south edges in the highlighted zones in those figures.

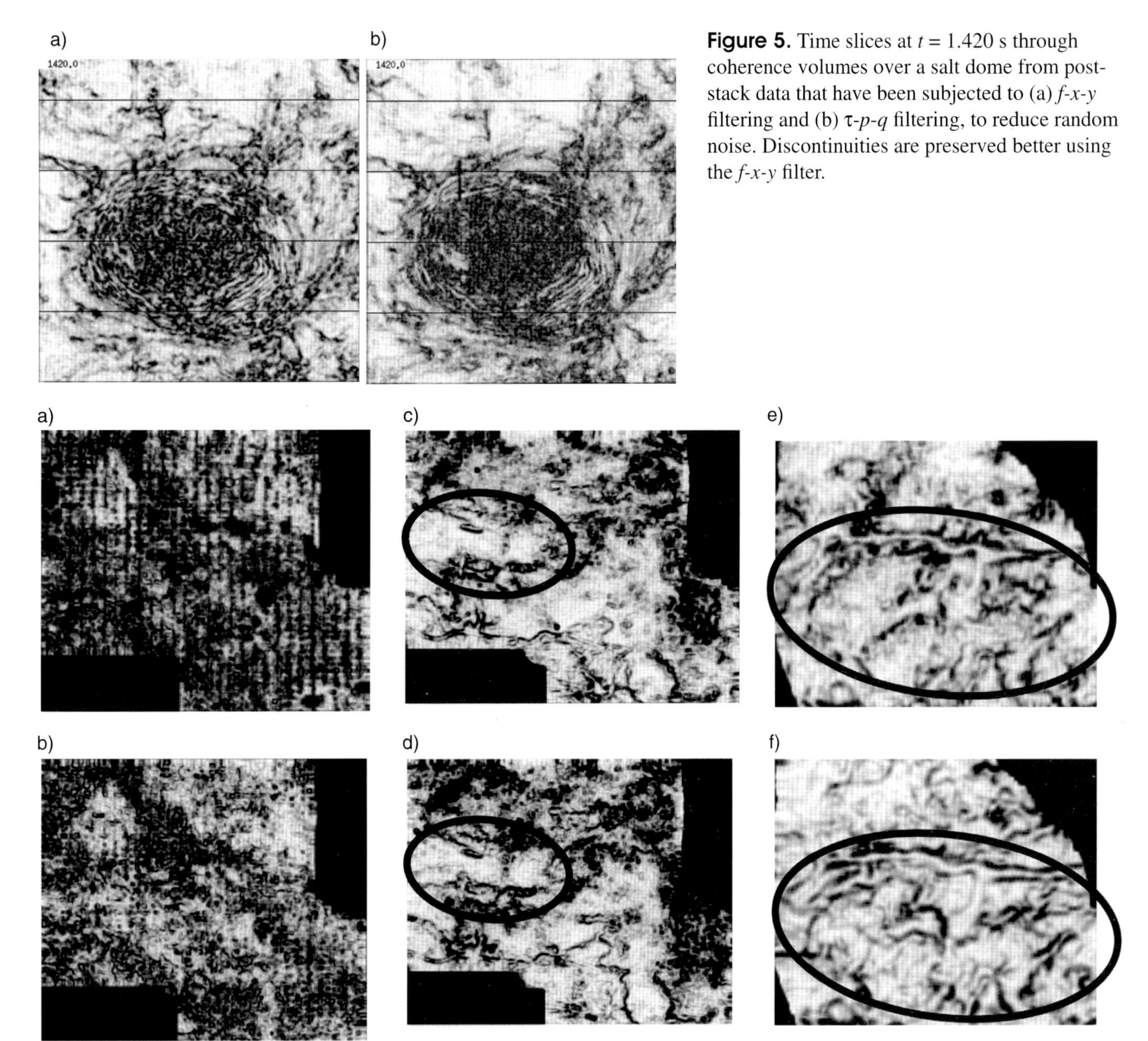

Figure 5. Time slices at t = 1.420 s through coherence volumes over a salt dome from poststack data that have been subjected to (a) f-x-y filtering and (b) τ-p-q filtering, to reduce random noise. Discontinuities are preserved better using the f-x-y filter.

Figure 6. (a)-(b). Time slices at t = 0.320 s through coherence volumes computed from data (a) before and (b) after AMO processing. (c)-(d). Time slices at t = 1.324 s through coherence volumes computed from the same data volumes used for (a) and (b), again (c) before and (d) after azimuth moveout (AMO) processing. (e)-(f). Time slices at 1.778 s through coherence volumes run on a different data volume (e) before and (f) after AMO processing. Ellipses indicate a channel system that is imaged better after AMO processing. After Negut et al. (2005) and Chopra (2005). Data are courtesy of Arcis Corporation, Calgary.

The traditional way to assess migration velocities has been to look for overmigration or undermigration effects on vertical sections. Running coherence on a suite of migration outputs allows the analyst to look specifically at features and evaluate which velocity field produces the best-focused fault terminations. In Figure 7, we show the same seismic slice imaged using 90% (Figure 7a), 100% (Figure 7b), and 110% (Figure 7c) of the stacking velocity field. In Figure 8a-c, we show the corresponding coherence slices. Comparison of Figures 7 and 8 demonstrates the convenience with which differences can be identified on coherence slices in preference to seismic slices. We have circled in red the events that are best focused, thereby defining an interpreter-driven, variable-velocity field that provides overall image improvement.

Acquisition Footprint

Stacking combines traces obtained at different offsets and azimuths. Because of surface-acquisition geometry, different bins may contain different combinations of offsets and azimuths in addition to differences in the total number of traces to be stacked. Often this variation of bin ingredients is larger for land 3D data than for marine 3D data.

Let us consider two cases. In the trivial case, assume only that all of the traces in a stacking bin are identical. That will be the case if, with the application of a proper NMO velocity correction, there are no residual moveout events, such as multiples or linear interference, and there is no amplitude variation with offset and azimuth. In this trivial case, if different bins have differing numbers of traces, an inadequate fold-of-stack amplitude compensation will produce lateral amplitude variations that reflect this fold-of-stack variation. In this trivial case, a modestly time-dependent amplitude correction that tracks the time-dependent changes in the fold-of-stack amplitude will attenuate the amplitude problem.

We term the second case the insidious case. In this case, the traces to be stacked together are not identical. They may differ because of combinations of (1) residual NMO resulting from incorrect NMO primary velocity correction and/or multiples and/or source-generated noise; (2) AVO; or (3) azimuth variations of amplitudes. Because the stacking process only attenuates and does not eliminate such trace-to-trace differences, the amplitudes seen on the stacked traces include any or all of these unwanted features, depending on the offsets and azimuths of the collection of traces within a bin.

We label this case insidious because the unwanted amplitude contributions are highly time dependent, thereby shifting the lateral pattern of contamination from one time slice to the next over a characteristic vertical distance of the wavelet in the data. The lateral periodicity of the pattern is determined by the lateral periodicity of the surface geometry.

a)

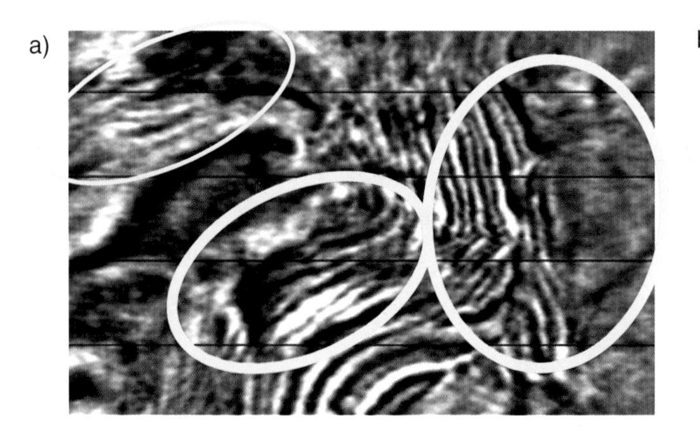

b)

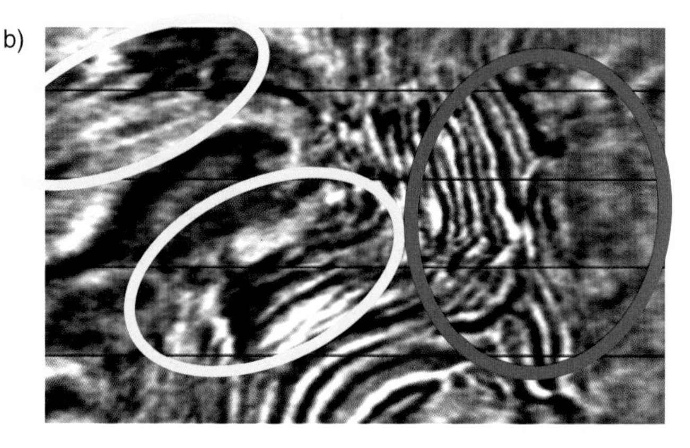

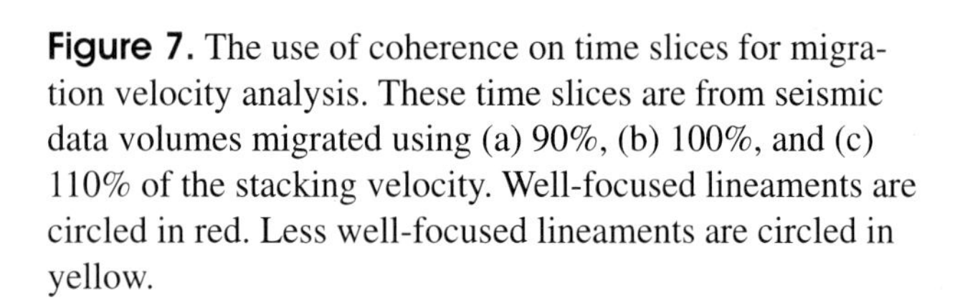

Figure 7. The use of coherence on time slices for migration velocity analysis. These time slices are from seismic data volumes migrated using (a) 90%, (b) 100%, and (c) 110% of the stacking velocity. Well-focused lineaments are circled in red. Less well-focused lineaments are circled in yellow.

c)

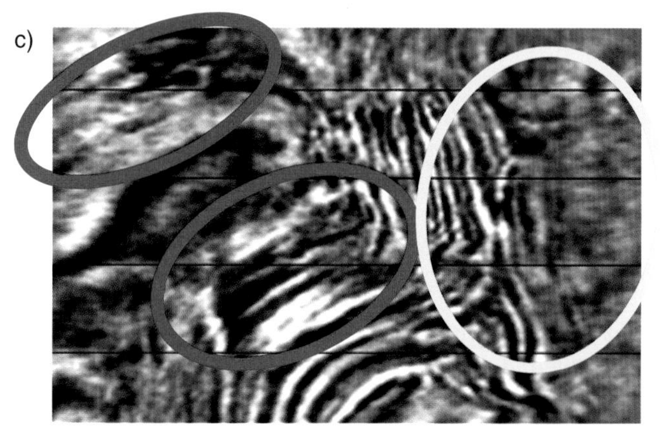

Think of looking through a kaleidoscope as it is rotated. The internal arrangement of its mirrors determines the periodicity of the pattern, even though the pattern itself is ever changing. In addition to the time dependence of the pattern, this insidious footprint may add amplitude to or subtract amplitude from the desired reflections. Such a shifting pattern inhibits our ability to find a one-size-fits-all inverse pattern to apply to the entire survey.

Solutions for the insidious case are compromises. Because of lateral changes in the offset and azimuth contributions to the stacked trace, an acquisition design that minimizes those lateral variations is preferred. Marine data, with consistent cable feathering and no skips, satisfy this criterion. A similar geometric solution for land data, although feasible, increases acquisition cost.

A few processing solutions exist, albeit with compromises. With some acquisition geometries, the largest variation in the offset occurs at the near offsets. Thus, a systematic elimination of the near offsets may be beneficial. If residual moveout from multiples is the primary challenge, then because the near offsets do little to attenuate the contributions from those multiples, eliminating the near offsets may be beneficial.

A second solution is to apply a lateral mix to the data, laterally smearing the unwanted amplitude variations and the data themselves. This mix may also be applied through a sophisticated k_x-k_y filter.

A third solution is to increase the lateral extent of the stacking bin, thereby increasing the regularity of the offset and azimuth contributions while decreasing the lateral resolution in the stacked data. Bins whose lateral extent becomes greater than one-quarter of the wavelength in the ground produce decreased lateral resolution in the migrated data.

Seismic migration of the stacked data provides an automatic fourth solution. Although the migration process improves the lateral resolution of the desired data, it laterally smears the unwanted amplitudes by a distance on the order of the Fresnel zone. Thus, the migration-induced lateral smearing of the footprint pattern is depth dependent.

We begin by examining a typical land seismic line in Figure 9. We note that in the shallow section, the associated lower fold and larger incidence angles give rise to a change not only in signal-to-noise ratio (thereby contaminating coherence), but also in amplitude (contaminating coherent energy gradients) and in dip and azimuth (contaminating curvature).

Budget constraints dictate that we acquire high-quality data that illuminate the largest possible area for a fixed budget. In this survey, we have no difficulty in constructing a time-structure map (Figure 10a) of the shallowest horizon of interest, the Yates. However, the Yates amplitude extraction is contaminated by acquisition footprint (Figure 10b). Such contamination should come as no surprise because

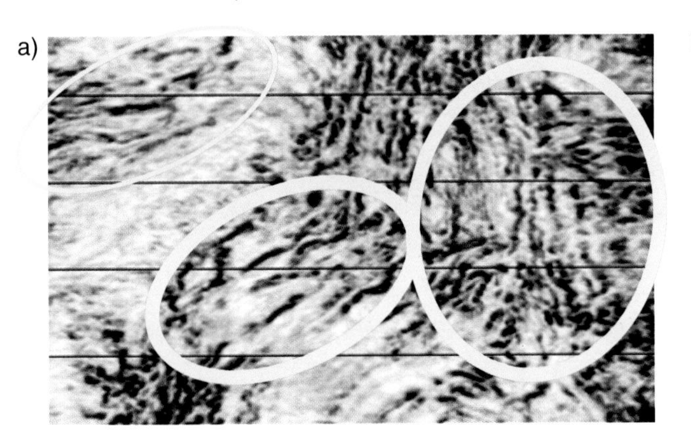

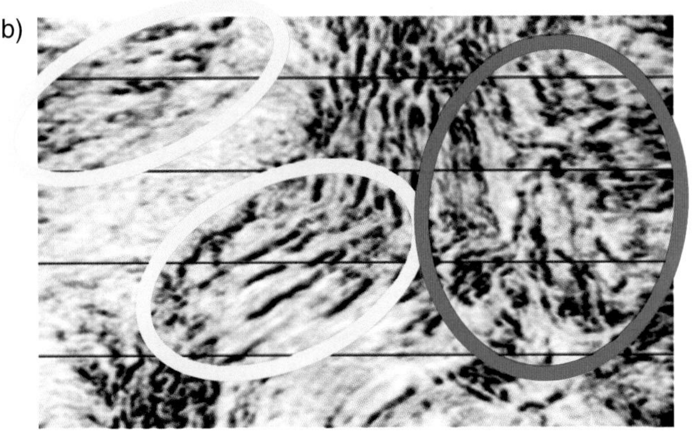

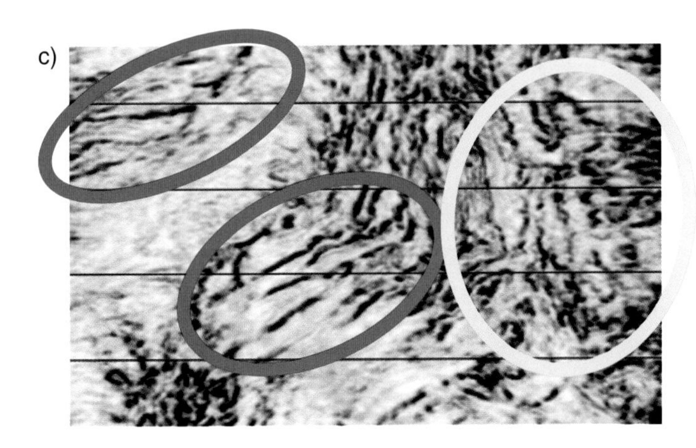

Figure 8. The use of coherence on time slices for migration velocity analysis. These time slices are from coherence volumes corresponding to the time slices shown in Figure 7, using (a) 90%, (b) 100%, and (c) 110% of the stacking velocity. Well-focused lineaments are circled in red. Less-well-focused lineaments are circled in yellow.

geometric attributes extract subtle lateral changes in waveform, amplitude, and dip azimuth — all characteristics that are especially sensitive to contamination by the acquisition footprint.

Footprint is strongest on shallow time slices and in general heals with depth (Figure 11). As seen on the coherence slices in Figure 11, the footprint is very pronounced and spread all over at 400 ms (Figure 11a), it is seen only in patches at 600 ms (Figure 11b), and is not conspicuous at 800 ms (Figure 11c). Reasons for healing with depth can be: increased fold of stack, decreased far-offset angle, and less-aliased migrations.

Footprint contaminates not only coherence, but also curvature and amplitude gradients (Figure 12). The time-slice displays at 800 ms from the most-negative curvature (Figure 12a), the most-positive curvature (Figure 12b), and the east-west component of the energy-weighted coherent-amplitude gradient (Figure 12c) all show contamination with acquisition footprint. The most important action that an interpreter can take when encountering footprint is to study the pattern on the shallow time slices and commit them to memory. In general, a good interpreter can see through acquisition footprint. Unfortunately, autopickers, geostatistics, and neural networks rarely are as clever as a human interpreter.

Given the trade-off between increasing the regularity of the offsets and of the total fold (and in general diminishing footprint) and extending the lateral size of the survey for a fixed cost, geoscientists and their managers often choose the latter to illuminate more geology. They then have a skilled interpreter manage the artifacts. Therefore, an acquisition footprint often appears on seismic images, particularly for land data. Such artifacts can mar amplitude extractions, overprint subtle stratigraphic features, and, most vexing of all, become intermixed with linear fracture features of interest.

Acquisition footprints may occur for various reasons, but Drummond et al. (2000) distinguish two general types of causes of a footprint. First, acquisition footprint can occur as a function of acquisition geometry. Second, a footprint can arise from errors or limitations in signal processing.

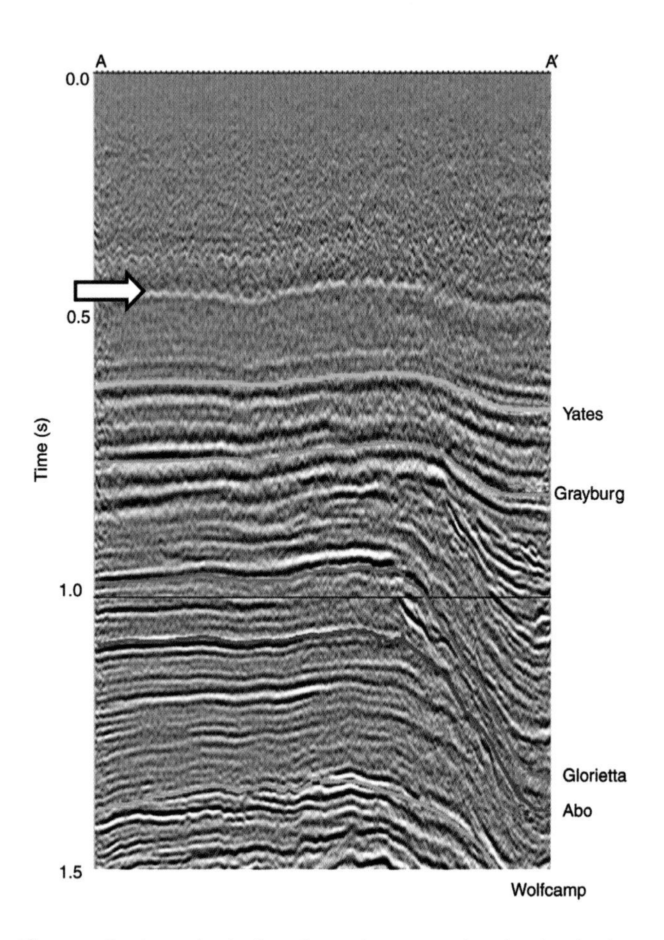

Figure 9. A vertical slice through conventional seismic data acquired over the Delaware Basin, New Mexico, U.S.A. The Yates and Grayburg strata are important producing horizons on the carbonate platform. The arrow indicates the appearance of an acquisition-footprint amplitude contamination at a horizon above the Yates. After Famini (2005).

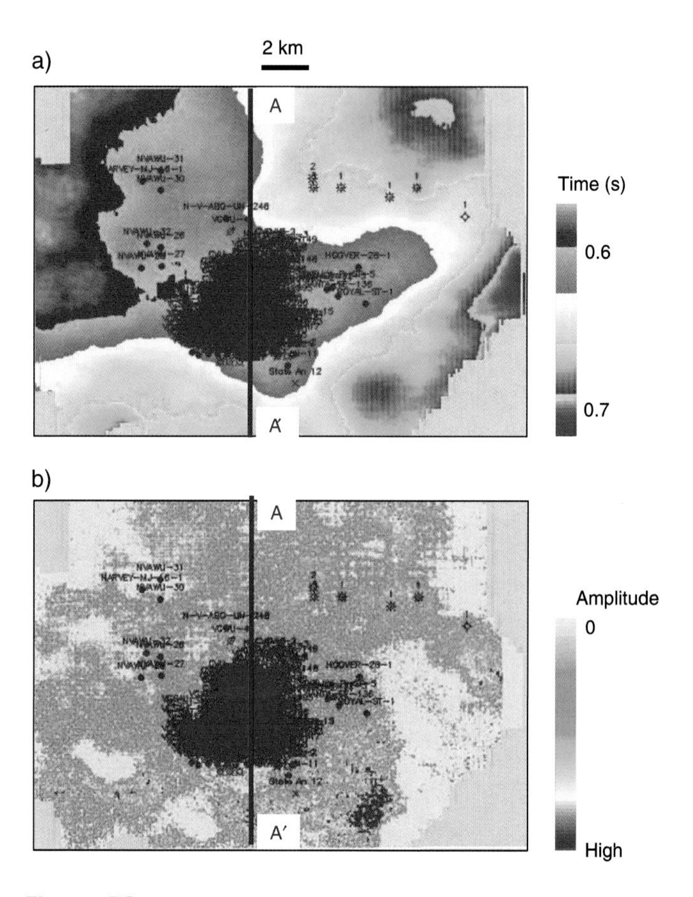

Figure 10. (a) A time-structure map and (b) an amplitude-horizon slice, both corresponding to the Yates horizon shown in Figure 9. An acquisition footprint contaminates the amplitude horizon slice. After Famini (2005).

Causes of acquisition footprint

The choice of acquisition design determines a particular distribution of fold, offset, and azimuth from one bin to the next. Apart from some variation in the taper zone, the total fold for most common geometries is designed to be uniform for all seismic bins. In spite of the uniformity of the total fold, however, offset and azimuth distributions can vary from bin to bin or can be uniform in the inline direction and irregular in the crossline direction.

Backscattered noise is without question the most common cause of acquisition footprint on land data because the

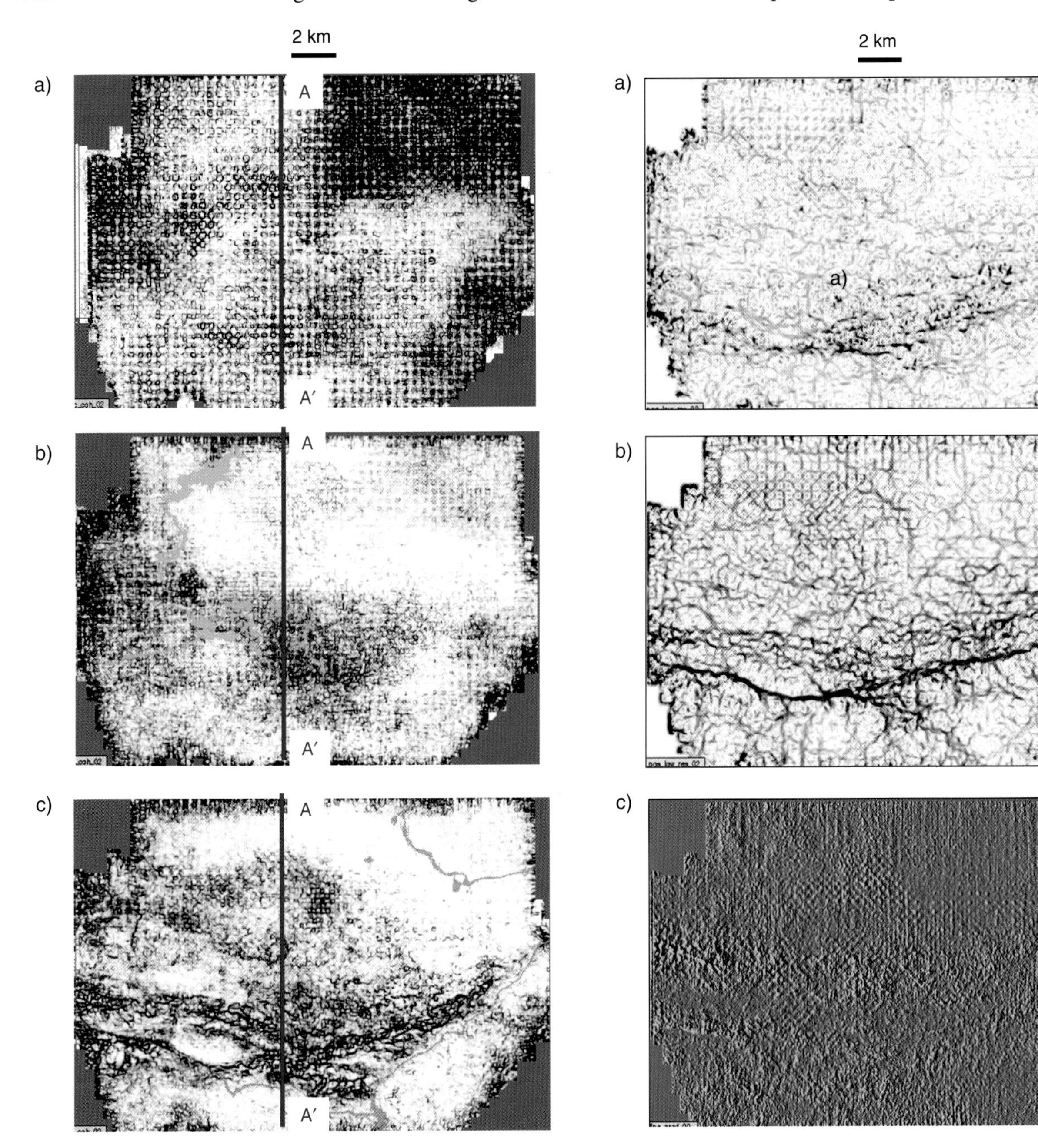

Figure 11. Time slices at (a) $t = 0.400$ s, (b) $t = 0.600$ s, and (c) $t = 0.800$ s through a coherence volume from a survey acquired over the Delaware Basin, New Mexico, U.S.A. Note how the acquisition footprint diminishes in deeper slices. Colors indicate horizons of interest cutting through the time slice. After Famini (2005).

Figure 12. Time slices at $t = 0.800$ s, through (a) the most-negative-curvature component, (b) the most-positive-curvature component, and (c) an east-west component of the energy-weighted coherent-amplitude-gradient volume for the same Delaware Basin data shown in Figure 11. The acquisition footprint impacts all attributes, including curvature, as can be seen on the vertical section in Figure 9. After Famini (2005).

bin-to-bin variations in the distributions of offset and azimuth allow that backscattered noise to leak through to the stack in a bin-dependent fashion. Azimuthal dependence occurs because source and receiver groups, as well as the stack array, preferentially accept or reject backscattered noise depending on azimuth. Such variations can lead to undesirable effects on the reflected signal.

In addition to the above-described lateral changes in offset and azimuthal distributions, unwanted lateral variations in the total stack fold also can occur. Obstacles on land, such as lakes, villages, highways, and untrusting farmers, cause deviations from the desired, regular geometry pattern that provides constant fold. The seismic crew is forced to undershoot the obstacle, thereby generating images whose lateral changes in the signal-to-noise ratio reflect the location of that undershooting. In a marine environment, obstacles commonly include production platforms, with cable feathering caused by tides and currents also adding variability to folds and offsets.

Very often, economic considerations compel us to choose a coarse sampling scheme for acquiring 3D data. Sparse recording of data causes artifacts during data processing. Coarse spatial sampling creates spatial aliasing, and aliased steeply dipping coherent noise resulting from ground roll or multiples, for example, creates artifacts.

For regular acquisition patterns such as those commonly used in land surveys, aliased noise leaks into the stack volumes as spatially periodic events. The periodicity (as opposed to randomness) allows that noise to pass through the noise-rejection filters used in processing and in so doing to cause footprints.

In addition to spatial aliasing during the acquisition stage, other processes that tend to accentuate footprints are (1) residual NMO caused by incorrect velocities, unflattened multiples, or any other process that causes the traces in a bin to differ from each other on the basis of their offset, such as AVO (Hill et al., 1999); (2) systematic errors in computed offsets or amplitude variations caused by an inadequate 3D DMO formulation (Walker et al., 1995; Budd et al., 1995); or (3) 3D prestack-migration signal enhancements based on *f-x-y* random noise attenuation and coherency filtering (Moldoveanu et al., 1999).

Effects of acquisition footprint

Whether it is the result of acquisition design or of accentuation during processing, an acquisition footprint is a nuisance for the interpreter. Sometimes we make efforts to avoid accentuation of the footprint during processing. We usually do this by applying interpolation or extrapolation on input data to avoid operator aliasing before we apply multichannel processes. If that does not help, we may use trace mixing of the output data, which tends to minimize the aliasing effect and also decreases lateral resolution.

As a possible solution, Gulunay (1999) suggested using a more specific type of mix that employs wavenumber-domain filtering on time slices. Migration is the only process that we know of that can "smart-mix" the data (such as through a Kirchhoff migration algorithm) and improve lateral resolution. In addition, migration laterally smears the footprint, so that the greater the depth, the greater the lateral smear. Sometimes, unfortunately, none of these approaches is effective, and the interpreter proceeds with an analysis of the seismic data that could lead to uncertain recommendations for drilling locations.

When an interpreter works on a footprint-contaminated seismic data volume, each subsequently derived attribute volume is contaminated by the acquisition imprint. Such footprint-contaminated amplitudes have questionable fidelity. Figure 13a shows an example of an amplitude time slice from a seismic volume riddled with footprint in the east-west direction. The time slice from the derived acoustic-impedance volume shown in Figure 13b exhibits a similar pattern. Any impedance analysis on the impedance volume would entail a high measure of uncertainty.

A significant problem arises when an acquisition footprint is not prominent on the amplitude seismic data but a pronounced gridlike pattern can still be seen on impedance slices. Compared with the original amplitude data, the impedance data should have low frequencies boosted by the implicit frequency filter of inversion ($1/i\omega$). However, residual-velocity analysis has more difficulty in attenuating low-frequency residual moveout than in attenuating high-frequency residual-moveout errors. In such cases, attempts to remove the footprint are not effective.

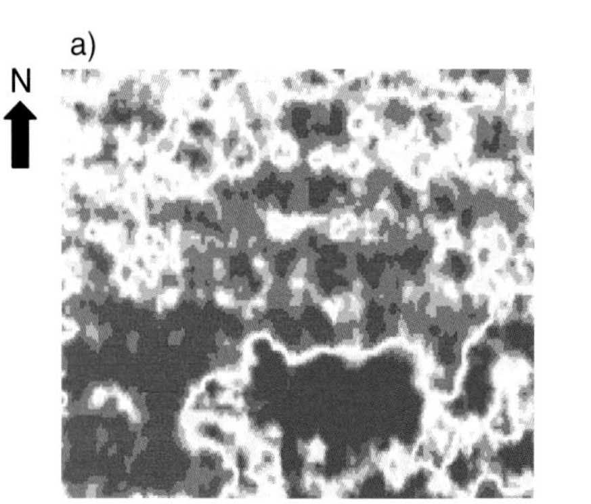

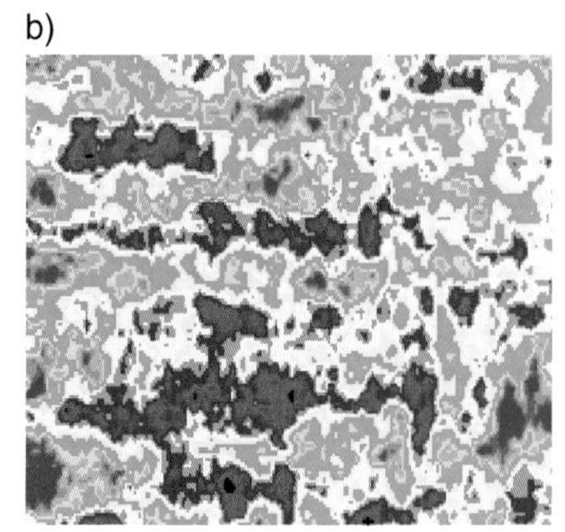

Figure 13. Time slices through (a) a seismic data volume and (b) the corresponding acoustic-impedance volume, from Alberta, Canada, exhibiting contamination from an east-west acquisition footprint.

Figure 14 displays progressively deeper pairs of time slices from a seismic data volume (Figure 14a) and the corresponding coherence volume (Figure 14b). The narrow north-south lineations on the slices are a processing artifact that has trickled through the processing sequence. The wider, east-west lineations corresponding to the receiver lines are subtler and less obvious on the seismic slices. Unfortunately, these subtle artifacts resulted in impedance slices (not shown) with a strong east-west stripe pattern as well as the north-south pattern, thereby preventing any meaningful analysis. The coherence slices show the lineations clearly in both the north-south and east-west directions.

Too often, 3D seismic-data processing is checked only for quality on vertical slices. From those vertical sections, it often is difficult to recognize an acquisition footprint on the data. Because the effects of footprint are distributed spatially, it is crucial that intermediate 3D seismic volumes be evaluated on constant-time slices or on depth slices to evaluate the presence and severity of the acquisition footprint.

The processing shop provides the next-best venue for suppressing acquisition footprint, second only to acquisition design. For example, compare alternatives in the use of a dip filter for attenuating the visibility of acquisition footprint. In the prestack, unmigrated domain, reflector terminations against faults appear as relatively fast, continuous hyperbolas. Backscattered noise generally has slower velocities. For that reason, dip filters applied before migration do not greatly alter the signal. In contrast, dip filters applied after migration smear the high-wavenumber fault-plane terminations we wish to retain.

Unfortunately, seismic interpreters rarely have the luxury to request reprocessing of their data from field tapes. Instead, one means of dealing with acquisition footprint is to analyze the (footprint-contaminated) poststack migrated data, time slice by time slice, in the k_x-k_y wavenumber domain. The seismic volumes and coherence volumes are sliced at every sample and the slices are animated through to examine typical time zones in which the acquisition footprint is most pronounced. For the data shown in Figure 14, footprints masked the seismic reflections between 0.6 and 1.5 s. The coherence slices were transformed into the k_x-k_y domain, and the filter was designed manually at every 100 ms. Interpolation between these filters yielded one k_x-k_y filter per time slice, and those filters were applied to the data shown in Figure 14a.

Figure 15a shows the same times slices as those in Figure 14a, but here we see them after k_x-k_y filtering (Chopra and Larsen, 2000). The coherence shown in Figure 15b was calculated from the seismic data shown in Figure 15a. The coherence slices confirm that the seismic volume is clear of any footprint lineations and represents a significant improvement in data quality that leads to a more confident interpretation. The derived impedance volumes also did not show any undesirable patterns.

Figures 16 and 17 show another example of k_x-k_y footprint removal. In Figure 16, we see a section of a seismic line before footprint removal (Figure 16a) and after (Figure 16b). Notice how after footprint removal the section in Figure 16b looks clear of the jitter in Figure 16a.

Figure 17a-b shows time slices through the seismic volume from Figure 16 before and after footprint removal, respectively, and Figure 17c-d shows time slices through the corresponding coherence volumes. Again, notice how the amplitude intensity looks more coherent on the seismic time slice after footprint removal. The footprint is clear in the east-west direction on the coherence time slice of Figure 17c and is suppressed in Figure 17d.

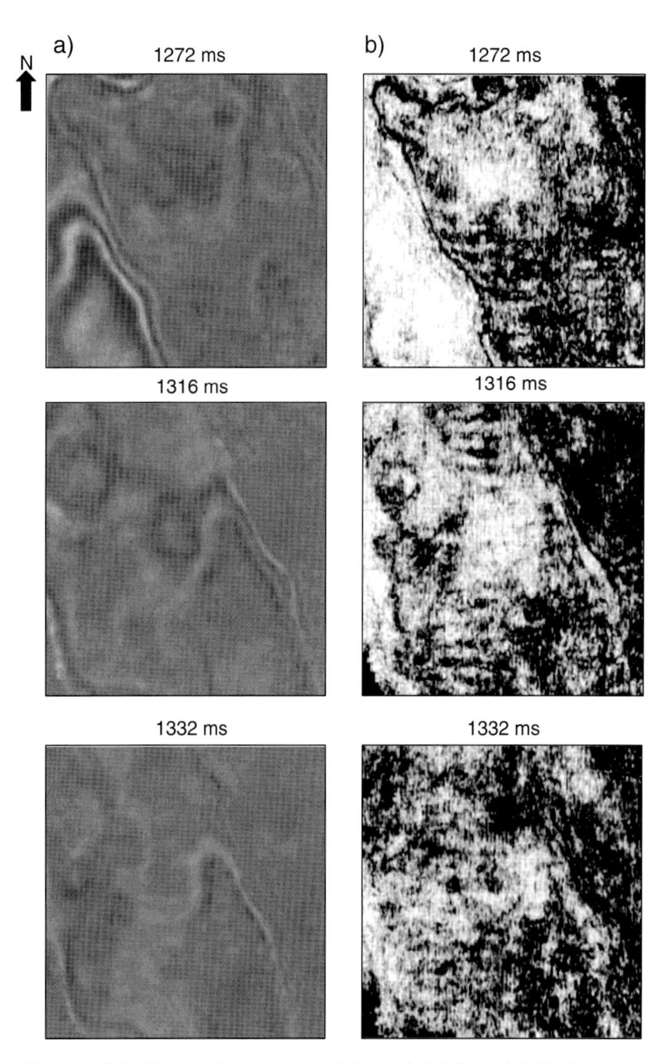

Figure 14. Time slices, at t = 1.272, 1.316, and 1.332 s, through (a) a seismic data volume and (b) the corresponding coherence volume. The acquisition footprint does not impede our ability to interpret the original seismic amplitude data, but it is exacerbated by the coherence calculation, in which we see wide east-west and narrow north-south artifacts. After Chopra and Larsen (2000).

It is important to ensure that no geologic reflection events are removed from the data during k_x-k_y filtering. As an example of such an unwanted attenuation, Marfurt et al. (1998) found that k_x-k_y filtering removed north-south-trending faults of interest over a compartmentalized reservoir, offshore Trinidad (Figure 18a is before and Figure 18b is after k_x-k_y filtering). Strong cable feathering that resulted in stripes of low-fold data plagued this data volume (Figure 18d). These problems were exacerbated by a poor DMO algorithm used at the time. Careful 3D dip filtering of the migrated seismic data cube eliminated most of the DMO artifacts and produced the improved coherence image

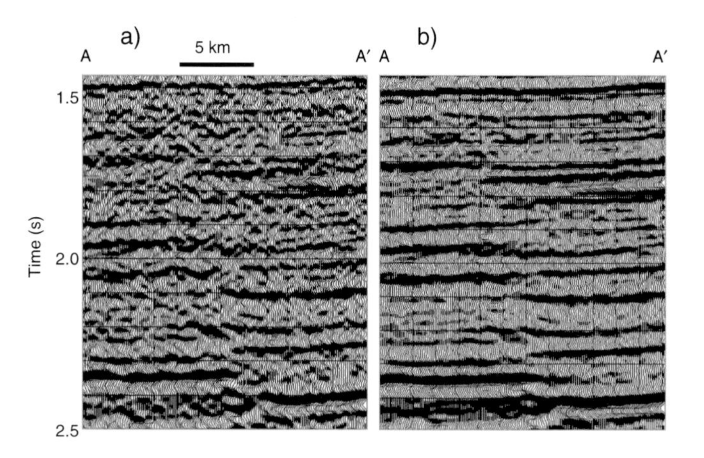

Figure 16. A seismic line (a) before and (b) after footprint removal using careful dip filtering. Note that the strong back-scattered ground-roll noise has been suppressed.

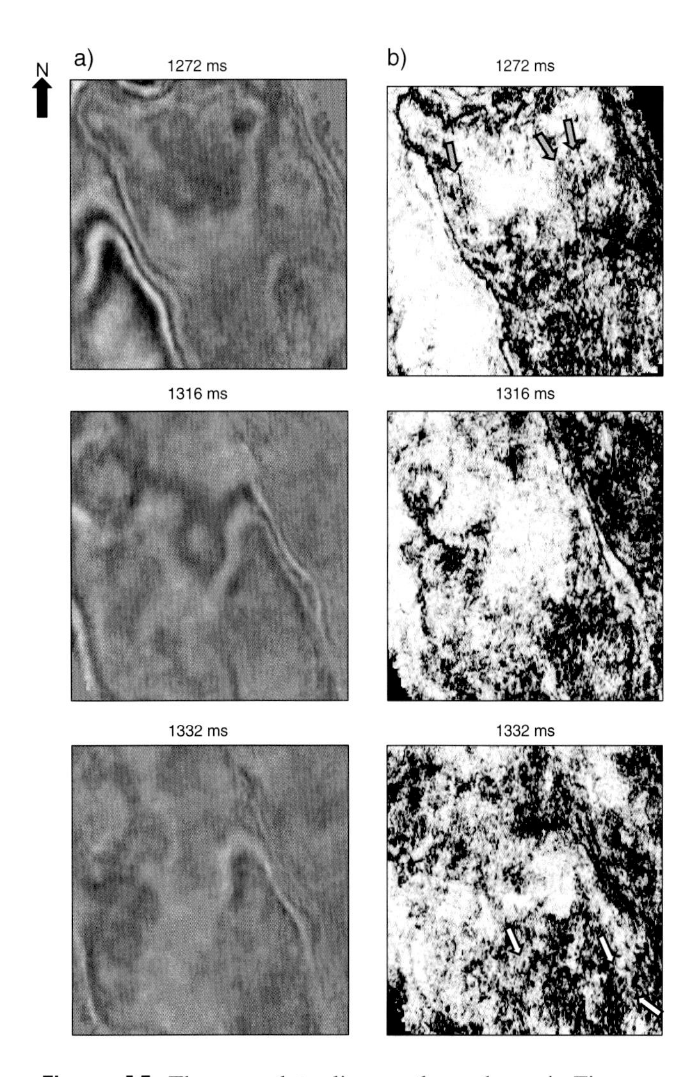

Figure 15. The same data slices as those shown in Figure 14, but displayed here after additional seismic processing (balancing, statics, and improved velocity analysis) to minimize the acquisition footprint. Although the impact on the original seismic data is minimal, we now can discern minor faults (indicated by gray arrows) and possible stratigraphic features (indicated by white arrows) that previously were masked by the acquisition footprint. After Chopra (2001a).

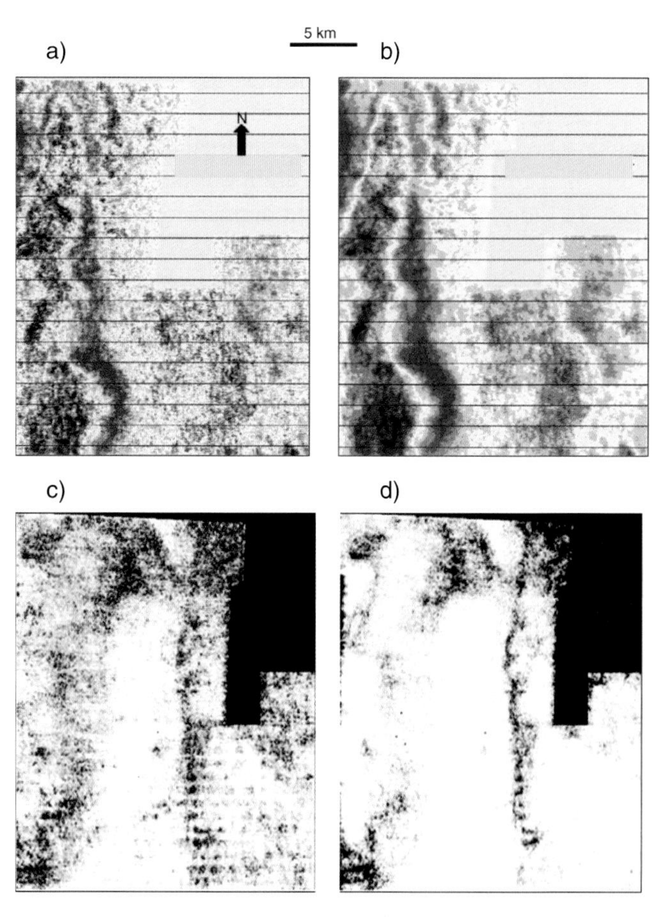

Figure 17. (a)-(b).Time slices at t = 1.000 s through the seismic data volume shown in Figure 16 (a) before and (b) after footprint attenuation. (c)-(d).Time slices at t = 1.000 s through the corresponding coherence volumes (c) before and (d) after footprint attenuation. Note the strong east-west acquisition footprint resulting from backscattered ground roll in (a). The processor uses coherence images of the acquisition footprint to judge the effectiveness of alternative processing flows and parameters.

shown in Figure 18c. However, postmigration dip filtering must be done with great care, because not only can it eliminate fault-plane reflections of interest, it also can cause the desired flat-reflector signal to alias into the reject band.

Drummond et al. (2001) improved on the post-migration k_x-k_y filter by first predicting the noise and then least-squares fitting it to the data using a series of lateral coefficients. That process generated a 2D matched filter. Figure 19a shows a time slice through a seismic data volume from onshore Algeria. The north-south-trending footprint is seen covering the slice. Adaptive filtering was run on the data volume and Figure 19b shows the filtered slice equivalent to the slice in Figure 19a. Figure 19c shows the difference between the slice in 19a and the one in 19b and shows the footprint removed from 19a. Our experience has taught us that if we cannot reprocess the data from field tapes, such adaptive filters give us the most promising means of suppressing acquisition footprint on migrated data volumes.

We conclude this section by showing time slices at t = 1.000 s through the coherence volume from the survey conducted in the Delaware Basin, New Mexico, U.S.A., and shown in Figure 11. The coherence volume in Figure 20a was generated from the original data volume, whereas the coherence volume in Figure 20b was generated from a reprocessed seismic volume that had improved statics and a velocity designed to improve the frequency content. We

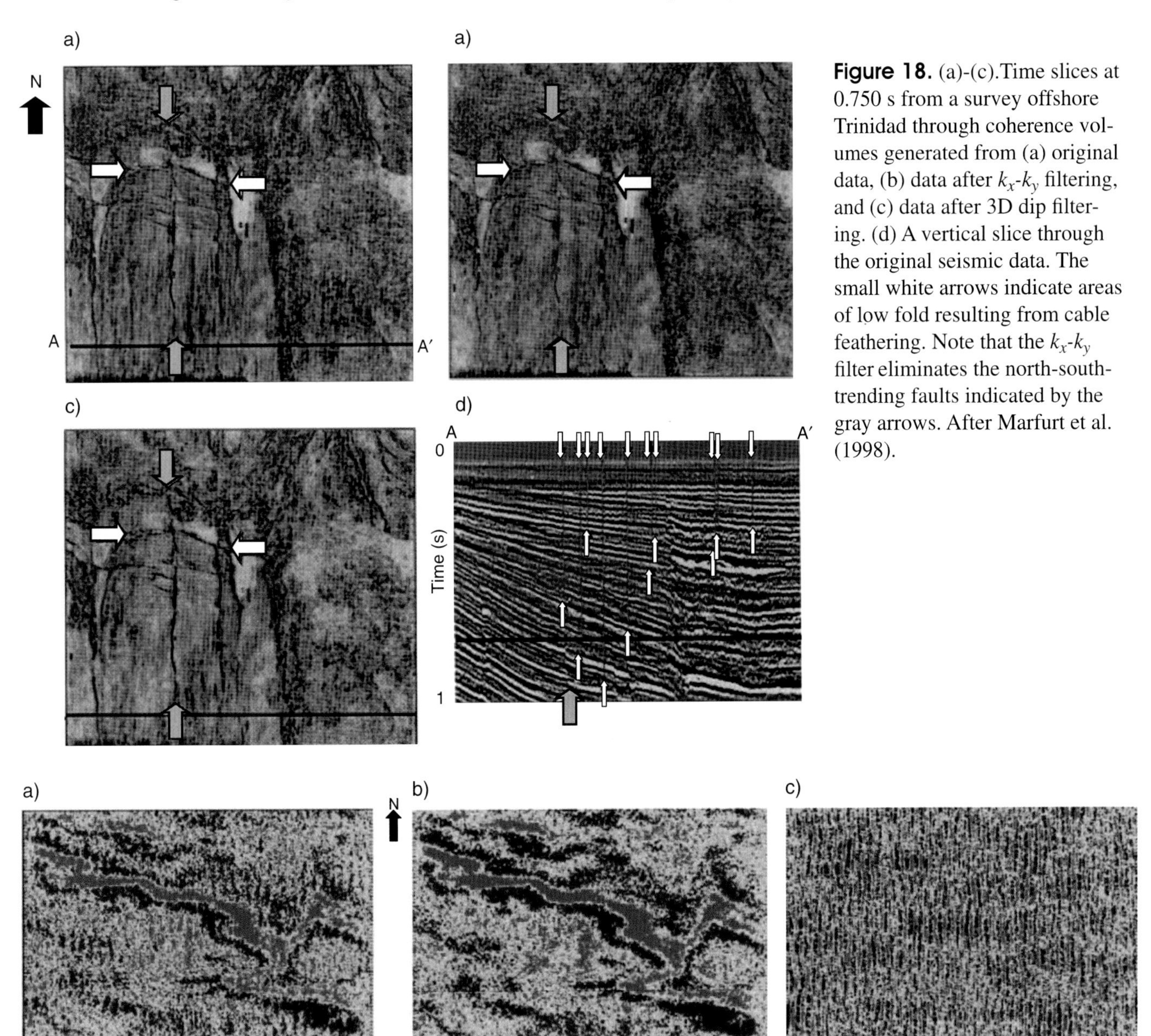

Figure 18. (a)-(c).Time slices at 0.750 s from a survey offshore Trinidad through coherence volumes generated from (a) original data, (b) data after k_x-k_y filtering, and (c) data after 3D dip filtering. (d) A vertical slice through the original seismic data. The small white arrows indicate areas of low fold resulting from cable feathering. Note that the k_x-k_y filter eliminates the north-south-trending faults indicated by the gray arrows. After Marfurt et al. (1998).

Figure 19. A time slice through a data volume from onshore Algeria, (a) showing a strong acquisition footprint and (b) after adaptive filtering designed to suppress the acquisition footprint. (c) Rejected noise obtained by subtracting the data shown in (b) from those in (a). After Drummond et al. (2001).

note that the lateral resolution of the Brushy Canyon mass-wasting deposits indicated by the white arrow has been improved significantly by reprocessing. However, we note that the lateral resolution of the acquisition footprint indicated by the gray arrow on the platform also has increased. Given the choice, any interpreter would prefer to have the improved stratigraphic images, although that may require mentally filtering out the overlying footprint pattern in some parts of the survey.

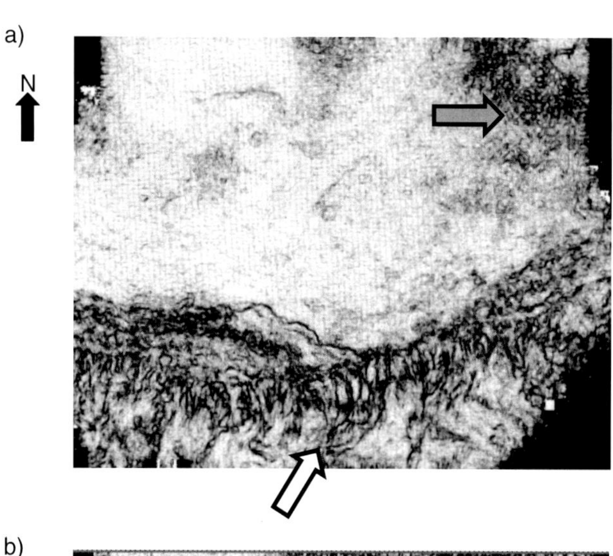

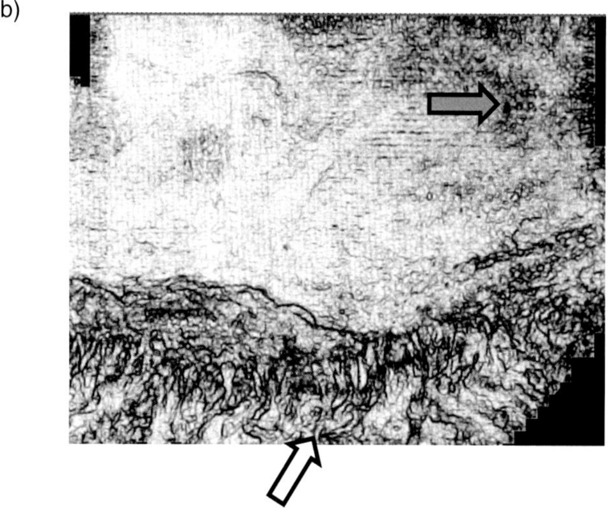

Figure 20. Comparison of a time slice at t = 1.000 s through coherence volumes generated for a survey from the Delaware Basin, New Mexico, U.S.A. (a) The coherence slice from original processing and (b) the same coherence slice after careful reprocessing to improve lateral resolution. Note the trade-off between the increased acquisition footprint in the northeast corner, indicated by the gray arrow, and improved resolution in the Brushy Canyon slump features, indicated by the white arrow. After Famini (2005).

Factors Influencing Vertical and Lateral Resolution

Lateral resolution can be defined as the minimum horizontal distance separating two visibly distinct features on a seismic section. The basis of lateral resolution is spectral bandwidth (see Figure 1 in Chapter 6). Kallweit and Wood (1982) concluded that resolution of migrated data is a function of effective frequency, which they defined for a broadband signal as the reciprocal of the trough-to-trough distance of a zero-phase wavelet. Hilterman (1982) defined lateral resolution of unmigrated stacked data in terms of the half-wavelet Fresnel zone (Figure 21).

Horizontal resolution of migrated data is limited by acquisition geometry and can be improved by decreasing the size of shot and group arrays, by increasing the acquisition spread to acquire greater angular subsurface illumination, and by increasing the migration aperture (Figures 22 and 23). By removing unwanted noise from data and balancing the frequency content of the signal, seismic processing enhances input for migration. That enhanced input, together with an accurate velocity model, is essential for improving lateral resolution.

Seismic migration maps the seismic-reflection energy recorded on the earth's surface to its correct spatial and depth location, while at the same time collapsing the width of the Fresnel zone to the size of the seismic wavelet in the earth.

Migration provides this ultimate improvement in resolution for an infinite migration aperture. For smooth reflectors, Sun and Bancroft (2001) showed that we can reconstruct accurate amplitudes by retaining no more than two Fresnel zones in our migration aperture. That economy occurs because we are using a broadband wavelet such as the one shown in Figure 24c versus the monofrequency signal shown in Figure 24a. Figure 24 shows the energy of the reflected signal as a function of the reflector radius, for three different source wavelets, namely (a) a monochromatic wavelet, (b) a narrow-band wavelet, and (c) a broadband Ricker wavelet. For a monochromatic wavelet (Figure 24a), the energy is oscillating, and for a narrowband wavelet wavelet (Figure 24b) the energy again oscillates. For a broadband signal (Figure 24c), the energy function first builds up to a maximum but then stabilizes. This comparison suggests that the boundary of the first Fresnel zone corresponds to the position of maximum energy buildup (Bruhl et al., 1996).

Although such an economy sounds quite fortuitous, we still are faced with the challenge that we do not always know the size and shape of these Fresnel zones, particularly for complex velocity models and for discrete diffractors such as curvilinear fault edges. We evaluate the influence of including and excluding different sizes of Fresnel zones later in this chapter. Migration algorithm developers devote a great deal of effort to estimating the size and location of Fresnel zones. Optimal estimates lead to accurate reflector-amplitude fidelity with minimal computational effort.

For large apertures and simple velocity structures, a good migration algorithm provides a lateral resolution that is approximately one-quarter of the effective wavelength at depth, which in essence turns Figure 1 from Chapter 6 on its side. In this ideal case, we simply define our resolution in terms of wavenumber, k_x, instead of in terms of frequency, f.

For moderate migration apertures and deeper targets, raypath illumination prevents us from reaching this maximum resolution. In Figure 22, we see how lateral resolution is determined by the distance (or migration aperture) between a surface midpoint and a subsurface scatterer, plus depth and velocity gradient.

For shallow point-diffractor targets or fault edges, the rays turn nearly horizontal beyond a certain distance, so that increasing the migration aperture does not improve lateral resolution. Indeed, the opposite occurs, because our velocities usually have errors, and rays traveling longer distances accumulate greater errors and later events have a lower signal-to-noise ratio. Hilterman (2000) showed in an AVO study that the impact of transverse anisotropy increases with the angle of incidence. For shallow reflections, transverse anisotropy decreases the Fresnel zone and further decreases the migration aperture required to provide a given resolution.

We have determined that vertical resolution and lateral resolution for a flat layer are the minimum vertical and horizontal distances, respectively, between two points that can be resolved on a seismic section. An inaccurate velocity model results in destructive interference of higher-frequency components summed along the diffraction curves, thereby reducing vertical and lateral resolution (Figure 25a). In

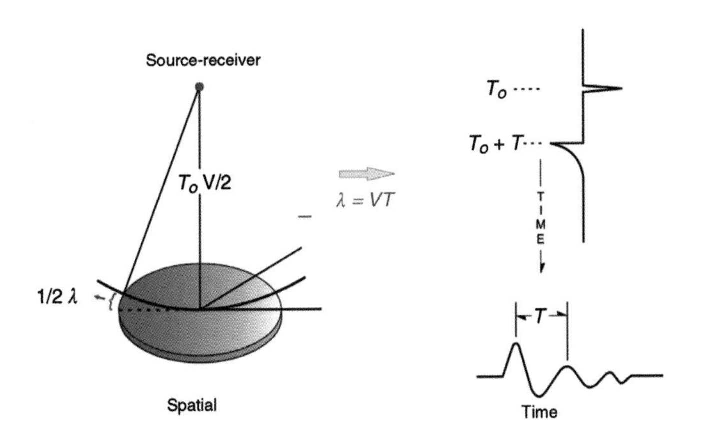

Figure 21. Description of the Fresnel zone in spatial and temporal domains. Here, λ is the dominant wavelength, T is the two-way traveltime to the target from the surface, and V is the average velocity of the overburden. After Hilterman (1982).

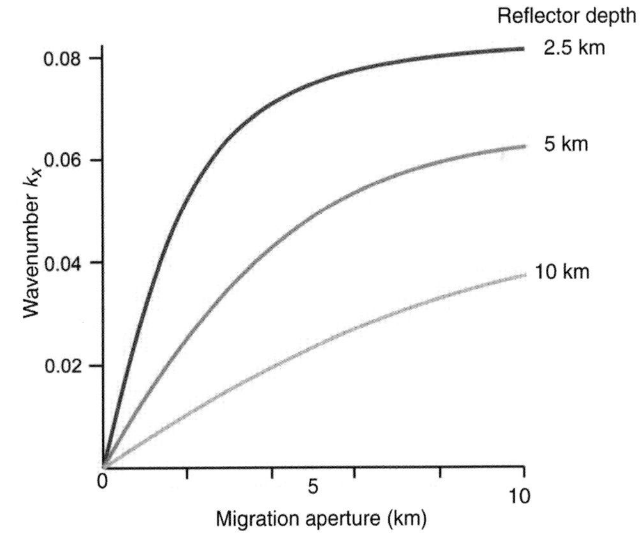

Figure 22. Lateral resolution at depth depends on the wavelength at depth, the incidence angle, and the placement and size of the migration aperture. The wavelength at depth in turn depends on the velocity and frequency. After Lazarevic (2004).

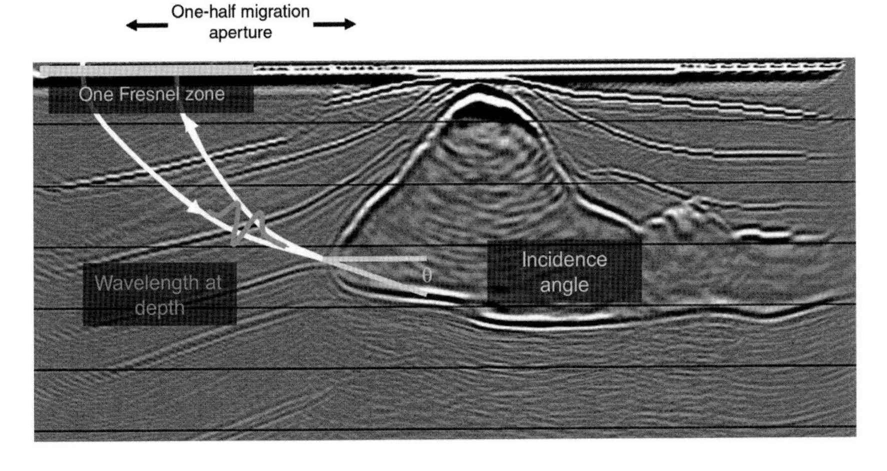

Figure 23. Lateral resolution as a function of depth and migration aperture, for a velocity function that has the form $v = v_0 + kz$, with values $v_0 = 3$ km/s and $k = 0.3$ s^{-1}. The wavenumber increases more slowly with the size of the aperture for deeper reflectors, which indicates that for a fixed aperture, lateral resolution decreases with depth. Note that increasing the migration aperture much beyond the aperture being equal to depth results in a diminishing increase in horizontal wavenumber bandwidth. After Lazarevic (2004).

complex media, the concepts of vertical and lateral resolution are mixed. For a vertical salt face in a sedimentary basin with a typical velocity compaction gradient, the frequency bandwidth determines the lateral resolution of layers against the salt flank, whereas the migration aperture determines the vertical resolution of layer terminations (Figure 25b).

The accuracy of our subsurface images, and thus the quality of any seismic attributes generated from those images, depends on (1) the seismic bandwidth, (2) seismic noise in the data, (3) the accuracy of the velocity-depth model, (4) the migration algorithm used, and (5) the migration aperture.

Seismic noise

The baseline of the usable bandwidth, and thus of the vertical and lateral resolution, is determined by the signal-to-noise ratio. Properly sampled low-velocity noise, such as backscattered ground roll, can be attenuated by a good migration algorithm. Unfortunately, we rarely sample such noise adequately, so that we migrate the aliased noise as if it were a signal that has a different moveout. Once we have migrated the noise, there is no easy way to attenuate these aliased events. If we are fortunate, the aliased ground roll appears as overlapping migration smiles. If we are unlucky,

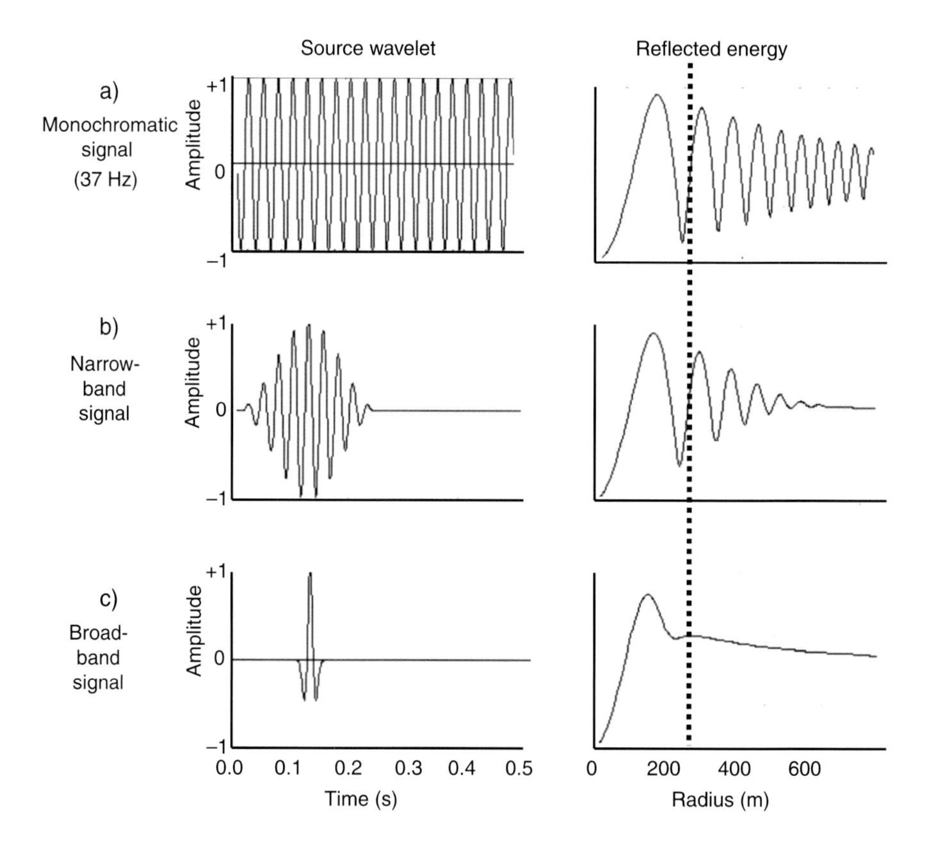

Figure 24. Reflected amplitude as a function of reflector radius (Fresnel zones) for (a) monochromatic, (b) narrow-band, and (c) broadband sources. All three wavelets have a center frequency of 37.1 Hz. Reflector depth is 1000 m, and velocity is 2000 m/s. In each of the three cases the Fresnel zone is defined by the maximum of the energy function. After Bruhl et al. (1996).

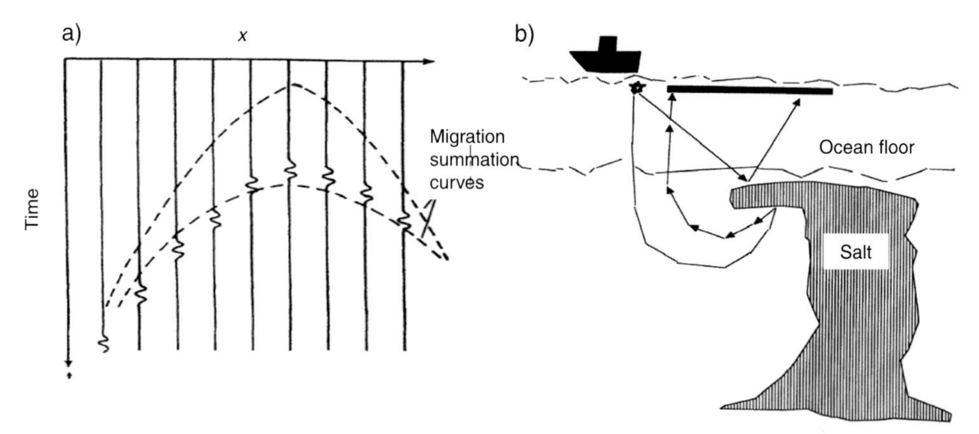

Figure 25. The impact of migration on resolution. (a) Correct migration velocities sum along an accurate diffraction hyperbola and thereby produce high-resolution images. After French (1975). (b) Migration also rotates our estimates of resolution so that frequency content controls lateral resolution and migration aperture controls vertical resolution along a steep salt flank. After Brown (1994).

the aliased component of the noise becomes organized and forms false reflector images. In either case, crossing events are nongeologic and cause havoc with geometric attributes such as coherence.

In contrast, operator aliasing is an artifact of the migration algorithm itself. Although operator aliasing was troublesome when migration algorithms were first being written, almost all commercial service providers now address these problems and prevent operator aliasing in a reasonable manner, typically by eliminating higher frequencies (and of course the associated resolution) of steeply dipping events.

The velocity-depth model

The key to accurate migration and lateral resolution is an accurate velocity-depth model. An inaccurate velocity model results in the diffraction hyperbola being misaligned with the data, which leads to a loss of high frequencies, overall defocusing of the image, mispositioning of the energy (as shown in Figure 26), and, most vexing for geometric attributes, crossing of otherwise juxtaposed events that have different dips and azimuths.

Migration using a velocity model that is slower than the true subsurface velocity (which is shown in Figure 26b) images horizons that are too shallow in depth, makes the events less continuous, and contaminates them by undermigrated smiles (Figure 26a). Dipping events are less steep and also are shifted to a shallower depth. Generally, the slower velocity cannot collapse diffractions completely, and that results in deterioration of the faults on the migrated section. Fault-plane reflections do not line up with reflection terminations, a problem that is exacerbated if the medium is anisotropic. Figure 26a also shows the effect of a slower velocity on imaging a fault. The fault in this image is not defined clearly and appears as two blurry events rather than one. The fault is less steep compared with its position using correct velocities (Figure 26b), and it is moved toward the hanging wall.

In contrast, migration using velocities that are too high images horizons too deep and makes dipping structures both steeper and deeper. Figure 26c shows overmigrated smiles on both the top of the reflections and the termination of the layers on the fault plane. The single fault is imaged as a double fault because of the crossing of the smile, and it is steeper and is moved toward the footwall. Reflections that correspond to a given geologic structure are both deformed and mispositioned because of incorrect velocities.

Figure 27 illustrates structural deformation and mispositioning caused by incorrect velocity models by showing horizons picked on Figure 26. In Figure 28, we display horizon slices through coherence volumes computed from data migrated with velocities that were 100% (Figure 28a) and 110% (Figure 28b) of the correct velocity and that correspond to the seismic data images in Figures 26b and 26c. The limitation of the stair-step finite-difference model approximation to the dipping reflectors in the SEG-EAGE salt-dome model produces useful discontinuities that we can map with coherence. An accurate migration, such as that in Figure 26b, exactly reproduces these modeling stair-step artifacts. We note that using too high a velocity blurs these stair-step discontinuities and both blurs and mispositions the fault indicated by blue arrows.

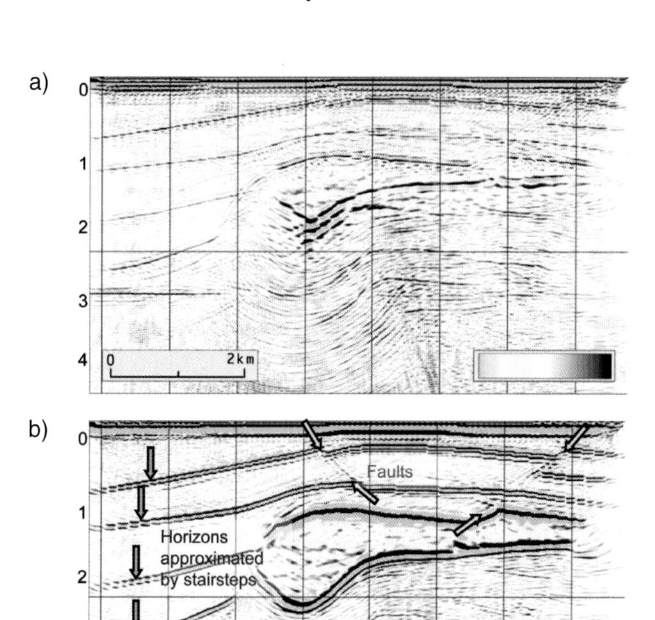

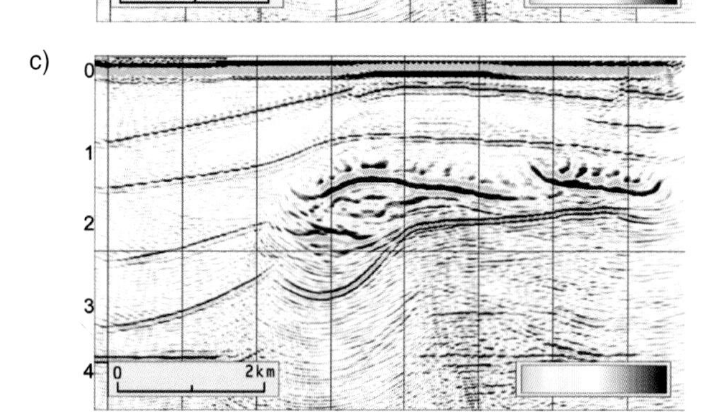

Figure 26. The impact of incorrect migration velocity on lateral resolution. Results of 3D prestack Kirchhoff depth migration on the SEG-EAGE salt model, using velocities that are (a) 90%, (b) 100%, and (c) 110% of the correct velocity. After Lazarevic (2004).

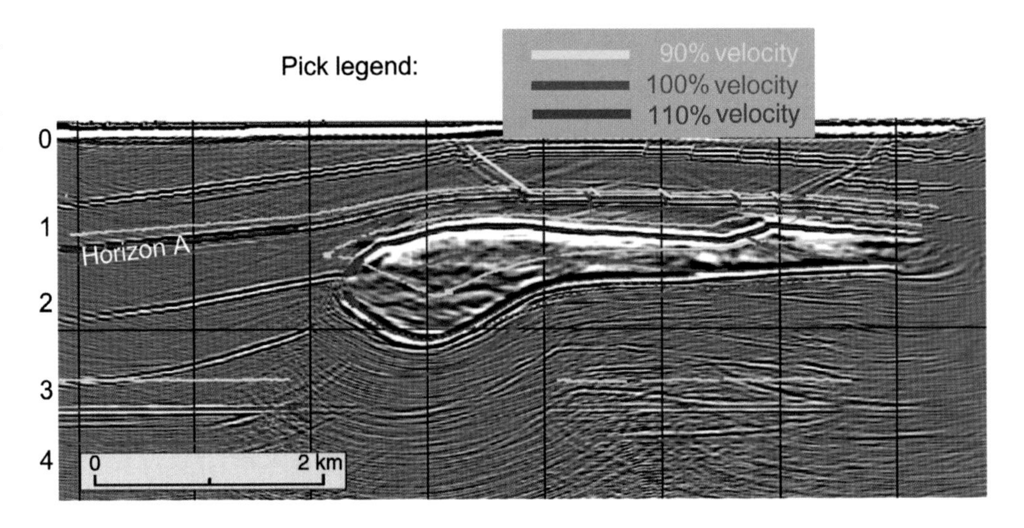

Figure 27. The impact of incorrect velocity on lateral resolution. Orange, red, and blue picks were made on the images shown in Figure 26a and 26c, respectively. After Lazarevic (2004).

Migration algorithm

Migration algorithms can be divided into three broad classes. First, we categorize migration by its output domain — time versus depth — with time migration being less sensitive to an incorrect velocity model than depth migration is. Second, we categorize migration by its input data — prestack versus poststack — with prestack migration handling Snell bending effects more accurately than poststack migration does, where the Snell bending is approximated (in part) by the NMO correction. Third, we categorize migration by algorithm — Kirchhoff versus wave equation — pitting the ray-based Kirchhoff family of algorithms against the wave-equation-based family of algorithms.

One of the most important advantages of Kirchhoff migration compared with conventional one-way wave-equation algorithms is its ability to image very steep dips. For a fixed total number of output samples, the cost of Kirchhoff migration is independent of the seismic bandwidth. Furthermore, Kirchhoff migration can be implemented to image only a subset of lines or a range of depths, thereby providing a target-oriented capability. Kirchhoff migration provides poor images below salt and fault-shadow zones because conventional implementations typically handle only one raypath from a source to an image point and back to a receiver.

In contrast, for highly heterogeneous velocity models, wave-equation migration provides images that are superior to those produced from Kirchhoff migration because wave-equation migration can correctly image data that follow multiple paths between source, image point, and receiver. Wave-equation migration requires data that have been sampled regularly in space — a requirement that must be achieved as a preprocessing step using interpolation. The cost of wave-equation migration increases as the fourth power of the uppermost frequency, effectively limiting its bandwidth for all but research and demonstration studies.

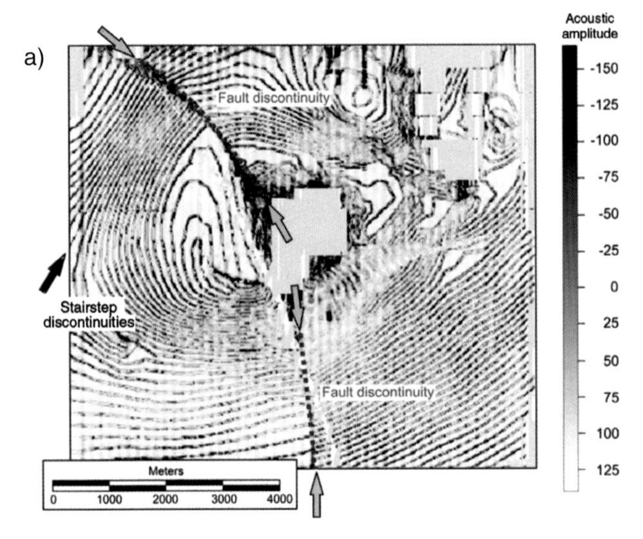

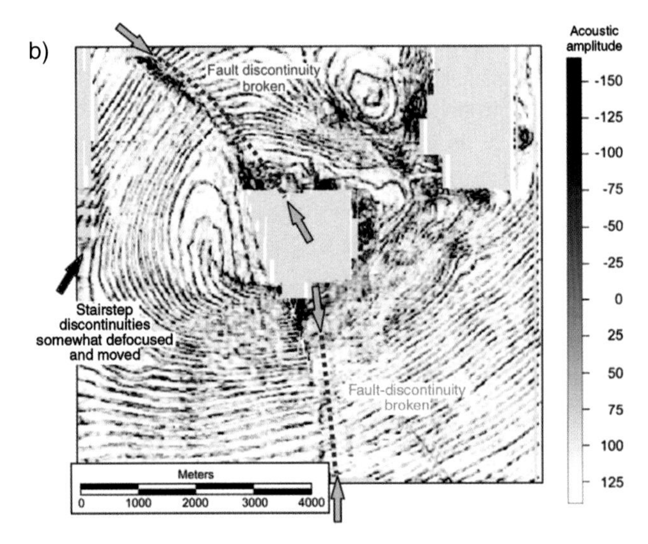

Figure 28. Coherence along horizon A, shown in Figure 27, from (a) a 100% velocity coherence volume and (b) a 110% velocity coherence volume. The fault marked with the blue arrows is laterally moved and broken, and stair-step modeling discontinuities are defocused because of incorrect velocity. After Lazarevic (2004).

Influence of prestack versus poststack depth migration

In Figures 29–33 we compare the output from poststack depth migration versus the output from prestack depth migration. Both of our examples, one from offshore Trinidad and the other from offshore the Netherlands, use a velocity model that can be approximated by simple $v(z)$ functions. Changes in image quality result from the improved stacking in depth that is gained by including Snell bending effects.

In Figure 29, we show poststack (Figure 29a) and prestack (Figure 29b) depth-migrated images from part of a survey acquired offshore Trinidad. Gray arrows indicate fault-plane reflections that are imaged much better by the prestack depth migration. We also note that the reflector indicated by the white arrows is considerably more continuous.

In Figure 30, we display a folded image with the seismic data as a vertical slice and with coherence as a horizontal depth slice. Although it may appear to be counterintuitive, the prestack depth migration image in Figure 30b is less coherent than the poststack image in Figure 30a. This decrease in coherence results from an increase in lateral resolution, which causes focusing of a multitude of microfaults common in a deformed shale. Those microfaults can be seen clearly offsetting the reflectors in the vertical slice.

In Figure 31, we show poststack (Figure 31a) and prestack (Figure 31b) vertical slices through the seismic data from a survey acquired offshore Netherlands. White arrows indicate the position of the time slices shown in Figures 32 and 33. The incoherent zone seen in Figure 31 on the vertical seismic slice corresponds to a shale-dewatering feature.

The depth slices (in Figure 32) from the seismic-data and envelope volumes show the polygonal faults associated with shale dewatering to be much better organized on the prestack depth-migrated image (Figure 32b) than on the poststack image (Figure 32a). This is borne out by depth slices through the coherence volumes and the energy-weighted coherent-amplitude-gradient volumes in Figure 33. Figure 33a and Figure 33b compare depth slices at the level indicated by the white arrows in Figure 31 and corresponding to the same level as in Figure 32, through coherence, after poststack and prestack depth migration. Figure 33c and Figure 33d compare the equivalent slices from the north-south component of energy-weighted coherent-amplitude-gradient volumes after poststack and prestack depth migration. The polygonal geometries believed to be associated with shale dewatering are resolved much better in the prestack depth-migrated images. Although prestack depth migration often is justified for imaging structurally complex terrains, here we note that it also has a major influence on the lateral resolution of stratigraphic features.

Comparing Kirchhoff migration with wave-equation prestack depth migration

As we mentioned above, cost constraints, not algorithmic capabilities, implicitly limit the frequency content of prestack-depth-migration images. Although many research-

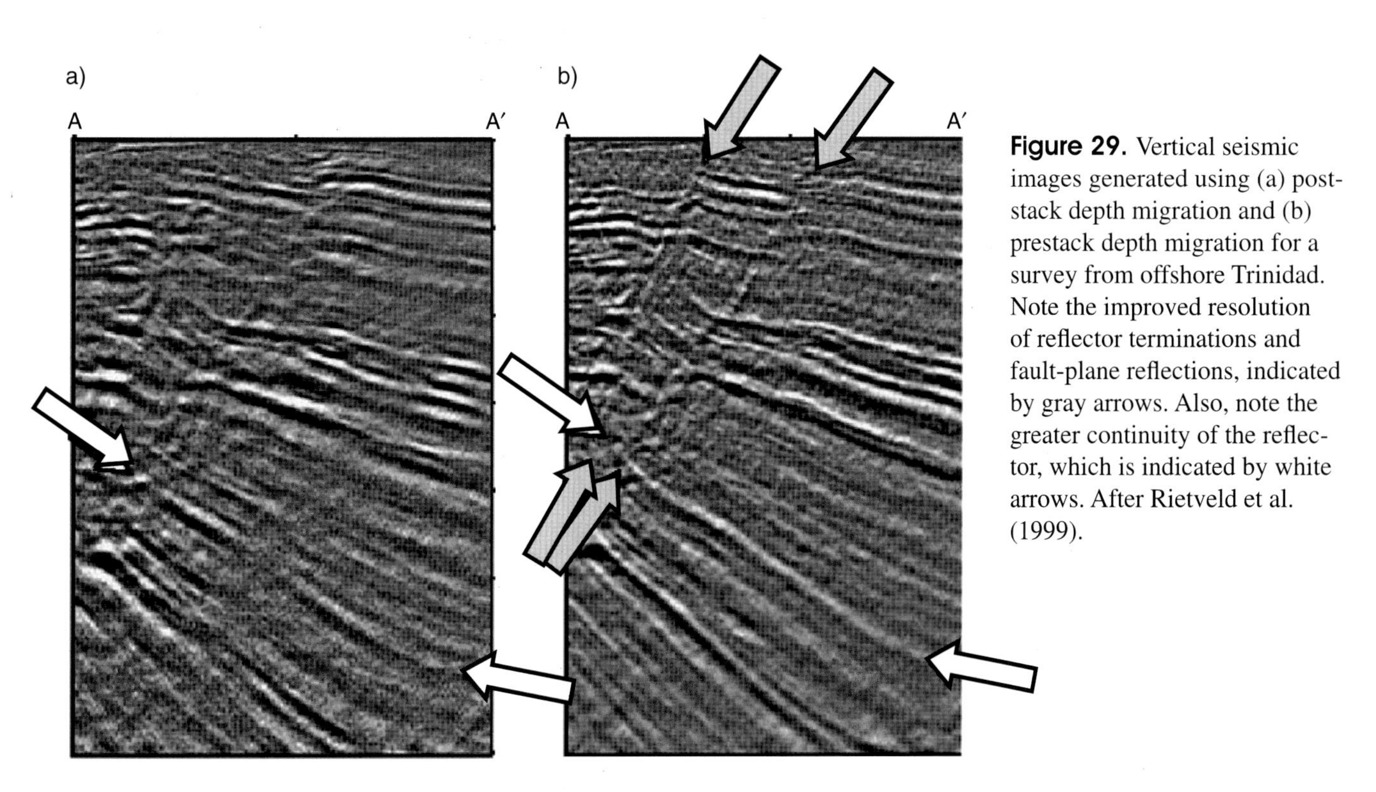

Figure 29. Vertical seismic images generated using (a) poststack depth migration and (b) prestack depth migration for a survey from offshore Trinidad. Note the improved resolution of reflector terminations and fault-plane reflections, indicated by gray arrows. Also, note the greater continuity of the reflector, which is indicated by white arrows. After Rietveld et al. (1999).

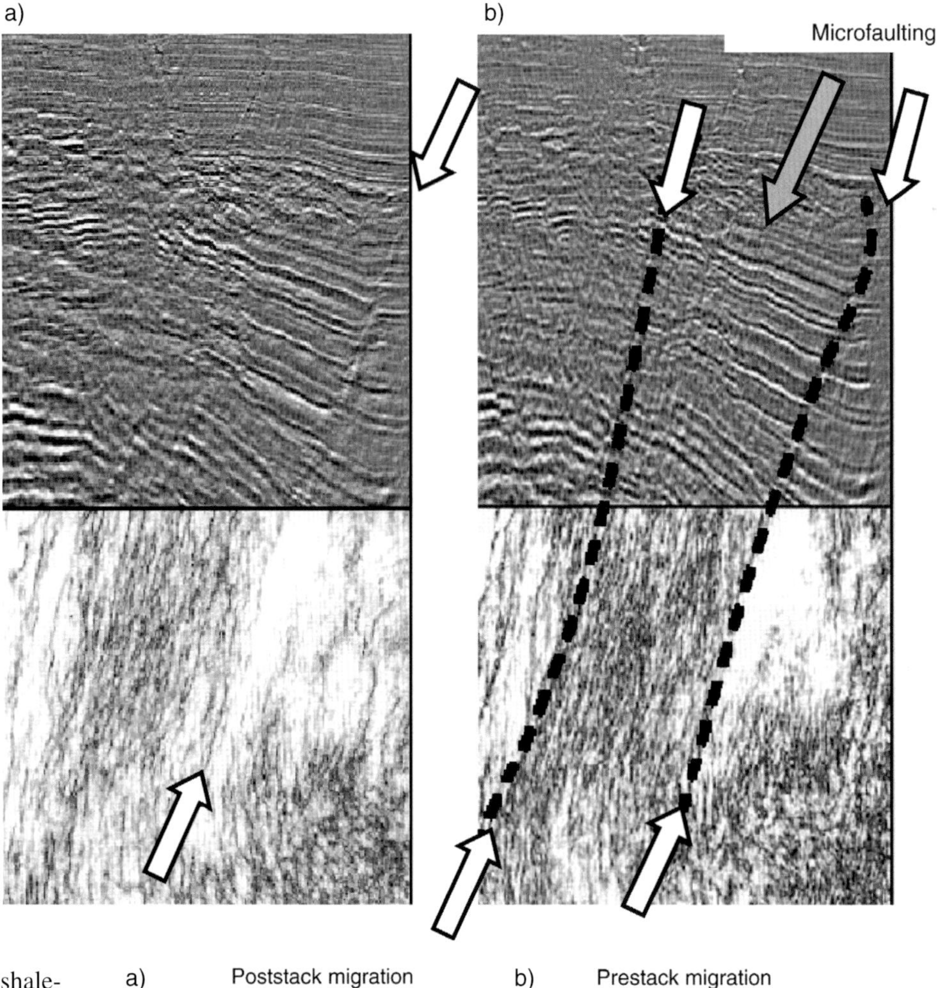

Figure 30. Folded images with a vertical slice through the seismic data volume and a horizontal slice through the coherence volume of (a) post-stack and (b) prestack depth-migrated data. White arrows indicate major faults. The gray arrow indicates micro-faulting, which is common in shale-dominated lithologies. The microfaulting appears as a broad, incoherent zone on the depth slice. After Rietveld et al. (1999).

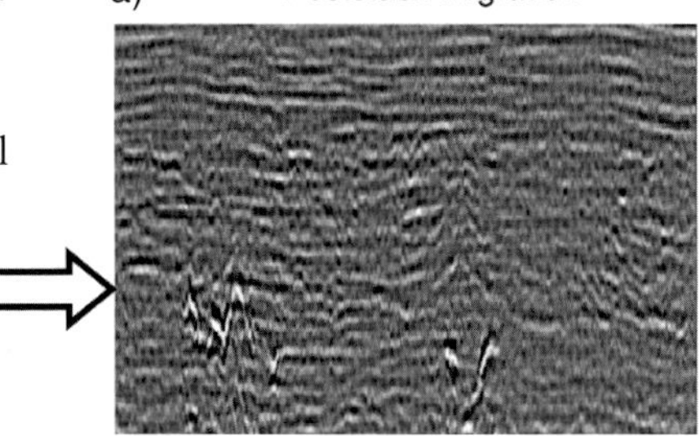

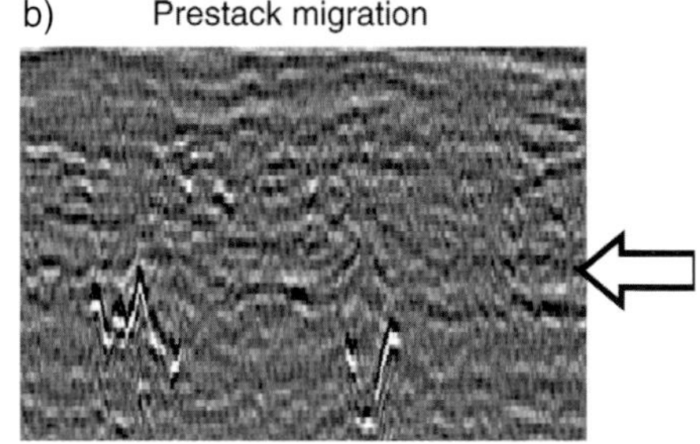

Figure 31. Vertical slices through a shale-dewatering sequence from offshore the Netherlands, taken from poststack and prestack depth-migrated volumes. Minimal structural definition is present. After Rietveld et al. (1999).

ers have shown that wave-equation migration is nearly always superior to Kirchhoff migration, those workers always compared comparable frequency content. Lazarevic (2004) compared how these products are provided in practice. We reproduce in Figure 34 her analysis of frequency content for two output images (one from a Kirchhoff migration, the other from a shot-domain wave-equation migration) for a land survey over the Yucatan Peninsula, Mexico. Even at 25% of the cost, the Kirchhoff image has a bandwidth that is approximately double that of the wave-equation image.

In Figure 35, we show a line through the Kirchhoff-migration and wave-equation prestack-depth-migration images. We note that the discontinuities (faults and karst features) in the shallow part of the section (indicated by yellow arrows) are sharper in the Kirchhoff image (Figure 35a) than in the wave-equation image (Figure 35b). We attribute this improved lateral resolution to the increased bandwidth, which is exhibited as improved vertical resolution in the shallow section as well.

In the deeper part of the section, the situation is different. Although the input bandwidth was higher for the Kirchhoff migration, the output images appear to have similar frequency contents at depth. We attribute that loss of frequency to the migration hyperbolas being misaligned with the unmigrated data, either because of a poor velocity, or more likely (because both images used the same velocity model) because of an inability to model multiple source-image-receiver raypaths.

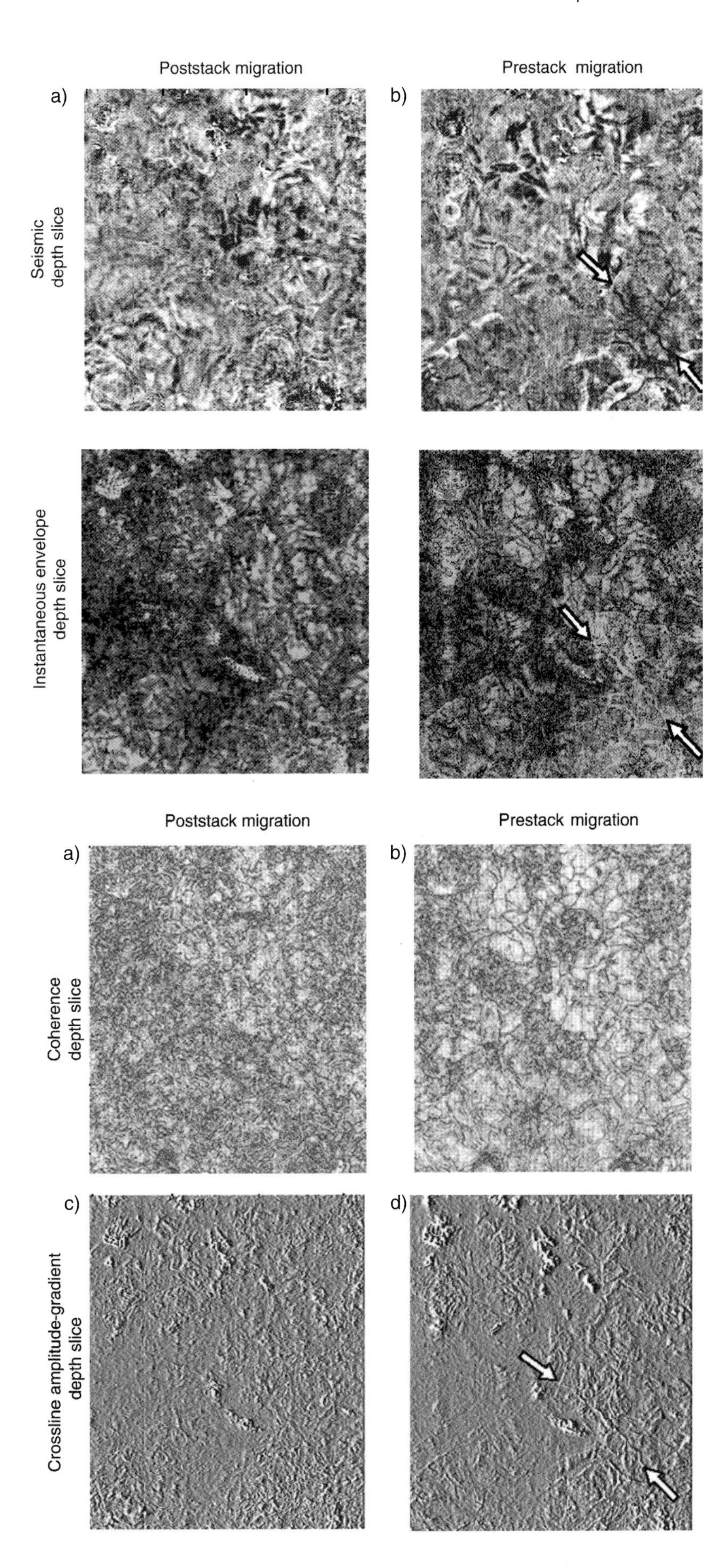

Figure 32. Depth slices at the level indicated by the white arrows in Figure 31, shown here through the seismic data volume and an energy-envelope (reflection-strength) volume after (a) poststack and (b) prestack depth migration. Note the improved lateral resolution on the envelope slice after prestack depth migration. After Rietveld et al. (1999).

Figure 33. Depth slices at the level indicated by the white arrows in Figure 31 and corresponding to same time level as Figure 32, shown here through (a)-(b) the coherence volume and (c)-(d) the north-south component of the energy-weighted coherent-amplitude-gradient volume, after poststack and prestack depth migration. The polygonal geometries associated with the dewatering process are resolved much better in the prestack depth-migration images. After Rietveld et al. (1999).

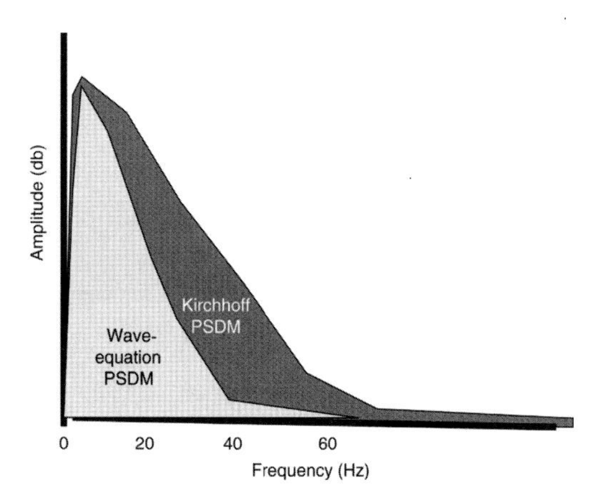

Figure 34. Frequency content of Kirchhoff and wave-equation prestack depth-migration (PDSM) images from a Yucatan Peninsula, Mexico, data volume corresponding to Figure 35. The Kirchhoff image is at 20 db at 40 Hz, and the wave equation is at 20 db at 20 Hz. After Lazarevic (2004).

Closer inspection shows significantly improved lateral resolution in the wave-equation-migration image (Figure 35b), as indicated by the blue arrows. Furthermore, we are able to carry the interpretation of the reflector around the survey to the right side of the image on the wave-equation image (Figure 35b) but not on the Kirchhoff image (Figure 35a).

Finally, we note that the area in the center of each image is nearly uninterpretable. Surface obstacles, including swamps and farms, sparse acquisition, and overlying salt and associated illumination problems prevented the analysts from obtaining a sufficiently accurate velocity model to image subsalt reflectors.

In Figure 36, we show inline (northwest-southeast) energy-weighted coherent-amplitude gradients extracted along the horizon indicated by the yellow arrows in Figure 35. Because the Kirchhoff migration (Figure 36a) used a broad-

Figure 35. Vertical slices through (a) a Kirchhoff prestack depth-migration volume and (b) a wave-equation prestack depth-migration volume. Lateral discontinuities in the shallow horizon (yellow arrows) are defined better on Kirchhoff migration. At depth, the more accurate physics implemented by the multiarrival wave-equation-migration algorithm provides a better image, with improved continuity and lateral resolution (blue arrows), even though its frequency content is less. After Lazarevic (2004).

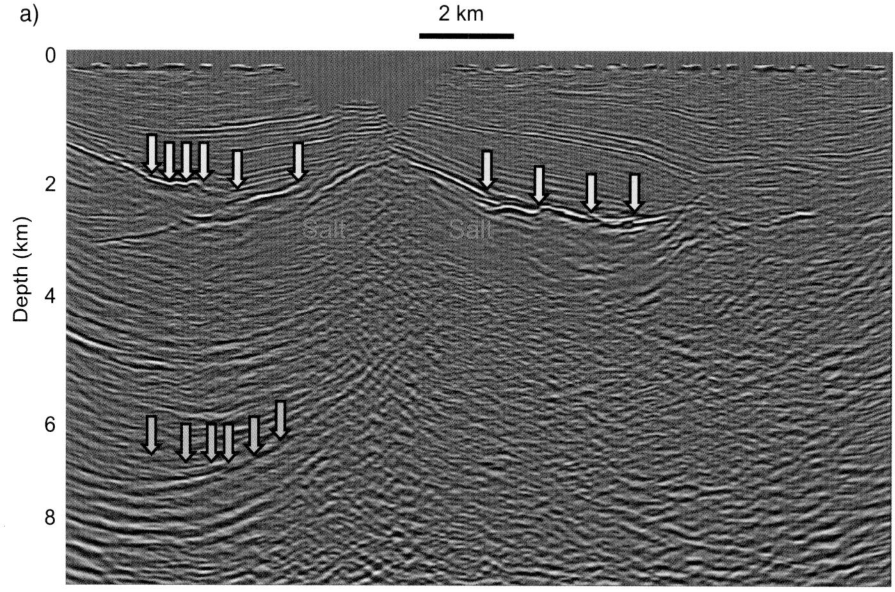

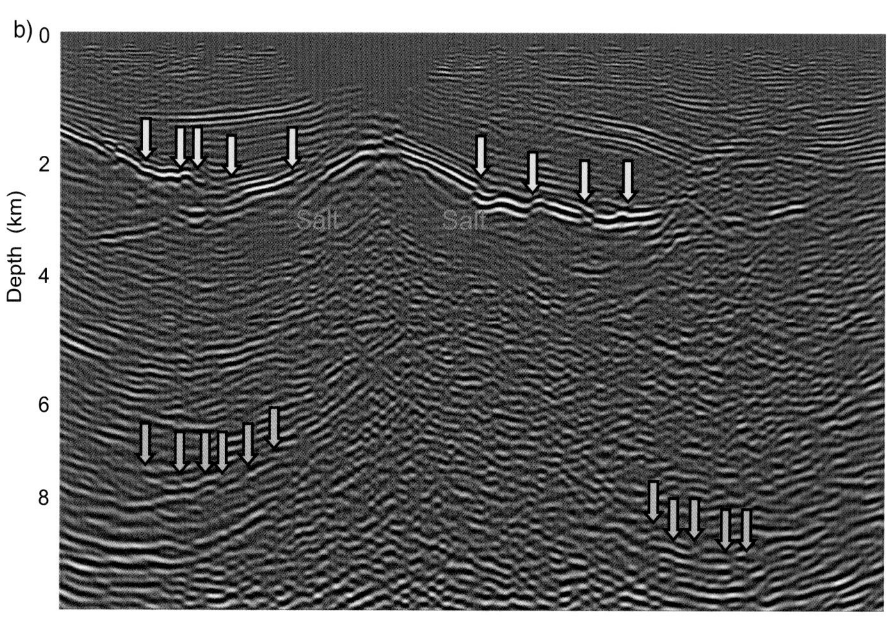

er bandwidth than that used by the wave-equation migration (Figure 36b), we note that the Kirchhoff image has both a higher dynamic range and a higher lateral resolution.

Figure 37 shows depth slices at $z = 8$ km (no continuous horizons spanned the survey at this level) through coherence volumes generated from a Kirchhoff prestack-depth-migration volume (Figure 37a), a wave-equation prestack- depth-migration volume (Figure 37b), and the corresponding depth slices through most-positive-curvature volumes from a Kirchhoff prestack-depth-migration volume (Figure 37c) and a wave-equation prestack-depth-migration volume (Figure 37d). We see good images in the minibasin in the southwestern part of the survey. Although the Kirchhoff coherence images appear to be better resolved than the wave-equation coherence images in this area, the opposite is true for the long-wavelength most-positive-curvature images. Everywhere else, the attribute images are useless. We wish to state bluntly that poorly migrated images produce poor attribute images.

Excluding the first Fresnel zone to enhance discontinuities

Now that we have reviewed some of the other factors that determine the quality of a migrated image, we return to the Fresnel zone. As we noted earlier, Sun and Bancroft (2001) demonstrated that we can construct accurate amplitudes of horizontal continuous reflectors if we include the width of only two Fresnel zones in our migration aperture.

Kozlov et al. (2004) reasoned that the strong reflection amplitudes that Sun and Bancroft (2001) wanted to preserve can easily overwhelm subtler amplitude anomalies that result from discontinuities. In Figure 38, we reproduce Kozlov et al.'s depth-slice images obtained by conventional migration, shown here with all the Fresnel zones possible included (Figure 38a), the innermost Fresnel zone excluded (Figure 38b), and only the further Fresnel zones included (Figure 38c). In essence, we migrate the wings of the diffractions and not their crests. In particular, note the increased lateral resolution shown in Figure 38b, in which all but the nearest Fresnel zones were used.

Migration aperture often is limited by survey size in land data, as shown in Figure 39a. The Fresnel zone grows with depth, so that we can include more Fresnel zones when we migrate shallower reflectors. In Figure 39b, we see the Fresnel zones used in a complete migration (in which we migrate every data trace we have). Figure 39c shows a more efficient migration algorithm that preserves amplitudes on continuous reflectors by including only two Fresnel zones. Finally, we see Kozlov et al.'s (2004) algorithm that excludes the innermost Fresnel zone (Figure 39d).

In Figure 40, from Kozlov et al. (2004), we compare depth slices (at 842 ms) through a coherence volume (Figure 40a) calculated from an image using all Fresnel zones

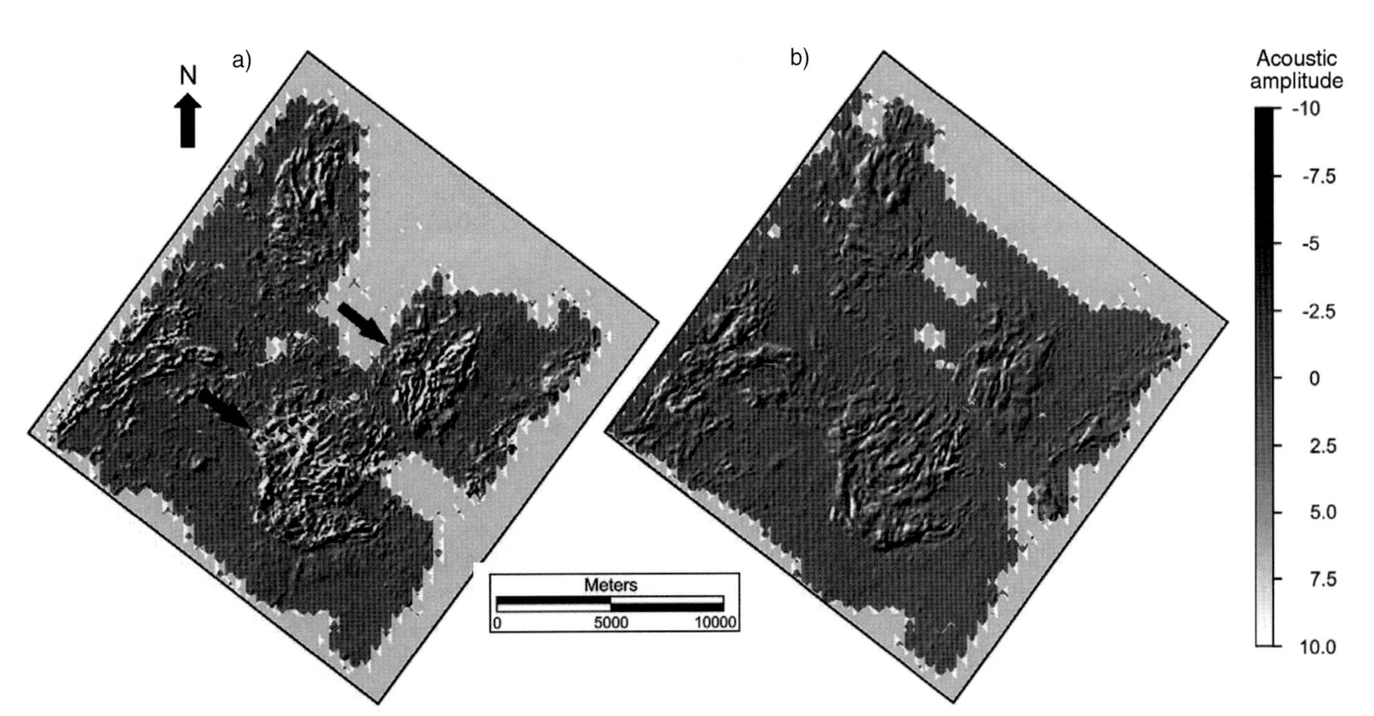

Figure 36. Shallow horizon slices, corresponding to the yellow arrows in Figure 35, of the inline energy-weighted coherent-amplitude gradient on (a) a Kirchhoff prestack depth-migration image and (b) a wave-equation prestack depth-migration image. Note the improved lateral resolution of the Kirchhoff image, which shows indications of channels and other stratigraphic features. After Lazarevic (2004).

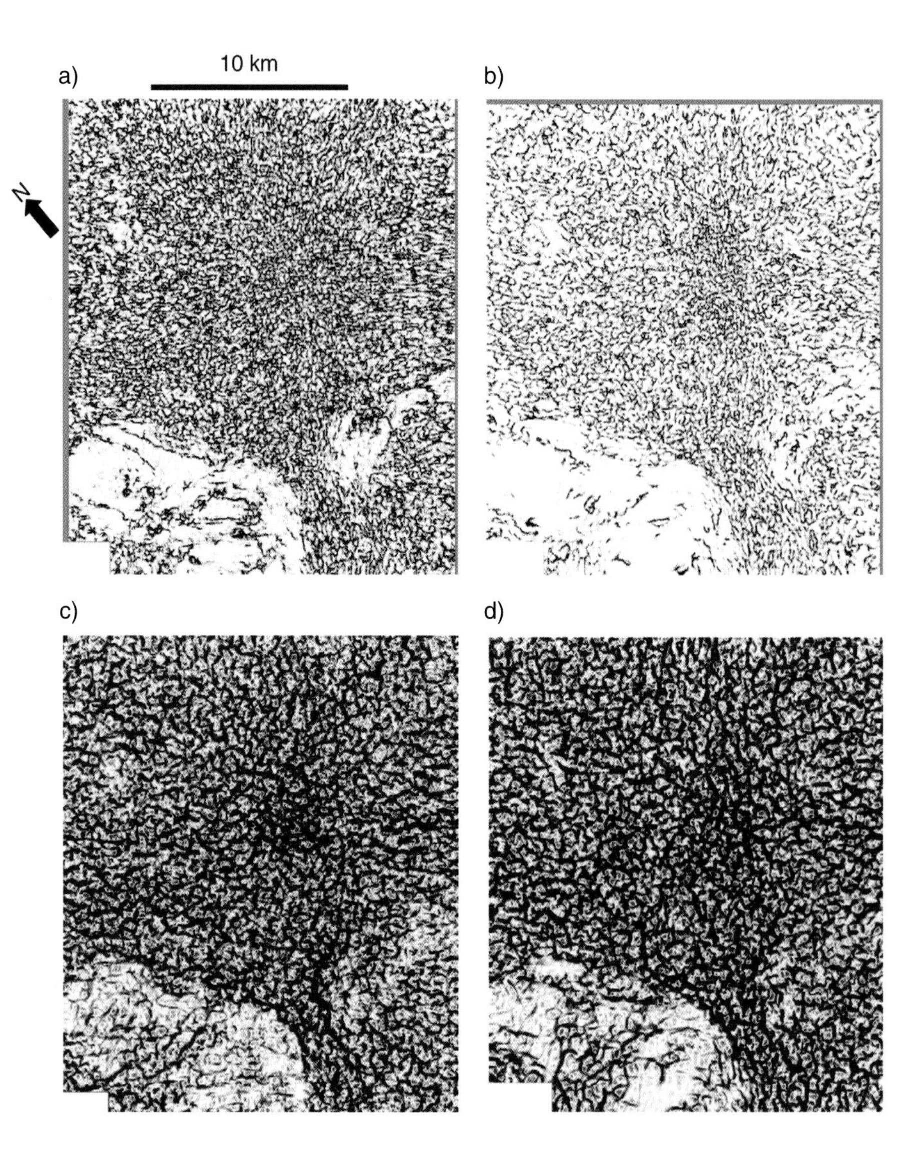

Figure 37. (a)-(b). Depth slices at z = 8 km through coherence volumes generated from (a) a Kirchhoff prestack depth-migration volume and (b) a wave-equation prestack depth-migration volume. (c)-(d). Corresponding depth slices through most-positive-curvature volumes from (c) a Kirchhoff prestack depth-migration volume and (d) a wave-equation prestack depth-migration volume. The poor attribute images outside the minibasin in the lower left corner are the result of overlying salt and carbonates. To state it succinctly, fancy attributes cannot help a poorly migrated image. After Lazarevic (2004).

with a seismic data volume (Figure 40b) (which they called a scattering-object-image volume) with the width of a Fresnel zone excluded from the center of the Kirchhoff migration operator. A similar set of images at 1762 ms is shown in Figure 40c and d. Although the coherence images show some features not seen on their scattering-object images, we also see features on the scattering-object images that we do not see in coherence. Simply stated, additional information exists in the data, and our conventional migration followed by coherence flow is not extracting that information.

The Role of Frequency Enhancement on Seismic Attributes

Inversion for acoustic impedance

Seismic inversion for acoustic impedance combines sparse, high-resolution well control with dense, moderate-resolution seismic data, thereby providing images that exhibit improved vertical resolution (Latimer et al., 2000). Seismic amplitudes reveal impedance changes between lithologic units. The observed seismic amplitude changes, however, may not indicate whether the amplitude changes relate to variations in lithology above or below an interface.

Acoustic impedance is a physical rock property, given as the product of density and interval velocity. Well logs measure both these entities directly, so that by dividing the density log by the traveltime measured by the sonic log, we can generate an acoustic-impedance log.

Acoustic impedance is also a layer property. If our objective is to quantitatively interpret our data in terms of thin, stratal interval properties, then we should use impedance instead of interface reflection properties. Because acoustic impedance is a layer property, it simplifies lithologic and stratigraphic identification and may be more directly linked to lithologic or reservoir properties such as porosity, fluid fill, and net pay.

In particular, impedance inversion allows direct interpretation of three-dimensional geobodies. Impedance inversion plays an important role in seismic interpretation, reservoir characterization, time-lapse seismic monitoring, pressure prediction, and other geophysical applications. Several different techniques and methodologies commonly are used to perform acoustic-impedance inversion (Oldenburg et al., 1983; Haas and Dubrule, 1994; Russell, 1988). They entail different levels of sophistication, including recursive inversion, model-based inversion, sparse-spike inversion, stratigraphic inversion, and stochastic inversion. No matter what technique is adopted to invert the seismic data volume, the impedance volume proves to be very useful.

In this section, we examine the advantages of calculating coherence on an inverted impedance volume rather than on the original seismic data volume. In such a case, the al-

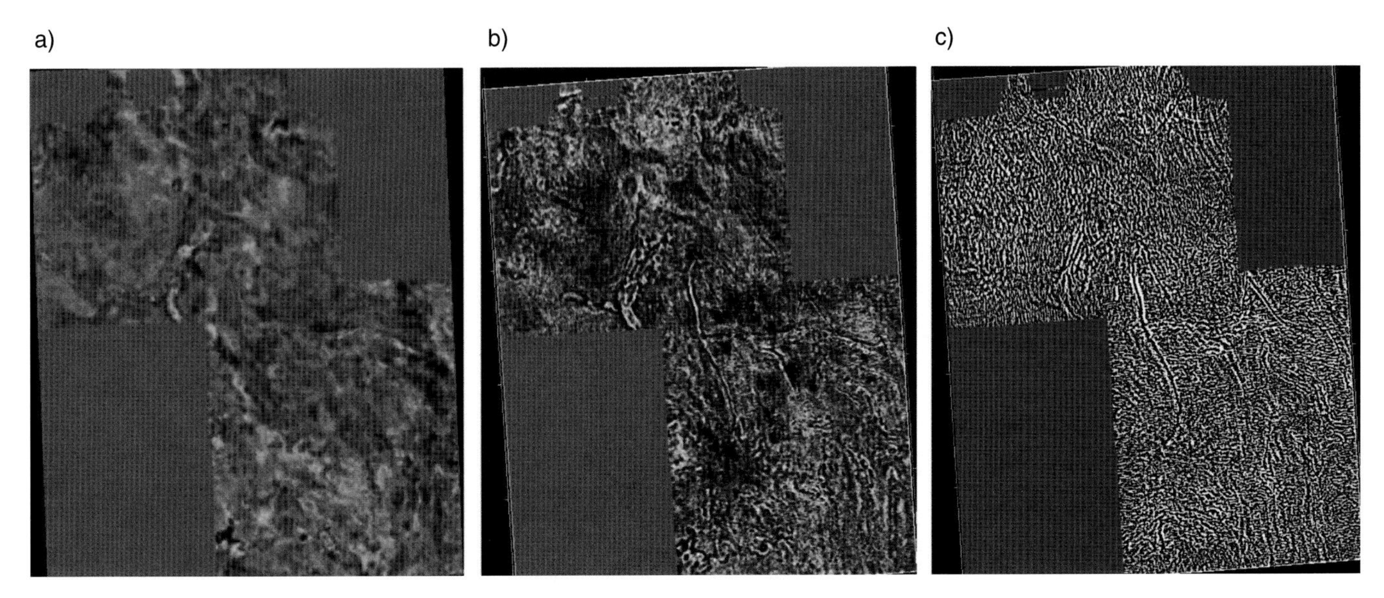

Figure 38. Depth slices at 3296 m through a survey from eastern Siberia, using (a) all Fresnel zones, (b) a gentle mute of the nearest Fresnel zones, and (c) a harsh mute of the nearest Fresnel zones. Note the improved illumination of stratigraphic discontinuities. After Kozlov et al. (2004).

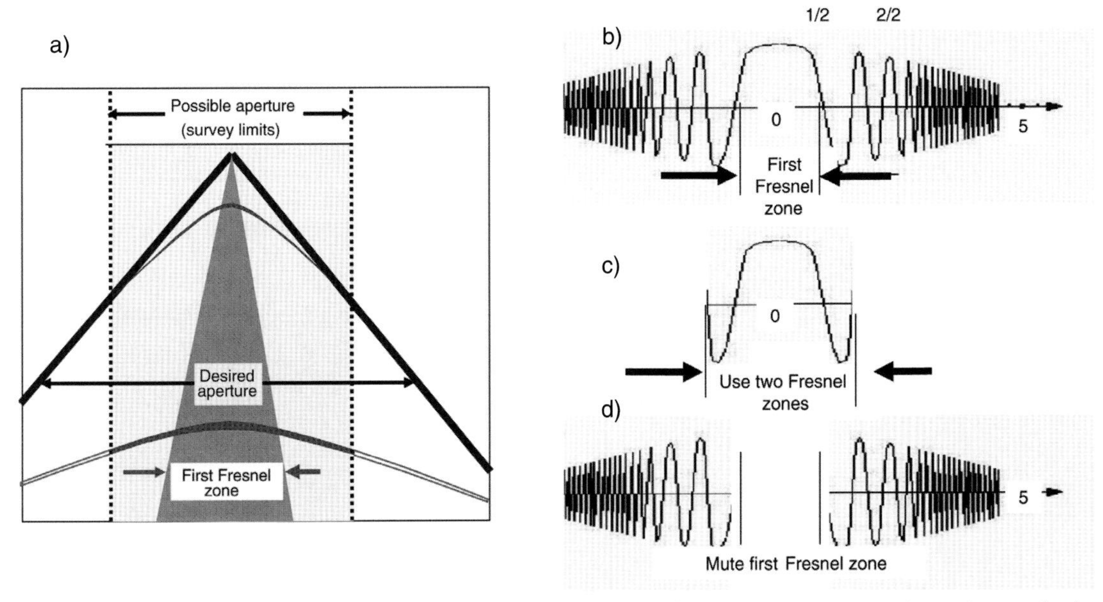

Figure 39. (a) A schematic diagram showing the size of the Fresnel zone at a given time level for a given velocity. Theoretically, in conventional migration, we wish to include as many Fresnel zones as are permitted by the limits of acquisition and computation. (b) Each Fresnel zone is defined by an annulus (for constant velocity), in which all the amplitudes are summed together with the same sign. (c) Typically, cost constraints, errors in the velocity modeling, and operator aliasing lead us to limit our migration aperture to about two Fresnel zones. (d) To enhance scattering objects versus specular reflectors, we exclude the interior Fresnel zones from our computation, as shown here. After Kozlov et al. (2004).

gorithm searches for similar patterns in acoustic impedance rather than measuring local waveform similarities. The output volume is still coherence, but it is coherence of acoustic impedance rather than of seismic data. Because the inversion volume has a higher vertical resolution than the input seismic data have, along with enhanced signal-to-noise ratio, the resulting coherence resolution (derived by laterally comparing adjacent waveforms) should be significantly higher. Indeed, a seismic processor might consider acoustic-impedance inversion to be the optimal wavelet-shaping deconvolution algorithm, with the seismic wavelet being driven in a smooth, spatially varying way that is defined by well control. A careful impedance algorithm also rejects noise that does not fit the a priori model and therefore acts as a spatial filter.

In Figure 41, we show a comparison of time slices at 1044 ms through a coherence volume run on the original seismic data (Figure 41a), through acoustic impedance generated from the original seismic data (Figure 41b), and through coherence generated from that acoustic-impedance volume (Figure 41c). In Figure 41a, we see a prominent east-west-running channel and also some low-coherence features above the channel. In Figure 41c, this low-coherence zone appears to be distinct boundaries of a second channel. We conclude that two channels are running almost east to west in the image.

As we mentioned earlier, reflection is an interface property and impedance is a layer property, so that an inherent phase difference exists between the two attributes. Thus, we could argue that although the coherence slice in Figure 41c represents the same time as that in Figure 41a, it may not be equivalent to the coherence slice in Figure 41a.

Impedance inversion also has increased the low-frequency component of the data, so we may fear looking at geology farther above and below the target time slice. We therefore need to examine adjacent time slices to verify what we see in Figure 41. Figure 42 shows such a series of images. For a fair comparison of the appearance of the northern portion of the data, the volumes was flattened on a marker horizon above the channel and then sliced through. Each of the slices confirms the conclusion stated above.

In Figures 43 and 44, we show an example wherein a coherence volume is combined effectively with seismic inversion to improve our understanding of the morphology of stratigraphic features recorded by 3D seismic surveys. This example is a Tertiary oil play from the North Sea, and it il-

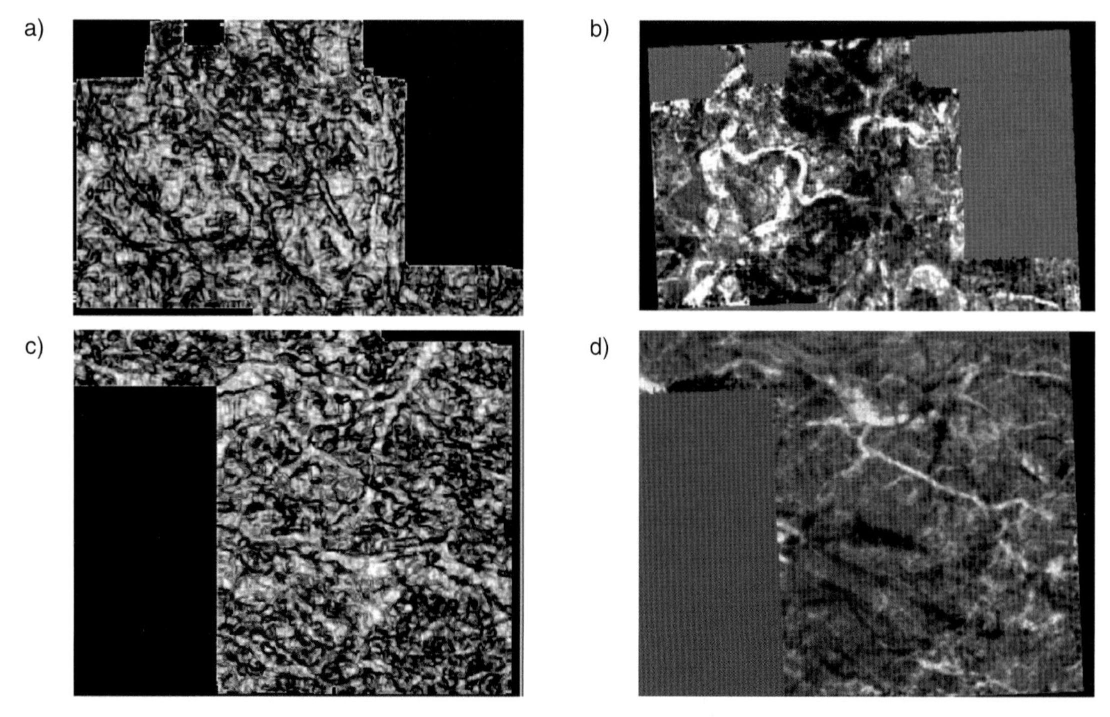

Figure 40. (a)-(b). Depth slices at 842 m, in data from a survey acquired in eastern Siberia through (a) a coherence volume calculated from conventional prestack depth migration using the full migration aperture, encompassing all Fresnel zones, and (b) a scattering-object image volume, obtained using the same depth-migration algorithm but limited to only the outermost Fresnel zones. In this algorithm, the Kirchhoff migration diffraction summation operator excludes contributions from the crest of the operator where that width of the exclusion crest is measured in terms of Fresnel zone diameters. (c)-(d). Using data from the same survey, depth slices here at 1762 m through (c) the coherence volume calculated from conventional prestack depth migration using the full migration aperture, encompassing all Fresnel zones, and (d) a scattering-object image volume, obtained using the same depth-migration algorithm but limited to only the outermost Fresnel zones. After Kozlov et al. (2004).

lustrates significant imaging improvement that resulted in unparalleled detail of subtle sedimentary depositional features. The principal aim of the study was to delineate the extent of a Tertiary reservoir and identify the nature and extent of lower Paleocene sand bodies and to gain a better understanding of their depositional environments.

Inversion was performed on this multiple-well 3D seismic volume. In Figure 43, we display a 2D seismic profile passing through a well location extracted from the 3D volume. The estimated wavelet was convolved with the well-derived reflectivities and the synthetic traces inserted in the seismic profile at the well position. A good match was obtained between the two data sets.

One well was excluded from the inversion process. That was done to be able to perform a blind well test on the inverted volume and evaluate the effectiveness of the inversion process itself and the level of resolution of the impedance volume. Figure 43b shows the acoustic-impedance profile corresponding to the 2D profile in Figure 43a; inserted in between is the acoustic-impedance log. Because this well was excluded from the inversion, the good match between the two is a valid check of the inversion's ability to predict the well.

A comparison between the impedance detail in the seismic inversion result and the overall vertical resolution of seismic data clearly showed that seismic inversion substantially enhanced subsurface resolution. In Figure 44b, we show the impedance time slice corresponding to the seismic slice in Figure 44a and the coherence slice in Figure 44c. This acoustic impedance is more highly correlated to the well logs and lithology, thereby enabling a more consistent interpretation of the subsurface than is possible from the seismic data and well logs alone.

In Figure 44d, we display the time slice of the coherence computation performed on the acoustic-impedance volume. Notice that the slice displays higher resolution and lower noise levels, and thus sharper geologic detail. By deconvolving the wavelet, we have minimized mixing structural and stratigraphic features present at shallower and deeper levels and thereby have preserved both vertical and lateral resolution.

Finally, we corendered the coherence volume and the impedance volumes to generate a composite volume using the techniques discussed in Chapter 9. The time slice in Figure 44e shows the stratigraphic features clearly and the acoustic-impedance range across them. With reasonably high-

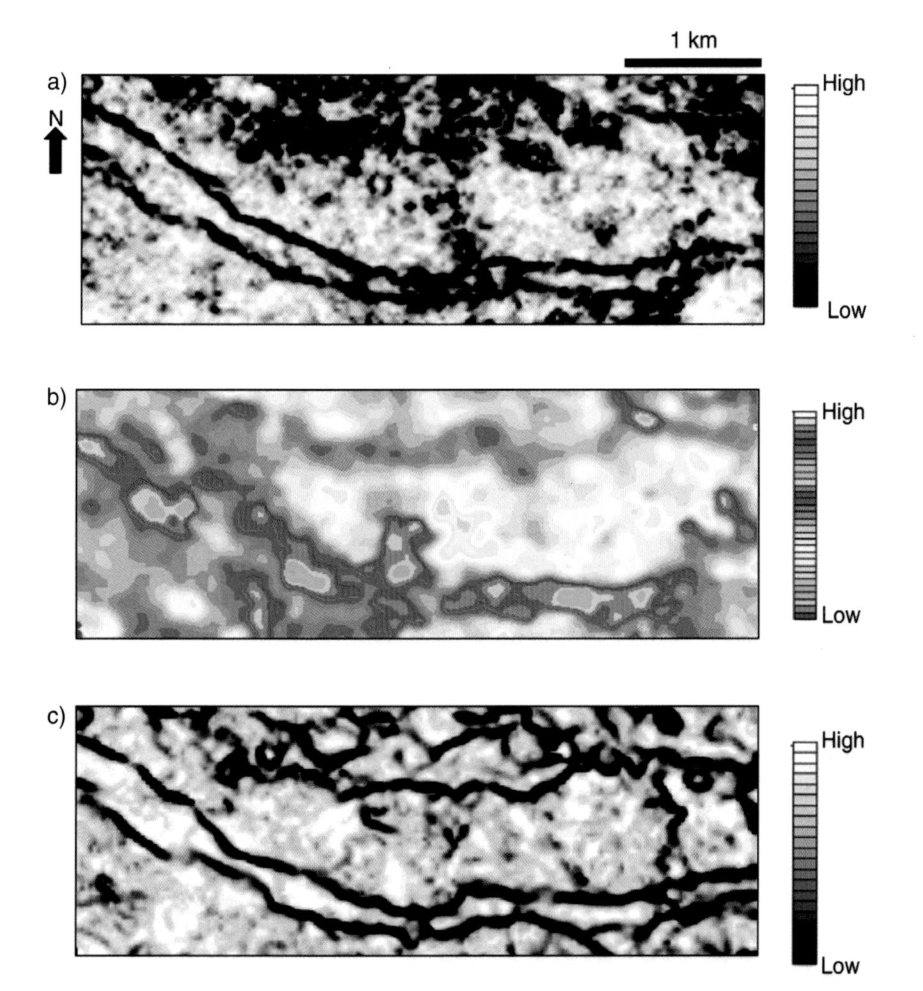

Figure 41. Time slices through (a) a coherence volume generated from original seismic data, (b) an acoustic-impedance volume generated from original seismic data, and (c) a coherence volume generated from the acoustic-impedance volume in (b). Note the improved resolution in the north part of (c). One of the benefits of impedance inversion is a nearly optimal deconvolution, which increases the bandwidth, decreases stratigraphic mixing, and improves the signal-to-noise ratio. After Chopra (2001b).

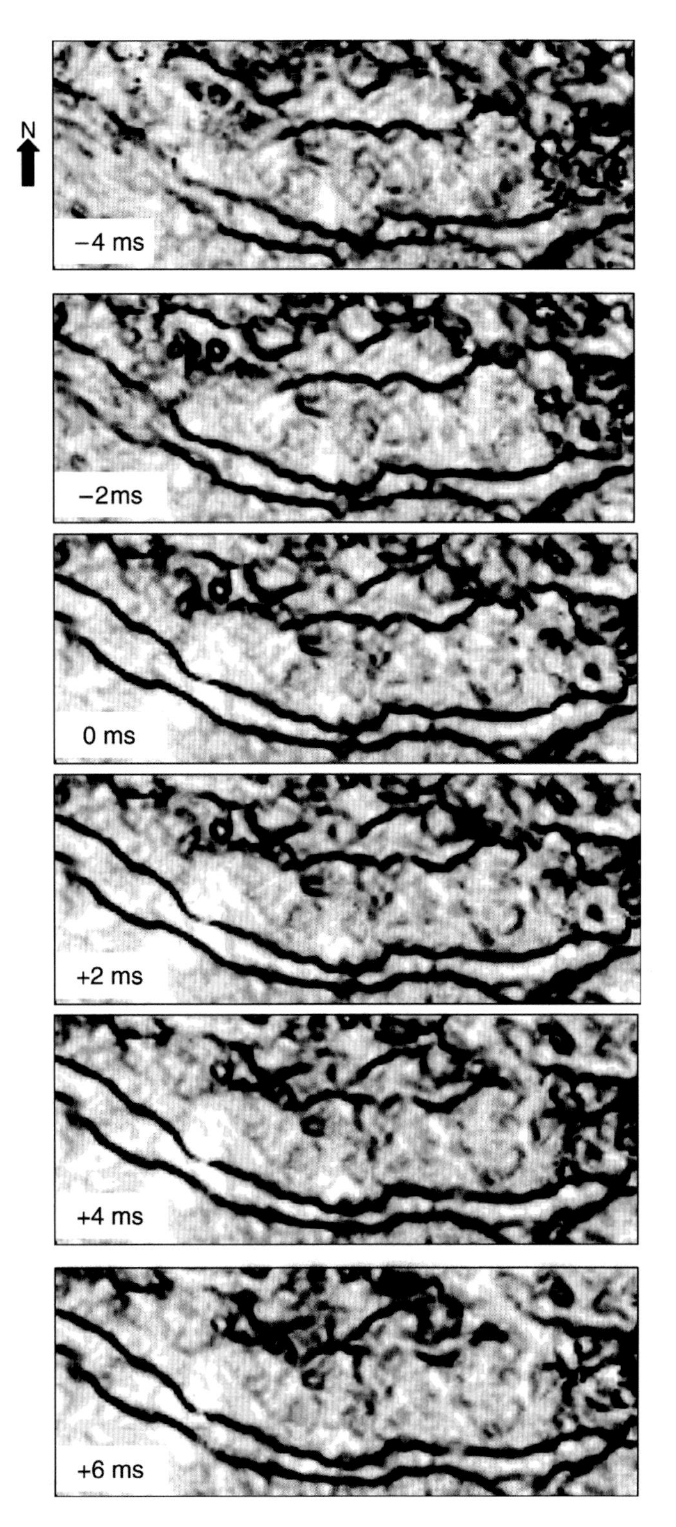

Figure 42. Horizon slices above and below the channel horizon from Figure 41c, run on the acoustic impedance derived from the original seismic data. Note the high vertical resolution provided by coherence computed from the acoustic-impedance volume. In contrast, the coherence image shown in Figure 41a, which was generated from the narrower-bandwidth original seismic data, mixes the reflectivity of the diverse stratigraphic units in the north part of the image. After Chopra (2001b).

quality data, such an analysis would extract higher levels of detail for the interpreter and would offer a clearer window on reality.

In Figure 45, we show a comparison of a small zoomed portion of the coherence and composite displays shown in Figure 44. Notice that the coherence shows the boundaries of the stratigraphic features. The composite display shows alpha-blended coherence in black, with blue indicating low and red indicating high values of impedance.

Frequency enhancement of seismic data using vertical seismic profiles

Whereas conventional well logs provide measurements of impedance at every foot, and those measurements can then be indirectly tied to seismic data via synthetic data, a vertical seismic profile (VSP) is a direct measure of the seismic waveform at depth. With care, a seismic analyst can use those measurements (VSPs) to estimate seismic attenuation (1/Q) with depth. Such estimates, together with an appropriate attenuation model, can then be used to compensate the surface data for change in amplitude and phase (caused by attenuation).

We emphasize that a significant difference exists between deterministic, VSP-driven amplitude compensation and simple statistically driven spectral balancing, which makes no attempt to correct for phase. Details on such a comparison are given in Chopra et al. (2002).

For VSP downgoing signals recorded at different depth levels, the ratio of change in amplitude of the first arrivals at successive depths describes the decay of frequency components between those observation points. This fact is used first to determine the amplitude decay resulting from frequency attenuation from downgoing VSP traces and then to try to restore the frequency components that have been attenuated in the data.

The change in amplitude and length of the wavelet on first arrivals at successive depth levels is used to estimate the change in the frequency components. An inverse operator (in the time domain) is designed to compensate for those changes.

In Figure 46, we show seismic data before and after VSP-driven wavelet shaping. Notice the improvement in resolution and continuity of the reflection events in Figure 46b compared with those in Figure 46a. The increase in frequency bandwidth after enhancement leads to a far better correlation with well data, as seen from the overlays of sonic-log and synthetic seismograms.

In Figure 47, we show times slices at t = 0.984 and 1.024 s through coherence volumes, computed from the data shown in Figure 46a and b, before and after frequency enhancement. We can see the northeast-southwest-trending channel in the center of the image with its definition and

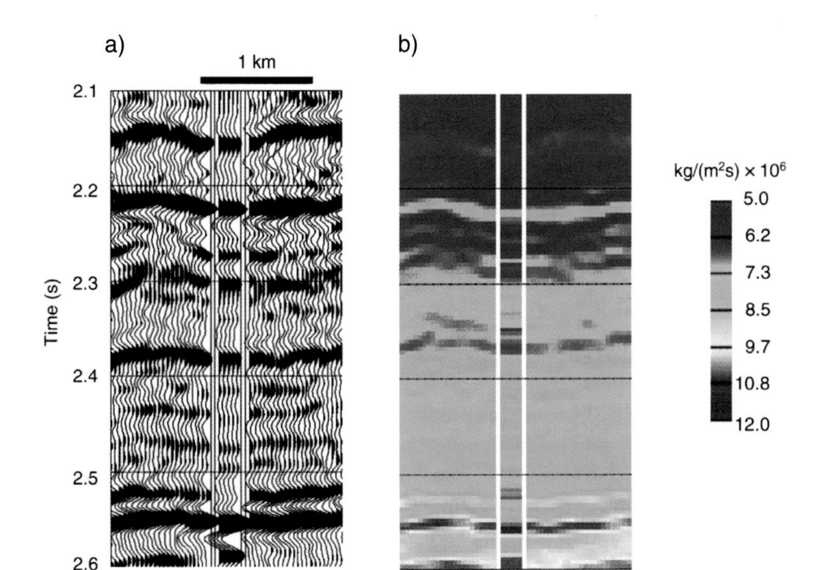

Figure 43. (a) A seismic data profile and (b) derived acoustic impedance through a survey acquired in the North Sea. The modeled synthetic seismogram from inversion is inserted in the seismic image, and the acoustic impedance from the well log is inserted in the impedance image.

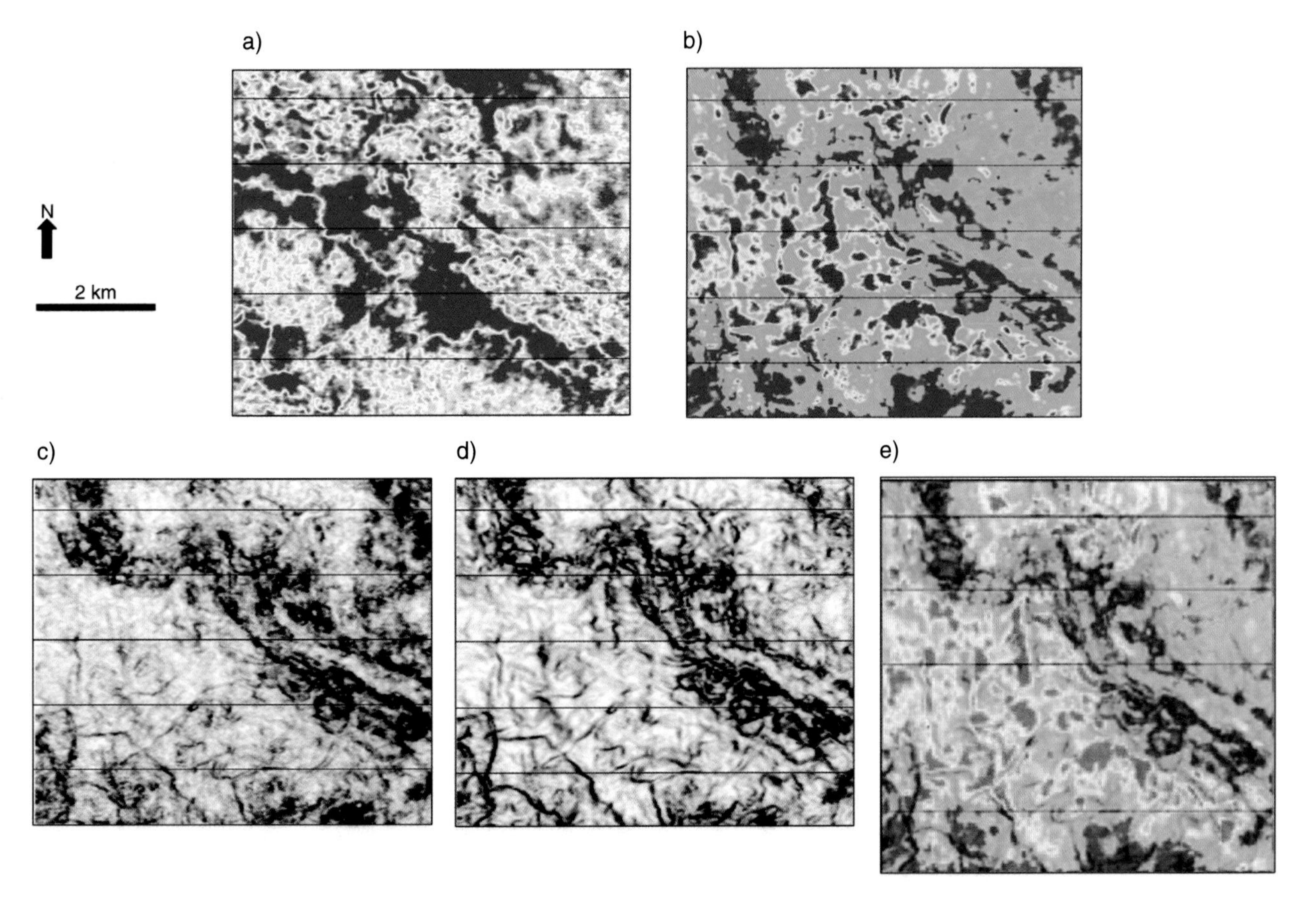

Figure 44. Time slices from the same survey shown on the vertical slices in Figure 43. (a) A seismic data volume, (b) an acoustic-impedance volume, (c) a coherence volume computed from the seismic data volume displayed in (a), and (d) a coherence volume computed from the acoustic-impedance volume displayed in (b). Note the improved resolution shown in (d). In contrast, image (c) shows that the discontinuities occurring within a narrow stratigraphic window are blended with events above and below, through the narrower-bandwidth longer seismic wavelet. (e) The coherence volume shown in (d) is alpha-blended here with the impedance shown in (b).

detail more focused than before (Figure 47a and b). Similarly, the northwest-southeast fault trend, which is not obvious on the slice in Figure 47c, can be tracked in Figure 47d. Frequency enhancement helped define trends better and so leads to a more confident interpretation.

In Figure 48, we show time slices through coherence volumes calculated from the originally processed seismic data (Figure 48a), from seismic data reprocessed using coherence as a quality control, as discussed in Figure 2 (Figure 48b), and from seismic data reprocessed using VSP-driven frequency enhancement (Figure 48c). After VSP frequency enhancement, notice that the signal-to-noise ratio is higher and the faults appear clearly with a northeast-southwest trend.

Similarly, Figure 49 shows a seismic representation on a reef before (Figure 49a) and after (Figure 49b) VSP frequency enhancement. Notice that the seismic events after frequency enhancement have become more pronounced and continuous (both above and below the horizon tracked in red). The reef's boundary cannot be seen clearly on the horizon slice from a coherence volume run on data before frequency enhancement (Figure 49c), but it appears quite clearly on the coherence horizon slice after frequency enhancement (Figure 49d).

Acoustic-impedance inversions have been performed on seismic volumes before and after frequency enhancement. Inversion algorithms generally assume a stationary wavelet in the convolutional model of the seismogram. That assumption is often satisfactory if the time window of the inversion is not too long.

We might expect that any processing that can remove the predictable time-varying wavelet decay resulting from earth-transmission processes would contribute to the stationarity of the wavelet, although that is not always the case. Wavelets extracted from different windows of a seismic line after VSP-frequency-enhancement processing are found to be stable. In inversion, obvious differences that stem from the greater stability of the seismic wavelet can be observed on frequency-enhanced impedance sections.

Impedance inversion performed on data with a larger bandwidth also yields more information than does inversion performed on data with a narrow bandwidth. Hirsche et al. (1984) studied the estimation of formation-dependent absorption (Q) using drift correction from logs and also its use for subsequent Q-compensation of seismic data. They found that inverted seismic traces after Q-compensation compare favorably with time-converted sonic logs. Stratigraphic features that cannot be detected on seismic-inversion results before Q-compensation are clearly visible afterward, and they enable us to interpret important stratigraphic features in detail.

Figure 50 shows vertical sections through an impedance volume. In Figure 50a, a gas-producing well, W, is seen intersecting the highlighted portion corresponding to a

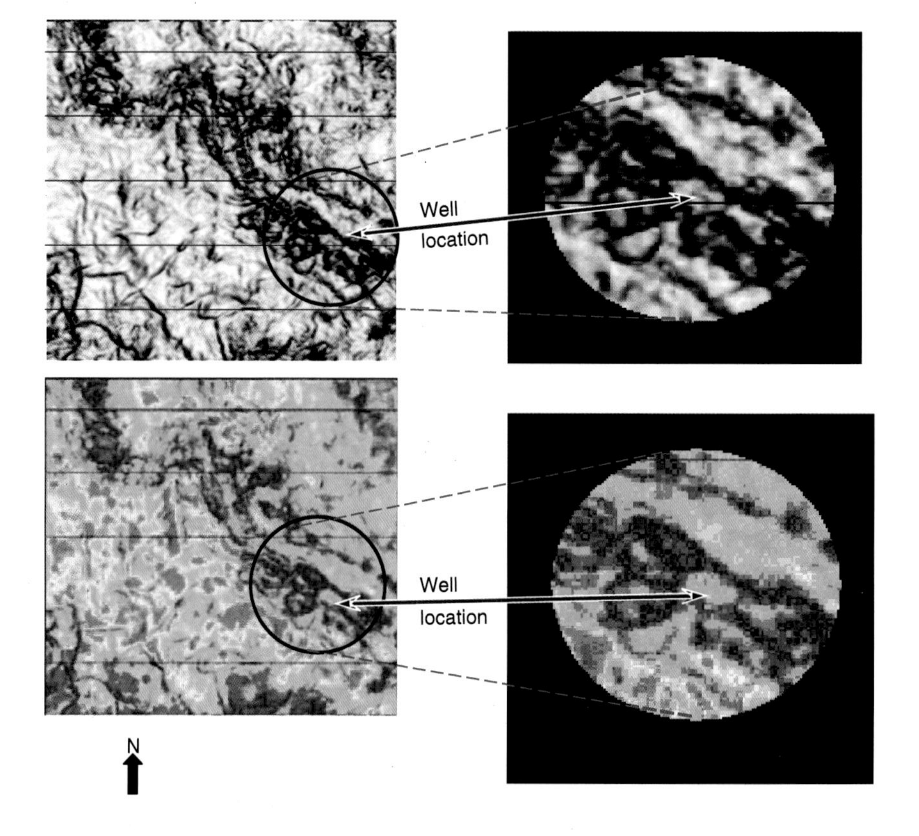

Figure 45. Zoom showing the well location on the images from Figure 44d and e. This producing well intersects a geologic formation that is more coherent (white versus gray or black) and has lower impedance (cyan versus blue).

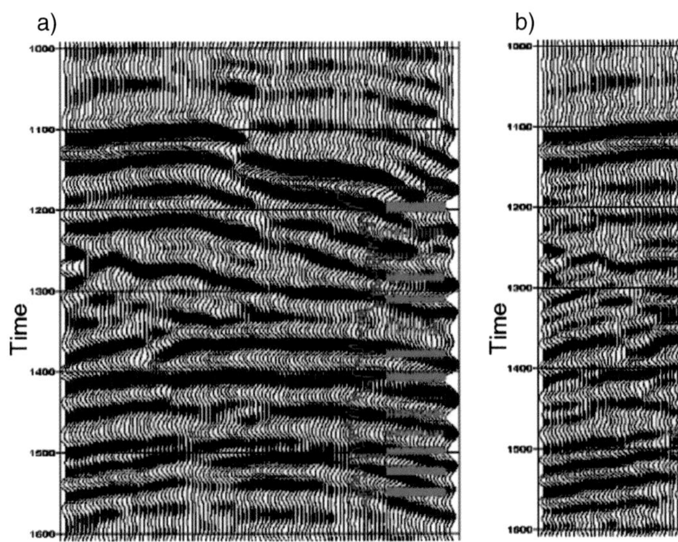

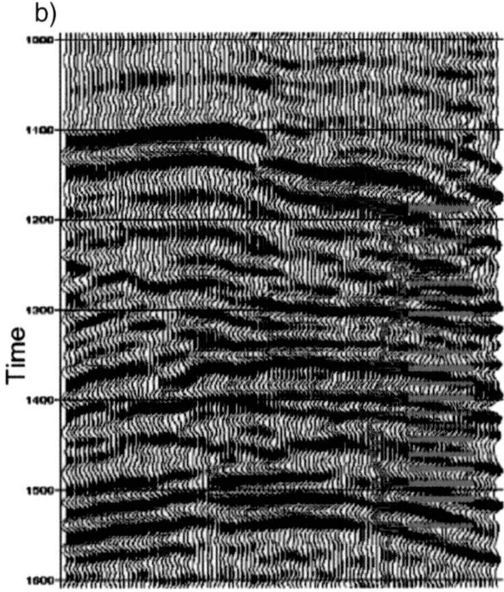

Figure 46. Vertical slices through a seismic volume (a) before and (b) after VSP-driven spectral enhancement. The sonic-log and filtered synthetic seisomograms (generated for the portion of the sonic log available with bandpass 8-12-45-50 Hz and 8-12-65-70 Hz) are shown overlaid on the two sections. Images courtesy of Core Laboratories.

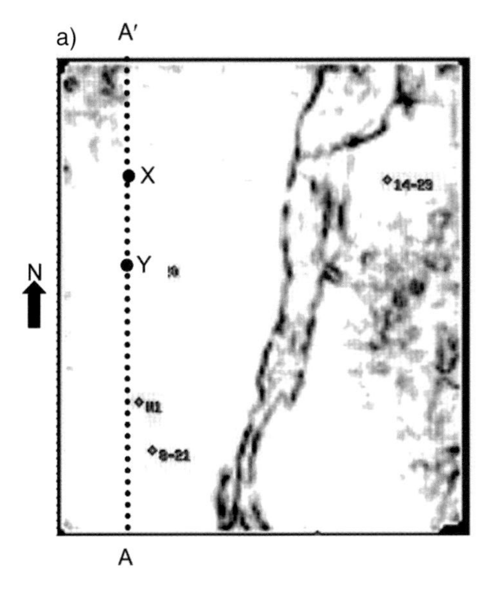

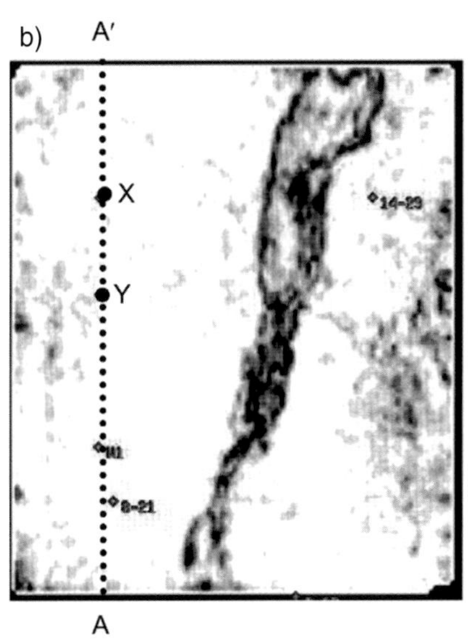

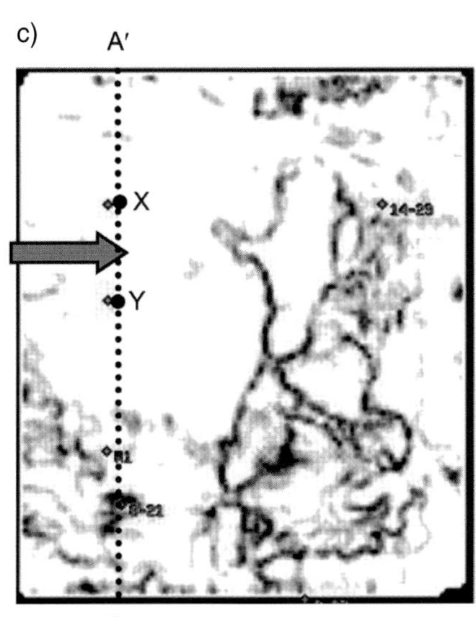

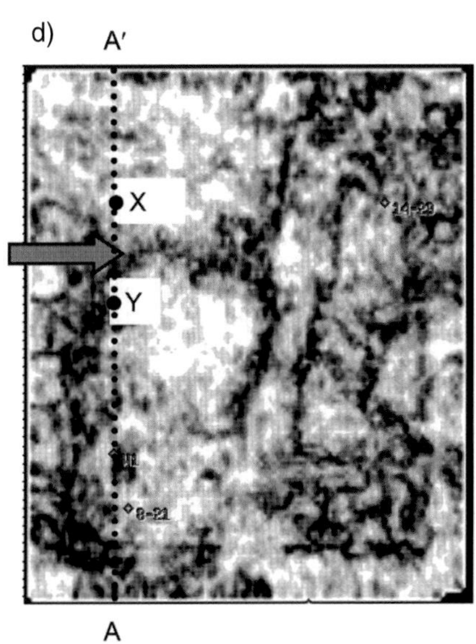

Figure 47. Time slices through coherence volumes generated from the seismic data from Figure 46, before and after VSP frequency enhancement. The slices are shown here at (a) $t = 0.984$ s and (b) $t = 0.984$ s, and at (c) $t = 1.024$ s and (d) $t = 1.024$ s. The arrow indicates a zone in which no communication existed between wells X and Y. Images courtesy of Core Laboratories.

gas sand. However, the green streak continues across the segment and does not identify the gas sand. Frequency enhancement was run on that seismic section and impedance inversion was performed (Figure 50b). Note the dark streak (registering low impedance, within the highlighted portion) that clearly represents the gas sand. This example provides findings similar to those of Hirsche et al. (1984) using VSP-driven frequency enhancement, and amply corroborates their work.

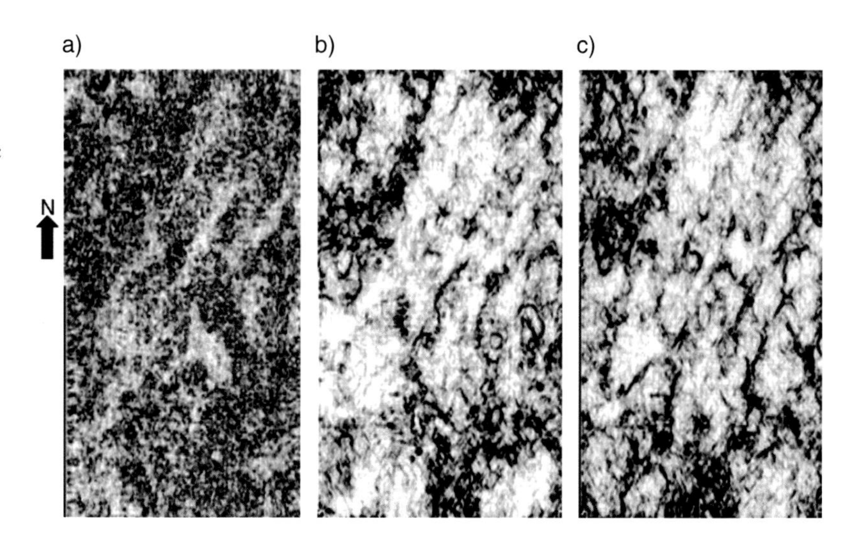

Figure 48. Time slices at t = 1.210 s through coherence volumes calculated from (a) originally processed seismic data, (b) those seismic data reprocessed using coherence for quality control, as discussed in Figure 2, and (c) the seismic data reprocessed using VSP-driven spectral enhancement. Images courtesy of Core Laboratories.

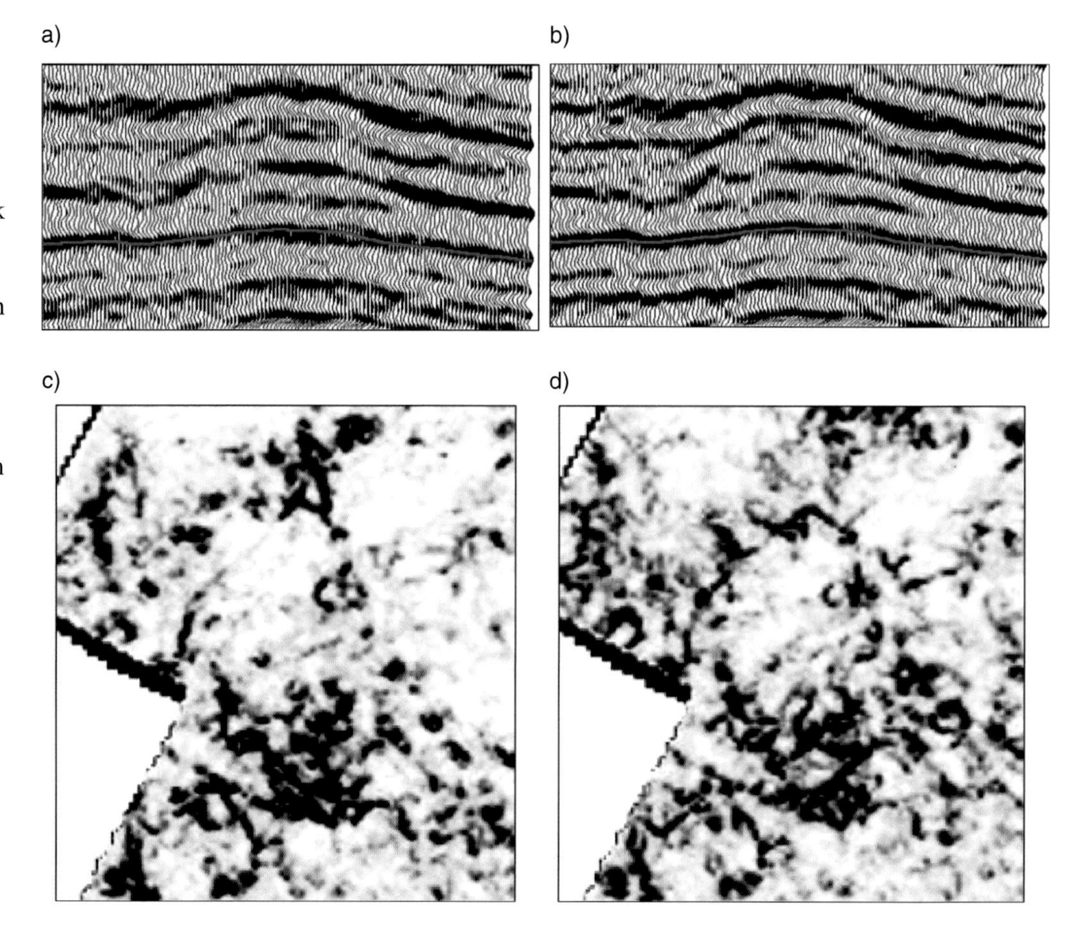

Figure 49. Seismic data (a) before and (b) after VSP-driven spectral enhancement. (c) A horizon slice along the red pick through the coherence volume corresponding to the conventional data shown in (a), and (d) a horizon slice along the red pick through the coherence volume corresponding to the spectrally enhanced data shown in (b). Images courtesy of Core Laboratories.

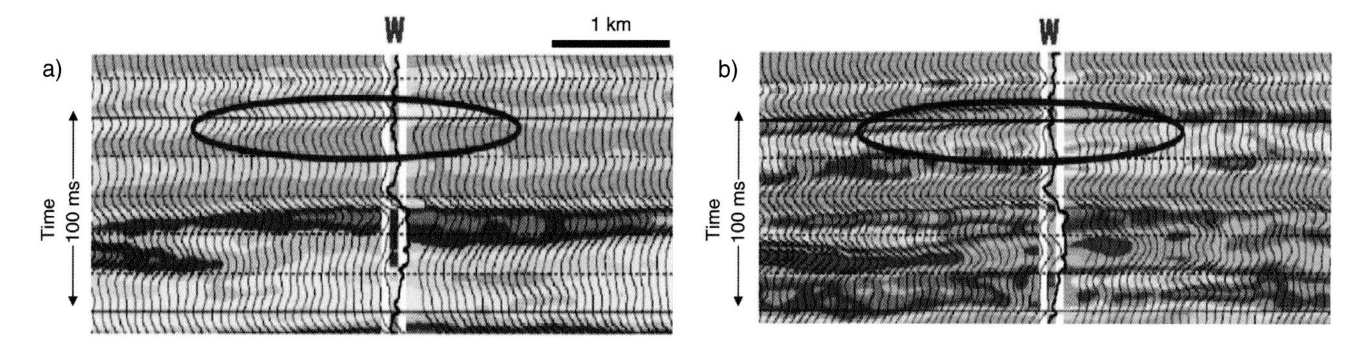

Figure 50. Vertical slices through impedance volumes generated from (a) conventional seismic data and (b) those seismic data after VSP-driven spectral compensation. The ellipse denotes the improved resolution of low-impedance gas sand. Images courtesy of Core Laboratories.

Chapter Summary

Seismic attributes are only as good as the seismic data from which they are derived. Errors in geometry, statics, wavelet shaping, and velocities all reduce the spectral bandwidth, signal-to-noise ratio, and lateral resolution of the resulting seismic image. Coherent noise, including multiples and backscattered headwaves and ground roll, produces events that cross and may be stronger in amplitude than the true reflection events of interest. Coherence treats such crossing events as discontinuities at their intersections, thereby producing erroneous time-slice images that might be misinterpreted as faults or stratigraphic boundaries.

Fortunately, geometric attributes can be a tool to help minimize such data-quality issues. We recommend using coherence at each stage of the seismic processing flow, (1) to safeguard the quality of results and (2) to drive selection of processing parameters and noise-rejection algorithms to ensure their appropriateness to the geologic objective at hand.

Acquisition footprint plagues almost all land-data volumes, as well as marine volumes in which obstacles or currents prevent uniform coverage. Although acquisition footprint mimics features of the acquisition geometry, most often it is the result either of backscattered noise or of poorly chosen processing parameters.

The ideal junctures for attacking acquisition footprint are at the time of the survey design and in the processing shop. Also, in many cases, careful k_x-k_y filtering of time slices of the migrated data volume can help reduce footprint artifacts. We recommend designing such filters on the basis of the exacerbated footprint artifacts seen on the coherence time slices, and then applying those filters to the seismic data.

Acquisition footprint degrades geometric attributes and also autotrackers, clustering algorithms, geostatistics, and neural nets. Footprint can be particularly troublesome in any attempt to map fractures and other lineaments.

In general, acquisition footprint diminishes with depth. Thus, we advise interpreters always to begin by examining attribute time slices in the shallowest part of the section (e.g., at $t = 0.2$ s for land data) and from that information to form a mental image of what not to interpret deeper in the section.

Seismic migration collapses diffraction hyperbolas and increases lateral resolution. Given a good velocity model, prestack migration algorithms provide higher lateral-resolution images than do poststack migration algorithms.

Poorly focused images, such as those that occur below salt, provide almost useless seismic-attribute volumes. If one finds that generating a time-structure map on a nearby reflector is extremely difficult, we advise against using attributes. At present, the human interpreter is nearly always smarter than a computer algorithm.

Impedance inversion, and other processes (such as VSPs) that use well control to improve the frequency content of an image, generate improved attribute volumes. Higher-resolution data produce less mixing of overlying and underlying lithologic units, thereby providing attribute images that have improved vertical and lateral resolution.

References

Biondi, B., S. Fomel, and N. Chemingui, 1998, Azimuth moveout for 3D prestack imaging: Geophysics, **63**, 574–588.

Brown, R. L., 1994, Image quality depends on your point of view: The Leading Edge, **13**, 669–673.

Bruhl, M., G. J. Vermeer, and M. Keihn, 1996, Fresnel zone for broadband data: Geophysics, **61**, 600–604.

Budd, A. J. L., K. Hawkins, A. R. Mackewn, and J. W. Ryan, 1995, Marine geometry for optimum 3D seismic imaging: 57th Annual Conference and Exhibition, EAGE, Extended Abstracts, B030.

Chopra, S., 2001a, Adding the coherence dimension to 3D seismic data: CSEG Recorder, **26,** no. 1, January 2001, 5–8.

———, 2001b, Integrating coherence cube imaging and seismic inversion: The Leading Edge, **20**, 354–362.

———, 2005, Azimuth moveout — A promising application for pre-stack data: 2005 CSEG National Convention, Expanded Abstracts, 419–423.

Chopra, S., and G. Larsen, 2000, Acquisition footprint — Its detection and removal: CSEG Recorder, **25**, no. 8, 16–20.

Chopra, S., E. Blias, L. Chavina, V. Alexeev, and V. Sudhakar, 2002, High frequency restoration of surface seismic data: CSEG Recorder, **27**, no. 6, 5–12.

Drummond, J. M., A. J. L. Budd, and J. W. Ryan, 2000, Adapting to noisy 3D data — Attenuating the acquisition footprint: 70th Annual International Meeting, SEG, Expanded Abstracts, 9–12.

Drummond, J., J. Ryan, and R. Kasmi, 2001, Adapting to noisy 3D data: Enhancing Algerian giant field development through strategic planning of 3D seismic in Berkine Basin: The Leading Edge, **20**, 718–728.

Famini, J., 2005, Impact of seismic processing on seismic attribute analysis — Application to a survey from the Delaware Basin, NM, USA: M.S. thesis, University of Houston.

French, W. S., 1975, Computer migration of oblique seismic reflection profiles: Geophysics, **40,** 961–980.

Gulunay, N., 1999, Acquisition geometry footprints removal: 69th Annual International Meeting, SEG, Expanded Abstracts, 637–640.

Haas, A., and O. Dubrule, 1994, Geostatistical inversion — A sequential method of stochastic reservoir modeling constrained by seismic data: First Break, **12**, 561.

Henry, S., 2004, Understanding seismic amplitudes: AAPG Explorer, July, www.aapg.org/explorer/geophysical_corner/2004/07gpc.cfm. Accessed August 2006.

Hill, S., M. Shultz, and J. Brewer, 1999, Acquisition footprint and fold-of-stack plots: The Leading Edge, **18**, 686–695.

Hilterman, F. J., 1982, Interpretative lessons from three-dimensional modeling: Geophysics, **47**, 784–808.

———, 2000, AVO examples of long offset 2-D data in the Gulf of Mexico: The Leading Edge, **19**, 1200–1213.

Hirsche, W. K., B. E. Cornish, C. B. Wason, and G. A. King, 1984, Model-based Q compensation: 54th Annual International Meeting, SEG, Expanded Abstracts, S18.7.

Kallweit, R. S., and L. C. Wood, 1982, The limits of resolution of zero-phase wavelets: Geophysics, **47**, 1035–1046.

Kozlov, E., N. Barasky, E. Korolev, A. Antonenko, and E. Koshchuk, 2004, Imaging scattering objects masked by specular reflections: 74th Annual International Meeting, SEG, Expanded Abstracts, 1131–1134.

Latimer, R. B., R. Davison, and P. van Riel, 2000, An interpreter's guide to understanding and working with seismic-derived acoustic impedance data: The Leading Edge, **19**, 242–256.

Lazarevic, I., 2004, Factors impacting lateral velocity resolution: M.S. thesis, University of Houston.

Marfurt, K. J., R. M. Scheet, J. A. Sharp, and M. G. Harper, 1998, Suppression of the acquisition footprint for seismic sequence attribute mapping: Geophysics, **63**, 1024–1035.

Moldoveanu, N., S. Ronen, and S. Mitchell, 1999, Footprint analysis of land and TZ acquisition geometries using synthetic data: 69th Annual International Meeting, SEG, Expanded Abstracts, 641–644.

Negut, D., S. Cilensek, A. M. Popovici, S. Crawley, and D. Bevc, 2005, Azimuth moveout (AMO) for data regularization and interpolation: application to shallow resource plays in western Canada: 2005 CSEG National Convention, Expanded Abstracts, 313–317.

Oldenburg, D.W., T. Scheuer, and S. Levy, 1983, Recovery of the acoustic impedance from reflection seismograms: Geophysics, **48**, 1318.

Rietveld, W. E., J. H. Kommedal, and K. J. Marfurt, 1999, The effect of prestack depth migration on 3D seismic attributes: Geophysics, **64**, 1553–1561.

Russell, B., 1988, Introduction to seismic inversion methods: SEG Course Notes Series, **2**.

Sheriff, R. E., 1975, Factors affecting seismic amplitudes: Geophysical Prospecting, **23,** 125–138.

Sun, S., and J. C. Bancroft, 2001, How much does the migration aperture actually contribute to the migration result?: 71st Annual International Meeting, SEG, Expanded Abstracts, 973–978.

Walker, C. D., A. R. MacKewn, A. J. L. Budd, and J. W. Ryan, 1995, Understanding the effects of modern marine 3D geometries: 65th Annual International Meeting, SEG, Expanded Abstracts, 942–944.

Chapter 8

Structure-oriented Filtering and Image Enhancement

Chapter Objectives

After reading this chapter, you will be able to

- choose a filtering technique that follows structure and suppresses crosscutting noise
- identify the limits of attribute analysis on data that have been poorly imaged
- recognize the need for special filters to preserve narrow lineaments such as fractures on attribute volumes
- evaluate the application of image processing to enhance attribute volumes

Introduction

Almost all seismic-data volumes are contaminated by both random and coherent noise. Ideally, the juncture at which to address these noise problems is in acquisition design, preprocessing, and migration. Realistically, however, such options are rarely available to the interpreter. Seismic data may come from sources such as speculative (spec) surveys, trade data, and even data acquired by buying other companies. For spec surveys, time and cost constraints may preclude reprocessing the data. For other-party acquisition and trade data, the original field tapes may have been lost or destroyed.

In Chapter 7, we state clearly that if the data are poorly migrated, little can be done to improve the results. We also claim that, in general, if long-period multiples contaminate a migrated section and have dips similar to those of the underlying geology of interest, again we can do very little to remove those multiples at the interpretation stage.

However, many data volumes that are reasonably well migrated and multiple free are still contaminated by noise. Although such noise may not deter a skilled interpreter from creating an accurate time-structure map, it may prevent the use of autotrackers and produce poor-quality attribute volumes.

Most filters work very well with random noise. However, most noise that plagues seismic data is not truly random — it is coherent, although sometimes it is so poorly sampled spatially that it appears to be random. The common forms of contaminating noise seen on migrated images are aliased backscattered ground roll and head waves, both of which survive preprocessing and migration steps and generate organized patterns of conflicting dip that overprint geologic features of interest.

Because such noise often has a very steep dip, we expect an accurate 3D dip filter to help. Let us examine the application of such a dip filter intended to reject steeply dipping noise, as seen in Figure 1a. Figure 1b shows the noise rejected by the filter. This rejected noise was not aliased. In Figure 1c, we have attempted to reject the aliased noise also. Note that the resulting seismic image in Figure 1d is much cleaner than that in Figure 1a, thereby resulting in a much more continuous attribute image in Figure 1f compared with that in Figure 1e. However, we also have rejected some of the signal shown in Figure 1c.

Although we often think of noise as being aliased, the signal also can alias into the domain of a steep-dip filter (Marfurt et al., 1998). For the example in Figure 1, the rejected signal is acceptable. However, if we wish to map fractures or other subtle discontinuities, we want to avoid using such a broad filter.

Gulunay et al. (1993) and Linville and Meek (1995) designed dip filters that first estimated the dip of the most-coherent noise event and then subtracted it in a least-squares sense from the data. Done (1999) used a principal-component filter to achieve the same result. Fomel (2002) used prediction-error filters to design a plane-wave destructor to reduce aliased noise.

Clearly, a close relationship exists between geometric attributes and coherent-noise estimation and subtraction. Indeed, the same prediction-error filter used by Fomel (2002) to attenuate noise was used by Bednar (1998) to estimate coherence (Figure 27 in Chapter 3). The criterion for successfully applying these kinds of filters to migrated data volumes is to avoid smoothing across faults and other discontinuities.

In this chapter, we present two families of tools that interpreters can use on already-migrated data to aid their interpretation. The first tool, structure-oriented filtering, operates on the seismic data. The second tool, image enhancement, operates on the resulting attributes.

Structure-oriented Filtering

The goal of structure-oriented processing is to apply filtering along seismic events and in so doing to remove random noise and enhance lateral continuity. The key to structure-oriented filtering is to differentiate between the dip azimuth of the reflector and that of the overlying noise. Once we have estimated this dip and azimuth, we apply a filter to enhance signal along the reflector, much as interpreters do with time-structure and amplitude-extraction maps using interpretation workstation software. The most familiar filters are mean, median, and α-trim mean filters. We first describe the operation of these filters.

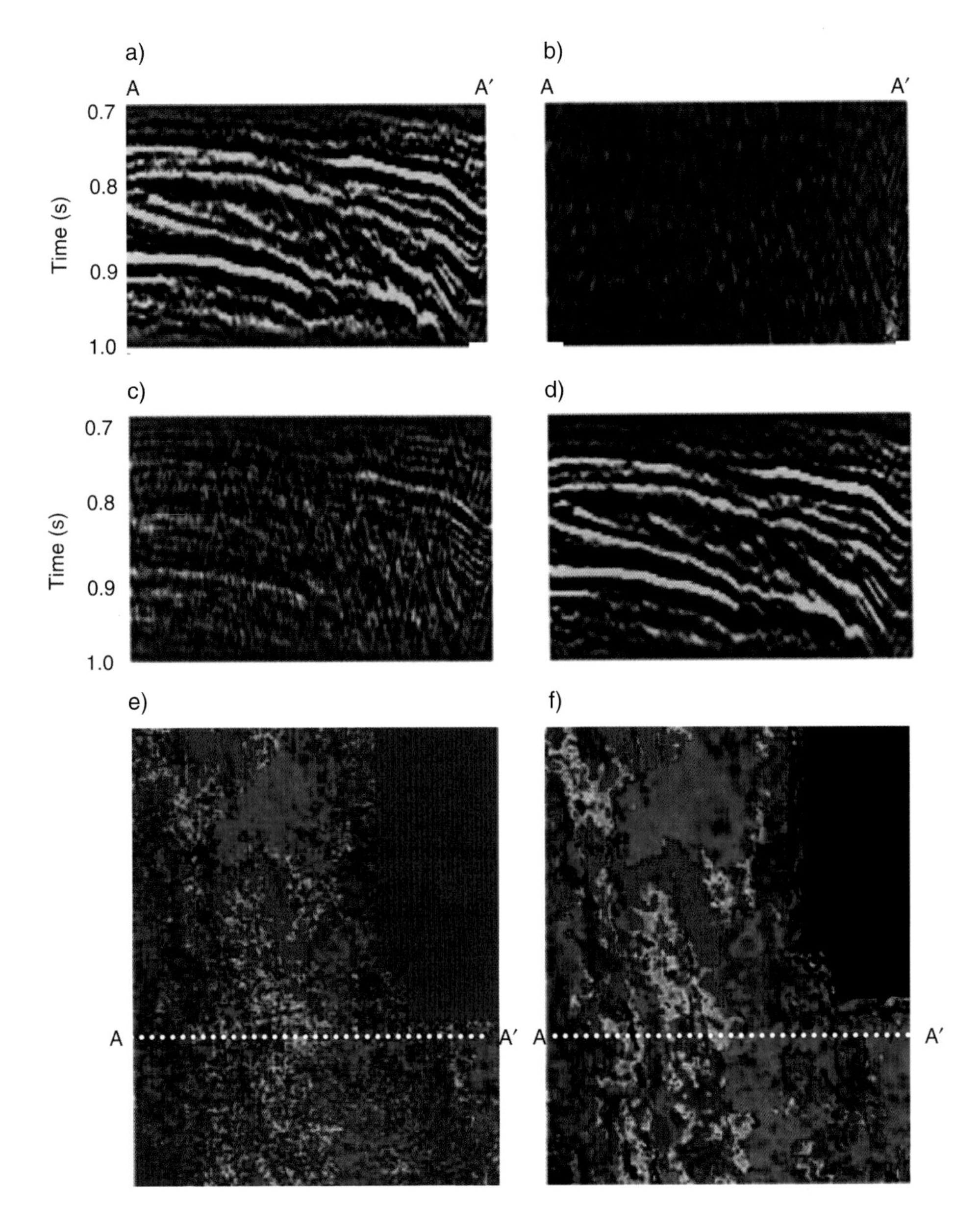

Figure 1. (a) A vertical slice through a time-migrated seismic data volume from the Permian Basin, Texas, U.S.A. (b) Rejected seismic data from a conservative least-squares dip filter and (c) rejected seismic data from an aggressive least-squares dip filter. (d) Filtered data that are the result of subtracting the noise in (c) from the original data in (a). (e) A time slice at t = 0.832 s through the wavelet phase volumes generated directly from the unfiltered seismic data shown in (a), and (f) a time slice at 0.832 from the dip-filtered seismic data shown in (d). Both (e) and (f) were followed by a 3D five-trace running sum along the reflector dip and azimuth. After Marfurt et al. (1998).

The mean filter

The mean filter is the best-known and simplest random-noise suppression filter and forms the basis of most seismic stacking algorithms. On maps, the mean filter is a low-pass filter that typically is implemented as a running-window-average filter. The output-data value is the average of all the samples that fall within a centered analysis window. The window size is usually an odd number, such as three by three or five by five, and may be either rectangular or elliptical. The definition of the mean filter at time t is

$$u_{\text{mean}}(t) = \frac{1}{J}\sum_{j=1}^{J} u_j(t), \qquad (8.1)$$

where $u_j(t)$ denotes the jth of J traces falling within the analysis window.

The median filter

The median filter is one of the most widely used nonlinear techniques in signal and image processing and also is used routinely to filter VSP data. The median filter replaces each sample in a window of a seismic trace by the median of the samples that fall within the analysis window; in so doing it rejects outliers. The window size is typically an odd number (e.g., 3×3 or 5×5). One way to calculate the median is simply to order all of the J samples in the analysis window using an ordering index, k:

$$u_{j(1)}(t) \le u_{j(2)}(t) \le \ldots \le u_{j(k)}(t) \le u_{j(k+1)}(t) \ldots \le u_{j(J)}(t). \qquad (8.2)$$

The median is then given by

$$u_{\text{median}}(t) = u_{j(k=[J+1]/2)}(t). \qquad (8.3)$$

Figure 2 shows a segment of a seismic section before (Figure 2a) and after (Figure 2b) application of a five-by-five median filter. Notice the cleaner background and the focused amplitudes of the seismic reflections after median filtering.

Figure 3 exhibits time slices from a coherence volume generated before (Figure 3a) and after (Figure 3b) median filtering of the data shown in Figure 2. Notice the cleaner-looking display and crisp features on the coherence time slice after median filtering.

The α-trimmed-mean filter

The α-trimmed-mean filter contains properties of both the mean filter and the median filter. It has been applied widely to stacking seismic data contaminated by strong spikes resulting from other seismic vessels, traffic noise, and other sources not correlated with the shooting program. If we order the data as in equation 8.2, the α-trimmed mean is given by

$$u_{\alpha}(t) = \frac{1}{(1-2\alpha)(J-1)+1} \sum_{k=\alpha J+1}^{(1-\alpha)J} u_{j(k)}(t), \qquad (8.4)$$

where the value of α varies between 0 and 0.5. If $\alpha = 0.5$, the normalization is 1, and we obtain the median filter. If $\alpha = 0.0$, the normalization is $\frac{1}{J}$, and we obtain the conventional mean filter. If $\alpha = 0.25$, we produce our result by rejecting the largest 25% and smallest 25% of the samples in our analysis window and averaging the 50% of the samples clustered around the median.

a)

b)

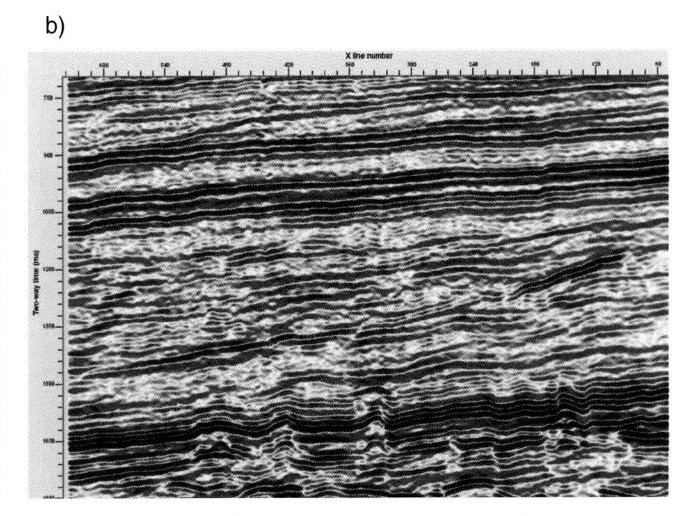

Figure 2. Segment of a seismic section (a) before and (b) after application of a five-by-five median filter. Notice the cleaner background and focused amplitudes of the seismic reflections after median filtering Data courtesy of Arcis Corporation, Calgary.

The modified-trimmed-mean (MTM) filter

The modified-trimmed-mean (MTM) filter (also called the range-trimmed-mean filter) is an enhancement of the α-trimmed-mean filter and was designed by Lee and Kassam in 1985 to lessen the edge blurring that is typical of the standard mean filter. We include it here because we will use it later in our discussion of lineament-preserving smoothing. Like the α-trimmed-mean filter, the modified-trimmed-mean filter is a running-window estimator that selects only a subset of the samples inside the window and uses them to calculate an average. The samples, u_j, in the analysis window are selected if they fall in the range

$$u_{\text{median}}(t) - q \le u_j(t) \le u_{\text{median}}(t) + q \tag{8.5}$$

where u_{median} is given by equation 8.3, and q is a preselected threshold value between edge preservation and smoothing efficiency. Unlike the case with the α-trimmed mean, with an MTM filter the ordered samples generally are selected in a nonsymmetric manner. The number of data samples used varies on the range of window width for any given estimate.

The result of the filter is the average of the selected samples:

$$u_{MTM} = \frac{1}{\text{N}} \sum_{j=1}^{J} b(u_{\text{median}}, q, d_j) u_j(t) \ , \tag{8.6}$$

where $b(u_{\text{medain}}, q, d_j)$ is the "boxcar" function defined as

$$b(u_{\text{median}}, q, u_j) = \begin{Bmatrix} 1 \\ 0 \end{Bmatrix} \begin{matrix} u_{\text{median}} - q \le u_j \le u_{\text{median}} + q \\ otherwise \end{matrix} \ . \tag{8.7}$$

where N denotes the number of samples that fall within the range of $\pm\, q$.

The value q is an important parameter in selecting the samples. If q has a value of zero, the resulting filter reduces to the median filter. As q increases, all of the samples in the window eventually are included, so that the filter becomes the mean filter.

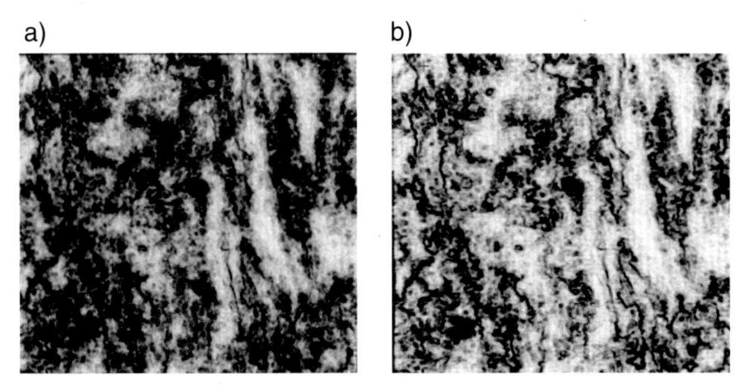

Figure 3. Time slices from a coherence volume generated (a) before and (b) after median filtering of the data shown in Figure 2. Notice the crisp features on the coherence time slices after median filtering. Data courtesy of Arcis Corporation, Calgary.

Application of mean filters to provide robust attributes

All of these filters have been used to enhance attribute calculations along reflectors. Figure 1f shows an example of response phase calculated from seismic data subjected to a 3D five-trace mean filter along reflector dip azimuth. The major edges are preserved, but the random salt-and-pepper appearance is diminished.

In Figure 4a, we show an example of instantaneous frequency calculated from seismic amplitudes, and in Figure

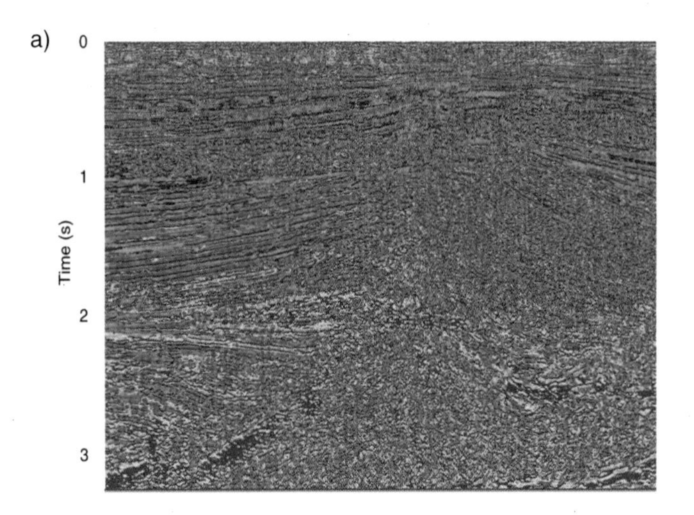

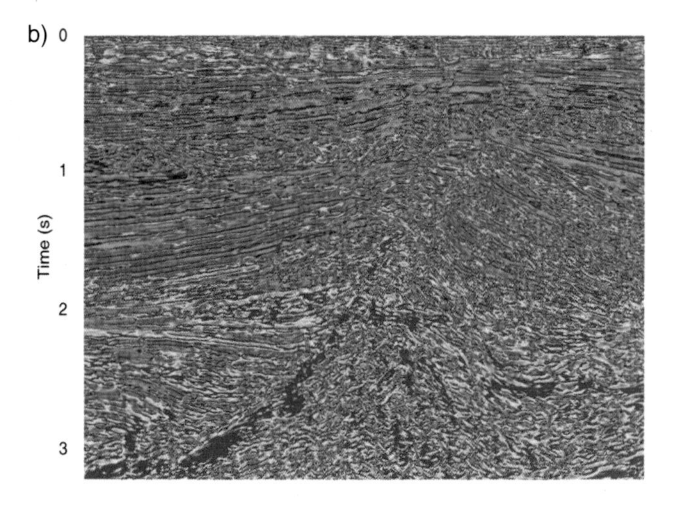

Figure 4. (a) Instantaneous frequency calculated from the original seismic data, and (b) instantaneous frequency calculated from a 2D running sum of seven traces along the dip direction. Note that in (b) the signal-to-noise ratio is improved but the lateral discontinuities are smeared. Courtesy of Tury Taner, Rock Solid Images.

4b, we see instantaneous frequency subjected to a 2D seven-trace mean filter along reflector dip. In both these examples the signal-to-noise ratio is improved, but some of the lateral discontinuities have been smeared.

A limitation of these filters is that they smooth across discontinuities. In Figure 5, we show the effect of a five-trace running-window mean filter across an idealized discontinuity. If each of the input traces is weighted equally, the abrupt discontinuity becomes a continuous linear ramp of length five.

Of course, we can generate a more continuous filter response by using filter coefficients that weight samples near the center of the analysis window more than those at its edges. However, when we implement those coefficients, the response of the mean filter is to smooth desired discontinuities. In Figure 6a, we show the result of applying a running-sum or mean filter to an idealized fault, and in Figure 6b we show a similar application to a channel. Hoecker and Fehmers (2002) applied such a mean filter to noisy data, the results of which we show in Figure 7a. In Figure 7b, we display the result of applying structure-oriented filtering with no edge preservation.

Anisotropic diffusion

Although median and α-trimmed-mean filters behave somewhat better for the simple example shown in Figure 6, they still smear faults. To address this problem, Hoecker and Fehmers (2002) described an anisotropic-diffusion smoothing algorithm. Although it is an accurate analog for numerical analysts familiar with the diffusion equation, the name anisotropic diffusion (and its associated equation) do not provide much insight for interpreters. Instead of reproducing the details of the algorithm, we display an idealized flow diagram in Figure 8.

The anisotropic part of anisotropic diffusion is so named because the smoothing takes place parallel to the reflector. No smoothing takes place perpendicular to the reflector. Thus, the algorithm begins by estimating reflector dip azimuth at each sample in the volume. Hoecker and Fehmers (2002) estimated dip azimuth using the gradient structure tensor (GST) described in Chapter 2.

Next, the algorithm estimates a measure of continuity. Hoecker and Fehmers (2002) mentioned that coherence is one such measure, but clearly others, such as curvature (lateral change in dip), may work as well. If the discontinuity is strong, the algorithm does not smooth it. If the discontinuity is weak, the algorithm does smooth it. If the discontinuity is moderate, the algorithm mixes the output of smoothing with the original sample value. This process is repeated for all samples until the entire volume has been smoothed once. Then, just as we do for time-structure and amplitude-extraction maps, we can elect to smooth again, which yields an iterative algorithm that with each iteration implicitly increases the size and changes the weights of the effective smoothing operator.

In Figure 7c, we display Hoecker and Fehmers's (2002) results of structure-oriented filtering using anisotropic diffusion. Note how the overall signal-to-noise ratio is improved relative to the input data volume shown in Figure 7a. Also, the faults not only are preserved but are sharp-

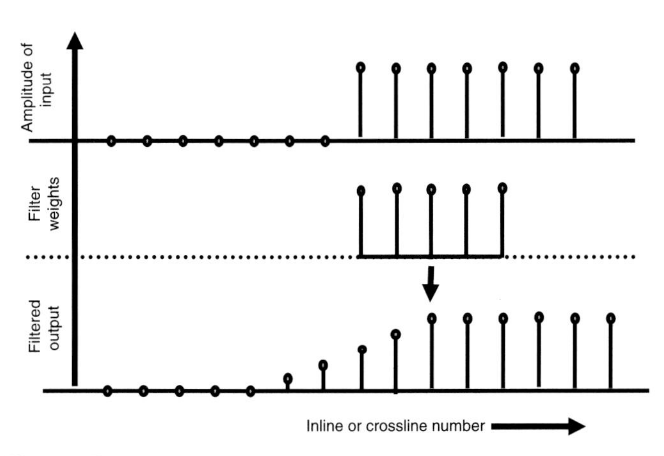

Figure 5. Cartoon showing implementation of a running-sum filter or a mean filter, which, with the median filter, commonly is applied by interpreters to maps of seismic traveltime, amplitude, and attributes. In this cartoon, the filter moves from left to right, with the output being the average of five adjacent traces that fall within the operator gate. After Luo et al. (2001).

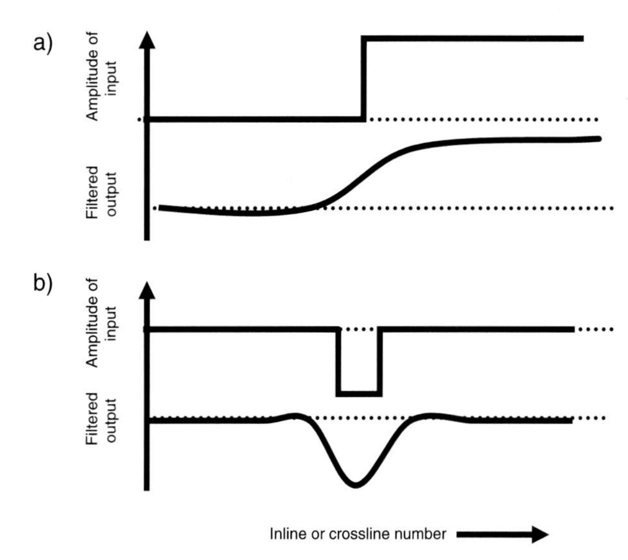

Figure 6. The result of applying a runningsum filter or a mean filter to an idealized (a) fault and (b) channel. The discontinuity in amplitude (or dip, or whatever component is being smoothed) is blurred, thereby decreasing lateral resolution. After Luo et al. (2001).

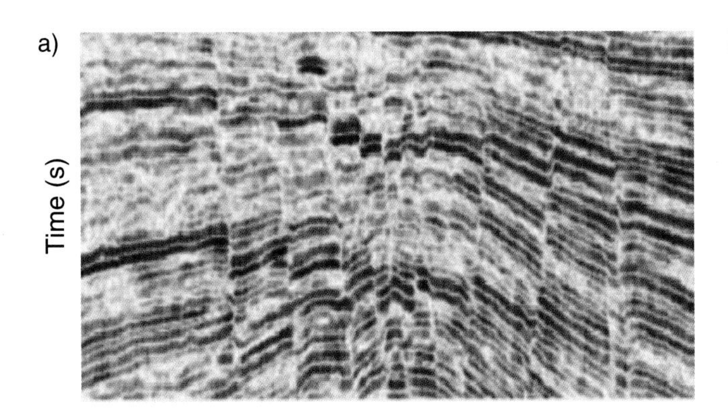

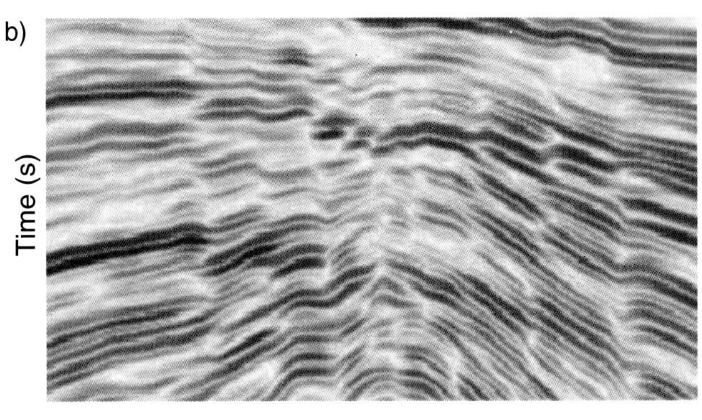

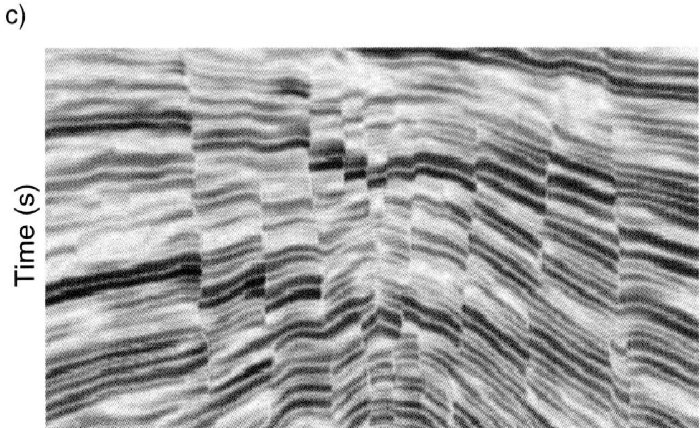

Figure 7. Seismic data (a) before and (b) after structure-oriented filtering (SOF) with no edge preservation, and (c) seismic data after structure-oriented filtering using an anisotropic diffusion operator. Note how the fault edges are preserved in (c). After Hoecker and Fehmers (2002).

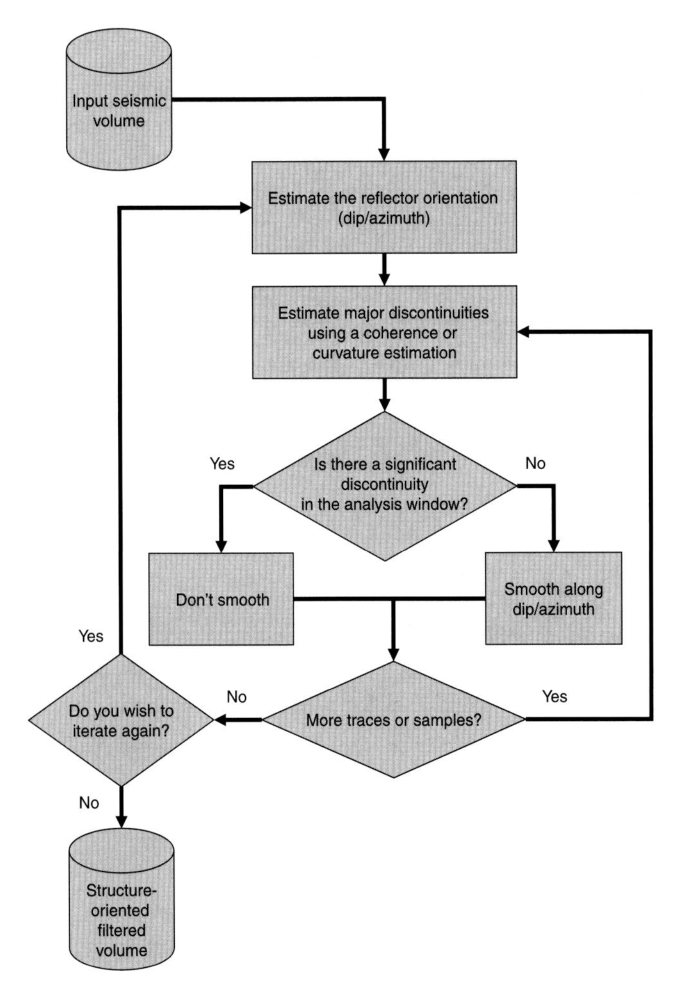

Figure 8. A simplified flowchart of Hoecker and Fehmers' (2002) structure-oriented filtering algorithm, expressed by equation 8.1. In actual implementation, the amount of smoothing varies between the two yes and no extremes shown in this figure.

ened, unlike the case with the simple mean filter shown in Figure 7b.

One benefit of such filtering is to precondition the data for computer autotracking. In Figure 9, we show how a 3D autotracker fails to track a seeded horizon on the original data (Figure 9c) but produces a rather complete horizon on the structure-oriented-filter data (Figure 9d). If an interpreter is suspicious of filtered data, he or she can always snap the results of this preconditioned autotracker to the original data and extract amplitudes from there.

In Figure 10, we show the results of using structure-oriented filtering with anisotropic diffusion on a survey acquired from Oman. Masaferro et al. (2003) found that structure-oriented filtering produced smoother time-structure and amplitude-extraction maps, less-ambiguous stratigraphic terminations, and coherence images that were less contaminated by noise.

The multiwindow (Kuwahara) filter (edge-preserving smoothing filter)

Faced with noisy land data volumes from the Arabian Peninsula, Luo et al. (2002) also analyzed mean, median, and α-trimmed-mean filters in an effort to improve interpretability and the behavior of seismic attributes. Instead of turning off the smoothing operator, as anisotropic diffusion does, Luo et al.'s edge-preserving-smoothing algorithm

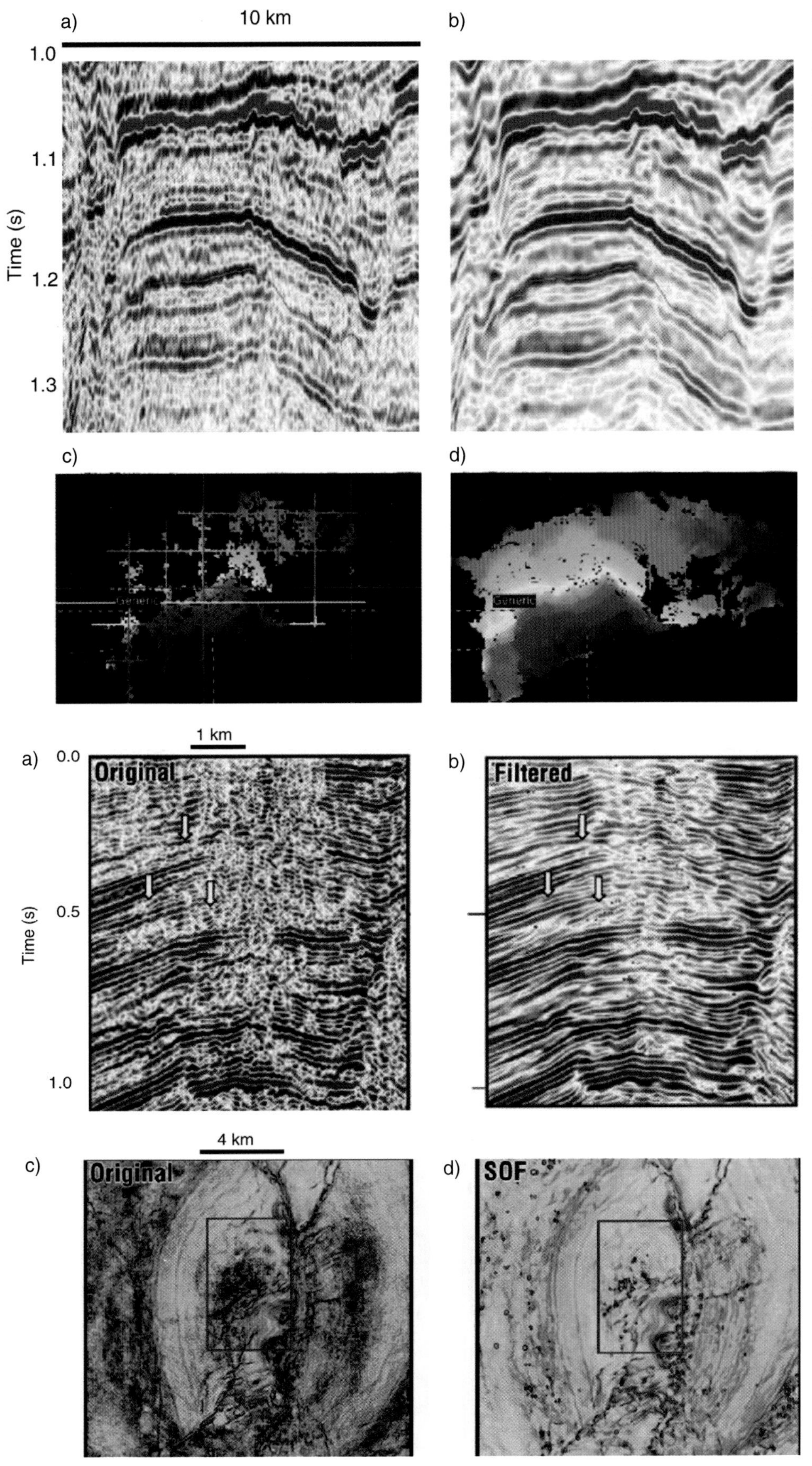

Figure 9. The influence of structure-oriented filtering on autotrackers. A vertical slice (a) before and (b) after structure-oriented filtering. An autotracked horizon (c) before and (d) after structure-oriented filtering using an anisotropic diffusion equation. The autotracker fails to pick the complete horizon when it is applied to the noisy original data, but it succeeds when it is applied to the filtered data. After Hoecker and Fehmers (2002).

Figure 10. The influence of structure-oriented filtering on geometric attributes for a survey from Oman. (a)-(b). Vertical slices through the seismic volume (a) before and (b) after structure-oriented filtering. (c)-(d). Time slices at $t = 0.420$ s through the semblance estimate of coherence (c) before and (d) after structure-oriented filtering. After Masaferro et al. (2003).

shifts the smoothing operator to an adjacent window that does not span the discontinuity (in the extreme, the operator may become one-sided).

Luo et al.'s (2002) work was based on earlier work done by Kuwahara et al. (1976) in the biomedical field. Luo et al. began by calculating a statistic such as the variance of the data in each of the laterally overlapping analysis windows, each with a different center point. In the window that had the best statistic (e.g., the minimum variance), they smoothed the data using a mean, median, α-trimmed-mean, or other filter and then assigned the data to the analysis point.

In Figure 11, we reproduce Luo et al.'s (2002) example of an idealized amplitude discontinuity contaminated by noise. The signal-to-noise ratio is approximately 1:1. The 21-point running-window mean filter smooths out the discontinuity (Figure 11c), whereas the multiwindow Kuwahara filter preserves it (Figure 11d).

Next, in Figure 12a we show the results of applying the Kuwahara filter to a noisy data volume from the Arabian Peninsula. In Figure 12b, we display the result of applying the Hilbert transform edge detector described in Chapter 5 to the unfiltered data. In Figure 12c, we show the results of the same edge detector applied to the seismic data after several passes of multiwindow Kuwahara filtering using nine overlapping three-trace by three-trace analysis windows. A meandering channel (arrows) can now be clearly seen.

Luo et al. (2002) showed how this technique also can be used to suppress acquisition footprint (Figure 13). To do so, the size of the analysis window must be larger than the scale of the footprint; otherwise, the edge-preserving filter will enhance the artificial discontinuities. Unfortunately, larger windows will also eradicate any geologic features smaller than the analysis window. Thus, we should apply such smoothing with care or we may eliminate closely spaced faults, fractures, and thin channels.

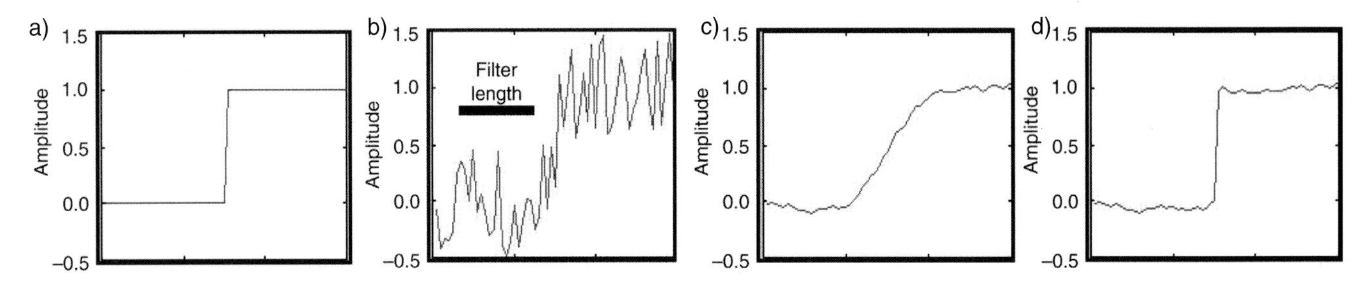

Figure 11. A simple example showing multiwindow (Kuwahara) filtering. An idealized amplitude discontinuity (a) without and (b) with additive noise. (c) The result of filtering the noisy signal in (b) with a 21-point running-window mean filter and (d) with a 21-point multiwindow Kuwahara filter. After Luo et al. (2002).

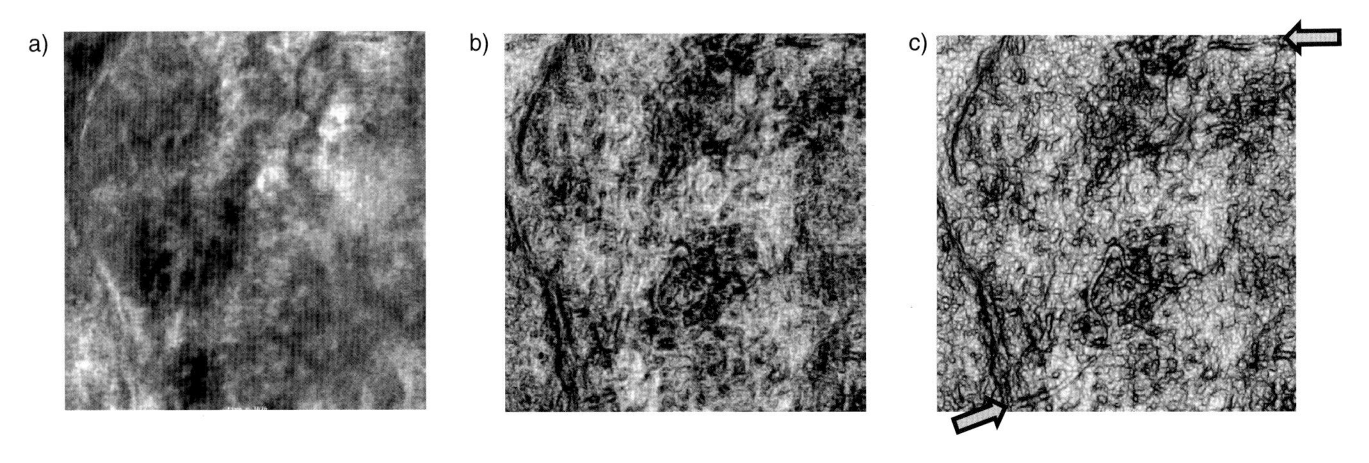

Figure 12. (a) An amplitude time slice at t = 1.026 s from a survey acquired in Saudi Arabia. (b) The corresponding time slice through an edge-detection volume generated using the Hilbert transform edge-detection algorithm described in Chapter 5. (c) The corresponding time slice through the long-wavelength Hilbert transform edge-detection algorithm applied to the seismic data after multiwindow Kuwahara edge-preserving smoothing. Arrows indicate a narrow channel that meanders through the survey. After Luo et al. (2002).

Principal-component filtering (the KL filter)

Use of a mean filter in either the anisotropic-diffusion or multiwindow Kuwahara filter has the disadvantage that lateral changes in amplitude for features of geologic interest also are smoothed. In particular, the appearance of narrow channels is diminished. Median filters and α-trimmed-mean filters can help but will still obliterate features that are only a few traces wide.

The principal-component filter (also known in seismic processing as the Karhunen-Loeve filter, or simply the KL filter) is used commonly by seismic processors to estimate linear noise and multiples and subsequently to subtract them from the data. In our case, we will do the opposite — we will determine the linear event having a fixed seismic waveform that best fits the data along the estimated reflector dip and azimuth and retain it as the coherent component of the reflected signal. We discussed this process in cartoon form in Figure 17 of Chapter 3. We showed how we used the result to generate energy-weighted coherent-amplitude gradients in Figures 18 and 19 from Chapter 5. Here we provide some of the arithmetic.

If m is the analysis point in the laterally shifted Kuwahara window, the principal-component-filtered data are given by

$$u_m^1(t) = \left[\sum_{j=1}^{J} u_j(t) v_j^1(t) \right] v_m^1(t), \tag{8.8}$$

where $\mathbf{v}^1(t)$ is the first eigenvector (which is the vector that best represents the lateral amplitude variation across the J traces in the analysis window) corresponding to the covariance matrix, $\mathbf{C}$:

$$\begin{aligned} C_{ij}(t,p,q) = &\sum_{k=K_s}^{K_e} \left[u_i(t+k\Delta t - px_i - qy_i) - \mu(t,p,q) \right] \\ &\left[u_j(t+k\Delta t - px_j - qy_j) - \mu(t,p,q) \right] \\ + &\sum_{k=-K}^{+K} \left[u_i^H(t+k\Delta t - px_i - qy_i) - \mu^H(t,p,q) \right] \\ &\left[u_j^H(t+k\Delta t - px_j - qy_j) - \mu^H(t,p,q) \right] \end{aligned} \tag{8.9}$$

presented earlier as equation 3.17. Here, i and j are trace indices in the laterally shifted Kuwahara window (Chapter 2, Figure 7a), p and q are the components of reflector dip, μ is the mean across traces at each sample, and the time samples between K_s and K_e straddle the analysis point (Chapter 2, Figure 7b). The superiority of the principal-component filter comes from the vertical samples that are used to design the filter: The principal-component filter uses ($K_e - K_s + 1$) vertical samples, rather than using simply one sample as the simpler mean and median filters do.

We choose a smoothing window by evaluating which window has the most coherent waveform, so we avoid spanning faults and angular unconformities, as was discussed in the estimation of reflector dip and azimuth in Chapter 2. Details can be found in Marfurt (2006).

In Figure 14, we apply this principal-component filtering algorithm to a land seismic survey from the Central Basin Platform, Texas, U.S.A., and display the results of coherence calculations. The seismic data underwent two passes of filtering, using nine overlapping, three-by-three-trace, ±10-ms analysis windows. Whereas the overall appearance of coherence applied to filtered data is sharper (Figure 14b and d), we note in particular that the ability to detect individual fault traces in complex fault zones (gray arrows) as well as preserved channels seen in the Thirtyone chert formation (white arrow) is more convincing. Many of the figures in this book have undergone structure-oriented principal-component filtering before calculation of attributes.

Lineament-preserving filtering

Although the principal-component (or KL) filter allows us to retain small amplitude variations that are only one seismic bin wide (as long as the waveform is consistent with its neighbors), this filter cannot be adapted readily to other attributes we may wish to filter, such as dip and azimuth. However, obtaining robust estimates of dip and azimuth is critical to obtaining accurate estimates of curvature and an-

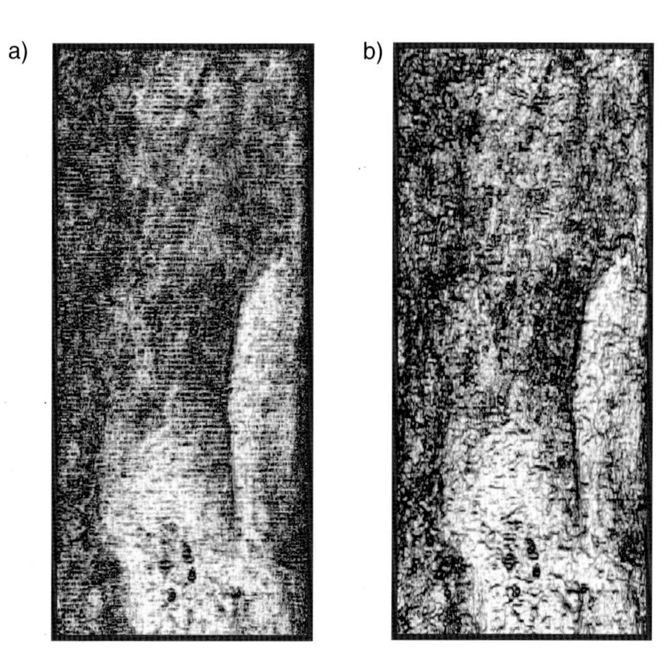

Figure 13. The influence of edge-preserving smoothing of the seismic data on an acquisition footprint from a survey acquired in Saudi Arabia. A time slice through edge-detection attribute volumes using the long-wavelength Hilbert transform edge-detection algorithm described in Chapter 5 and generated (a) before and (b) after 5 × 5 Kuwahara multiwindow edge-preserving smoothing. After Luo et al. (2002).

gular unconformities. In addition, accurately estimating dip and azimuth is critical to generating an accurate structure-oriented filter of the seismic amplitude discussed earlier in this section.

Whereas faults often are associated with a lateral change in reflector dip and azimuth, fractures often are seen as small changes in dip and azimuth, deviating from some smoother background mean. Narrow lineaments, only one seismic bin wide, are obliterated by mean, median, and α-trimmed-mean filters applied to larger analysis windows containing nine or more traces. The same filters applied to five-trace analysis windows eliminate lineaments that cut the window at 45°.

In Figure 15, we display two times slices through the north-south component of a vector dip volume computed for a survey from the Fort Worth Basin, Texas, U.S.A. The rectangular boxes in the southwestern portion of the survey indicate locations of two earlier surveys that were merged into the larger survey that covers the remainder of the image. In 1999, these three surveys were reprocessed as a unit, using the same software and processor. Because they were acquired by a suboptimal acquisition program, the two older surveys are noisier and provide the noisier estimates of apparent dip seen in this figure.

We then applied a simple nine-trace running-mean filter to the time slice shown in Figure 15a. Figure 16a displays the rejected noise obtained by subtracting the mean-filtered north-south dip from the original north-south dip. Although much random noise has been rejected, we also note that the short-wavelength component of the features of interest, such as the faults and channels indicated by arrows, also have been rejected. For that reason, Al-Dossary and Marfurt (2007) evaluated a long list of image-processing filters that could preserve details such as fractures yet that would suppress random noise. In Figure 16b, we show the results of their multistage-median modified-trimmed-mean (MSMTM) filter, which they found to work best for this problem and which is discussed in detail below. The following section is extracted almost verbatim from their paper.

The multistage-median (MSM) filter

Image-processing filters can be lumped into two broad categories: those that smooth, such as the mean filter, and those that sharpen, such as the median filter. (The MSMTM filter, which we will discuss momentarily, is a two-stage filter, the first stage of which sharpens and preserves narrow details such as our lineaments of interest and the second stage of which smooths by rejecting random noise.)

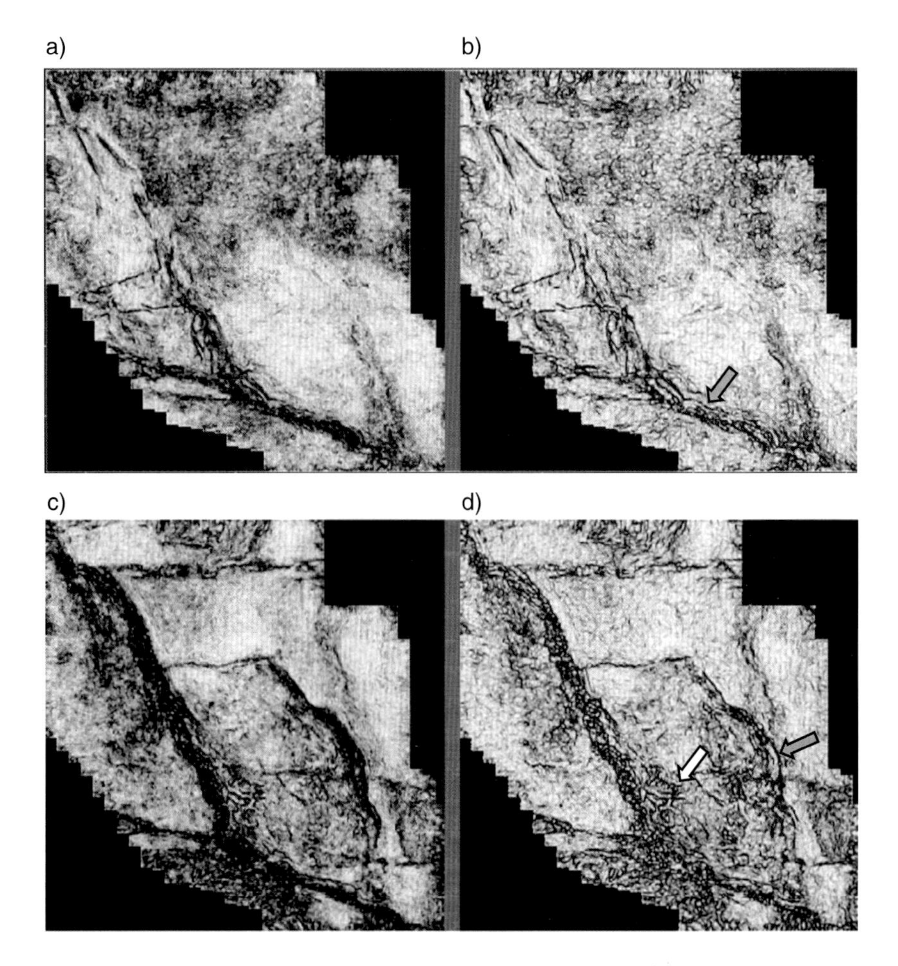

Figure 14. (a)-(b). Time slices at t = 0.800 s and (c)-(d) time slices at t = 1.040 s through eigenstructure coherence volumes generated from a survey acquired over the Central Basin Platform, Texas, U.S.A. Slices (a) and (c) were calculated from original time-migrated data, and slices (b) and (d) were calculated from the same data after two passes of structure-oriented filtering using a multiwindow principal-component filtering algorithm. Note the clarity of the individual fault traces in complex fault zones (gray arrows) in (b) and (d) and preserved channels in the Thirtyone chert formation (white arrow) in (d). Seismic data are courtesy of OXY.

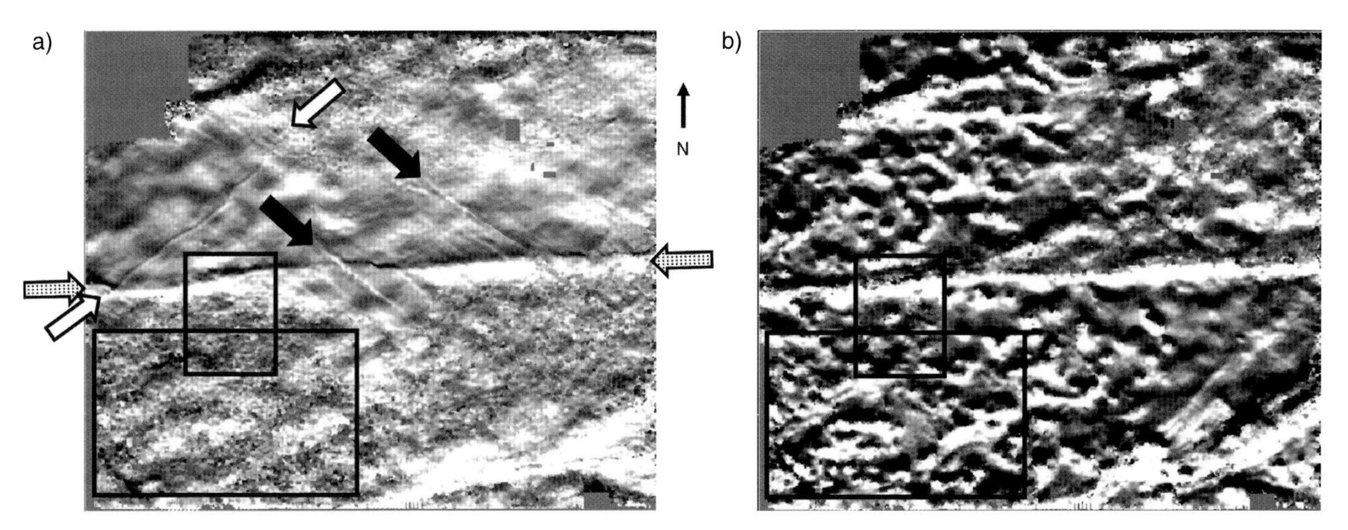

Figure 15. Time slices at t = (a) 0.800 and (b) 1.100 s through a north-south dip volume from a survey in the Fort Worth Basin, Texas, U.S.A. Speckled arrows indicate a broad east-west strike-slip fault. Black arrows indicate thinner northwest-southeast lineaments. White arrows indicate a northeast-southwest channel, which is visible because of differential compaction. Rectangles indicate two older, smaller surveys that were incorporated into a larger, merged survey. All three surveys were reprocessed as a unit, so differences in data quality are the result of acquisition rather than processing. After Al-Dossary and Marfurt (2007).

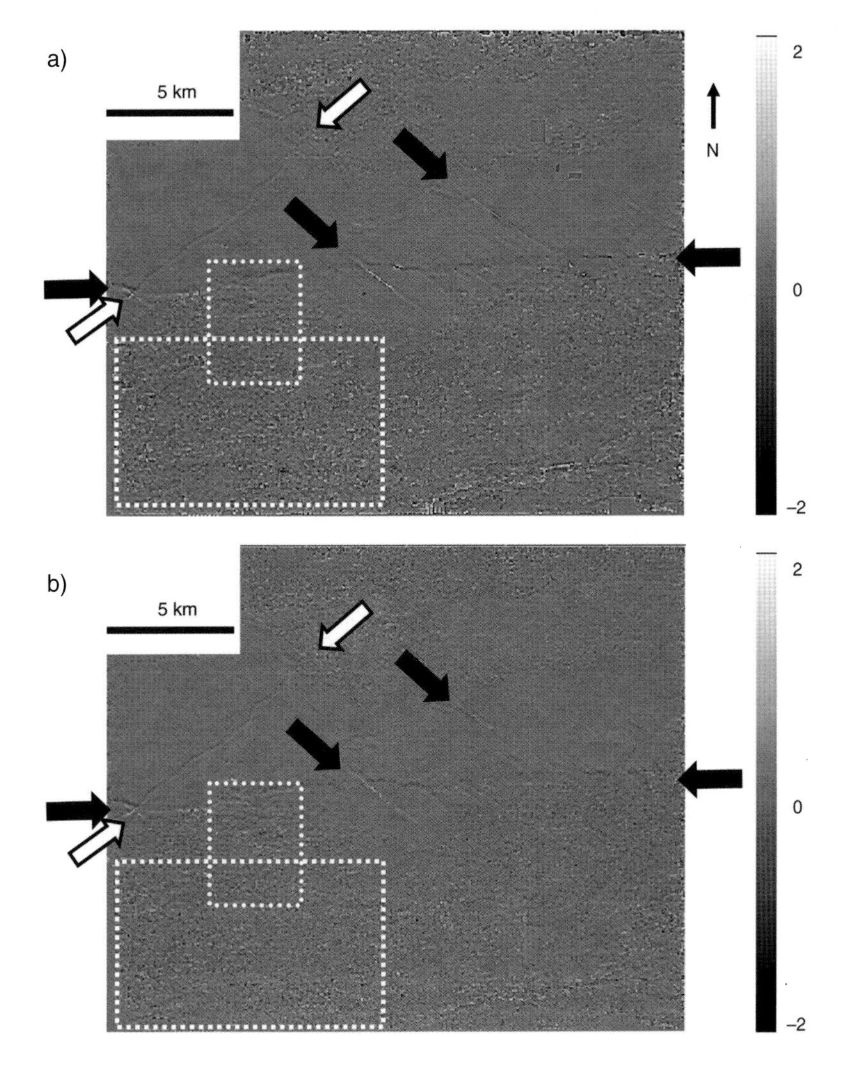

Figure 16. The rejected noise resulting from applying two passes of (a) a mean filter and (b) a multistage-median modified-trimmed-mean (MSMTM) filter to the image shown in Figure 15a and subtracting them from the original. Note that the mean filter rejects the short-wavelength components of the lineaments. The MSMTM filter rejects a smaller amount of random noise than the mean filter does. The MSMTM also rejects more long-wavelength components of the signal, thereby indicating that it has a sharpening aspect that is typical of median filters. After Al-Dossary and Marfurt (2007).

The multistage-median filter (MSM) is simply a sharpening filter. Given data, u, to be smoothed on a grid, we calculate the multistage median, u_{MSM}, using the following four steps:

1) Define four one-dimensional linear subwindows, W_k, (Figure 17), that are aligned along the north-south, east-west, and northeast-southwest and northwest-southeast axes of the larger two-dimensional area $(2N + 1) \times (2N + 1)$ centered about the trace at (m, n):

$$\begin{aligned} W_1 &= \{\, u_{m+i,n}\, , -N \le i \le N \,\}, \\ W_2 &= \{\, u_{m+i,n+i}\, , -N \le i \le N \,\}, \\ W_3 &= \{\, u_{m,n+i}\, , -N \le i \le N \,\}, \text{ and} \\ W_4 &= \{\, u_{m+i,n-\mathrm{i}}\, , -N \le i \le N \,\}. \end{aligned} \tag{8.10}$$

2) Calculate the median, $Z(W_j)$, of each of the four subwindows :

$$Z(W_j) = \text{median } [\, u_{ik}\, \varepsilon\, W_j]. \tag{8.11}$$

3) Calculate the second-stage medians, defined as

$$\begin{aligned} \mathrm{M}_{13} &= \text{median } [Z(W_1), Z(W_3)\, , u_{mn}], \\ \mathrm{M}_{24} &= \text{median } [Z(W_2), Z(W_4)\, , u_{mn}], \end{aligned} \tag{8.12}$$

where u_{mn} is the data value at the center of the analysis window.

4) Finally, calculate the final-stage median and obtain the multistage median, d_{MSM}:

$$u_{MSM} = \text{median } [M_{13}\, , M_{24}, u_{mn}]. \tag{8.13}$$

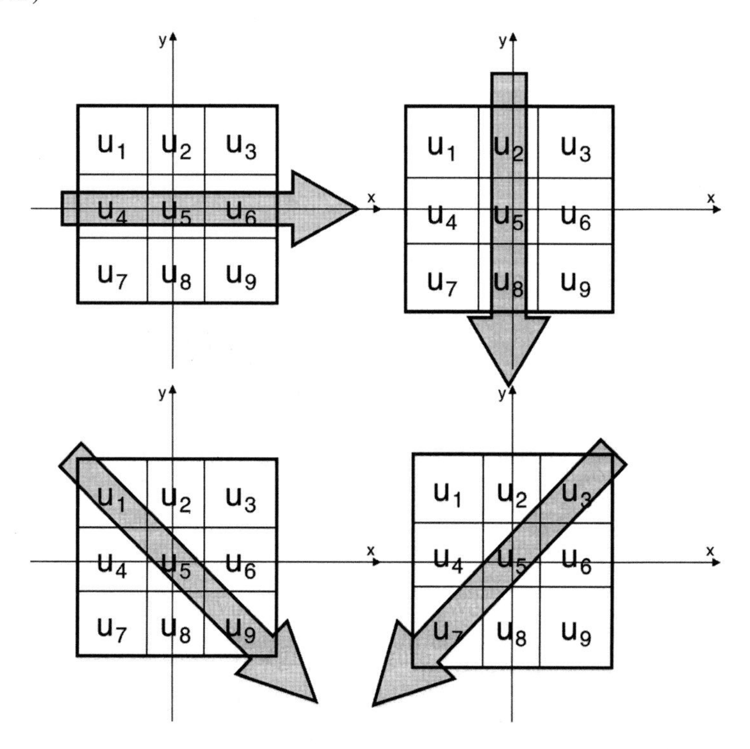

Figure 17. A multistage median filter (MSM) consists of four median filters each one-seismic-bin-wide. First, we obtain the median of u_4, u_5, and u_6. Then we obtain the median of u_2, u_5, and u_8. We now have two numbers, both of which are medians. Include in this collection the value u_5. Now we have three numbers. Take the median of those three numbers, which we will refer to as M_{13}. Repeat this procedure for medians calculated on the diagonals. Call that median M_{24}. Now take the median of M_{13} and M_{24} along with the value of u_5. We call this final (multistage) median, u_{MSM}. After Al-Dossary and Marfurt (2007).

The multistage-median modified-trimmed-mean (MSMTM) filter

Wu and Kundu (1991) combined the modified-trimmed-mean (MTM) filter with a detail-preserving filter, the multistage-median (MSM) filter. They dubbed the new filter the multistage-median modified-trimmed-mean (MSMTM) filter. Like the α-trimmed-mean and MTM filters, the MSMTM filter selects a subset of samples inside a window and calculates an average. The output of cascaded median calculations provides the numerical cutoff for inclusion in the subsequent calculation of the mean. Because the MSM filter is a detail-preserving filter, the MSMTM filter preserves lineaments. The MSMTM filter is efficient, smoothes noise, and preserves edges and lineaments. The MSMTM filter is implemented as a running-window estimator. As with the MTM algorithm, the samples are selected if they are in the range

$$u_{MSM} - q \le u_j \le u_{MSM} + q. \tag{8.14}$$

The result of the filter is the average of the selected samples

$$u_{MSMTM} = \frac{1}{\mathrm{N}} \sum_{j=1}^{J} b(u_{MSM}, q, d_j) u_j(t), \tag{8.15}$$

where N denotes the number of samples that fall within the range $\pm\, q$.

Al-Dossary and Marfurt (2007) used a three-by-three window to apply a mean filter and the MSMTM filter to the north-south-dip time slice from Figure 15a. They then subtracted the filtered data from the original data. We display the resulting differences in Figure 16, in which we note two changes. First, in Figure 16a, the mean filter has rejected some of the information associated with channels and faults. Second, in Figure 16b, some of those features have also been rejected. However, the MSMTM filter has retained some of the sharpening components of the median, so this is acceptable. A sharper version of such features is retained on the output.

To further display the effectiveness of the MSMTM filter, we applied it iteratively (three times using a three-by-three window) to the north-south components of dip shown in Figure 15. We also applied the same filter to the complementary east-west components of dip (not shown). We then calculated a short-wavelength estimate of most-negative curvature (in the notation of Chapter 4, using a value of α = 1.0) and display the results in Figures 18 and 19. Note that the overall noisiness has been reduced and the complex pattern of fractures and collapse features has been preserved. We conclude this section by noting that such filtering, which enhances the signal-to-noise ratio of the short-wavelength component of reflector dip azimuth, does not significantly alter long-wavelength estimates of curvature such as that shown in Figure 20f of Chapter 4.

Limitations and pitfalls of structure-oriented filtering

Conflicting dip

Structure-oriented filtering is based on an accurate estimate of reflector dip and azimuth. In the dip-scan estimate of reflector dip azimuths described in Chapter 2, dip and azimuth are defined by the most coherent event falling within the analysis window for the scanned dips. With structurally complex geologies in which we scan for dips exceeding 60°, we may encounter high-amplitude coherent noise with dips that fall within the search limits. In that case, the noise may be enhanced and the dipping reflector suppressed! A more common occurrence may be the appearance of strong amplitude coherent multiples overprinting lower-amplitude reflections. Once again, the multiples are enhanced and the primaries suppressed. Clearly, the interpreter must be aware of these pitfalls.

As is the case in any filtering process, identification of residual noise that the filter passed may be more difficult than identification of the noise on the unfiltered data volume. We show such an example in Figure 20. In Figure 20a, we have circled a poorly migrated diffraction at about 1.0 s. The diffraction tails are clearly evident. However, after structure-oriented filtering the tails of this diffraction have been attenuated, but the apex remains (Figure 20b and c). This survey was shot in a carbonate terrain in an effort to map the fractures better. Without knowing how the filter works and without looking at the original unfiltered data, an interpreter may be misled into interpreting this residual diffraction apex and the low-amplitude zone near it to indicate a carbonate reef.

In general, properly migrated seismic data do not have conflicting dips. However, anisotropy and errors in the velocity-depth model often cause misalignment of fault-plane and salt-flank reflections. Unless great care is taken during migration, these steeply dipping events often do not align with the reflector terminations. However, such events provide important information to a skilled interpreter, who can use them as a guide for accurately interpreting a salt flank or inferring lithologic changes across a fault. Unfortunately, if these valuable events are misaligned, they are suppressed by structure-oriented filtering.

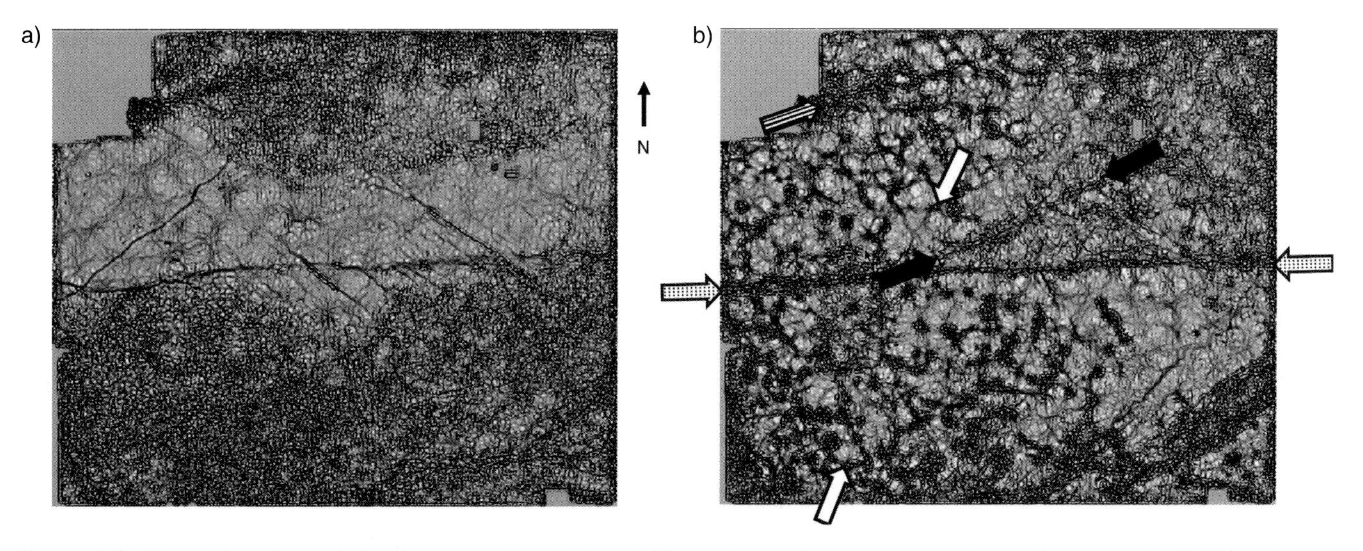

Figure 18. Time slices through the short-wavelength (α = 1.0), most-negative-curvature volume, k_{neg}, at t = (a) 0.800 and (b) 1.100 s. The most-negative curvature was calculated from the unfiltered vector dip, the north-south component of which is shown in Figure 15. After Al-Dossary and Marfurt (2007).

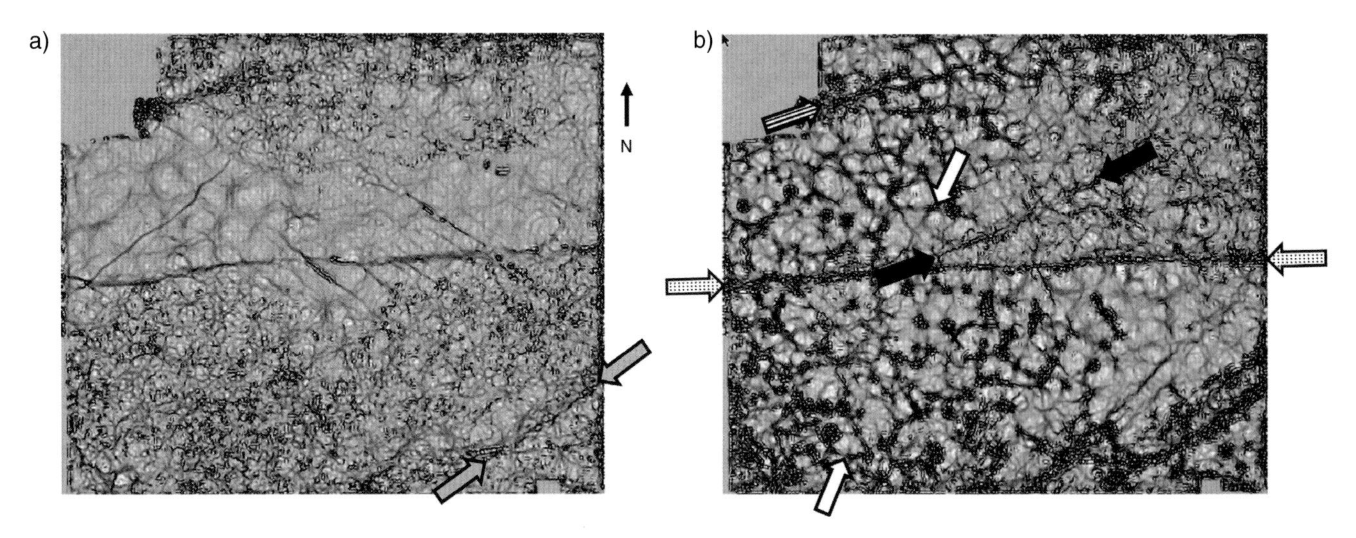

Figure 19. Time slices through the short-wavelength ($\alpha = 1.0$) most-negative-curvature volume, k_{neg}, at t = (a) 0.800 and (b) t = 1.100 s, calculated from the north-south and east-west components of vector dip after two passes of MSMTM filtering using a 3 × 3 window. The fault edge indicated by the gray arrows in (a) shows up more clearly than it did in Figure 18a. The Reidel shear zone (black arrows) branching off the strike-slip fault (speckled arrows) in (b) shows up as a clear lineament rather than as the incoherent zone seen in Figure 18b. Likewise, a north-northeast to south-southwest lineament connecting collapse features (white arrow) is more visible. Although the fault zone indicated by the striped arrow is still diffuse, it is significantly clearer here than it was in Figure 18b. After Al-Dossary and Marfurt (2007).

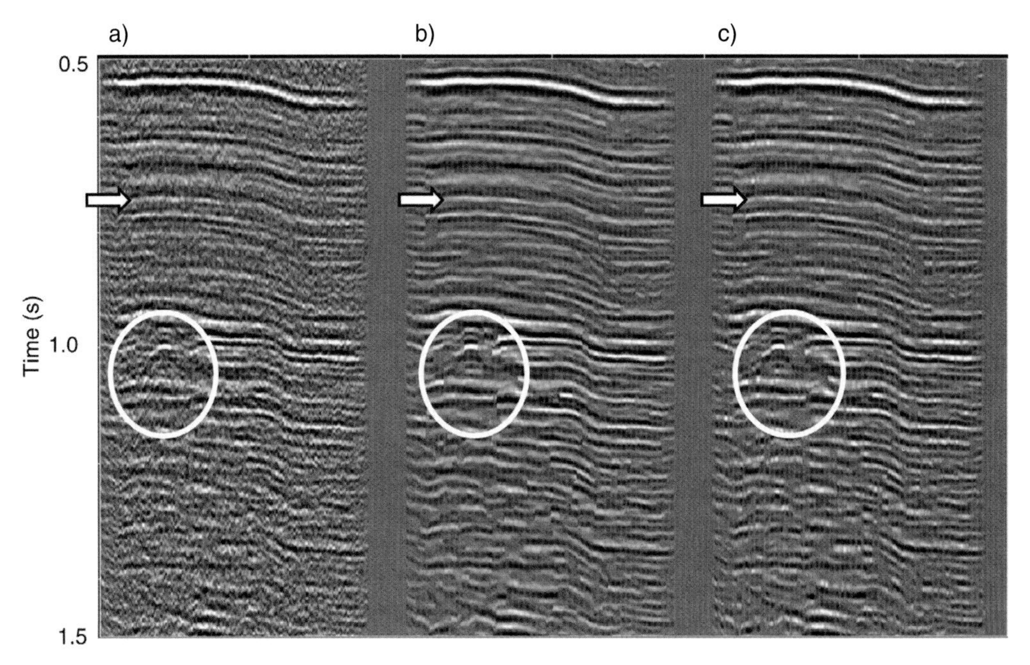

Figure 20. Pitfalls of structure-oriented filtering. (a) A vertical slice through original seismic data from a survey acquired in the Illinois Basin, U.S.A. (b)-(c). Vertical slices through the same data (b) after two passes of structure-oriented multiwindow filtering using a mean filter and (c) after two passes of structure-oriented multiwindow filtering using a principal-component filter. Note the conflicting dips of the diffraction tails circled in (a) and the underlying horizontal reflectors. After the filtering in (b) and (c), the tails of this diffraction have been eliminated so that the residual diffraction apex might be misinterpreted to be a carbonate buildup. Seismic data are courtesy of Continental Resources of Illinois, Inc.

Strong noise

The behavior of the principal-component filter is not always what we desire. To illustrate exactly what it does, we examine a noisy seismic survey acquired over the Illinois Basin, U.S.A. In returning to Figure 20a, we show a vertical slice through the original time-migrated data volume. We note that there is a strong overprint of highly aliased, backscattered ground roll contaminating the image. We apply two passes of multiwindow Kuwahara filtering using nine overlapping three-trace by three-trace windows with a vertical extent of ±10 ms. We show the result of a mean filter and a principal-component filter in Figure 20b and c, respectively. Note that the reflector amplitudes of the event indicated by the white arrow are more continuous (and more geologically reasonable) on the mean-filtered data (Figure 20b) than on the principal-component-filtered image (Figure 20c). In contrast, the principal-component-filtered data more closely honor the amplitude holes in the original data. Both filters do what we asked them to do. The interpreter's job is to decide which filter provides more useful geologic information.

In Figure 13, we showed how Luo et al.'s (2002) multiwindow mean filter can suppress acquisition footprint. If the acquisition footprint results from leakage of side-scattered noise with some amount of dip across the vertical analysis window, the principal component generally does a better job of reducing the footprint.

However, acquisition footprint also can be a function of signal variability resulting from differences in fold, source-receiver offset, or source-receiver azimuth between adjacent bins. Such differences are particularly sensitive to errors in velocity-induced NMO errors (Hill et al., 1999). In that case, when the footprint pattern varies slowly in the vertical direction, a principal-component filter preserves and even enhances the acquisition footprint, whereas a mean or median filter suppresses it.

Fractures that are nearly vertical are almost indistinguishable from that kind of acquisition footprint. If we are interested in mapping fractures, we recommend using the principal-component filter, and advise the interpreter to accept some image contamination resulting from acquisition footprint.

Poorly migrated images

Although structure-oriented filtering can greatly reduce coherent noise, it cannot fix certain errors caused by reflectors having been placed incorrectly because of inaccurate migration. In Figure 21, we show coherence images before (Figure 21a and b) and after (Figure 21c and d) two passes of structure-oriented filtering using a principal-component algorithm. We note in Figure 21c a dramatic improvement of the shallow image at $t = 0.600$ s after structure-oriented filtering, versus before filtering (Figure 21a). However, deeper in the section, at $t = 1.500$ s, the changes are less dramatic, as Figure 21b and d show. As we discussed in Chapter 7, one problem resulting from an inaccurate migration is partially focused discontinuities, which generate coherence images that have fewer features.

A second problem is improper location of the reflectors, causing reflectors to cross each other and resulting in artificial discontinuities and a generally wormy appearance. The example discussed previously from the Yucatan Peninsula and shown in Figures 34–36 of Chapter 7 was extreme. The example in Figure 21 from Vinton Dome, Louisiana, U.S.A., is subtler.

In Figures 22b and 23, we see a major fault dividing geologic blocks that have different dips. We apply structure-oriented filtering to the data shown in Figure 22a and display the result in 22c. It is always a good practice to examine which information has been discarded by any filtering process. In Figure 22d, we show the rejected noise from our filter, and we are comfortable that we have not rejected an undue amount of coherent reflector energy. We also note that the terminations of the reflectors in Figure 22c are sharper than those in Figure 22a.

We examine those reflector terminations in greater detail in Figure 24 and note that although they are sharper after filtering (Figure 24b), new simple fault planes are cutting through the section. Although some complex movement about antithetic faults may have caused the misalignment of fault blocks indicated by the white arrows in Figure 24b, no such explanation exists for the misalignment of the much simpler fault indicated by the gray arrows. However, a much simpler explanation is that the migration velocity was either too high or too low, so that when the inaccurate velocity model was coupled with the different reflector dip on either side of the fault indicated by the red and blue zones in Figures 22b and 23, the result was an interfingering of the reflection images.

Such incorrect imaging on migration produces overlapping fault blocks, as shown by Figure 25's vertical slices through the coherence volumes, which correspond to the data slices shown in Figure 22. The fault indicated by the white arrows is well aligned in the shallow section but becomes progressively more distorted with depth. The fault indicated by the gray arrows makes little geologic sense for this simple salt diapir in a sand-shale environment. Although the signal-to-noise ratio of the coherence image is improved after structure-oriented filtering, the locations of the discontinuities are unchanged. To put these discontinuities in their proper location, we would need to modify our velocity-depth model and remigrate the data.

We should be very careful when we interpret fault edges on poorly migrated images, but we do not always need to use state-of-the-art prestack depth migration. For example, the images shown in Figure 14 from the Central Basin Platform in Texas were migrated using a simple post-stack time migration. Although here the velocity shows considerable lateral changes, the geology in this area consists of flat reflectors that have undergone wrenching, with some blocks popped up and others dropped down, and the blocks separated by reverse and strike-slip faults. Because the dip of the reflectors on either side of these faults does not exceed 10° and the velocity is fast, an inaccurate migration simply results in an image that is somewhat overfocused or underfocused and does not cause the reflectors on either side of the fault to interfinger.

Fortuitously, this robustness allows us to examine stratigraphic features of the Vinton Dome survey that lie away from the mismigrated faults. In Figure 26, we show a vertical slice through the seismic data, with picks along the top of the middle Miocene and Hackberry formations. In Figure 27, we display two coherence horizon slices along the horizons from Figure 26; the coherence volumes were calculated from the structurally oriented filtered data. As we did with the time slices shown in Figure 21, we note in Figure 26 considerably better lateral resolution along the shallower middle Miocene than along the deeper Hackberry horizon slice.

In contrast, the coherent-energy gradients in Figure 27 show considerable detail even along the Hackberry horizon, where we note several channels and other stratigraphic features corresponding to zones of high coherence in Figure 27b. We attribute this good lateral resolution to the fact that away from the faults we are relatively free from reflector interfingering, so our images suffer only from suboptimal focusing and mispositioning.

In Figure 28, we show extractions through the north-south (Figure 28a) and east-west (Figure 28b) energy-weighted coherent-amplitude-gradient volumes along the Hackberry horizon corresponding to the coherence volume shown in Figure 27b. Note that although we see radial faults (indicated by the gray arrow), stratigraphic features such as channels (indicated by white arrows) appear to be less affected by the inaccurate migration. In summary, given an inaccurate depth image, we cannot determine ex-

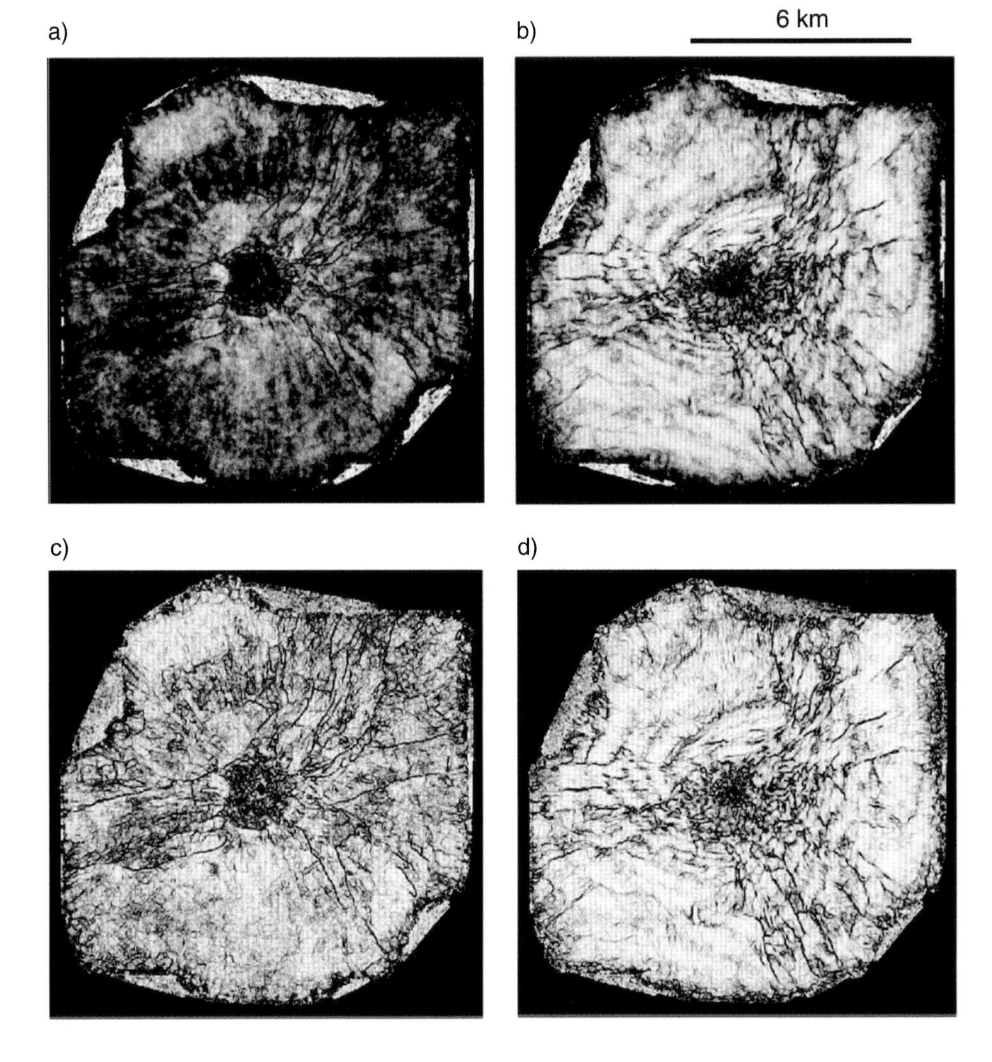

Figure 21. Time slices at $t =$ (a) 0.600 and (b) 1.500 s through coherence volumes calculated from a prestack time-migrated seismic survey over Vinton Dome, Louisiana, U.S.A. (c)-(d). The corresponding coherence time slices generated after the seismic data had undergone structure-oriented filtering. After Marfurt et al. (2002). Seismic data are courtesy of OPEX.

actly where the channels are but we can still detect them. That information may justify a more careful velocity analysis and remigration.

Image Enhancement

Many of the filters described above, including the mean, median, α-trimmed-mean, modified-trimmed-mean, multistage-median, and MSMTM filters, fall within the realm of image processing. Other filters discussed earlier in the book include variations of the Sobel (edge-detection) filter discussed in Chapter 5. Most filters in image-processing literature have been applied to 2D images, with particular emphasis on digital photographs. In the preceding part of this chapter we emphasized applying filters to migrated seismic data volumes, or to dip-azimuth volumes before

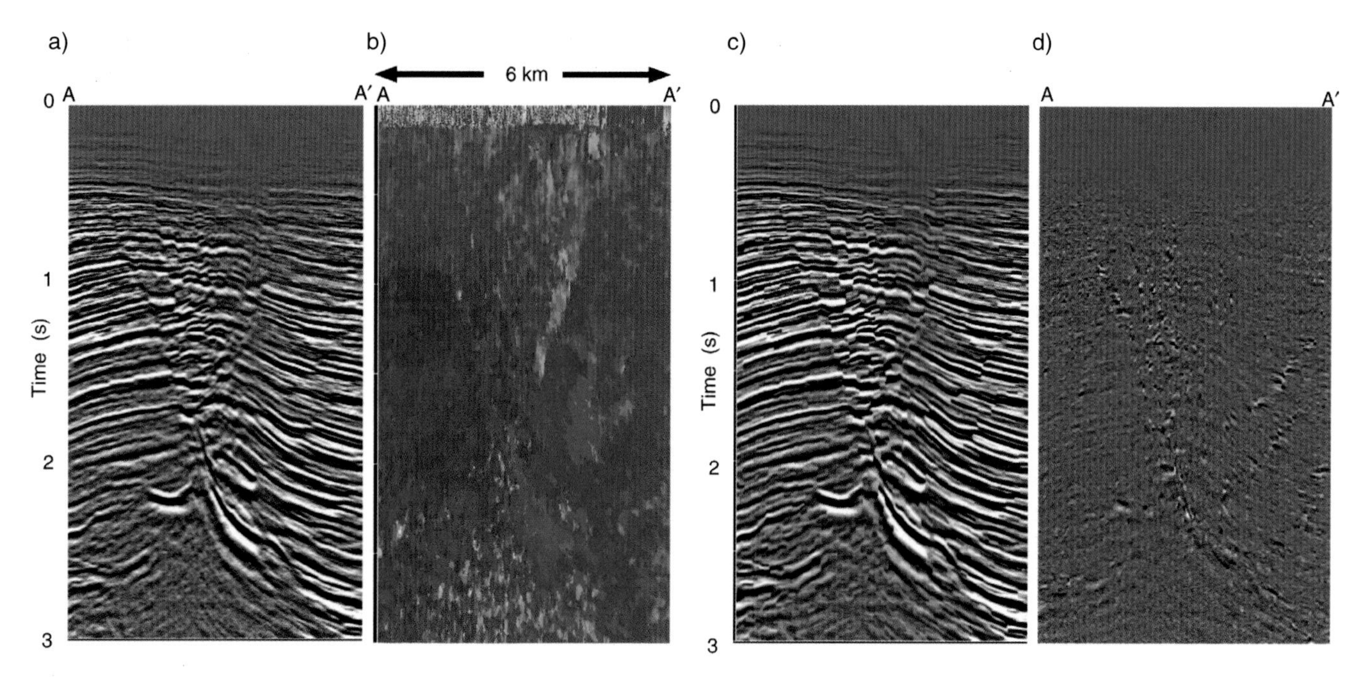

Figure 22. (a) A vertical slice (a) through a prestack time-migrated data volume, (b) through the corresponding dip azimuth cube, and (c) after two passes of structure-oriented filtering using a multiwindow principal-component algorithm. (d) The difference, or rejected noise, between the data shown in (c) and in (a). The color wheel and location of line AA′ are shown in Figure 23. After Marfurt et al. (2002).

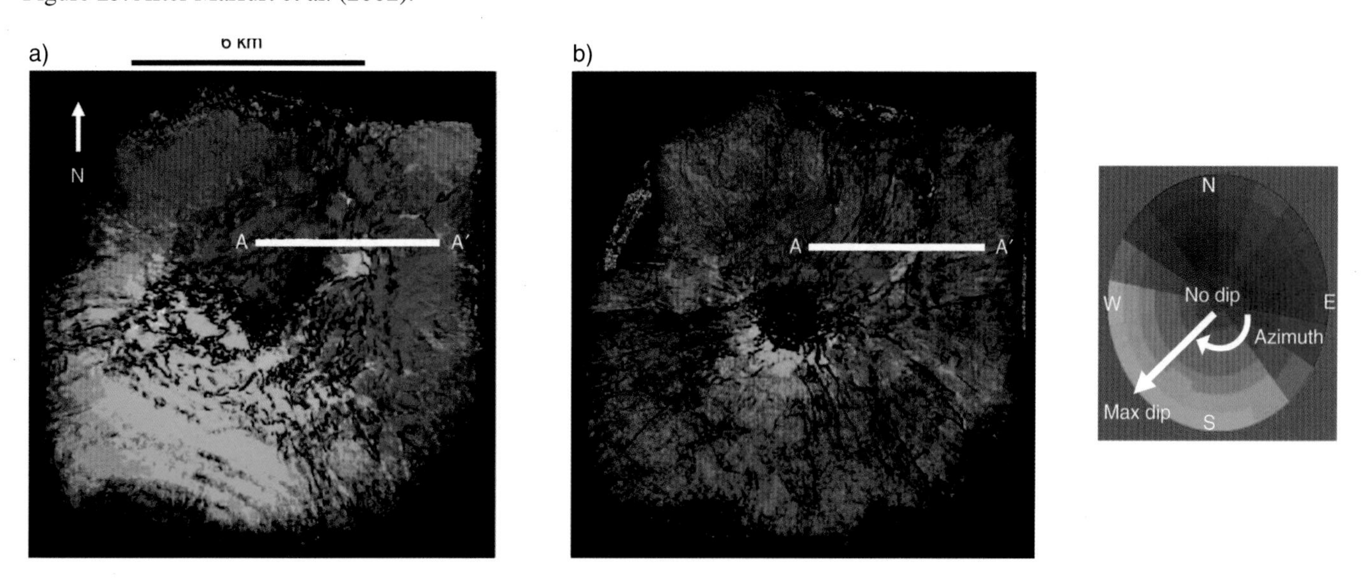

Figure 23. Time slices at t = (a) 0.750 and (b) 2.250 s through a dip/azimuth/coherence composite volume, using the techniques described in Chapter 9. Note the change in azimuth from north (red) to east (blue), intersected by line AA′. Such a change indicates a rotation of the sediments around a complicated fault zone. After Marfurt et al. (2002).

curvature calculation. Next we apply image-processing filters to the attributes themselves.

Sharpened coherence volumes

One of the simplest components in photographic analysis is the sharpening filter. The simplest sharpening filter is based on the Laplacian operator, and is the second-derivative filter:

$$a_{\text{sharp}} = \frac{\partial^2 a}{\partial x^2} + \frac{\partial^2 a}{\partial y^2} \tag{8.16}$$

The second-derivative sharpening filter is related to the first-derivative edge-detection algorithm we discussed in Chapter 5. Geophysicists are familiar with equation 8.16 being applied to gravity and magnetic data to obtain short-wavelength, enhanced second-derivative maps.

One difficulty of applying equation 8.16 to coherence volumes is that it produces overshoots and undershoots of the image amplitude, thereby generating side lobes along discrete edges. Thus, we believe that the sharpening algorithm applied to the seismic data volume in Figure 29a, from off the east coast of Canada, is likely to have been an implementation of a filter similar to the multistage-median filter described by equation 8.13. Unfortunately, the details of the algorithm used in Figure 29c have been lost through retirements of the scientists involved. The output is a 3D volume of sharpened coherence coefficients (Figure 29c). We note that the fracture detail is clearer and the faults look crisper here than on the equivalent coherence display (Figure 29b).

We apply this same Laplacian sharpening filter first to a stratigraphic-sequence coherence volume (Figure 30) and then to another coherence volume from the Cook Inlet, Alaska, U.S.A. (Figure 31). Note that the channel edges and the faults are crisper and better focused on the sharpened display (Figure 31b) than on the equivalent coherence slice in Figure 30a. Similarly, the fault trends seen on the sharpened displays in Figure 31c are crisper and easier to interpret than they are on the equivalent coherence displays (Figure 31b).

Relief-enhanced coherence volumes

We will discuss shaded-relief and other multiattribute display techniques thoroughly in Chapter 9. Briefly, we note here that a shaded-relief display calculates the normal to a surface at each point in a seismic volume and projects either a diffuse or specular light source upon it. The surface we refer to here is the coherence seen on any given slice.

However, because coherence is a measure of discontinuity, exaggerating such coherence values through shaded

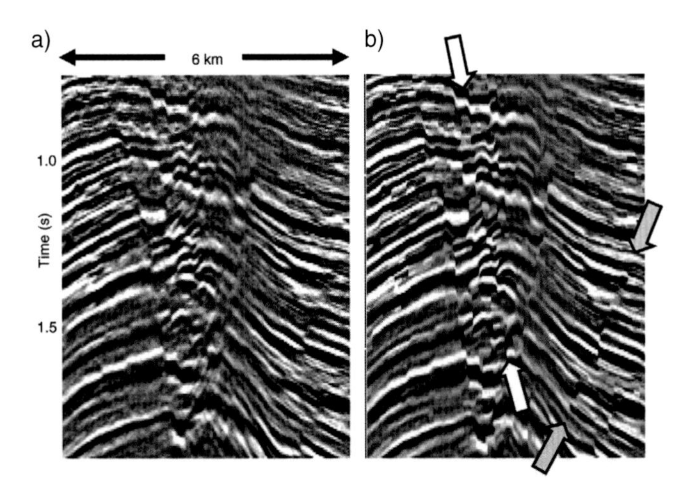

Figure 24. Close-up views of data (a) before and (b) after two passes of structure-oriented filtering, shown respectively in Figure 22a and c. Note that although the edges are indeed sharper in (b), they do not line up along smooth faults. Because the geology consists of easily deformed sands and shales, we attribute this misalignment to an inaccurate velocity model, exacerbated by the conflicting reflector dip shown in Figure 23. These two factors result in a geologically unacceptable interfingering of reflectors. After Marfurt et al. (2002).

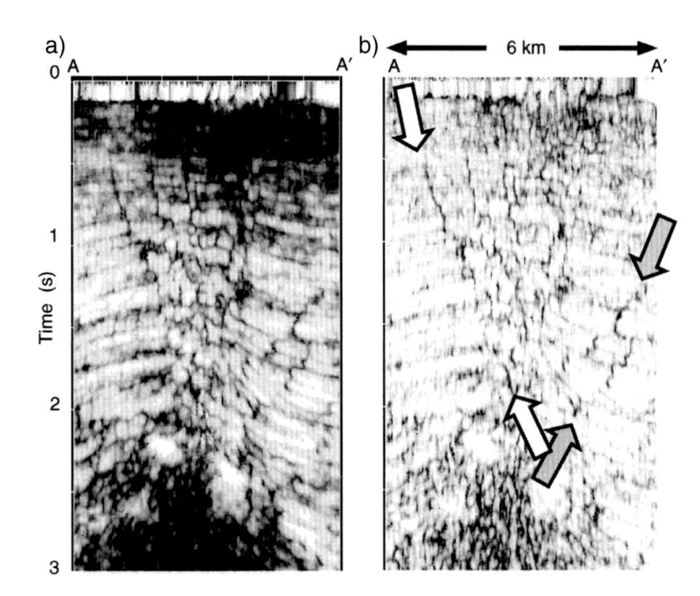

Figure 25. Vertical sections through coherence volumes corresponding to Figure 22a and c. Note that although structure-oriented filtering reduces noise in the shallow section (the black area), it does not realign poorly imaged faults. Such misalignment generates the wormy faults seen on the coherence image in Figure 21d. Although the misalignment of faults is the result of poor seismic imaging, faults do not always need to align. In Chapters 11 and 16, we will present examples of faults misaligned because of brittle deformation of carbonates embedded in plastically deformed shales. After Marfurt et al. (2002).

relief would be too extreme. Rather, in Figure 32 we mix the results of shaded relief with the original coherence calculation to generate a relief-enhanced image (Figure 32b) of the faults and fractures originally displayed in Figure 29. As part of this process, we filter out horizontal bands of low coherence, which usually are associated with either chaotic deposition (such as slump deposits) or low signal-to-noise ratios (such as shale-on-shale reflections). In Figure 33, we display a 3D view of a different survey after suppression of these stratigraphic features.

Fault Enhancement

Coherence and other geometric attributes are local measures of changes in waveform shape, amplitude, frequency, and dip azimuth. Human interpreters organize such features into fault planes, meandering channels, slump blocks, karst collapses, and other features that fit their geologic model and interpretation experience.

Image processors are hard at work to help accelerate this interpretation process. In medicine, significant progress has been made in the development of "snake" algorithms that help track blood vessels in the human kidney on CAT-scan images. Clearly, such algorithms could be generalized to track meandering channels like those shown in Figure 30.

Interpretation of faults on 3D seismic data volumes still remains a time-consuming and tedious exercise. Faults are manually picked on inlines, crosslines, and time slices via discontinuities seen on the seismic amplitude. Although coherence and other edge-detector attributes enhance the visual appearance of abrupt lateral changes in 3D seismic volumes, automated workstation tools have been slow to exploit those attribute-generated enhancements. However, recently this trend has been changing for the better and approaches have been developed for using seismic attributes to automatically detect faults.

Filtering coherence volumes to enhance faults

Barnes (2005) described a filter for improving seismic-discontinuity-attribute data to aid interpretation of faults. Filter parameters specify the dip, planarity, and resolution of the discontinuities that the filter allows to pass, so it can enhance steeply dipping discontinuities. In the process, the filter removes discontinuities resulting from stratigraphy, noise, and other artifacts. After application of this discontinuity filter, the disjoint fault segments must be connected into fault surfaces for which some of the existing methods could be used.

Figure 34a shows a vertical slice through a seismic volume from a survey acquired in southern Louisiana, U.S.A.

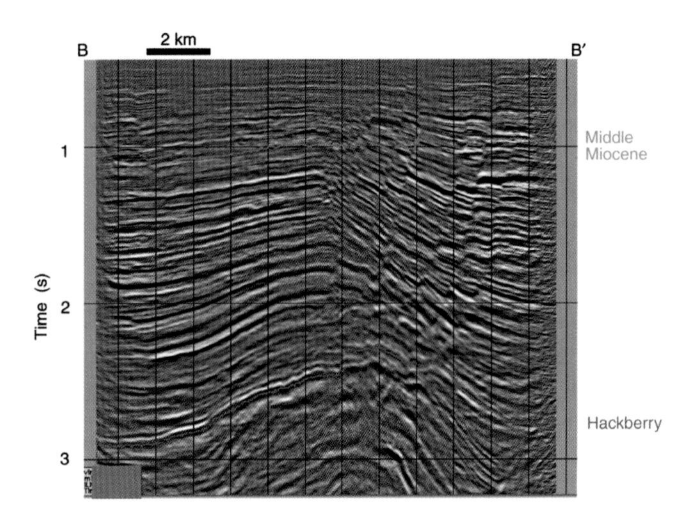

Figure 26. A vertical section through the southern part of a Vinton Dome, Louisiana, U.S.A. survey. The quality of the seismic data is characterized by higher vertical and lateral resolution along the shallow middle Miocene horizon than along the deeper Hackberry horizon. Line location is shown in Figure 27. After Marfurt et al. (2002). Data courtesy of OPEX.

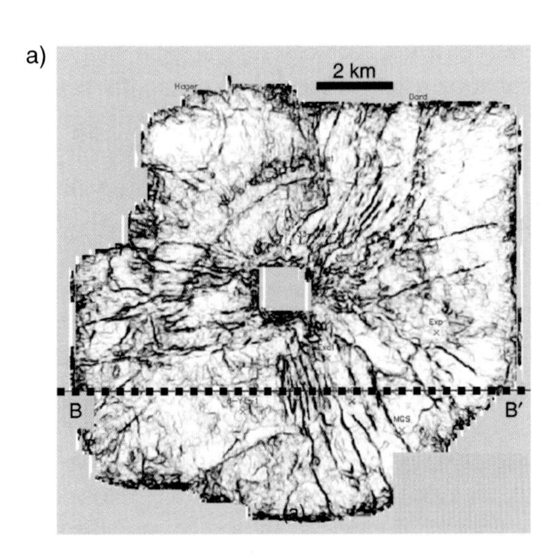

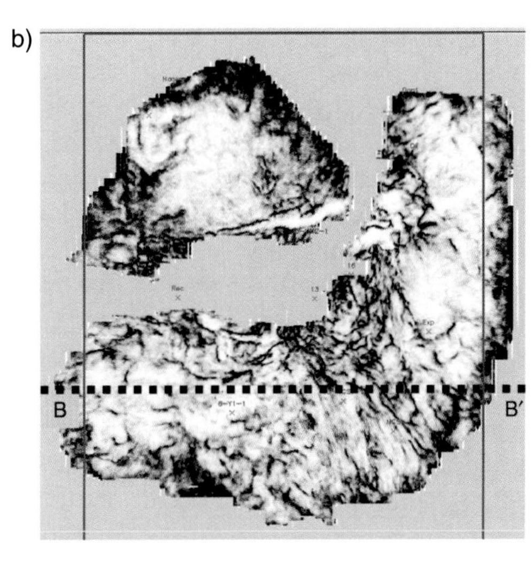

Figure 27. Coherence horizon slices along (a) the middle Miocene horizon and (b) the Hackberry horizon from Figure 26. Note the lack of fault resolution at the Hackberry level.

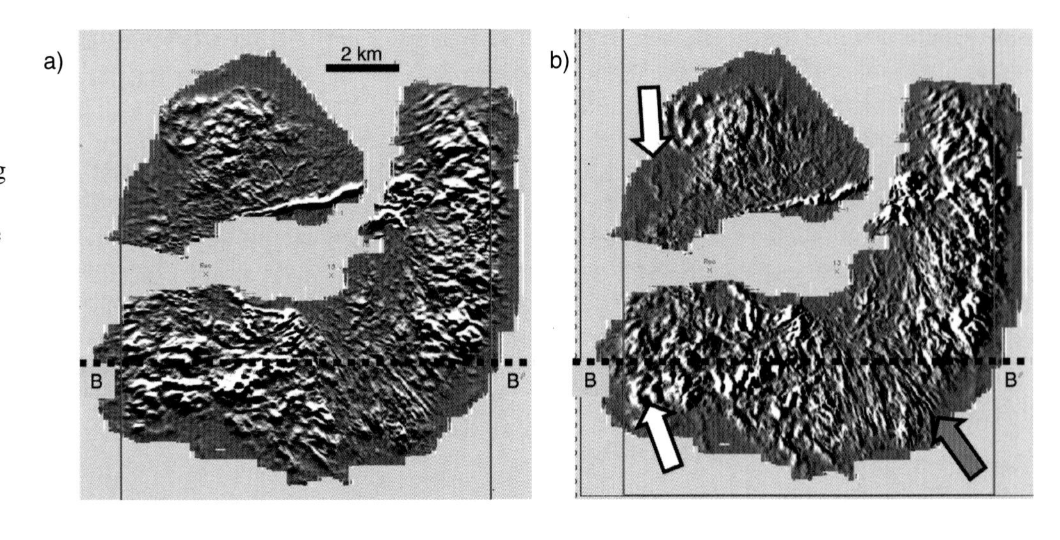

Figure 28. Horizon slices through the (a) north-south and (b) east-west energy-weighted coherent-amplitude-gradient volumes along the Hackberry horizon corresponding to the coherence horizon slice shown in Figure 27b. Although we can see indications of radial faults (gray arrow), stratigraphic features — such as the channels indicated by the white arrows — appear to be less affected by the inaccurate migration.

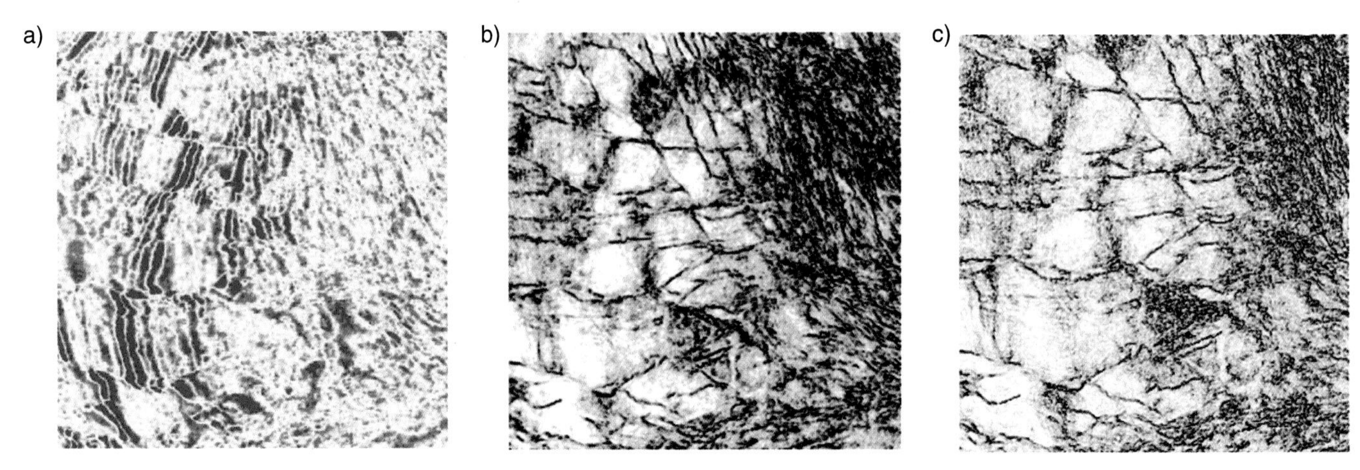

Figure 29. Time slices at $t = 1.200$ s through (a) a seismic data volume, (b) a coherence volume, and (c) a sharpened coherence volume, off the east coast of Canada. Notice the clarity with which the oblique faults stand out on the coherence display, compared with the seismic equivalent in (a). Besides, the fractured zone in the top right of these images is easy to locate and decipher on the coherence display. The definition of these features is crisper on the sharpened coherence display.

The corresponding vertical slice through the discontinuity volume is shown in Figure 34b. Notice the two main faults seen to the left and several faults in the lower half of the data.

Figure 35 shows a time slice at 3.000 s through the seismic data volume and the corresponding time slice through the discontinuity volume indicated by the yellow dotted line in Figure 34. The faults are clearly visible on the coherence volume, most of them running east to west.

Figure 36 displays the results of successive filtering of the discontinuity volume shown on the vertical slice in Figure 34b, displayed here after (a) suppression of horizontal discontinuities, (b) after image dilation, and (c) after image erosion. A composite image of the discontinuity and seismic data is shown in Figure 36d. Likewise, Figure 37 is a set of similar displays, here for the time slice at $t = 3.000$ from Figure 35b.

Lees (1999) demonstrated that just as horizons are picked on seismic data by voxel tracking, a similar process can be used to construct surfaces representing faults. He began by calculating a coherence volume from the seismic volume. Next, he generated a composite volume using a technique discussed in detail in Chapter 9 on color display. If coherence was low, he mapped the coherence value to the lower 128 values of his 8-bit voxel range. If coherence was high, he mapped the complete seismic data range to the upper 128 values of his 8-bit voxel range. In that manner, conventional voxel-picking technology can either pick coherence (faults) or reflectors (seismic) by defining seed points and a range of neighboring voxel values.

Figure 38a is a segment of a seismic section showing some faults clearly; Figure 38b is a magnified view of a portion of this segment. Figure 38c shows the corresponding coherence volume. Figure 38d shows the combined display, with black corresponding to points that have low semblance values. Note the composite color bar with the lower half (blue/black/red) used to display semblance and the upper half (blue/white/red) used to display seismic data.

Next a seed point is picked and made to grow within the low-coherence values. Such growth usually does not form continuous sheets, so iterations may be necessary to grow the cloud of points into sheets or planes in the inline or crossline directions. Figure 38e shows a triangulated surface interpolated from a cloud of points.

Dorn et al. (2005) described another process that uses the coherence attribute. Figure 39 shows a coherence volume that is used for automatic fault extraction, taken from a survey acquired offshore the U. K., at Wytch Farm field. First, a classical destriping operator is run on the data (a time or depth slice) to remove any remnant acquisition footprint or stripes. Then the resulting volume is processed to enhance linear features on each time or depth slice.

Linear features associated with faults are expected to show a minimum length that exhibits low coherence. A window of adjacent samples is created for examining each

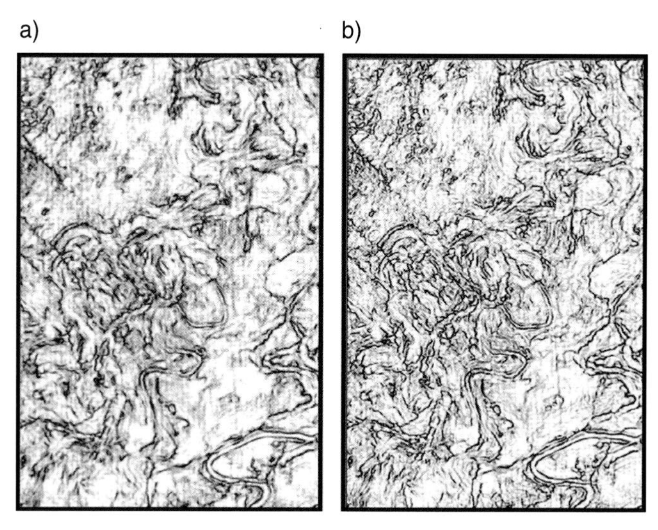

Figure 30. Time slices at t = 1.200 s through (a) a coherence volume and (b) a sharpened coherence volume from a survey, showing a crisper and more focused definition of a complex system of meandering channels and the faults intersecting them.

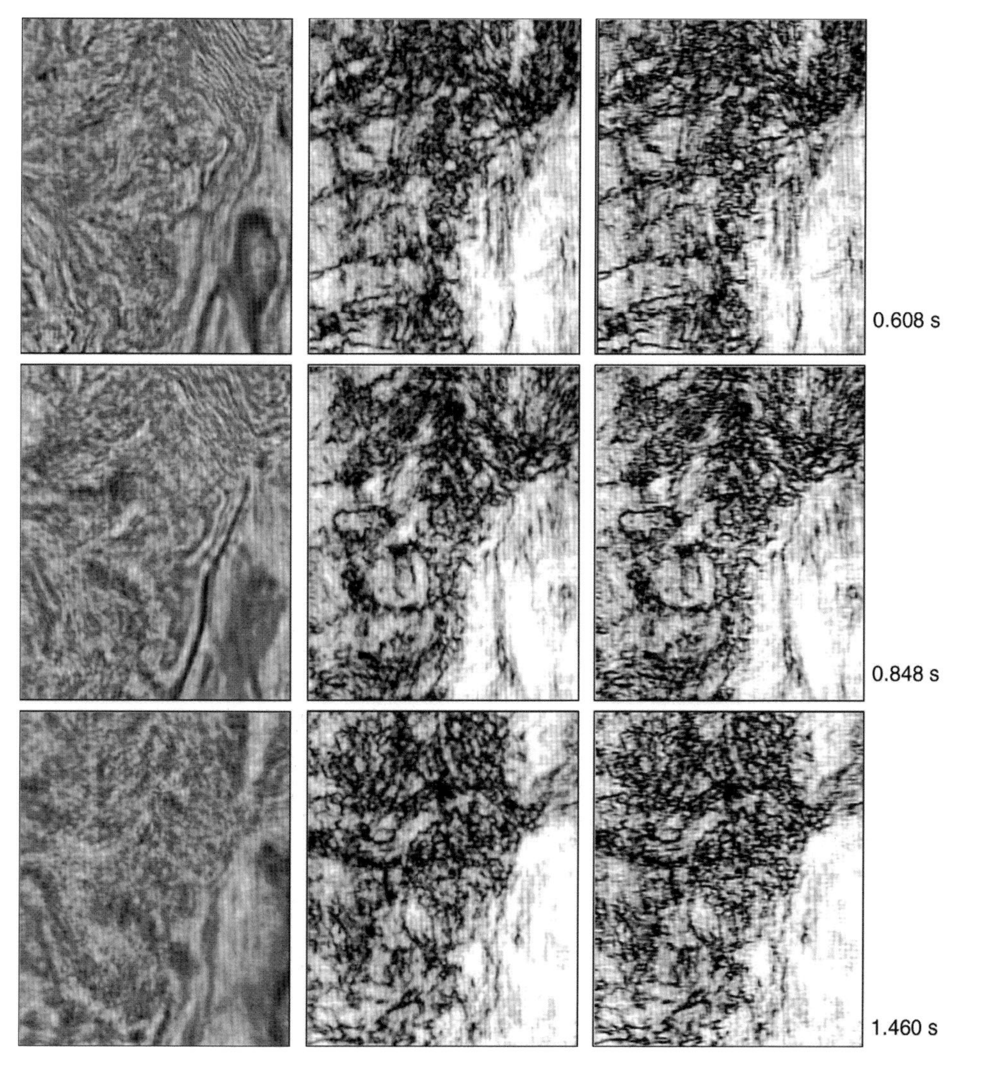

Figure 31. Time slices at t = 0.608, 0.848, and 1.460 s through (a) a seismic data volume, (b) a coherence volume, and (c) a sharpened coherence volume from a survey through the Cook Inlet of Alaska, U.S.A. The fault trends are easier to interpret on the sharpened displays.

a) 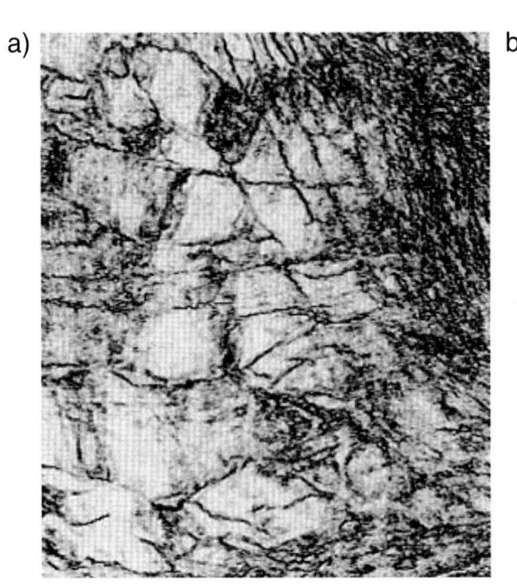

b) 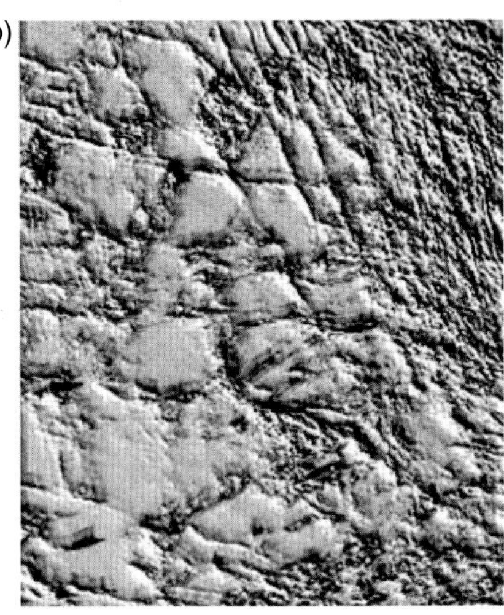

Figure 32. Time slices, corresponding to that shown in Figure 29b, of (a) a coherence volume and (b) a relief-enhanced coherence volume that eliminates many of the low-coherence values associated with horizontal stratigraphy.

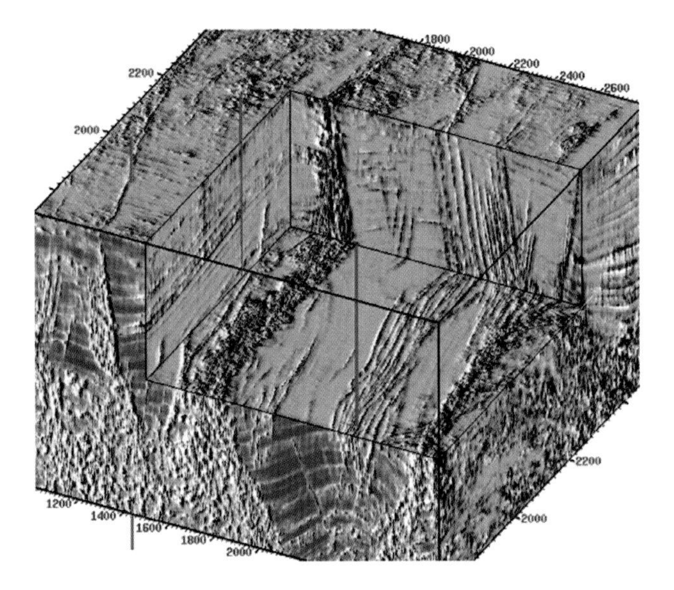

Figure 33. Cutaway volume of a relief-enhanced coherence data volume, with structural attenuation of the data shown in Figure 32. Note the enhanced lineations depicting the faults, which are now easier to detect. The vertical magenta line denotes the positions of wells that have been drilled into the faulted zones.

sample in a slice. The goal is to see if a linear segment can be created that links samples of low coherence so that they form a line segment. This step yields a relative-probability volume, wherein each sample represents the relative probability that it belongs to a horizontal linear feature. Here, filters can be set to restrict the azimuth range or to exclude linear features that do not reach a certain length. Figure 40a shows a lineament-enhanced volume derived from the volume shown in Figure 39.

Next, the line-enhanced volume in Figure 40a is subjected to a fault-enhancement process in which linear features are traced in time or depth as well as azimuth. Linear features corresponding to channel boundaries, pinch-outs, and unconformities, which do not have appreciable vertical extent, are filtered at this step.

Figure 40b shows a fault-enhanced relative-probability volume. Notice the improved continuity and signal-to-noise ratio for faults on the vertical section in the volume. This volume can be used to pick fault polylines using a 3D interpretation system, linking the polylines in 3D space, segregating them into separate faults, and producing named fault surfaces. Figure 41 shows fault surfaces selected from the many surfaces generated by this procedure.

A similar approach is followed by a commercial package (from Ikon Science Ltd.), using advanced automated image-processing techniques to reveal fault trends in 3D volumes. The coherence attribute is used to pick horizontal fault segments, after which trend analysis and reconnaissance are performed to gain structural understanding and optionally to add surfaces to collate segments.

Figure 42a shows fault segments seen in a 3D view, picked on the coherence attribute (time slice), and shown in color by azimuth according to the color wheel in Figure 42b. The 3D view contains a crossline that helps us examine the correlation of faults with their corresponding seismic signatures. Figure 42c shows the same fault segments seen in Figure 42a, but displayed here on seismic-amplitude reflectivity. This is another display that is used to check the accuracy of the fault picking.

Figure 43 shows the fault planes that were generated by joining the picked fault segments from Figure 42 and overlaid here on the coherence attribute slice. The fault planes retain the colors of the azimuths used to display the fault segments in Figure 42.

Ant tracking

The ant-tracking algorithm is an iterative scheme that progressively tries to connect adjacent zones of low coherence that have been filtered to eliminate horizontal features associated with stratigraphy. Ant-tracking nomenclature was

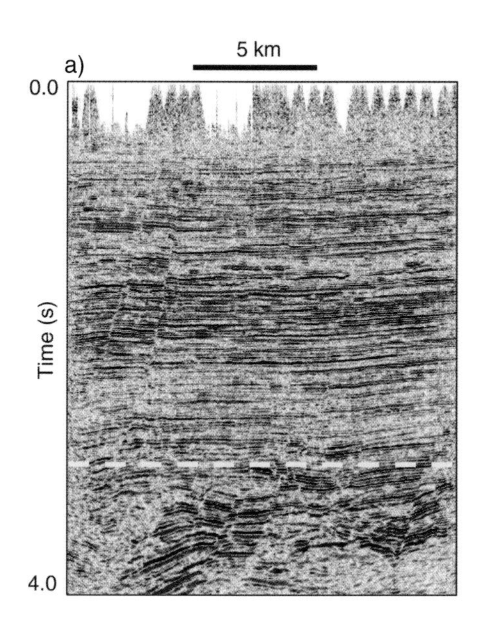

Figure 34. Vertical slices through (a) a seismic volume and (b) the corresponding discontinuity volume, from a survey acquired in southern Louisiana, U.S.A. Notice the two main faults to the left tend to stand out on the coherence display. Data are courtesy of Seitel, and the attribute analysis is courtesy of Landmark Graphics. After Barnes (2005).

assigned by workers who clearly were not familiar with the overly aggressive fire ants feared by geoscientists living in Houston, Texas, U.S.A. Rather, the ants used in Randen et al.'s (2001) ant-tracking algorithm are the organized, disciplined ants spoken about in Aesop's fables.

The ant-tracking method draws on an analogy from ants finding the shortest distance between their nest and their food source and then communicating by making use of a chemical substance called a pheromone, which attracts other ants. Ants following the shortest path reach their destination soonest, so ants that follow are influenced by the pheromone on the traversed path. Thus, the shortest path is followed the most and is marked with the most pheromone.

In the practical case, artificial electronic ants are distributed in the seismic-discontinuity attribute volume and allowed to follow different paths. Ants deployed at different positions in the discontinuity volume traverse the fault surface by following an electronic pheromone. In contrast, surfaces that do not represent faults or noise are marked weakly and can be removed by setting a filter threshold. As these ants traverse different surfaces in the discontinuity volume, they estimate the orientation of those surfaces. In fact, the orientation of the faults and the values of attribute strength are stored as surface measurements and those two properties are then used to extract fault surfaces.

Figure 44b shows results (on a time slice through a coherence volume) from application of ant tracking to fault attributes. Notice how crisp and continuous the faults are in Figure 44b, compared with the pre-ant-tracking input data in Figure 44a. Similarly, Figure 44d shows a vertical section from the coherence volume after application of ant tracking to fault attributes. Again, the faults appear continuous in a clearer background.

The surfaces extracted using the above procedure are essentially segments and not complete surfaces. Joining the

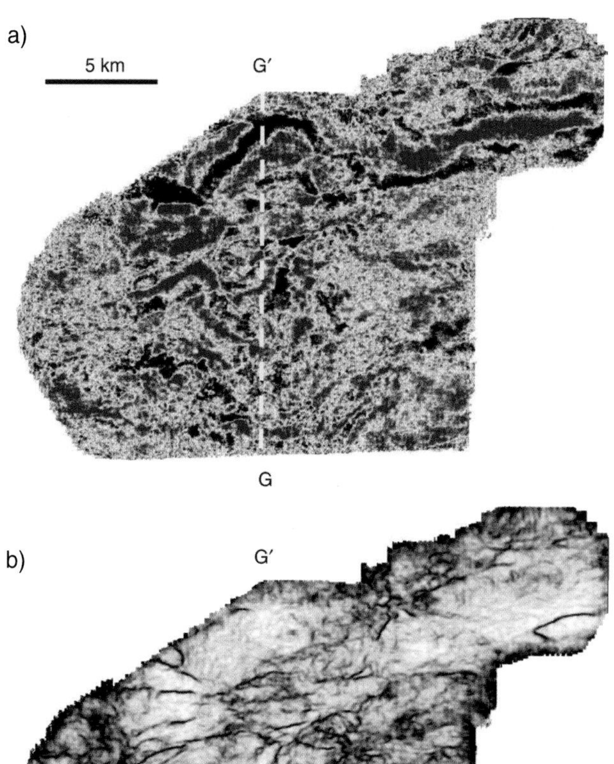

Figure 35. (a) A time slice at $t = 3.000$ s through the seismic data volume and (b) the corresponding time slice through the discontinuity volume computed from the survey shown in Figure 34. The east-west-trending faults are seen clearly on the coherence display. Data are courtesy of Seitel, and the attribute analysis is courtesy of Landmark Graphics. After Barnes (2005).

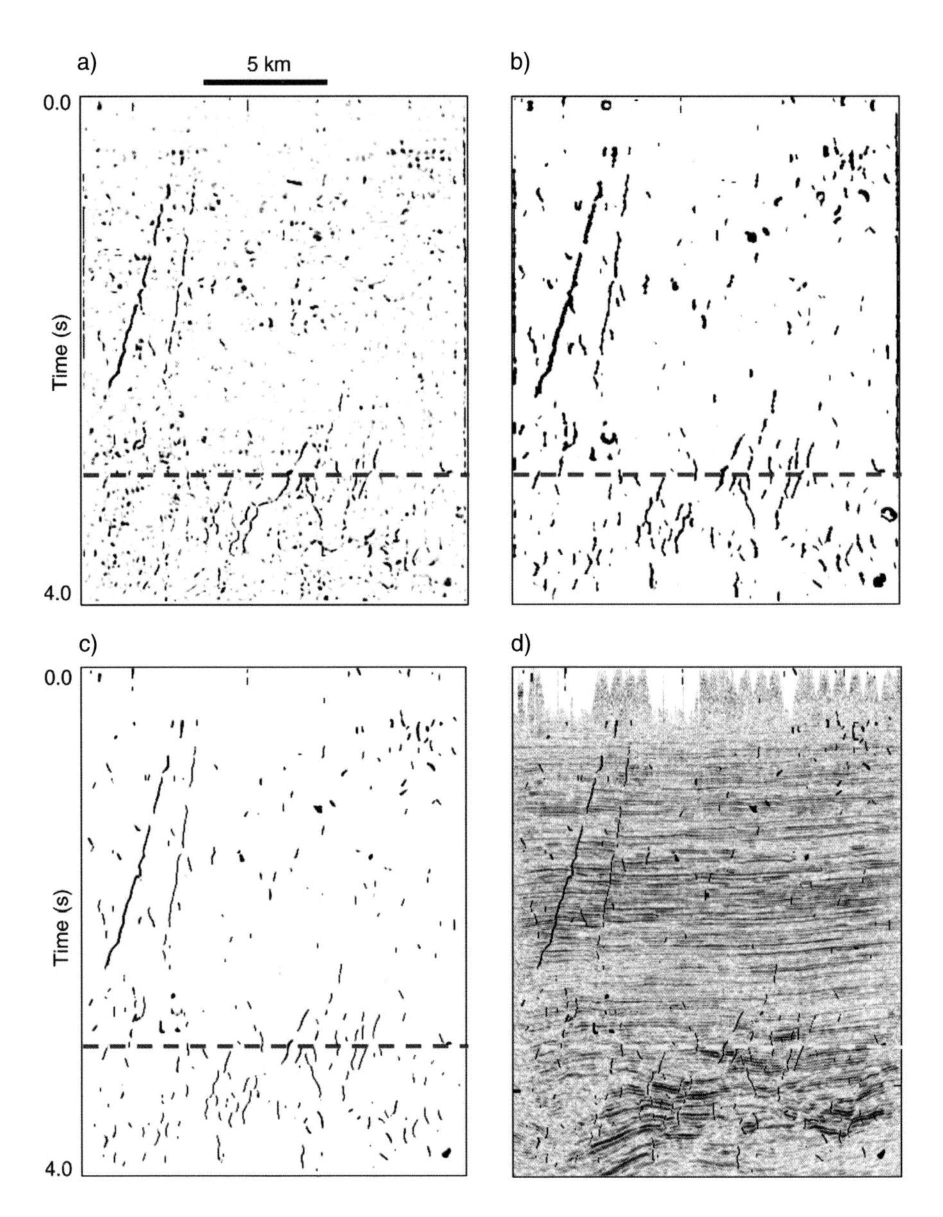

Figure 36. The results of successive filtering of the discontinuity volume from which a vertical slice is displayed in Figure 34b, (a) after suppression of horizontal discontinuities, (b) after image dilation, and (c) after image erosion. (d) A composite image of discontinuity and seismic data. Notice how the unwanted low-coherence noise has been filtered out. After Barnes (2005).

segments into surfaces comprises the final phase of the ant-tracking method, when fault segments are split into separate systems defined by their orientation. Here, fault segments are split into groups having similar orientation, with no segments intersecting.

In Figure 45a, we show a coherencelike volume generated using the gradient structure tensor first described in Chapter 2. In Figure 45b, we display the results of filtering out the horizontal stratigraphic features. Note that the discontinuities associated with faults are preserved but are not yet aligned. Each of these surfaces is then thinned (Randen et al., 2001) so that each surface is one voxel thick. The extracted surfaces emerge connected and are output as fault interpretations (Figure 45c). Application of the ant-tracking algorithm connects these disconnected discontinuities into a suite of discrete fault surfaces. Figure 46 displays the enhanced fault surfaces visualized in a seismic subvolume extracted from a bigger volume used to generate the coherence volumes in Figures 44 and 45.

Hough transform

The Hough transform is used in image processing for detecting shapes. It maps line or edge points (pixels) in an image to lines in parameter space. It also is sometimes referred to as a point-to-curve transformation.

If we parameterize lines by their slope and intercept ($y = mx + c$), then for all lines passing through each edge pixel (x,y) in the image, that pixel is mapped onto the line $b = -xm + y$ in the parameter space (m,x,b). The equation that converts pixels from the space domain to the polar-parameter domain or vice-versa is $\rho = x\cos\theta + y\sin\theta$.

Duda and Hart (1972) summarized the properties of the Hough transform:

- A point in the picture plane corresponds to a sinusoidal curve in the parameter plane.
- A point in the parameter plane corresponds to a straight line in the picture plane.

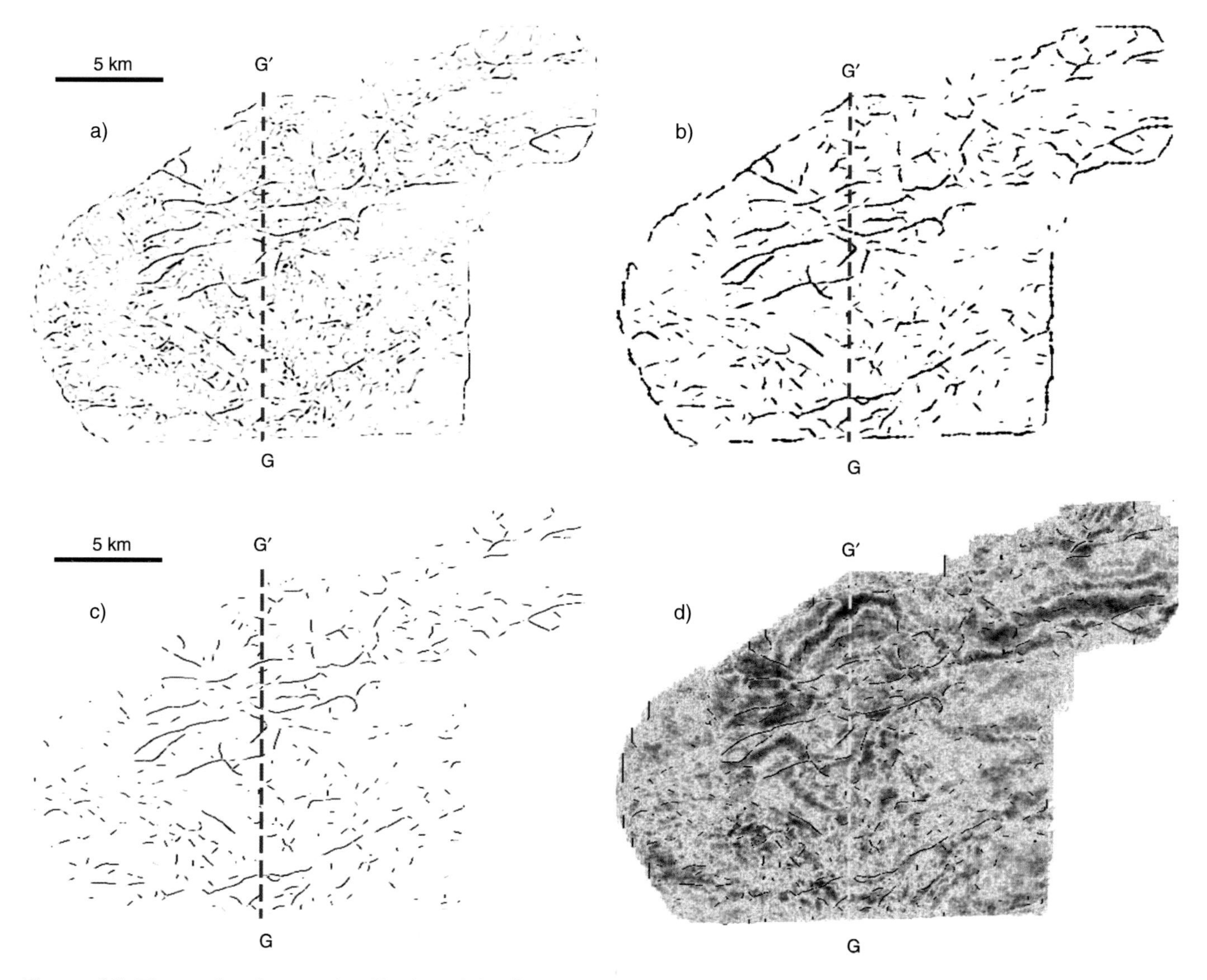

Figure 37. The results of successive filtering of the discontinuity volume from which a time slice at t = 3.000 s is displayed in Figure 35b, (a) after suppression of horizontal discontinuities, (b) after image dilation, and (c) after image erosion. (d) A composite image of discontinuity and seismic data. Again, notice how the unwanted low-coherence noise has been filtered out. After Barnes (2005).

- Points lying on the same straight line in the picture plane correspond to curves through a common point in the parameter plane.
- Points lying on the same curve in the parameter plane correspond to lines through the same point in the picture plane.

Application of Hough transforms for detecting faults was first reported by AlBinHassan and Marfurt (2003). They demonstrated the application of a Hough transform on seismic-attribute (curvature and coherence) 3D data. Using a running-window approach on 2D slices, the method detects faults as straight lines. However, the method is sensitive to noise.

Jacquemin and Mallet (2005) proposed applying a double Hough transform for automatic fault extraction. The intersection of a fault by a series of (x,z) cross sections is essentially a family of straight lines. Application of the Hough transform maps each of these straight lines to a point in the first parametric space. For each fault, the set of points thus obtained comprises a new straight line and can again be mapped to a point in the second-parameter space by using another Hough transform. Thus, by using a cascade of Hough transforms, each fault is represented as a point in the parametric space. Using an automated process, such points that correspond to faults in the (x,y,z) space and that are located on planes pertaining to points in the parametric space can be retrieved and used to detect faults.

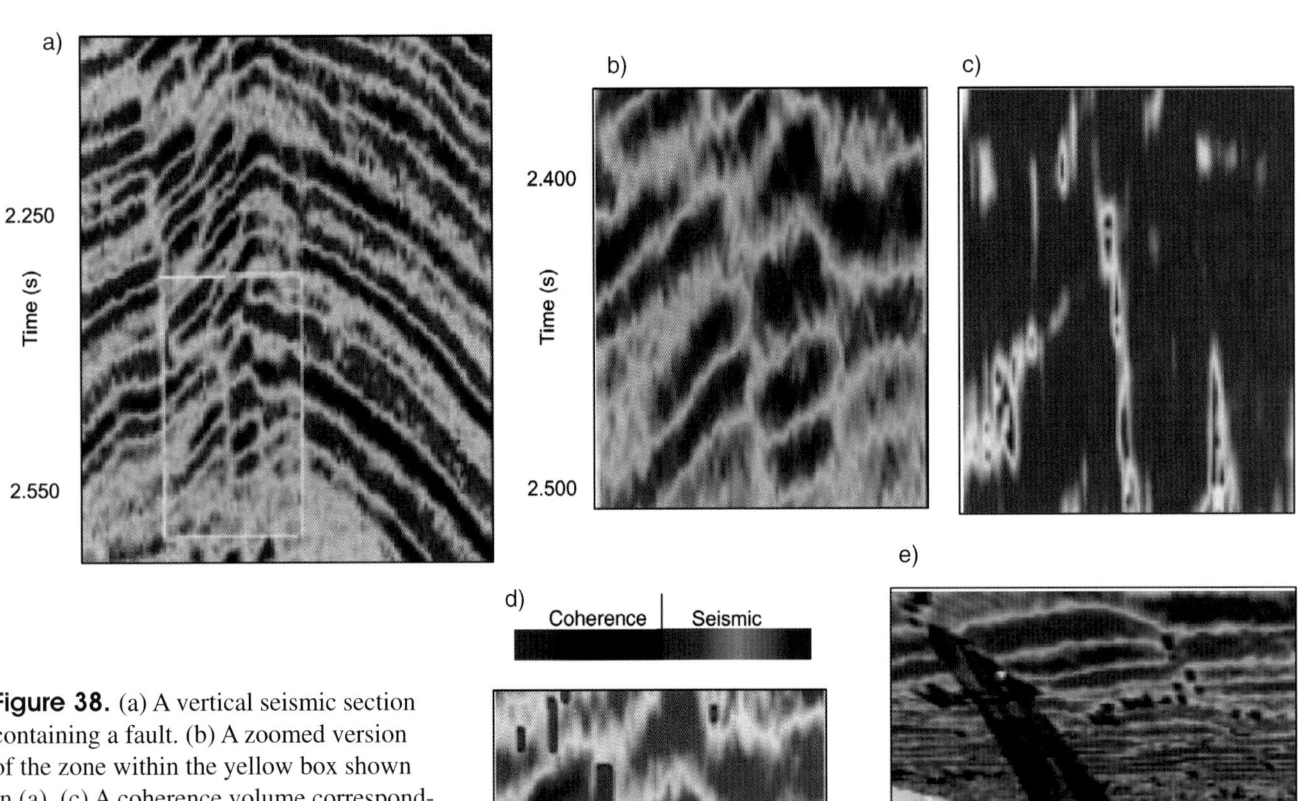

Figure 38. (a) A vertical seismic section containing a fault. (b) A zoomed version of the zone within the yellow box shown in (a). (c) A coherence volume corresponding to the data area in (a). (d) A composite image of coherence data and seismic data, using the composite color bar above. Black corresponds to points with low coherence values. (e) A triangulated surface showing the fault plane from the fault we see in images (a)-(d). Notice how the low-coherence points can be joined in an automated way to generate fault planes. After Lees (1999).

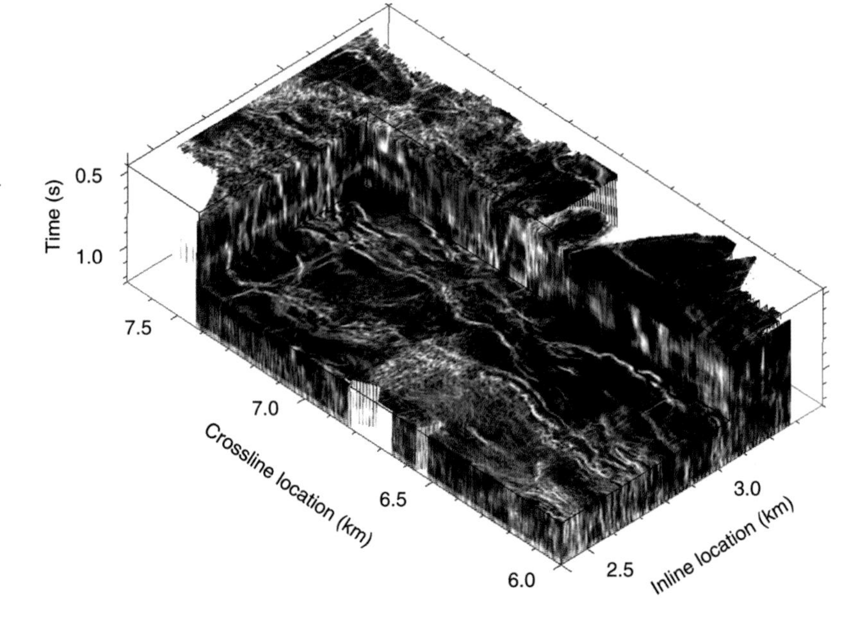

Figure 39. A coherence volume generated for the Wytch Farm survey, U. K. The low-coherence lineations (in white) are used as input to an automatic fault-extraction algorithm. Data are courtesy of BP, Premier Oil, ONEPM, Kerr-McGee Oil (U. K.), and Talisman North Sea. After Dorn et al. (2005).

The first step in such a process is to generate a coherence volume from the seismic data that then is used to enhance the faults. Because the Hough transform is sensitive to noise, we may subject the seismic data to structure-oriented filtering or other filtering before we calculate coherence. The coherence volume is transformed into a binary data volume in which the presence or absence of faults is coded by 1 and 0 values. Threshold filtering at this stage could help remove acquisition footprint noise. After we apply the double Hough transform, we retrieve and store the points corresponding to planes in (x,y,z) space. Reverse transformation of those points yields the subset of points in (x,y,z) space that we then interpolate to generate fault planes.

Figure 47a and b show vertical slices through a seismic volume and the corresponding coherence (semblance) volume. Using the methodology explained above, the faults extracted from the data are shown in three dimensions in Figure 47c. The method works well for planar faults, but for curved paths it may be necessary to interactively merge some subsets of points that are extracted separately but that correspond to the same fault.

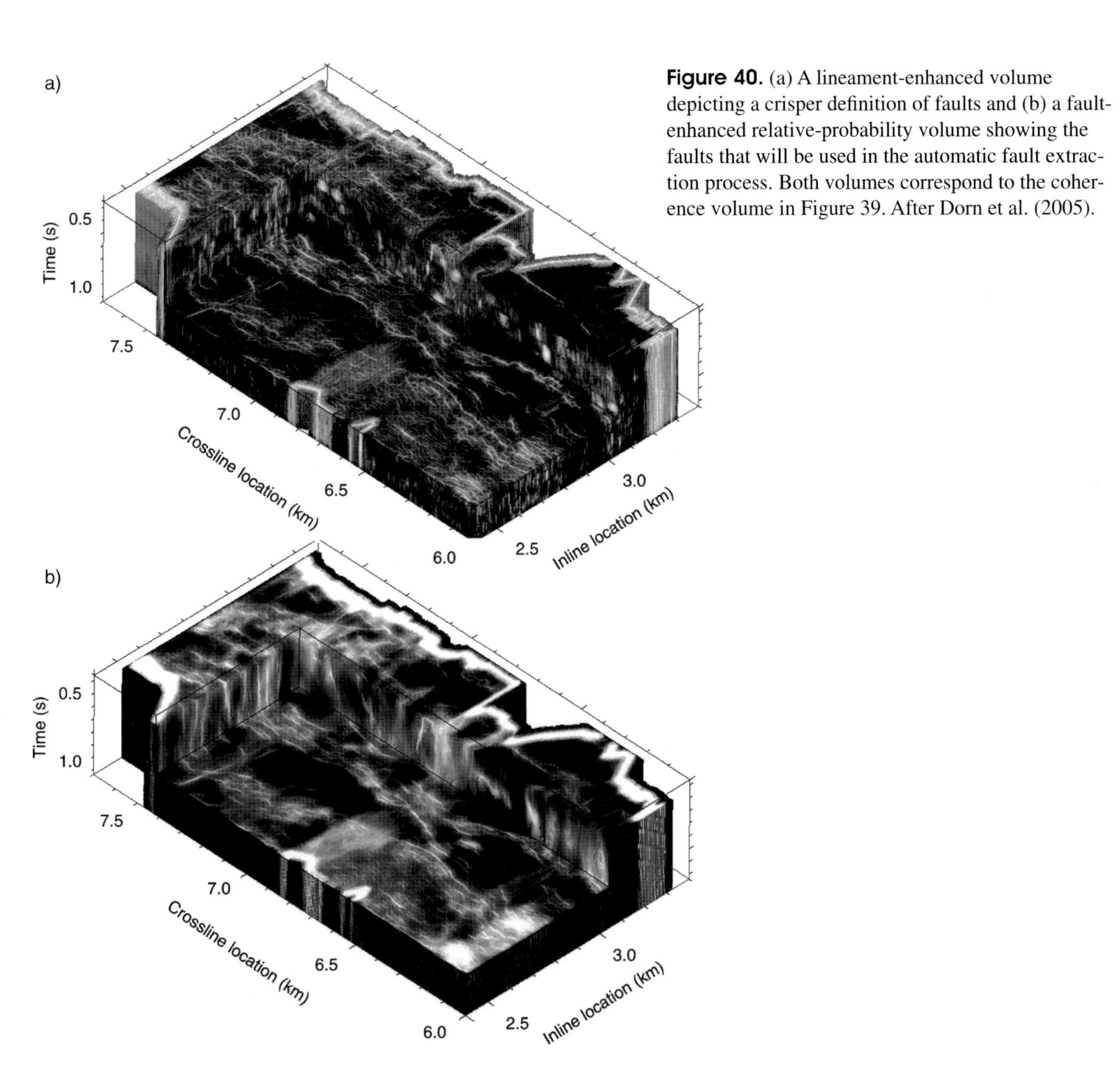

Figure 40. (a) A lineament-enhanced volume depicting a crisper definition of faults and (b) a fault-enhanced relative-probability volume showing the faults that will be used in the automatic fault extraction process. Both volumes correspond to the coherence volume in Figure 39. After Dorn et al. (2005).

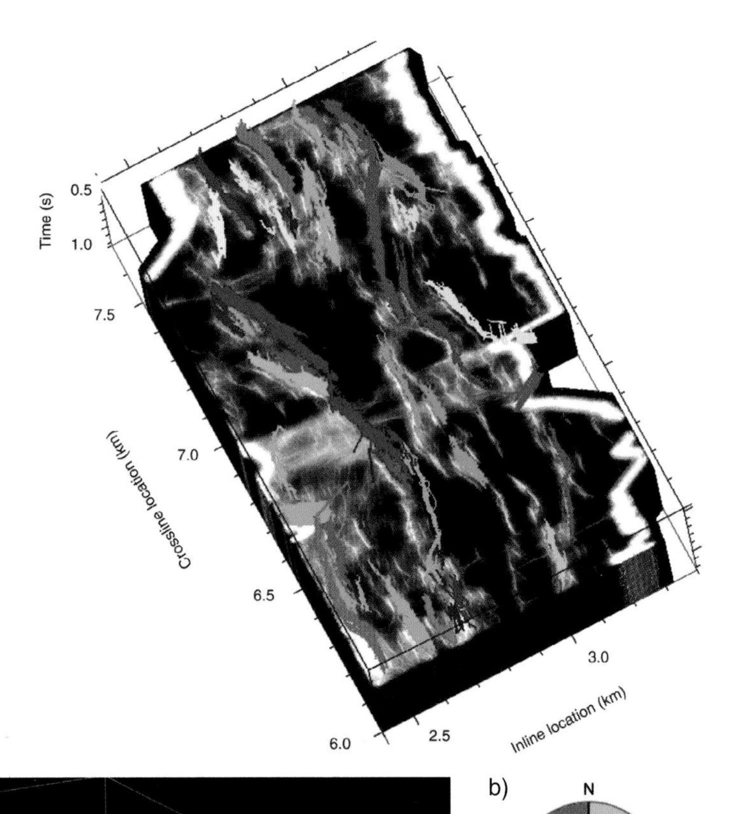

Figure 41. The 40 largest faults of 133 faults extracted using the technique described in the text. To preserve image clarity, the remaining 93 faults are not shown. After Dorn et al. (2005).

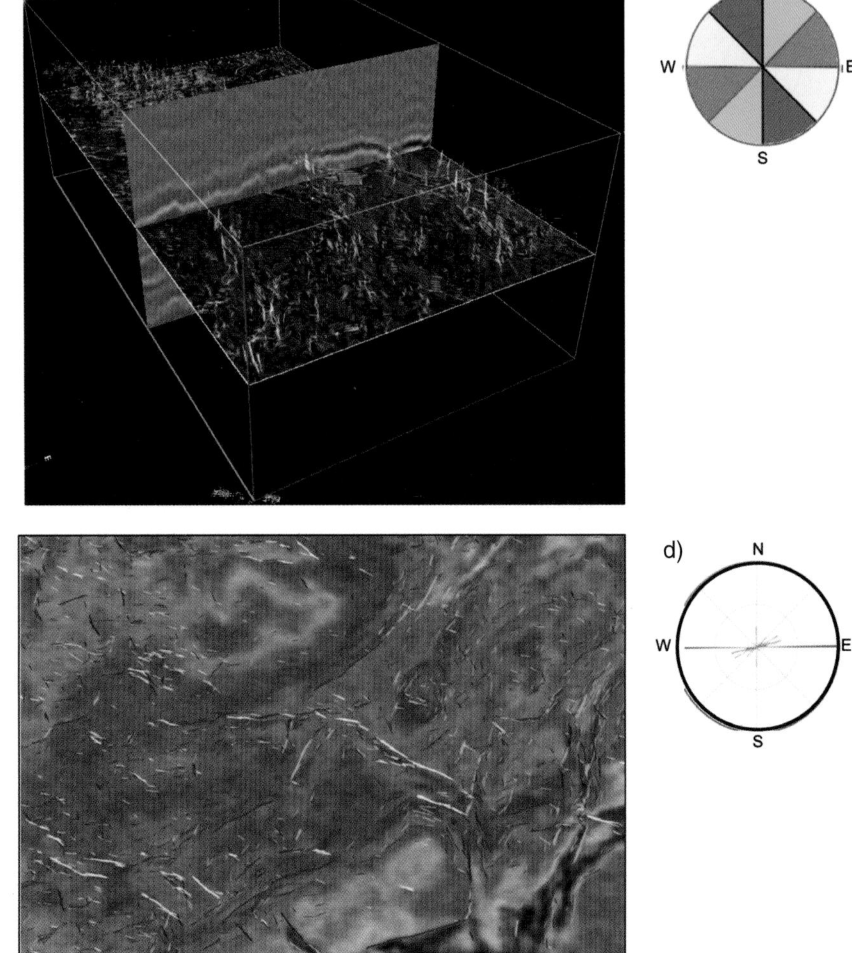

Figure 42. (a) A 3D view of fault segments picked on the coherence attribute (time slice) and colored by the azimuth scale shown in (b). A crossline also is seen in the 3D view and helps us examine the correlation of faults with their corresponding seismic signatures. (c) The same faults shown in (a), displayed here on seismic amplitude. (d) The corresponding rose diagram. These displays illustrate the approach adopted in automatically tracking faults on a coherence volume and checking whether the tracked faults correlate with the seismic information. Images courtesy of Ikon Science Ltd.

Figure 43. A 3D view of the azimuth color-coded fault planes shown in Figure 42, displayed here on a seismic time slice. These fault planes have been tracked automatically and are useful aids to an interpreter. Image is courtesy of Ikon Science Ltd.

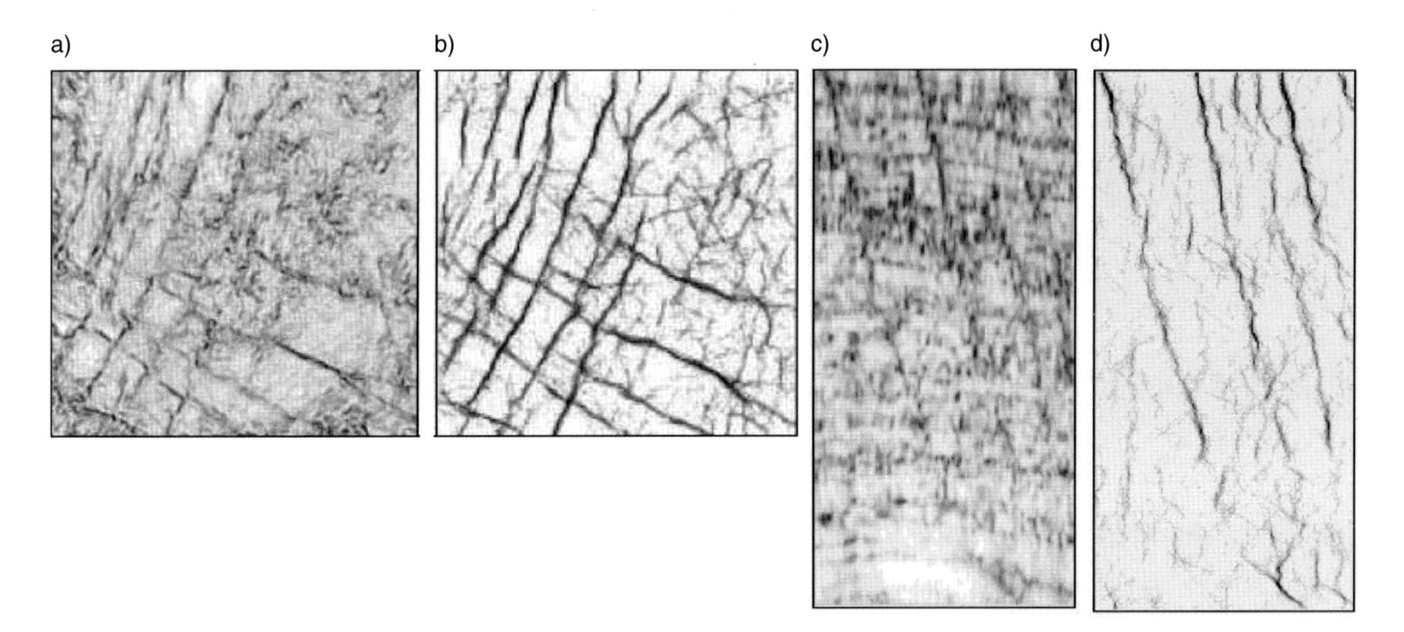

Figure 44. (a)-(b). Time slices through a coherence volume (a) before and (b) after application of the ant-tracking algorithm. (c)-(d).Vertical slices through the same coherence volume (c) before and (d) after application of the ant-tracking algorithm. Notice how crisp and continuous the faults appear on both the horizontal and vertical displays. After Pedersen et al. (2001).

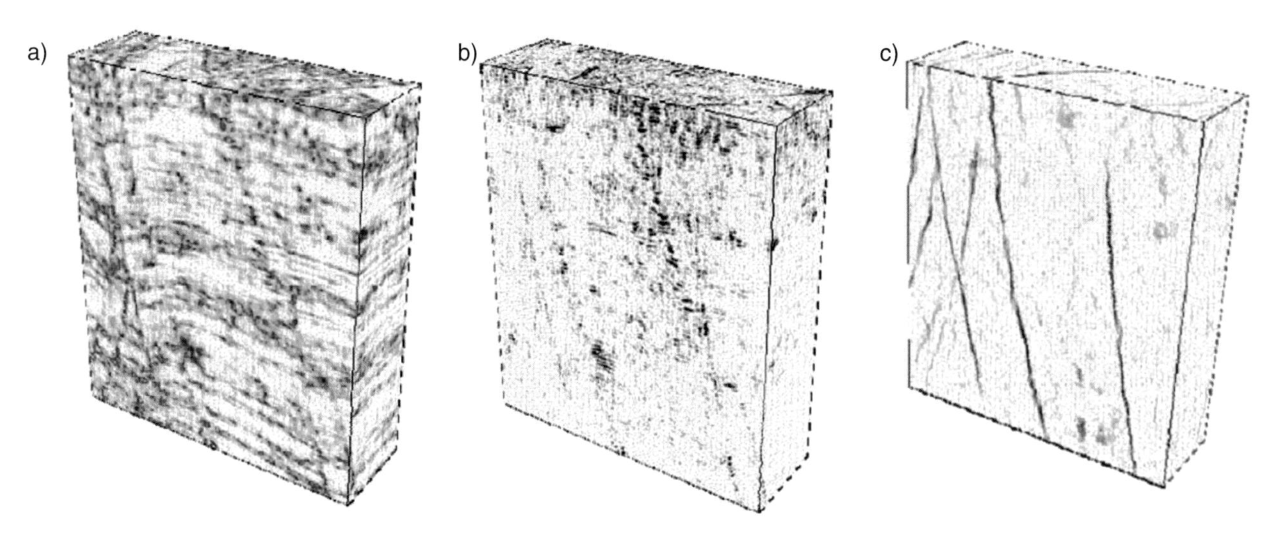

Figure 45. (a) A coherencelike volume (e.g., showing chaos), (b) a coherence volume filtered to minimize low-coherence effects associated with stratigraphy, and (c) fault planes enhanced using an ant-tracking algorithm on the same data volume. Notice the continuity of the fault planes in Figure 45c after application of the ant-tracking algorithm to filtered coherence volume in Figure 45b. After Randen et al. (2001).

Figure 46. The extracted fault surfaces, visualized as computer objects that slice through the seismic data subvolume extracted from a bigger volume used for generating the coherence volumes in Figures 44 and 45. Such a display is useful for checking the accuracy with which the faults have been tracked by the automated process and gives the seismic interpreter confidence. After Randen et al. (2001).

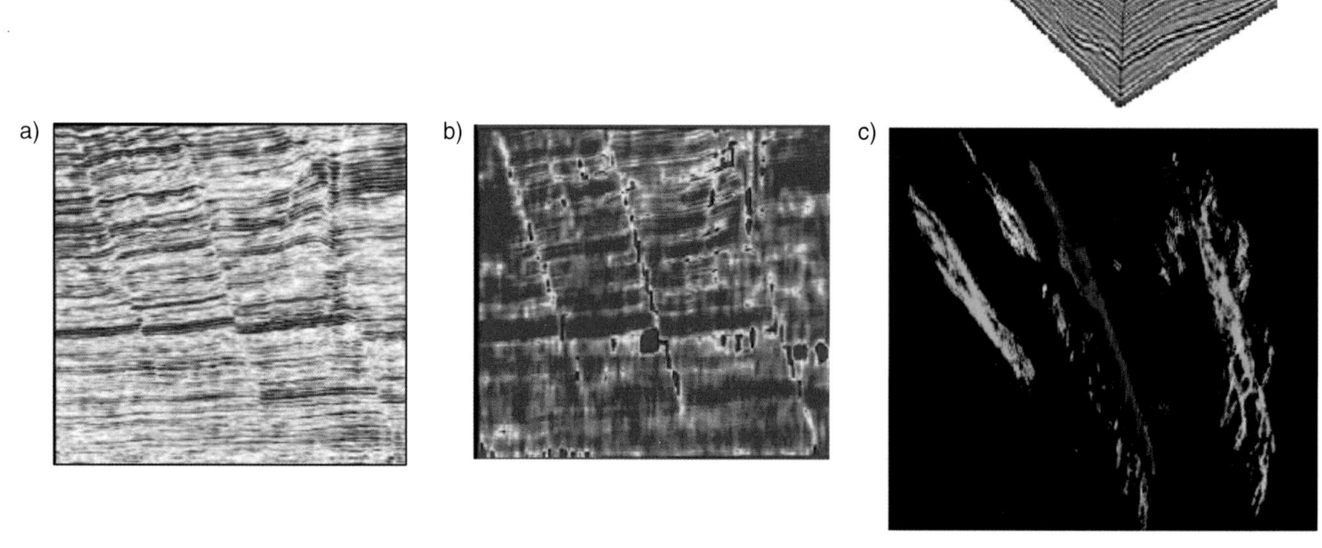

Figure 47. (a) Vertical slices through a seismic data volume and (b) the corresponding coherence volume, showing faults. (c) A 3D view of faults extracted from the coherence volume shown in (b), here using the double-transform method. For approximately planar faults, the method allows their full automatic extraction from a 3D seismic volume. For curved faults, however, one may need to extract subsets of the fault planes and to merge those subsets later. After Jacquemin and Mallet (2005).

Chapter Summary

Structure-oriented filtering can significantly improve the signal-to-noise ratio of migrated seismic data. If the data are free of multiples and are migrated properly, an image of only one reflector should exist at any subsurface location away from a discontinuity. Unlike conventional dip filters that pass or reject a band (or fan) of dips at any analysis point, structure-oriented filtering accepts only one value of dip azimuth — that of the estimated reflector. Thus, the filter does not suffer from the aliasing that plagues conventional dip filters.

Structure-oriented filters are designed to avoid smoothing across discrete discontinuities. Implicit in all structure-oriented filtering algorithms is some calculation to recognize those discontinuities, such as a calculation of the variance, coherence, or curvature.

Structure-oriented filtering improves the behavior both of 3D autotrackers and of attribute calculations. Seismic data that have been subjected to structure-oriented filtering generally have a higher signal-to-noise ratio, sharper discontinuities, and enhanced images of faults, fractures, and stratigraphic features such as channels. The interpreter should be forewarned, however, that not all features of geologic interest appear as discrete boundaries. Identification of gas chimneys, diagenetically altered dolomites, and other diffuse features may be hindered by structure-oriented filtering.

Common filters, such as mean, median, and α-trimmed-mean filters, smear or even eliminate narrow features that comprise fewer than half of the samples in the data-analysis window. For that reason, larger windows may help suppress acquisition footprint.

In contrast, even small three-by-three analysis windows suppress lineaments that are only one sample wide. Thus, the interpreter should use some of the more sophisticated detail-preserving filters. The multistage-median modified-trimmed-mean (MSMTM) filter is one such filter that suppresses noise but preserves these narrow lineaments. The principal-component (or KL) filter is a less general filter that works well in preserving lineaments on seismic-amplitude data.

Structure-oriented filters can improve signal-to-noise ratio but cannot properly reposition mismigrated subsurface discontinuities. Application of structure-oriented filtering to detect reflector edges separating regions of conflicting dip that have been improperly migrated results in sharper edges that do not align properly, thereby leading to an ambiguous geologic interpretation. In contrast, inaccurate migration using a simple velocity model of reflectors that have a similar dip results in mispositioning, and either in overfocusing or underfocusing but not in reflector interfingering, thereby generating attribute volumes that can be very useful.

In general, we recommend the following progression to obtaining improved attribute images. First, properly acquire, process, and migrate your data. Second, if necessary, apply structure-oriented filtering. Third, if you cannot attempt the previous two steps, apply image enhancement. At the publication time of this book, image-enhancement algorithms available to the interpreter typically are limited to two dimensions, are adapted from photographic enhancement, and do not exploit the data richness available in 3D seismic data and corresponding 3D seismic-attribute volumes. We expect this area to progress rapidly during the next decade, when simple 3D visualization software arrives on every interpreter's desktop.

References

AlBinHassan, N. M., and K. J. Marfurt, 2003, Fault detection using Hough transforms: 73rd Annual International Meeting, SEG, Expanded Abstracts, 1719–1721.

Al-Dossary, S., and K. J. Marfurt, 2003, Fracture-preserving filtering: 73rd Annual International Meeting, SEG, Expanded Abstracts, 378–381.

———, 2007, Lineament-preserving: Geophysics, **72**, no. 1, P1–P8.

Barnes, A. E., 2005, Fractal analysis of fault attributes derived from seismic discontinuity data: 67th Annual Conference and Exhibition, EAGE, Extended Abstracts, P318.

Bednar, J. B., 1998, Least-squares dip and coherency attributes: The Leading Edge, **17,** 775-776.

Done, W. J., 1999, Removal of interference patterns in seismic gathers, *in* R. L. Kirlin and W. J. Done, eds., Covariance analysis for seismic signal process: SEG Geophysical Developments, **8**, 185–225.

Dorn, G. A., H. E. James, L. Evins, 2005, Automatic Fault Extraction (AFE) in 3-D seismic data: CSEG National Convention, 247–250.

Duda, R. O., and P. E. Hart, 1972, Use of the Hough transformation to detect lines and curves in pictures: Graphics and Image Processing, 11–15.

Fomel, S., 2002, Application of plane-wave destruction filters: Geophysics, **67**, 1946–1960.

Gulunay, N., V. Sudhaker, C. Gerrard, and D. Monk, 1993, Prediction filtering for 3-D poststack data: 63rd Annual International Meeting, SEG, Expanded Abstracts, 1183–1186.

Hill, S., M. Shultz, and J. Brewer, 1999, Acquisition footprint and fold-of-stack plots: The Leading Edge, **18**, 686–695.

Hoecker, C., and G. Fehmers, 2002, Fast structural interpretation with structure-oriented filtering: The Leading Edge, **21**, 238–243.

Jacquemin, P., and J. L. Mallet, 2005, Automatic fault extraction using double Hough transform: 75th Annual International Meeting, SEG, Expanded Abstracts, 755–758.

Kuwahara, M., K. Hachimura, S. Eiho, and M. Kinoshita, 1976, Digital processing of biomedical images: Plenum Press, 187–203.

Lee, Y., and S. Kassam, 1985, Generalized median filtering and related nonlinear filtering techniques: IEEE Transactions on Acoustics, Speech, and Signal Processing, **33**, 672–683.

Lees, J. A., 1999, Constructing faults from seed picks by voxel tracking: The Leading Edge, **18,** 338–340.

Linville, A. F., and R. A. Meek, 1995, A procedure for optimally removing localized coherent noise: Geophysics, **60,** 191–203.

Luo, Y., S. Al-Dossary, and M. Alfaraj, 2002, Edge-preserving smoothing and applications: The Leading Edge, **21,** 136–158.

Luo, Y., S. Al-Dossary, and M. Marhoon, 2001, Generalized Hilbert transform and its application in geophysics: 71st Annual International Meeting, SEG, Expanded Abstracts, 1835–1838.

Marfurt, K. J., 2006, Robust estimates of dip and azimuth: Geophysics, **71**, P29–P40.

Marfurt, K. J., W. S. Duncan, P. Constance, 2002, Comparison of 3-D edge detection seismic attributes to Vinton Dome, Louisiana:72nd Annual International Meeting, SEG, Expanded Abstracts, 577–580.

Marfurt, K. J., R. M. Scheet, J. A. Sharp, and M. G. Harper, 1998, Suppression of the acquisition footprint for seismic sequence attribute mapping: Geophysics, **63**, 1024–1035.

Masaferro, J. L., R. Bourne, and J.-C. Jauffred, 2003, 3-D seismic imaging of carbonate reservoirs and structures: The Leading Edge, **22**, 18–25.

Pedersen, S. I., T. Randen, L. Sonneland, and O. Steen, 2002, Automatic fault extraction using artificial ants: 72nd Annual International Meeting, SEG, Expanded Abstracts, 512–515.

Randen, T, S. I. Pedersen, and L. Sonneland, 2001, Automatic extraction of fault surfaces from three-dimensional seismic data: 71st Annual International Meeting, SEG, Expanded Abstracts, 551–554.

Wu, W.-R., and A. Kundu, 1991, A new type of modified trimmed mean filter: Nonlinear image processing II: SPIE, **1451**, 13–20.

Chapter 9

Multiattribute Displays

Chapter Objectives

After reading this chapter, you will be able to

- identify good and bad color-display practices
- display multiple attributes in a single image
- apply color schemes that allow you to communicate these features effectively to others

Introduction

Conventional seismic displays use three schemes. The first to be developed was the original wiggle trace (WT), which displays seismic amplitude as a deviation of a line about a separate baseline for each trace. The second development in seismic displays was the variable-area (VA) display, which shades in the positive seismic lobe of the wiggle trace as black. Also, these two display models can be combined to generate a variable-area/wiggle-trace (VA/WT) display. A variation of the VA/WT display models colors in the negative lobe as red.

The third type of seismic display model dispenses with the wiggle trace concept and simply plots the seismic amplitude against a suitable color bar. The original (gray-scale) hard-copy plots using this technique were called variable-density plots. The subsequent CRT displays were called variable-intensity (VI) displays. This latter name is used more commonly and has been generalized to include color displays in general, whether they are on a CRT screen or on hard copy, and whether the intensity (or lightness) is variable or fixed, with amplitude being plotted against color hues.

Seismic attributes usually are displayed in color to capture as much detail as possible and often to display the attributes using a natural analog that is familiar to team members or investors who may not be geoscientists. As an example, a rainbow color scheme is usually used for complex-trace-envelope displays, with hot colors representing high values and cool colors used for low values. Time-structure maps are also displayed against a rainbow color scheme, but most commonly with shallow depths (low values) plotted against red and deeper values against blue, to draw the interpreter's attention to shallow structural features that may trap hydrocarbons.

We begin this chapter by reviewing different color models. After that we discuss conventional but effective 1D color bars for displaying seismic data and attributes. Finally, we discuss combining displays of attributes with seismic data and attributes with other attributes, using overlays, composite displays, 2D color bars, and 3D color bars.

Alternative Color Models

Experiments show that a combination of red- and blue-colored lights can produce magenta-colored light. Similarly, yellow light can be produced by mixing red- and green-colored lights. It is possible to produce light of any desired color by combining red, green, and blue lights (RGB), but these colors cannot be produced by any mixture of lights. Thus, red, green, and blue are called *primary* colors. Cyan, magenta, and yellow (CMY) are called *secondary* colors, because they can be produced by the combination of two primary colors.

The choice of which three colors to use to generate additional colors depends on whether the original colors will be added together, which is the case where light sources are used to produce the colors (e.g., on a CRT or other form of graphics screen), or subtracted, as in the case of pigment or ink in a hardcopy-plotting device, where the eye responds to light reflected from a printed or plotted surface (Russell, 1992).

Three color models are used commonly in computer displays of seismic (and photographic) images. The most familiar is the RGB (red, green, blue) color model used on computer and television screens (Figure 1a). Distinct input channels (often with the cable wires colored red, green, and blue) go from the computer into the CRT monitor. Most ordinary monitors define values of R, G, and B that range between 0 and 255 for 8-bit integer values. Because there are three such 8-bit channels, we have 3 × 8, or 24-bit, color. By driving each of these channels independently we can mix various levels of R, G, and B contributions to produce colors that span most of the range of human color perception (Figure 1b).

The corresponding hard-copy printed-color model uses cyan, magenta, and yellow (CMY) as the base colors. Because equal mixtures of C, M, and Y pigment generate a dark brown color, commonly black (represented by a capital K from the last letter of black to differentiate it from blue) is added to form a somewhat expanded CMYK color model. Unfortunately, the range of human color perception spanned by the CMYK model is smaller than that covered by the RGB model (Figure 1b), so printed copies of attribute images are sometimes inferior to what we can display on the computer monitor.

A third color model is defined by hue, lightness, and saturation (HLS) values. The HLS model does not directly map to either CRT or printer hardware, so color images defined using the HLS model need to be converted to RGB (and from there to CMYK) before their final display. Nevertheless, the HLS model relates better to the human psychology of color, with simple definitions of concepts like bright, dark, pastel, dirty, gray, and pure colors.

Although typically the HLS model is defined in computer-graphics textbooks as a double helix, we find it more useful to morph the HLS model to the sphere shown in Figure 2a. In particular, note that along the equator, the hue or *H*-axis rotates from blue at 0°, through magenta at 60°, to red at 120°, to yellow at 180°, to green at 240°, to cyan at 320°, and back to blue at 360°. We find the hue axis to be particularly useful in mapping cyclic attributes such as phase, azimuth, and strike. Note that along the vertical axis we have a pure gray scale, going from black at the south pole, through gray at the center of the sphere, to white at the north pole. This is the lightness or *L*-axis. We have mapped saturation along the radius (*S*-axis), which we will use later when we display dip-azimuth images.

Single- and Dual-Gradational Color Bars

In Chapter 2 of AAPG Memoir 42, Alistair Brown (2004) strongly recommended that interpreters use either single- or dual-gradational color bars to map seismic data and attributes. We strongly agree, and in Figure 3 we display several of the color bars that we use in this book.

Single- and dual-gradational color bars have two advantages. First, the interpreter intuitively remembers which values represent high, low, zero, or intermediate values. Second, the addition of more colors (say, by upgrading hardware and software from an 8-bit to a 24-bit display capability) improves resolution but does not greatly modify the overall appearance of a given attribute. The extra colors are merely interpolated between the original colors. Deviation from these simple color-display models can result in overly busy and difficult-to-interpret images.

In Figure 3a-d, we show single-gradational color bars that are useful in displaying data having a single polarity,

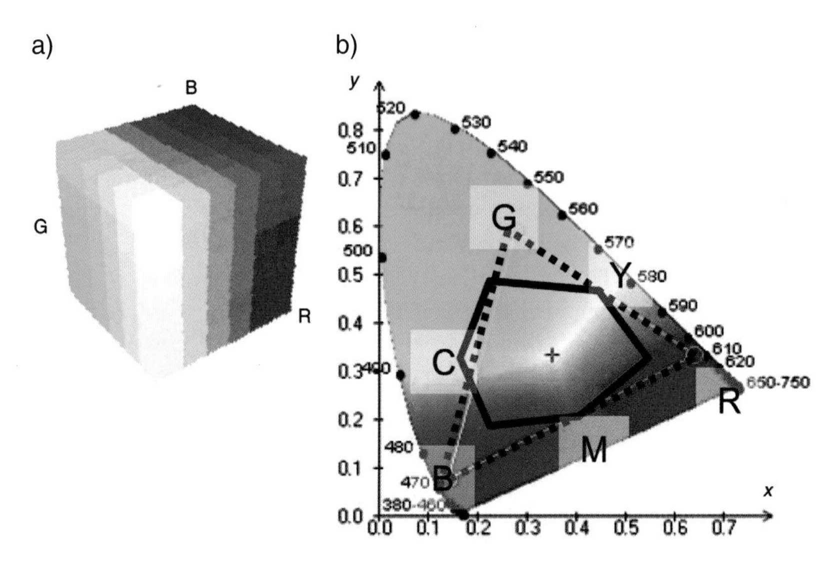

Figure 1. (a) RGB color model (red, green, and blue, commonly used for visual displays, such as computer monitors and TV screens). (b) RGB model and CMYK model (cyan, magenta, yellow, and black, used in printing), mapped here to the human visual system defined by the Commission Internationale de l'Éclairage (CIE) standard (the area between the RGB triangle and the perimeter of the CIE color model). Not all colors perceivable by humans can be created using positive amounts of red, green, and blue. In addition, many colors displayed on a monitor cannot be generated with printing inks using the CMYK model [the area between the CMYK polygon and the RGB triangle in (b)]. Modified from http://www.hf.faa.gov.

which may or may not include the value zero. In this book, we use the color bar in Figure 3a to display coherence, with high coherence being white and low coherence being black. We may also use this color bar to map amplitude extractions (or a horizon slice) along a seismic peak in which we display strong negative values as black and zero values as white.

We use the color bar Figure 3b to display dip magnitude, with strong dip being plotted as black and zero dip being plotted as white. We also use this color bar to display seismic-amplitude extractions through a picked seismic peak, with zero values being displayed as white and strong positive values displayed as black.

The single-gradational rainbow color bar shown in Figure 3c also is useful in displaying amplitude or envelope data, with high values appearing as red. To map time and structure, we often reverse that color bar, as shown in Figure 3d, using red to draw attention to shallow topographic features.

Generally, time-structure maps are much more continuous than most attribute extractions. For that reason, we often use the color bar shown in Figure 3e to provide a contoured appearance. Such a variation does not wildly invalidate our rule of simplicity. Careful inspection reveals that this color bar is simply a suite of six different single-gradational color bars — one red, one yellow, one green, one cyan, one blue, and one magenta — that subliminally links to the contour model used in conventional topographic maps.

In Figure 3f-h, we display three dual-gradational models. Figure 3f and Figure 3h are used routinely in seismic displays. We use the color bar in Figure 3h to display curvature throughout this book.

The key to dual-gradational maps is to use a neutral background color for expressing data that have little interpretational interest, such as zero-amplitude values in conventional seismic displays in which the signal-to-noise ratio is small, or zero values of curvature that display planar rather than deformed reflectors of interest. Kidd (1999) recommended the use of black, white, or gray as neutral colors.

Because gray is the central value of the single-gradational gray scale, it is also very effective in displaying conventional seismic data (Figure 3i), particularly when we wish to overplot colored-horizon and fault interpretations. Finally, certain attributes, such as phase, azimuth, and strike

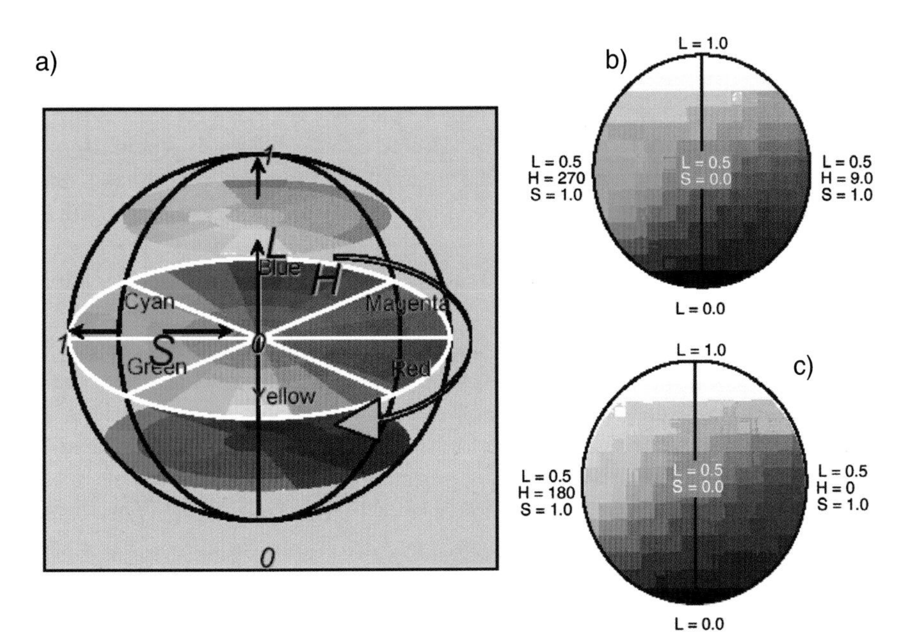

Figure 2. (a) The HLS (hue-lightness-saturation) color model mapped to spherical coordinates. Here we link the hue, $0° < H < 360°$, to azimuth; the lightness, $0.0 < L < 1.0$ to the vertical axis; and saturation, $0.0 < S < 1.0$, to radius. (b) An east-west vertical slice through the HLS color model and (c) a north-south vertical slice through the HLS color model. We will use the horizontal plane of this image for dip and azimuth images. By mapping coherence to the vertical axis, we obtain a three-attribute display that is simple to interpret. After Lin et al. (2003).

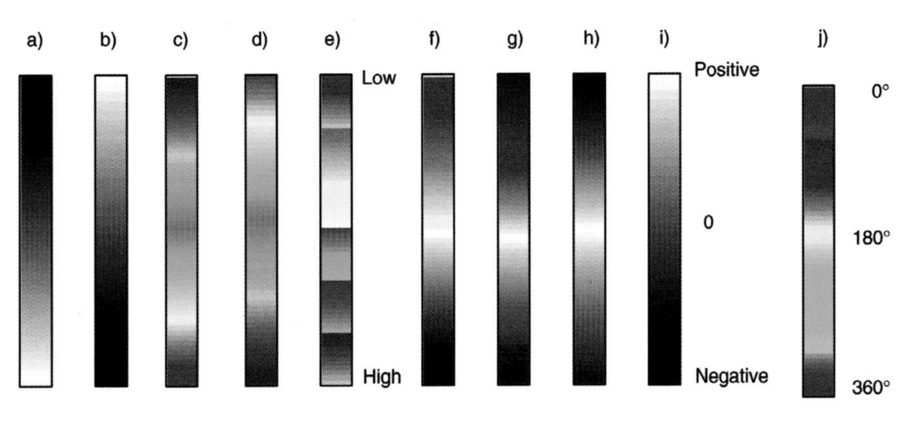

Figure 3. 1D color bars used to display (a)-(d) single-polarity attributes. (e) Specialized color bar used to provide a contoured appearance. (f)-(h) Dual-polarity color bars used to plot attributes. (i) Single-gradational 1D color bar also used commonly to plot dual-polarity-attribute data, particularly when the interpreter wishes to plot interpreted faults and horizons. (j) 1D cyclical color bar useful for displaying phase and azimuth.

are cyclic and require a cyclical color bar such as that shown in Figure 3j. In that type of display, the color at 0° is identical to the color at 360° for phase and azimuth and at 180° for strike.

Seismic Overlays

Seismic overlays have long been used in attribute displays, with some color displays comprising attributes represented along with the original seismic data. In that technique, the attribute of interest is plotted in color to form a background. Next, the seismic data are plotted in variable-area format and overlaid on the background attribute (shown in Chapter 1, Figure 2). (Note: Although this is how seismic overlays are prepared now, in the early days, the underlying section comprising the seismic was plotted first, and the color modulation was done over it, as indicated in the caption for Figure 1.) In the computer, each raster that falls within a positive seismic lobe is simply set to black.

As a variation of this method, Lindseth (1979) colored the seismic lobe by the value of the acoustic-impedance attribute (shown in Chapter 1 as Figure 4). One limitation of seismic overlays is that traditionally, in wiggle-trace displays, we have not displayed the negative lobe of the seismic amplitude and thus in such cases we lose half of our data. One way to overcome that shortcoming is to plot negative lobes in gray, as shown in Figure 4. Even so, variable-area plotting limits the lateral trace interval of the seismic data displayed because displaying a meaningful lateral extent of amplitude requires 5–10 pixels per trace.

Blended or Mixed Displays

In contrast to seismic overlays, blended or mixed displays attempt to render two seismic attributes simultaneously at all points. The actual implementation of these blended, mixed, and interleaved displays depends greatly on the programmer who implements it.

The more modern way to implement this technique is to use the graphical concept of alpha blending. In alpha blending, each voxel in attribute number one is expressed by the red-green-blue triplet (R_1, G_1, B_1). Likewise, each voxel of attribute number two can be expressed by (R_2, G_2, B_2). The blended image is simply the weighted average of the two input images: $R = \alpha R_1 + (1 - \alpha) R_2$, $G = \alpha G_1 + (1 - \alpha)G_2$, and $B = \alpha B_1 + (1 - \alpha)B_2$ where α varies between 0 and 1.

This technique is most effective when one of the images is displayed in (saturated) color and the other is displayed in shades of (unsaturated) gray. Adding gray to a color image does not alter the hue but does change the lightness and saturation. Thus, we readily recognize the gray seismic data lying behind the green fault location in Figure 5. Likewise, blending a colored peak-frequency image (Figure 6a) with a gray-scale coherence image (Figure 6b) yields the blended or mixed image shown in Figure 6c, which provides hues that look either more pastel (if they are in a zone of high coherence) or darker (if they are in a zone of low coherence). In contrast, mixing two colored attributes with variable hues generally results in images that are somewhat muddied and more difficult to interpret, just as randomly mixing the pure colors in a watercolor set usually creates a muddy brown color.

Composite Displays

Whereas blended or mixed images average the RGB components of two attributes, a composite display subdivides our 1D color bar into two smaller 1D segments. We then use Boolean logic to determine which part of the color bar to use in the display.

To visually separate two possible attributes, we customarily represent the values of the first attribute using saturated color levels and the values of the second attribute using shades of gray (unsaturated colors). In Figure 7, we have mapped two 1D color bars — a gray scale for coherence and a cool-to-hot color bar for reflector envelope — into a single 1D composite color bar. Simply stated, if, at a given location, the value of the envelope e is greater than some threshold ($e > e_{min}$), we plot the envelope value at that location using the high end of its color bar. If $e < e_{min}$, we plot the coherence value instead at that same location. As a result, we get a view of the data that is equivalent to having the second attribute (envelope) become transparent if it is below a threshold value, thereby revealing the black-and-white image of a second layer (coherence) behind it. The simplest way to implement this technique is to read in both data volumes, perform the logic, and assign the color index (which in the case of Figure 7 ranges between 0 and 255) to an output volume. The output volume of color indices then can be mapped directly to the composite color bar shown in Figure 7.

It is not uncommon to encounter strong seismic reflectors (with large envelope values) in channels, point bars, or reefs. The composite images in Figure 8 leave most of the coherence images unchanged but map the bright spots within them. The high envelope values corresponding to the events of interest often stand out as bright spots on coherence slices. Notice that such bright spots (in color) appear within the reef boundaries in Figure 8a, as do higher envelope values within the channels in Figure 8b.

In Figures 9–12, we show composite displays for several reef and channel features. Such displays help interpreters to identify the nature and extent of depositional features

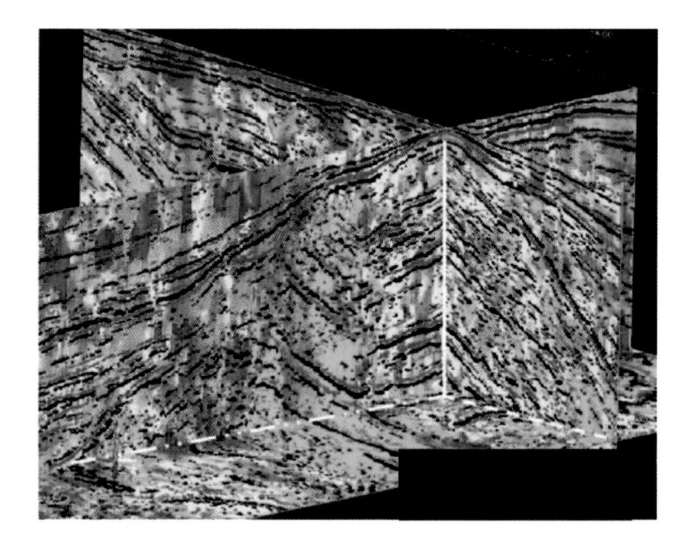

Figure 4. Seismic amplitude overlaid on reflector azimuth. Here, the variable-area positive seismic amplitudes are plotted in black, and negative amplitudes are plotted in gray. After Kerr et al. (2002).

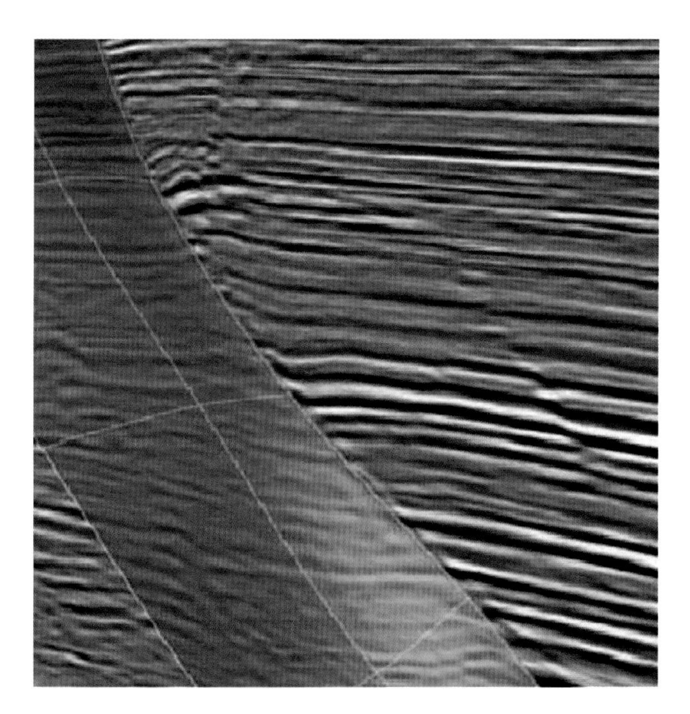

Figure 5. A blended or mixed attribute image. Here, the two seismic attributes to be blended are the seismic data (plotted against a single-gradational gray scale) and the green fault plane. Each voxel of the seismic display has its own R_1, G_1, B_1 color components. The green fault plane has the color components $R_2 = 0.0$, $G_2 = 1.0$, $B_2 = 0.0$. The blended image is simply the weighted average of the two input images: $R = aR_1 + (1-a)R_2$, $G = aG_1 + (1-a)G_2$, $B = aB_1 + (1-a)B_2$. In this example, the blending factor $a = 0.5$. After Meyer et al. (2001).

a)

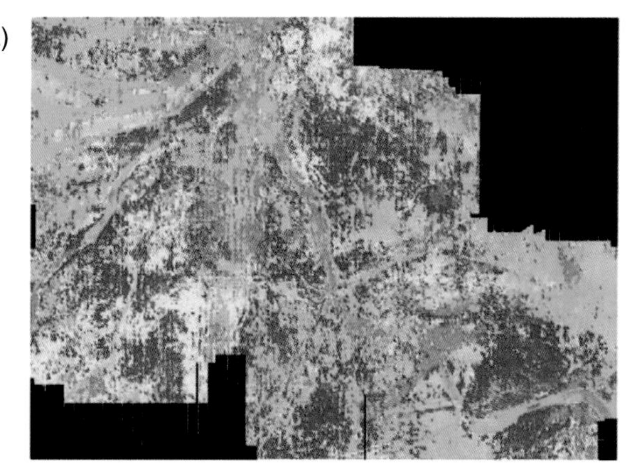

b)

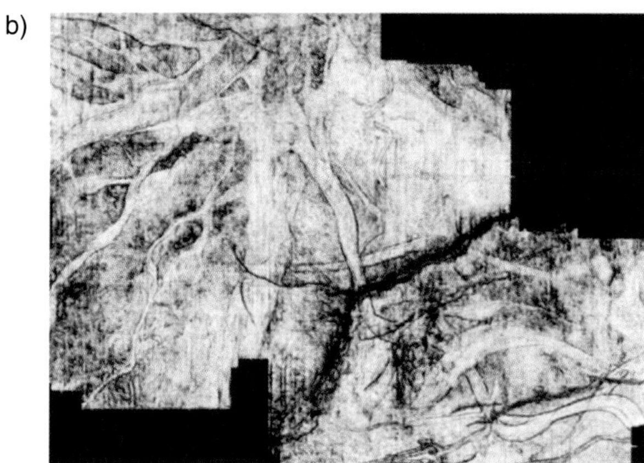

c)

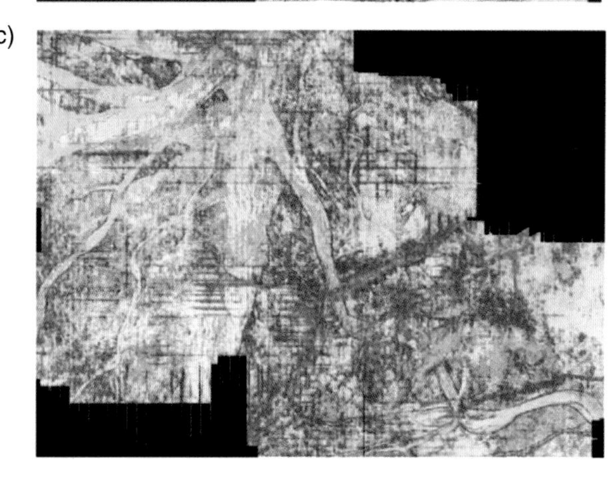

Figure 6. (a) A peak spectral-frequency image, (b) a coherence volume, and (c) a blended or mixed image of the two input attributes. Blue corresponds to a peak frequency of 10 Hz, and red corresponds to 60 Hz. The blending factor $a = 0.5$. This blended image is particularly effective in that coherence is sensitive to channel edges, and the peak frequency is sensitive to channel thickness. Blended images work well when one of the inputs is plotted against a single-gradational gray scale. In particular, the impact of coherence is to maintain the same hue in zones of high coherence, thereby rendering them simply more pastel. Blended or mixed images of two colored attributes result in mixed hues, which produce muddier, more difficult-to-interpret results. After Marfurt and Kirlin (2001).

and to understand the depositional environment. Figure 9a is a seismic section with a bright spot corresponding to a gas accumulation; a time slice at 1.320 s is shown in Figure 9b. The equivalent coherence slice (Figure 9c) and the amplitude envelope slice (Figure 9d) are shown as a composite slice in Figure 9e. Figure 9f displays the slice in Figure 9e, here with a colored version of the vertical seismic section.

In Figure 10a, we show a time slice at 2.144 s from a seismic volume, displayed here in a black-and-white gradational color scheme and depicting a channel system from a deltaic environment. The same seismic time slice is displayed in color in Figure 10b, the equivalent coherence slice is in Figure 10c, and the composite display of coherence and high values of envelope are in Figure 10d. Notice the direct correlation of high values of coherence and envelope — a typical characteristic commonly observed when the reflectivity of gas in a reservoir overwhelms subtler lateral variations in lithology. Figure 11 exhibits a similar set of slices at two different times: (a) at 2.248 s and (b) at 2.272 s. Again, notice the direct correlation of high values of coherence and the envelope attribute.

Figure 12a shows a time slice from a seismic volume acquired in a survey in Alberta, Canada, depicting a channel that runs east to west. The definition of the channel is clear on the equivalent coherence slice (Figure 12b) and the composite display of coherence and envelope (Figure 12c) indicates high envelope values within the channel, as dictated by the local geology. The seismic signature of the edges of the channel can be studied by drawing the seismic section (AA′ in Figure 12) cutting the channel orthogonally, as shown in Figure 12d.

A more quantitative estimate of thickness and porosity can be obtained through seismic inversion to obtain acoustic impedance. A coherence volume offers a high-resolution unbiased image of structural and stratigraphic edges within that volume. In contrast, an acoustic-impedance volume displays what lies between these edges, thereby providing

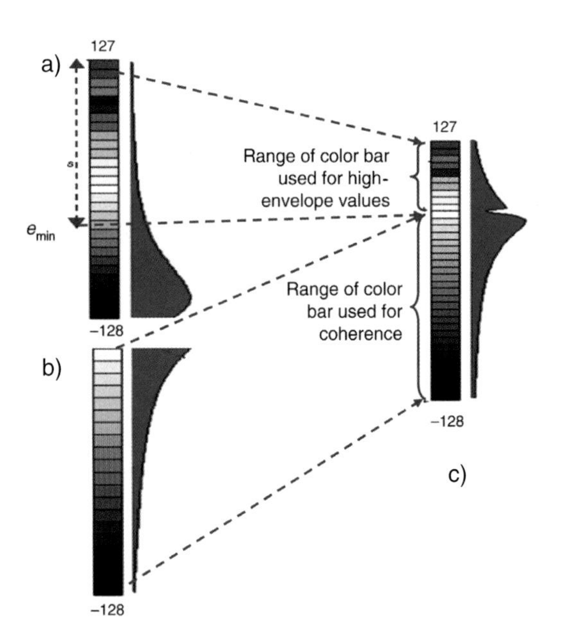

Figure 7. Integrating seismic attributes and seismic data using a composite display: (a) an amplitude envelope color bar, (b) a coherence gray-scale bar, and (c) a composite multiattribute color bar. We generate our composite attribute displays in two steps. First, assuming our graphics software is limited to 256 colors, we construct the color bar shown on the right. Second, we perform Boolean arithmetic on the two input attributes and generate a third volume that has values ranging between 0 and 255. In this example, if our envelope value is greater than some threshold ($e > e_{min}$), we assign a color index that uses one of the higher (64) colors corresponding to the envelope portion of the composite color bar. If $e < e_{min}$, we assign a color index that uses one of the lower (192) colors corresponding to the coherence attribute. After Chopra (2001a).

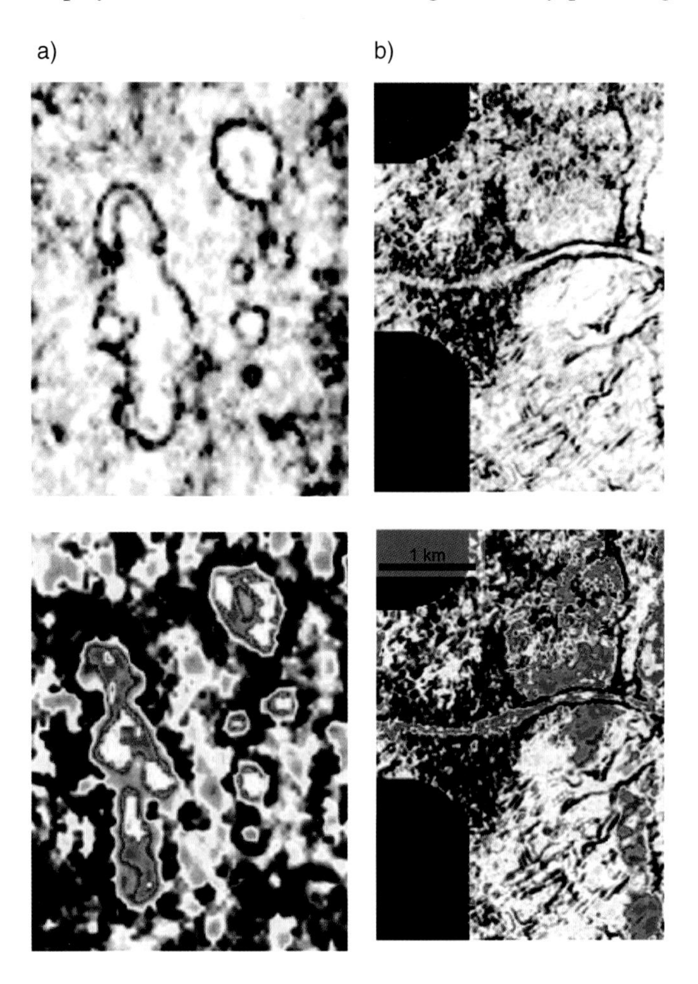

Figure 8. Composite displays depicting the high end of envelope amplitudes superimposed on coherence, using the composite color bar described by Figure 7. (a) A low-impedance porous carbonate reef. (b) A low-impedance channel. After Chopra (2002).

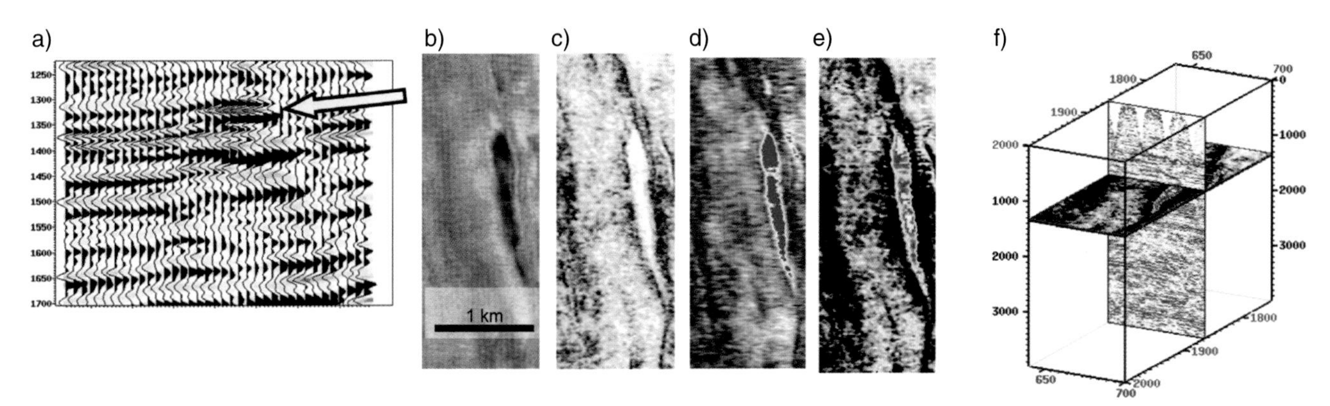

Figure 9. Coherence and its relation to bright spots. (a) A seismic section with a bright spot indicated by the arrow. (b)-(e). Time slices, at t = 1.320 s, of (b) seismic data, (c) coherence, (d) an envelope along the reflector dip, and (e) a composite of (c) and (d). (f) Display of the time slice shown in (e) and a color version of the vertical section shown in (a).

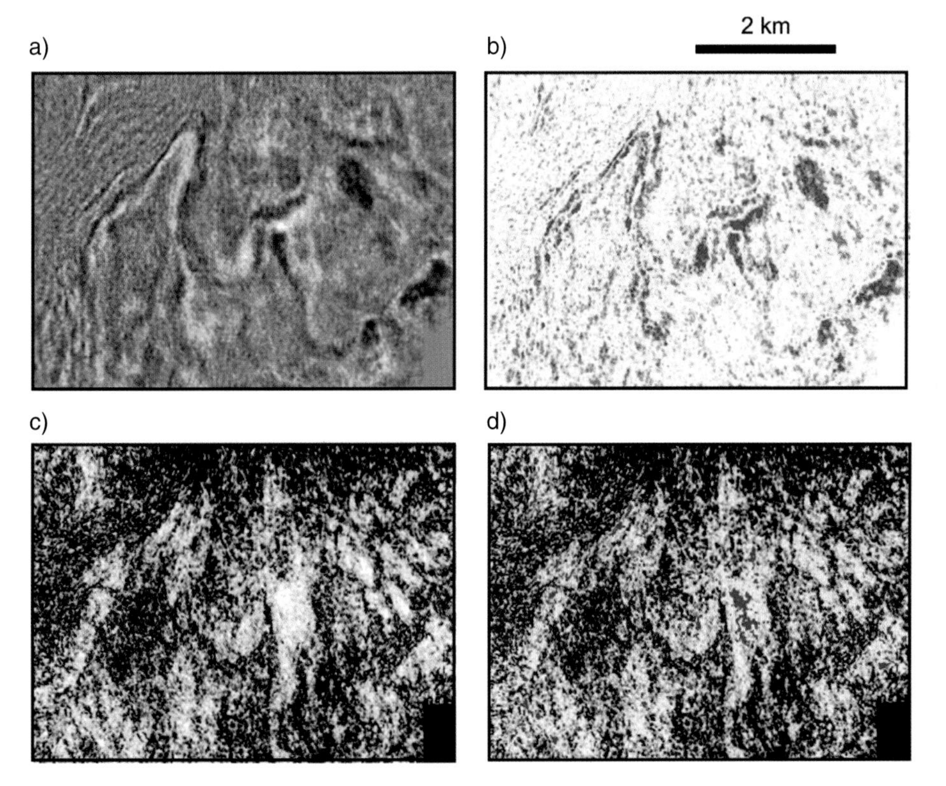

Figure 10. Time slices at t = 2.144 s, depicting a channel system from a deltaic environment, of (a) seismic amplitude plotted using a single-gradational (gray) color bar, (b) seismic amplitude plotted using a dual-gradational blue-white-red color bar, (c) coherence, and (d) a composite display of envelope $e > e_{min}$ and coherence, using the composite display described in Figure 7.

information that can be used for lithologic and stratigraphic interpretation. By integrating coherence and impedance volumes, we can readily identify acoustic-impedance changes in sedimentary systems and can gain unparalleled details of subtle sedimentary depositional features.

Acoustic-impedance results can be combined numerically with coherence results to produce a volume that allows the interpreter to display stratigraphic images from the 3D seismic data and to examine the acoustic-impedance contrast across them. For example, sand in a gas-charged channel exhibits low impedance. Thus, a range of low-impedance values representing the gas sands can be selected and merged with the coherence cube. The resulting composite merged volume can be sliced through again to see low impedance (in color) displayed within the boundaries of the channel.

Figure 13 illustrates such a situation and shows how the low end of the impedance range of values is cut off from the impedance volume and merged with the coherence volume. We will now see how to use such a color bar.

Channel-sand reservoirs are difficult to develop efficiently for hydrocarbon extraction, but often such reservoirs have excellent production characteristics. Because the depositional mechanisms involved in channels can create sand bodies whose thickness and quality can vary rapidly over short distances, they can be difficult exploration targets.

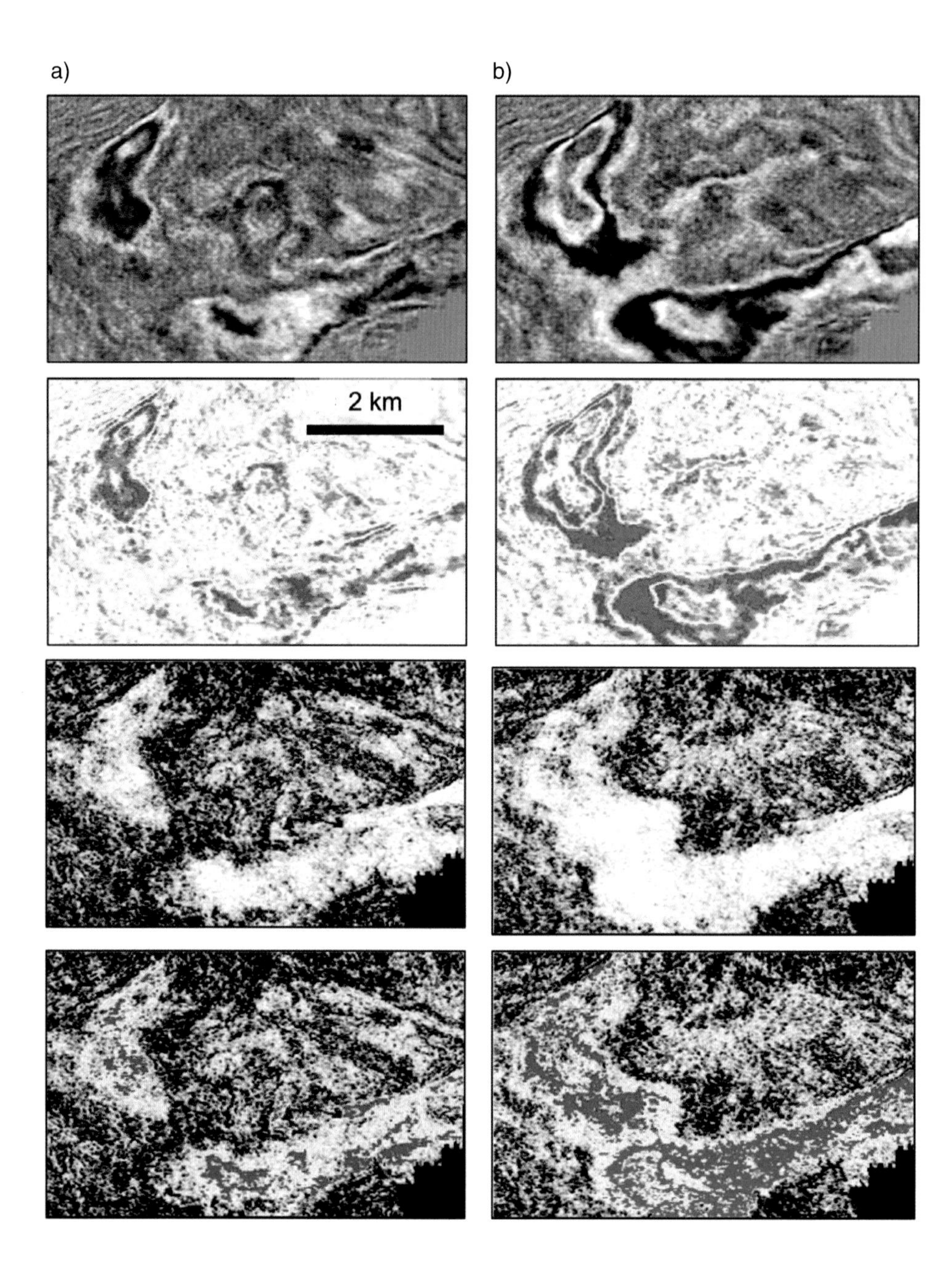

Figure 11. Time slices from a deltaic environment (a) at t = 2.248 s and (b) at t = 2. 272 s. Moving from top to bottom, we see seismic amplitude plotted using a single-gradational (gray) color bar, seismic amplitude plotted using a dual-gradational blue-white-red color bar, coherence, and a composite display of envelope $e > e_{min}$ and coherence, using the composite display described in Figure 7. Notice the direct correlation of high values of both coherence and envelope — a common characteristic when the reflectivity of gas in the reservoir overwhelms subtler lateral variations in lithology.

However, once found, good sands provide excellent production characteristics. By revealing the effects of overlying and underlying lithologies, impedance inversion helps us map rapidly varying sand thicknesses that often are difficult to understand on conventional seismic-amplitude data.

Figure 14a shows a time slice through a coherence volume with two channels that stand out clearly in a high-coherence background. The time slice through the corresponding impedance volume (Figure 14b) reveals low-impedance values within the channels, which imply the presence of hydrocarbon-bearing sands. However, the low end of the impedance values can be merged with the coherence values and stretched over a suitable scale (Figure 14c) to show the variation in the low end of the range of the impedance values chosen. Such composite plots can be used to define precise reservoir and nonreservoir facies boundaries and reservoir compartments.

Estimates of λ, μ, and ρ are a natural extension of impedance inversion that exploits subtle AVO aspects of prestack data. (Recall that λ, μ, and ρ represent respectively the incompressibility, rigidity, and density of the rocks. Gas sands exhibit low values of $\lambda\rho$ and high values of $\mu\rho$, or low values of the ratio λ/μ). In Figure 15, we show a composite image of coherence and low values of the ratio λ/μ.

2D Color Bars

Many seismic attributes have meaning only when used in conjunction with a second attribute. For instance, dip

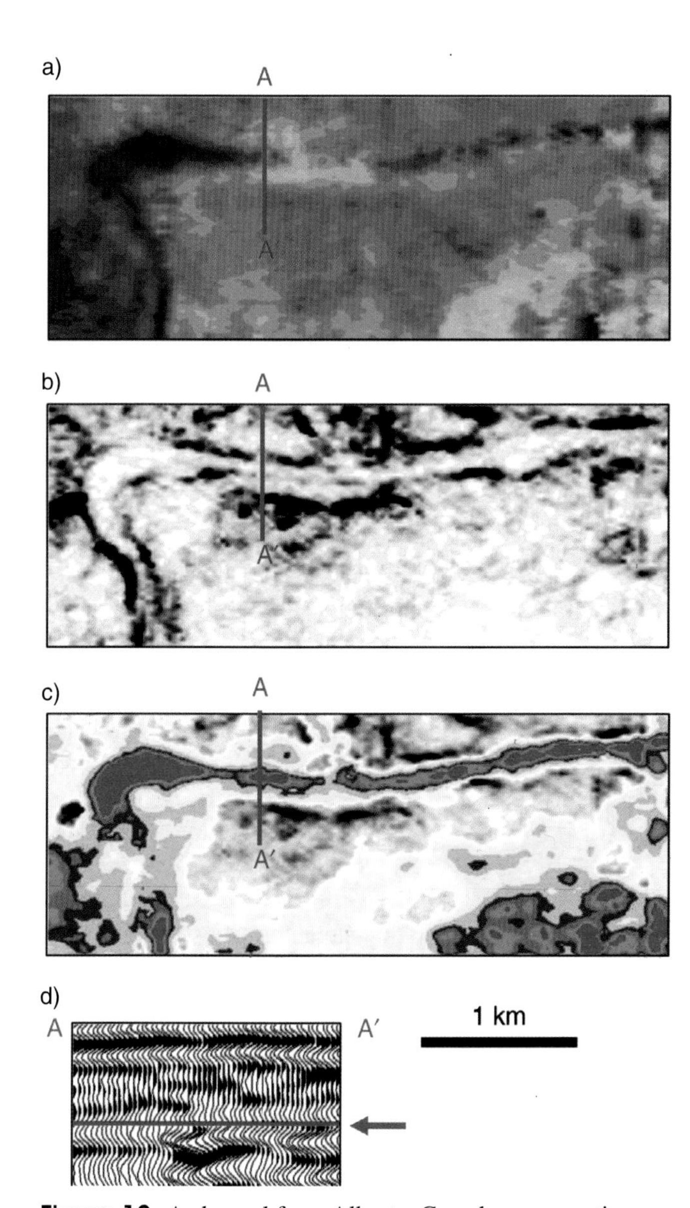

Figure 12. A channel from Alberta, Canada, seen on time slices through (a) seismic data, (b) coherence data, and (c) a composite coherence and reflector envelope, using the color bar described in Figure 7. (d) A vertical slice through the channel corresponding to line AA′. The arrow indicates the level of time slices. After Chopra (2001b).

azimuth has little meaning when the dip magnitude is close to zero and is contaminated by noise. Wavelet phase has little meaning when the wavelet envelope is smaller than the noise level. Reflector shape has little meaning if the total reflector curvedness is small. We can display such dependencies by using a 2D color bar rather than the traditional 1D color bar. To our knowledge, Knobloch (1982) was the first to apply a 2D color bar to seismic data when he plotted instantaneous phase against hue and instantaneous envelope against lightness. In Figure 16, we illustrate his technique on a data volume from the Gulf of Mexico.

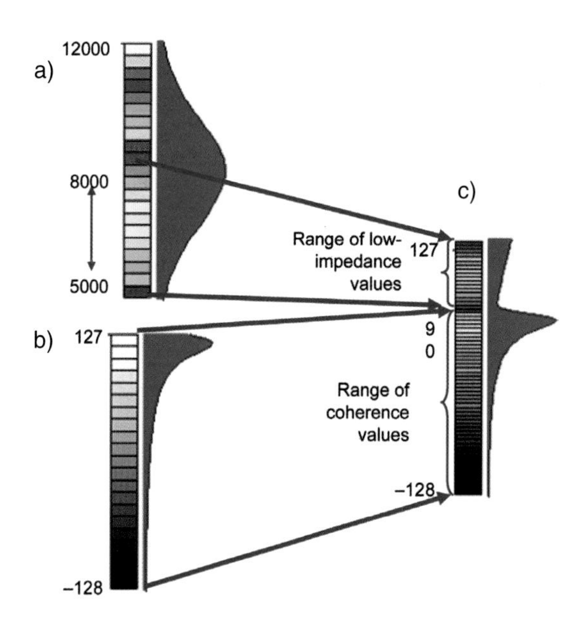

Figure 13. A composite-attribute display of impedance and coherence. The method is analogous to that described in Figure 7, except that now (a) is the impedance color bar, (b) is the coherence color bar, and (c) is the composite-attribute color bar. Here, we wish to accentuate zones of low acoustic impedance, which are indicative of higher porosity.

Figures 16a and b show vertical sections of reflector envelope and reflector phase, respectively, which by using the composite color scale shown in Figure 16c have been combined to form the composite image shown in Figure 16d.

We also can use a 2D color bar to display seismic amplitude and coherence simultaneously. Common practice is to plot coherence against a gray scale (Figure 17a) and seismic amplitude against a double-gradational (red-white-blue) scale (Figure 17b), in which white corresponds to zero amplitude. In Figure 17c, we generalize this concept and generate a 2D color bar in which the hue, lightness, and saturation, H, L, and S, are defined as

$$H = 120° \text{ (red) if } a < 0,$$
$$H = 360° \text{ (blue) if } a > 0;$$
$$S = |a|/a_{max}, \text{ and}$$
$$L = (1.0 - 0.5|a|/a_{max})\, c, \tag{9.1}$$

where a is the seismic amplitude clipped to be $|a| < a_{max}$, a_{max} is the amplitude clipping value, and c is coherence, here assumed to be scaled between 0.0 and 1.0.

As shown by the color bar in Figure 17c, for $c = 1$, the peak amplitudes are mapped to values of $L = 0.5$ and $S = 1.0$ and zero amplitude values are mapped to $S = 0$ and $L = 1$ (white). As coherence decreases, the values become progressively darker.

In the next two illustrations, we show another example of a 2D color bar, this time with spherical coordinates. We first show the results of applying a 1D color bar. In Figure 18, we show conventional horizon-attribute displays generated using commercial interpretation workstation software. Rijks and Jauffred (1991) showed how interpreters can extract additional information from 3D seismic horizons by generating dip-magnitude and dip-azimuth maps such as those shown in Figure 18b and 18c, respectively. However, Rijks and Jauffred (1991) went a step farther and plotted dip azimuth against hue and dip magnitude against lightness, with 0° dip corresponding to $L = 1$ (white) and maximum dip corresponding to $L = 0.5$ (solid colors vary according to the value of H).

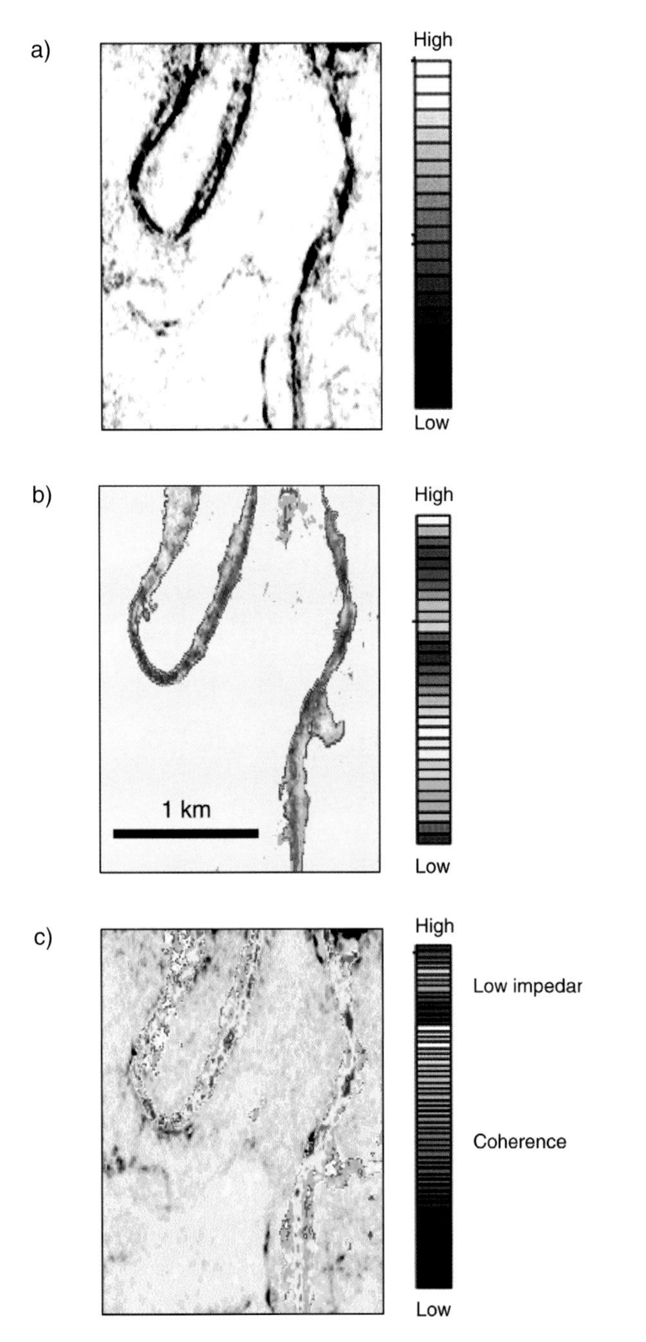

Figure 14. A channel system appearing on time slices through (a) a coherence volume, (b) an acoustic-impedance volume, and (c) a composite acoustic-impedance and coherence volume. The respective color bars for (a), (b), and (c) are indicated. Notice that the low-impedance values in the channels in Figure 14b do not exhibit as much variation as is seen on the composite plot in Figure 14c. After Chopra (2002).

We display a variation of this approach in Figure 19, but here we have applied it to a volume of vector dip and we display a time slice at 1.000 s. In Figure 19a, we follow Rijks and Jauffred (1991) and plot dip azimuth against hue, but differ by plotting dip magnitude against saturation, S. If the dip magnitude is zero, we set $S = 0$ and display gray. At progressively larger dips (up to 50° in this image) we increase the saturation to $S = 1$ to obtain pure colors clearly displaying azimuth. Note that the 2D color display of Vinton Dome in Figure 19a closely mimics the color legend, showing that the reflectors are dipping radially away from the center of the dome. Far from the center of the dome, the image becomes grayer, indicating that the reflectors are nearly horizontal.

3D Color Bars

In Figure 19b, we plot coherence against a gray scale. Next we follow Marfurt et al. (1998) and combine that coherence with the dip-azimuth image in Figure 19a to generate the dip-azimuth/coherence image shown in Figure 19c.

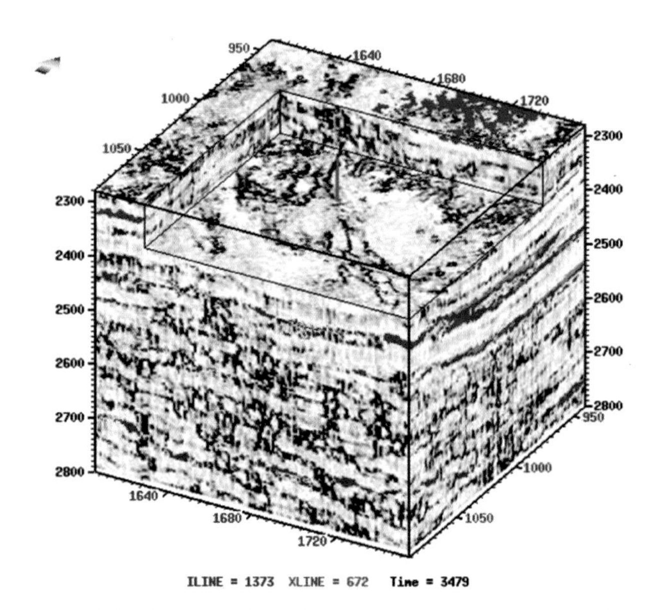

Figure 15. A composite cube consisting of coherence values and low values of the ratio λ/μ (in color), which indicate prospective hydrocarbon zones.

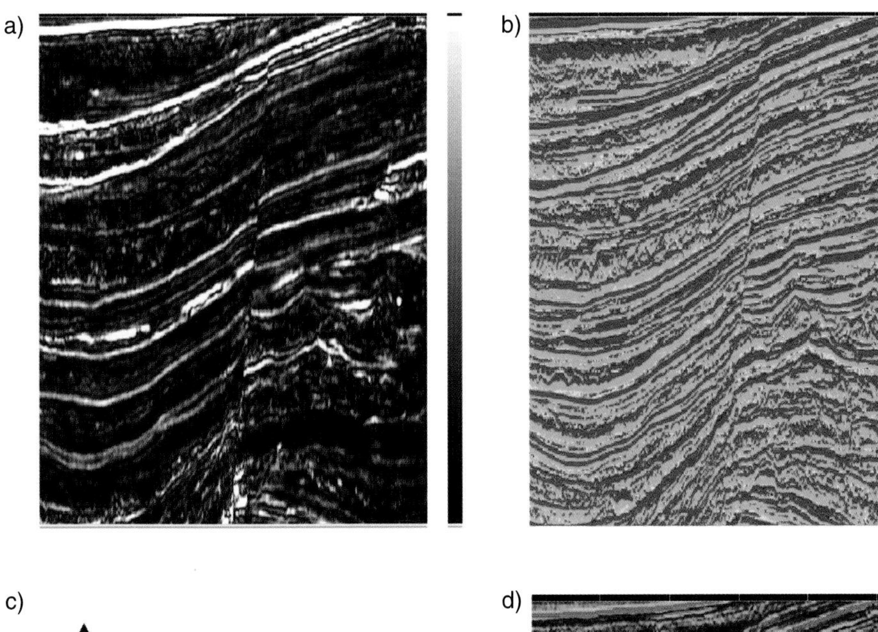

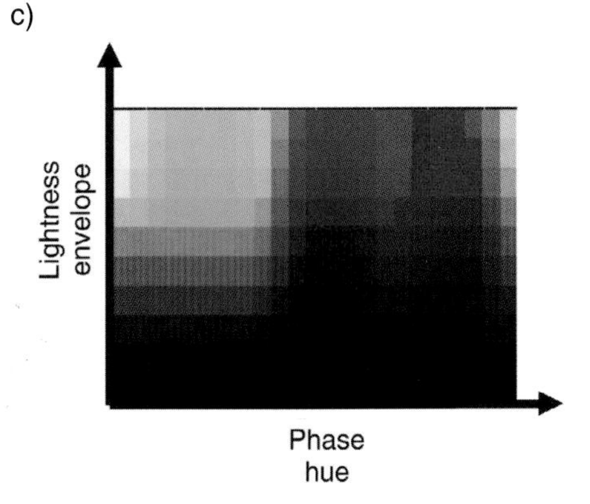

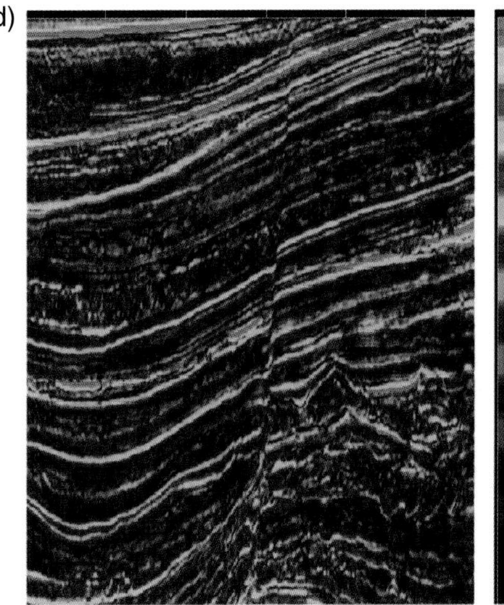

Figure 16. Combining (a) reflector envelope against (b) reflector phase, using (c) a composite color scale to form (d) a composite image. Conventional 256-color 1D color bars used by the plotting software are displayed on the right of (a), (b), and (d). This technique, originally presented by Knobloch (1982), emphasizes the phase of the stronger reflection events and provides an effective tool for tracking waveforms across faults. Note that the 2D color legend in (c) has been mapped to a more conventional 1D color legend in (d), to use conventional plotting software.

In this image, we use a 3D color bar and have plotted dip azimuth against hue, dip magnitude against saturation, and coherence against lightness. Vinton Dome has very strong dips that exceed 50°.

In Figure 20, we show the value of such a display on an area from the Central Basin Platform, Texas, U.S.A., that has dips clipped to 10°. Such an image allows us to better visualize the transformation from faults (with low coherence) to folds and flexures (with higher coherence but with measurable dip). Of course, some of these folds and flexures may actually be overmigrated or undermigrated faults.

As a final 3D color bar example, Figure 21 shows a composite image of dip azimuth and seismic data corresponding to line AA′ in Figures 17–19. We use the larger part of the color bar to map dip azimuth, exactly as we did in Figure 19a. However, we reserve the remainder of the color bar to plot the seismic amplitude against a gray scale. Specifically,

$$\text{if } |a| > a_{min},\ L = 0.5a/a_{max} + 0.5,\ H = 0,\ S = 0$$
$$\text{and if } |a| < a_{min},\ L = 0.5,\ H = \varphi,\ S = d/d_{max}, \qquad (9.2)$$

where a_{max} is the amplitude clipping factor, $a_{min} = 0.1a_{max}$ is a threshold below which we plot the dip azimuth, φ is the dip azimuth, d is the dip magnitude, and d_{max} is the maximum (or clipping) dip magnitude.

Note that even though this is an east-west section, we see considerable dip to the south (yellow) because we are on the southern flank of the salt dome. Smaller areas (either rotated blocks or mismigrated data) dip to the north (in blue).

Unconventional Attribute Displays

Although wiggle-trace (variable-area) and variable-density displays for seismic data have been used conventionally, both of these display modes have limitations that cause us to miss pertinent information. Lynch (2000) and Lynch and Lines (2004) have suggested a novel type of display that enables the interpreter to extract subtle information from seismic attributes.

Figure 22a is a segment of seismic section in a common variable-intensity display. Figure 22b shows the same section in a new type of display in which the amplitudes have excursions in the plane of the paper, in both positive and negative directions. The seismic traces are displayed as subsurface landscapes. With the powerful graphics cards available today, such displays can be generated rapidly and displayed on PCs.

Envelope-amplitude displays

Figure 23a shows a seismic-amplitude terrainlike display, and Figure 23b shows the corresponding complex-trace envelope. The envelope often is used for lithologies because it is relatively insensitive to lateral changes in reflection phase. For a consistent lithologic environment, the phase is constant, so that the position between the peak of the envelope and the peaks and troughs of the seismic amplitude remains constant. In contrast, changes in lithology

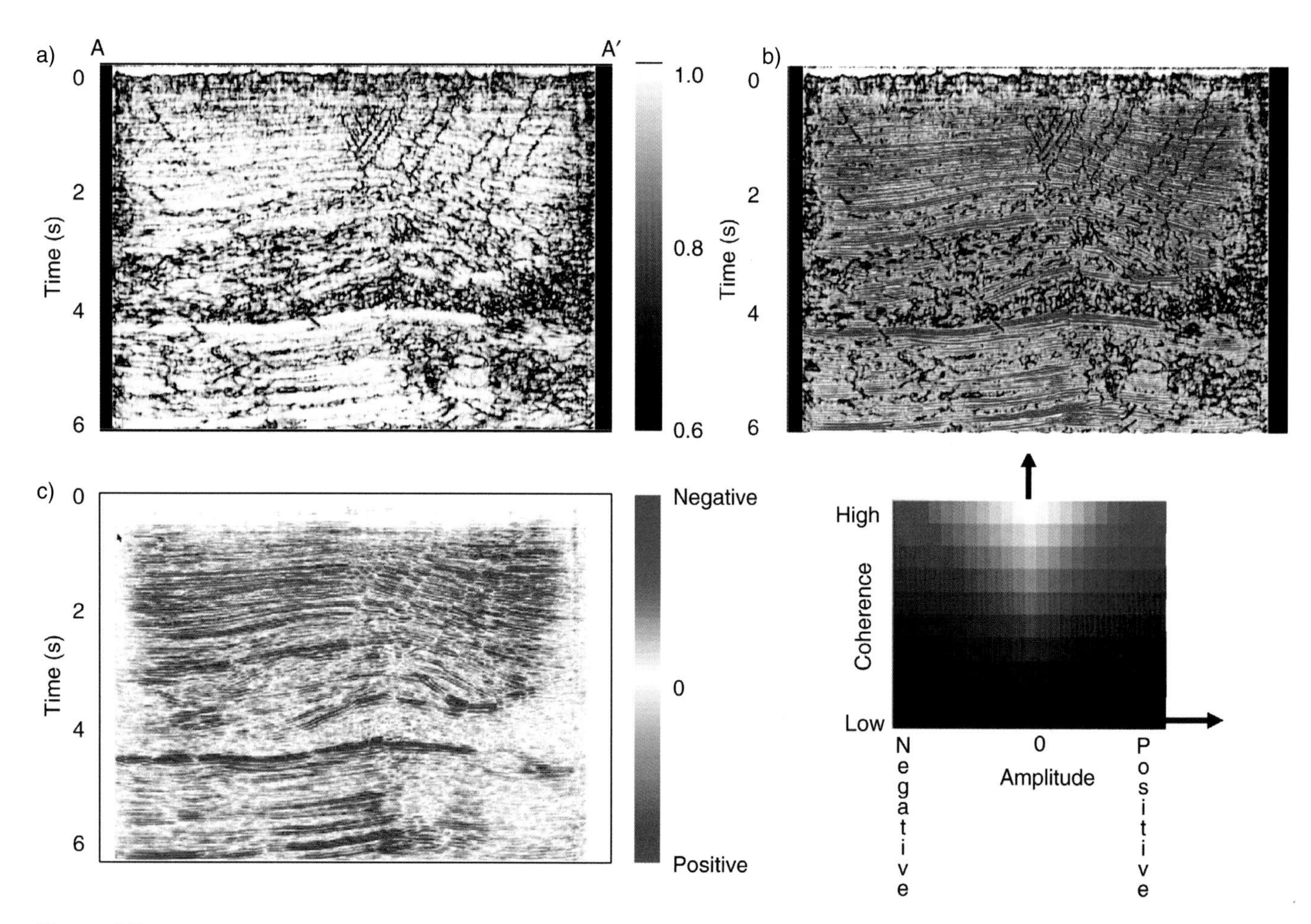

Figure 17. (a) Coherence plotted using the lightness axis, L. (b) Seismic amplitude using a conventional dual-gradational red-white-blue color bar. (c) Composite coherence and seismic amplitude obtained by using the 2D color bar shown to the right. Location of line AA′ is shown in Figure 18. After Lin et al. (2003).

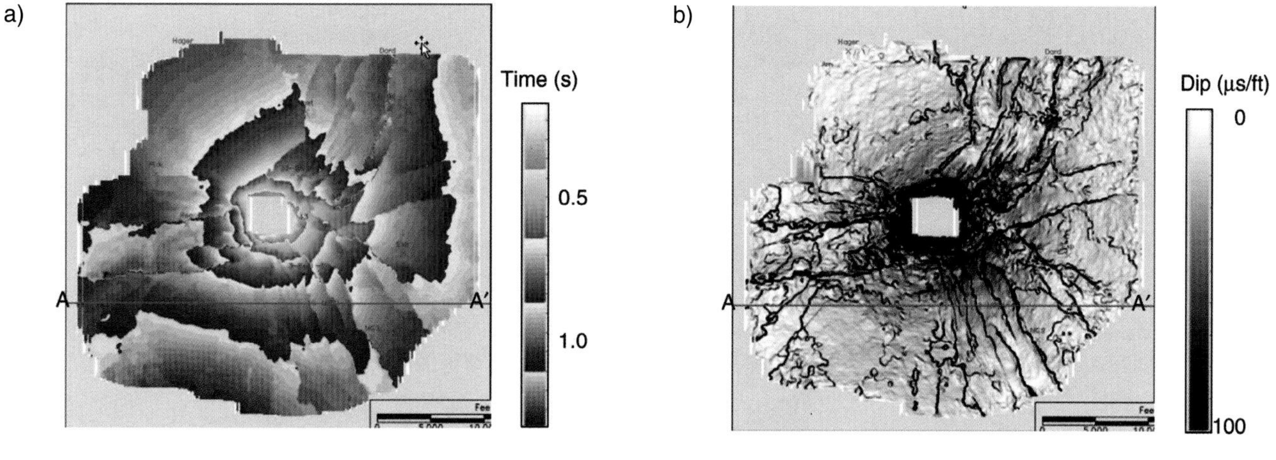

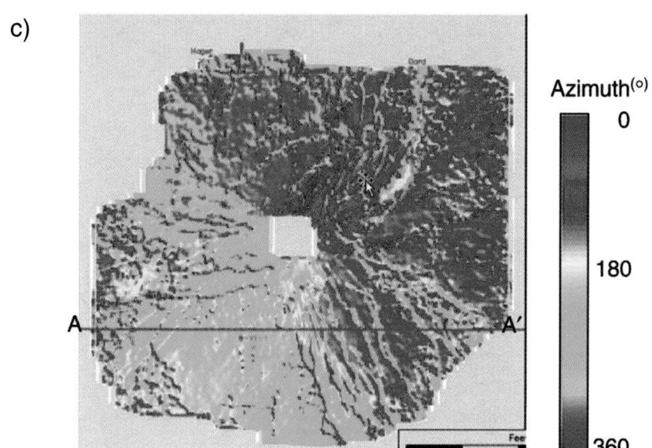

Figure 18. Conventional workstation displays of horizon attributes extracted along the middle Miocene strata of Vinton Dome, Louisiana, U.S.A.: (a) time, (b) time and dip magnitude, and (c) time and dip azimuth. Here, we have mapped time against a discontinuous color scale, thereby providing a contour effect at each discontinuity. We have mapped dip magnitude against lightness, which ranges from $L = 0.0$ for strong dip to $L = 1.0$ for zero dip. Finally, we have mapped dip azimuth against hue (H), with the values of H ranging between 0 and 360 and with $H = 0$ and $H = 360$ (blue) being north, and $H = 180$ (yellow) being south. Because this horizon lies over a salt dome, the azimuth follows the color wheel. Data are courtesy of OPEX.

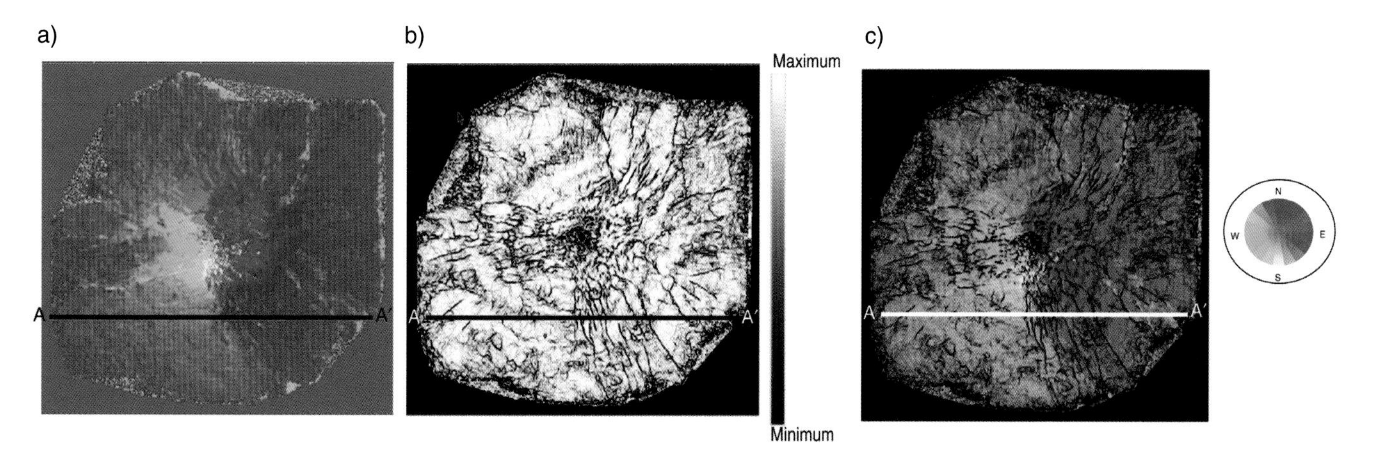

Figure 19. Time slices at $t = 1.000$ s through the Vinton Dome survey, corresponding approximately to the middle Miocene horizon displayed in line AA′ of Figure 18a. (a) A dip azimuth slice displayed using a 2D color bar, with dip azimuth mapped to hue and dip magnitude mapped to saturation. The maximum dip magnitude of 50° is plotted at full saturation. The minimum dip magnitude of 0° is plotted as zero saturation, or gray. Lightness is fixed at $L = 0.5$. (b) A coherence slice displayed using a single-gradational color bar along the lightness axis. (c) Dip azimuth and coherence displayed using a 3D color bar. Here, dip azimuth is mapped as it was in (a), and coherence is mapped against lightness, where $0 < L < 0.6$. Data are courtesy of OPEX.

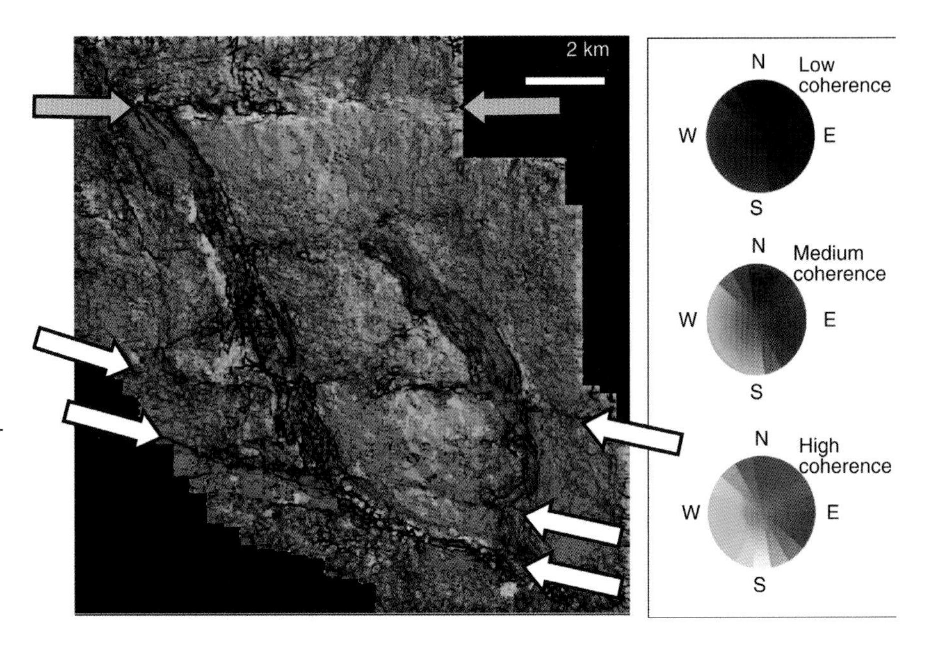

Figure 20. A time slice through a survey acquired over the Central Basin Platform, Texas, U.S.A., using a 3D color legend. Here, we have plotted dip azimuth against hue, dip magnitude against saturation, and coherence against lightness. Note how the low-coherence fault indicated on the northwest by a gray arrow becomes in the northeast a more coherent flexure dipping to the south. The two faults farther south, indicated by the white arrows, are seen either as a band of low coherence or as a flexure dipping to the north. The juxtaposition of magenta (northeast dip) and green (southwest dip) in the center of the image indicates a local anticlinal feature that is associated with northwest- to southeast-trending reverse faults. Data are courtesy of OXY.

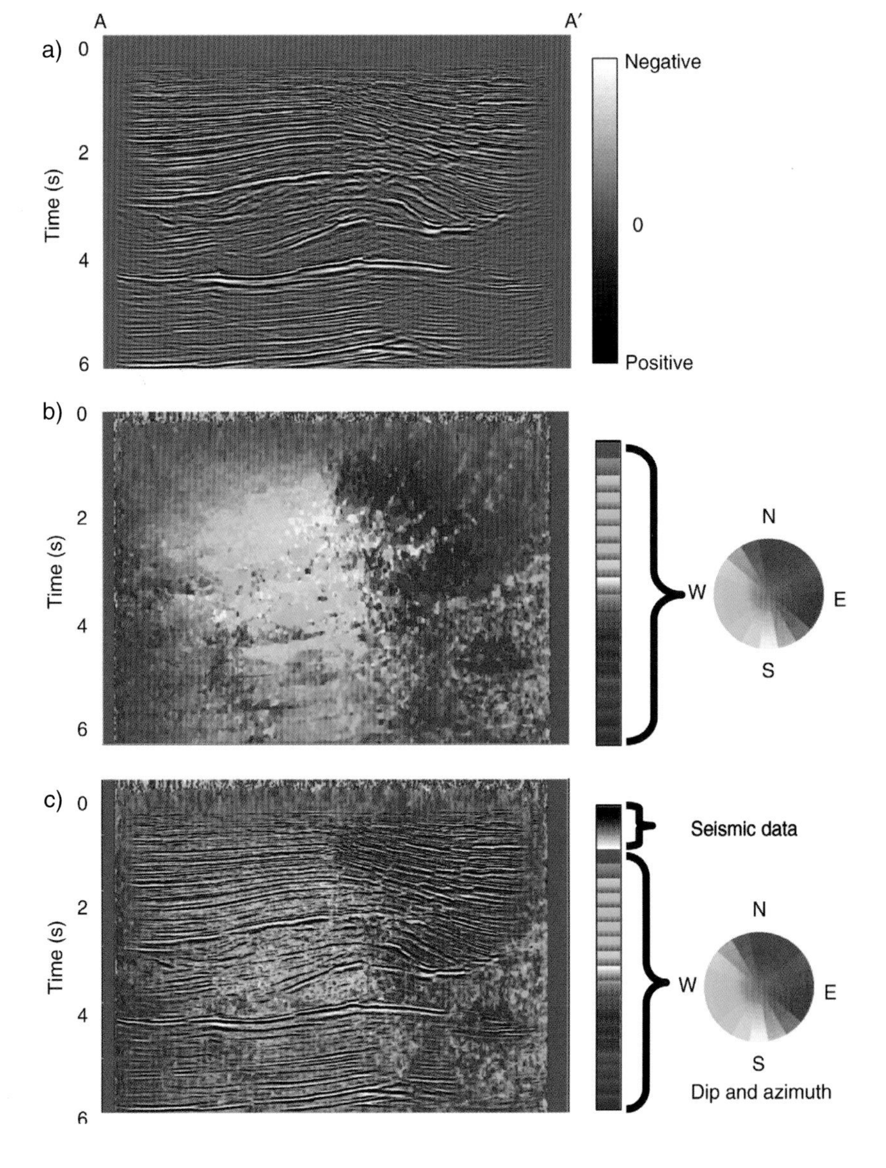

Figure 21. A vertical section corresponding to line AA′ in Figures 17, 18, and 19 from Vinton Dome, Louisiana, U.S.A. (a) Seismic data plotted using a conventional single-gradational gray-scale color bar. (b) Dip azimuth plotted using a 2D hue-saturation color map with dip magnitude plotted against saturation, S, and dip azimuth plotted against hue, H. (c) A composite image obtained by plotting the seismic data at voxels where $|a| < a_{min}$, and plotting the dip azimuth where $|a| < a_{min}$. After Lin et al. (2003). Data are courtesy of OPEX.

a)

b)

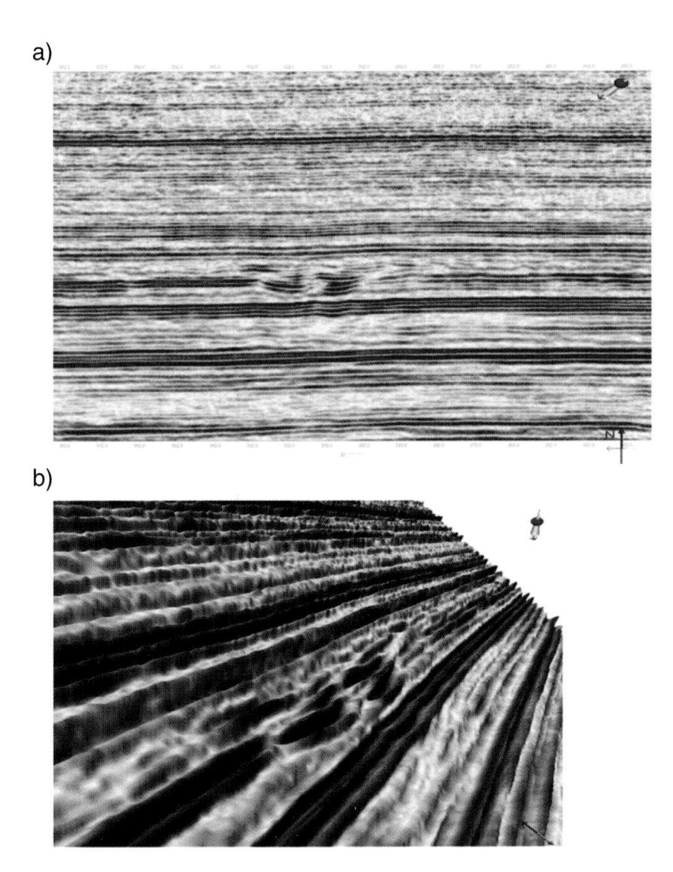

Figure 22. (a) A vertical slice through seismic data, displayed using a red-white-blue dual-gradational color bar. (b) A display of the same section, using a terrain display in which the amplitudes are presented so that they have excursions in the plane of the paper. Such landscape displays help extract subtle information from seismic attributes. After Lynch and Lines (2004).

a)

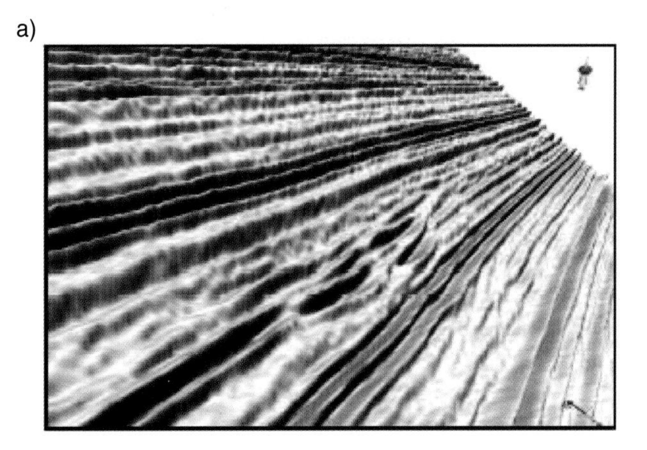

b)

Figure 23. (a) Seismic-amplitude data and (b) their complex-trace envelope, both displayed using a terrainlike surface. Changes in lithology or thickness usually modify the phase of the waveform, giving rise to changes in the position of the envelope peak with respect to the peaks and troughs of the amplitude data. Terrainlike displays help us understand these differences. After Lynch and Lines (2004).

or thickness modify the phase of the waveform, causing changes in the position of the peak of the envelope with respect to the peaks and troughs of the amplitude data. We can display these differences using the terrain display.

Figure 24 shows a prominent peak (in the foreground) that closely corresponds to the peak on the seismic data (peaks are yellow, troughs are blue). If we follow this event, we see that the yellow peak-seismic amplitudes seem to twist off the peak of the envelope-amplitude display. Such behavior means that the peak energy is moving down the seismic peak, which clearly indicates a change in lithology.

Instantaneous-frequency displays

Complex-trace estimates of instantaneous frequency produce a display of the sample-by-sample variation of a seismic trace's dominant frequency. Such displays have been used for varied tasks, including identifying gas sands, determining edge terminations of stratigraphic plays, and identifying faults in two dimensions and in three dimensions.

A combination display can be generated that relates high-frequency events on the instantaneous-frequency display to the seismic data. The seismic data are displayed as a variable-density plane and the high-frequency events are associated correspondingly, coming through the seismic amplitudes. Instantaneous-frequency displays often are contaminated by spikes that correspond to low-amplitude areas in which wavelets from different reflectors overlap. (In Chapter 6, we described how the SPICE algorithm exploits such discontinuities).

Figure 25a shows several high-frequency events that clearly are not caused by low-amplitude variations. Figure 25b shows the two-attribute display, in which instantaneous frequency defines the terrain and amplitude defines the color. In such cases, the interpreter can conclude with confidence that what appears around the channel results from lithologic changes rather than from just noise.

Figure 26a is the weighted-average frequency display. This display effectively shows where the actual frequency

Figure 24. A two-attribute display of the data shown in Figure 23, here with the envelope defining the terrain excursions and the seismic amplitude defining the color. Notice the yellow-peak seismic amplitude seen twisting off the peak of the envelope display, indicating that the peak energy is moving down the peak — an indication of changing geology. After Lynch and Lines (2004).

highs and lows are, but the interpreter is not sure how those frequency highs and lows relate to the seismic data. Figure 26b is a combination display in which a weighted-average frequency display is colored by the seismic data itself. Such a combination display makes it easy to see where the high frequencies are in relation to the seismic peaks and troughs. One can easily follow the changes in frequency in and around the channel.

Displaying vector attributes with icons

It is natural to think of plotting vector data by using vectors. Although we can use 2D and 3D color bars to display such data in a cube, we may also wish to overlay those data on top of a fourth attribute. We conclude this chapter with such a display generated by Simon (2005).

Here, Simon's attributes are measures of P-wave velocity anisotropy: the magnitude of the fast velocity (v_f), the magnitude of the slow (perpendicular) velocity (v_s), and

a)

b)

Figure 25. (a) Instantaneous-frequency data shown in a terrainlike display, corresponding to the data in Figure 23a. (b) A two-attribute image of those data, here with instantaneous frequency (defining the terrain) and amplitude (defining the color). The input data were shown previously in Figures 25a and 23a. Such displays help an interpreter conclude that the changes seen around the channel are the result of lithologic changes and not just the noise. After Lynch and Lines (2004).

a)

b)

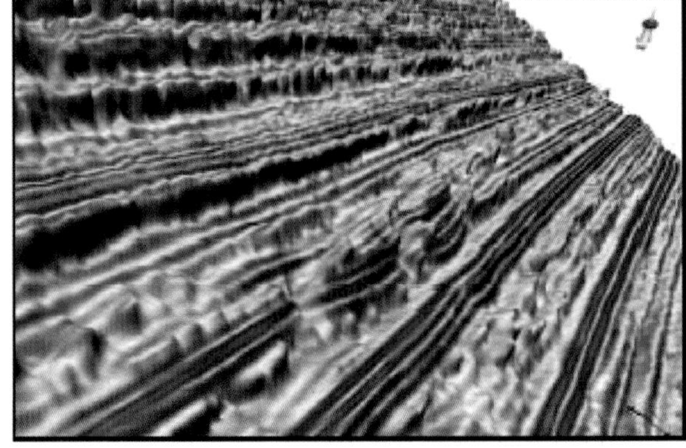

Figure 26. (a) Weighted-average frequency data corresponding to the seismic data shown in Figure 23a, displayed here as a terrain display. (b) A two-attribute image, with weighted-average frequency defining the terrain and seismic amplitude defining the color. Notice that it is easy to see where the high frequencies are in relation to the seismic peaks and troughs, and one can easily follow the changes in frequency in and around the channels. After Lynch and Lines (2004).

the azimuth of the fast velocity. In Figure 27, Simon maps the magnitude and azimuth of v_f against the length and azimuth of a simple line-segment icon. He color codes each icon with a measure of anisotropy, v_f-v_s. Then he plots these icons on top of a horizon slice through the middle of the reservoir, in a maximum-curvature volume, which allows him to visually correlate the relation (if any) between curvature and velocity anisotropy. We summarize key aspects of Simon's (2005) effort in Chapter 10 where we discuss prestack attributes.

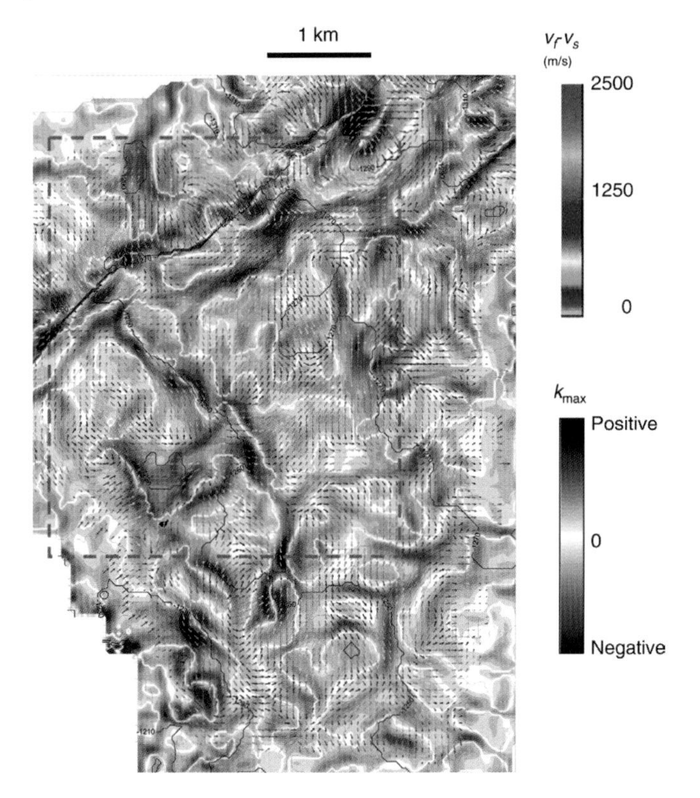

Figure 27. Use of colored icons (arrows) to display vector data. The color of the icon represents the magnitude of the P-wave velocity anisotropy. The length and orientation of the arrow represent the magnitude and azimuth, respectively, of the faster velocity, $\mathbf{v_f}$. These icons are overlaid on a horizon slice through a maximum-curvature volume displayed using a dual-gradational red-white-green color bar. After Simon (2005).

Chapter Summary

For each seismic data volume a multitude of corresponding attributes may exist. Some attributes, such as dip and azimuth, and inline and crossline coherent-energy gradients, are pairs of components of a two-dimensional vector attribute that are naturally mapped to a two-dimensional color map.

Often, attribute calculations are meaningful only if the underlying seismic data are sufficiently strong and/or coherent. We have shown how we can effectively combine information from more than one attribute into a single display. The most commonly used techniques include seismic overlays and blended or mixed maps.

Less commonly, interpreters use composite color maps that map one attribute with its color bar if its amplitude exceeds a given threshold and map a second attribute with a distinctive color bar if it does not exceed that threshold.

Finally, 2D and 3D color tables are extremely powerful in mapping vector data, such as dip magnitude and dip azimuth, or in modulating one attribute by another, such as modulating reflector shape by reflector curvedness.

Through meaningful color-coding schemes, multiattribute seismic-visualization tools allow interpreters to link selected attributes visually. Thus, such visualization tools enhance geoscientists' efficiency in data analysis, communication, and presentation.

References

Brown, A. R., 2004, Interpretation of three-dimensional seismic data: AAPG Memoir **42,** 6th edition.

Chopra, S., 2001a, Integrating coherence cube imaging and seismic attributes: Presented at the 2001 CSEG National Convention.

———, 2001b, Adding the coherence dimension to 3D seismic data: CSEG Recorder, **26**, 5–8.

———, 2002, Coherence cube and beyond: First Break, **20**, 27–33.

Kerr, J. D., W. Shea, and J. Henderson, 2002, Seismic volume processing — An investigation of its use for geologic interpretation: 64th Annual Conference and Exhibition, EAGE, Extended Abstracts, G-42.

Kidd, G. D., 1999, Fundamentals of 3D seismic volume visualization: The Leading Edge, **18**, 702–709.

Knobloch, C., 1982, Pitfalls and merits of interpreting color displays of geophysical data: 52nd Annual International Meeting, SEG, Expanded Abstracts, 112.

Lin, I., K. J. Marfurt, and O. Johnson, 2003, Mapping 3D multiattribute data into HLS color space — Applications to Vinton dome, Louisiana: 73rd Annual International Meeting, SEG, Expanded Abstracts, 1728–1731.

Lindseth, R. O., 1979, Synthetic sonic logs — A process for stratigraphic interpretation: Geophysics, **44,** 3–26.

Lynch, S., 2000, Ancient evenings: Seismic visualization using very old techniques: CSEG Recorder, **25**, no. 8, 5–6.

Lynch, S., and L. Lines, 2004, Combined attribute displays: 74th Annual International Meeting, SEG, Expanded Abstracts, 1953–1956.

Marfurt, K. J., and R. L. Kirlin, 2001, Narrow-band spectral analysis and thin-bed tuning: Geophysics, **66,** 1274–1283.

Marfurt, K. J., R. M. Scheet, J. A. Sharp, and M. G. Harper, 1998, Suppression of the acquisition footprint for seismic sequence attribute mapping: Geophysics, **63**, 1024–1035.

Meyer, D. E., E. L. Harvey, T. E. Bulloch, J. C. Voncannon, and T. M. Sheffield, 2001, Use of seismic attributes in 3D geovolume interpretation: The Leading Edge, **20,** 1377–1380,1400.

Rijks, E. J. H., and J. C. E. M. Jauffred, 1991, Attribute extraction: An important application in any detailed 3D interpretation study: The Leading Edge, **10,** 11–19.

Russell, B., 1992, Using color in seismic displays: The Leading Edge, **11,** 13–18.

Simon, Y. S., 2005, Stress and fracture characterization in a shale reservoir, North Texas, using correlation between new seismic attributes and well data: M.S. thesis, University of Houston.

Chapter 10

Prestack Geometric Attributes

Chapter Objectives

After reading this chapter, you will be able to

- exploit changes in amplitude variation with offset and azimuth to produce multiple-attribute images that illuminate different geologic features of interest
- identify limitations to seismic processing that may result in smeared attribute images from multiazimuth and multioffset data
- interpret attributes computed from multiple azimuth-limited seismic volumes to better characterize faults and fractures
- recognize opportunities to use P-wave and S-wave anisotropy to map in situ stresses and fractures on attribute volumes

Introduction

Interpretation of amplitude variation with offset (AVO) is an endeavor that may be even more useful than interpretation of attributes that are sensitive to structure and stratigraphy. Recently, AVO was the subject of an SEG/EAGE distinguished lecturer short course (Hilterman, 2001). Because the seismic response across seismic offsets is sensitive to changes in lithology, porosity, and fluid content (which we call AVO effects), it should be obvious that the attribute images generated from offset-limited volumes also show that sensitivity. In general, AVO practitioners inform us that structural effects have the greatest influence on near-offset range, whereas lithology and fluid have the greatest effects on longer offsets (as cartooned in Figure 1). As a sum over all offsets, the seismic stacked response typically produces an average of these responses. Figure 1a shows a typical geometry for a common-midpoint gather. Figure 1b indicates that the structural effects often are seen best at the near-angle seismic volumes, whereas lithofluid effects often are seen best on the farther-angle seismic images.

One step in traditional AVO analysis includes fitting a parametric curve to seismic amplitudes across amplitudes or incident angles. Sometimes, more robust estimates of the curve-fitting parameters can be obtained by fitting the curve to amplitude or envelope peaks within a short temporal-analysis window.

Recently, considerable research has been directed at estimating the impact that thin-bed tuning has on determination of AVO amplitudes. Accommodation for thin-bed-tuning contamination of the underlying AVO phenomenon requires analysis of the seismic waveform across offsets or angles. Clearly, if the attributes discussed in this book, such as coherence, energy-weighted coherent-amplitude gradients, and spectral decomposition, are applied to limited-offset ranges, those attributes will be sensitive to such AVO tuning effects. In spite of complications introduced by thin-bed-tuning contamination, coherence analysis on these offset-limited volumes can provide spectacular results, especially in areas where hydrocarbon accumulations are involved.

As is the case with AVO, to obtain useful offset-limited volumes we must process the gathers in a way that compensates for loss of frequencies and amplitude as a function of increasing offset (Figure 2). Seismic attributes can then be determined from each offset volume over a window of interest. In the workflow shown in Figure 2, time slices for each offset are generated and then grouped by time. In this chapter, we show how the interpreter can animate through

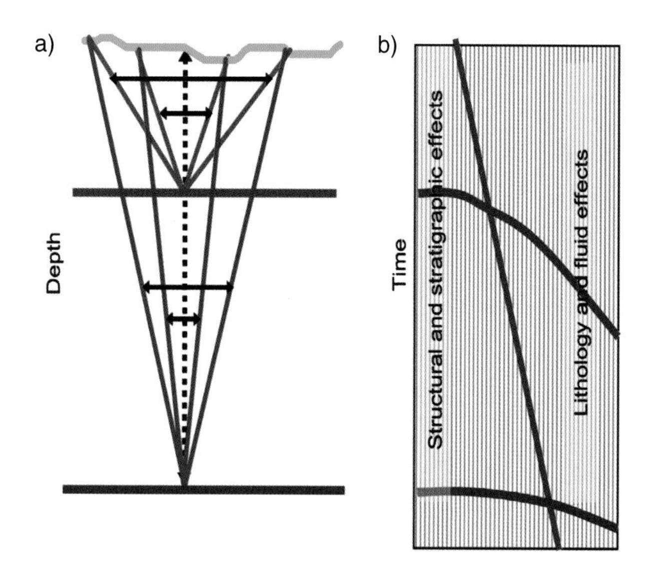

Figure 1. Idealized (a) geometry and (b) seismic data, corresponding to a common-midpoint (CMP) gather. Often, structural and stratigraphic effects are seen best on near-angle seismic volumes, and lithology and fluid effects are seen best on far-angle seismic images.

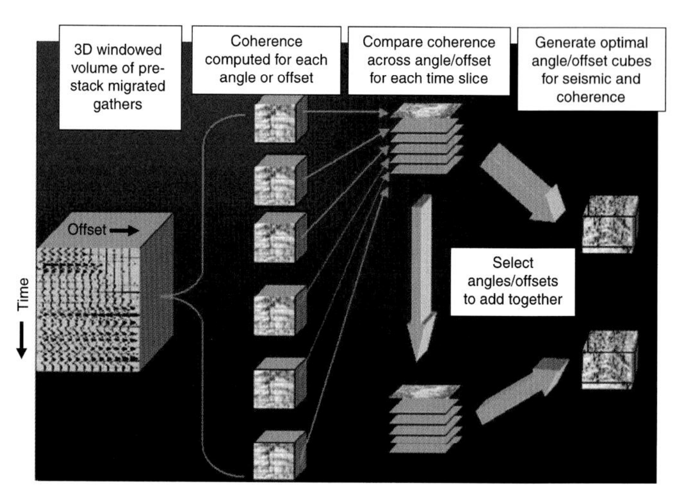

Figure 2. A flowchart for generating prestack coherence. Figure courtesy of Core Lab.

these volumes and choose offsets that best illuminate features of interest.

Whereas hydrocarbons cause changes in seismic response with incident angle, aligned vertical faults and fractures cause azimuthal variations in the seismic amplitude, phase, and velocity (Grimm et al, 1999). Conventional 3D processing sequences typically stack all azimuths and thus obliterate the azimuthal variation of moveout and amplitude. In this chapter, we discuss a simple but effective methodology for detecting faults and fractures in 3D seismic data by taking advantage of the azimuthal variation of seismic signatures and coherence.

Fractures can be detected by P-wave, S-wave, and converted-wave reflections. Thus, in addition to seismic volumes associated with a given offset (or incident angle) and azimuth, we can acquire and sort data by its polarization and mode of propagation. Each mode of propagation responds to the subsurface geology differently. In the extreme case, a given geologic feature may be nearly transparent to a given mode (say, to near-offset P-P waves) but may be a good reflector to a different mode (say, to moderate-offset converted waves).

Application of geometric attributes to prestack data volumes is undergoing active study at the time of this publication. Therefore, this method fittingly comprises the last chapter in Part 1 of this book. Prestack attribute analysis is tightly linked to amplitude variation with offset, amplitude versus azimuth, and azimuthal anisotropy. Indeed, we consider velocity anisotropy estimates to be attributes amenable to the same manipulation in an interpretation workstation or to the same analysis by geostatistics and neural nets as are the geometric and spectral-decomposition attributes that make up the bulk of this book. Our goal here is to show the promise that such analysis holds. We fully expect others to produce excellent examples within the next several years.

Attributes Applied to Offset-limited and Angle-limited Stacks

We begin our discussion with a suite of ten offset-limited volumes generated from a survey acquired over Louisiana, U.S.A. Coherence was computed on each of 10 offset-limited volumes. We show time slices at t = 1.200 s through each of these 10 volumes in Figure 3.

We note a significant variation in the character with offset: Some faults and stratigraphic edges show up at near offsets, others at mid-range offsets, and still others at far offsets. We also note that some offsets (such as the one at 2170 m) appear less coherent, which indicates a lower signal-to-noise ratio. Two situations cause such variability with offset. First, multiples may be present in the data and may interfere with a given offset at a given depth. Such multiples can be reasonably well attenuated by using a Radon transform or other multi-offset subtractive technique.

The second cause of variability with offset may result from AVO. If the amplitude response changes polarity between the near and far offsets, it will cross zero at some intermediate offset. In that case, a reflection may effectively disappear at some intermediate offset. Because we have seen in previous sections that low reflectivity (such as shale-on-shale reflectors) in a fixed level of noise results in incoherent images, we expect a similar phenomenon on selected reflectors over particular offset intervals.

In Figure 4, we show the sensitivity of coherence to a known hydrocarbon accumulation. Data were acquired over a Tertiary field in the North Sea and sorted into a near-offset volume (Figure 4b) and a far-offset volume (Figure 4c) in addition to the conventional full-offset volume (Figure 4a). Subtle AVO waveform responses with offset or incident angle cause changes in both amplitude and waveform. Using coherence, we can easily map the edges of the reservoir.

In Figure 5, we show a different reservoir, also in the North Sea. Well control allows us to map the gas-oil contact in the far-offset volume (Figures 5b and 5d) but not in the near-offset volume (Figures 5a and 5c), which instead maps the edge of a sand body. Because amplitude and waveform are mathematically independent, traditional amplitude maps provide a second independent view of a reservoir, and that view emphasizes the internal characteristics rather than the edges.

Figures 6–8 were generated from a survey acquired over South Marsh Island, on the shelf of the Gulf of Mexico, U.S.A. We analyzed two coherence volumes, one comprising far-incident angles (>20°) and the other near-incident angles (<20°). Figure 6 reveals more similarities than differences. Nevertheless, we note that a north-south-trending fault (indicated by the gray arrow) shows up better on the far-angle image in Figure 6a, whereas we see a channel

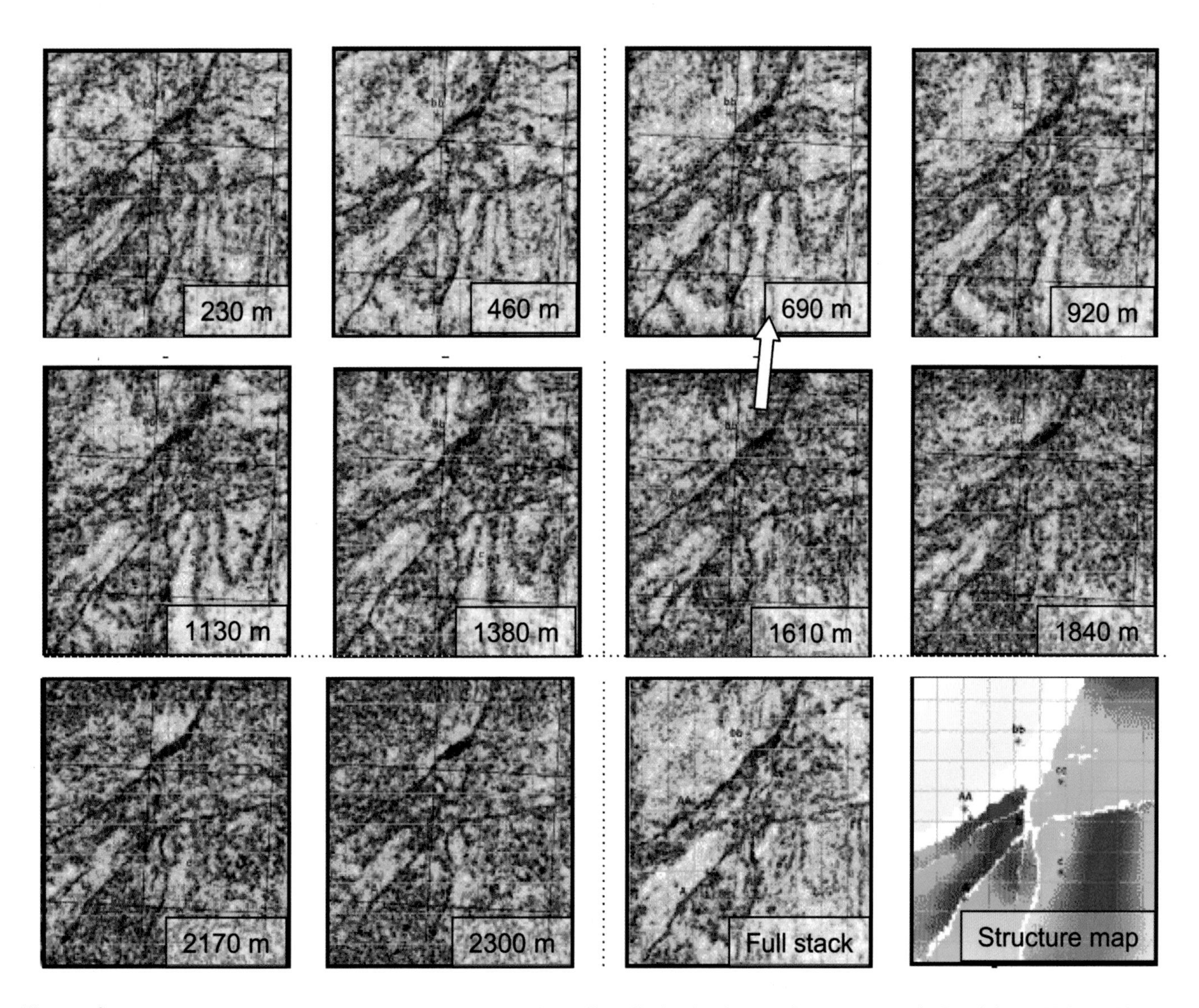

Figure 3. Illumination of faults using coherence applied to offset-limited volumes, from a survey in Louisiana, U.S.A. The time slice is at $t = 1.200$ s. The coherence images change because signal changes with offset (as a result of AVO effects), as does noise (such as multiples and backscattered energy). The near offset is at 230 m; the far offset is at 2300 m. Note the fault at the mid-offset of 690 m, indicated by the arrow. That fault is not obvious on either the near offset of 230 m or the far offset of 2300 m.

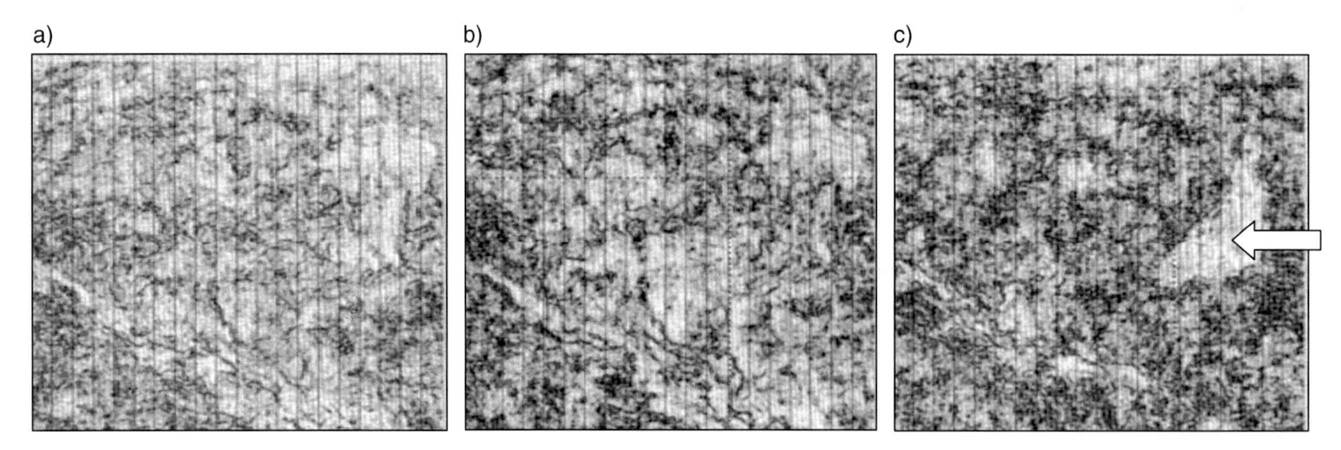

Figure 4. Coherence slices through a lower Tertiary gas reservoir from a survey acquired in the North Sea. Coherence was computed from the (a) full-offset, (b) near-offset, and (c) far-offset seismic volumes. The gas response for this AVO class can be seen clearly on the coherence slice of the far-offset volume, as indicated by the arrow in (c), but a gas response cannot be seen on the full-offset volume or the near-offset volume.

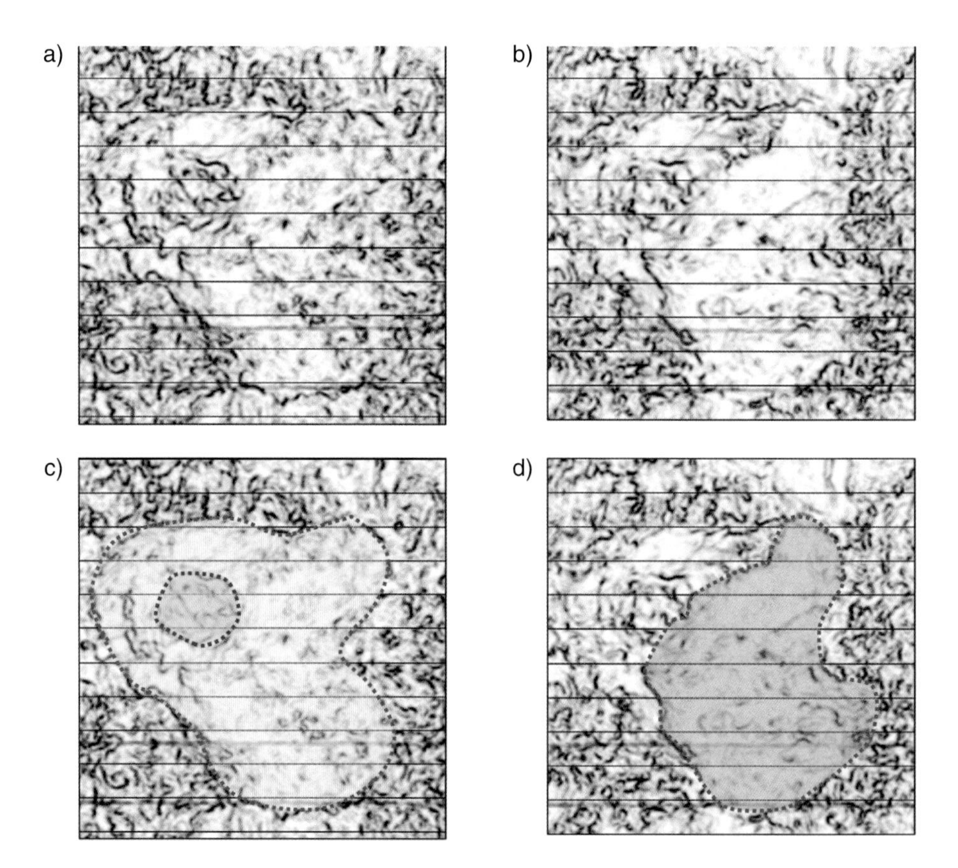

Figure 5. Coherence slices through (a) a near-offset volume and (b) a far-offset volume over a producing Tertiary field in the North Sea. Interpreted versions are shown in (c) and (d). The gas-oil contact outlined by the edge of the magenta feature, which was established from well control, is clearly visible in the far-offset slice shown in (d) but is not apparent in the near-offset slice in (c). In contrast, the near-offset slice better illuminates the overall extent of the sand body (in yellow) as well as an injection feature (the small green circle within the yellow patch). This injection feature is interpreted to be a throat into which the sand was injected.

feature (white arrow) that shows up better on the near-angle image in Figure 6b.

Figure 7 shows corresponding time slices through the north-south component of the energy-weighted coherent-amplitude gradient volumes determined for the same data as in the images in Figure 6. The white arrow indicates the same channel feature described in Figure 6. The black arrows indicate a channel that is somewhat better delineated in the near-angle image in Figure 7b than it is in the far-angle image in Figure 7a but that is barely detectable in the coherence images in Figure 6. We attribute the lack of detection by coherence to a longer-wavelength gradational change in thickness across the channel, as discussed in Chapter 5. The narrow channel indicated by the gray arrow in the near-angle image in Figure 7b also is defined better here than in any of the other images.

In Figure 8, we display a deeper time slice through these same two north-south energy-weighted coherent-amplitude-gradient volumes. Here we see a sinuous channel that is clearly defined on the near-angle image (Figure 8b, white arrows) and a fault that can be traced farther on the far-angle image (Figure 8a, gray arrows). Given point well control, we would feel confident extrapolating channel properties along its path anywhere that it maintains a similar appearance.

In summary, by using a full suite of attributes and by applying this attribute suite to angle-limited volumes, we are presented with a wealth of information that helps us quantify reservoir heterogeneity.

On the basis of observations made from the coherence response for the near-angle and far-angle traces, we can determine whether a prestack or a poststack inversion is war-

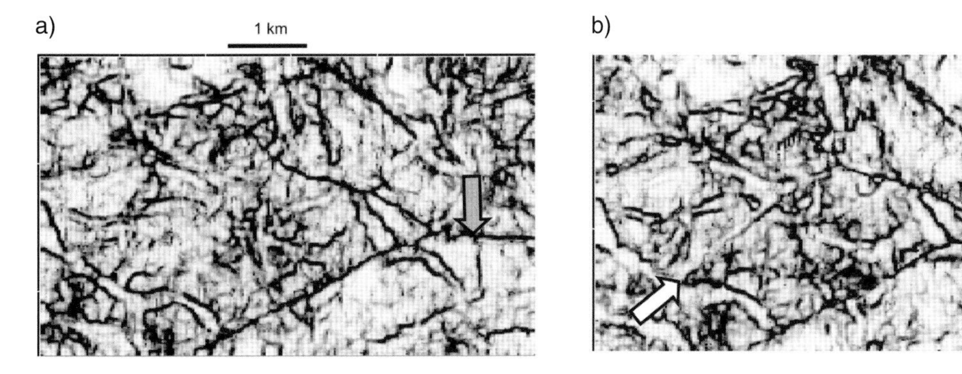

Figure 6. Time slices at $t = 1.218$ s through coherence volumes generated from (a) a far-angle and (b) a near-angle migrated stack. The fault indicated by the gray arrow is illuminated better on the far-angle stack, whereas the channel indicated by the white arrow is illuminated better on the near-angle stack. Data courtesy of Fairfield.

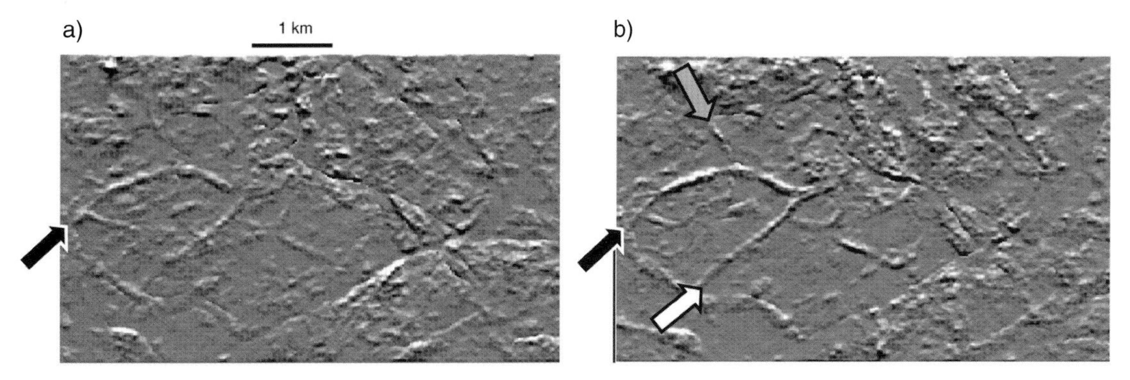

Figure 7. Time slices at $t = 1.218$ s through north-south energy-weighted coherent-amplitude-gradient volumes generated from (a) a far-angle and (b) a near-angle migrated stack. The channel indicated by the black arrow is well illuminated on both the near-angle stack and the far-angle stack. The channels indicated by the white, black, and gray arrows are illuminated better by the far-angle stack. Data courtesy of Fairfield.

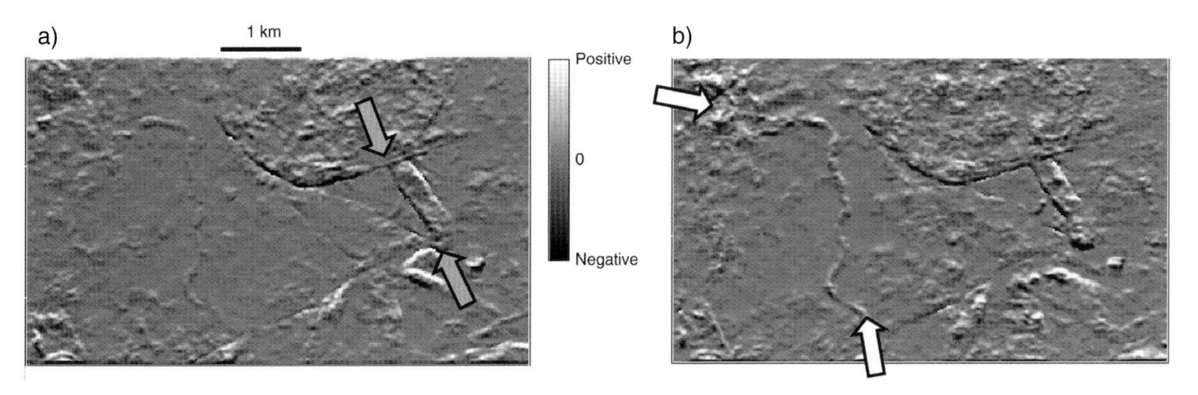

Figure 8. Time slices at $t = 1.482$ s through north-south energy-weighted coherent-amplitude-gradient volumes generated from (a) a far-angle and (b) a near-angle migrated stack. The fault indicated by the gray arrows is illuminated better on the far-angle stack, whereas the channel indicated by the white arrows is illuminated better on the near-angle stack. Data courtesy of Fairfield.

ranted. If we see no appreciable difference between near-offset and far-offset volumes in terms of amplitude and coherence slices, we may assume that a poststack inversion is sufficient. However, if we see significant differences, a prestack inversion should be employed to exploit this variation. This latter case lends itself to performing either a full or partial (minimum of three subvolumes) prestack elastic inversion to derive the compressional (P-wave) and shear (S-wave) reflectivities followed by a joint inversion to derive the P- and S-wave impedances. Those impedances can then be used to derive λ-μ-ρ attributes, where λ, μ, and ρ represent, respectively, the incompressibility, rigidity, and density of the rocks.

Geometric Attributes Applied to Azimuth-limited Stacks

Mapping faults in hydrocarbon reservoirs is critical for assessing prospects, characterizing reservoir compartmentalization, and simulating reservoirs with the goal of maximizing hydrocarbon recovery. Mapping fractures accurately is more difficult. However, we need such mapping to evaluate and rank prospects, optimize well locations, decide on test intervals, and evaluate the formation for optimal well development and reservoir management.

Routine acquisition of high-quality 3D seismic data and the eventual interactive interpretation of those data on workstations have helped interpreters immensely in resolving faults and fractures. Picking fault surfaces can be time consuming. Smaller faults may have a minute reflector offset and in many cases may appear as inconsequential disruptions. Minor faults often are seen best on dip or azimuth maps, where seemingly insignificant displacements laterally align to help confirm that we are looking at a fault. Often, minor faults are not seen directly as reflector displacements on vertical seismic sections, but they can be detected by examining localized amplitude reduction. Illumination of major and minor faults varies with azimuth.

Commonly, 3D land and OBC seismic surveys are designed to record a range of azimuths. Among the various reasons for acquiring a wide-azimuth survey is the desire to image small faults and locate fracture systems. Because the orientation of faults and fractures varies within a prospect, our 3D seismic survey must be designed so that some raypaths illuminate these azimuthally oriented systems. If vertical faults and fractures are aligned in significant numbers, we may experience an azimuthal variation in velocity.

During conventional processing of the seismic data, we typically stack all azimuths together so that subtle azimuthal variations in moveout and amplitude are obliterated. If significant azimuthal anisotropy exists, commonly we obtain an image that is smeared and therefore has lower lateral and vertical resolution.

We have two ways to address this smearing. The first is to perform an azimuthal velocity analysis followed by azimuth-sensitive NMO corrections or migration. Although such a process is an improvement over stacking all azimuths with an incorrect velocity, the process averages out subtle variations resulting from varying illuminations.

The second approach is simpler. We process different azimuthal bins independently, perhaps stacking them at the end if we so desire. Because many seismic processes (such as DMO and prestack migration) are linear operations with costs proportional to the number of input traces, generating these intermediate seismic volumes costs little more than the disk space they occupy.

In general, azimuth-limited (and the previously discussed offset-limited) volumes have a lower signal-to-noise ratio than do full-azimuth volumes. Clearly, one can design filters across the azimuth-limited bins (akin to Radon filters) to suppress noise that normally would be suppressed by stacking all the data together. However, none of the examples shown in this chapter has had such a filter applied.

In Figure 9, we show time slices through coherence volumes at t = 1290 ms, computed from a full-azimuth migrated stack (Figure 9a) and an azimuth-limited (112.5° to 157.5°) migrated stack (Figure 9b) for a survey acquired over southern Alberta, Canada. The coherence slice for the azimuth-limited volume is less coherent overall. Some of this decreased coherence results from the decreased signal-to-noise ratio.

However, in Figure 9b we also can identify several faults that could not be seen on the full-azimuth volume (arrows). Our experience to date has been that faults typically appear on data azimuths that are either perpendicular or parallel to the fault. In the first case, diffractions from a fault will be recorded best by raypaths that propagate perpendicularly to it, a fact well understood by those doing velocity analysis for prestack depth migration.

Unfortunately, our velocity analysis is not always as accurate as we would like it to be. In this second case, raypaths parallel to a fault are least sensitive to fault displacement and to velocity errors. Such decreased sensitivity to the fault results in a simple NMO correction followed by stack producing a signal with a good signal-to-noise ratio. If we have an accurate estimate of migration velocity (which we cannot obtain from data with offsets limited to being parallel to strike), we can then image the fault best by migrating the azimuthally limited stack made parallel to the fault. This phenomenon also is well known and was a preferred means of acquiring 3D marine seismic data in the 1980s (before depth migration and migration-driven velocity analysis became available).

In Figure 10, we show vertical slices through a coherence volume computed from a full-azimuth stack and a coherence volume generated from an azimuth-limited stack for a land survey acquired in Tunisia. Both coherence volumes were computed along structural dip. The low-coherence zone could result from decreased signal-to-noise associated with the limited-azimuth seismic volume. However, a more reasonable explanation, consistent with the location on the flank of the anticline, proximity to faults, and knowledge of the geology, is that the azimuth-limited stack illuminates fractures better.

Example 1 — Western Canada

Our first example comes from a land-data volume acquired over western Canada (Chopra et al., 2000). The conventional standard processing sequence applied to 3D data volumes is shown on the left side of Figure 11. After surface-consistent statics and zero-phase deconvolution had been applied to the CMP gathers, the gathers were binned into four different azimuth volumes according to the direction between source and receiver, but within 45° of the dominant fault strike. The range of azimuths fixed for each

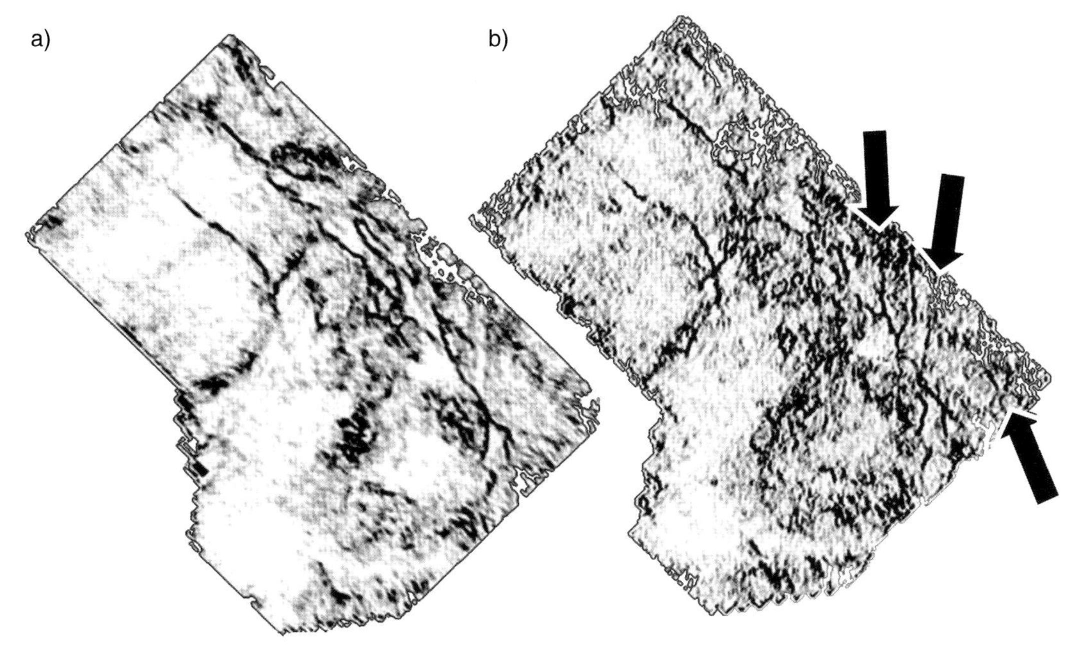

Figure 9. The impact of azimuthal binning on coherence. (a) A coherence image run on all azimuths. (b) A coherence image run on azimuths restricted to 45. The coherence slice in Figure (b) is less coherent overall, and part of the decreased coherence results from the decreased signal-to-noise ratio. However, it does show the improved definition of some of the features indicated with arrows. Figures Courtesy of Core Laboratories.

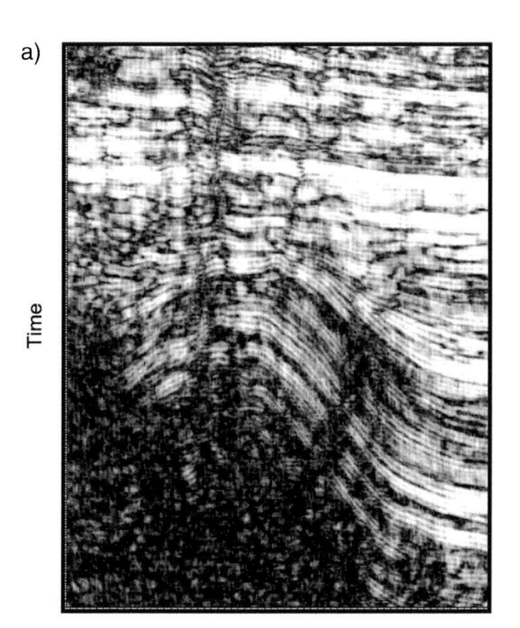

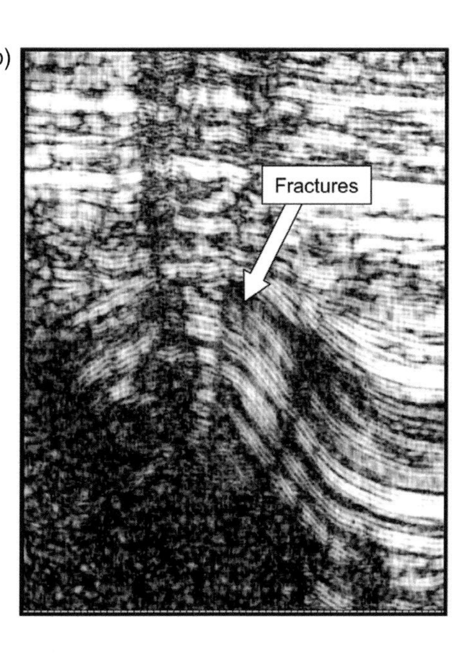

Figure 10. The impact of azimuthal binning on coherence. (a) Coherence generated from a full-azimuth stack does not show significant low-coherence faults or fractures associated with deformation of the reflectors. (b) In contrast, coherence generated from an azimuth-limited stack shows low-coherence anomalies where we expect faults and fractures to be initiated. Figure courtesy of Core Laboratories.

volume was 45° to 90°, 90° to 135°, 135° to 180°, and 180° to 225°. Thereafter, processing was carried out independently for each of the four volumes. The choice of azimuth ranges is dictated by the orientation of faults that must be imaged and of the fold of the seismic data being processed. Our experience indicates that a four-azimuth division of the full-azimuth range works well.

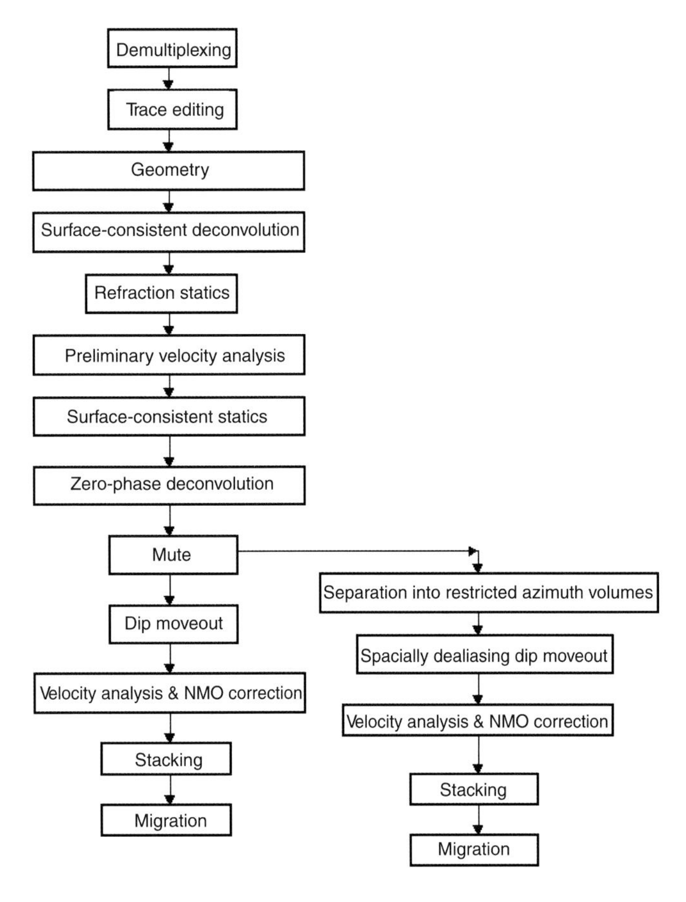

Figure 11. The conventional processing flow (left) and an azimuth-limited processing flow (right).

The independent processing flow shown on the right side of Figure 11 included spatially dealiasing dip moveout or DMO (Beasley and Mobley, 1998), velocity analysis and NMO correction, and stacking. A good DMO algorithm should preserve the seismic amplitudes. To achieve that objective, several issues have to be addressed: binning of the input data to ensure that the offset bins are balanced, spatial sampling of the DMO operator, and DMO-oriented weighting of the DMO stack to compensate for the effects of acquisition geometry on the stack amplitudes. In the spatially dealiasing DMO algorithm used, instead of summing a DMO response to the nearest bin center, the trace was weighted and summed to the four bin centers, which are the corners of the smallest rectangle containing the response trace (Beasley and Mobley, 1998). The weighting was determined by the distance from the output trace to the bin center of the input traces.

Figure 12a shows vertical line JJ′ through the full-azimuth seismic volume. Figure 12b shows a horizon slice 30 ms below the red pick through the corresponding coherence volume. We note a system of faults trending northeast to southwest. This fault pattern could not explain the waning of initial pressure levels in and around well W1, which is indicated by the arrow.

In contrast, Figure 13 shows vertical line JJ′ through the four different azimuth-limited seismic volumes. As expected, both azimuth-to-azimuth variation and increased lateral resolution occur in the restricted-azimuth sections, compared with the full-azimuth section shown in Figure 12a.

In Figure 14, we display horizon slices 30 ms below the red pick through coherence volumes corresponding to the azimuth-limited seismic volumes from Figure 13. Different azimuth coherence slices show reasonably good alignment not only in the northeast-southwest direction but in the orthogonal northwest-southeast direction as well. Well W1 is now seen to be located within a faulted area, which helps explain the waning of pressure initially observed in the well.

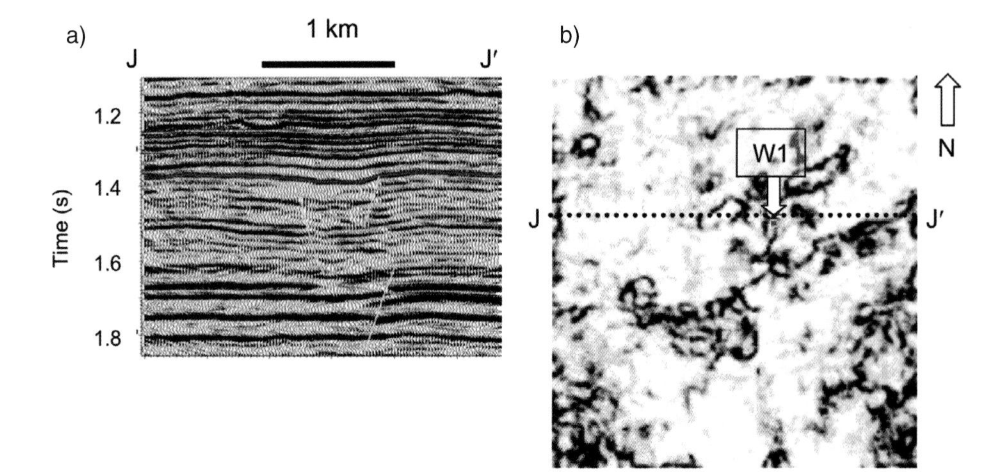

Figure 12. (a) Line JJ' through a full-azimuth seismic data volume. (b) A horizon slice 30 ms below the red pick in (a), through the corresponding coherence volume.

Example 2 — Offshore West Africa

Our next example comes from a wide-azimuth OBS (ocean-bottom seismometer) line acquired offshore West Africa. Because this is an OBS line (unlike the customary towed-cable line), the marine data obtained contain a full suite of azimuths. On the basis of the orientation of faults in this volume, four azimuth-limited volumes were generated: 22.5° to 67.5°, 67.5° to 112.5°, 112.5° to 157.5°, and 157.5° to 202.5 (Chopra et al., 2000). Figures 15a and b show lines AA′ and BB′ through the full-azimuth seismic volume. Figure 15c shows a time slice at t = 1.312 s through the corresponding coherence volume, in which we note a northeast-southwest fault system that corresponds to discontinuities seen on the vertical seismic data.

Next, we display vertical lines AA′ (Figure 16) and BB′ (Figure 17) through the four different azimuth-limited seismic volumes. As expected, lateral resolution is greater in the azimuth-limited volumes than in the full-azimuth volume shown in Figures 15a and 15b. Also, significant variation exists between each azimuth-limited volume seen in Figures 16 and 17.

In Figure 18, we display times slices at t = 1.312 s through the four coherence volumes computed from the four azimuth-limited seismic volumes displayed in Figures 16 and 17. The images in Figure 18 show not only the northeast-southwest faults but also faults in the orthogonal direction, such as those indicated by arrows in Figures 18a and 18c.

Despite significantly lower fold in the azimuth-limited volumes, superior imaging (compared with full-azimuth stacks) is seen in the direction perpendicular to fractures. This result is intuitive to standard practices and suggests that both the fault-parallel and fault-perpendicular volumes need to be analyzed for accurate fault interpretation.

Effect of Sharpening on Azimuth-limited Coherence Volumes

In Chapter 8, we showed how a simple sharpening algorithm could improve coherence images. We have now applied that methodology to a 3D seismic land-data set from western Canada. In Figure 19, we display time slices

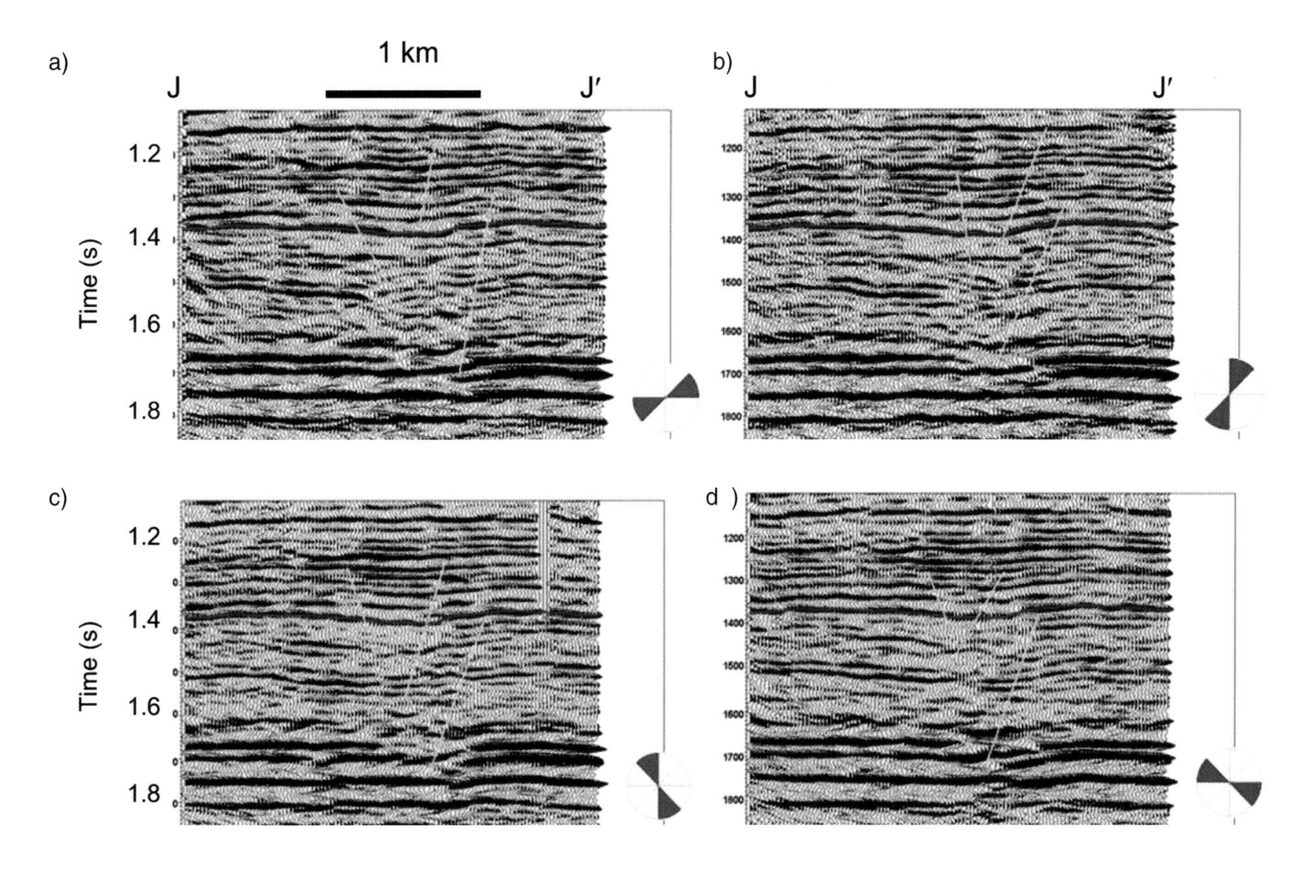

Figure 13. Line JJ' from Figure 12, here through azimuth-limited seismic volumes: (a) at about 67.5° and 247.5°, (b) at about 22.5° and 202.5°, (c) at about 157.5° and 337.5°, and (d) at about 112.5° and 292.5°. Note the different appearances of the faults as they intersect the red horizon.

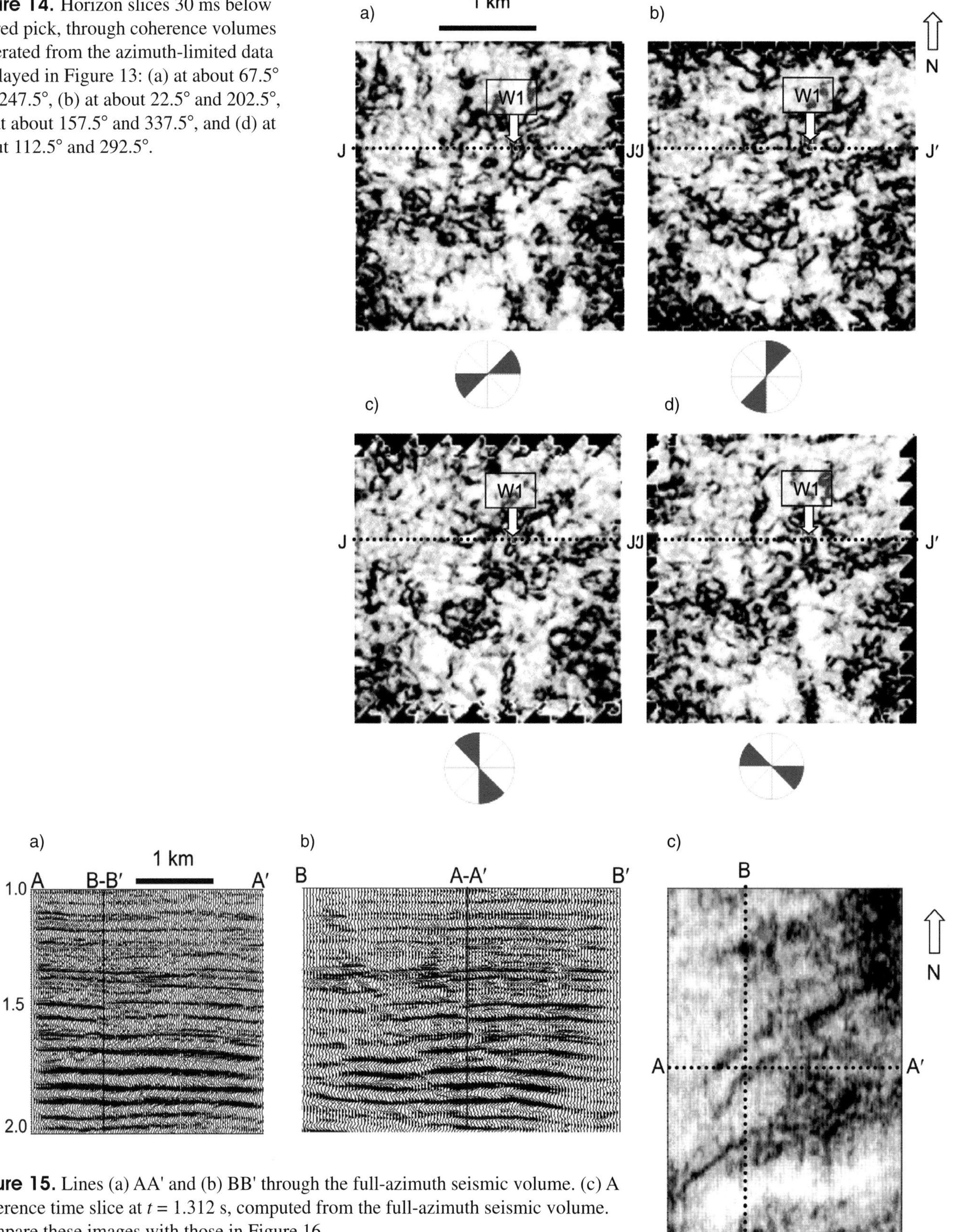

Figure 14. Horizon slices 30 ms below the red pick, through coherence volumes generated from the azimuth-limited data displayed in Figure 13: (a) at about 67.5° and 247.5°, (b) at about 22.5° and 202.5°, (c) at about 157.5° and 337.5°, and (d) at about 112.5° and 292.5°.

Figure 15. Lines (a) AA' and (b) BB' through the full-azimuth seismic volume. (c) A coherence time slice at t = 1.312 s, computed from the full-azimuth seismic volume. Compare these images with those in Figure 16.

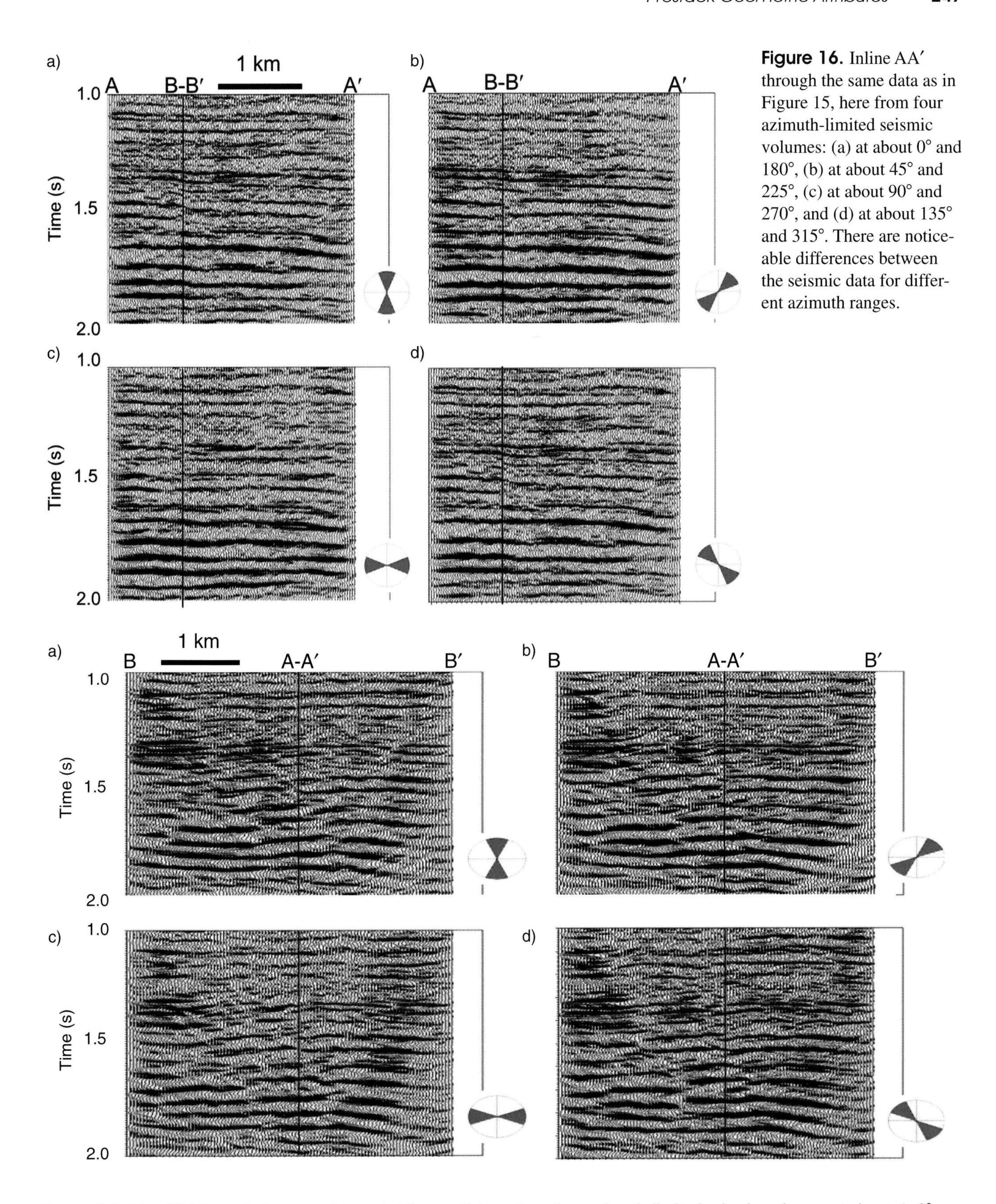

Figure 16. Inline AA′ through the same data as in Figure 15, here from four azimuth-limited seismic volumes: (a) at about 0° and 180°, (b) at about 45° and 225°, (c) at about 90° and 270°, and (d) at about 135° and 315°. There are noticeable differences between the seismic data for different azimuth ranges.

Figure 17. Line BB' through the same data as in Figure 15, here from four azimuth-limited seismic volumes, at about: (a 0° and 180°, (b) 45° and 225°, (c) 90° and 270°, and (d) 135° and 315°. Noticeable differences exist between the seismic data for different azimuth ranges.

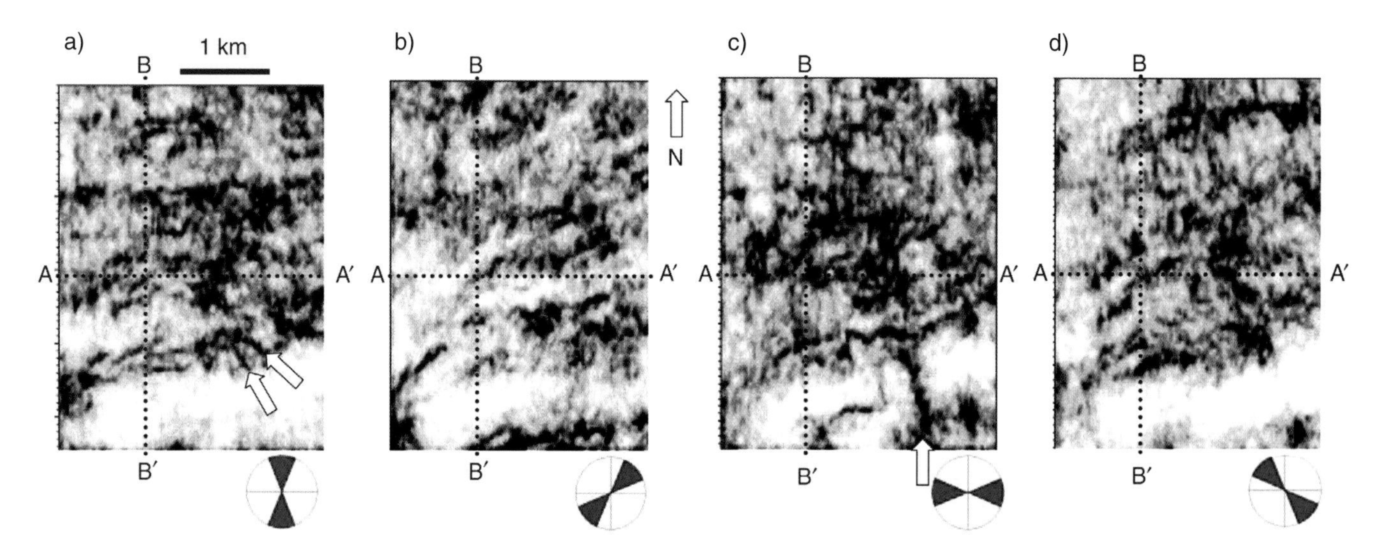

Figure 18. Times slices at t = 1.312 s through coherence volumes computed from the azimuth-limited seismic volumes shown in Figures 16 and 17, at about: (a) 0° and 180°, (b) 45° and 225°, (c) 90° and 270°, and (d) 135° and 315°.

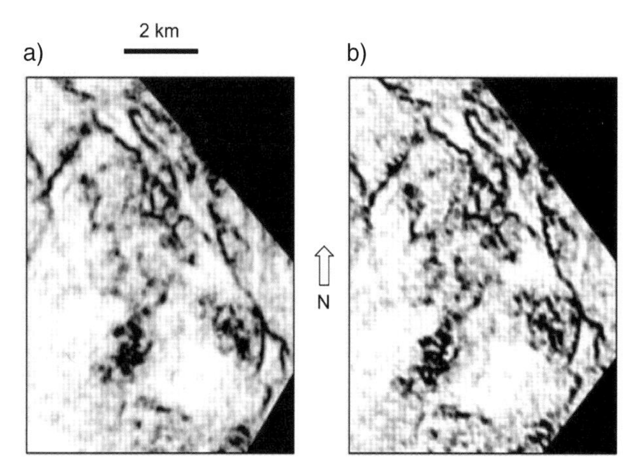

Figure 19. Time slices at t = 1.524 s through coherence volumes computed from a full-azimuth seismic volume (a) before and (b) after image sharpening. Image sharpening was described in Chapter 8.

at t = 1.524 s, which represents the Precambrian level. Although several faults appear clearly in the images both before (Figure 19a) and after sharpening (Figure 19b), the effect of sharpening is minimal because the desired level of detail is missing from the data.

After application of surface-consistent statics and zero-phase deconvolution to the CDP gathers, the 3D seismic volume was binned into four different azimuth volumes according to the direction between source and receiver, but within 45° of the dominant fault strike (Chopra and Sudhakar, 2000). The range of azimuths fixed for each volume was 45° to 90°, 90° to 135°, 135° to 180°, and 180° to 225°. Thereafter, processing was carried out independently for each of the four volumes, including spatially dealiased dip moveout (Beasley and Mobley, 1998).

In Figure 20, we show time slices at t = 1.524 s through coherence volumes computed from each of the azimuth-limited seismic volumes generated above. The solid blue wedge next to the coherence slice in each of the images (a) to (d) denotes the individual azimuths. Each azimuth-limited volume illuminates different faults. Whereas the overall signal-to-noise ratio of each azimuth-limited image is decreased, the lateral resolution is improved here compared with that of the coherence slice generated from the full-azimuth seismic volume displayed in Figure 19a. Where we have narrow coherence lineations in Figure 20, we have broader, smeared lineations in Figure 19a because of the data smearing during stack.

In Figure 21, we show the impact of sharpening. Because the signal-to-noise ratio of the azimuth-limited volumes was less than that of the full-azimuth volume, the impact of sharpening was greater because of the higher lateral resolution, as we see on each of the coherence slices (Figures 21a to d). Indeed, the impact of sharpening was significant, as shown by the north-south-trending faults indicated by the arrows in Figure 21d.

Interazimuth Coherence

Al-Dossary et al. (2004) noted that one of the main effects of azimuthal anisotropy is a change in the temporal thickness of a geologic formation as a function of different azimuthal viewing angles. If the formation is thin, we cannot pick the top and bottom of the formation, nor can we calculate an accurate interval velocity. However, if we subdivide our survey into azimuthal bins that are parallel and perpendicular to the principal axes of anisotropy, we should

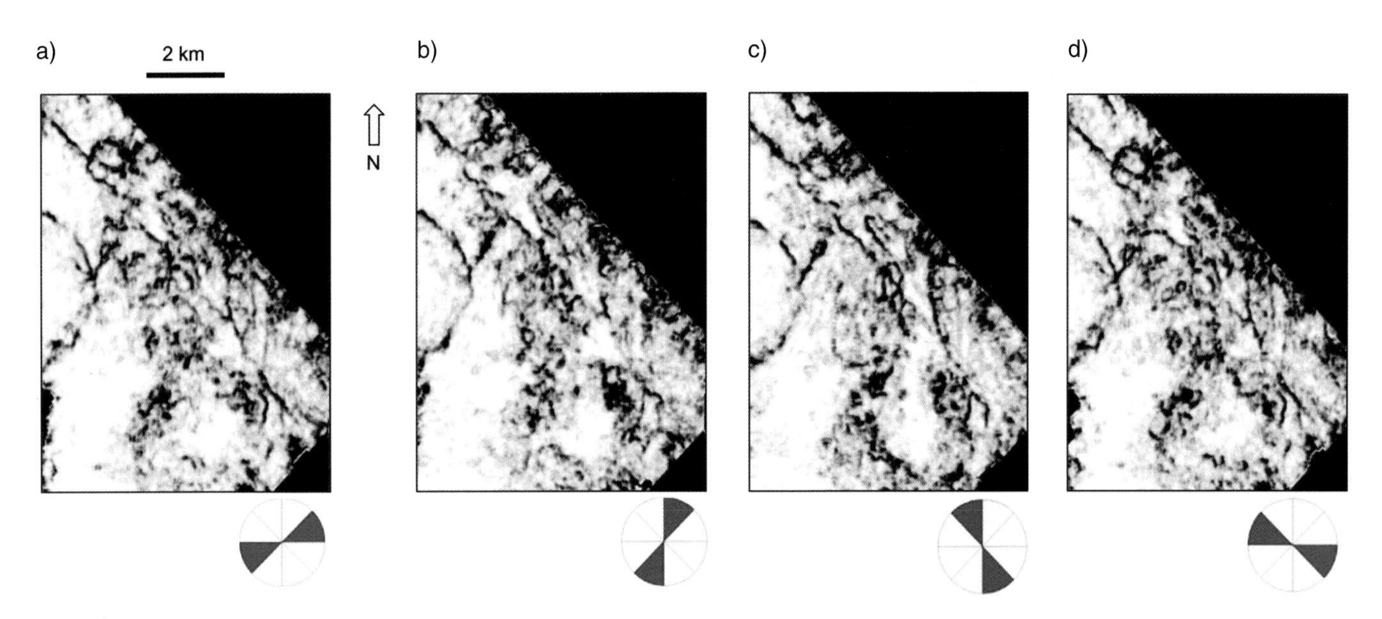

Figure 20. Time slices corresponding to those shown in Figure 19, through coherence volumes generated here on azimuthally limited seismic data volumes. The solid blue wedge in each image denotes azimuths.

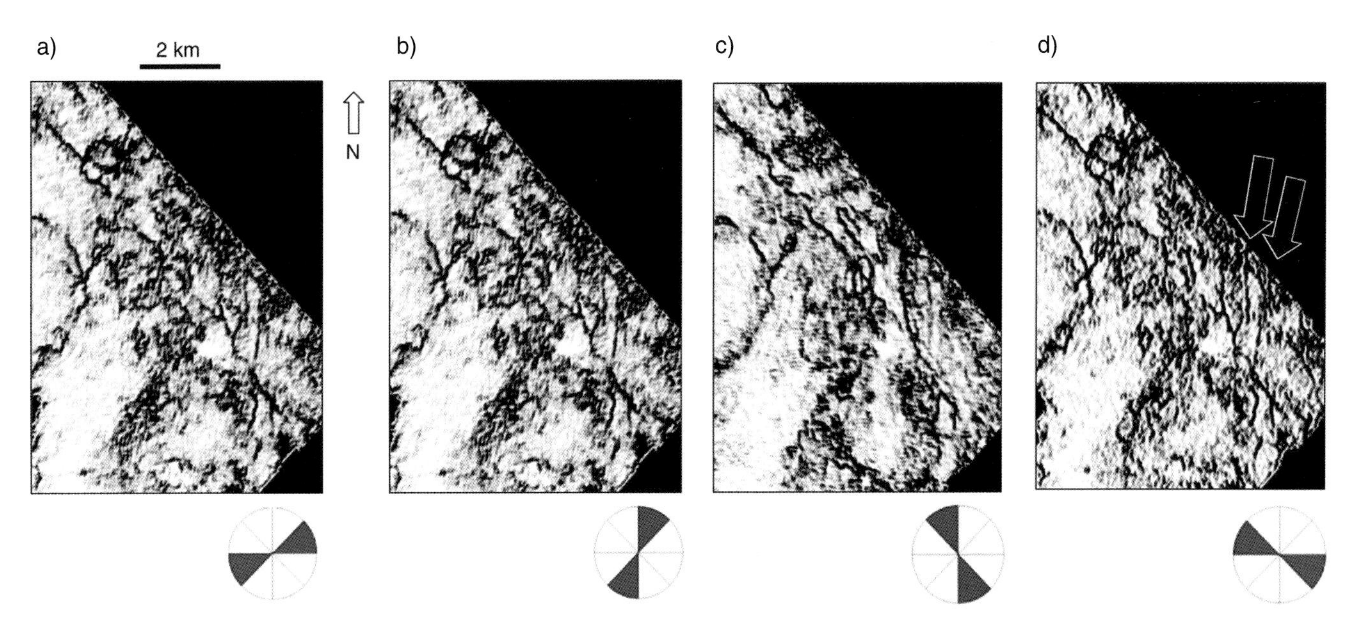

Figure 21. Time slices corresponding to those shown in Figure 20, through coherence volumes generated on azimuthally limited seismic data volumes after image sharpening as described in Chapter 8. The solid blue wedge in each image denotes azimuths. Comparison of the individual images (a) to (d) with their corresponding images in Figure 19 shows the crisp definition of the features after running sharpened coherence.

be able to see subtle differences in thin-bed tuning effects that could be measured by comparing the two waveforms. Figure 22 is a cartoon illustrating this interazimuth-coherence concept. Figure 22a shows an idealized earth model with a thin (25-m-thick) fractured zone. The synthetic data corresponding to a source-receiver azimuth that is parallel to the fractures is shown in Figure 22b, and one that is perpendicular to the fractures is shown in Figure 22c. The similarity between Figures 22b and 22c shows significant change and is displayed as a function of lateral position in Figure 22d.

Al-Dossary et al. (2004) applied this azimuthal binning technique to two offset- and azimuth-limited seismic volumes over a fractured reservoir in north Texas (Figures

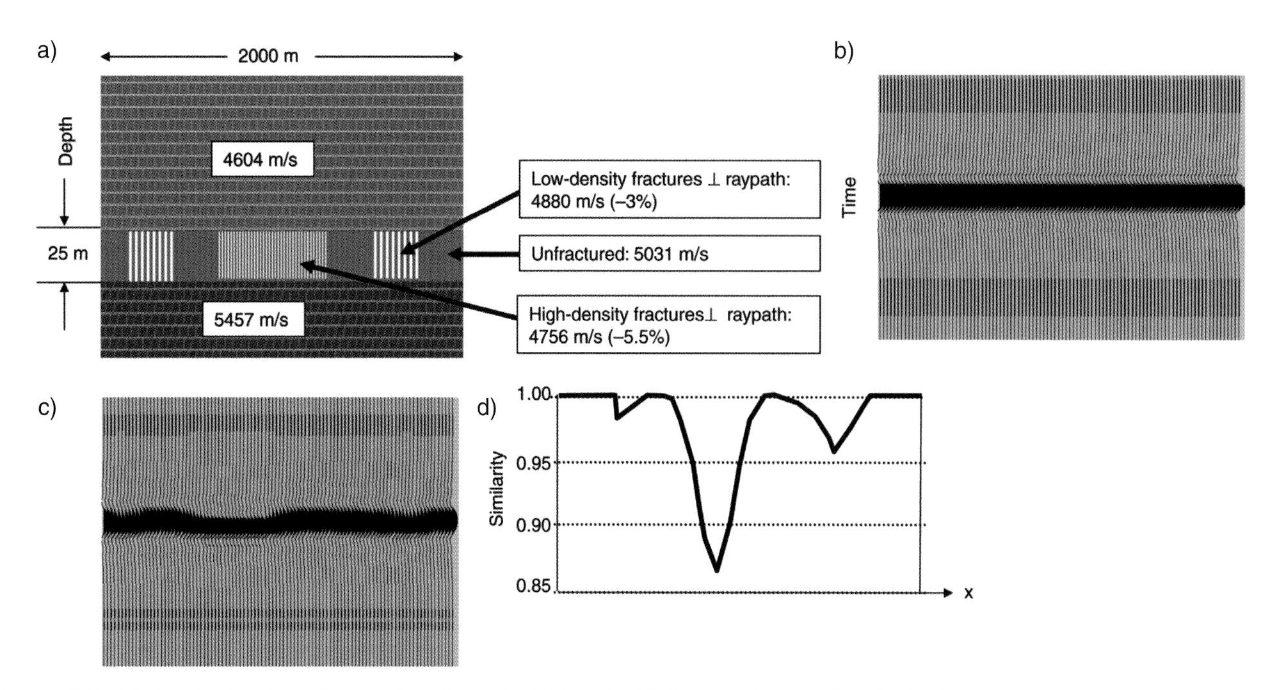

Figure 22. (a) An idealized earth model with a thin (25-m-thick) fractured zone. Synthetic data correspond to a source-receiver azimuth that is (b) parallel to the fractures and (c) one that is perpendicular to the fractures. (d) The similarity between (b) and (c), displayed as a function of lateral position. After Al-Dossary et al. (2004).

23a and 23b). Although the images are intriguing, Simon (2005) showed that the correlation of interazimuth coherence (similarity) (Figure 23c) with estimated ultimate recovery (EUR) from wells was insignificant. Simon (2005) attributed this lack of correlation to the rapid change in the azimuth of velocity anisotropy across the survey, which we will discuss later when we examine Figure 26.

Although interazimuth coherence between two fixed azimuths should provide a good estimate of fracture density (or stresses) for a single, predetermined azimuth, applying the method to variable azimuths requires a search over azimuths such as the algorithm designed by Jenner (2001) for velocity anisotropy.

P-wave Velocity Anisotropy

We refer the reader to recent books by Thomsen (2002) and Tsvankin (2001) for a detailed discussion of velocity anisotropy. In this chapter, we simply note that volumetric estimation of azimuthal anisotropy based on algorithms like those developed by Jenner (2001) is suitable for the same analysis workflows as are other volumetric attributes such as coherence and spectral decomposition.

Simon (2005) reexamined the survey shown in Figure 23 with the goal of determining which seismic attribute was the best predictor of EUR from each of 102 wells. To review, Figure 23 shows time slices at t = 1.200 s through (Figure 23a) northeast-southwest, and (Figure 23b) northwest-southeast azimuth-limited and offset-limited seismic volumes. Both volumes are offset-limited to 20°–50° at target depth. Figure 23c shows the interazimuth coherence between the data shown in Figures 23a and b using a 20-ms analysis window. The north Texas reservoir in question has many natural fractures, almost all of which are filled with calcite. Production from this tight reservoir required hydrofracturing. The induced fractures are controlled more by the local stress field than by preexisting natural fractures. Figure 24 shows fractures seen on an acoustic log (Figure 24a) and a resistivity image log (Figure 24b) from the survey shown in Figure 25. White arrows indicate vertical and petal fractures induced by drilling; these fractures allow the interpreter to determine the direction of maximum horizontal stress. Figure 24c is a rose diagram showing the direction and count of natural (blue) and induced (red) fractures. It is unclear which has greater influence on velocity anisotropy — natural fractures or local stress.

Simon (2005) used the methodology described by Bourne et al. (2000) to determine that the direction of movement along the strike-slip fault in the northwestern corner of the image in Figure 25 was right-lateral. More important, he found that the anomalies in velocity anisotropy correlated strongly with EUR and with the performance of several microseismic experiments done during hydrofracturing.

In Figure 25a, we display Simon's (2005) image of a microseismic experiment with a well that has a relatively low EUR. We note that the microseismic experiment shows fractures that are aligned almost entirely northeast-southwest in a narrow band. As determined by seismic velocity analysis over limited azimuthal ranges, the azimuth of the fast velocity, v_f, aligns with the direction of the regional stress, which is also northeast-southwest.

In Figure 25b, we display Simon's (2005) image of a microseismic experiment with a well that has high EUR.

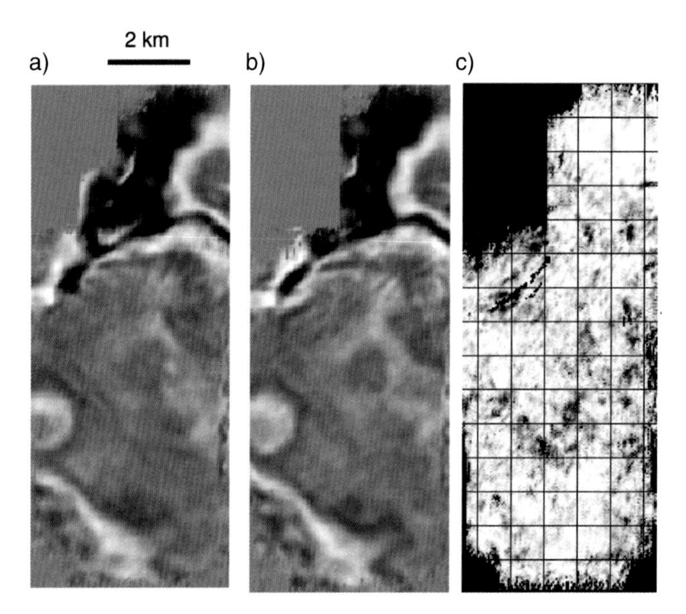

Figure 23. Time slices at t = 1.200 s, through azimuth-limited and offset-limited seismic volumes oriented (a) northeast-southwest and (b) northwest-southeast. Both volumes are offset-limited to 20–50° at target depth. (c) Interazimuth coherence between the data shown in (a) and the data in (b), using a 20-ms analysis window. After Al-Dossary et al. (2004). Data courtesy of Devon Energy.

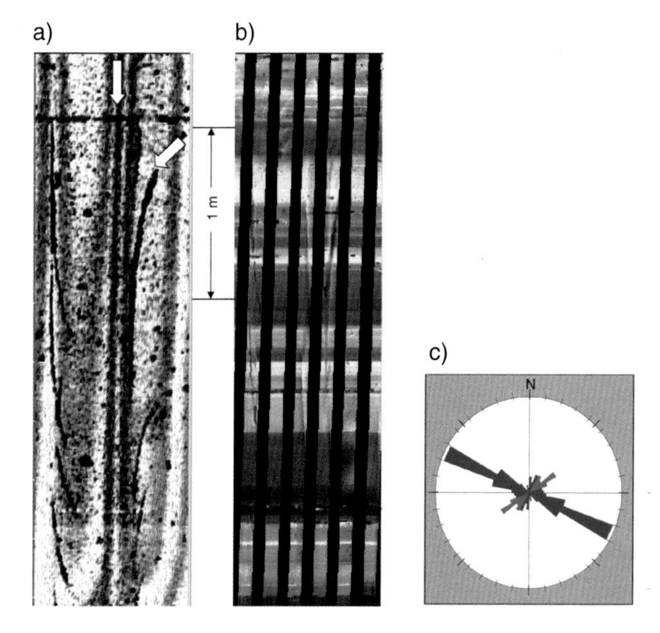

Figure 24. Fractures seen on (a) an acoustic log and on (b) a resistivity image log, from the survey shown in Figure 25. White arrows indicate drilling-induced vertical and petal fractures that allow the interpreter to determine the direction of maximum horizontal stress. (c) A rose diagram showing the direction and count of natural (blue) and induced (red) fractures. After Simon (2005). Data courtesy of Devon Energy.

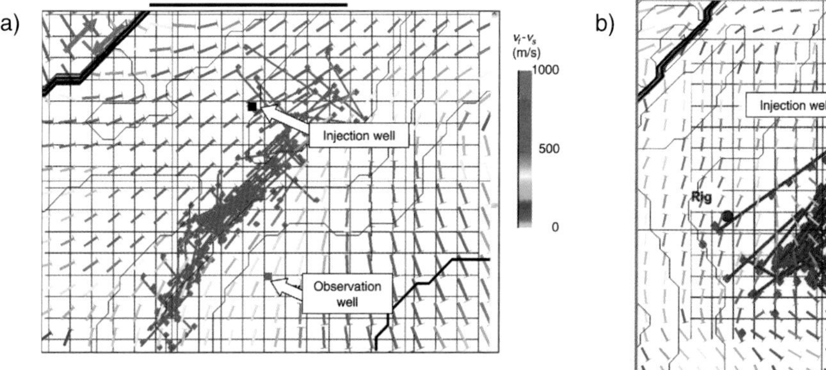

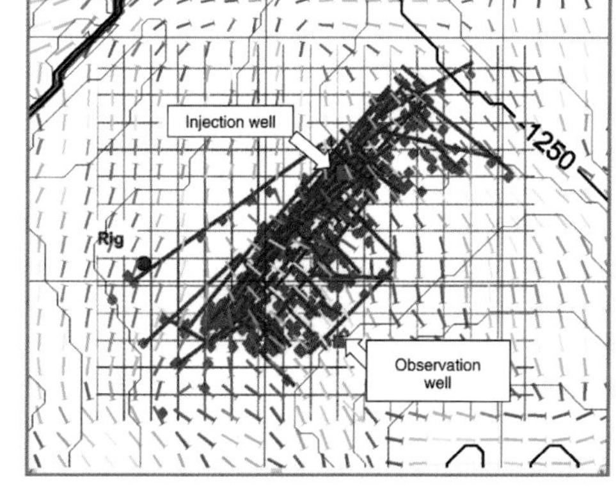

Figure 25. Velocity anisotropy at the reservoir level, plotted as icons. The azimuth and length of each icon reflect the azimuth and magnitude of the fast velocity, v_f. The color of each icon is proportional to the difference between the fast and slow velocity values, $v_f - v_s$. Black lines indicate fractures induced by hydrofracturing, mapped here using microseisms recorded in the observation well. (a) An injection well that subsequently had moderate production and has moderate EUR, probably resulting from a network of fractures that drains a moderate-sized area and has predominantly one azimuth, aligned with a strong anisotropy (red arrow). (b) An injection well that subsequently had moderate production and has excellent EUR, probably resulting from a network of fractures that better drains a larger area and is associated with weak anisotropy (green and blue arrows). After Simon (2005). Data courtesy of Devon Energy.

Here, the microseismic experiment shows a grid of fractures that covers a wider zone than do the fractures shown in Figure 25a (and because this injection well has the higher EUR, presumably a larger area of the reservoir will be drained). Although the regional stress is in the northeast-southwest direction, the azimuth of the fast velocity, v_f, appears to be diverted locally to be northwest-southeast.

Simon (2005) also found an intriguing visual correlation between the azimuth of the fast velocity and curvature (Figure 26). Here, the azimuth of v_f appears to align with the major linear ridges and valleys. Although the various curvature attributes correlated poorly with EUR, Simon found a significant numerical correlation between the magnitude of v_f and EUR (about 30%), and very strong visual correlations between v_f and both the hydrofrac patterns and the curvature seen on map overlays.

Geoscientists' understanding of the correlation between production and fracture-sensitive attributes is in its infancy. We clearly need to design methodologies beyond simple multiattribute crosscorrelation. We will evaluate one such approach when we review recent work by Nissen in Chapter 15.

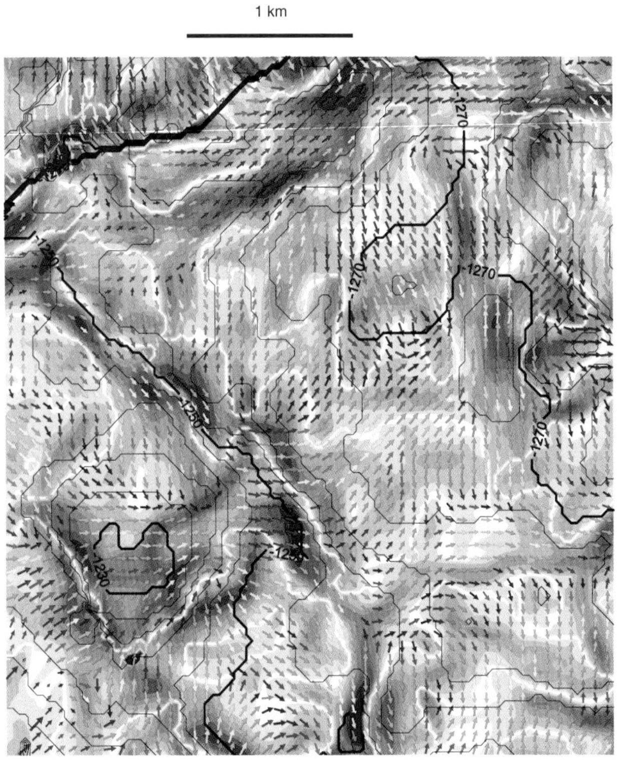

Figure 26. P-wave anisotropy, overplotted onto maximum curvature. Note how the azimuth of the fast velocity, v_f, lines up with the ridges and valleys seen in the curvature. After Simon (2005). Data courtesy of Devon Energy.

Seismic-attribute Images from Multicomponent Data

We conclude this section with several attribute images computed from multicomponent data. Because we obtain different attribute images from offset-limited and azimuth-limited volumes, we should not be surprised that we obtain different images from wavefields having different polarizations. D'Agosto Palladino (2003) processed a three-component seismic survey (explosive source and three-component geophones) acquired in the Barinas Basin, Venezuela, with the goal of mapping fractures in the carbonate Escandalosa Formation. Figure 27 is a representative core showing the intersection of natural fractures and vugs in an otherwise tight matrix.

D'Agosto Palladino (2003) found that the P-P (Figure 28a) and P-S data (Figure 28b) from the Barinas Basin survey had very similar frequency contents (Figure 28c) — a finding that differs from most multicomponent survey results. Because the velocity of shear waves is about half that of P-waves, the converted wave-data volume has considerably greater vertical resolution than does the corresponding P-P data volume. (In contrast, the lateral resolution is similar because of the difficulty in accurately estimating the shear-wave velocities).

In Figure 29, we display a representative line through the P-P data from Figure 28, indicating here (with white arrows) the reverse fault through the Escandalosa Formation. The lateral resolution is less than optimal because of difficulties in estimating the S-wave velocity from the data. We also

Figure 27. The connection between vugs and fractures in an Escandalosa Formation core sampled at Borburata field, Barinas Basin, Venezuela. After D'Agosto Palladino (2003), in turn after www.pdv.com/lexico. Image courtesy of PdVSA, copyright Edgar Chacín.

indicate some migration (or DMO) artifacts by black arrows. Although such artifacts do not negatively impact a conventional structural interpretation, they appear as acquisition footprint on the energy-weighted coherent-amplitude-gradient attribute images shown in Figure 30b and 30c.

The main north-south fault in the Escandalosa data is easily identified in Figure 30 and appears to bifurcate in the northern part of the survey. There is also a second, less-pronounced system of northeast-southwest faults in the southeastern corner of the survey (Figure 30a).

D'Agosto Palladino (2003) followed a well-established processing workflow of rotating the multicomponent seismic data into both radial and transverse polarizations that are based on the acquisition geometry. Once the data were rotated, he then broke the data volume into six azimuth-limited subvolumes as a preface to later birefringence analysis (akin to the P-wave anisotropy analysis discussed in the previous section). In Figure 31, we display the same seismic line shown in Figure 29 for six azimuths of P-S reflections, here having both radial polarizations (Figure 31a) and tangential polarizations (Figure 31b). We note that the north-south-trending reverse fault (indicated by arrows) is best resolved on azimuths close to the strike of the fault. D'Agosto Palladino (2003) attributed this appearance to the robustness of the common conversion point stack and moveout parallel to strike. An accurate calculation perpendicular to strike would require not only a more accurate velocity but also a ray-trace-driven moveout curve, with a better solution being simple prestack P-S depth migration.

Finally, we display representative converted wave-attribute images from along the Escandalosa horizon through attributes generated from the radial component P-S data volume. Figure 32a shows the coherence display, and Figure 32b shows the east-west component of the energy-weighted coherent amplitude gradient. We still see the main north-south fault illuminated by the P-P images in Figure 30. We do not see any significant acquisition footprint, perhaps because of the extra care D'Agosto Palladino (2003) took to reject low-velocity ground roll that otherwise would interfere with the low-frequency component of his P-S reflections. A northeast-southwest fault (gray arrows) appears in the northwestern corner of the image; that fault is not seen on P-P data. A suite of antithetic faults appears in Figure 32c but was masked by acquisition footprint in Figure 30c.

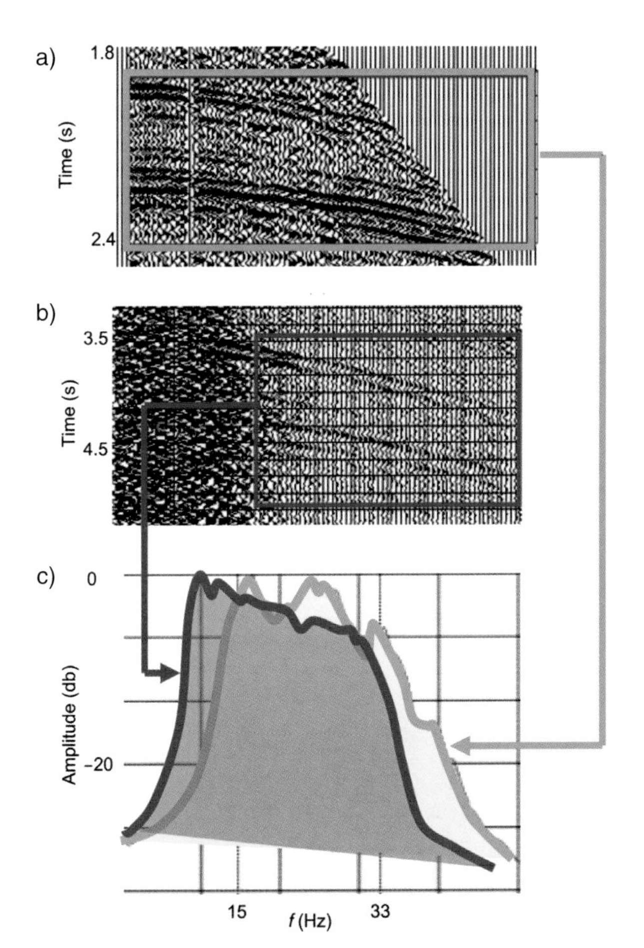

Figure 28. Data windows from (a) a common-midpoint (CMP) gather of the vertical-component P-P reflections and (b) a common-conversion point (CCP) gather of the radial-component P-S reflections. (c) Note that the spectral bandwidths of unprocessed P-P and P-S reflections are the same size. After D'Agosto Palladino (2003). Data courtesy of PdVSA.

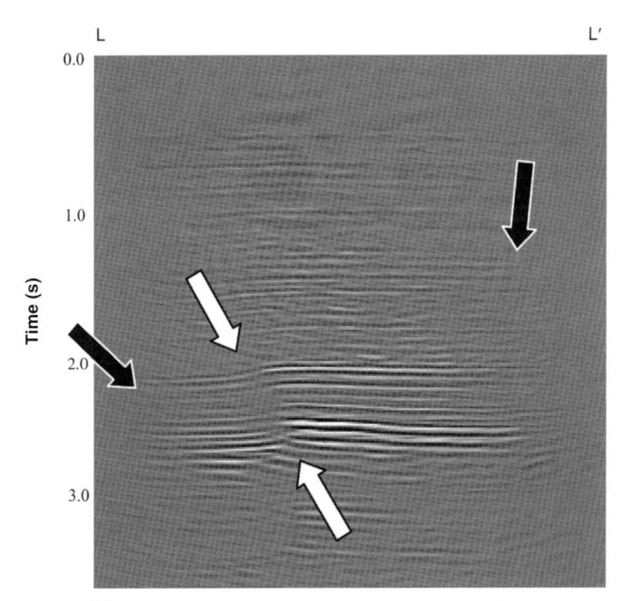

Figure 29. Line LL' through a prestack time-migrated P-P volume. White arrows indicate the reverse fault seen in Figure 30. Black arrows indicate noise (from an acquisition footprint) that has been organized by either the DMO (dip-moveout) or migration operators. After D'Agosto Palladino (2003). Data courtesy of PdVSA.

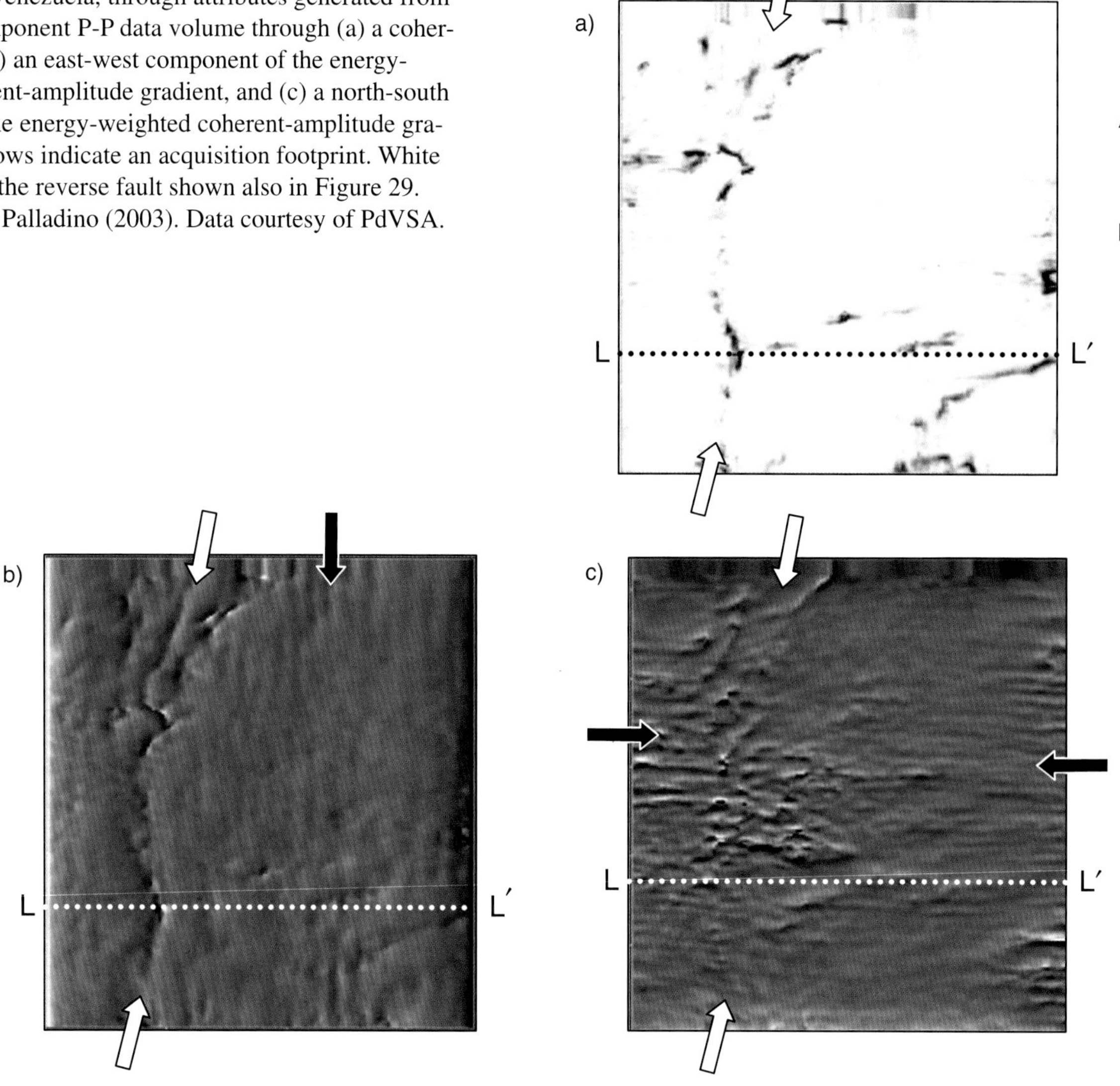

Figure 30. Time slices near the Escandalosa horizon, Barinas Basin, Venezuela, through attributes generated from the vertical-component P-P data volume through (a) a coherence volume, (b) an east-west component of the energy-weighted coherent-amplitude gradient, and (c) a north-south component of the energy-weighted coherent-amplitude gradient. Black arrows indicate an acquisition footprint. White arrows indicate the reverse fault shown also in Figure 29. After D'Agosto Palladino (2003). Data courtesy of PdVSA.

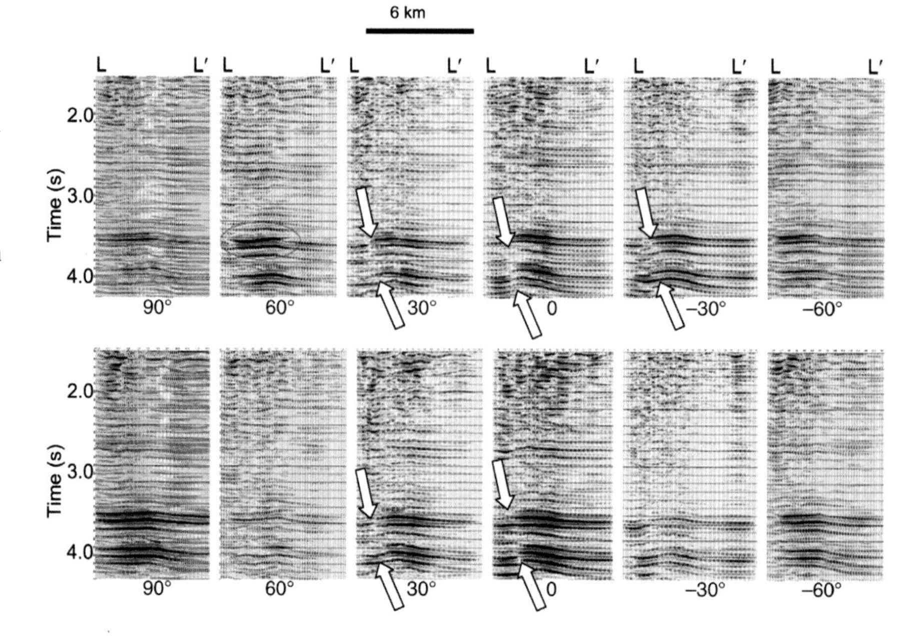

Figure 31. Line LL' through azimuth-limited prestack time-migrated P-S volumes, showing (a) radial components and (b) transverse components. White arrows indicate the reverse fault seen also in Figure 29. Here, the reverse fault (indicated by arrows) appears more distinct on azimuth-limited volumes running parallel to the fault. Time and distance scales differ here from those used in Figure 29. After D'Agosto Palladino (2003). Data courtesy of PdVSA.

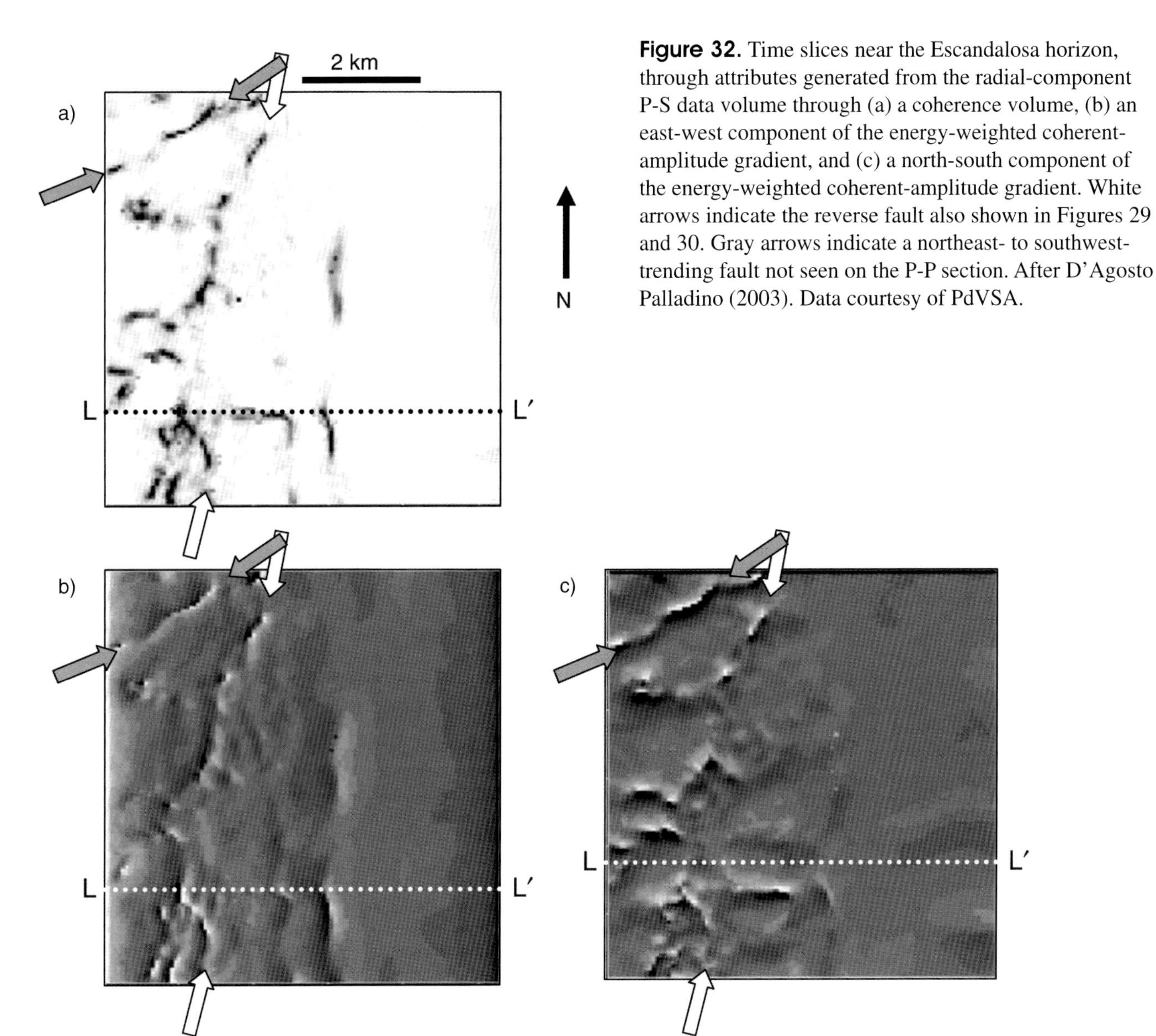

Figure 32. Time slices near the Escandalosa horizon, through attributes generated from the radial-component P-S data volume through (a) a coherence volume, (b) an east-west component of the energy-weighted coherent-amplitude gradient, and (c) a north-south component of the energy-weighted coherent-amplitude gradient. White arrows indicate the reverse fault also shown in Figures 29 and 30. Gray arrows indicate a northeast- to southwest-trending fault not seen on the P-P section. After D'Agosto Palladino (2003). Data courtesy of PdVSA.

Chapter Summary

Different offsets (incident angles) not only illuminate different geologic features, they influence seismic reflectivity even for flat geologies. For this reason, seismic-attribute volumes computed from offset-limited or incident-angle-limited seismic volumes are different from full-offset volumes. Coupled with conventional AVO analysis, attributes such as conventional amplitude extractions, coherence, and energy-weighted coherent-amplitude gradients can be used to better delineate the edges of hydrocarbon reservoirs and lithologic boundaries than can full-offset stacked data volumes. Although generally the variability between different offset images is only moderate, we can use those images to identify detailed stratigraphic features that may help us produce better maps of reservoir heterogeneity for efficient reservoir management.

Seismic reflections are also sensitive to fractures and regional stress, both of which can contribute to P-wave and S-wave anisotropy. We find that the four-azimuth method detects azimuthal anisotropy with arbitrary orientation much better than the conventional, all-azimuth stacking method does. Compared with the use of conventional, all-azimuth stacking, attributes computed from restricted azimuth 3D seismic volumes offer superior lateral resolution of fault systems in different orientations.

Such processing is more costly because it requires a greater processing effort. In addition, the partial-azimuth stacks produce lower fold and poorer S/N ratios compared with results from conventional full-azimuth volumes. This is tolerable because of the high multiplicity of the original 3D data and also because of the spatially dealiasing DMO algorithm, which tends to take care of amplitude preservation and aliasing.

Of course, volumetric estimates of velocity anisotropy are an attribute in themselves and provide information that is not measured by dip and azimuth, curvature, coherence, textures, and spectral-decomposition attributes, all of which are the primary focus of this book. In particular, volumetric estimates of anisotropy can be used to estimate both fracture density and orientation. At present, we believe that anisotropic effects resulting from fractures are seismically indistinguishable from anisotropic effects resulting from regional stress.

In addition to offset and azimuth, we can acquire seismic data that have different modes of propagation. For the same surface acquisition, P-P and P-S waves illuminate different regions of the earth and have different reflectivities, thereby generating independent and complementary attribute images of the subsurface. Each of those volumes results in complementary attribute maps that can help us delineate faults, fractures, and stratigraphy.

References

Al-Dossary, S., Y. Simon, and K. J. Marfurt, 2004, Inter-azimuth coherence attributes for fracture detection: 74th Annual International Meeting, SEG, Expanded Abstracts, 183–186.

Beasley, C. J., and E. Mobley, 1998, Spatial dealiasing of 3-D DMO: The Leading Edge, **17,** 1590–1594.

Bourne, S., J. F. Brauckman, L. Rijkels, B. J. Stephenson, A. Weber, and E. J. M. Willemse, 2000, Predictive modeling of naturally fractured reservoirs using geomechanics and flow simulation: 9th Abu Dhabi International Petroleum Exhibition and Conference (ADIPEC), 0911.

Chopra, S., and V. Sudhakar, 2000, Fault interpretation — The coherence cube and beyond: Oil & Gas Journal, July 31, 71–74.

Chopra, S., V. Sudhakar, G. Larsen, and H. Leong, 2000, Azimuth based coherence for detecting faults and fractures: World Oil, **21,** September, 57–62.

D'Agosto Palladino, C., 2003, Birefringence analysis at Borburata field for fracture characterization: M.S. thesis, University of Houston.

Grimm, R. E., H. B. Lynn, C. R. Bates, D. R. Phillips, K. M. Simon, and W. E. Beckham, 1999, Detection and analysis of naturally fractured gas reservoirs: Geophysics, **64**, 1277–1292.

Hilterman, F. J., 2001, Seismic amplitude interpretation: SEG Distinguished Instructor Series, no. 4.

Jenner, E., 2001, Azimuthal Anisotropy of 3-D compressional wave seismic data, Weyburn field, Saskatchewan, Canada: Ph.D. thesis, Colorado School of Mines.

Simon, Y. S., 2005, Stress and fracture characterization in a shale reservoir, north Texas, using correlation between new seismic attributes and well data: M.S. thesis, University of Houston.

Thomsen, L., 2002, Understanding seismic anisotropy in exploration and exploitation: SEG Distinguished Instructor Series, no. 5.

Tsvankin, I., 2001, Seismic signatures and analysis of reflection data in anisotropic media: Handbook of Geophysical Exploration, Section 1, **29**, Pergamon Press.

Section II

Use of Geometric Attributes in 3D Interpretation

Chapter 11

Attribute Expression of Structural Deformation

Chapter Objectives

After reading this chapter, you will be able to

- use coherence to accelerate interpretation of faults on 3D volumes
- use volumetric attributes to provide a preliminary interpretation across multiple surveys having different amplitude and phase
- identify the appearance and structural style of salt and shale diapirs on geometric attributes
- use curvature to define axial planes
- use coherence and curvature as aids in predicting fractures

Introduction

Geometric attributes such as coherence allow interpreters to quickly visualize and map complex fault systems, salt and shale diapirs, and, in some cases, incoherent overpressured shales (Chopra, 2002). Volumetric curvature provides not only images of folds, domes, and collapse features, but also helps interpreters map faults whose vertical throw falls below seismic resolution. Color displays of volumetric dip and azimuth on vertical sections and time slices allow interpreters to easily visualize the rotation of fault blocks within the 3D seismic volume and can be an important aid in estimating four-way closure. Together, coherence, curvature, volumetric dip, and volumetric azimuth contribute to a more complete understanding of the deformation process, thereby allowing interpreters to link a system of faults via connecting folds and also to link folds to blocks of undeformed sediments.

Geometric attributes allow us to map on time slices faults that are not readily seen on conventional amplitude slices. The following series of examples illustrates this point.

In Figure 1a, we can map some obvious east-west-trending faults that trend perpendicularly to strike; however, it is difficult to place additional faults on the seismic slice. The corresponding coherence slice in Figure 1b not only shows these additional faults but also the faults parallel to strike. In addition, we see an intensively fractured region in the northeastern corner of the image. Overlaying the coherence slices on the corresponding seismic slices (Figure 1c) can help us understand the seismic expression of the faults. By doing that at different time levels, we can transfer faults to the seismic volume (Figure 1c). We can do that either by creating workstation maps for different horizons and fault locations or by associating the faults to the seismic volume. Then we can use 3D visualization to see the disposition of fault planes in the 3D volume.

Correlating coherence patterns with their corresponding seismic expressions can be done conveniently using dual-screen workstation software, which now is quite common. An interpretation can then display a time slice through coherence on one screen and a vertical slice through the seismic data on a second screen. Choosing an arbitrary line perpendicular to the now clearly imaged fault allows the interpreter to begin by picking the fault in the dip direction (using the cursor-connect option) where it will be most accurately resolved and unambiguously interpreted. In Figure 2, for a seismic volume from the Gulf of Mexico, we show the coherence slice (Figure 2a) correlated with the reflection breaks seen on the vertical seismic section (Figure 2b).

Bifurcations of faults, en echelon faults, and/or fault relays often are particularly challenging to interpret. Conventional interpretation of vertical seismic slices can lead

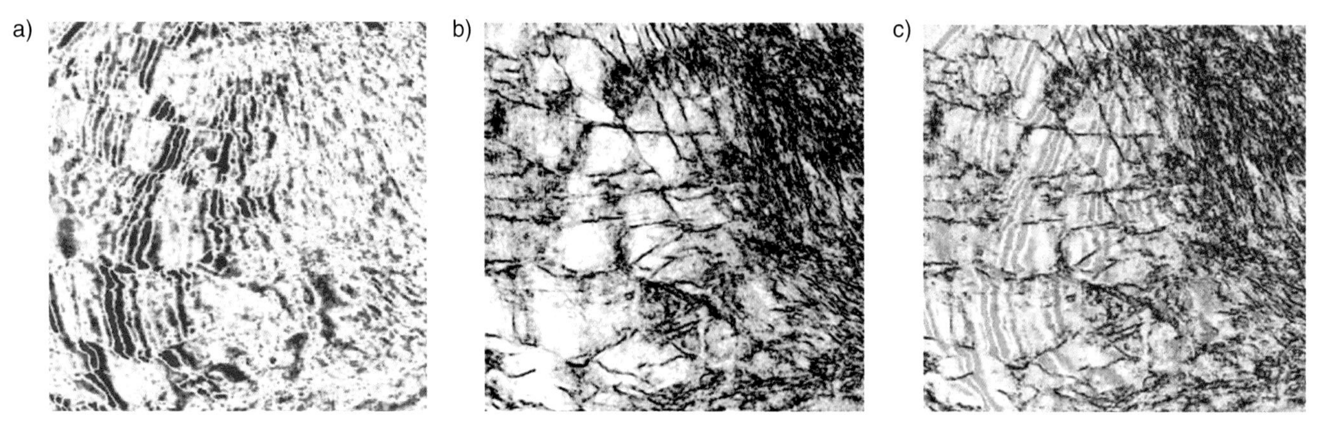

Figure 1. Time slices through (a) a seismic data volume, (b) a coherence volume, and (c) a coherence volume overlaid on seismic data, from a survey off the eastern coast of Canada.

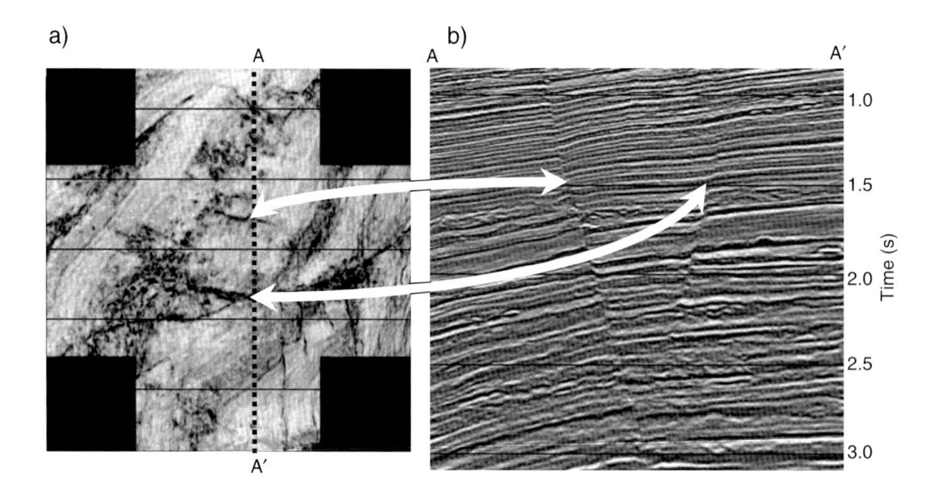

Figure 2. Faults seen on (a) a coherence time slice at $t = 1.500$ s and on (b) vertical seismic line AA′, from the Gulf of Mexico. We see here how normal faults that appear on vertical seismic displays can be tracked on coherence time slices.

interpreters to incorrectly assign two en echelon faults to a single fault, thereby creating the appearance of a very different, less risky trap closure. In Figure 3, we note how the bifurcated and en echelon faults are much easier to interpret on the coherence slice in Figure 3b than on the seismic data volume in Figure 3a. Thus, we used the coherence volume to produce the interpretations shown in Figure 3c. We note radial faults emanating from two salt domes, which appear as low-coherence zones (black). Arrows indicate low-coherence shales.

Note that we can differentiate the shales on a coherence time slice by the presence of higher-coherence lineaments and meandering features encased in larger generally low-coherence areas. Such features are common is mass-transport complexes (MTCs), which we will discuss in greater detail in Chapter 14.

In a typical workflow, fault interpretation is done by naming and picking major faults on a coherence slice such as that shown in Figure 3b and then picking those faults on a coarse grid of vertical slices through a few arbitrarily chosen seismic lines that are perpendicular to the strike of the fault trace. With that template, the interpreter then proceeds to pick faults on coarse time slices (say, 0.200 s) through the coherence volume. Finally, the interpreter concludes with conventional fault interpretation using inlines and crosslines through the seismic data. Using that simple workflow, the interpreter defines the fault families and interrelations early in the interpretation process and avoids significant mislabeling and reassignment of faults.

In contrast to the previous example, Figure 4 shows a very different fault pattern on a time slice through seismic data volumes and coherence volumes from a survey acquired in southern Alberta, Canada. Although the seismic time slice in Figure 4a indicates some of the breaks corresponding to the faults, we note an incoherent area in the southwestern corner of the survey, whereas the more coherent reflectors to the northeast are broken into several large blocks (Figure 4b). The arrow in Figure 4b indicates an area where the two faults appear to horsetail toward each other. They do not link directly, which could cause problems with a potential reservoir seal. Figure 4c shows an overlay of coherence on the seismic data to clarify the seismic signatures corresponding to the interpretation we make of faults or incoherent regions on the coherence slice in Figure 4b.

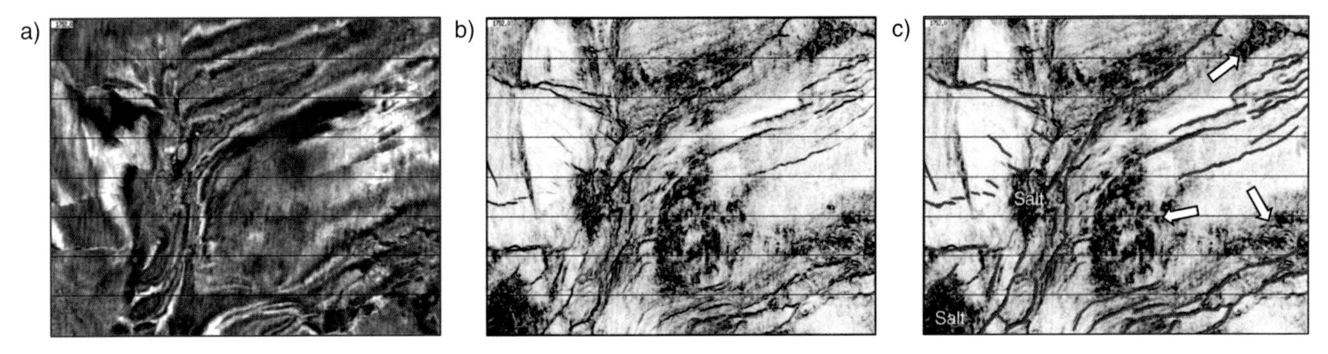

Figure 3. Time slices at t = 1.752 s through (a) a seismic data volume and (b) the corresponding coherence volume from a survey in the Gulf of Mexico, U.S.A. (c) Two salt domes appear as round, incoherent features in the lower left corner of the image and give rise to a system of radial faults. These and other faults are easily picked and displayed in red. Other incoherent zones, indicated by arrows, correspond to channels and mass-transport complexes. The seismic data are courtesy of Geco-Prakla.

Figure 4. Time slices at t = 1.200 s through (a) a seismic data volume, (b) a coherence volume, and (c) a coherence volume overlaid on a seismic data volume, from a survey in southern Alberta, Canada. The arrow indicates a zone where the faults appear to horsetail — a situation that could endanger the quality of the seal in a reservoir.

The following example also illustrates use of a coherence volume to reveal fault locations. Figure 5 is from a survey acquired over South Marsh Island, offshore Louisiana, U.S.A., and it shows a fault pattern that does not exhibit the radial pattern we commonly see over salt domes in this part of the world. Because the salt is deeply seated we see instead the linear patterns more common to the western Gulf of Mexico. Notice the northeast-southwest-trending main fault (white arrows in Figures 5b, c, and d) with multiple faults perpendicular to it. By animating through a suite of such slices in a movie loop (including the ones shown in Figures 5a–d), the interpreter can rapidly determine which are the main, through-going faults and which are antithetic faults. Animation also helps the interpreter distinguish between faults and channels (indicated by black arrows in Figure 5a, c, and d), which generally have a very different location and form at each stratigraphic horizon.

As is the case with seismic-amplitude interpretation, 3D visualization aids us greatly in interpreting coherence volumes. In Figure 6, we show chair diagrams through a seismic data volume (Figure 6a) and a coherence volume (Figure 6b) over a salt dome from the Gulf of Mexico, U.S.A. Faults are clearly visible on the coherence volume.

Low-coherence banding following stratigraphy has two major causes in clastic terrains. The more common cause is low reflectivity associated with shale-on-shale lithologies within a fixed (higher) background of incoherent seismic noise. A less common but not infrequent cause is truly chaotic geology that is associated with slumping, channel cannibalization, and laterally reworked tidal complexes.

The quality of coherence images depends on the quality of the input data. Commonly, not all parts of the seismic volume are imaged equally well. The challenge in creating an accurate subsalt image is one such example. Although inaccurate imaging of the salt generally produces poor seismic images below the salt, and correspondingly poor attribute images (such as shown earlier in Figure 37 of Chapter 7), the degree of subsalt defocusing increases with increased velocity contrast between the salt and the neighboring lithologies.

Figure 7a shows a vertical seismic slice through a survey acquired in the North Sea. The top of the salt is poorly imaged, with obvious poorly collapsed diffraction hyperbolae remaining. Nevertheless, the deeper Carboniferous faults are imaged well, and we can see them clearly on the seismic and coherence time slices (Figure 7b and c, respective-

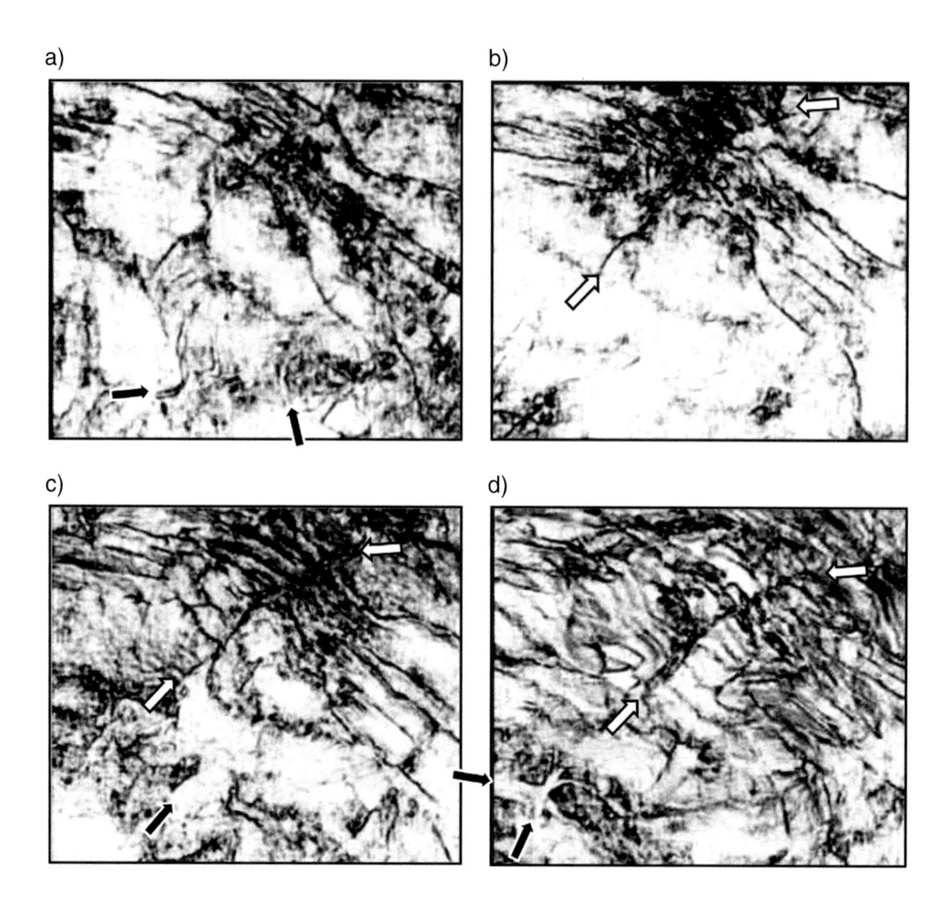

Figure 5. Time slices through a coherence volume at t = (a) 1.140 s, (b) 1.216 s, (c) 1.520 s, and (d) 1.930 s, showing fault patterns over a salt dome in the South Marsh Island area of the Gulf of Mexico, U.S.A. White arrows indicate a master fault. Black arrows indicate stratigraphic features. Note how the fault patterns change slowly from time slice to time slice.

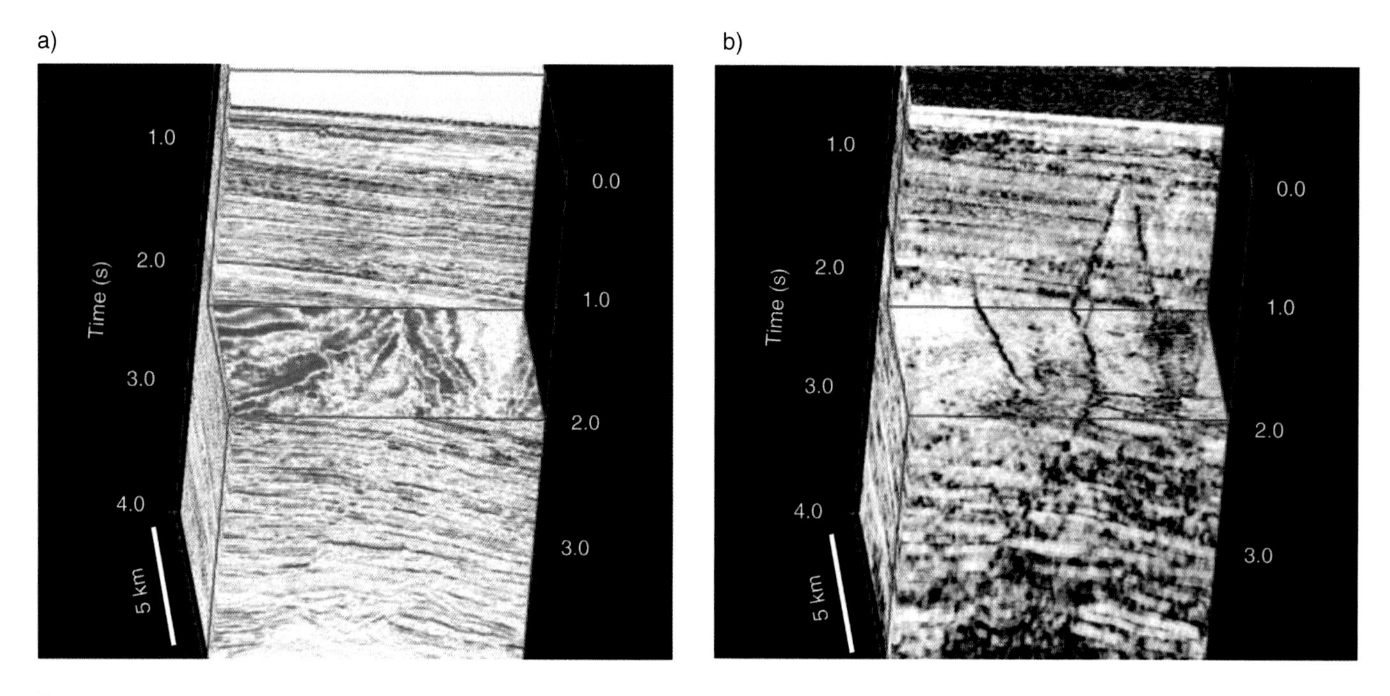

Figure 6. Chair diagrams through (a) a seismic data volume and (b) a coherence volume, over a salt dome from the Gulf of Mexico, U.S.A. Faults are seen clearly on the coherence volume. The low-coherence banding following the stratigraphy has two major causes in clastic terrains. The more common cause is low reflectivity associated with shale-on-shale lithologies within a fixed (higher) background of incoherent seismic noise. A less common but not infrequent cause is truly chaotic geology, associated with slumping, channel cannibalization, and laterally reworked tidal complexes.

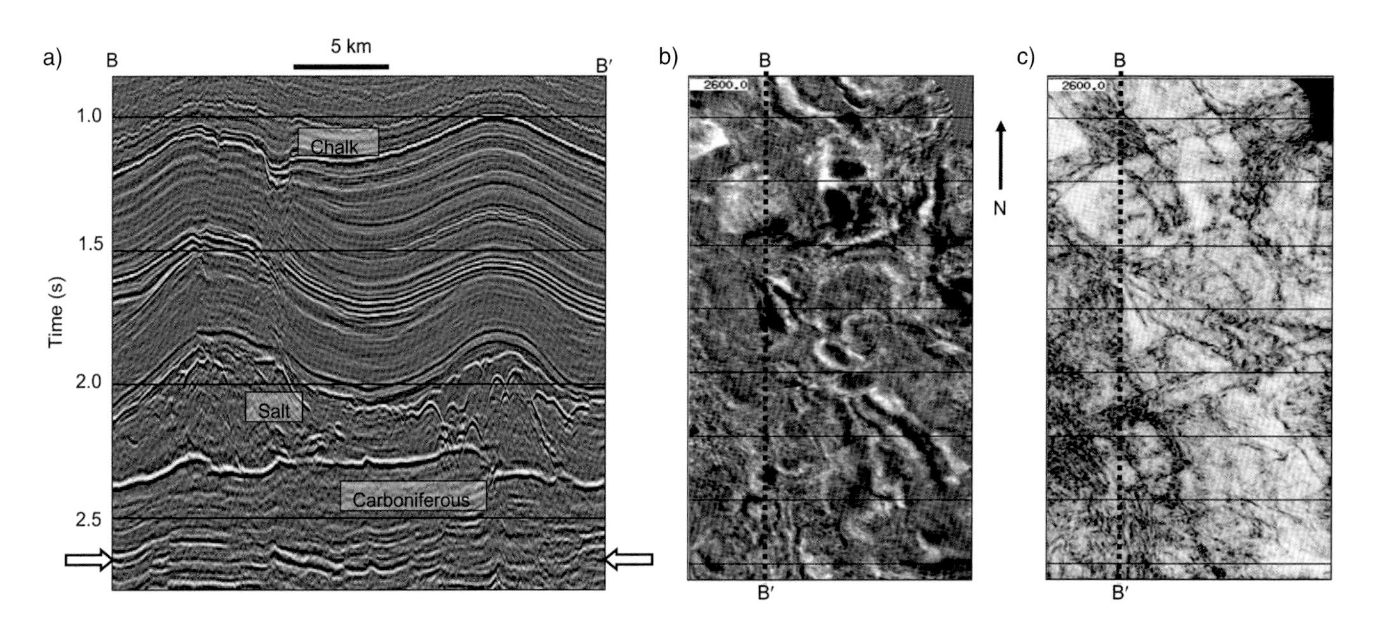

Figure 7. (a) A vertical slice, AA', through seismic data, and (b)-(c) time slices at t = 2.600 s in the Carboniferous section. The vertical slice passes through (b) a seismic data volume and (c) a coherence volume, from a North Sea survey. Note that even though the top of the salt is not imaged accurately (as evidenced by the diffraction hyperbolae), we can still map deeper faults. We expect the images of such faults to be inaccurate and perhaps displaced laterally from their true position because of the incorrect salt-velocity model.

ly). We expect these faults to be displaced laterally and perhaps to be deformed from their true position because of the incorrect salt velocity model.

In Figure 8a and b, we display a time-structure map of a Carboniferous horizon and a corresponding horizon slice through the coherence volume. The inaccurate velocity model causes artificial discontinuities in the horizon slice image. Notice the bands of low-coherence features in place of faults in the upper half of the image. We avoid such artifacts by using the less-biased time slice at t = 2.600 s through the coherence volume shown in Figure 8c. In general, we recommend using time slices to map faults and horizon slices to map stratigraphy.

Geometric attributes are sensitive to lateral changes in waveform similarity, dip azimuth, and energy and typically are measured within a vertical analysis window. For this reason, geometric attributes are less sensitive to the phase and frequency content of the seismic-source wavelet. As we discussed in Chapter 1, the initial application of coherence was motivated by the need to analyze merged surveys to obtain a more regional view of tectonism and sedimentary environments. Figure 9 shows the product of just such a coherence application. This figure is a time slice at t = 1.000 s through seismic-coherence volumes originating from four different surveys acquired over the Central Basin Platform, Texas, U.S.A. These surveys were acquired and processed by four different companies over a period of time ranging from 1994 through 2005.

In Figure 9, we see the lateral changes in overall values of the coherence, which result from geologic differences and not from the different vintages in the surveys. We note that the westernmost survey overall is considerably less coherent than the two to the southeast. The area covered by the westernmost survey is uplifted, so our time slice covers considerably older rocks that have experienced a greater amount of tectonic deformation. In contrast, the eastern portion of the northernmost survey also has low coherence. Here the time slice cuts across chaotic sediments spilling into the basin to the east.

The next figure shows the overall trend in changes in structural depth. Figure 10 is a time-structure map of the Ellenburger horizon. Note that the Ellenburger is deepest in the northernmost survey and shallowest in the westernmost survey.

Figure 11 shows a horizon slice along the Ellenburger horizon through the most-positive-curvature volumes, and those images indicate the east-west strike-slip faults.

Figures 12 and 13 shows two sets of images of two different salt domes. In Figure 12, some of the radial faults are not seen very clearly on the seismic time slice (Figure 12a), but the equivalent coherence slice (Figure 12b) makes many of these radial faults show up clearly, thereby facilitating a more rapid and more accurate interpretation.

Figure 13 shows another salt dome that is associated with several radial faults, some of which actually pass through the shale diapir above the salt, which is seen as a very low-coher-

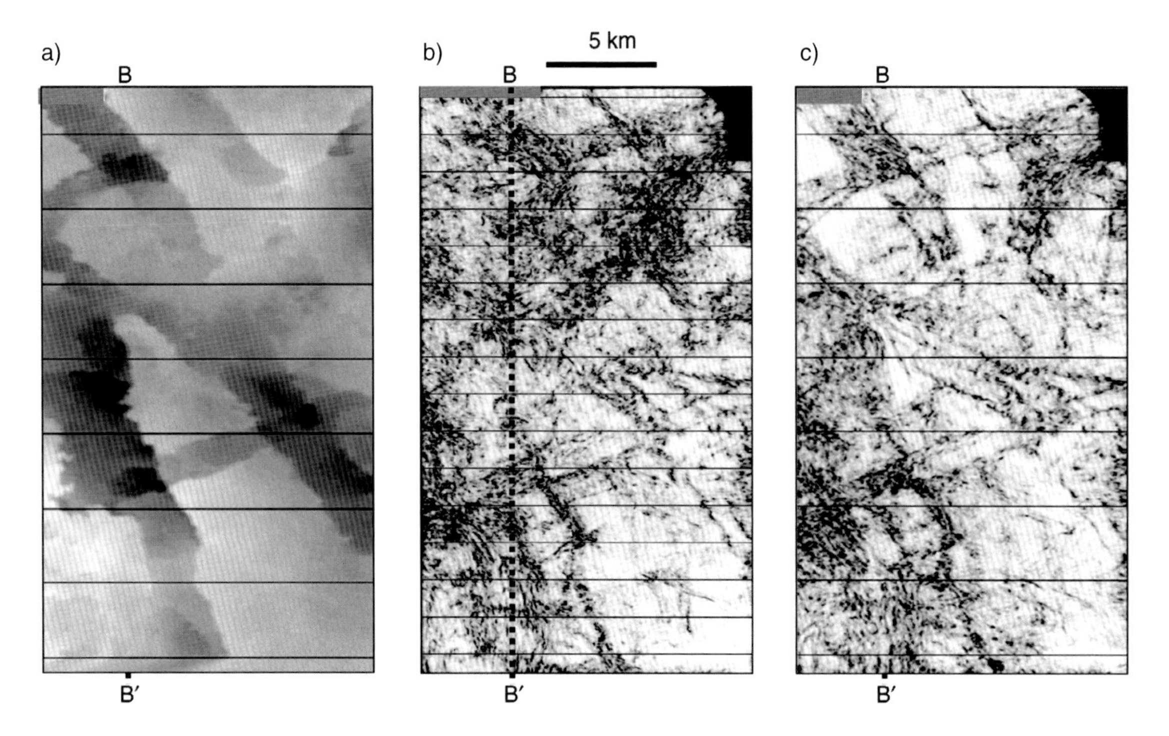

Figure 8. (a) A time-structure map of a Carboniferous horizon, and (b) the corresponding horizon slice through the coherence volume for the survey shown in Figure 7. The inaccurate velocity model causes artificial discontinuities in the horizon-slice image. (c) We avoid such artifacts by using a less-biased time slice at $t = 2.600$ s through the coherence volume.

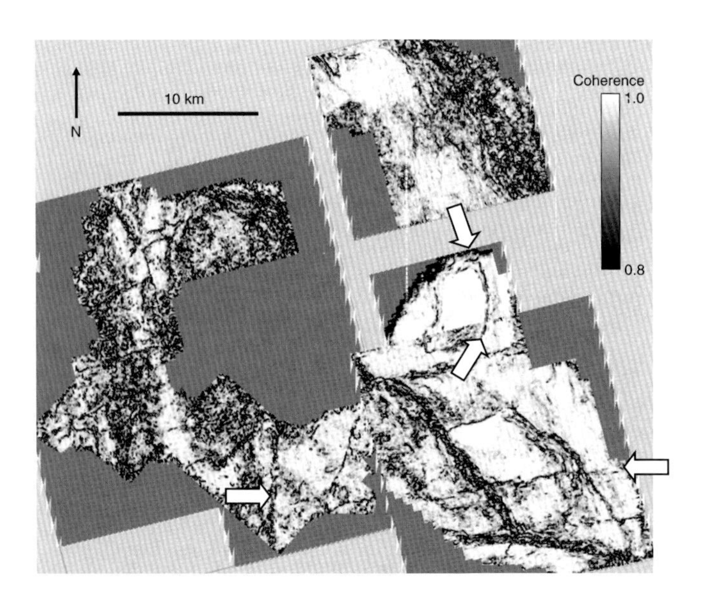

Figure 9. Time slices at $t = 1.000$ s through coherence volumes generated for four surveys conducted on the Central Basin Platform, Texas, U.S.A. by different operators over a 15-year period. Arrows indicate faults that can be carried across surveys. The seismic data are courtesy of Oxy Permian, Devon, Burlington, and BP.

ence (black) patch on Figure 13a and b. A thin channel to the left (marked in blue) also is visible (Figure 13b).

We now continue this chapter by first summarizing why certain tectonic features sometimes appear on coherence and curvature images and sometimes they do not. Then we show how to use coherence to help accelerate fault interpretation and horizon picking, and we include an interpretation workflow that employs geometric attributes to help track and manage fault types using conventional workstation software. We follow by examining geometric-attribute expressions of a wide range of structural-deformation processes, including compressional, extensional, and strike-slip faulting, salt and shale diapirism, and fractures.

Appearance of Faults on Geometric Attributes

Coherence, curvature, and other attributes sensitive to faults and folds are computer algorithms that are based on very simple measurements. Such measurements are simpler but also more localized than the measurements human interpreters use with their brains and eyes. Human interpreters

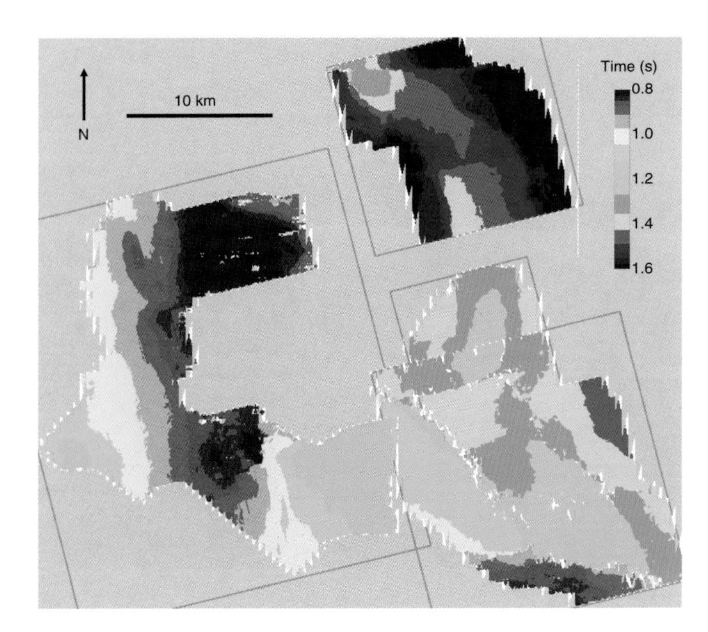

Figure 10. A time-structure map of the Ellenburger horizon, from the four surveys shown in Figure 9. Note the structural misties among the surveys. Interpretation is courtesy of Chuck Blumentritt, University of Houston.

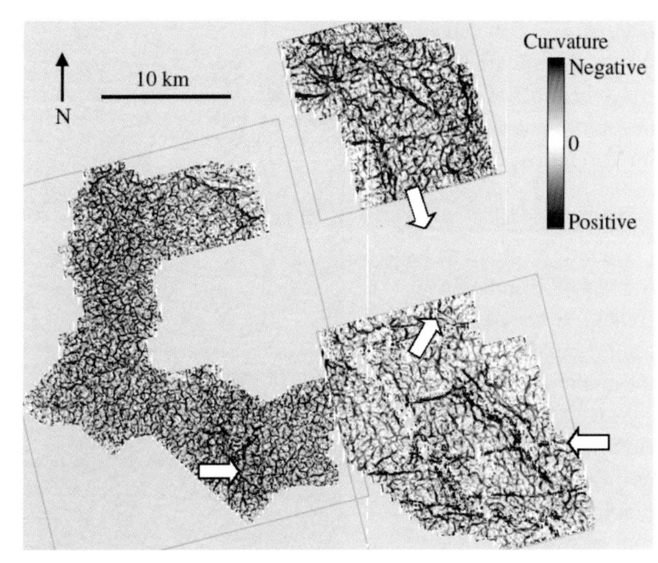

Figure 11. Horizon slices along the Ellenburger horizon shown in Figure 10, displayed here through the most-positive-curvature volumes. Interpretation is courtesy of Chuck Blumentritt, University of Houston.

a)

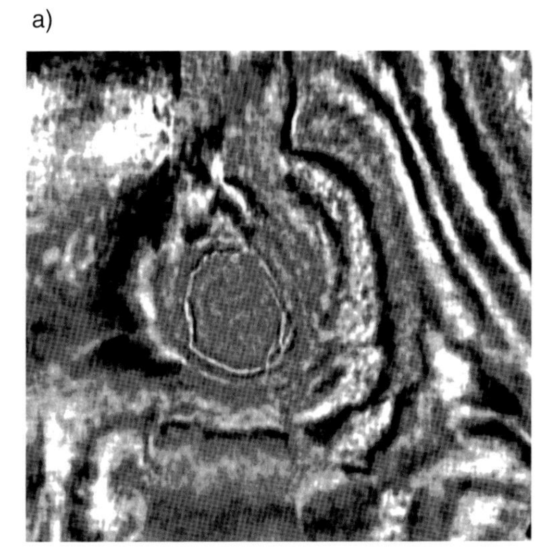

b)

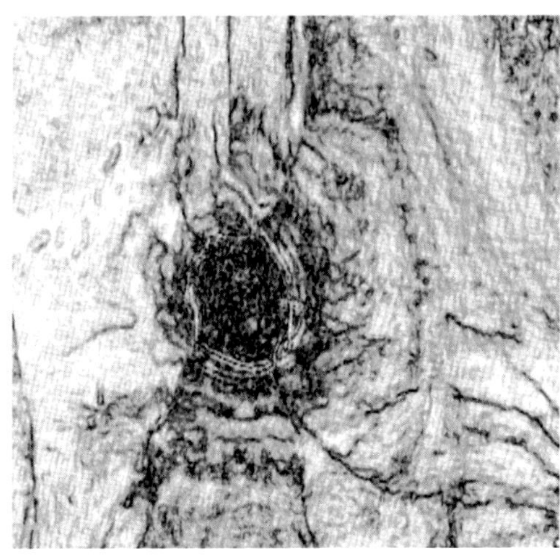

Figure 12. Time slices from (a) a seismic data volume and (b) a coherence volume, from the Gulf of Mexico. Radial faults, both big and small, are seen very clearly.

typically analyze several seconds of seismic data as they decide where to place a fault. In contrast, geometric attributes analyze only 20–40 ms of data around each analysis point.

When we manually pick a fault, we do more than recognize discontinuities and link them together. We also apply well-established geologic models that tell us where a fault should be, whether or not we explicitly see it. That is commonly the case in shaly parts of our sections where the seismic data quality may be poorer, or where the shale deforms ductilely rather than brittlely.

In Figure 14a, we show an example of a listric fault. Finite reflector offset across the faults will make this listric fault easily detected by coherence. The reflectors exhibit rotation as the fault slides down, so that the fault also will be seen by curvature.

The fault shown in Figure 14b also will be seen by coherence. However, little or no reflector rotation occurs about the fault, so it will not be seen by volumetric curvature. Although a human interpreter may be talented enough to draw a surface along the dashed reflector (second from the bottom in Figure 14b) and then envision tight curvature across the fault, we need to remember that our curvature algorithms work on estimates of volumetric dip. There is never a picked horizon. Because the dip of any given reflector on either side of the fault is the same in this example, the volumetric estimate of curvature will be zero.

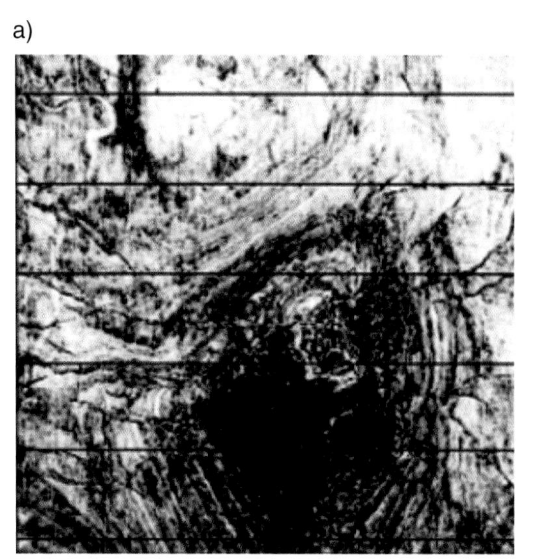

Figure 13. Time slice from a coherence volume from the Gulf of Mexico (a) before and (b) after interpretation. Notice the radial faults emanating from the salt mass (interpreted in red) seen as having very low coherence (black). Some of the radial faults actually pass through the shale diapir above the salt. Also note a channel (interpreted in blue) meandering to the left of the salt diapir.

In Figure 15a, we show a fault that has a displacement of significantly less than one-quarter wavelength. Coherence will not show this fault. However, the reflector will appear to have a subtle change in dip. Unlike the example in Figure 14, in this case a computer can easily track local changes in a horizon if those changes fall within a fraction of a wavelength. For that reason, the fault in Figure 15a will appear on a curvature-attribute volume.

The structure shown in Figure 15b is similar to that shown in Figure 14b. Because the reflectors have finite offset (greater than one-quarter wavelength) the fault will be seen by coherence. However, because the dip does not change, the fault will not be revealed by curvature.

In Figure 16a, we depict a situation that interpreters often interpret as a fault. In essence, a continuum exists between vertical offset of horizons over a short lateral distance (what we commonly call faulting), and the same vertical offset of horizons taking place over longer lateral distances (which may be either folding or a sequence of multiple faults, having smaller offsets, that we may wish to interpret as a fault zone). Whatever the geologic basis, what looks like a fault in Figure 16a generally will not be seen by coherence. It will be seen by curvature.

The situation in Figure 16b is similar. At depth we have either a small graben or collapse feature. The edges of that feature show finite reflector offset and thus will appear on a coherence image. In contrast, the sediments above have filled in this low during or after its formation. Differential compaction or continued subsidence may allow these patterns to progress a significant distance toward the surface. Gentle synclines or bowls like these will not be seen by coherence, but they will be seen by curvature.

Attribute-assisted Fault Interpretation

In the following examples we illustrate how one can use coherence and other geometric attributes as an aid in fault interpretation. These attributes serve as the building blocks for the computer-assisted fault-interpretation software development shown in Figures 34–47 in Chapter 8. Here, we will address more mundane workflows accessible to anyone with a conventional interpretation workstation.

Our first example is that of picking faults on a survey from the deep-water Gulf of Mexico, U.S.A. In Figure 17, we display a coherence time slice at t = 2.700 s. In the northwestern corner of the survey, we recognize incoherent energy that is associated with a salt dome. We also recognize several radial faults extending from the salt dome, which we will examine by choosing lines AA′ and BB′ (displayed in Figure 18a and b). Note in Figure 17 that line AA′ cuts the fault indicated by the white arrow perpendicularly to its strike. Likewise, line BB′ cuts the fault indicated by the black arrow perpendicularly to its strike as well. Line BB′ cuts the fault indicated by the white arrow at an oblique angle.

The most accurate means of picking a fault is to pick it perpendicularly to its strike. Note in Figure 18b how steep and well focused the fault indicated by the black arrow is and how diffuse the fault indicated by the white arrow is. Picking a suite of what are commonly called *fault segments* on seismic lines that are perpendicular to strike generally results in clean fault surfaces (see the faults identified by the white arrow in Figure 18a and the black arrow in Figure 18b). In contrast, picking fault segments on seismic lines that are oblique or nearly parallel to the strike (such as the

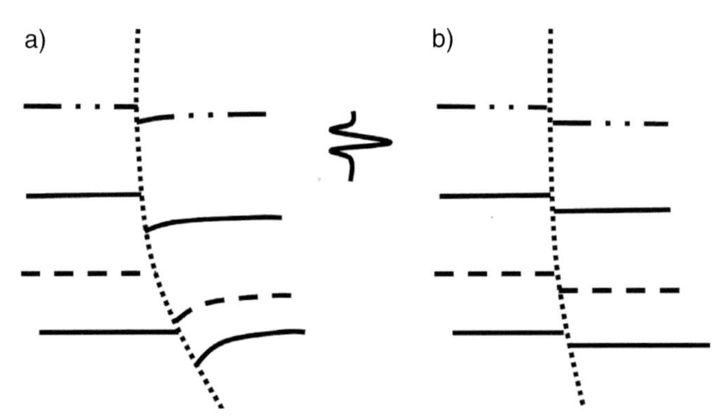

Figure 14. Attribute sensitivity to faults, where the amount of fault throw is measured in terms of a seismic wavelet. (a) An idealized growth fault. Such a fault will be seen on both curvature and coherence attribute volumes. (b) An idealized strike-slip fault. This fault will be seen on a coherence-attribute volume but not on a curvature-attribute volume.

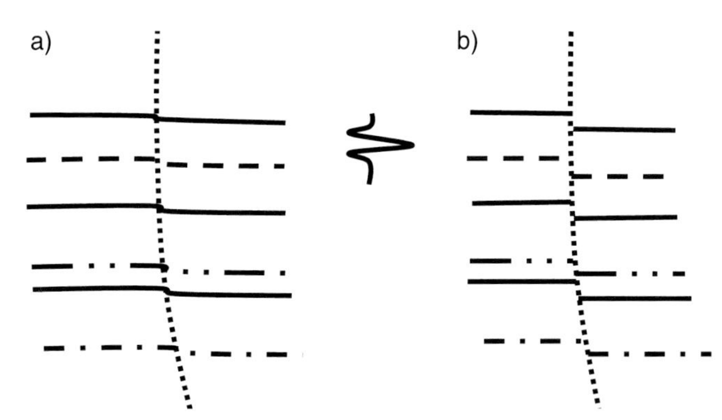

Figure 15. Attribute sensitivity to faults, where the amount of fault throw is measured in terms of a seismic wavelet. (a) An idealized fault with an offset much less than one-quarter of the size of the seismic wavelet. This fault will be seen on curvature-attribute volumes but not on coherence-attribute volumes. (b) An idealized fault with finite offset and no reflector rotation. This fault will be seen on coherence attribute volumes but not on curvature attribute volumes.

fault identified by the white arrow in Figure 18b) results in very irregular and geologically unreasonable fault surfaces. Using coherence time slices allows us to determine the fault strike before we start picking, thereby resulting in rapid, more accurate interpretations.

Often, it is difficult to correlate horizons across a fault, particularly if a significant strike-slip component exists so that the layer thicknesses vary nonuniformly across the fault. One means of circumventing that problem is to use coherence images as a guide in picking a seismic traverse. We start the traverse at point C in Figure 17, proceed in the direction of the yellow arrow, cross the fault indicated by the black arrow, and then choose a traverse (indicated by the green line) that runs around the ends of the other faults and closes the loop at point C. We display this traverse in Figure 18c and show a picked horizon (the trace at the left and right of the image is the same) that is easily carried around the fault. This process works particularly well on large surveys that capture the full extent of radial and en echelon faults. Once seeded, the entire fault block can be picked either by using traditional manual picking on a 20-inline by 20-crossline grid, or if data quality permits, by using machine-guided picking.

Our next examples are from a survey acquired in a salt province in northwestern Louisiana, U.S.A.; we will use these as examples of an interpretation workflow. In addition to plays against the salt domes themselves, plays in this region include the limestones of the Cotton Valley Formation and the Buda Limestone, and more recently include the Bossier Formation (shale), the latter of which workers hope will be as productive as the neighboring Texas Fort Worth Basin's Barnett Shale.

Figure 19 displays time slices at $t = 2.600$ s through an uninterpreted coherence volume and an uninterpreted seismic volume, respectively (Figures 19a and 19b). We begin interpretation by simultaneously displaying both slices and picking unassigned faults. Faults that cut across the seismic fabric (magenta arrows) are easy to pick on the seismic time slice (Figure 19d), whereas those that cut subparallel to the seismic fabric (yellow arrows in Figure 19d) are easier to identify by using coherence. For the moment, we avoid picking the event indicated by the green arrow (Figure 19c), because it may be the edge of a channel or a low-coherence dipping shale.

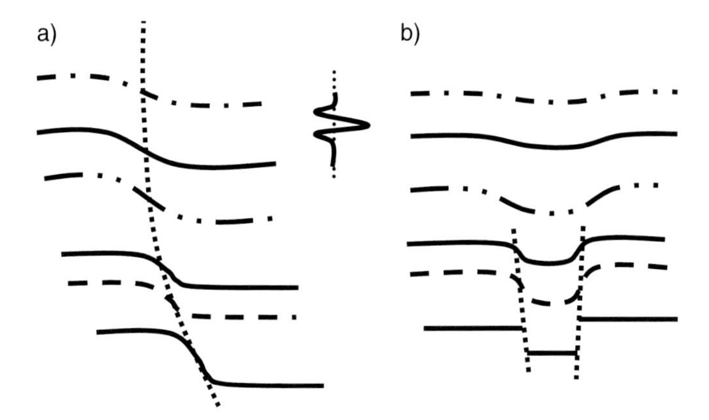

Figure 16. (a) Attribute sensitivity to folds and flexures. This fault will be seen on curvature-attribute volumes but not on coherence-attribute volumes. (b) Attribute sensitivity of infill/collapse features. The deeper part of the fault will be seen on coherence-attribute volumes, whereas the shallower part of the fault and the overlying infill will be seen on curvature-attribute volumes.

Next we choose an appropriate seismic line perpendicular to faults of interest. In Figure 20a, we have chosen line

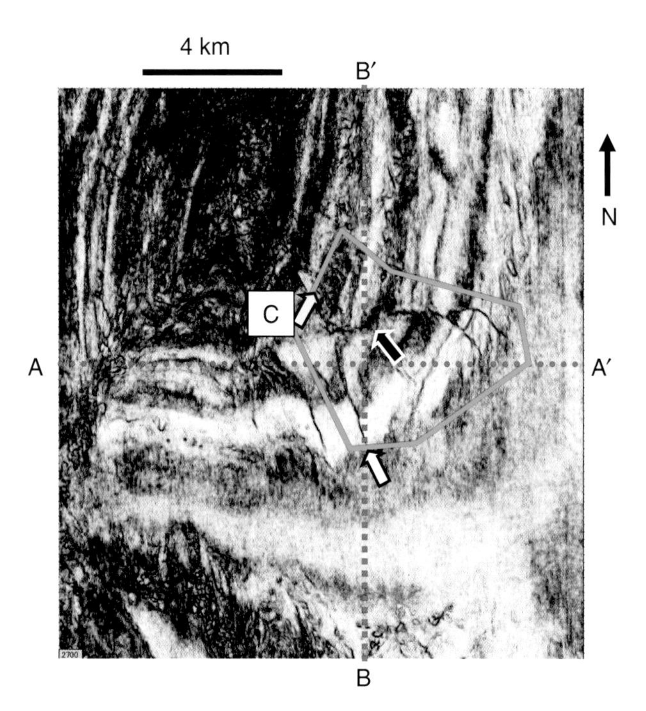

Figure 17. Using coherence to help pick faults and horizons: Lines AA′ (Figure 18a) and BB′ (Figure 18b) will cut through the fault indicated by the yellow and black arrows, almost perpendicularly to the dip. We will choose not to interpret the fault indicated by the white arrow, because we cut it at a steep angle. The green traverse that begins and ends at C (Figure 18c) was chosen to avoid cutting all but the main fault, thereby allowing us to correlate horizon picks by running around their ends. The time slice is at $t = 2.700$ s. Seismic data are courtesy of BP.

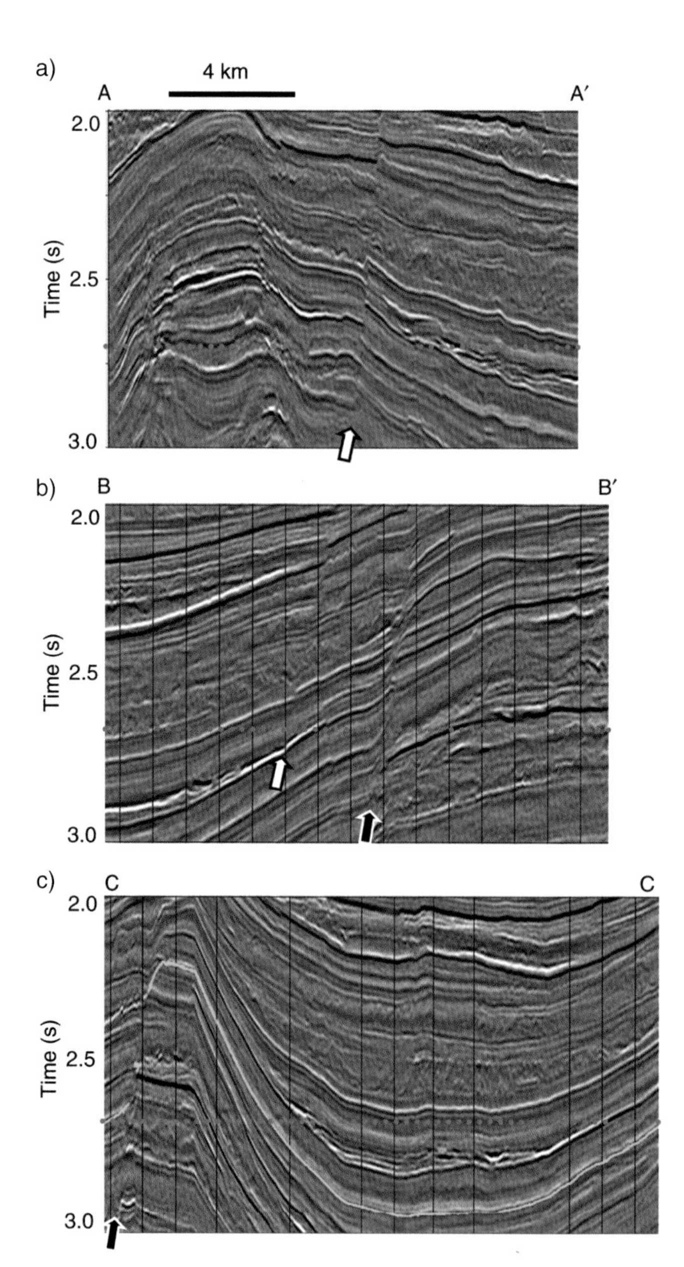

Figure 18. Using coherence to help pick faults and horizons. Locations of lines AA′ and BB′ and the traverse that begins and ends at point C are shown in Figure 17. The faults indicated by the white arrow in (a) and by the black arrow in (b) are cut nearly perpendicularly to the strike of the fault and can be picked easily. In contrast, the fault indicated by the white arrow in (b) is seen in Figure 17 to be cut nearly parallel to the fault strike. We recommend not picking it on this line. Correlating horizons across faults can be difficult, particularly if there is a strike-slip component along the fault. The traverse displayed in (c) cuts the major fault indicated by the black arrow but avoids all other faults, thereby allowing the interpreter to tie the green horizon pick rapidly and unambiguously. The time slice was at $t = 2.700$ s and is indicated by the dotted magenta line. The seismic data are courtesy of BP.

AA′. The choice of seismic lines depends not only on the interpretation software package but also on the interpreter's mental organizational skills. Several current interpretation packages cannot interpolate faults picked on arbitrary lines, thus requiring a two-step approach of first picking the ideal faults on arbitrary lines and then repicking the faults on either inline or crosslines that subsequently can be interpolated. The mental organizational skill arises in that the interpreter might need to save his or her arbitrary line as a named traverse in order to erase any inaccurate fault picks later in the interpretational process.

In Figure 20b, we pick and assign a unique name and color to these faults one at a time, causing the corresponding fault picks made on the coherence slice to change appropriately. We add an additional purple fault on the seismic section and note its location (purple arrow) in Figure 20a; we pick it in Figure 20c.

Next, in Figure 20d, we display seismic section BB′ 100 lines to the north and note the posted faults. We acti-

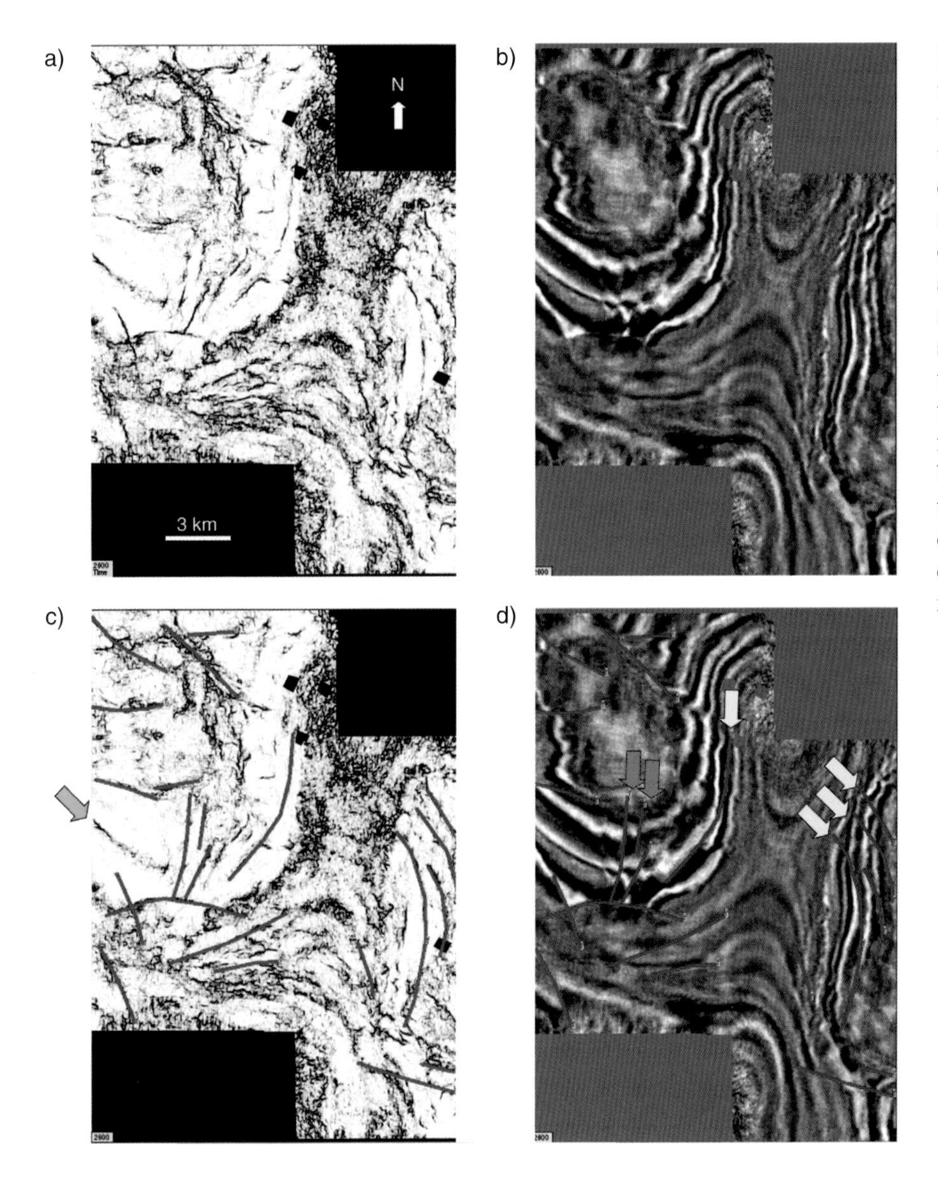

Figure 19. Time slices at $t = 2.600$ s through (a) an uninterpreted coherence volume and (b) an uninterpreted seismic volume and through (c) the interpreted coherence volume and (d) the interpreted seismic volume. Interpretation begins by displaying both slices at the same time and picking faults that will be assigned subsequently. Faults that cut across the seismic fabric (magenta arrows) are easy to pick on the seismic time slice, whereas those that cut subparallel to the seismic fabric (yellow arrows) are more visible by using coherence. In contrast, the feature indicated by the green arrow in (c) does not cut across the seismic fabric. We delay picking it for the moment. The seismic data are courtesy of Seitel.

vate each fault name one at a time and pick that fault as we see it on the vertical seismic section.

To begin naming some of the east-west faults, in Figure 21b we display north-south seismic line CC′ from the coherence volume in Figure 21a. We do not pick the purple and tan faults (indicated by arrows) because we are cutting them closer to their strike direction. We add a blue fault and extend the previously unassigned red fault. Next, in Figure 21d, we display seismic section DD′ 100 lines to the west, and then extend a previously assigned red fault and assign it a teal color. We note that the green fault extends farther to the west and we modify both the green and red picks on the coherence slice in Figure 21c. We also add a pink and a violet fault.

Next we display coherence slices in Figure 22 at (a) $t =$ 2.500 and (b) $t = 2.700$ s, 0.100 s above and below the image shown in Figure 21a. We follow the same process, checking accuracy of our previous interpretation picks and identifying new faults seen on coherence and seismic volumes, until a consistent fault map is generated. By following this process, we can generate a coarse fabric of the major faults rapidly and assign them names or colors that relate them to appropriate fault systems, thereby laying the framework for conventional fault interpretation on a more conventional 20-line grid.

Diapirism

Salt domes

Because salt domes initiate the formation of hydrocarbon traps and can form a seal themselves, they are one of the most important structural elements in hydrocarbon exploration. Salt domes and ridges are found in many parts of the world, including the Gulf of Mexico, eastern Canada, offshore Brazil, West Africa, and the North Sea. Halokinesis, or salt tectonics, is a complex and evolving branch of

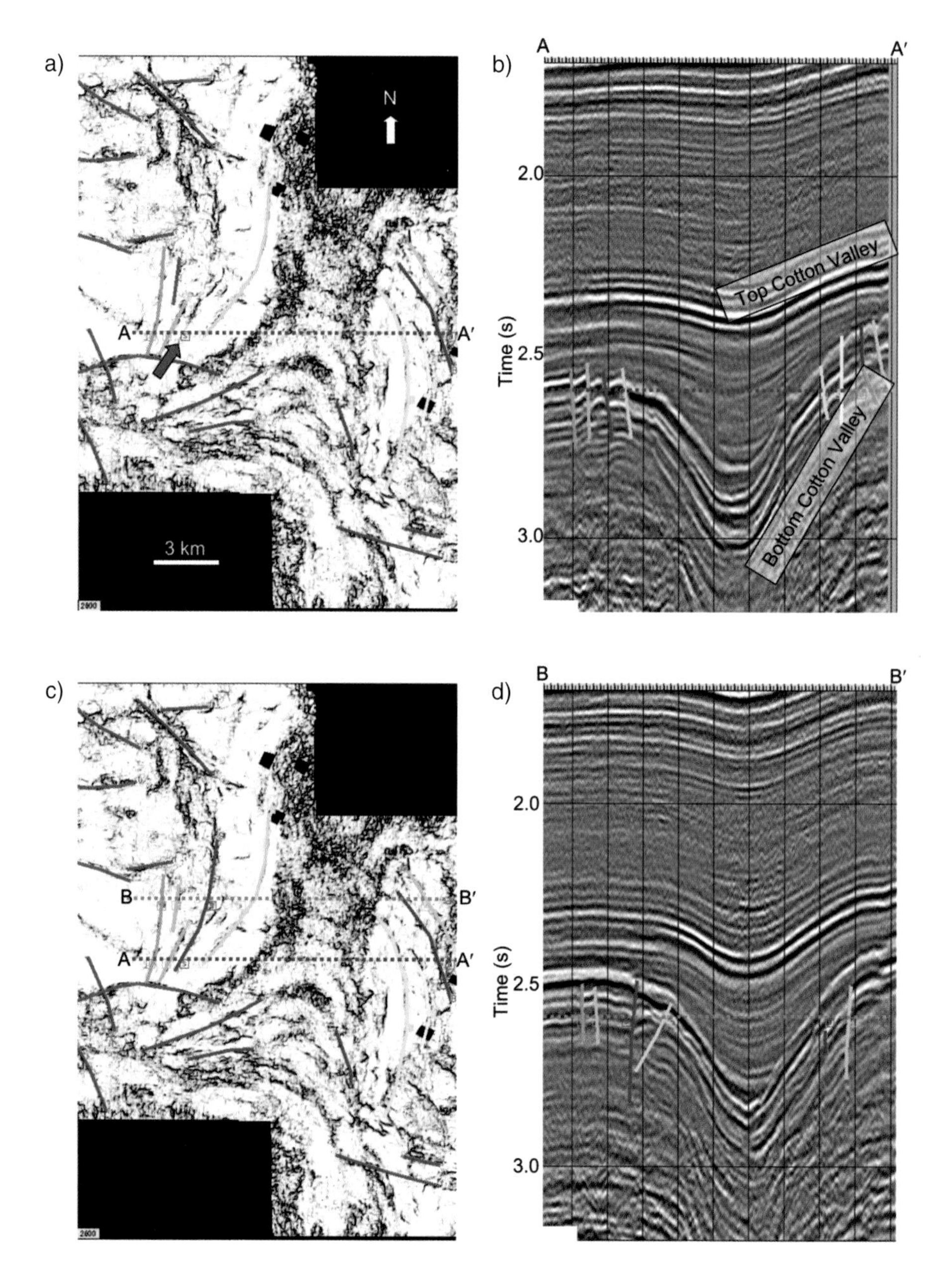

Figure 20. Fault assignment using coherence and seismic volumes. In the vertical seismic slice in (b), we have chosen an east-west section roughly perpendicular to several suspected faults seen in the coherence volume in (a). We pick and assign a unique name and color to these faults, one at a time. We add an additional purple fault on the seismic section in (b), note its location (purple arrow) in (a), and pick it in (c). Next, in (d), we display a seismic section 100 lines to the north and note the posted faults.

geologic study in itself. Simply stated, salt deposited in confined seas becomes mobile when sediments load it. If such loading is uniform, the salt may form large allochthonous sheets that are squeezed out away from the shore (much like an engineer would systematically squeeze a tube of toothpaste from the end). Such sheets may emerge at the continental margin, like the example of the Sigsbee Escarpment discussed in Chapter 14. If a salt deposit is loaded less uniformly, say by sediments dumped by large river systems (or as a geophysicist might randomly squeeze a tube of toothpaste), salt domes may be generated, such as those that occur in Louisiana and east Texas, U.S.A.

Various types of salt structures often are characterized as sheets, pillows, ridges, domes, and canopies. Multiple salt structures can join together, squeezing sediment out and forming a salt weld. Most workers currently believe that salt structures are built downward, with the formation of a minibasin being the driving force for the upwelling of a salt dome.

The example used in the interpretation tutorial illustrated by Figures 19–22 (and also in Figures 26 and 27) is an excellent example of a salt-withdrawal basin in northwestern Louisiana and eastern Texas, U.S.A. As a salt deposit moves, less-ductile sediments above the salt deform by faulting. Such faults often form hydrocarbon traps of exploration interest.

Biles et al. (2003) provide a unique view of the results of halokinesis over the northern Gulf of Mexico, U.S.A., using a survey that covered an area about 400 by 100 km in size. In a variance slice through this huge merged survey (Figure 23), we can identify more than 40 individual salt

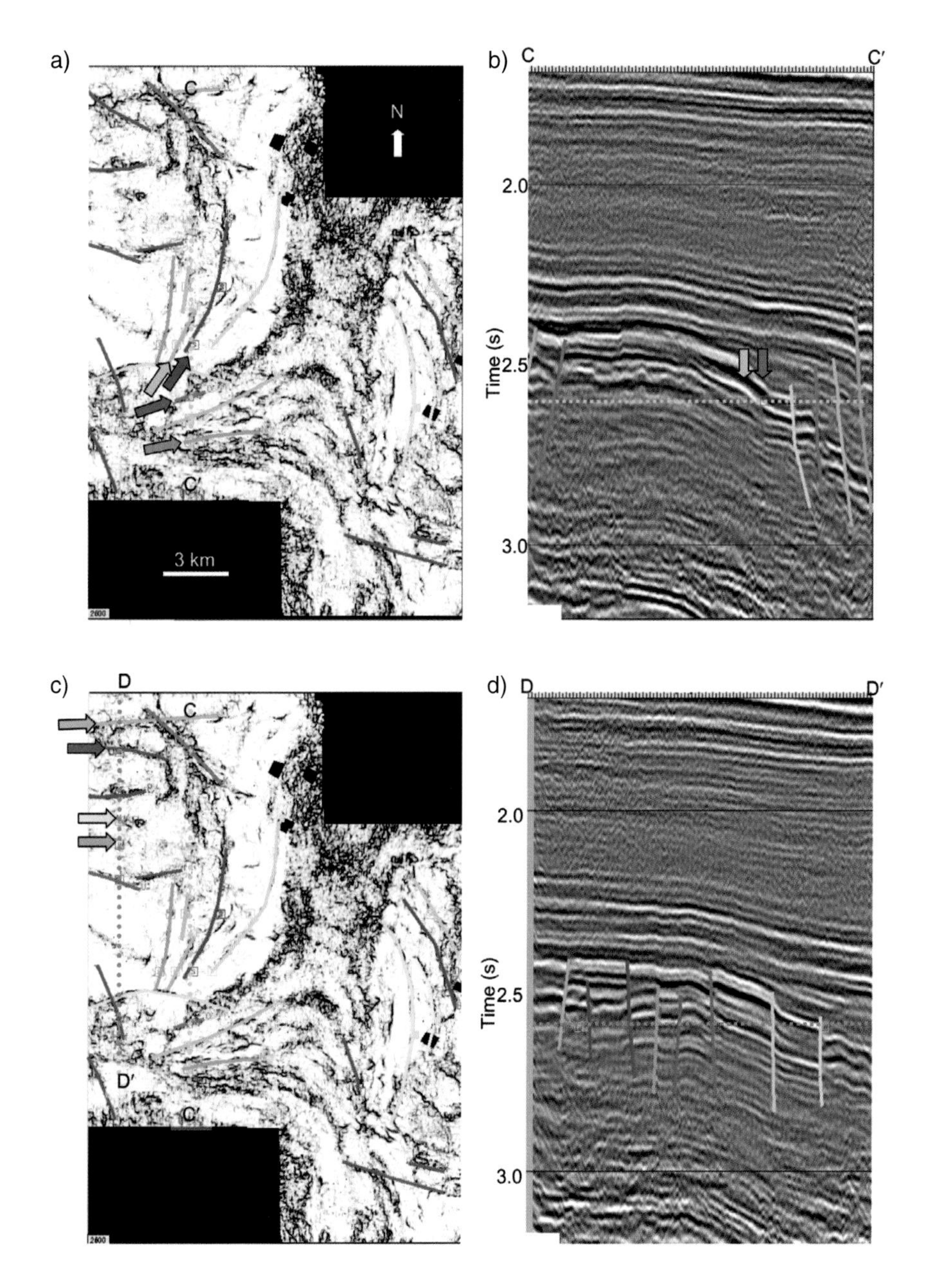

Figure 21. Fault assignment using coherence and seismic volumes. (a) and (c). The coherence volume from Figures 19 and 20 is shown again here as we continue our interpretation. (b) We display the cyan dotted north-south seismic line shown in (a), on which we assign unique names and colors to faults trending roughly east-west. Note that we do not pick the purple and tan faults (indicated by arrows) because we are cutting them closer to their strike direction. We add a blue fault and extend the previously unassigned red fault. (c) The magenta-dotted north-south seismic section 100 lines to the west, on which we (d) extend a previously assigned red fault. We note that the green fault extends farther to the west, and we modify both the green and red picks on the coherence slice in (c). We also add a pink fault and a violet fault.

domes. These salt domes are linked to each other by a complex sequence of radial faults. We can also see the edges of large down-to-basin listric faults that sole out onto the salt-evacuation surfaces or welds (arrows).

We showed one of these salt domes and associated radial faults from the South Marsh Island area of the Gulf of Mexico in Figure 19 of Chapter 3.

In Figure 24, we show three time slices, at t = (a) 0.500s, (b) 1.000 s, and (c) 1.500 s, through a coherence volume generated from a seismic survey acquired over Vinton Dome, southwestern Louisiana, U.S.A. A salt diapir appears as a black, incoherent circular patch in the center of the image. Radial faults emanate out in all directions.

Line KK′ does not cut any of the radial faults in Figure 24, as is shown in Figure 25a and c. Some of the low-coherence features in Figure 25c are geologic and correspond to slumps and pinch-outs as we approach the salt flank. Others result either from low signal-to-noise ratios (associated with shales that have low reflectivity) or from crossing events (in which the insufficiently accurate time migration improperly positions the salt flank).

In Figure 25b and d, we display line LL′, which cuts the radial faults. Careful examination of Figure 25d shows that the faults do not appear as a simple continuous line but instead have a subtle stair-step appearance. The reasons for this appearance are geophysical rather than geologic. First, because the coherence calculation was performed within a ±10-ms vertical-analysis window, the strongest reflector falling anywhere within that window, rather than the reflector at the window's center, dominates the coherence calcu-

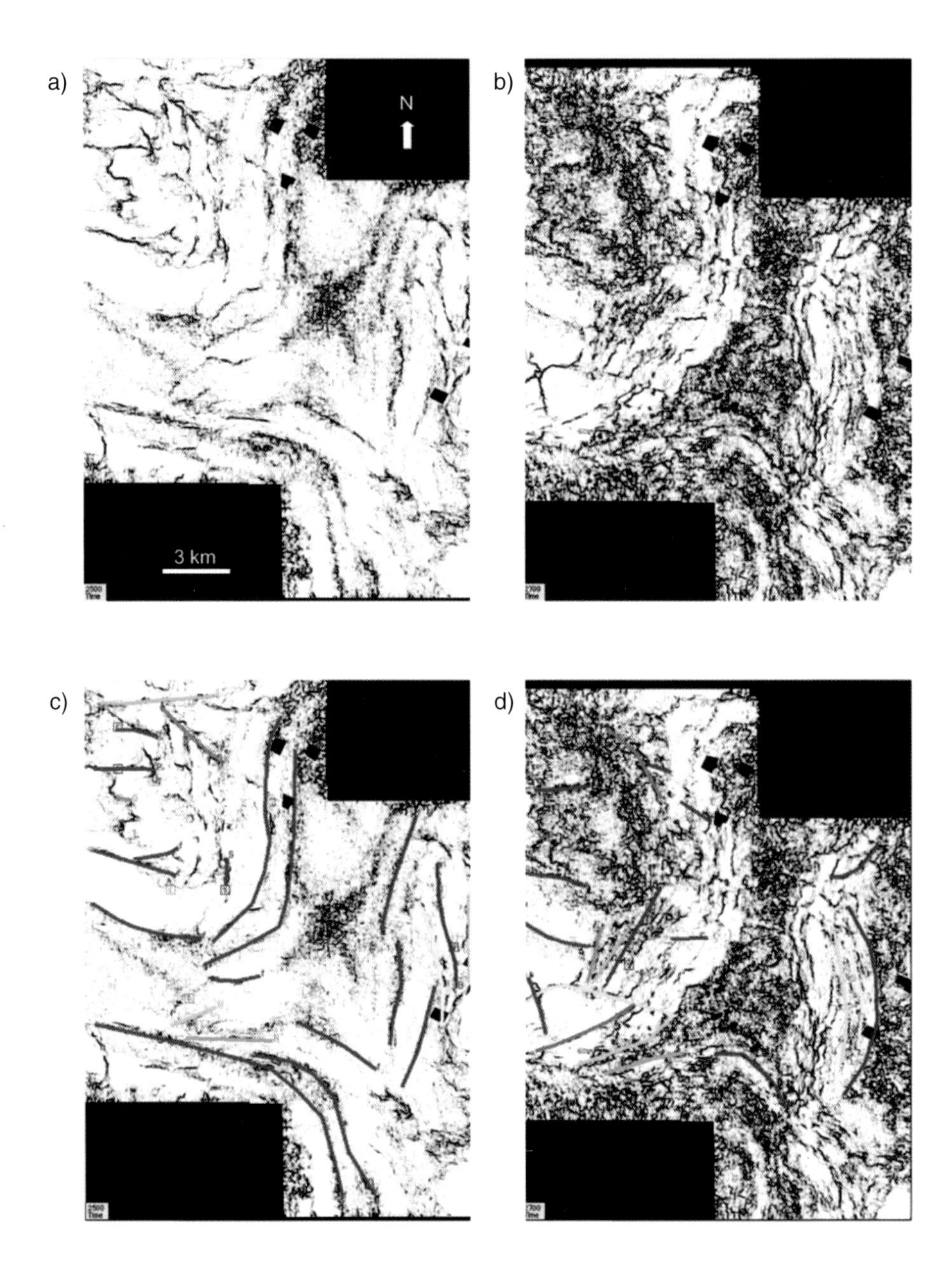

Figure 22. Fault assignment using coherence and seismic volumes. Next, we display coherence time slices at t = (a) 2.500 s and (b) t = 2.700 s, which are respectively 0.100 s above and below the image shown in Figure 19a. In (c) and (d) we follow the same process as before, checking the accuracy of our previous interpretation picks and identifying new faults seen on coherence and seismic volumes, until we have generated a consistent fault map.

lation. Second, although coherence calculations are performed along dip, most implementations resample the data vertically, not vertically and horizontally, thereby resulting in progressively less accurate results as the faults sole out (as indicated by the arrows).

Figure 26 displays a very different fault pattern associated with salt diapirism. In this example from east Texas, U.S.A., the salt is interpreted to have formed a salt glacier at the seafloor during geologic time, and that salt glacier left a circular salt-withdrawal basin in its wake (Maione, 2001). Stresses associated with this geometry resulted in ring faults rather than the more commonly observed radial faults. In the southwestern corner of Figure 26, we also see ring faults associated with salt withdrawal in the same geologic province.

In the next section, we will see smaller-scale, near-surface ring faults associated with shale diapirism. In Chapter 14, we will see ring faults associated with pockmarks associated with shale diapirism.

Maione (2001) stated that "the structural style of high-angle ring faults creates a multitude of possible fault traps in a previously unattractive, synclinal, structural setting." We provide his work as Chapter 16, one of our case studies. For now, we inspect Figure 27 from his data and note that the faults (as seen in Figure 27b) are not continuous toward the surface. These ring faults (indicated by red lines in Figure 27a and b) were interpreted first on the coherence image (Figure 27b) and then transferred to the seismic image (Figure 27a). Unlike the algorithmic limitations discussed earlier for Vinton Dome in Figure 25d, the cause here is geologic. As was the case in Figures 19–22 through the same geologic section from northwestern Louisiana, the limestones of the James Limestone and the Cotton Valley Formation de-

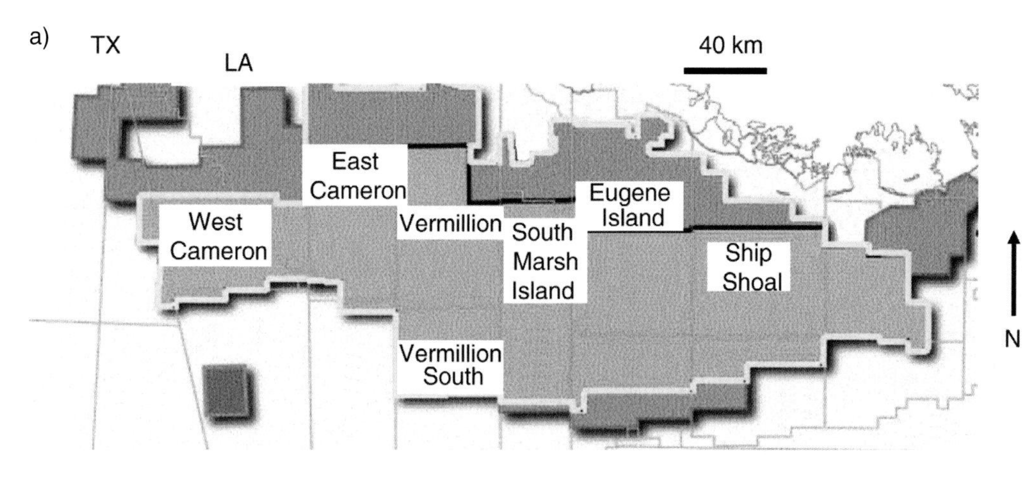

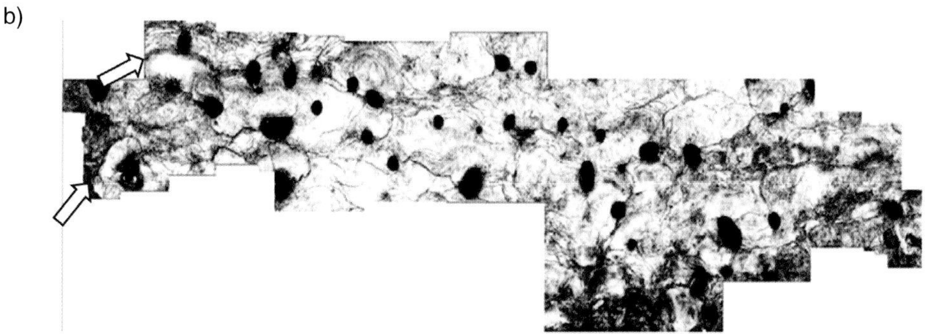

Figure 23. (a) The area of a very large regional study over the northern Gulf of Mexico, U.S.A. (b) A time slice at t = 2.000 s through a variance volume for the area in (a) bordered in yellow. This time slice shows more than 40 salt domes, many of which are linked by faults. After Biles et al. (2003).

form brittlely, whereas the intervening shales deform plastically, so we cannot trace the fault from limestone to limestone across the shales.

Shale ridges and diapirs

Shale ridges and diapirs are nearly as common as salt ridges and diapirs and often are difficult to distinguish from them seismically. Shale diapirs are important trap-generating mechanisms in West Africa, the Caspian Sea, and other parts of the world. Haskell et al. (1999) described a system of large (3- to 5-km-wide by 30-km-long) shale ridges on the Nigerian continental shelf (Figure 28). These ridges are separated by long minibasins that have faults (identified by the arrow) linking the ridges on either side.

As they approach the surface, the offshore-Nigeria shale ridges give rise to diapirs (Figure 29). Figure 29 shows the vertical seismic sections corresponding to the lines indicated as BB′, CC′, DD′, and HH′ in Figure 30. Shale ridges and diapirs consist of chaotic complexes of highly deformed shale that often include more-competent carbonate and/or sandstone.

In general, shale diapirs appear to be incoherent in both seismic and coherence volumes. However, Haskell et al. (1999, p. 376) noted that "Random high-coherence zones within the ridges indicate that the ridges are texturally heterogeneous." Vertical seismic sections show that some of these low-coherence zones may contain locally coherent zones within them (Figure 29d). Figure 30 shows time slices though a coherence volume at 0.225s (Figure 30a), 0.725 s (Figure 30b), 1.225 s (Figure 30c), and 1.725 s (Figure 30d) below the seafloor, cutting a shale ridge and associated diapirs that correspond to the area shown by the black box in Figure 28. Haskell et al. (1999, p. 376) interpreted such zones to be "blocks of the adjacent substrate which were incorporated into the ridges." Shale ridges form the base of the complex and are indicated in the two deeper images in Figure 30 by gray arrows. The shale diapirs are circular features, 1–2 km in diameter, and are seen in the shallower slices where they initiate radial faults (black arrows) and ring faults (white arrows). The mechanical genesis of these ring faults is similar to those reported by Maione (2001; reprinted as our Chapter 16) for an east Texas salt dome. We note doming along line DD′ in Figure 29c and collapse features in lines BB′ (Figure 29a) and CC′ (Figure 29b).

Reverse and Strike-slip Faults

Complex faulting near Galeota Ridge, offshore Trinidad

Gersztenkorn et al. (1999) described using coherence and volumetric dip and azimuth in conjunction with conventional amplitude interpretation and well control to analyze complex faulting seen on an offshore Trinidad 3D sur-

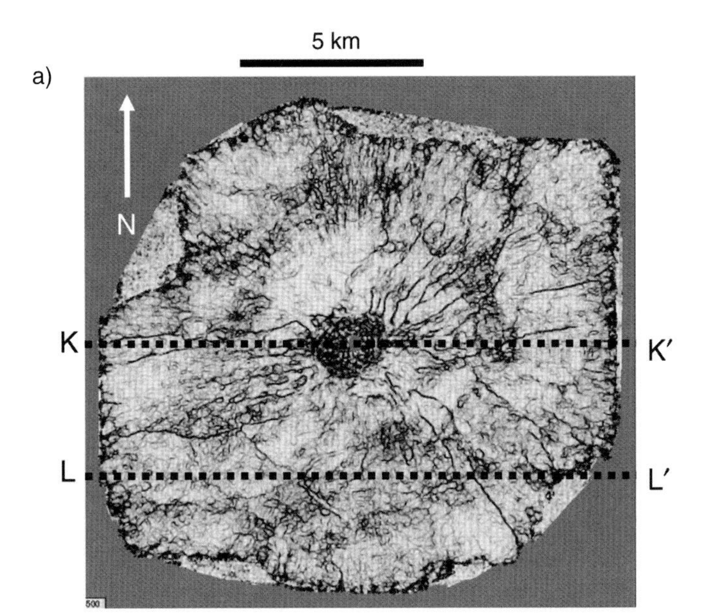

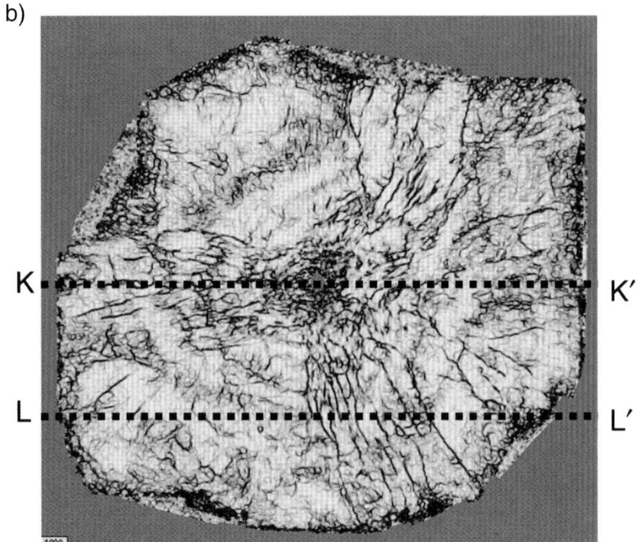

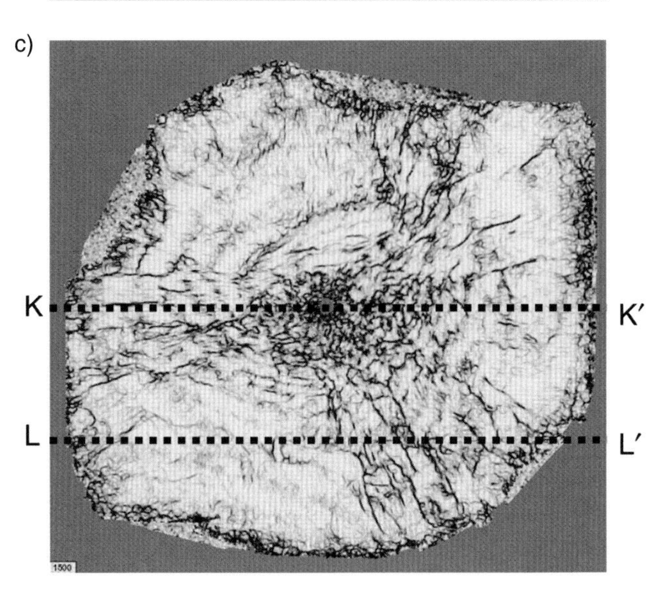

Figure 24. Radial faults emanating from Vinton (salt) Dome, southwest Louisiana, U.S.A., and appearing here in time slices at t = (a) 0.500 s, (b) 1.000 s, and (c) 1.500 s through a coherence cube. The seismic data are courtesy of OPEX.

vey. The region has been interpreted as being transpressional — with compressive stresses in one direction forming the Galeota Ridge, and extensional stresses in the other direction, toward the Columbus Basin. The input data were prestack depth migrated and yielded particularly well-focused fault terminations. The depth volumes then were converted back to time to link them to other surveys in the basin.

Figure 31 shows a time slice at t = 1.200 s through a seismic data volume (Figure 31a) and the corresponding coherence volume (Figure 31b). We note a series of northwest-southeast-trending extensional faults (black arrows) that cut the Galeota Ridge. We also note a series of northeast-southwest-trending compressional faults (white arrows) that define several blocks in the southwestern half of the survey. Gersztenkorn et al. (1999) noted that the faults are significantly easier to interpret on the coherence slices than on the seismic time slices.

Figure 32 displays time slices at t = 1.100 s through the coherence volume (Figure 32a) and dip-azimuth volume (Figure 32b) corresponding to the area in the dotted black rectangle in Figure 31. Corresponding vertical slices through the seismic data along DD′ and EE′ are shown in Figure 33. Line DD′ runs parallel to the extensional faults and crosses the northern flank of the Galeota Ridge (Figure 33a). The monoclinal dip on the seismic section shown on line DD′ appears as a region of magenta and blue in Figure 32b. Line EE′ shows a series of faulted blocks caused by extensional forces (gray arrows in Figure 33b). Figure 33b reveals that there is no rotation about these faults. In contrast, reflectors to the east of the fault indicated by white arrows have been rotated significantly and dip toward the southeast (yellow), southwest (green), and west (blue). The reflectors are hard to tie across this fault in Figure 32. We suspect that movement along the fault has a significant strike-slip component.

In Figure 34, we display coherence time slices at 0.800 s (Figure 34a), 1.060 s (Figure 34b), and 1.200 s (Figure 34c) through the discovery area indicated by the white rectangle in Figure 31a. Vertical seismic line AA′ (Figure 34d) shows extensional features, whereas seismic line BB′ (Figure 34e) shows compressional features.

Gersztenkorn et al. (1999, p. 1006) stated

> This area was drilled in 1995 and contains a gas field with reserves estimated at 1.1 trillion ft^3 (tcf). Gas accumulations in the area display bright amplitudes and occur at the intersection of orthogonal fault trends. The relationship between amplitude and coherence allows interpreters to quickly screen a series of 3D coherence time slices and identify potential gas accumulations at the intersections of faults. The actual gas accumulation manifests itself on a coherence time slice as a high-coherence response; faults show up as a linear zone of low coherence. This time-slice information was used to plan out a mapping strategy that focused on the area of strong coherence response. Detailed mapping and subsequent attribute analysis of several coherence indicators verified the presence of several stacked gas accumulations that were later successfully drilled. The structural culmination of the Galeota Ridge is the approximate location of the 1995 discovery well.

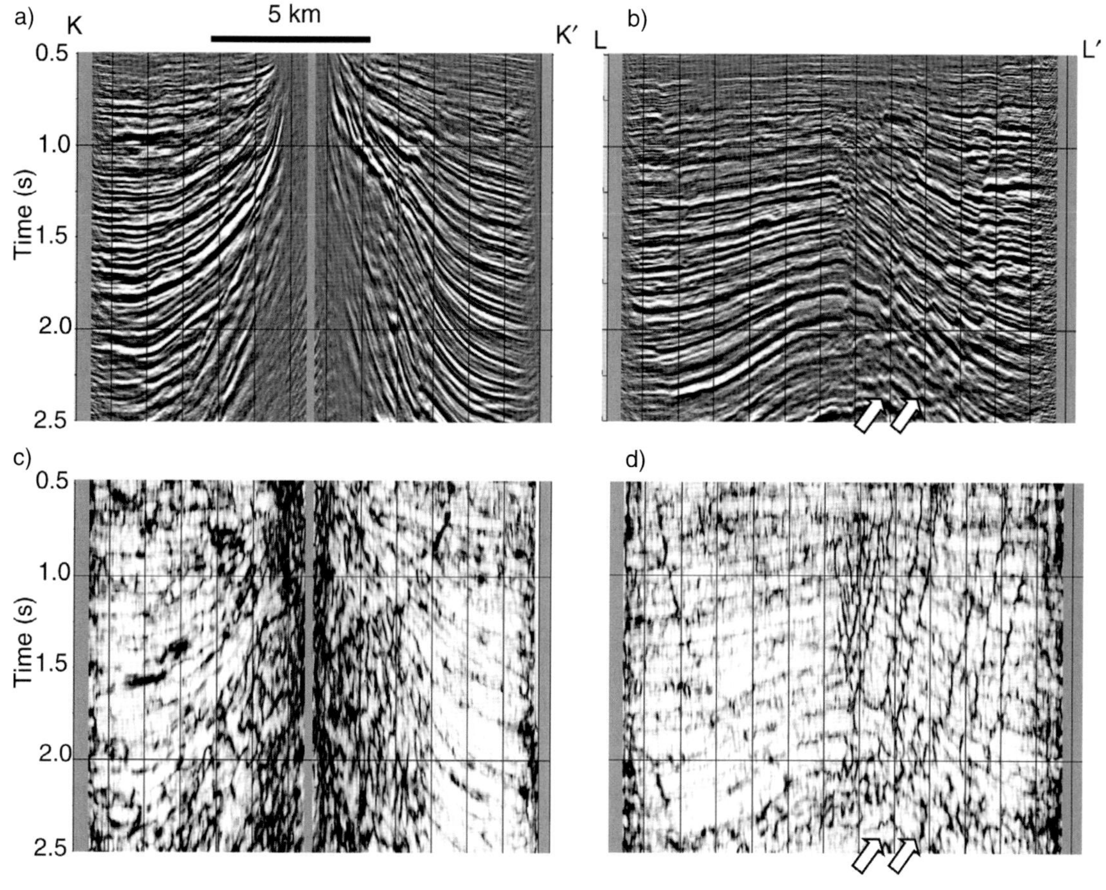

Figure 25. (a)-(b) Vertical slices through seismic data volumes and (c)-(d) vertical slices through coherence volumes, from the Vinton Dome survey, corresponding to lines KK′ and LL′ in Figure 24. The diapir comes almost to the surface, which is covered by a lake, resulting in the dataless area in the center of line KK′. Radial faults are clearly imaged in (d).

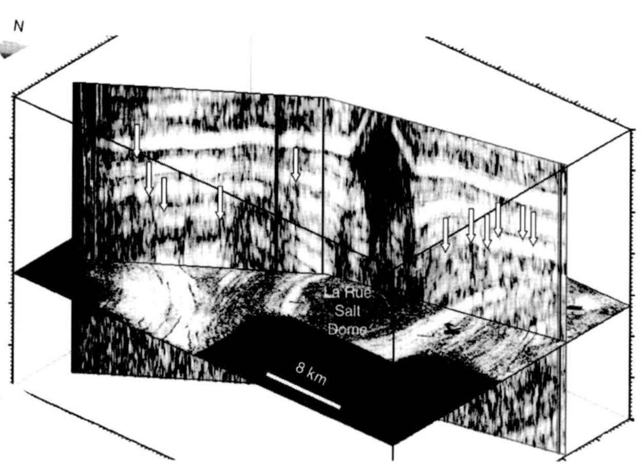

Figure 26. A 3D view from the south of a coherence volume over the La Rue salt diapir, east Texas, U.S.A. Arrows denote ring faults associated with salt withdrawal. After Maione (2001).

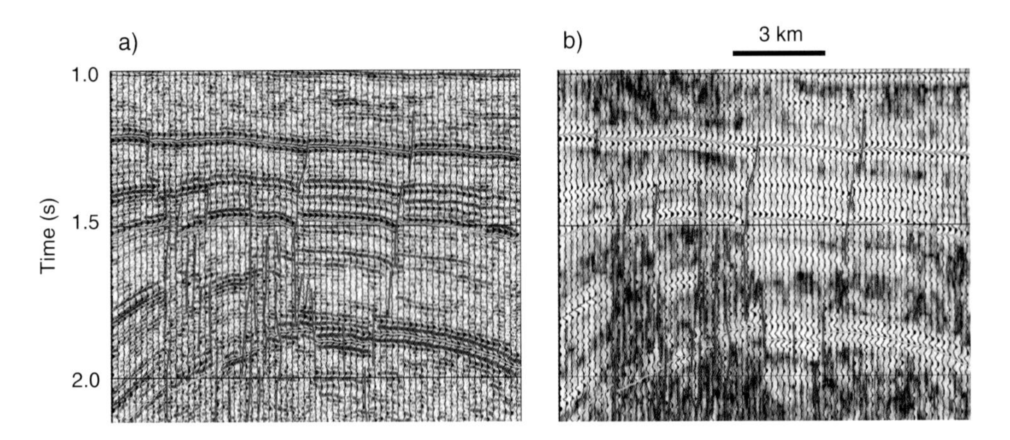

Figure 27. Vertical sections from along the northern part of a survey between two salt-withdrawal basins, cutting through (a) a seismic data volume and (b) a seismic volume overlaid on coherence. Ring faults (red lines) were interpreted first on the coherence image and then transferred to the seismic image. After Maione (2001).

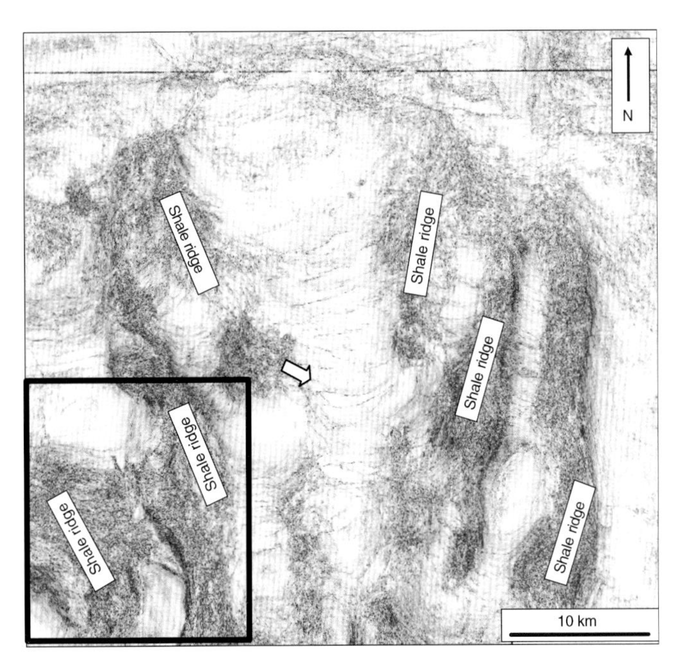

Figure 28. A phantom-horizon slice from a coherence volume 1.175 s below the water bottom from a large survey offshore Nigeria, showing multiple shale ridges. These ridges are linked by faults in the long minibasins between the ridges (arrow). The area indicated by the box is redisplayed in Figure 30. After Haskell et al. (1999).

Reverse faults, Central Basin Platform, Texas, U.S.A.

The Central Basin Platform of west Texas is host to some of the oldest and most prolific oil fields in North America. Although mature, these fields provide much of the exploration money needed to finance exploration in frontier basins. These fields are highly compartmentalized by faulting, lithologic variability, and diagenesis. We discuss the Dollarhide field in Chapter 15. We also have included Blumentritt et al.'s (2006) case study on the polyphase deformation of this area as our Chapter 17. Here, we simply wish to present how this complex structure appears on geometric attributes.

We begin in Figure 35 with a suite of time slices through a composite dip-azimuth/coherence volume, 100 ms apart, starting at 1.000 s and ending at 1.500 s. Note that most of this survey area dips gently to the northeast (magenta color), although it is interrupted by east-west-trending zones that dip steeply to the north (bright blue). On the west, a north-south-trending zone dips steeply to the west (bright green), and in the northwestern corner, a zone dips steeply toward the south (bright yellow). Note also that the northeastern third of the survey is considerably more chaotic (less coherent, with more bands of black) than the part of the survey to the south and west.

To confirm our observations, we examine lines MM′ (west to east) and NN′ (north to south) in Figure 36 shown here after principal-component structure-oriented filtering.

Coherence slices (not presented separately here) do not clearly define the faults we see in Figure 36. In many places, the reverse fault (indicated by the white arrow) appears as a fold (the bright green zone discussed earlier), with little to no discontinuity in the waveform. Similarly, the strike-slip faults (indicated by black arrows) also appear to have continuous waveforms in many parts of the section. However, we note an abrupt change in dip near these faults, which suggests that we can use curvature to map these features.

We present time slices corresponding to and computed from those in Figure 35, here cutting through the most-positive-curvature volume in Figure 37 and through the most-negative-curvature volume in Figure 38. These images have so much detail that they can overwhelm an interpreter unfamiliar with this technology.

First, curvature illuminates many subtle features that are underused in traditional interpretation. Unlike coherence, which sees fault discontinuities, curvature sees the

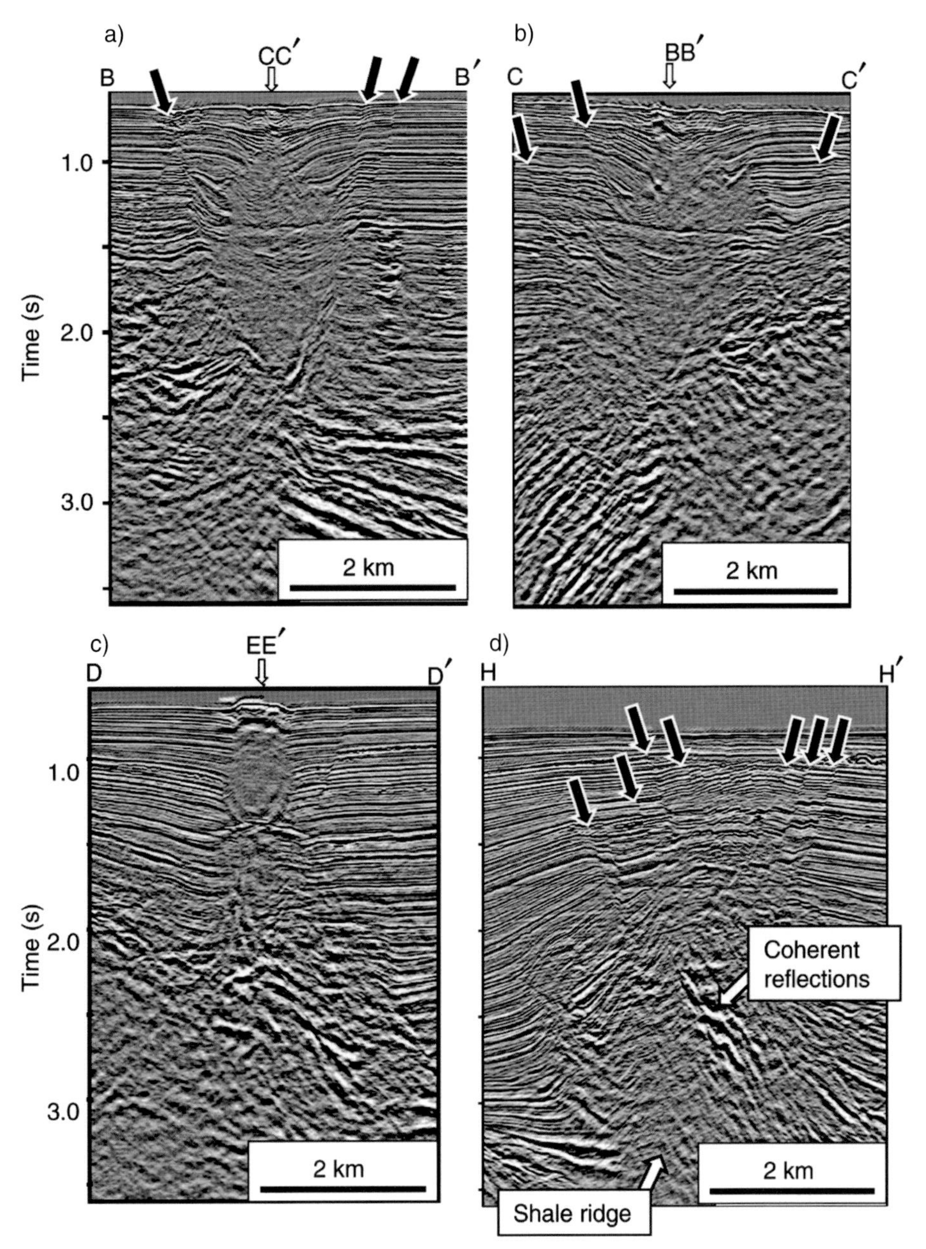

Figure 29. Vertical slices through a seismic survey acquired offshore Nigeria. Line locations are shown in Figure 30. The diapirs are rooted in a deeper shale ridge, such as that shown in (d) in line HH'. The faults (indicated by black arrows) in (d) are linked to radial faults emanating from a shale diapir to the north. The faults indicated by black arrows in (a) and (b) are ring faults associated with a collapse feature. In contrast, line DD′ in (c) shows doming. Other cross sections are displayed in the original paper. After Haskell et al. (1999).

flexures induced by faults and the apparent (or real) flexures at the faults themselves. The white arrow (Figure 36a) indicates a reverse fault that is associated with an anticline, and thus the fault should show up clearly on the most positive-curvature time slices. We indicate this feature with a white arrow in Figure 37c.

In contrast to Figure 36a, the strike-slip faults (for this survey) appear on Figure 36b to have a synclinal form. Thus, we look for them on the most-negative-curvature time slices and indicate them with black arrows in Figure 38c. We also can see major anticlinal highs of the blocks between the strike-slip faults on the most-negative curvature. Careful inspection of Figure 36b shows that some very subtle curvature anomalies also exist, such as the one indicated by the gray arrow. These subtle forms can be structural (resulting from folding or from faulting with displacements below the resolution of the seismic wavelet). Alternatively, they can be stratigraphic (resulting from slumping or in association with sand bars or dunes). These subtle anticlinal and synclinal forms appear in a very organized manner in Figures 37 and 38. In Chapter 17, a paper by Blumentritt et al., the authors show how these subtle folds can be used as a tool to unravel deformation history.

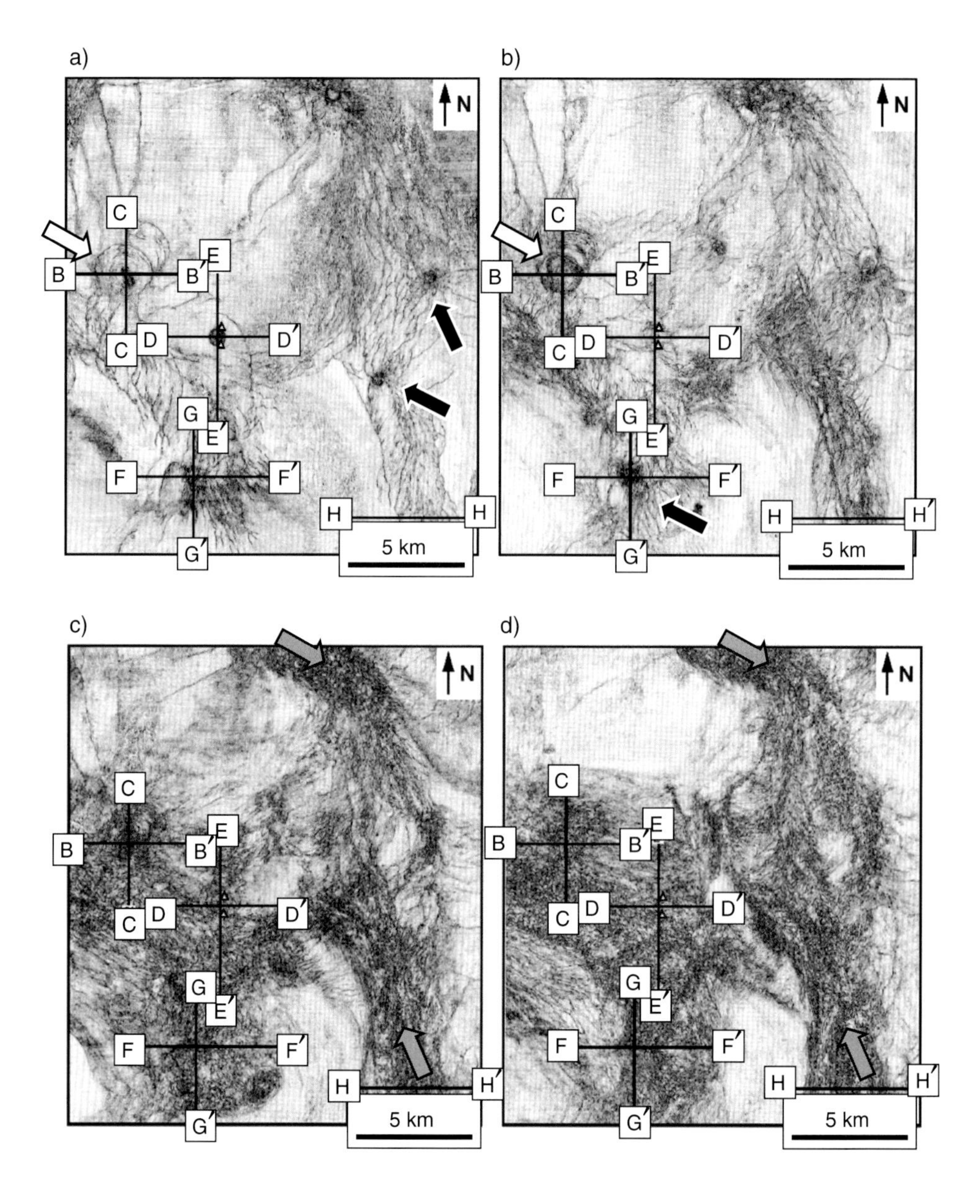

Figure 30. Time slices through a coherence volume at (a) 0.225, (b) 0.725, (c) 1.225, and (d) 1.725 s below the seafloor, cutting a shale ridge and associated diapirs corresponding to the area shown by the black box in Figure 28. Gray arrows in (c) and (d) indicate shale ridges. Black arrows and white arrows in (a) and (b) indicate radial faults and ring faults, respectively. After Haskell et al. (1999).

Reverse faults, Teapot Dome, Wyoming, U.S.A.

To illustrate further how different attributes illuminate geology differently, we display horizon extractions through coherence volumes, most-positive-curvature volumes, and most-negative-curvature volumes computed from a survey acquired over Teapot Dome, Wyoming, U.S.A. Figure 39 displays the results. Teapot Dome is one of the few reservoirs known to the average American high school history student — unfortunately more for its fractured politics than for its fractured rocks. It currently serves as an earth laboratory for the U. S. Department of Energy and is operated by the Rocky Mountain Oilfield Testing Center (RMOTC).

Although the acquisition and processing of the survey over Teapot Dome is of modern vintage, we do not readily see many indications of faults and fractures in the coherence slice (Figure 39a). However, we do see a great deal of information in the two curvature slices (Figure 39b and c). To better understand what these complex images mean, we take three seismic traverses through the data — one along dip (line PP′), one along strike (line QQ′), and a third line cutting the third azimuth of lineaments (line RR′) — and we display the results in Figure 40. The dip line, PP′, shows us the nose of an anticline associated with a reverse fault. Because it is continuous, we do not expect this anticline to appear on the coherence slice, but we do expect it to appear prominently on the most-positive-curvature slice (and it does).

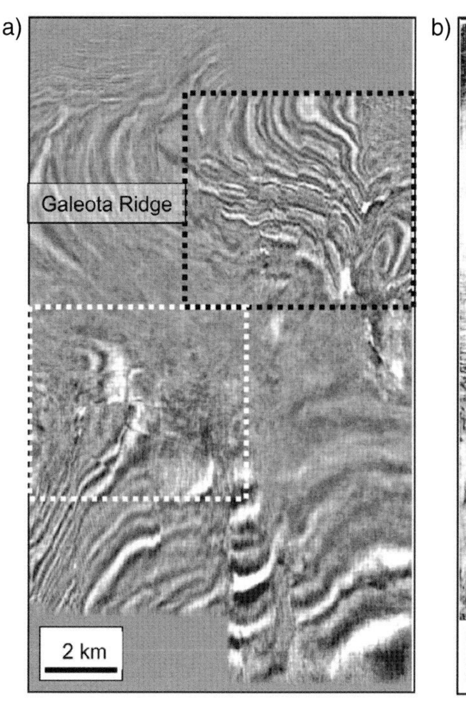

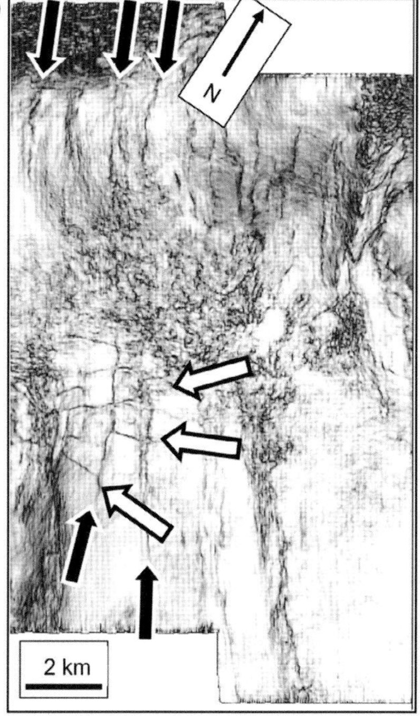

Figure 31. Time slices at t = 1.200 s, at the level of the El-Diablo-1 discoveries, offshore Trinidad, through (a) a seismic data volume and (b) a coherence volume. The discoveries were found in blocks bounded by strike-slip and antithetic faults such as those indicated by the arrows. Complex faulting is difficult to detect on the seismic time slice but is clear on the coherence slice. After Gersztenkorn et al. (1999).

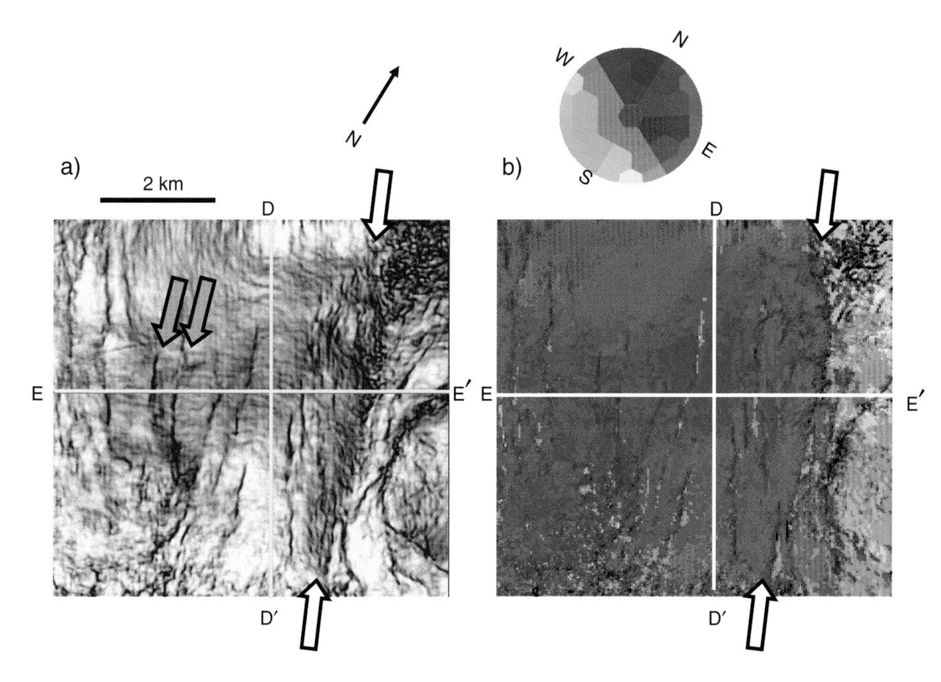

Figure 32. Time slices at t = 1.100 s, through (a) a coherence volume and (b) a dip-azimuth volume, corresponding to the area of the dotted black rectangle in Figure 31. In the western (left) half of the figures, the faulting is rather simple and the dip is gentle and toward the north and northeast (magenta and blue). To the east of the zone indicated by the white arrows, deformation becomes much more intense, which results in lower (blacker) coherence and reflectors that now dip toward the south, southeast, and west. After Gersztenkorn et al. (1999).

In Figure 40c, we indicate several strike-slip faults with black arrows. Deeper in the section (near the arrows), we see that the reflectors are broken. At that level, the strike-slip faults show up as a discontinuity on the coherence image. However, shallower in the section, these faults have the appearance of a flexure.

Several plausible theories can explain why this might happen: (1) The faults have small displacements that fall below the resolution of the seismic wavelet, (2) the faults become a fold or (3), along the fault, strike-slip movement occurs that does not cause a significant vertical displacement of the seismic waveform but instead causes a simple warping of the interface. For now, we content ourselves with the fact that we can map such subtle anomalies using volumetric curvature attributes.

We conclude this short discussion of Teapot Dome with Figure 40b, which shows seismic line RR′. Here we note two clear faults (indicated by white arrows) at the picked

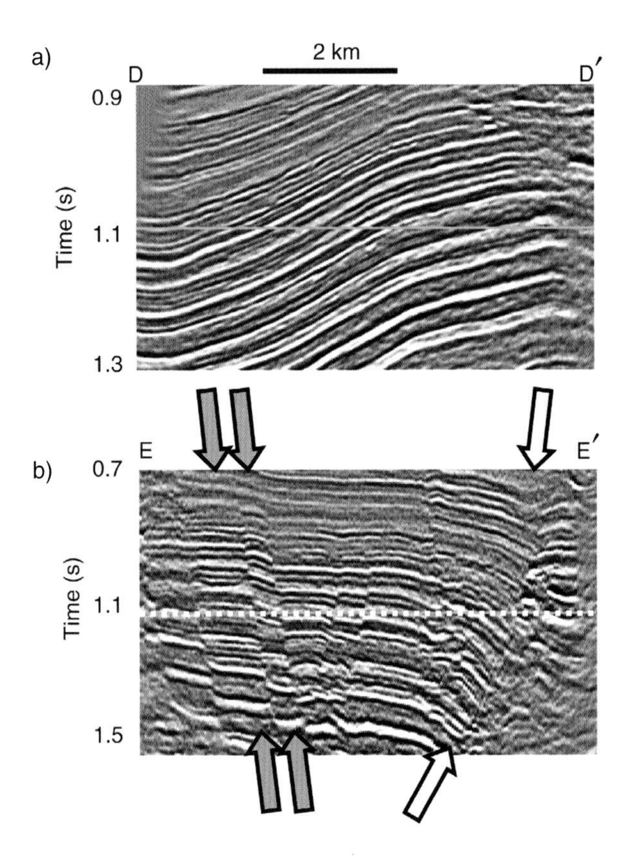

Figure 33. Seismic lines DD′ along strike and EE′ perpendicular to strike, as indicated on the time slices shown in Figure 32. Line EE′ shows a simple monocline. The reflectors do not rotate along the normal faults (indicated by gray arrows) on the west half of line DD′, so the colors in Figure 32b vary smoothly. In contrast, a significant change in dip occurs across the fault indicated by white arrows. Figure 32 shows that this rotation is complicated. Given these images and knowledge of the regional tectonism, we conclude that this is a wrench fault. After Gersztenkorn et al. (1999).

horizon, both of which show clearly on the coherence slice. Even so, these lineaments can be carried farther using the most-negative-curvature and most-positive-curvature slices, which measure changes in reflector shape rather than discontinuities in seismic waveform.

Fractures

Fractures are small cracks that occur in brittle rock when it is stressed to the point at which it breaks. Fractures often are seen in areas of significant geologic structure wherein the rocks fold, fault, and fracture. Because of their ability to trap hydrocarbons, fractured reservoirs are prolific sources of hydrocarbons. So, locating areas with high fracture density and determining the orientation of those fractures is very significant for hydrocarbon exploration. Seismic attributes can help interpreters determine whether a given reservoir is fractured. Figure 41 shows time slices through a seismic data volume (Figure 41a) as well as through the equivalent coherence volume (Figure 41b) from the Cook Inlet area of Alaska. Not only are the faults seen clearly on the coherence slices (arrows), the fractured areas can be marked as well.

Our next two examples of fractures come from the Arabian Peninsula. Figures 42–44 present images recently published by Neves et al. (2004), who used seismic attributes to map fractures in a sandstone reservoir and underlying source rock in order to map vertical hydrocarbon migration paths and fracture-permeability-enhanced reservoirs. A seismic line from their paper is shown here as Figure 42.

We take this opportunity to point out the area of conflicting dip indicated by the white arrow in Figure 42. This horizontal event is probably a multiple — a phenomenon that plagues much of the data acquired on the Arabian Peninsula. As was the case with the improperly migrated crossing reflectors discussed in Chapter 7, multiples generate coherence (and other attribute) pitfalls. Multiples are much easier to see on vertical seismic data than on an attribute map. For that reason, care should be taken always to inspect key seismic lines through an anomaly to determine whether the anomaly's cause is geologic or geophysical. Neves et al. (2004) presented such a line through their anomaly, and linked that with their interpretation on attributes, as we shall see.

Little indication of fractures appears on the time-structure and amplitude-extraction maps shown respectively in Figure 43a and b. Neves et al. (2004, p. 906) found that although conventional dip-magnitude and dip-azimuth maps of the interpreted horizon (Figure 43c and d, respectively) provide "an adequate image of the structural framework of the prospect, maps generated from volumetric attributes such as coherence and spectral decomposition (Figure 44a and b) reveal even more information." Neves et al. (2004, p. 906) noted the "southwest-northeast-striking lineaments (red dashed lines) on the west flank of the fault block. The existence of these en echelon faults, showing a right-lateral strike-slip component, might indicate lack of seal integrity." They also stated that "the faults on the west side of the structure (dashed red circle in Figure 44c) were better mapped on the coherence volume, [whereas] the faults on the eastern side (solid red circle in Figure 44c) were better mapped using the 26-Hz spectral-decomposition slice," and they recommended using a mixture of attributes and mapping tools to extract subtle fracture information.

Example from Abqaiq Field, Saudi Arabia

Ghawar, the largest oil field in the world, is located onshore in the eastern part of Saudi Arabia (Dasgupta et al., 2000). Abqaiq field represents the upper right limb of the

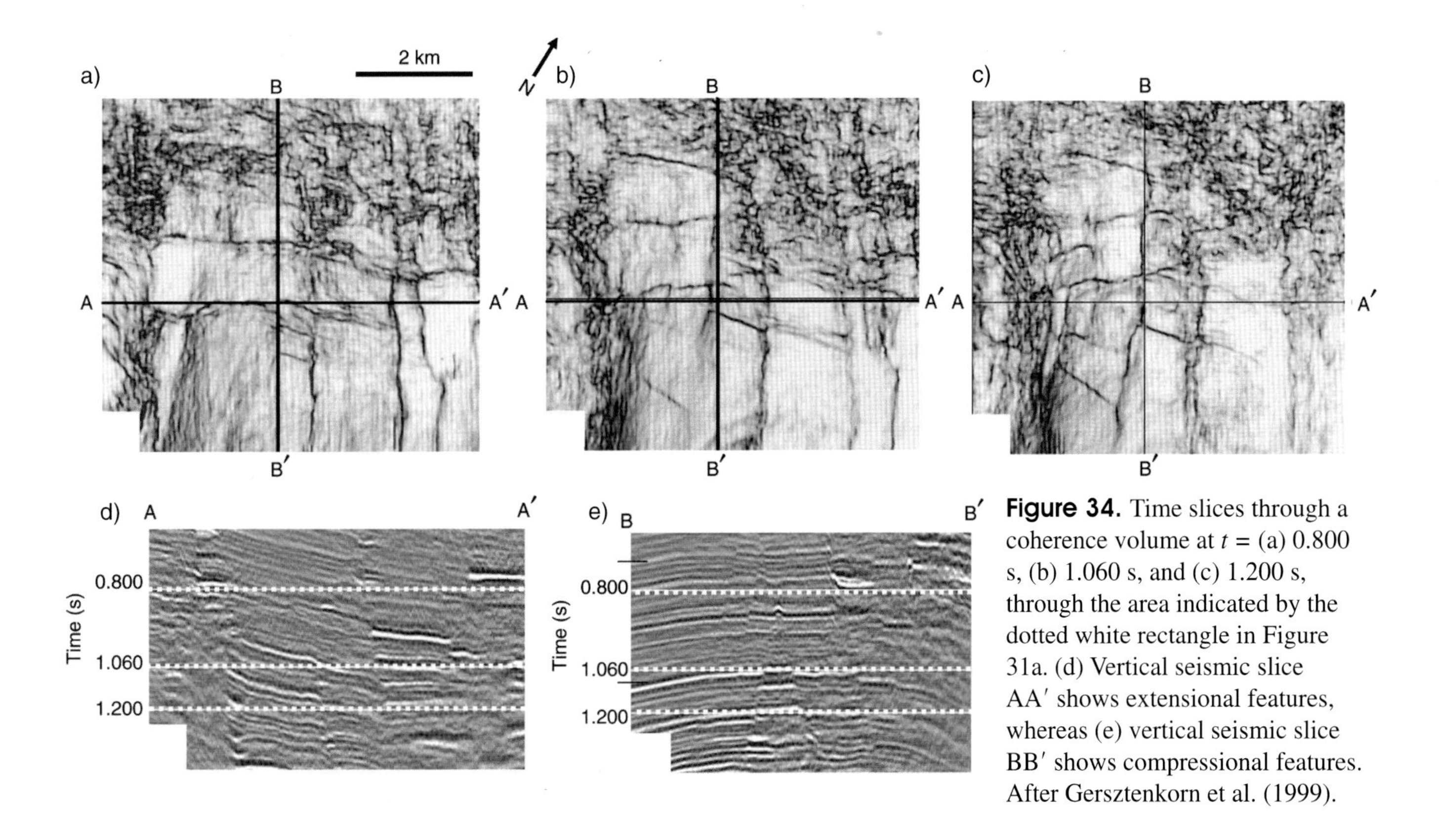

Figure 34. Time slices through a coherence volume at t = (a) 0.800 s, (b) 1.060 s, and (c) 1.200 s, through the area indicated by the dotted white rectangle in Figure 31a. (d) Vertical seismic slice AA′ shows extensional features, whereas (e) vertical seismic slice BB′ shows compressional features. After Gersztenkorn et al. (1999).

Ghawar oil field (Figure 45). The southern part of Abqaiq field has a domal structure believed to be the result of an anticlinal uplift that occurred during the Late Cretaceous and that may be related to deep-seated salt diapirism. The uplift resulted in extensional faults that exhibit maximum throws within the shallow formations and that decrease with depth.

Map views indicate a set of radial faults on the flanks of the domal structure and a system of axis-parallel faults on the structural crest. The reservoir in this field is the Late Jurassic-age Hanifa Formation, which is overlain by 100 m of nonporous limestone. Above this nonporous layer is the highly porous and permeable Arab–D reservoir. The two reservoirs have virtually identical pressure histories and a shared original oil-water contact, which together indicate that the reservoirs are in fluid communication with each other, possibly by way of faults and fractures.

Structural mapping from vertical well data has given no indication of faults or fractures cutting the reservoirs (Figure 46a). For that reason, a 450-km^2 3D seismic survey was acquired over this field (Lawrence, 1998), with the goal of detecting major faults and fractures that could explain the fluid communication across the reservoirs. Figure 47 shows time slices at t = 2.230 s through a seismic data volume (Figure 47a) and a coherence volume (Figure 47b). Note the radial faulting associated with the domal uplift.

Figure 48 displays corresponding vertical slices through a seismic data volume (Figure 48a) and a coherence volume (Figure 48b). Many of the vertical faults in the coherence volume shown in Figure 48b are not throughgoing. Their healing can be the result either of a lack of resolution because of statics and velocity errors, or more likely, of different fault/fracture responses for different lithologies, much like the situation we showed earlier in Figure 27. Figure 49 displays a 3D view of a slab of data and provides a direct correlation of the faults in the vertical section with those seen on the time slice for both the coherence volume in Figure 49a and the seismic volume in Figure 49b.

Interpretation of the 3D seismic data has provided considerably more detail than was possible with well data alone. As seen in a depth map at the level of the Arab-D reservoir (Figure 46b), now hundreds of faults appear where well data indicated none. Apparently, the western flank of the structure is highly faulted (believed to be the result of differential uplift along the flank) with a rotational trend around the domal structure.

Coherence was run on this 3D volume and analyzed at different reservoir levels. Lineations present on the time or horizon slices can be viewed directly on the chair or cube displays. This methodology for interpretation can be extremely revealing in identifying and understanding the coherence response and so makes fault interpretation more

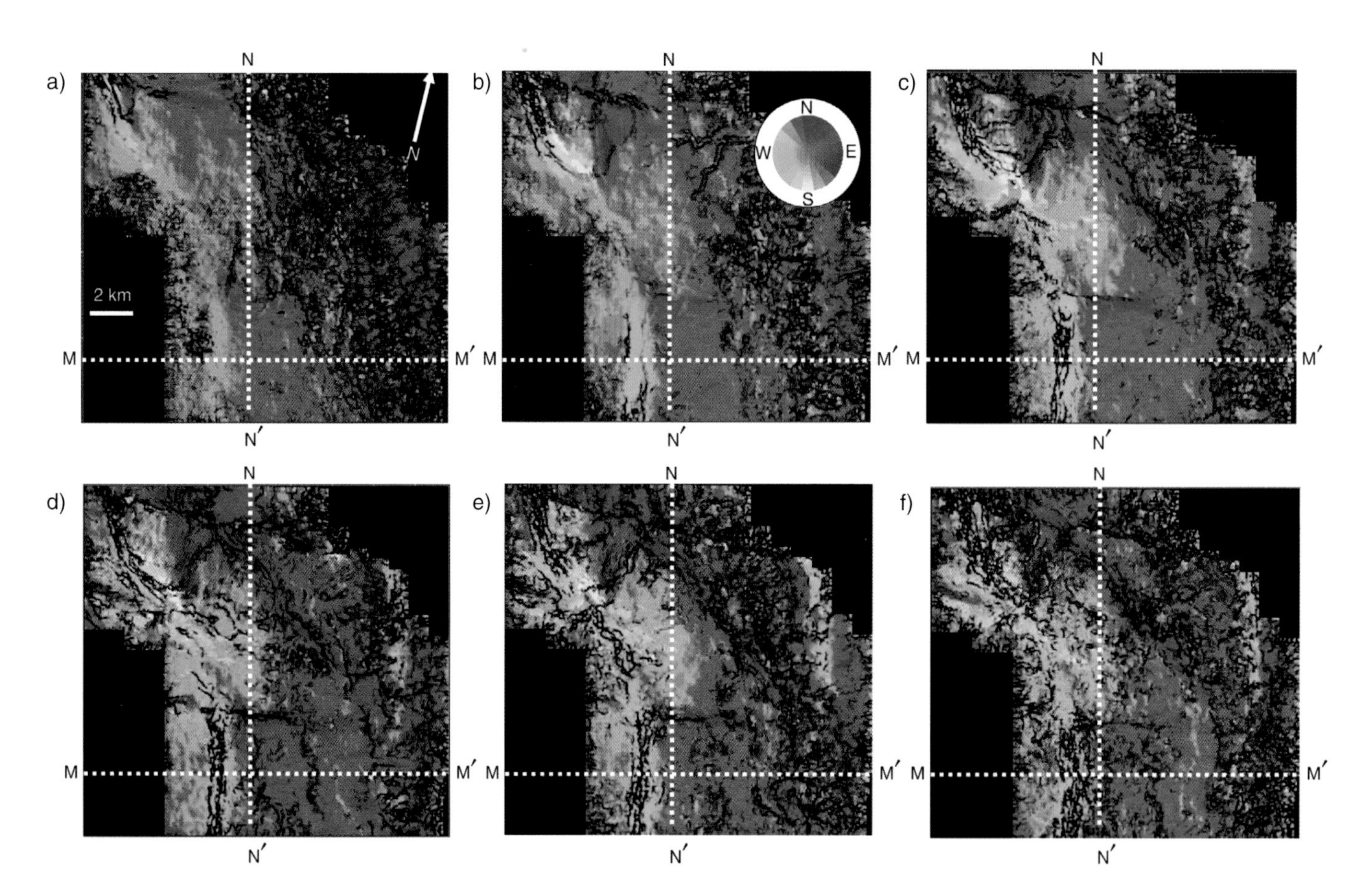

Figure 35. Composite dip-azimuth-coherence time slices at t = (a) 1.000 s, (b) 1.100 s, (c) 1.200 s, (d) 1.300 s, (e) 1.400 s, and (f) 1.500 s, through a survey acquired over the Central Basin Platform, Texas, U.S.A., using the color scheme described in Chapter 9. We note that the reflectors dip steeply to the south and west (yellow and green) in the northwest part of the images, to the west (green) in the southwestern part of the image, and gently to the northeast (magenta) elsewhere. A north-south-trending block appears to be rotated to the west (green) on the eastern part of (d)-(f). An east-west-trending strike-slip fault (the black low-coherence area in the center of (c)-(f) terminates in a flexure dipping to the north (blue) farther to the east. Vertical seismic lines are shown in Figure 38. The seismic data are courtesy of Burlington Resources.

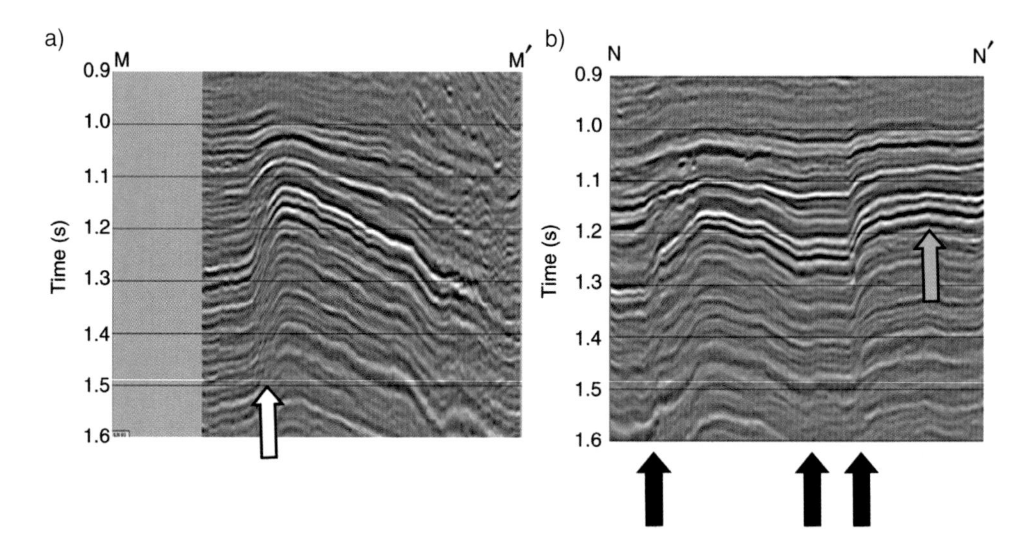

Figure 36. Seismic lines (a) MM′ and (b) NN′ indicated on the time slices in Figures 35 through 37, shown here after principal-component structure-oriented filtering. The white arrow indicates a reverse fault in (a). Black arrows indicate faults with a strike-slip component in (b). The gray arrow indicates subtle folding that can appear as lineaments in Figures 36 and 37. The seismic data are courtesy of Burlington Resources.

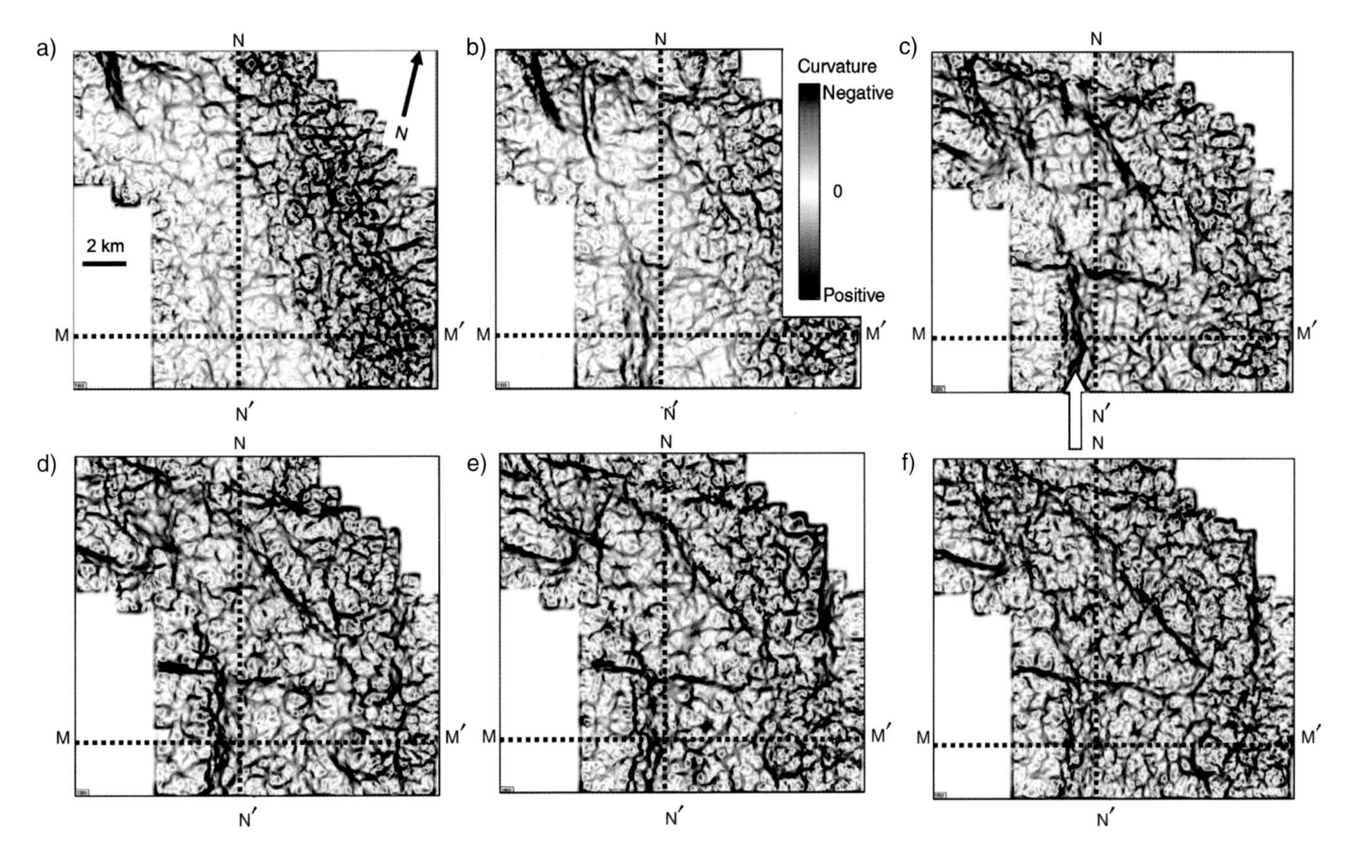

Figure 37. Most-positive-curvature time slices at t = (a) 1.000 s, (b) 1.100 s, (c) 1.200 s, (d) 1.300 s, (e) 1.400 s, and (f) 1.500 s, corresponding to and computed from the dip-azimuth time slices shown in Figure 35. The white arrow in (c) indicates a strong north-south anticlinal feature associated with a reverse fault shown on the vertical seismic data displayed in Figure 36a.

reliable and certain. The use of coherence allowed mapping of hundreds of faults and fracture zones at the Arab-D (Figure 46c) and Hanifa reservoir level where poor reflectivity required the presumption of extending Arab-D mapped faults to the underlying Hanifa reservoir. Further corroboration of such detailed mapping of small faults or fracture zones came from analysis of flowmeter, core, and borehole-image data, which suggested that many of the larger conventionally defined (reflector-offset-based) faults may affect the inter-reservoir fluid flow significantly less than small-scale coherence-defined faults or fractures do. Mapping of such small-scale faults is critical to our understanding of fluid flow.

Example from Alberta, Canada

Mapping of faults in 3D seismic volumes, in different directions, is important. Usually we see fault regimes being more prominent in one direction, a phenomenon that of course is controlled by the tectonic activity in the area. Mapping of cross faults could be very important, especially when we are identifying trap closures. Figure 50 shows a stratigraphic slab extracted from a coherence volume. Its disposition in 3D space gives the interpreter a good idea of structure at the level of interest.

The stratal slice in Figure 51a exhibits prominent faults in one direction (northwest-southeast). In this figure, we see the intermediate step that an interpreter would go through — that of examining the seismic signatures (Figure 51b) that correspond to the low-coherence lineations seen on the stratal slice (Figure 51a). Once convinced that the low-coherence lineations correlate correctly with their seismic signatures, the interpreter examines the stratal slices for other trends.

As Figure 52 shows, some fault trends are orthogonal to the prominent faults we see in Figure 51. We refer to such faults as cross faults. Notice at least three cross-fault trends marked on the stratigraphic slice in Figure 52b with a solid magenta line.

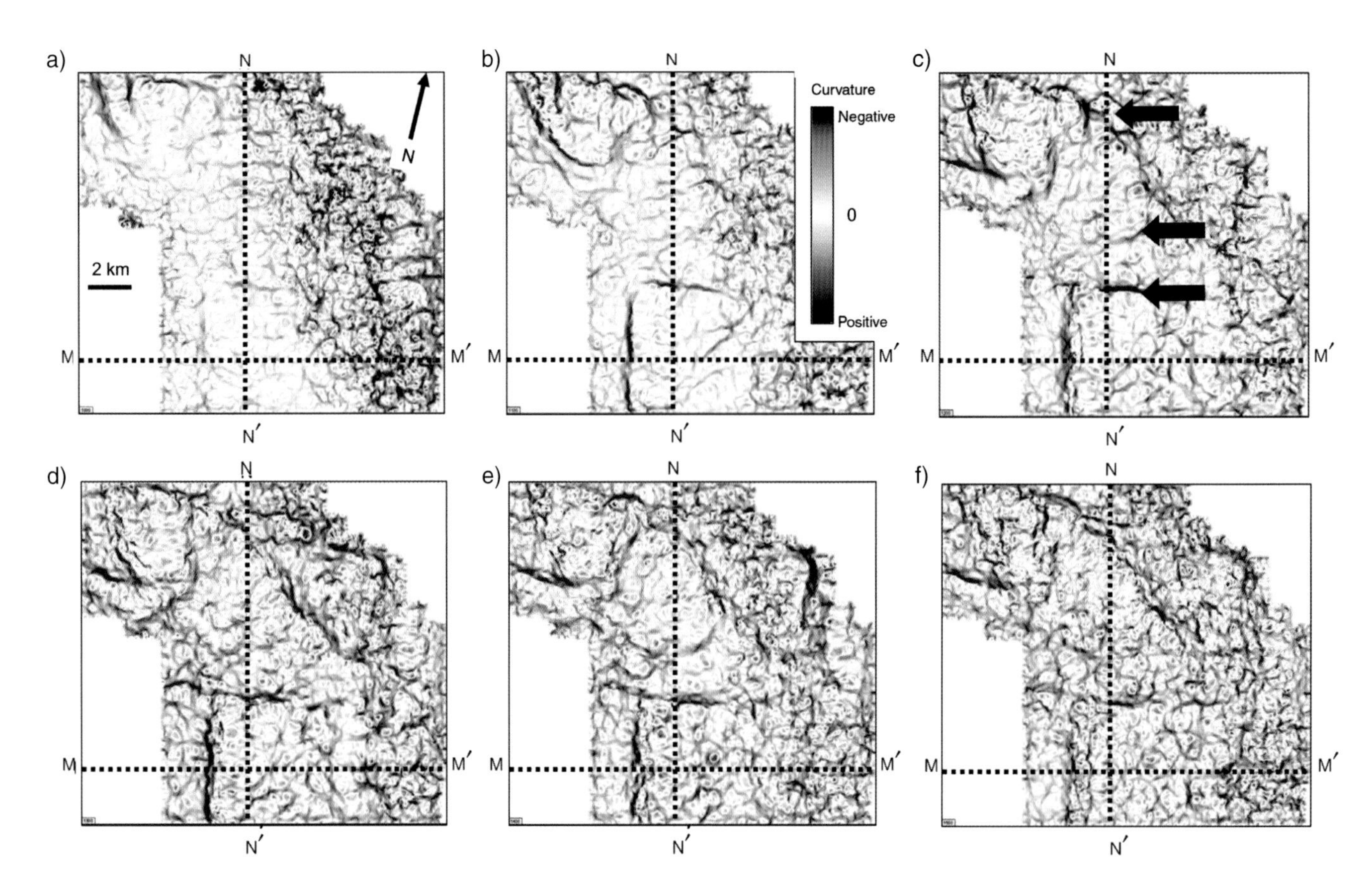

Figure 38. Most-negative-curvature time slices at t = (a) 1.000 s, (b) 1.100 s, (c) 1.200 s, (d) 1.300 s, (e) 1.400 s, and (f) 1.500 s, corresponding to and computed from the dip-azimuth slices in Figure 35 and corresponding to the most-positive-curvature slices in Figure 37. Black arrows indicate synclinal features that are shown on the vertical seismic data displayed in Figure 36b.

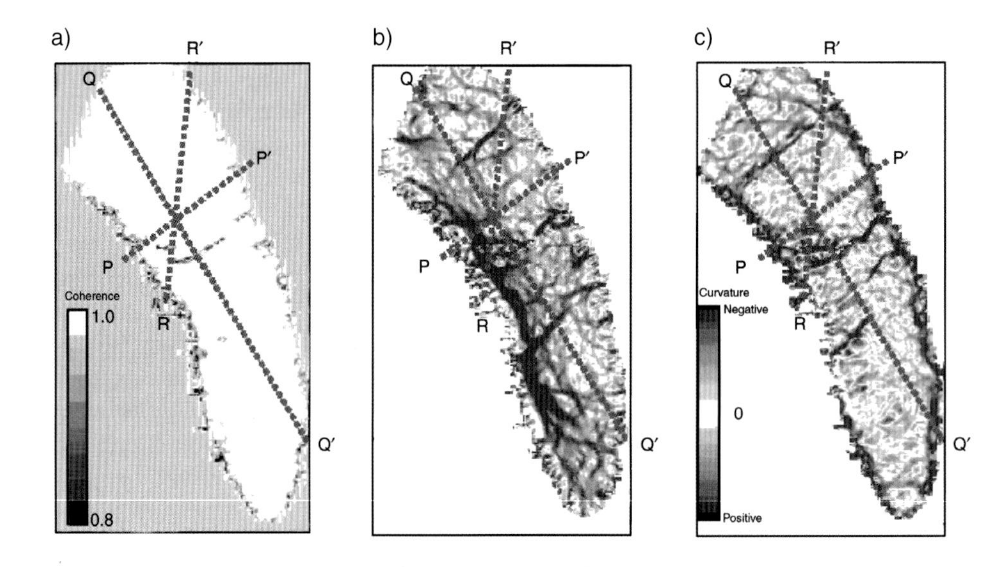

Figure 39. Reverse faulting that gives rise to strike-slip faulting and pop-up blocks, seen here through seismic attributes, from a survey conducted in the Teapot Dome area, Wyoming, U.S.A. Horizon slices along the purple horizon shown in Figure 40 cut though (a) a coherence volume, (b) a most-positive-curvature volume, and (c) a most-negative-curvature volume. The seismic data are courtesy of RMOTC.

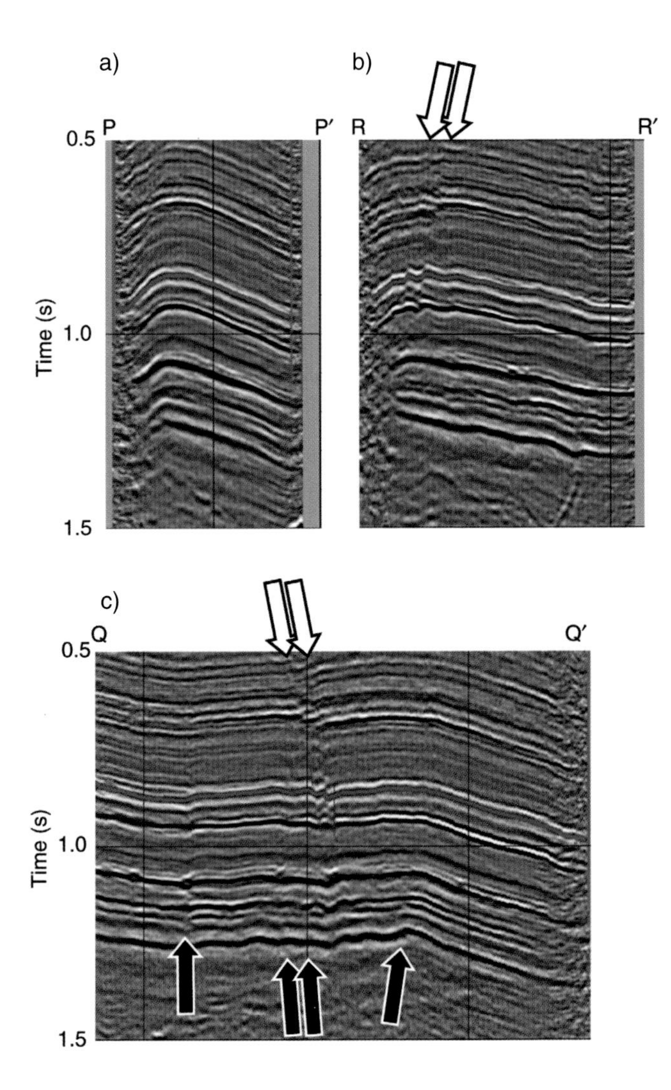

Figure 40. Seismic cross sections through faults seen in the curvature volumes in Figure 39: (a) dip line PP′, (b) line RR′, a line perpendicular to the third curvature lineaments, and (c) strike line QQ′. The strike-slip fault indicated by the white arrows is a distinct discontinuity at this level and therefore is seen in the coherence slice. The subtler faults indicated by black arrows are not seen in the coherence slice, but they do appear on the curvature horizon slices. Seismic data are courtesy of RMOTC.

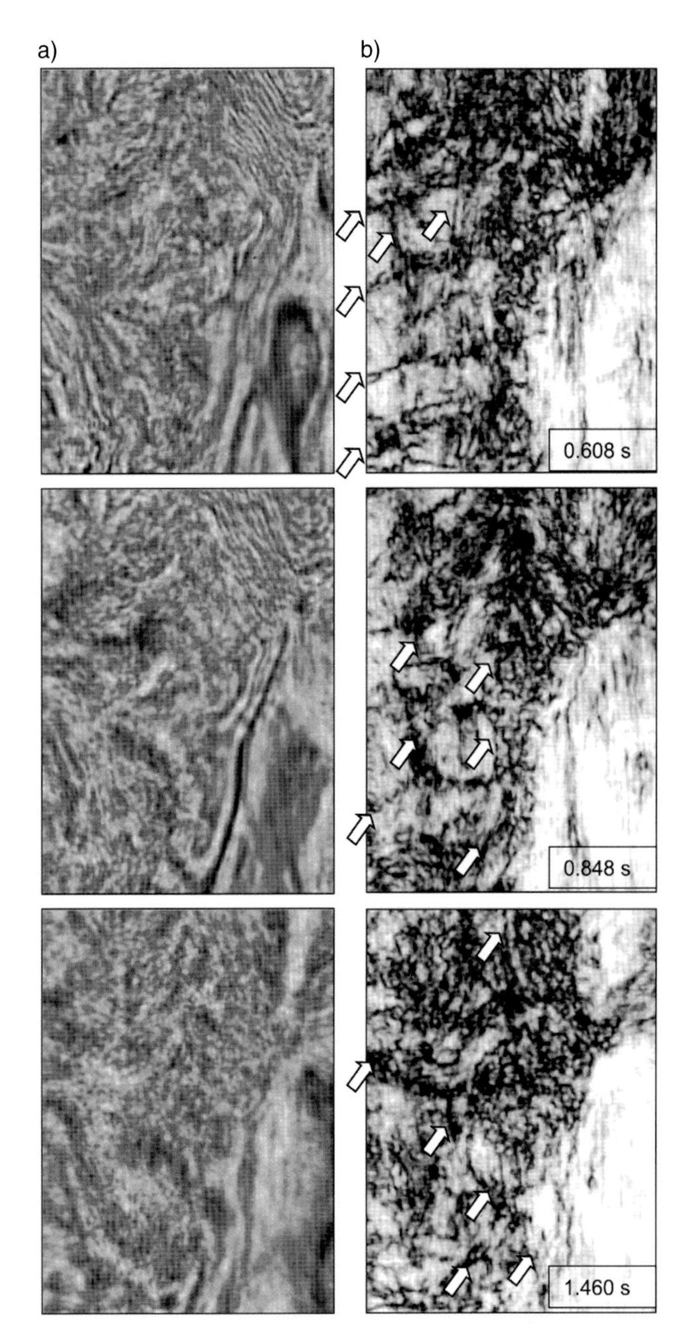

Figure 41. Time slices at $t = 0.608$ s, 0.848 s, and 1.460 s, through (a) a seismic data volume and (b) the corresponding coherence volume from a survey acquired over the Cook Inlet area of Alaska, U.S.A. Notice that not only are the faults seen clearly on the coherence slices (white arrows), but the fractured areas also can be marked.

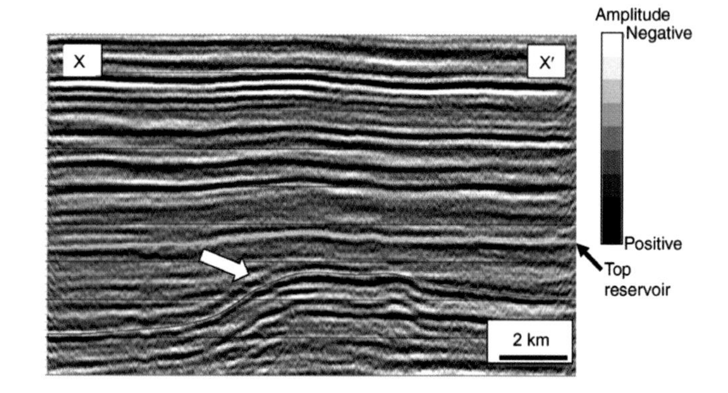

Figure 42. A seismic line through a fractured sandstone reservoir in Saudi Arabia. The picked horizon corresponds to the top of the reservoir. A white arrow indicates an area of conflicting dip. The horizontal event is most likely a multiple, a phenomenon that plagues much of the data acquired on the Arabian Peninsula. The interference of such crossing events with real reflectors causes coherence artifacts. After Neves et al. (2004).

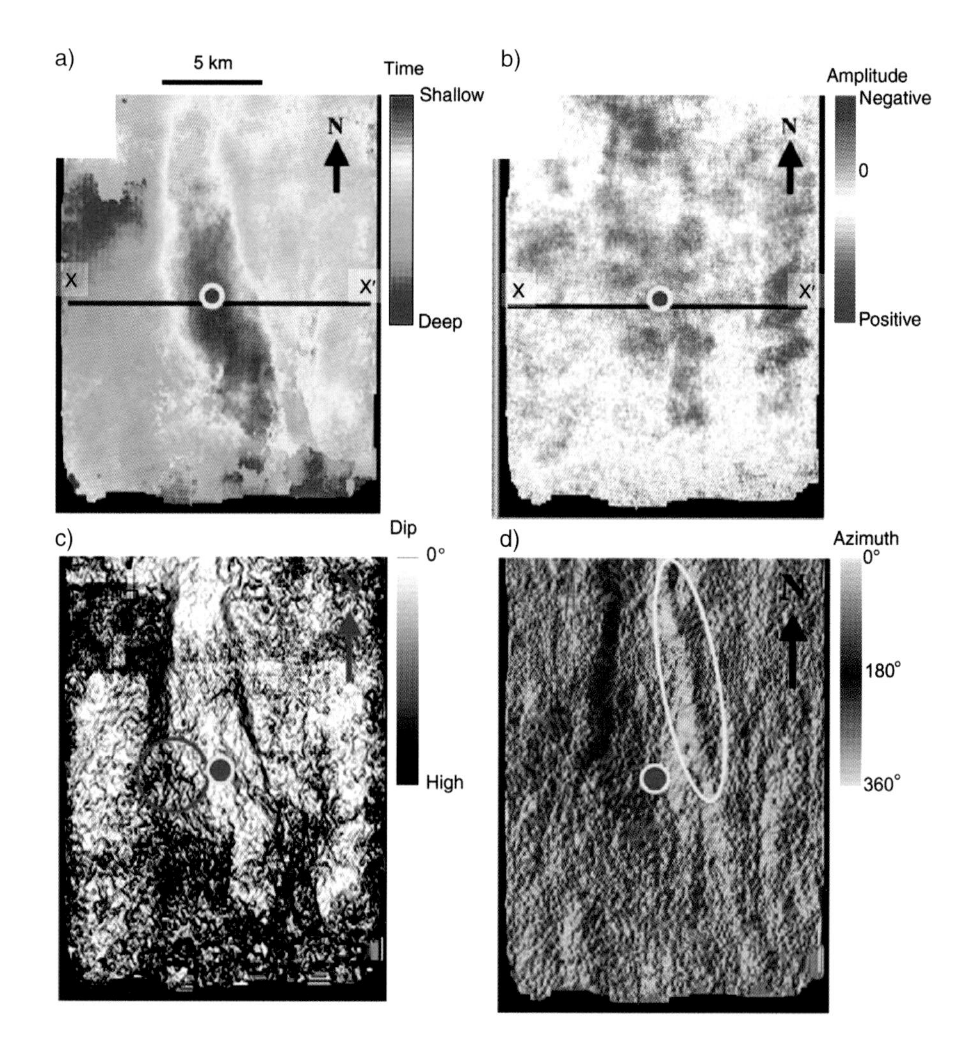

Figure 43. (a) A time-structure map, and its corresponding (b) horizon slice through the seismic data, (c) dip-magnitude map, and (d) dip-azimuth map, all corresponding to the top reservoir pick shown in Figure 42. The time-structure map indicates the existence of faults bounding the large red areas. The blue solid circle shows the location of a well on a structural high. The area of interest is west of the well. The full extent of the east flank of the fault block (circled in yellow) is delineated better by the dip-azimuth attribute (d), whereas an indication of a possible fractured zone (highlighted by the red circle) is inferred better from the dip-magnitude attribute in (c). Neither the dip-magnitude (c) nor the dip-azimuth (d) map provides a clear indication of fracturing. After Neves et al. (2004).

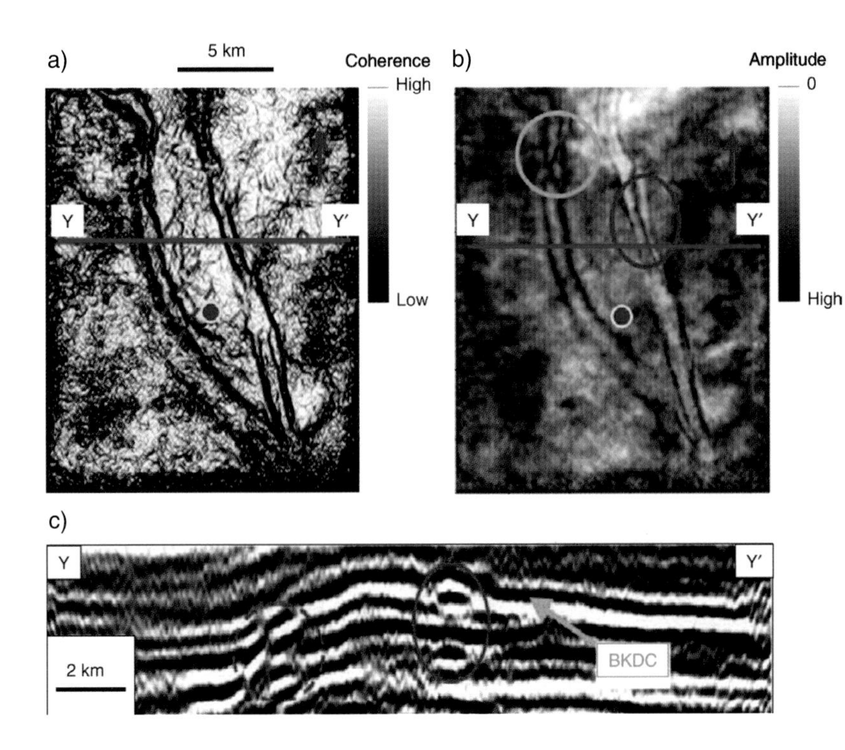

Figure 44. Horizon slices through (a) coherence and (b) the 26-Hz spectral component at the reservoir interval. The red dashed lines suggest the existence of en echelon faults cutting the west flank of the faulted block. In (b), the 26-Hz spectral component horizon slice provides additional information independently from the coherence horizon slice in (a). The red and green circles indicate areas where the 26-Hz spectral-component horizon slice shows a clearer image than the coherence map does. (c) A seismic crossline showing the existence of several faults. The dashed red circle indicates the interval where faults were mapped better using coherence, and the red solid circle shows faults that were mapped better by the spectral-decomposition attribute. After Neves et al. (2004).

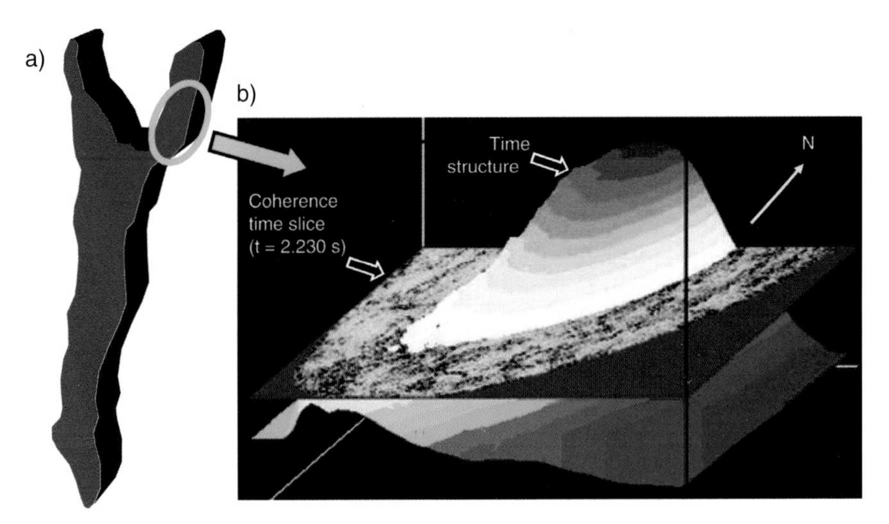

Figure 45. (a) An outline of Ghawar field, Saudi Arabia. The circle indicates the location of south Abqaiq field. (b) A 3D perspective view of a time-structure map of south Abqaiq field, showing its domal structure cut by a coherence slice at $t = 2.230$ s.

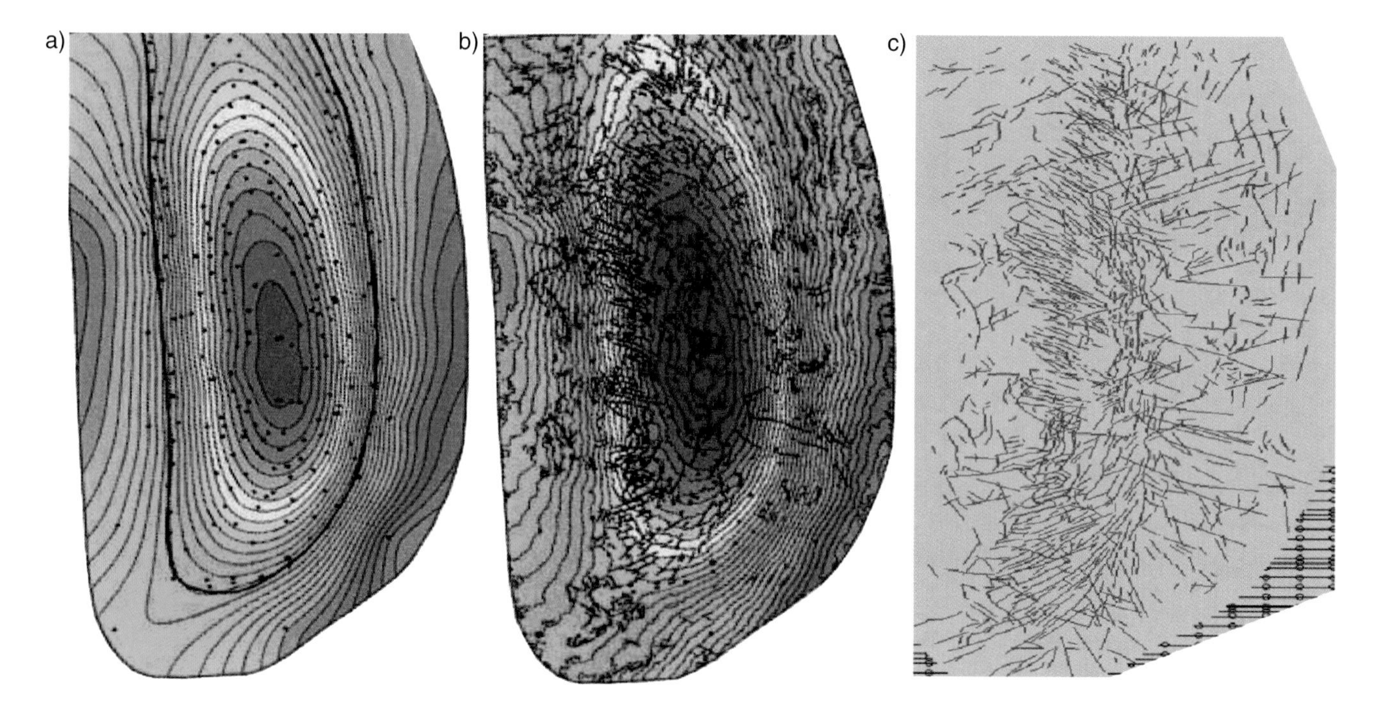

Figure 46. Depth-structure maps for the Arab-D level, south Abqaiq field, Saudi Arabia, prepared from: (a) well data only, (b) 3D seismic data integrated with well data, and (c) 3D seismic data integrated with coherence data and well data. The overall survey area is about 450 km^2. Hundreds of faults now are seen where well data indicated none. Apparently, the western flank of the structure is highly faulted (believed to be the result of differential uplift along the flank) with a rotational trend around the domal structure. Mapping of such small-scale faults is critical to our understanding of fluid flow.

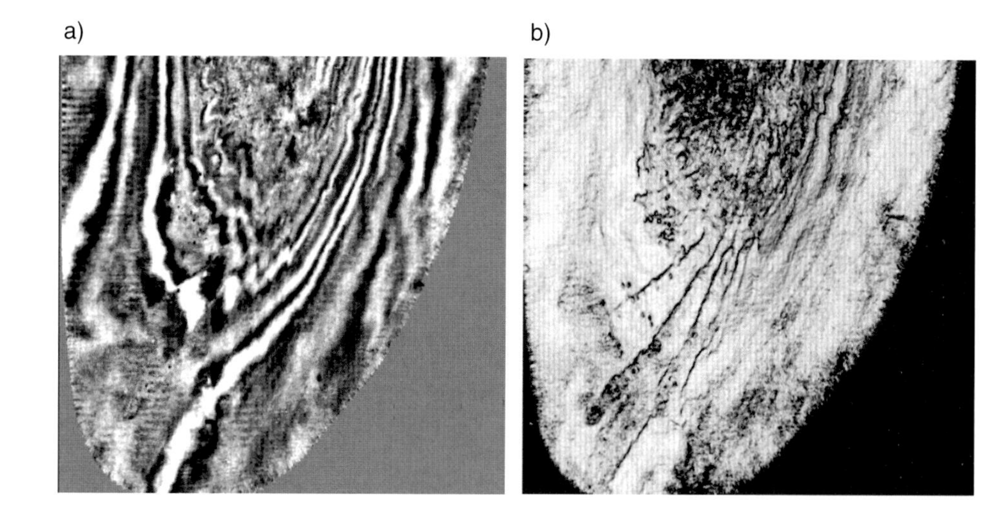

Figure 47. Time slices at t = 2.230 s through (a) a seismic data volume and (b) a coherence volume from south Abqaiq field, Saudi Arabia, showing radial faults.

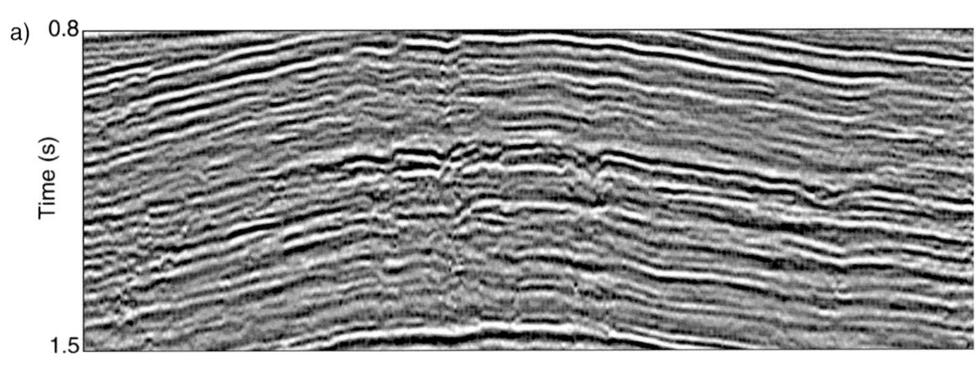

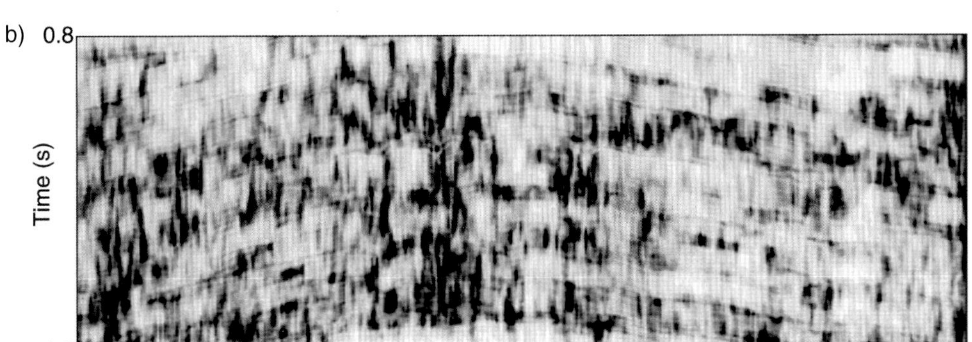

Figure 48. Vertical slices through (a) a seismic data volume and (b) a coherence volume, from south Abqaiq field, Saudi Arabia. Note how many of the vertical faults in the coherence volume do not appear to be through-going. Their healing can be the result of either a lack of resolution resulting from statics and velocity errors, or more likely, it can be the result of different fault/fracture responses for different lithologies. The former may be the less likely case because adequate precautions were taken during processing.

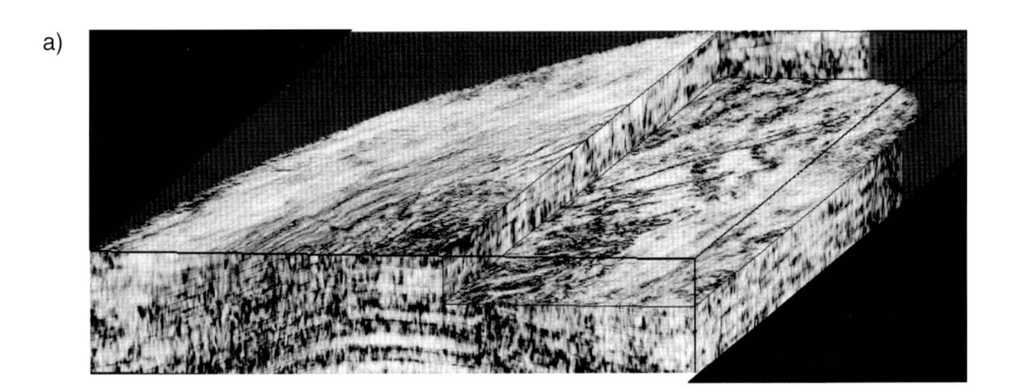

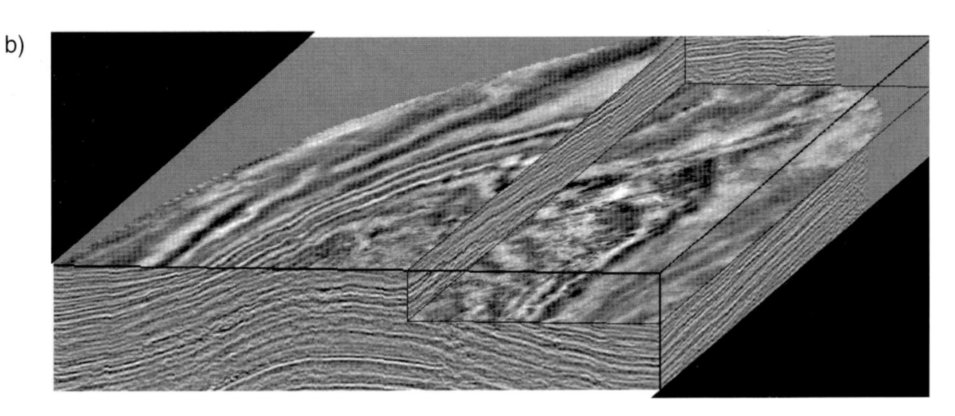

Figure 49. Windowed slabs of (a) a seismic data volume and (b) a coherence volume, from south Abqaiq field, Saudi Arabia, illustrating the expression of faults and channels.

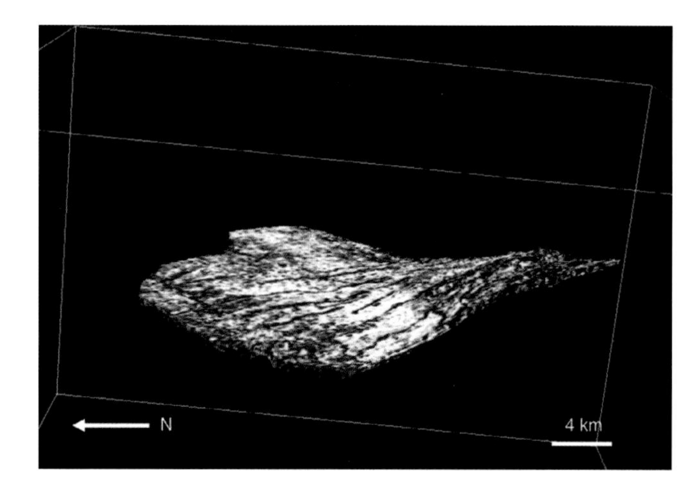

Figure 50. A stratigraphic cube from a coherence volume from Alberta, Canada. Apart from the structure that becomes obvious in such a 3D display, faults are seen in their true perspective. Images are courtesy of Arcis Corporation, Calgary. Data are courtesy of Olympic Seismic, Calgary.

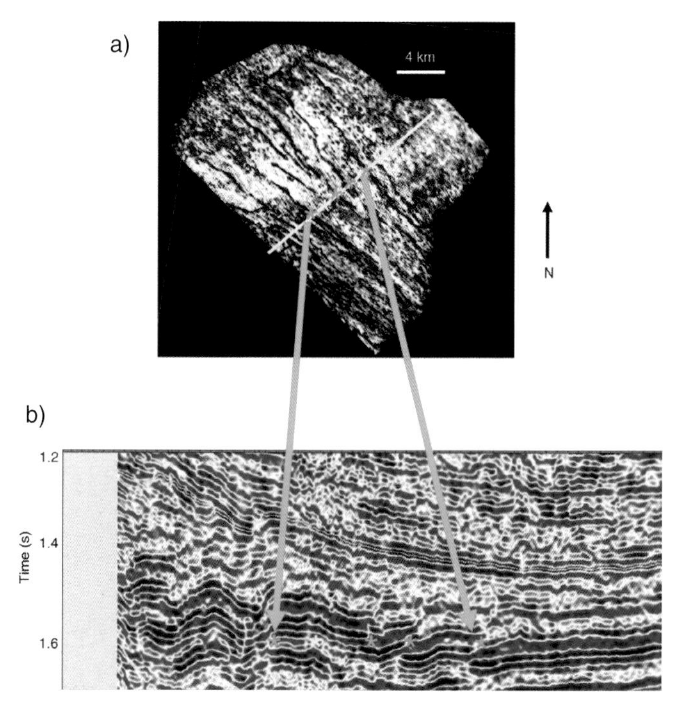

Figure 51. (a) Low-coherence lineations are interpreted to be faults on this coherence stratigraphic slice, and (b) those lineations are correlated with their corresponding seismic signatures (cyan arrows). Such correlations with the original seismic data allow the interpreter to confirm that lineaments are faults rather than crosscutting noise or other artifacts. Images are courtesy of Arcis Corporation, Calgary. Data are courtesy of Olympic Seismic, Calgary.

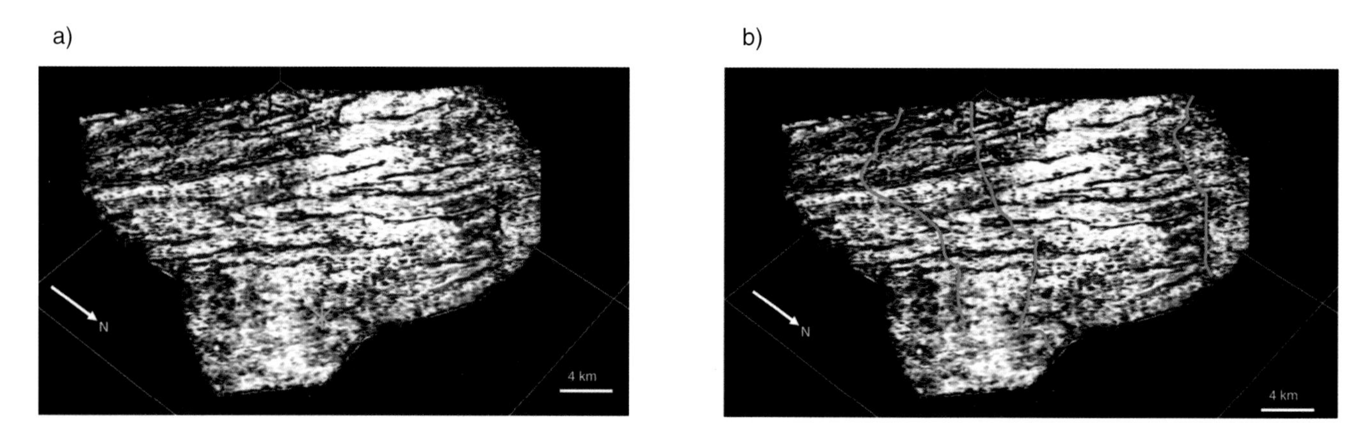

Figure 52. (a) An uninterpreted stratigraphic slice and (b) its interpretation, showing the main faults as crisp lineations in the east-west direction. Notice the three cross-fault trends that have been identified and are shown by solid magenta lines in the interpretation. Images are courtesy of Arcis Corporation, Calgary. Data are courtesy of Olympic Seismic, Calgary.

Chapter Summary

The use of volumetric attributes, including coherence, dip azimuth, and curvature, provides a natural and powerful extension of well-established workflows commonly used with time slices through seismic-amplitude volumes and dip-azimuth maps computed from picked horizons. Volumetric attributes have several advantages over attributes computed from a picked horizon, including saving the time needed to pick the horizon, avoiding interpreter error and/or bias, and using a vertical analysis window, which provides a more robust estimate in the presence of noise. Given sufficient time and skill, a human interpreter can avoid the first two constraints. However, volumetric attributes not only are calculated for an entire volume, they also are computed in a small volumetric-analysis window, thereby providing higher signal-to-noise estimates of reflector dip and azimuth.

Interpreting faults on seismic time slices works well when the faults cut perpendicularly to the seismic strike, but picking faults that run parallel to reflector strike on time slices is much more difficult. Volumetric curvature and dip-azimuth remove the seismic waveform, and although they result in a vertically blocky image, they provide the interpreter with a means of visualizing all faults at once.

Faults are not the only structural features of interest to interpreters. Salt and shale diapirs are readily recognized on coherence images. Folds and flexures, as well as faults with very little vertical throw, are recognized easily on curvature images. A 3D image of dip and azimuth is a very useful image, although modern workstation software still needs to adopt a 2D or 3D color table that easily shows these attributes.

References

Biles, N. E., A. E. Hannan, G. A. Jamieson, A. Krueger, D. L. Shelander, and F. Snyder, 2003, Regional evaluation and hydrocarbon potential of the deep section of the Gulf of Mexico offshore Louisiana continental shelf from modern 3D seismic data: 73rd Annual International Meeting, SEG, Expanded Abstracts, 414–417.

Blumentritt, C. H., K. J. Marfurt, and E. C. Sullivan, 2006, Volume-based curvature computations illuminate fracture orientations — Early to mid-Paleozoic, Central Basin Platform, west Texas: Geophysics, **71**, B159–B166.

Chopra, S., 2002, Coherence cube and beyond: First Break, **20**, 27–33.

Dasgupta, S. N., J. J. Kim, A. M. al-Mousa, H. M. al-Mustafa, F. Aminzadeh, and E. V. Lunen, 2000, From seismic character and seismic attributes to reservoir properties: Case history in Arab-D reservoir of Saudi Arabia: 70th Annual International Meeting, SEG, Expanded Abstracts, 597–599.

Gersztenkorn, A., J. A. Sharp, and K. J. Marfurt, 1999, Delineation of tectonic features offshore Trinidad using 3D seismic coherence: The Leading Edge, **18**, 1000–1008.

Haskell, N., S. E. Nissen, M. J. S. Hughes, J. Grindhaug, S. Dhanani, R. P. Heath, J. D. Kantorowicz, L. Antrim, M. Cubanski, R. Nataraj, M. Schilly, and S. Wigger, 1999, Delineation of geological drilling hazards using 3-D seismic attributes: The Leading Edge, **18**, 373–382.

Lawrence, P., 1998, Seismic attributes in the characterization of small-scale reservoir faults in Abqaiq field: The Leading Edge, **17**, 521–525.

Maione, S. J., 2001, Discovery of ring faults associated with salt withdrawal basins, Early Cretaceous age, in the East Texas Basin: The Leading Edge, **20**, 818–829.

Neves, F., M. S. Zahrani, and S. W. Bremkamp, 2004, Detection of potential fractures and small faults using seismic attributes: The Leading Edge, **23**, 903–908.

Chapter 12

Attribute Expression of Clastic Depositional Environments

Chapter Objectives

After reading this chapter, you will be able to

- use seismic attributes in the context of seismic geomorphology
- choose an appropriate workflow, based on time, horizon, or stratal slices, to meet your interpretation objectives within your time constraints
- determine when energy-weighted coherent–amplitude gradients, coherence, and curvature may help you to map channel features
- use spectral decomposition to add a third dimension to seismic geomorphology
- recognize and adjust your interpretation to account for differential compaction effects

Introduction

As we discussed in Chapter 1, the development of seismic attributes was closely linked to the development of seismic stratigraphy in the late 1970s (e.g., Vail et al., 1977). Seismic stratigraphy is one of the tools used in sequence stratigraphy, which in turn studies basin fill as a function of eustasy, sedimentation, and subsidence. In particular, seismic data (and seismic stratigraphy) can provide a basinwide, regional image of the subsurface that allows us to correlate major geologic events between outcrop data and more limited well-control data. Sequence stratigraphy allows us to map sea-level changes, lateral facies shifts, occurrences of unconformities, and tectonic activity through time. Given an understanding of geologic processes and paleoenvironments, sequence stratigraphy allows us to predict potential source and reservoir rocks.

Because this is a book about seismic attributes, we limit our discussion of sequence stratigraphy to the much more restricted topic of seismic stratigraphy. A key component of seismic stratigraphy is the mapping of seismic facies. Traditionally, seismic-facies analysis includes the mapping of continuous, discontinuous, and chaotic reflectors.

The presence of continuous reflectors suggests deposition in a relatively stable environment, whereas the presence of discontinuous reflectors suggests laterally heterogeneous depositional environments, such as areas of deposition and erosion by channels. Chaotic seismic reflectors suggest sedimentary rocks that have been fractured, mobilized, or diagenetically altered, respectively, or alternatively, crystalline basement or evaporites.

The morphological and geometric relations between reflectors are key components of seismic stratigraphy. Onlap occurs during transgression, with sediments being deposited on a dipping or eroded shoreline. In contrast, downlap occurs as the sediments prograde into deeper parts of the basin and may be deposited on top of an older, flatter seafloor. Toplap occurs when a strong horizontal reflector is deposited on top of downlapped strata. Finally, offlap defines strata that both prograde and aggrade outward into the basin. Figure 1 illustrates these geometries via a scan of two previously unpublished slides used by Tury Taner in his

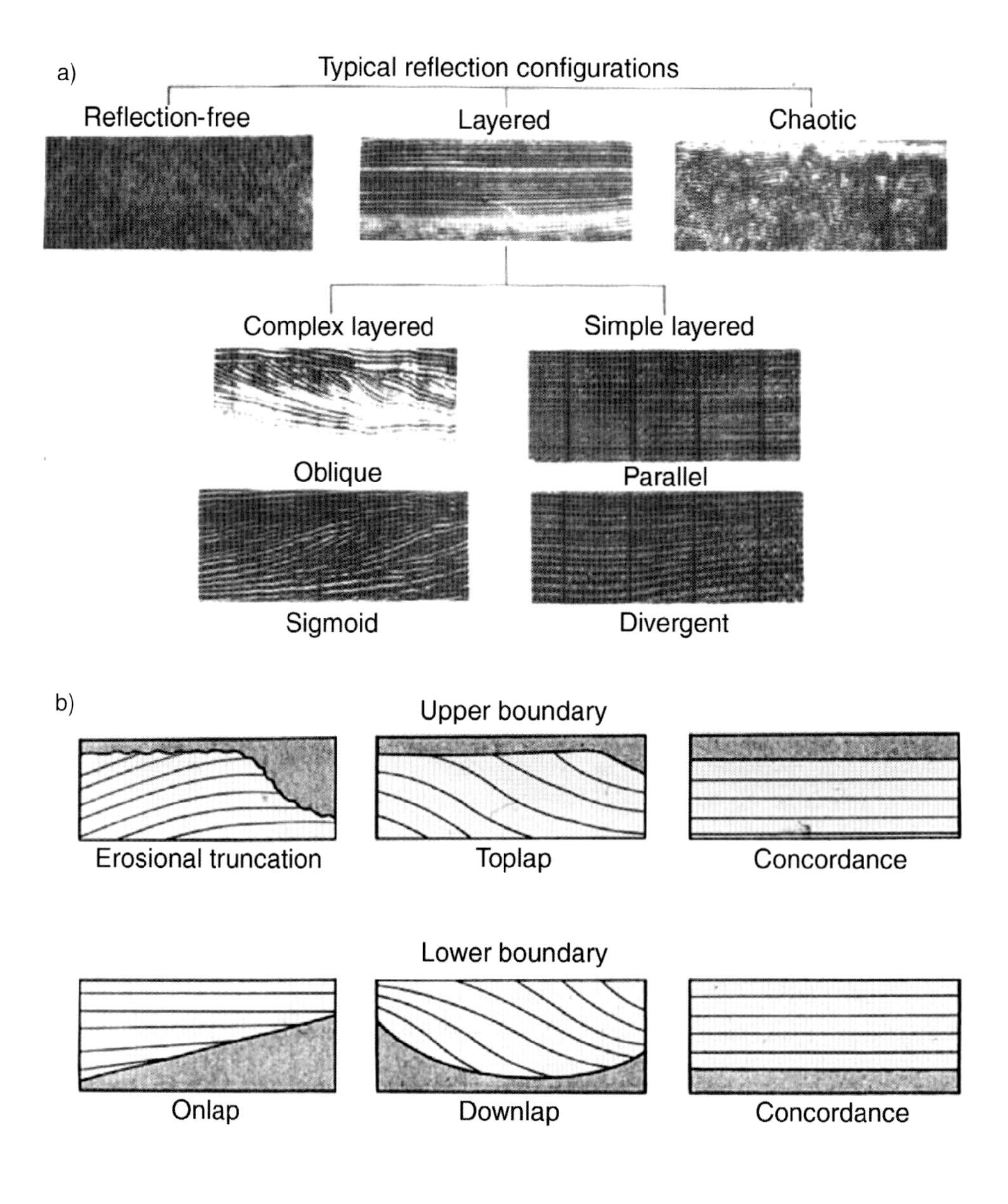

Figure 1. Scanned copies of two slides used by Tury Taner in the AAPG-sponsored school on seismic stratigraphy during the middle 1970s and the 1980s. (a) Representative reflection characters seen on 2D seismic lines. (b) Idealized characters used in seismic stratigraphy interpretation. These early interpretation-workflow concepts inspired later developments in geometric attributes (including volumetric dip and azimuth, reflector parallelism, continuity, and unconformity indicators). These images are courtesy of Tury Taner, Rock Solid Images.

AAPG-sponsored school on seismic stratigraphy in the late 1970s. Figure 2 provides a more modern (and somewhat more focused) illustration of seismic facies.

During the past five years, the term seismic facies has been applied to various seismic-classification techniques. In its original implementation, waveform classification was applied only to the waveform itself, and as such it provided very useful maps that were comparable to spectral decomposition. However, it did not provide quantification of reflector morphology, as defined by onlap, downlap, toplap, or offlap, or even of chaotic reflector morphology.

Quite recently, such classification technology has been generalized to work on attributes rather than on seismic data samples. In this new application, in which the input attributes include estimates of dip, azimuth, curvature, coherence, amplitude, and frequency content, the results can yield a seismic facies more like the classical seismic facies described in the late 1970s, such as those shown in Figure 1. In Chapter 14, Figure 30, we show one such example of this application to map a gas chimney.

Seismic attributes have helped workers map seismic facies since Taner and colleagues developed complex-trace attributes in 1979 (Taner et al., 1979). We have shown that coherence has been particularly helpful for mapping lateral changes in reflector continuity, as well as in highly chaotic areas, such as the salt and shale diapirs we discussed in Chapter 11.

Attribute mapping of angular unconformities is somewhat more challenging. Although we can accurately map dip and azimuth in 3D, changes in dip and azimuth occur not just vertically but also laterally. Although we can generate relatively low-resolution images of convergence and divergence (such as those in Chapter 2, Figure 21), higher-resolution images that attempt to map angular unconformities (such those in Chapter 2, Figure 22) currently are contaminated by other artifacts. We anticipate that future develop-

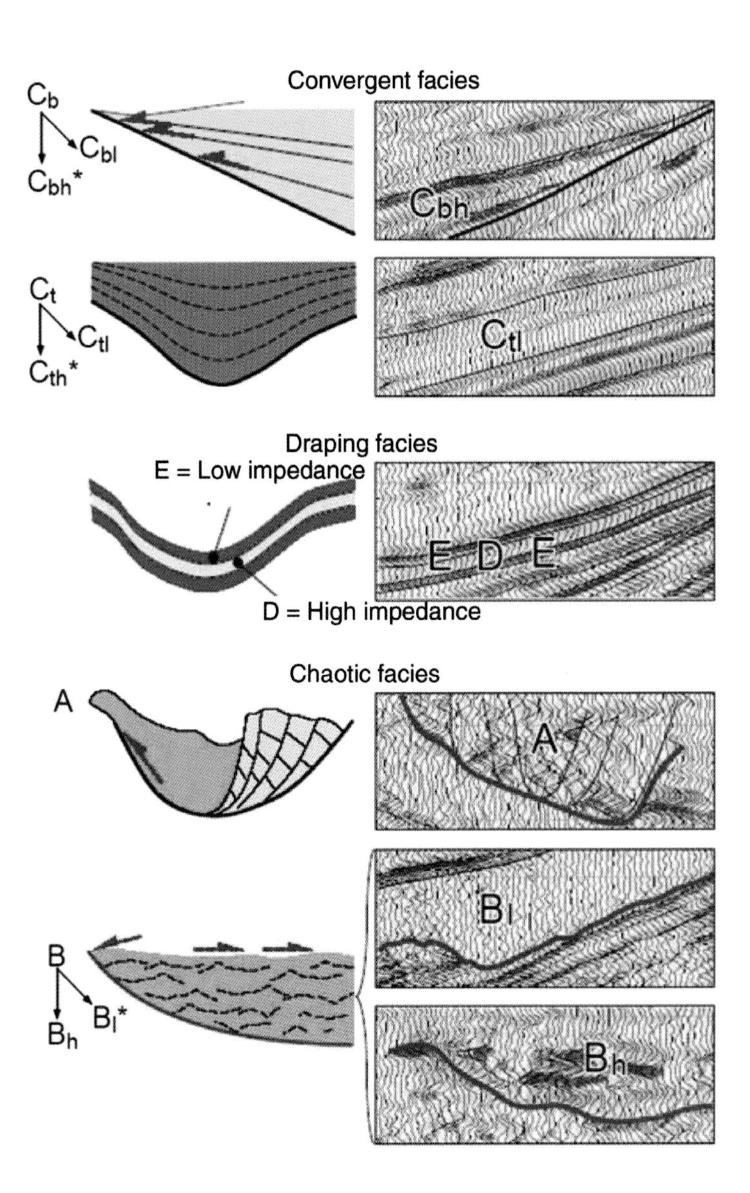

Figure 2. Idealized external and internal geometries that characterize seismic facies. Each subfacies marked by an asterisk is the more common of its subfacies pair. After Prather et al. (1998). AAPG©1998. Reprinted by permission of the AAPG, whose permission is required for further use.

ment of image-processing filters, such as those discussed for enhancing the appearance of faults on coherence volumes in Chapter 8, Figures 32–47, will allow us to achieve this goal.

Seismic Facies Analysis and Seismic Geomorphology

Combining observations of seismic facies and sedimentological and tectonic processes gives rise to a relatively new area of study dubbed seismic geomorphology (e.g., Posamentier and Kolla, 2003). The workflow of seismic geomorphology uses a combination of seismic attributes, time slices, horizon slices, and stratal slices (defined below) to map geologic features as they may have occurred at a particular instant in geologic time. Phantom-horizon slices most commonly are generated by first flattening a 100- to 200-ms slab of seismic data or attributes with respect to a picked horizon and then time slicing through the flattened slab. Even if the original picked horizon is a sequence boundary corresponding to a given instant in geologic time, shallower and deeper sequence boundaries generally are not parallel; thus, phantom horizons far from the original picked horizon cut formations of different ages. To avoid some of the limitations of the phantom-horizon slice, Zeng et al. (1998a, b) introduced the stratal slice. In that process, the interpreter picks two sequence boundaries and generates slices that are proportional between them, thereby more nearly producing intermediate horizon slices that correspond to a single geologic point in time.

Ideally, such a stratal slice gives us an image of paleogeography. Mapping paleogeography allows us to exploit our understanding of modern depositional processes, which in turn allows us to infer such things as whether a given channel system is sand prone or sand poor.

Modern geomorphologists use all data available to them, including logs, cores, seismic data, and seismic attributes. Root-mean-square (rms) energy and coherence attributes have proven to be particularly effective. Typical products of geomorphology are maps of the lateral form of geologic features, such as those shown in Figure 3.

In a sense, the seismic stratigraphy of the late 1970s has been absorbed into the broader discipline of seismic geomorphology. Posamentier predicted that pattern analysis based on geomorphic insights is where the next breakthroughs will be (Shirley, 2000). Seismic attributes will enable such pattern analysis. Posamentier also recommended that we look at the near surface down to about 400 m, where seismic resolution and data quality typically are higher, and develop expertise and understanding on how different depositional systems can be imaged and what kind of stratigraphic insights we can draw. Then, after we gain experience in the shallower zones, we can apply our understanding deeper where we have fewer pieces of the puzzle.

Thus, we begin our journey into seismic geomorphology with two high-resolution shallow studies that will help us understand the lower-resolution deeper-channel images we examine in this chapter. We investigate other shallow studies in Chapter 14.

Figure 4 displays a phantom-horizon slice 76 ms below the water bottom, through a coherence volume of a shallow channel system. The image was computed by Mark Deptuck (2003) for a survey over the Jeanne d'Arc Basin, offshore eastern Canada. The horizon slice cuts an inner levee-dominated facies that developed during an earlier phase (in blue) and through stacked channel forms that occupied the system during a later stage (yellow and red).

Figure 5 displays Deptuck's (2003) interpretation, which he derived from a suite of seven coherence slices at progressively deeper times in the stacked channel features. The interpretation is similar to one a geomorphologist would use on landforms — the only difference is that Deptuck's observations were made from seismic data and seismic attributes.

Turbidites

In his AAPG distinguished lecture, Jennette (2005, unpaginated) stated,

> Our knowledge of turbidite reservoirs has advanced rapidly over the past 15 years, owing largely to the petroleum industry's acquisition of ever larger and higher-frequency 3D marine seismic surveys. These surveys provide a stunning portfolio of high-resolution snapshots of ancient and modern submarine landscapes and illustrate the intricate details of their accompanying turbidite systems. As 3D volumes are stitched together and time-stratigraphy across large parts of continental slopes established, subsurface workers can reconstruct characteristics of the ancient shelf, shelf edge, slope, and basin-floor environments and deduce the suite of processes and controls that led to the development of the spectrum of turbidite reservoirs. Understanding these basic controls improves our ability to generate models that better predict the broad range of attributes required to ensure commerciality in costly offshore operating environments and/or settings where resolution of the objective is compromised by salt or deep burial.

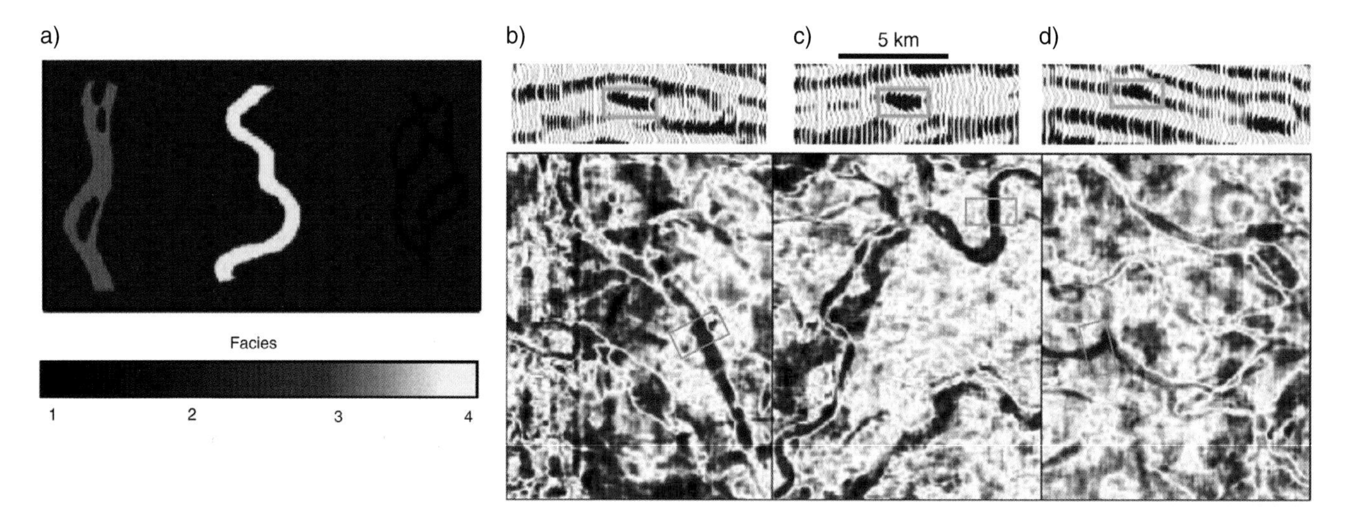

Figure 3. (a) Morphology-based facies classification of fluvial systems. Facies 1 = anastomosing (suspended load) channel. Facies 2 = floodplain. Facies 3 = straight (bed load) channel. Facies 4 = sinuous (mixed load) channel. (b)-(d) Amplitude stratal slices of three fluvial systems and related channel waveforms: (b) straight, (c) meandering, and (d) anastomosing. Although their channel morphologies differ, the three fluvial systems are characterized by a similar vertical seismic waveform. After Zeng (2004). AAPG©2004. Reprinted by permission of the AAPG, whose permission is required for further use.

Subsurface systems like those encountered in the Paleogene of the North Sea and the Tertiary of the Gulf of Mexico, offshore West Africa, and offshore Egypt, together with the outcropping systems of the Permian of west Texas and the Carboniferous Claire Group of western Ireland, provide comparative data sets from which to evaluate the principal mechanisms that establish turbidite reservoirs. We observe contrasting styles of architecture (channel-dominated to sheet-dominated), pattern (straight versus highly sinuous, dendritic versus lobate), sand percent, bed thickness, and grain size and sorting. These characteristics can be tied to (1) the sediment delivery system that, in conveyer-belt fashion, controls the composition and volume of sediment available to the shelf edge, (2) triggering mechanisms at the shelf edge that control the volume, feed rate, and concentration of the flows, and (3) seafloor gradients that influence the acceleration, steadiness, or deceleration of flows. Within any one system, much of the reservoir architecture we observe can be tied back to the sand: mud ratio of flows and to seafloor gradient. A fourth factor influencing final architectural character, particularly on the upper slope, is modification by slumping or headwardly migrating erosional nickpoints.

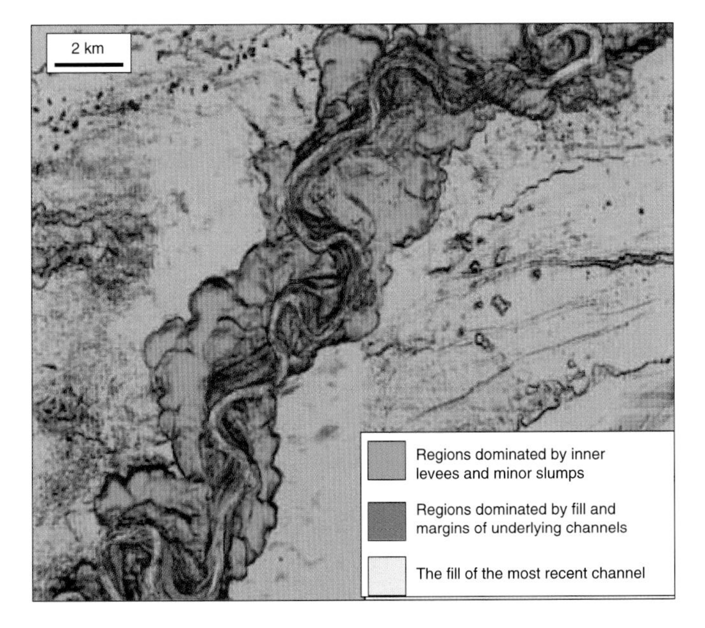

Figure 4. A phantom-horizon slice 76 ms below the seafloor through a coherence volume calculated from a survey acquired over the Jeanne d'Arc Basin in eastern Canada. The horizon slice cuts through the inner levee-dominated facies that developed during an earlier phase (in blue) and through the stacked channel forms that occupied the system during a later stage (yellow and red). After Deptuck (2003).

Figure 6 displays a coherence horizon slice generated by Saller et al. (2004) for a survey acquired offshore East Kalimantan, Indonesia. The data were extracted along the water bottom. Such shallow images provide a better understanding of the processes noted in the figure. These same processes also are evident on deeper images of exploration interest. In this figure, the slope extends from the shelf at about 100 m deep to the basin floor at 2000 m deep. Saller et al. (2004, p. 27) noted, "Most canyons on the slope are straight or gently curving, except one that has sharp sinuous bends and connects the earlier lowstand delta to a contemporaneous basin-floor fan. Sediment waves are common on the upper slope, upslope from the deep canyons, and on the lower slope."

In Figure 7, we show one of Saller et al.'s images of a coherence horizon slice near the water bottom, "showing a sinuous, meandering channel of an inner basin-floor fan passing into an unconfined outer basin-floor fan," (Saller et al., 2004, p. 27). Ridges outside of meander loops indicated by black arrows are sediment waves.

In Chapter 2, Figure 18, we showed a time slice at t = 1.000 s through a dip-azimuth cube computed from a survey acquired in the northern Delaware Basin, New Mexico, U.S.A. In that figure we noted that the sediments in the southern third of the survey were dumped (carried from shallower geologic features) from the platform into the basin, to form the Permian Brushy Canyon Formation. Here, in Figure 8, we display two Delaware Basin seismic lines that run (a) perpendicular to and (b) parallel to the platform edge. These

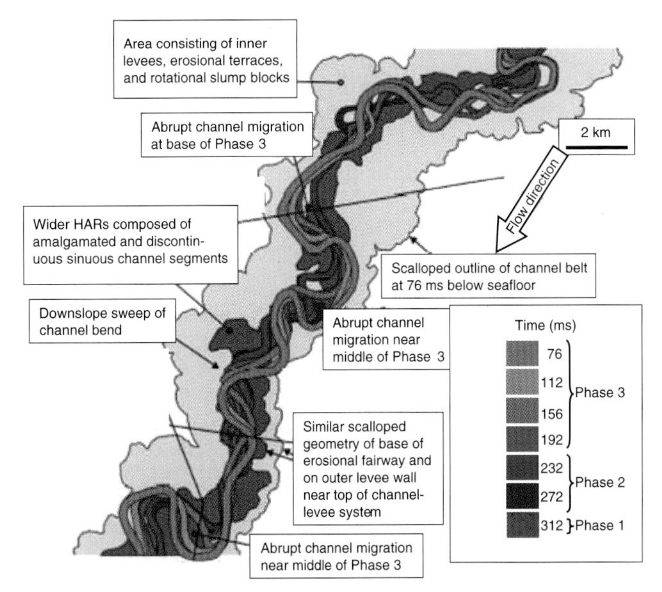

Figure 5. A drawing based on data from the Jeanne d'Arc Basin survey in the previous figure, showing here the planform geometry of the stacked channel-axis-deposit high-amplitude reflections (HARs) between 36 and 40 ms below the seafloor. The drawing was derived from a coherence horizon slice. After Deptuck (2003).

gravity-controlled slope deposits are quite chaotic, so that there is no meaningful surface to pick.

Instead, we flatten on the easy-to-pick overlying Grayburg Formation horizon (the orange pick in Figure 8). We then extract several horizons through the east-west component of the energy-weighted coherent-amplitude gradient and display the results in Figure 9. Although the difference between the depth of the basin and the shelf is not nearly as great here (with a relief of only approximately 300 to 400 m) as that shown in Figure 6, the morphology of the slump features in both environments is remarkably similar, with some slumps being straight and others meandering.

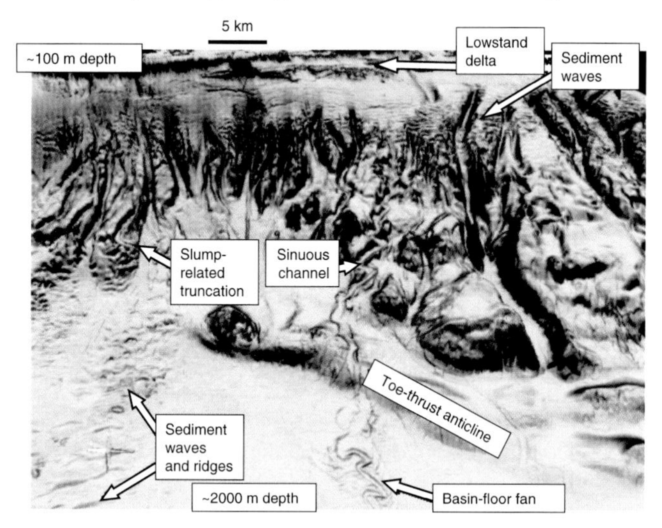

Figure 6. Sedimentary features commonly seen on a deep-water shelf margin, imaged by a coherence horizon slice along the water bottom from a survey acquired offshore East Kalimantan, Indonesia. The slope extends from the shelf, which is approximately 100 m deep, to the basin floor, which is approximately 2000 m deep. Most canyons on the slope are straight or gently curving, except one, which has sharp sinuous bends and connects the earlier lowstand delta to a contemporaneous basin-floor fan. Sediment waves are common on the upper slope, upslope from the deep canyons, and on the lower slope. After Saller et al. (2004). AAPG©2004. Reprinted by permission of the AAPG whose permission is required for further use.

Interpretation Workflows

Interpreting channels

Unlike faults, channels and other stratigraphic features usually are confined to a given stratigraphic horizon. Ideally, one would pick that horizon and then slice through the appropriate attribute volume to display the channel as it might have looked at a given point in geologic time. Unfortunately, any one of three things often prevents us from interpreting every horizon of interest. First, we may simply not have sufficient time to perform a detailed interpretation, or we may wish only to scan the data volume for features of interest before we perform a detailed interpretation. Second, the horizon may be highly faulted, thereby resulting in difficult (if not incorrect) correlations. Third, although the channel system itself may have a good signal-to-noise ratio,

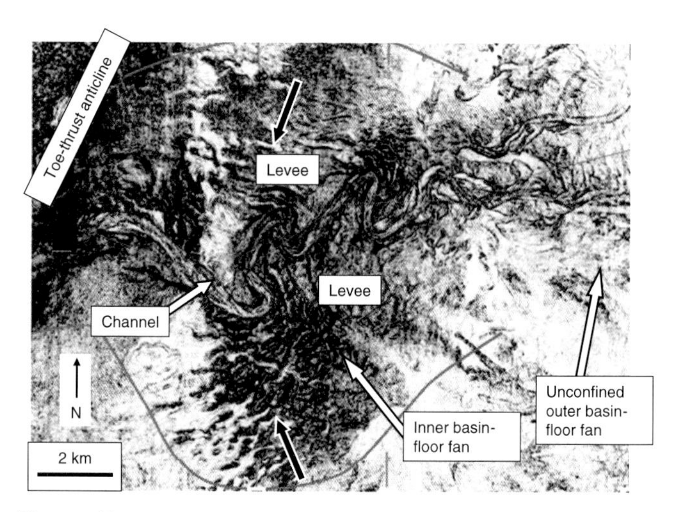

Figure 7. A coherence horizon slice that shows a sinuous, meandering channel in an inner basin-floor fan passing into an unconfined outer basin-floor fan. On the outside of the meander loops, the black arrows point to ridges that are sediment waves. After Saller et al. (2004). AAPG©2004. Reprinted by permission of the AAPG whose permission is required for further use.

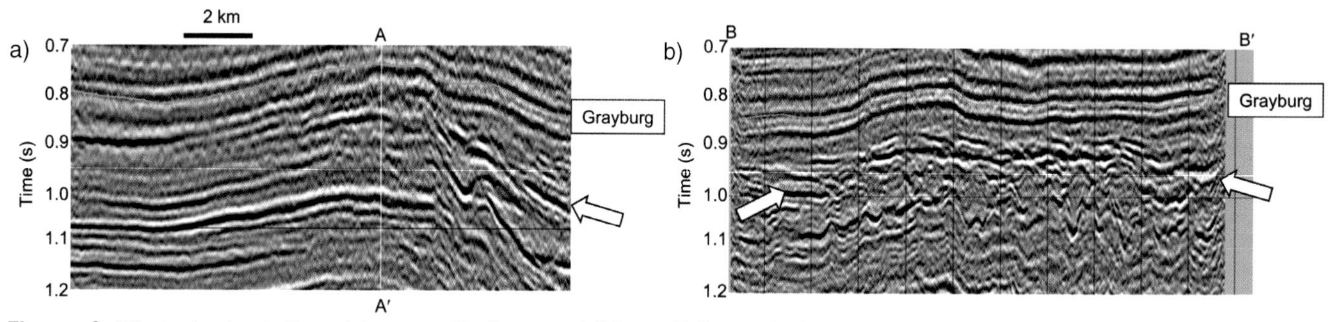

Figure 8. Vertical seismic lines (a) perpendicular to and (b) parallel to a platform edge, from a survey acquired over the northern Delaware Basin, New Mexico, U.S.A. A siliciclastic sequence (arrows) is too difficult to pick, so we image it by generating and displaying horizon slices parallel to the Grayburg horizon (see Figure 9). The data are courtesy of Marathon Oil Company.

the surrounding stratigraphy may not. In any of these three cases, the most common workflow is to generate either a phantom-horizon or stratal slice, such as those in Figures 4 and 9.

An alternative channel-mapping workflow that is useful when channels are clear is simply to paint them on time slices. We illustrate this concept in Figure 10, in which we display time slices at t = 1.164 s, 1.200 s, and 1.254 s through a coherence volume. In this figure, the green portion of the channel was picked on the 1.164-s slice, the blue portion on the 1.200-s slice, the magenta portion on the 1.254-s slice, and the cyan portion on an intermediate slice. The channel's geometry is then displayed in Figure 10c as a composite of the previously painted channel elements.

Such an interpretation strategy is achieved easily using conventional commercial interpretation software. First, we display a sequence of time slices and paint the features we interpret to look like channels on each slice, as shown in

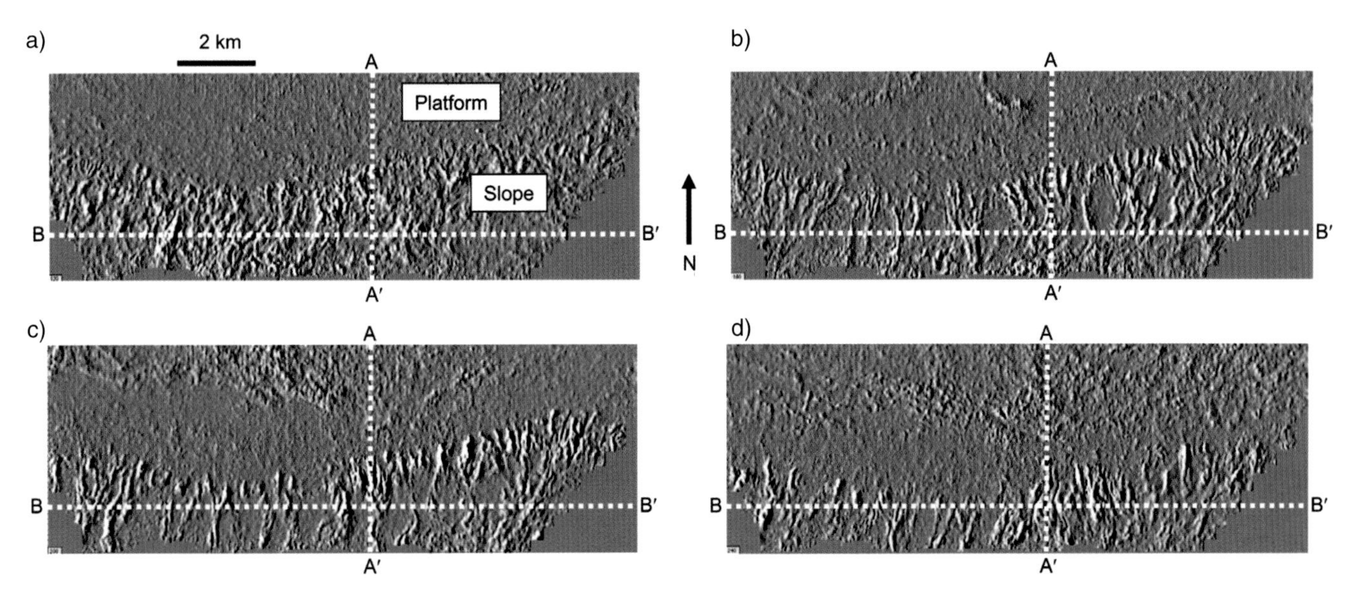

Figure 9. Phantom-horizon slices at t = (a) 0.120, (b) 0.160, (c) 0.200, and (d) 0.240 s below the orange Grayburg pick displayed in Figure 8. The slices cut through the east-west component of the energy-weighted coherent-amplitude gradient. The northern part of the slices cuts through the Permian carbonate platform. South of the platform are slumps and channel fill, sourced from eolian dunes, that gave rise to the Brushy Canyon and Cherry Canyon Formations of the Delaware Mountain Group.

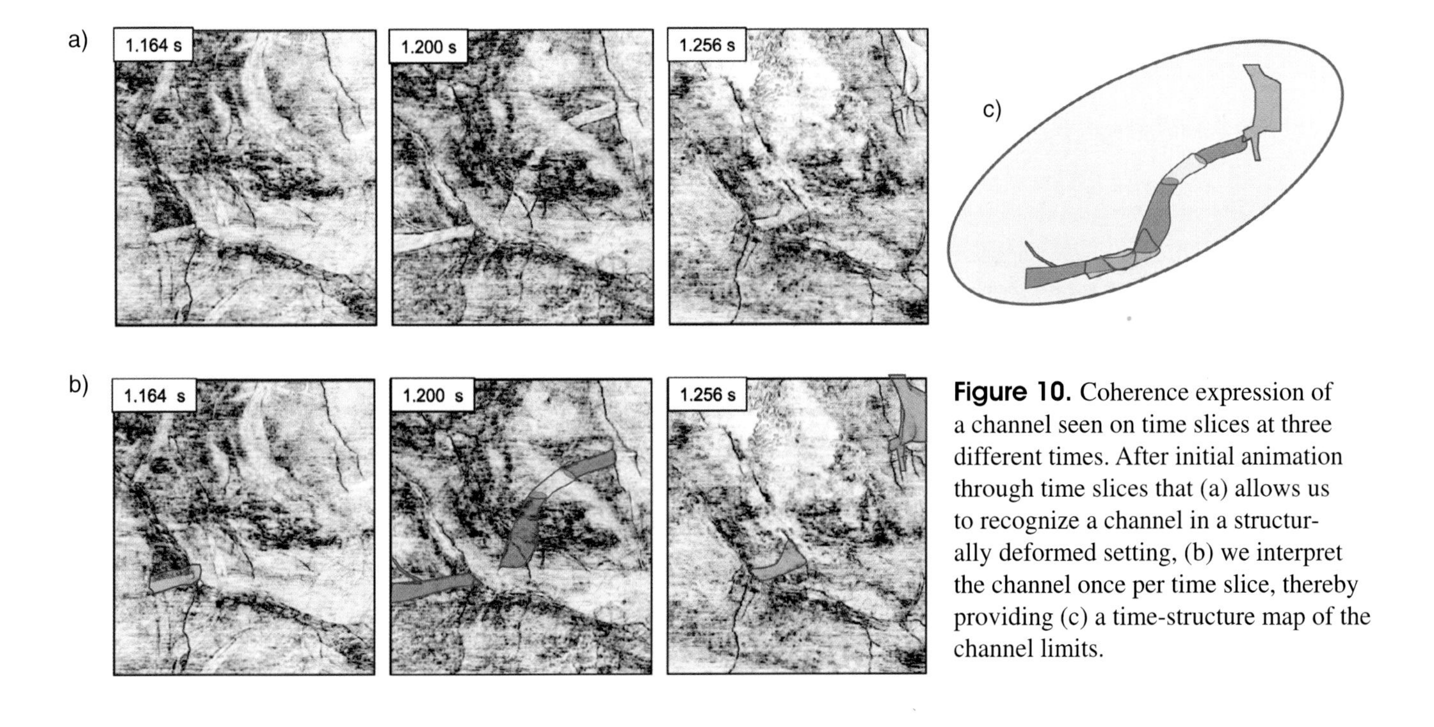

Figure 10. Coherence expression of a channel seen on time slices at three different times. After initial animation through time slices that (a) allows us to recognize a channel in a structurally deformed setting, (b) we interpret the channel once per time slice, thereby providing (c) a time-structure map of the channel limits.

Figure 11. In this case, we have turned off the snapping option (whereby the pick goes to the nearest peak or trough). If the channel has a significant vertical expression, successive picks will overwrite those made previously. Thus, if we wish to generate an image like the one by Deptuck (2003), in Figure 5, we may choose to assign a different channel name and color for each time slice.

In our present case, we simply display the time of each pick on a conventional time-structure map (Figure 12). Here, in this survey from the eastern Central Basin Platform, Texas, U.S.A., we note immediately the form of a channel system that is draining the erosional high on the west side of the survey and flowing toward the east into the Midland Basin.

Given this map view of the channel system, we can choose an arbitrary line perpendicular to the channel axis and display vertical slices through the seismic and coherence volumes (Figure 13). Comparing the interpreted (Figure 13b) with the uninterpreted seismic line CC′ (Figure 13a), we recognize that the picked events are consistent with a channel. Each channel pick is confined to a given stratigraphic horizon. Furthermore, we note several through-going faults (white arrows) on the vertical coherence slice shown in Figure 13c. The through-going fault indicated by the black arrow correlates with the channel, suggesting that the channel path is structurally controlled.

Interpreting unconformities

Interpreting sequence boundaries is one of the most important but most tedious tasks an interpreter performs. Because an unconformity cuts across lithologic units, it may appear alternatively as a peak, trough, or zero crossing, thereby frustrating the interpreter who has grown dependent on the autopicking, snapping, and seeding voxels used in modern software. In the hands of an experienced interpreter who is comfortable with picking unconformities on conventional seismic data, attributes can be an important aid in accelerating this process. The SPICE attribute (Smythe et al., 2004) discussed in Chapter 6 highlights interference between seismic waveforms and thus promises to be a very powerful sequence-boundary interpretation tool.

In our next example, we use coherence to map unconformities. Low-coherence anomalies associated with waveform interference significantly impair our ability to autopick faults on coherence volumes, so that the workflows discussed at the end of Chapter 8 on fault enhancement all begin by filtering out such stratigraphic anomalies. As we mentioned in Chapter 3, these anomalies may also be artifacts associated with zones of low (perhaps coherent) reflected energy that are overprinted by higher-energy incoherent noise. Although they are not geologic in origin, these zones often may be attributed to shale-on-shale reflectivity

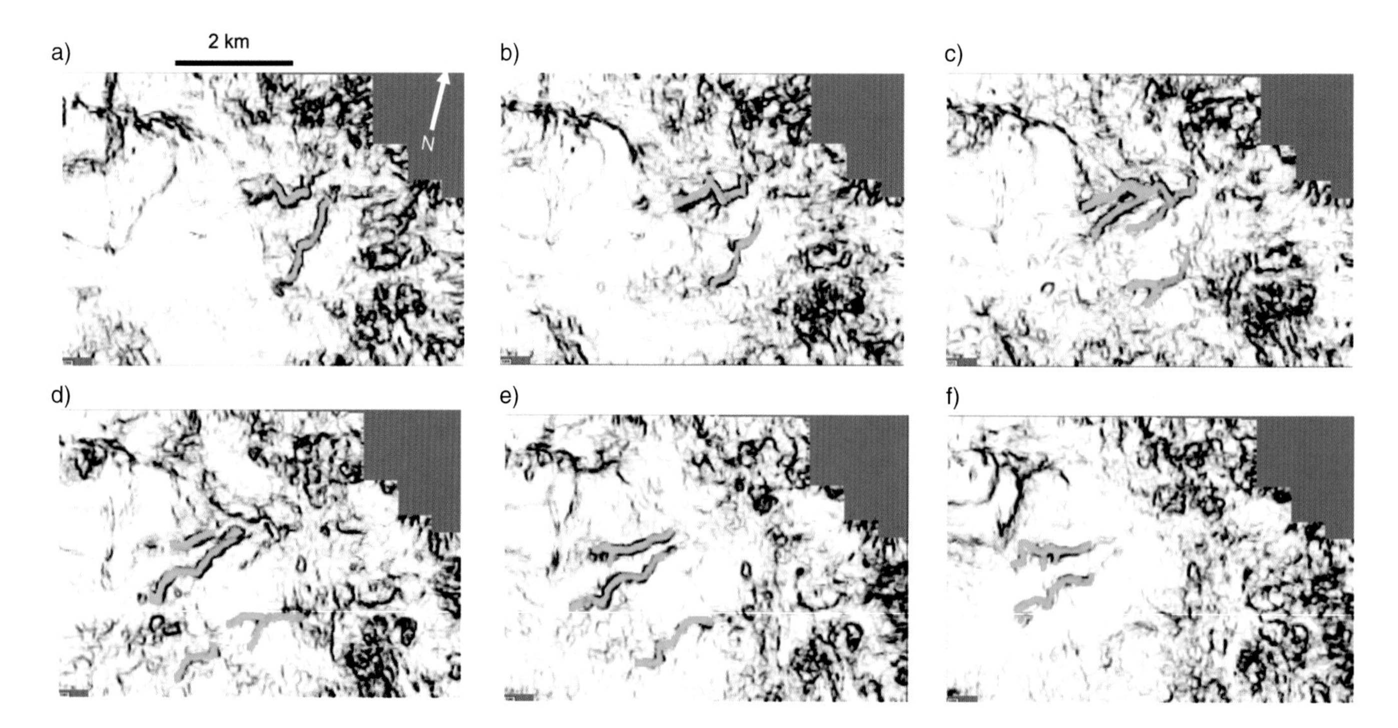

Figure 11. A workflow sequence showing how to quickly obtain a crude map of a channel without first interpreting the horizon in which it is confined After initial animation through the six time slices, we recognize a channel in a structurally deformed setting. Using commercial interpretation software, we paint the channel in green as we see it on each time slice, one slice at a time. The seismic data are courtesy of Burlington Resources.

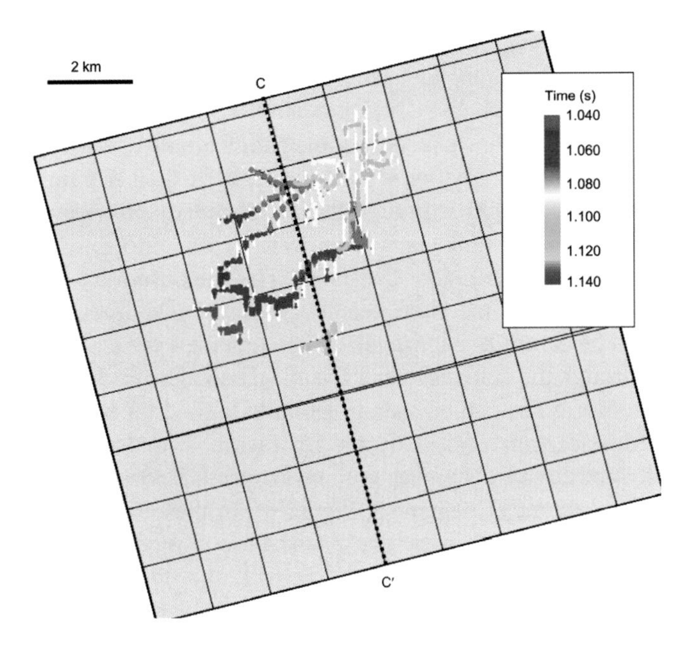

Figure 12. Commercial interpretation software generates a map of the painted picks from each time slice in Figure 11. Thus, we do not need to explicitly pick a horizon above or below the channel to map its location.

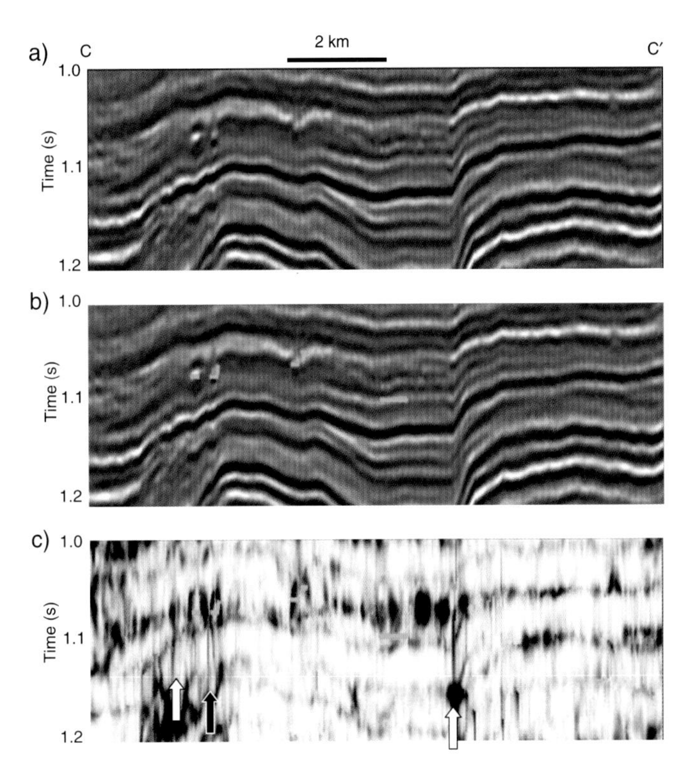

Figure 13. Line CC′ from Figure 12, shown here through the seismic data volume (a) without and (b) with the channel picks that were made in Figure 11 displayed on the data. (c) A vertical slice through the corresponding coherence volume. The seismic data have been subjected to principal-component, structure-oriented filtering, as described in Chapter 8.

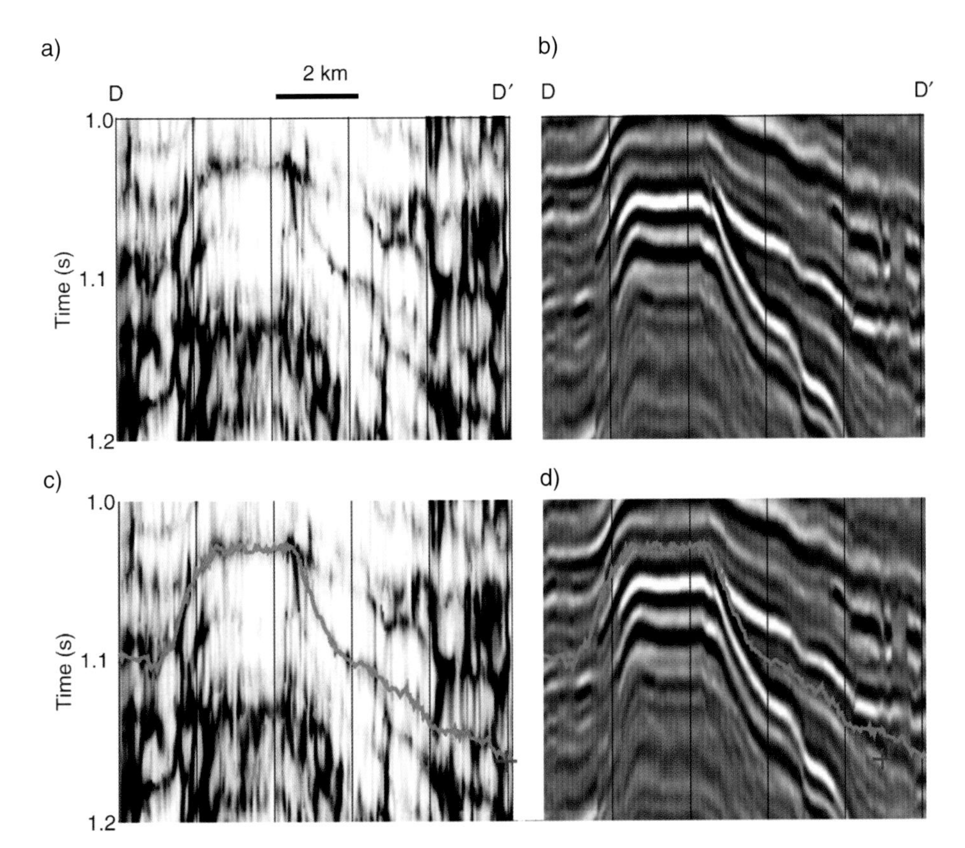

Figure 14. Coherence as an aid in picking angular unconformities. Vertical slices through (a) a coherence volume and (b) a seismic data volume, from the Central Basin Platform in west Texas, U.S.A. We recommend displaying the conventional seismic data and coherence data in dual-window mode, with the cursor (red plus sign) linked between the two windows. Although coherence helps us put the unconformity at a precise location, it leaves many choices to be made. Here, we made a choice by tracking where the cursor moved on the seismic data. We then snapped the pick to a nearby low value of coherence. The seismic data are courtesy of Burlington Resources.

and thus may indirectly indicate lithology. Erosional unconformities, and particularly angular unconformities, often produce low-coherence zones.

We suggest displaying attributes and seismic data with a linked mouse pointer using commercial interpretation software. Beginning with a coherence volume (Figure 14a) and a seismic volume (Figure 14b), we pick alternately on the seismic and coherence slices (Figure 14d and c, respectively). Generally, however, we snap to the coherence lows. Note that we could pick several possible low-coherence discontinuities. At present, such picking is not an automatic process. We need to watch the seismic data carefully to ensure that our coherence picks are consistent with a more traditional interpretation that uses the seismic data alone.

In Figure 15, we choose a somewhat shorter north-south line that is perpendicular to the one shown in Figure 14. The shorter line allows us room to show a vertical slice through the angular-unconformity attribute discussed in Chapter 2. Our unconformity attribute shown in Figure 15c is in an early stage of development — more-discriminating attributes can be generated using a mix of seismic attributes rather than just vertical changes in vector dip. Just as it is useful to filter out stratigraphic features seen on coherence for automatic fault enhancement, so it will be useful to filter out steeply dipping faults seen on the angular-unconformity volume. We see that the angular-unconformity image shown in Figure 15c identifies the angular unconformity about as well as the coherence image shown in Figure 15a does. However, both images suffer from spurious artifacts, so that attribute mapping of unconformities still needs considerable research and development.

In Figure 16, we display a line parallel to that shown in Figure 15, and in Figure 17, we display corresponding time slices at t = 1.000 s through those coherence and seismic data volumes. Orange arrows indicate the unconformity on the time slices in Figure 17a and b. This unconformity was picked on the time slice, thereby seeding other lines that could be carefully interpreted using combined vertical slices through the coherence and seismic data volumes. Similar unconformities can be seen in Dollarhide field on both the vertical seismic data (Chapter 15, Figure 4) and on time slices through a coherence volume and a most-positive-curvature volume (Chapter 15, Figure 6). In these latter time slices, the unconformity that has shallow dip complicates the image of the more steeply dipping faults. The channels seen on the east side of Figure 17a are the same channels discussed earlier in Figures 11 and 12.

Imaging Channels with Attributes

Seismic attributes, including rms amplitude, spectral decomposition, and geometric attributes, are all computed in a vertical analysis window and remove much of any overprint of the seismic wavelet from the image. The polarity of a channel reflection depends not only on the imped-

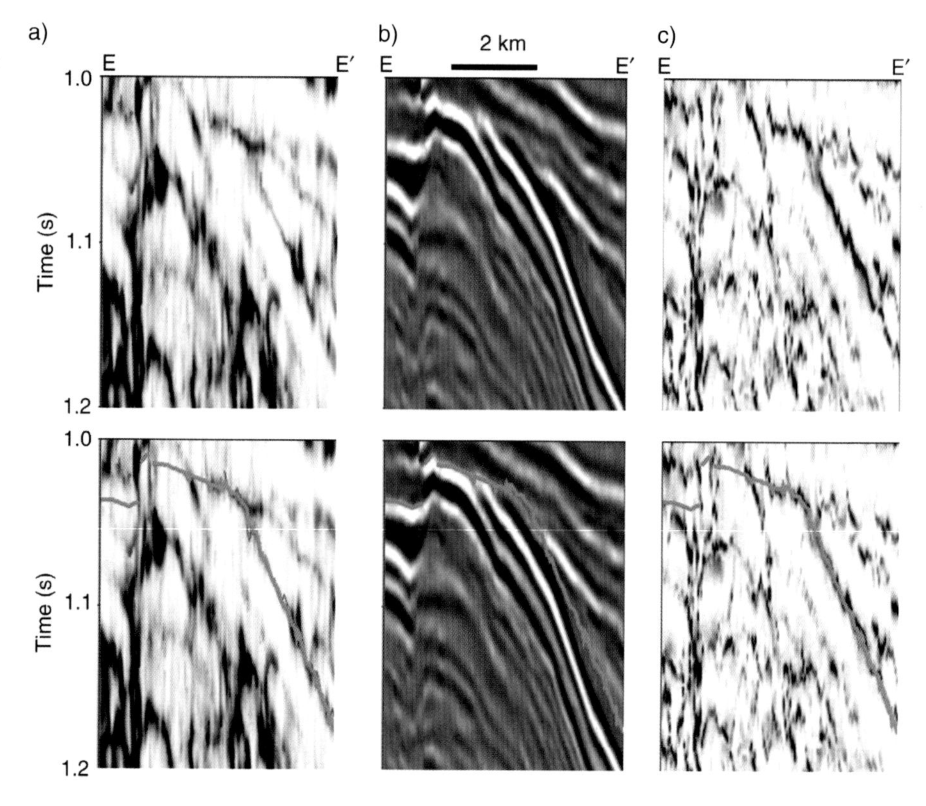

Figure 15. Vertical slices through (a) a coherence volume, (b) a seismic data volume, and (c) a measure of angular unconformity computed as the magnitude of the vertical derivative of reflector dip and azimuth. The location of line EE′ is shown in Figure 17. The northern end of the platform is cut by a steep fault. Clearly, more than one angular unconformity exists on the south flank. Here, we have tracked one that we interpret to be the Atoka unconformity.

ance of the channel fill (which changes within the channel system) but also on the impedance of lithologies that underlie and overlie the channel fill. Attributes that remove the seismic wavelet generate images that are more consistent visually to the interpreter when seen on map view. Attribute vertical analysis windows that are on the order of the dominant period of the seismic data also improve the signal-to-noise ratio of the image by stacking together the information content of similar time slices. However, vertical analysis windows that are much greater than the dominant period of the seismic data run the risk of mixing uncorrelated information from overlying and underlying strata.

In Figure 18, we present three alternative models of how a channel can appear on different seismic attributes. Figure 18a shows a thin, flat-topped channel below the tuning thickness. Reexamining Figure 1 in Chapter 5, we observe that no change in seismic waveform will occur across this event, so it will not be seen by eigenstructure coherence. However, the channel will be seen by rms amplitude (and other energy measures), spectral decomposition, semblance coherence, Sobel filters, and energy-weighted coherent-amplitude gradients.

Figure 18b shows a thin channel that has undergone differential compaction. This channel also will not give rise to an eigenstructure coherence anomaly, it will be seen by attributes sensitive to amplitude, and because it deforms the (thicker) sediments above it, it will now be seen as a most-positive-curvature anomaly.

Figure 18c shows a thicker channel above thin-bed tuning. The right side of the channel will be seen by coherence because the waveform of the composite reflection will change abruptly. The left side of the channel will be seen where it cuts an underlying reflector. The gentle taper generally will not be seen by coherence because the change takes place over a lateral area larger than the analysis window, such as the example shown in Chapter 5, Figure 8. The reflection from the bottom of the channel may be bro-

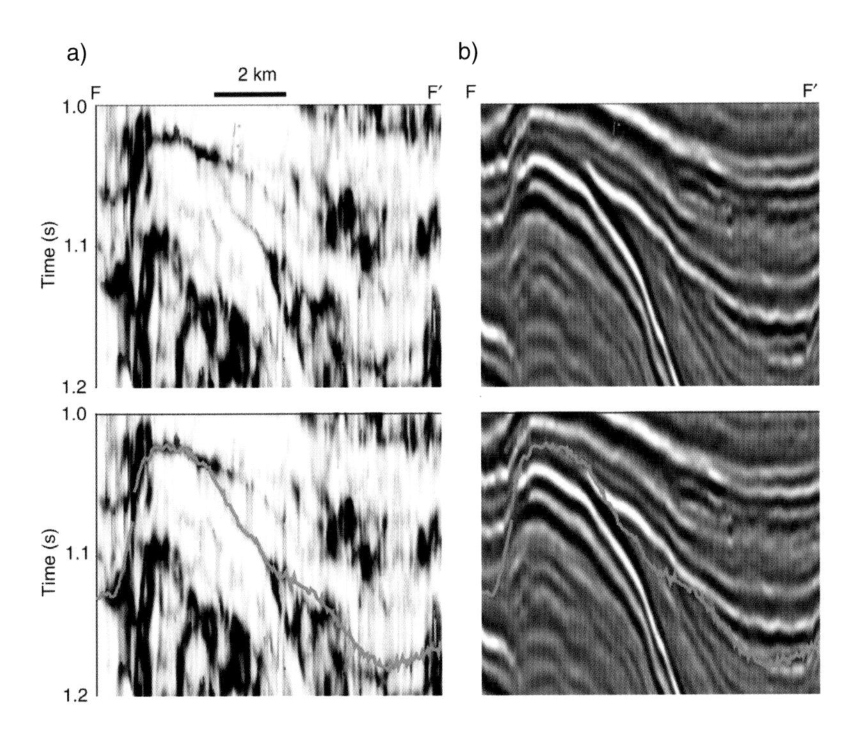

Figure 16. Vertical slices through (a) a coherence volume and (b) a seismic data volume east of the line shown in Figure 15. The location of line FF′ is given in Figure 17.

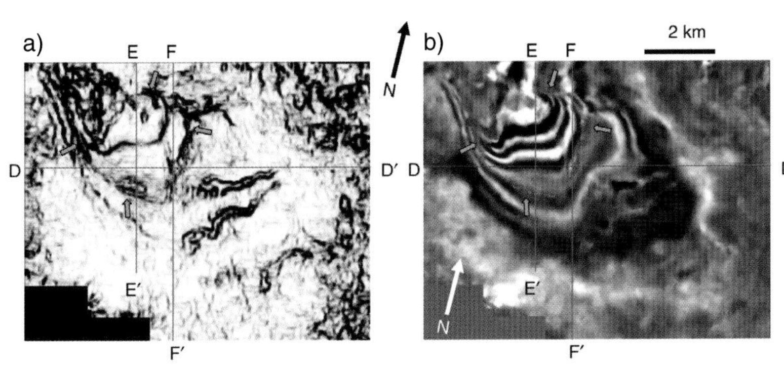

Figure 17. Time slices at $t = 1.000$ s through (a) a coherence volume and (b) a seismic data volume. Orange arrows indicate the location of an angular unconformity, which is nearly impossible to see on the seismic time slice. In contrast, the coherence time slice shows this unconformity as a zone of low coherence. Note the channels to the east that drained the unconformity. These channels were discussed previously in Figures 11 and 12.

ken because of laterally varying impedance and may not generate an accurate estimate of geologic dip. This channel probably will not be seen by curvature attributes.

Finally, Figure 18d shows a thicker channel that is aggradational. Our full suite of attributes will reveal that channel.

Channels Seen in Tertiary Rocks

We now turn to one of the first published examples of coherence-aided seismic geomorphology. Figure 19, from Haskell et al. (1995), displays the interpretation of a distributary channel system seen on a horizon slice along a Pleistocene-age boundary at approximately t = 1.200 s through a coherence volume. This survey from the South Marsh Island area of the continental shelf of the Gulf of Mexico, U.S.A. captures a distributary system that is remarkably like the present-day Mississippi River, which Haskell et al. used as a modern-day analog.

Haskell et al. (1995) interpreted the wide east-west channel A as the trunk channel of the paleo-Mississippi River, which bifurcates into three or more distributary channels. They noted that channels B and C are controlled by regional dip, except at locations D and E, where channel C crosses two faults trending N60°E. Channel C runs parallel to the fault channel on the down-thrown side of the fault and then resumes its southerly course at F. Lateral accretion generates a point bar near points E and F. Although often such large features are recognized on conventional amplitude horizon slices, Haskell et al. noted that the textures associated with laterally reworked deltaic sands at G, H, I, and J, and confirmed by the well control, are not readily identifiable on either vertical or horizontal amplitude slices. They noted that these zones consist of an abundance of short, straight to meandering segments that have a local northwest-southeast trend. The channel is controlled by a fault in the southern part of the figure, so that it turns and forms a point bar at K. The reader will recall seeing expressions of similar features using energy-weighted coherent-amplitude gradients in Chapter 5's Figures 12 through 16, and in Chapter 6's Figures 9, 10, and 22 using spectral decomposition.

Such channels often are well illuminated in Tertiary-age basins in which a strong impedance contrast exists between sand-dominated channels and shale-dominated matrix. We show another example from the Gulf of Mexico as Figure 20b, in which we can easily identify a channel by its morphology on a simple time slice through a coherence volume. The channel is much less apparent on the original seismic data time slice shown in Figure 20a. Indeed, we easily see a complicated pattern of at least three other channels imaged in the coherence time slice. In Figure 20c, we have interpreted a channel in blue that has been cut by a later channel.

In Figure 21, we display images of a more complicated meandering channel that is confined to a submarine canyon imaged from a survey acquired in the Eugene Island area, offshore Louisiana, Gulf of Mexico, U.S.A. The pattern is difficult to interpret on the time slice through the seismic data (Figure 21a), but it shows a distinct pattern of amalgamated channels on the coherence image (Figure 21b). By gen-

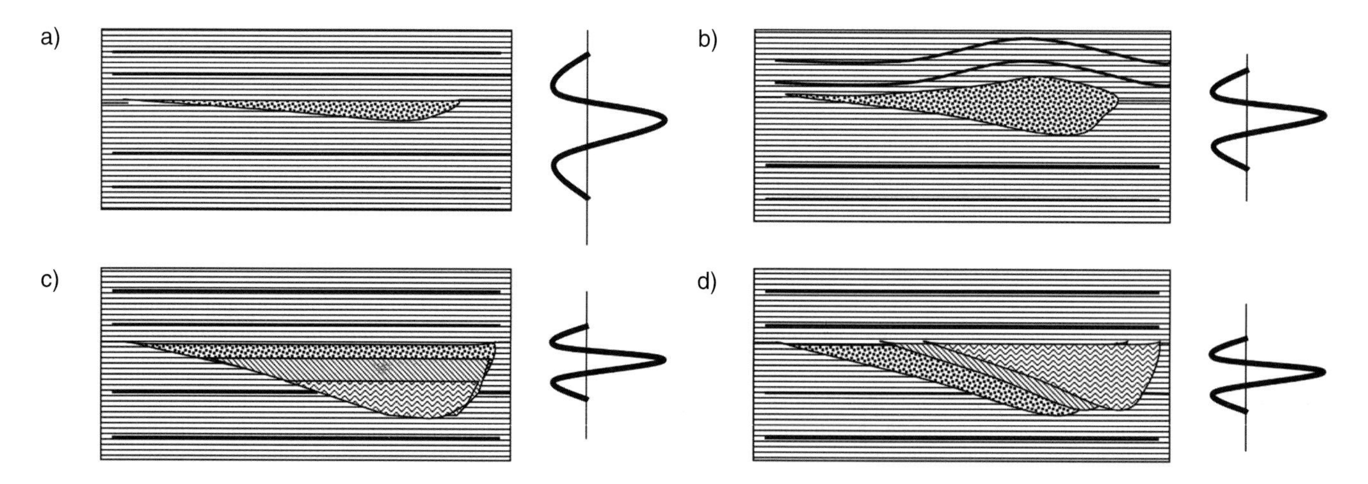

Figure 18. Attribute responses to channel features preserved in the geologic record. (a) Below thin-bed tuning, with homogeneous fill and no differential compaction. Only the amplitude changes. (b) Below thin-bed tuning, with homogeneous fill and differential compaction. Curvature and amplitude change; waveform does not change. (c) Above thin-bed tuning, with heterogeneous horizontal fill and no differential compaction. Curvature does not change; amplitude and waveform do change. (d) Above thin-bed tuning, with heterogeneous aggradational fill. Curvature, amplitude, and waveform all change.

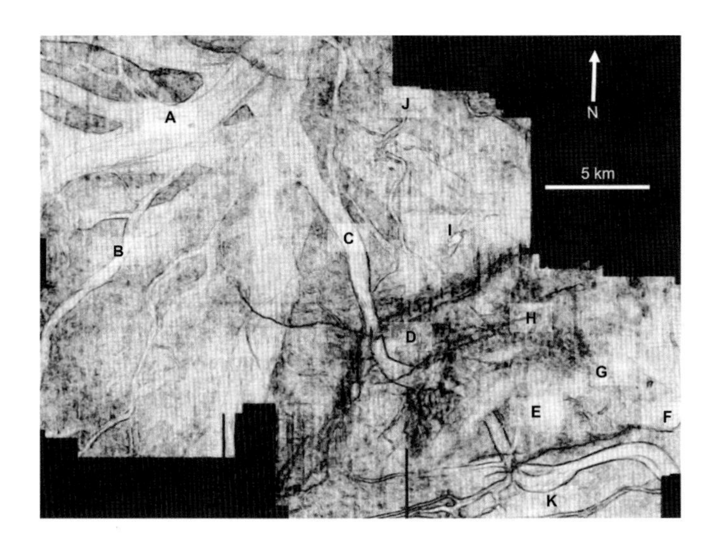

Figure 19. A horizon slice along a Pliocene-Pleistocene boundary at approximately t = 1.200 s through a coherence volume computed for a survey acquired over the paleo-Mississippi distributary channel system, South Marsh Island, Gulf of Mexico, U.S.A. After Haskell et al. (1995).

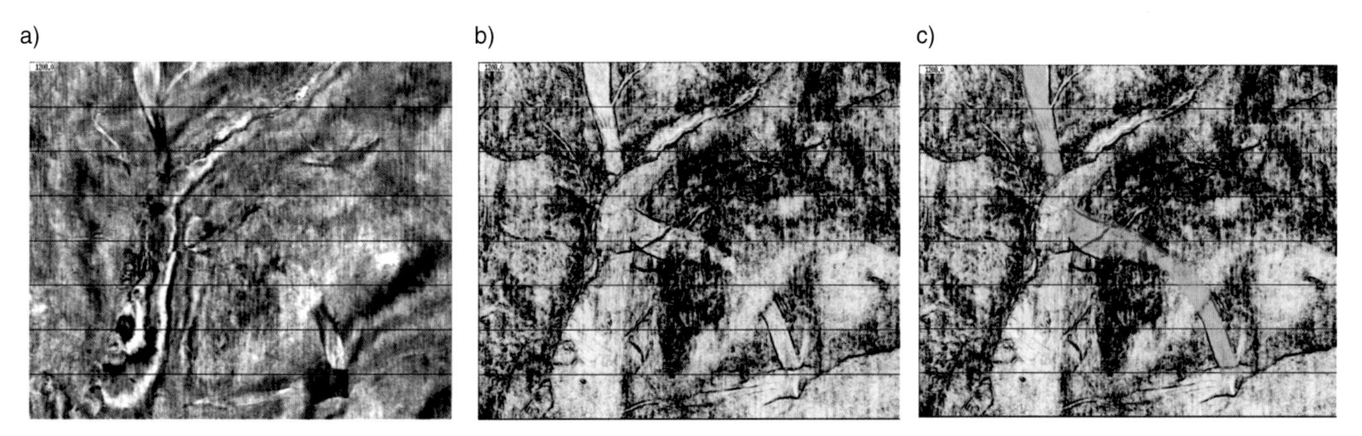

Figure 20. Time slices through (a) a seismic data volume and (b) a coherence volume from a survey from the Gulf of Mexico, U.S.A. (The survey area was 60 mi^2 or 155 km^2). (c) A coherence slice with an interpreted channel. Seismic data are courtesy of Geco-Prakla.

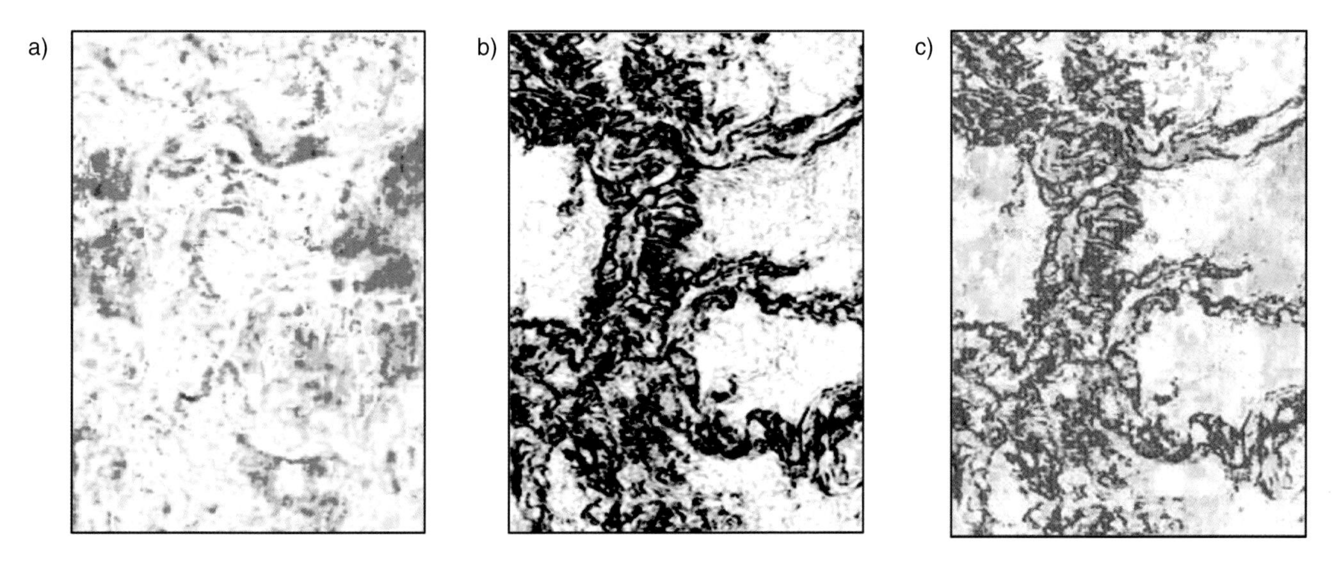

Figure 21. A time slice through (a) seismic data, (b) coherence, and (c) seismic data overlaid on coherence from the Eugene Island area, Gulf of Mexico, U.S.A. Note on the coherence images the enhanced resolution of the complex channel. The overlay aids in marking the extent of the channel features on time slices, which can then be used as a guide in picking the channels on the vertical sections.

erating a composite image of coherence with the seismic data (Figure 21c) we can facilitate linking our interpretation on map view to more traditional vertical seismic sections.

In Figure 22, we show that we can use a coherence image (Figure 22a) to identify subtler expressions of channels on vertical seismic sections (Figure 22b and c) and also to interpret the relative age of each channel. Here, we interpret channel A as having been cut by a later channel B, because we do not see preserved edges of channel A. In contrast, we do see the edges of channels C and D preserved in the region of channel B, implying that these two channels lie stratigraphically above or below channel B but appear mixed in this current time slice because of either the length of the seismic wavelet or the length of the coherence analysis window.

We can determine the vertical stacking of these channels by simply animating through shallower or deeper time slices. In Figure 23, we mimic such an animation by displaying time slices at t = 1.448 s (Figure 23b), t = 1.464 s (Figure 23c), and t = 1400 s (Figure 23a), for the same survey shown in Figure 22. We use a dashed red line to indicate the channel that is best focused at each time slice.

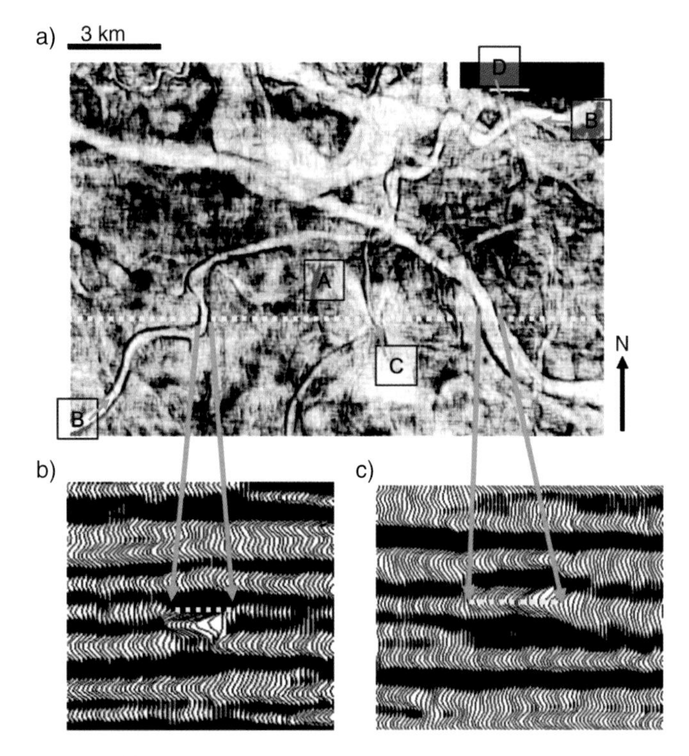

Figure 22. (a) Time slice at t = 1440 ms through a cannibalized channel system extracted from a survey offshore the Gulf of Mexico, U.S.A. (b-c) Expressions of that channel on the vertical seismic data. Ideally, stratigraphic analysis should be done on a horizon slice or a suite of time slices to remove the structural complexity of channels above and below the time slice. Channels that cut through older channels can be identified by their removal of the earlier channel's edge. Thus, channel A is probably cut by a later channel B, whereas channels C and D lie either above or below channel B.

An erosional scarp

Channels are not the only sedimentary features preserved in the Gulf of Mexico. We show the expression of slumps and other erosional features in Chapter 14. Here, in Figure 24, we show an image of an erosional scour from the Green Canyon area of the deepwater Gulf of Mexico. In Figure 24a we see the remains of nearly flat-lying sediments to the east. Sediments to the west of this scour have been eroded away and replaced with low-reflectivity material. The layered structure appears as a zone of high coherence (white) in the eastern half of Figure 24b, whereas the low-reflectivity area appears as an area of low coherence (black) in the western half. In Figure 24c, we display a time slice through the east-west component of the energy-weighted coherent-amplitude gradient. White arrows indicate narrow channels that have a subtle appearance, and black arrows indicate narrow channels that have a bright appearance. Because the coherent energy gradient measures lateral changes in energy, most commonly, the greater the reflectivity, the brighter the energy-weighted coherent-amplitude gradients will appear. Note that these narrow channels do not appear on the coherence image, which implies that they are thin enough to be below the thin-bed-tuning effect.

Multiple-attribute Images of the same channel features

In Figure 25, we display time slices through a seismic data volume (Figure 25a) and a coherence volume (Figure 25b) from a different survey in the South Marsh Island area of the Gulf of Mexico, U.S.A.; multiple channels are evident in these images. Figure 25c is a vertical seismic section through line AA′ in the time slices of Figure 25a and b. This vertical section reveals both faults (gray arrow) and channels (white arrows).

For comparison, in Figure 26 we show corresponding time slices through the most-negative-curvature (Figure 26a) and most-positive-curvature (Figure 26b) volumes. We see the faults on the most-negative-curvature image, which corresponds well to the reflector morphology in Figure 25c. In Figure 26, we do not see any strong indication of the channels, which do not appear to have been subjected to resolvable differential compaction.

We have found that curvature generally is not a good indicator of channels in the Tertiary section of the Gulf of Mexico in both the U.S.A. and Mexico. However, curvature maps of picked horizons are a well-established means of detecting channels in the Mesozoic section of the North Sea. The two curvature slices in Figure 26 appear quite complicated, but careful examination of Figure 25c shows that these features exist in the seismic data. In addition to faulting and folding, curvature anomalies can be associated with slumps (see Chapter 14), bars, levees, contourites, furrows, and other sedimentary features (such as those on the seafloor in Figures 6 and 7). The authors simply lack the experience in interpreting them at the present time.

In Figure 27, we show time slices corresponding to those shown in Figures 25 and 26, here of projections of energy-weighted coherent-amplitude gradients at 0°, 30°, 60°, 90°, 120°, and 150° from north. We note again the two wider channels seen on the coherence image in Figure 25b. However, here we see many additional, narrower channels (such as those indicated by the gray arrows) that do not appear clearly on the coherence image. Although such narrow features are too small to be exploration targets themselves, they may help us understand reservoir compartmentalization.

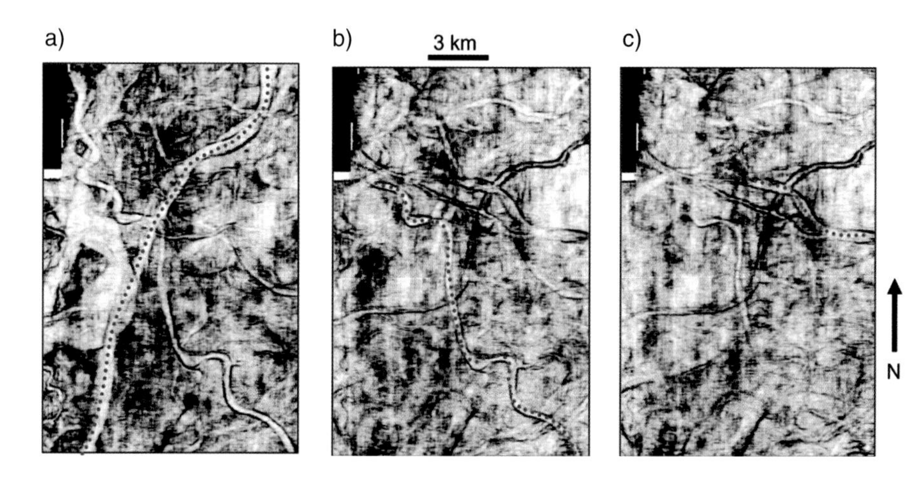

Figure 23. Time slices at t = (a) 1.400 s, (b) 1.448 s, and (c) 1.464 s, corresponding to the same survey shown in Figure 22. The red dashed lines indicate channels that appear strongest on each time slice, thereby indicating their relative depth, which when it is integrated with crosscutting relations with other channels, indicates relative age. Although some channels are prospective and can form important oil and gas reservoirs at depth, others, such as the shallow channels shown in this image, can form hazards associated with overpressures and need to be avoided when drilling deeper prospects.

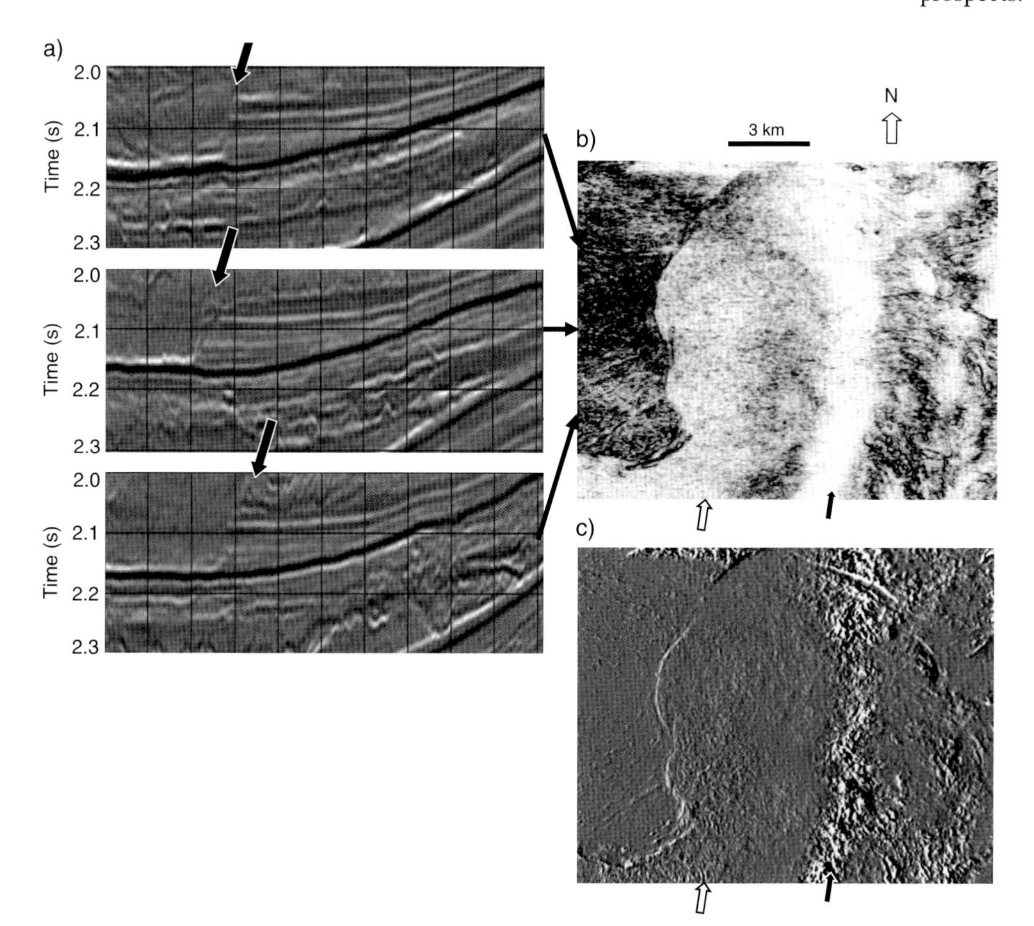

Figure 24. The appearance of an erosional scarp on (a) vertical seismic slices, and (b)-(c) on time slices at t = 2.100 s, through (b) a coherence volume and (c) an east-west energy-weighted coherent-amplitude-gradient volume.

Because channel edges show up well on the energy-weighted coherent-amplitude gradients, we computed most-negative curvature (Figure 28b and d) and most-positive curvature (Figure 28a and c) of the energy-weighted coherent-amplitude responses (rather than of structural responses). These images show us where the energy-weighted coherent amplitude most rapidly tunes in (forming local highs in coherent amplitude) and tunes out (forming local lows in coherent amplitude). For the wider channels seen in this time slice, the local highs correspond to the thalweg and the local lows correspond to channel edges.

Because these seismic data exhibit lateral changes in amplitude, we anticipate that spectral decomposition may help us extract further information. In Figure 29, we display spectral components at 30, 40, 50, 60, 70, and 80 Hz that were computed using the matched-pursuit algorithm described by Liu and Marfurt (2005). Taking each image individually, the images do not convey the clear information we saw in the coherence or energy-weighted coherent-amplitude-gradient images. However, by animating through these images, we can determine the approximate temporal thickness of the two major channels.

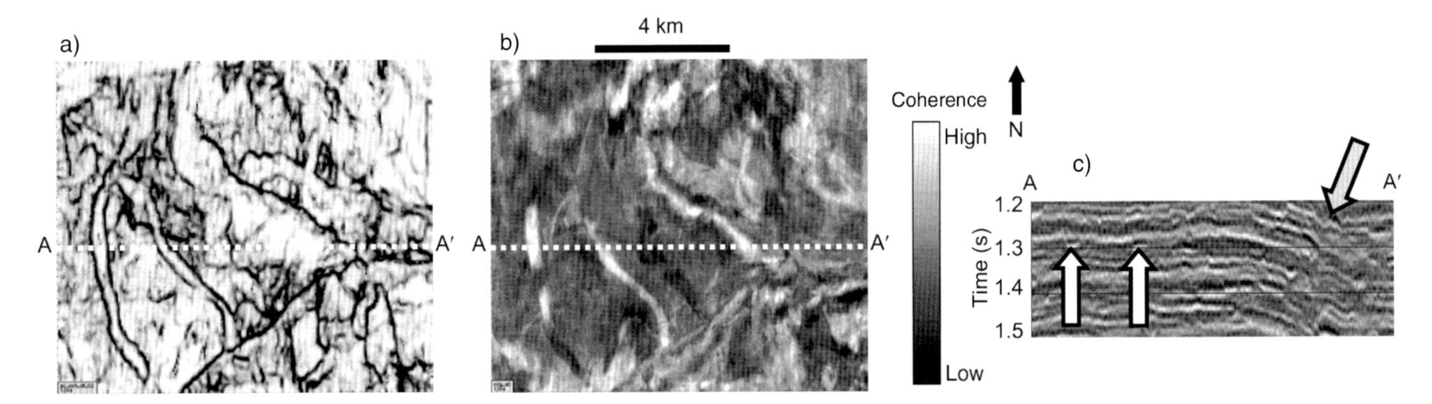

Figure 25. (a)-(b) Slices at t = 1.300 s, showing multiple channels through (a) a seismic data volume and (b) a coherence volume from a survey acquired in the South Marsh Island area, Gulf of Mexico, U.S.A. (c) A vertical section through the seismic data along line AA′. White arrows indicate the two prominent channels seen in the time slices. The gray arrow indicates a fault. Coherence was calculated using a nine-trace, ±30-ms analysis window. The seismic data are courtesy of Fairfield.

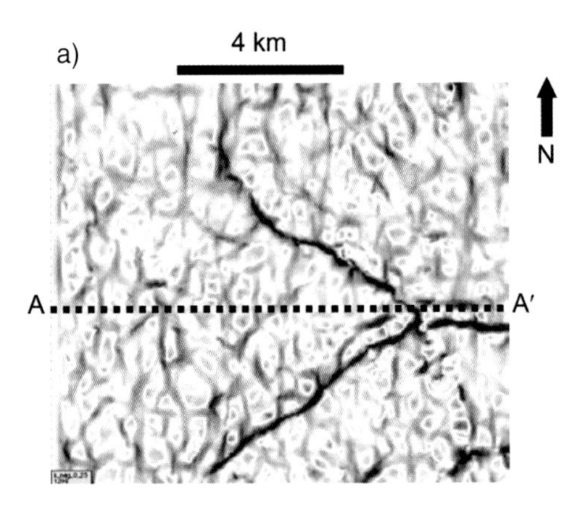

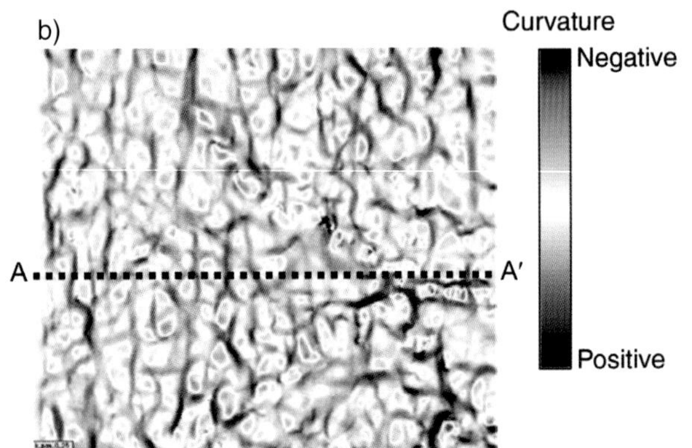

Figure 26. Time slices at t = 1.300 s, corresponding to those in Figure 25 and shown here through (a) a most-negative-curvature volume and (b) a most-positive-structural-curvature volume. Although the two intersecting faults show up well on the most-negative-curvature time slice, that slice bears little indication of the channels that are so obvious on the amplitude and coherence images in the previous figure. Careful inspection of Figure 25c reveals that the rather incoherent patterns are real and correlate perfectly with the hummocky nature of the sediments along seismic line AA'. We suspect that this hummocky pattern is associated with initial deposition or subsequent slumping rather than with differential compaction over the channels.

An alternative to animation for determining relative thickness is to estimate at each sample the peak (or mode) of the frequency spectrum, as we described in Chapter 6, Figure 20. In Figure 30, we plot the peak frequency using a 2D color bar. We plot frequency against hue, and note that the peak frequency of the channels appears as orange, corresponding to approximately 65 Hz. We plot the amplitude difference between this peak frequency component and the average spectral amplitude as lightness. Because the spectra have been balanced at each time slice (see Chapter 6 for a description), the average seismic spectrum is flat and thus appears to be black in Figure 30. Lateral variation in reflector thickness, such as that caused by channels, tunes the spectrum. By construction, this image shows channels that

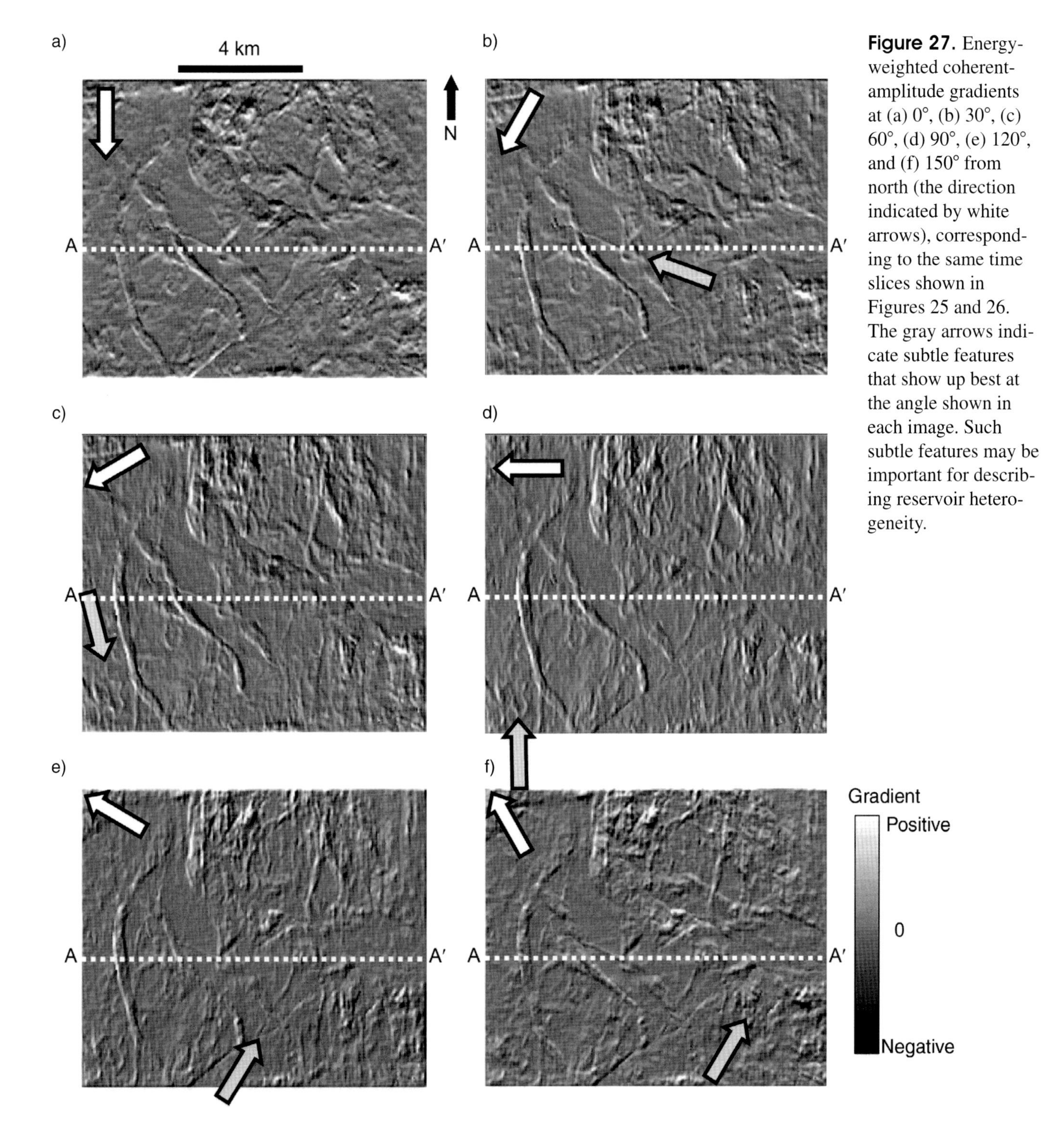

Figure 27. Energy-weighted coherent-amplitude gradients at (a) 0°, (b) 30°, (c) 60°, (d) 90°, (e) 120°, and (f) 150° from north (the direction indicated by white arrows), corresponding to the same time slices shown in Figures 25 and 26. The gray arrows indicate subtle features that show up best at the angle shown in each image. Such subtle features may be important for describing reservoir heterogeneity.

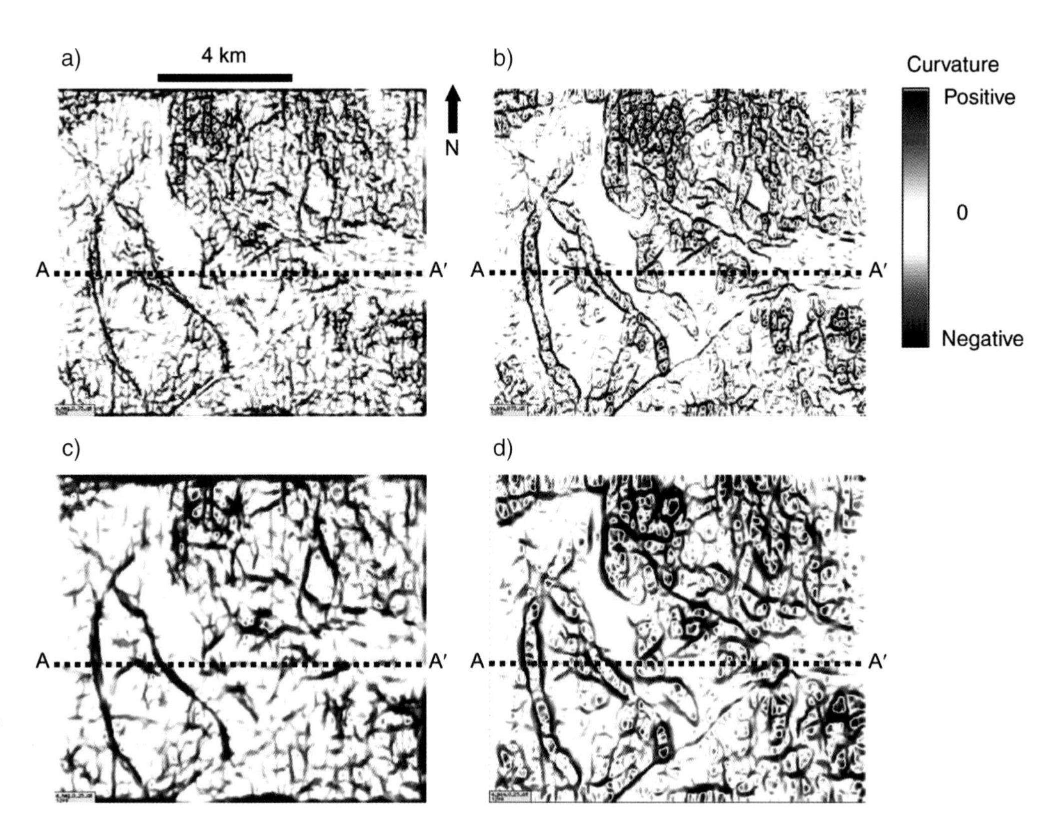

Figure 28. Time slices, corresponding to the time slice at t = 1.300 s shown in Figures 25 through 27. Images (a)-(b) are of moderate-wavelength (α = 0.75) (a) most-positive-curvature and (b) most-negative-curvature of the coherent amplitude. Images (c) and (d) are longer-wavelength (α = 0.25) images, again, of most-positive-curvature and most-negative-curvature, respectively. Strong red lineaments in (a) and (c) correspond to maximum constructive interference, and in this image, indicate the thalweg of the two channels. Strong blue lineaments in (b) and (d) indicate strong destructive interference and correspond to the edges of the channel. The vertical analysis window was ±30 ms.

are thick enough to produce thin-bed tuning as brightness. Other, thinner channels that have a less-peaked spectrum and overall lower-amplitude response do not show up.

The topmost image in Figure 30 allows us to add a third (vertical) dimension to a seismic geomorphology interpretation. We can estimate (qualitatively) not only the shape but also the relative thickness of the channels. That allows us to more accurately understand the depositional environment (and with well control, to infer possible grain sizes and sorting) using the methodology outlined by Zeng (2004), which we briefly discuss in the caption for Figure 3. The vertical slice shown in the middle image in Figure 30 shows how these channels tune laterally.

Appearance of a bright spot on geometric attributes and spectral decomposition

In Figure 31a and c, we note a bright amplitude (white arrow) wedged against a fault (gray arrow) deeper in the same survey, at t = 2.000 s. The coherence image (Figure 31b) shows the fault, a feature to the northeast of the bright spot that may be a channel (indicated by the speckled arrow), and the edges of the bright spot.

Because we recognized an amplitude anomaly, we plotted the inline and crossline energy-weighted coherent-amplitude gradients in Figure 32a and b, respectively. For comparison, we plotted the most-negative curvature and most-positive curvature in Figure 32c and d, respectively. Although both components of the energy-weighted coherent–amplitude gradient show the edges of the bright spot, the curvature images do not. Generally, no compelling physical reason explains why curvature would correlate with a bright spot.

In Figure 33, we display the peak frequency and the amplitude of the peak frequency generated using a matched-pursuit algorithm that employs the same 2D color bar used in Figure 30. The bright spot is bright, which we interpret to mean that it is both high in amplitude and tuned. The color of the bright spot appears to be green adjacent to the fault, corresponding to a peak frequency of about 40 Hz. In contrast, the color of the bright spot farther away from the fault is yellow, corresponding to a peak frequency of about 50 Hz. This change in peak frequency implies an increase in the tuning frequency away from the fault, which would be consistent with a gas-charged sand trapped by an updip fault.

Channels Seen in Mesozoic and Paleozoic Rocks

During the early development of coherence and spectral decomposition, many interpreters believed that these techniques only worked in Tertiary basins such as the Gulf of Mexico and West Africa. Older, less porous rocks have

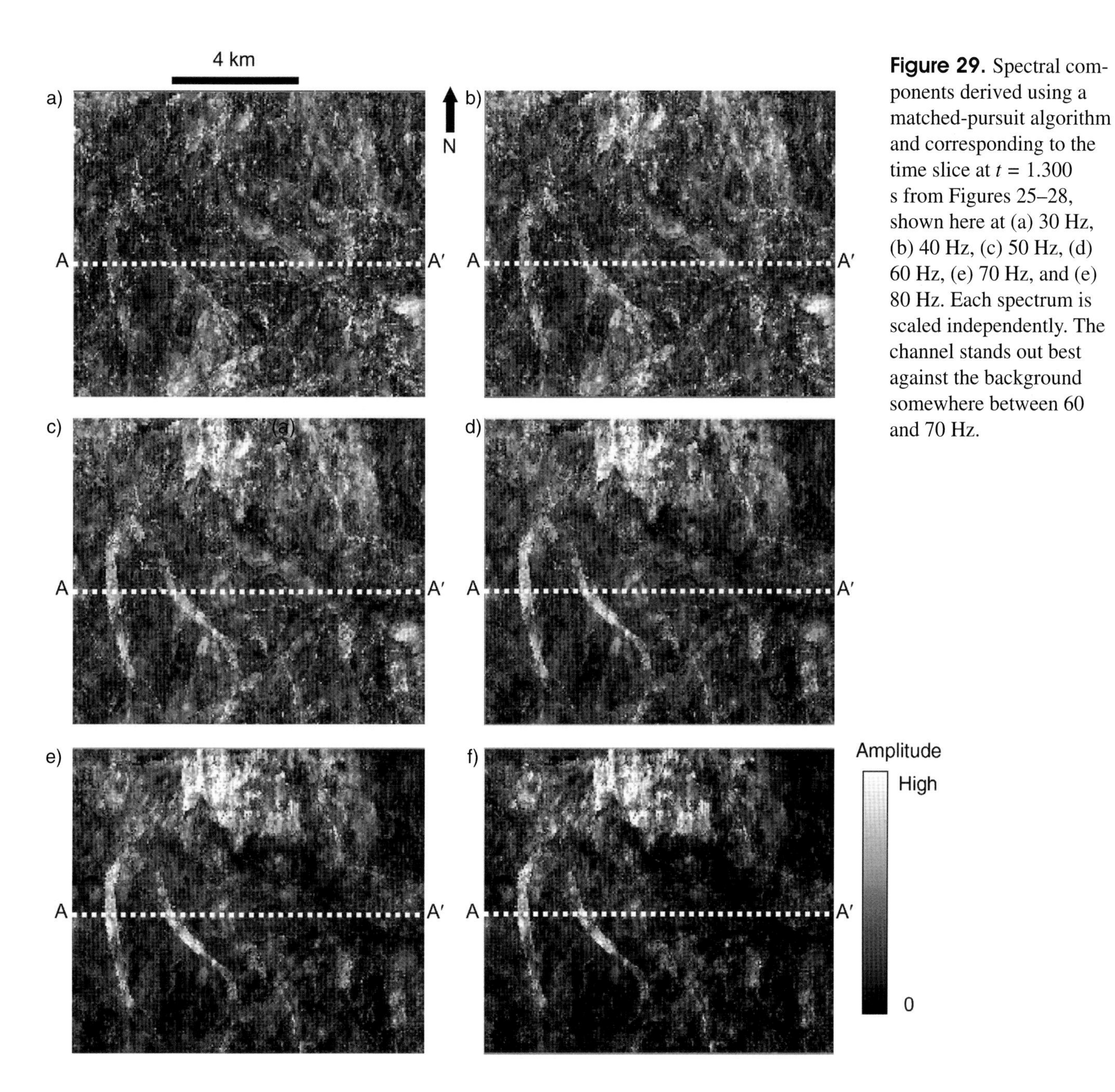

Figure 29. Spectral components derived using a matched-pursuit algorithm and corresponding to the time slice at t = 1.300 s from Figures 25–28, shown here at (a) 30 Hz, (b) 40 Hz, (c) 50 Hz, (d) 60 Hz, (e) 70 Hz, and (e) 80 Hz. Each spectrum is scaled independently. The channel stands out best against the background somewhere between 60 and 70 Hz.

faster velocities, thereby generating lower vertical and lateral resolution and often less variation in impedance from sands to shales.

Such fears were unfounded. The first published paper on spectral decomposition, by Peyton et al. (1998), directly addressed an older, Paleozoic channel system from the Midcontinent region of the U.S.A. We display some of their results in Chapter 6 as Figures 13 through 16. The turbidite example shown in Figures 8 and 9 and the channels shown in Figures 11 through 13 of this chapter are also Paleozoic in age. In this section, we will show a suite of examples of such older channels, most of them from Alberta, Canada. All are from land surveys.

We begin by examining a branching channel system that appears in images from a survey acquired in Alberta, Canada (Figure 34). We see here that the channels are very difficult to discern on the vertical seismic slices (Figure 34b) but are more clearly defined on the coherence time slice (Figure 34a).

Figure 35 shows time slices at various times through coherence volumes and a seismic data volume. We see a prominent east-west channel filled by glauconitic sandstone of Early Cretaceous age on the seismic data volume (Figure 35d) as well as on the coherence image from the same time (Figure 35c). In addition to this main channel, a second, north-south channel coming in from the northeast appears

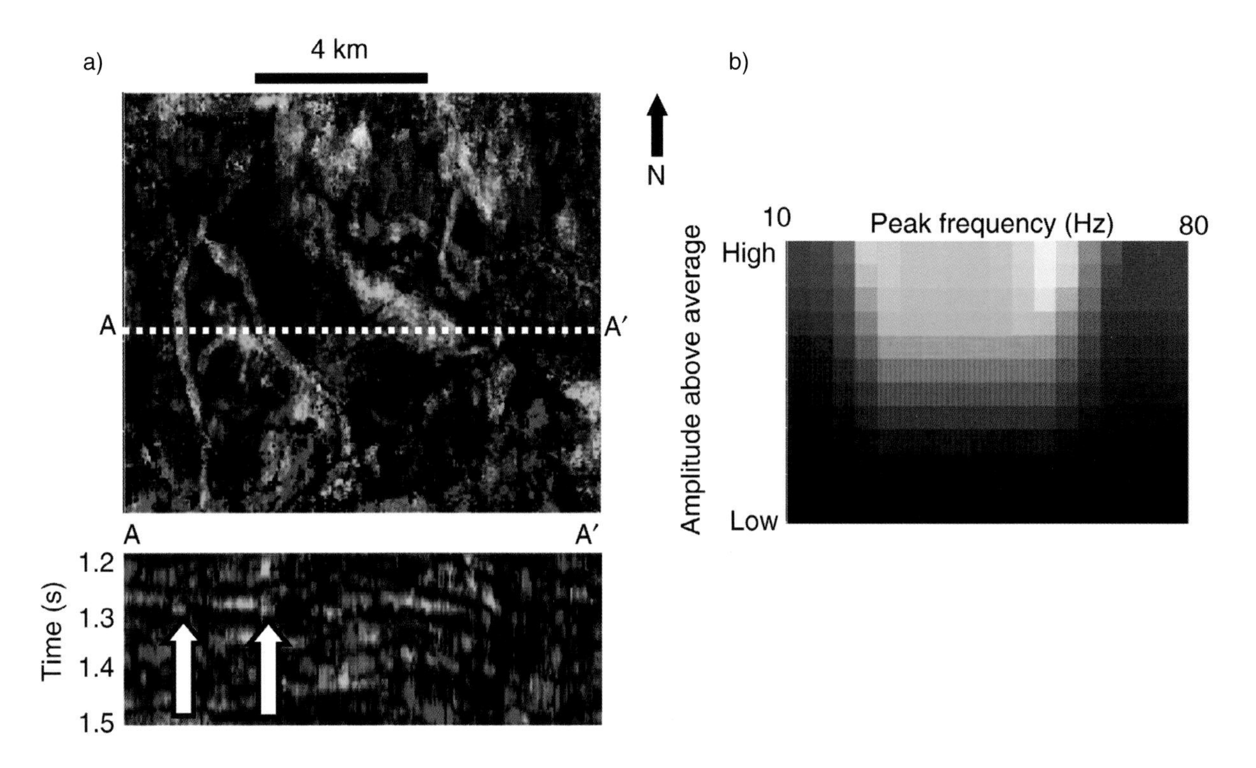

Figure 30. A composite image summarizing the information shown in Figure 29, here using a 2D color bar and plotting peak frequency against the amplitude of that peak frequency above the average normalized amplitude for all frequencies at each sample. Note that the two main channels tune in as orange, implying a peak frequency of about 65 Hz. Similarly, the bright blue area in the southern part of the image tunes in at 25 Hz. Such composite images can summarize much of the information contained in the individual components displayed in Figure 29.

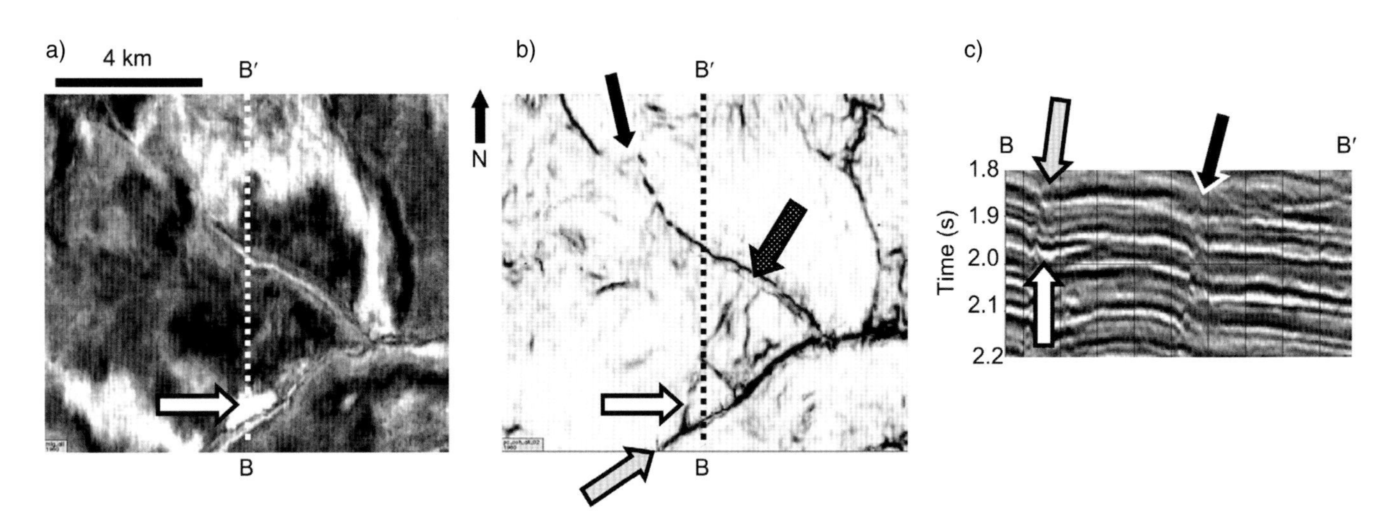

Figure 31. Time slices at $t = 2.000$ s through (a) a seismic data volume, (b) a coherence volume, and (c) vertical seismic data from a survey over South Marsh Island, Gulf of Mexico, U.S.A. The white arrow indicates a local bright spot. Gray and black arrows indicate faults; the gray arrow points to the southern boundary of the trap. Seismic data are courtesy of Fairfield.

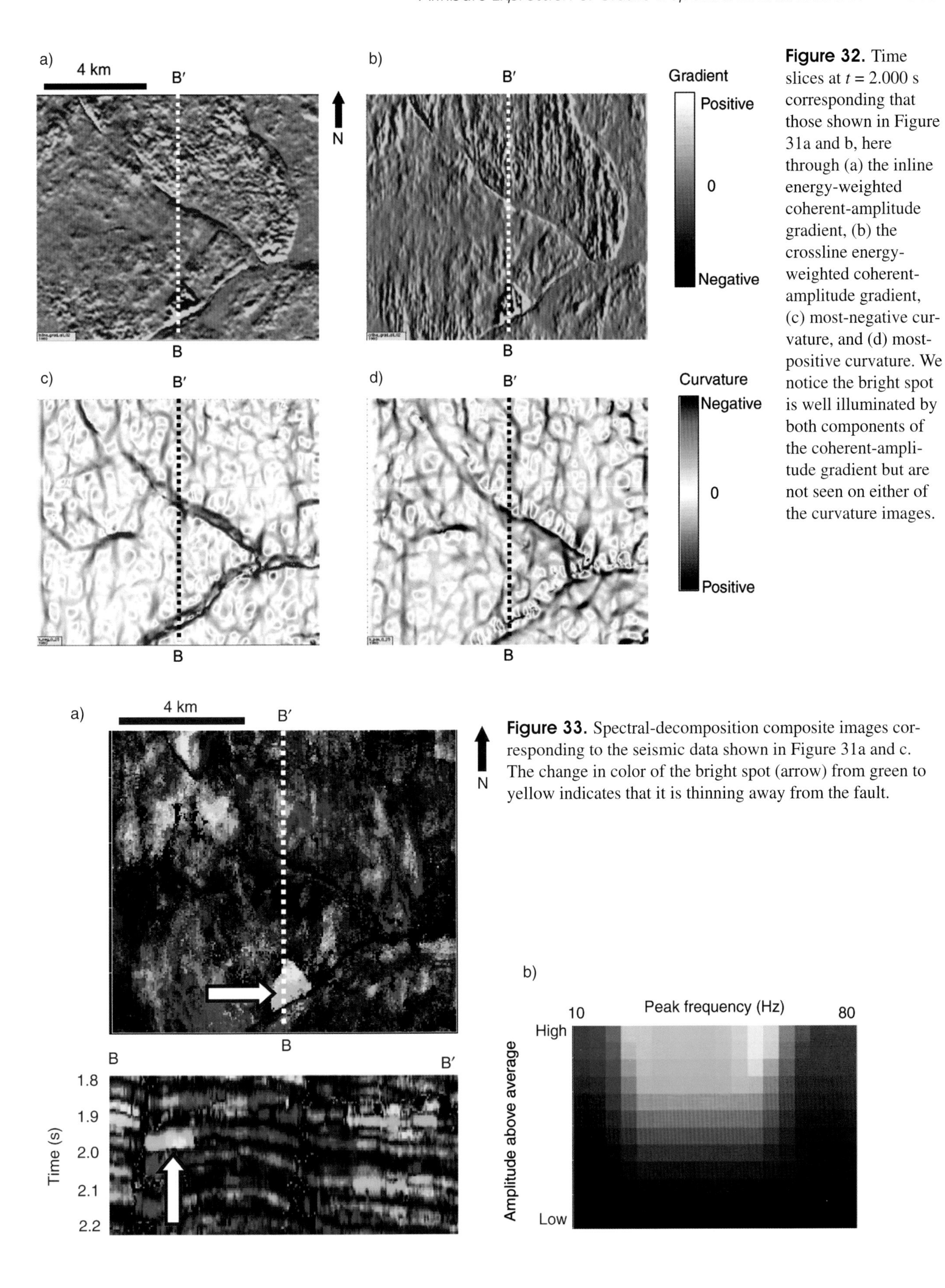

Figure 32. Time slices at $t = 2.000$ s corresponding that those shown in Figure 31a and b, here through (a) the inline energy-weighted coherent-amplitude gradient, (b) the crossline energy-weighted coherent-amplitude gradient, (c) most-negative curvature, and (d) most-positive curvature. We notice the bright spot is well illuminated by both components of the coherent-amplitude gradient but are not seen on either of the curvature images.

Figure 33. Spectral-decomposition composite images corresponding to the seismic data shown in Figure 31a and c. The change in color of the bright spot (arrow) from green to yellow indicates that it is thinning away from the fault.

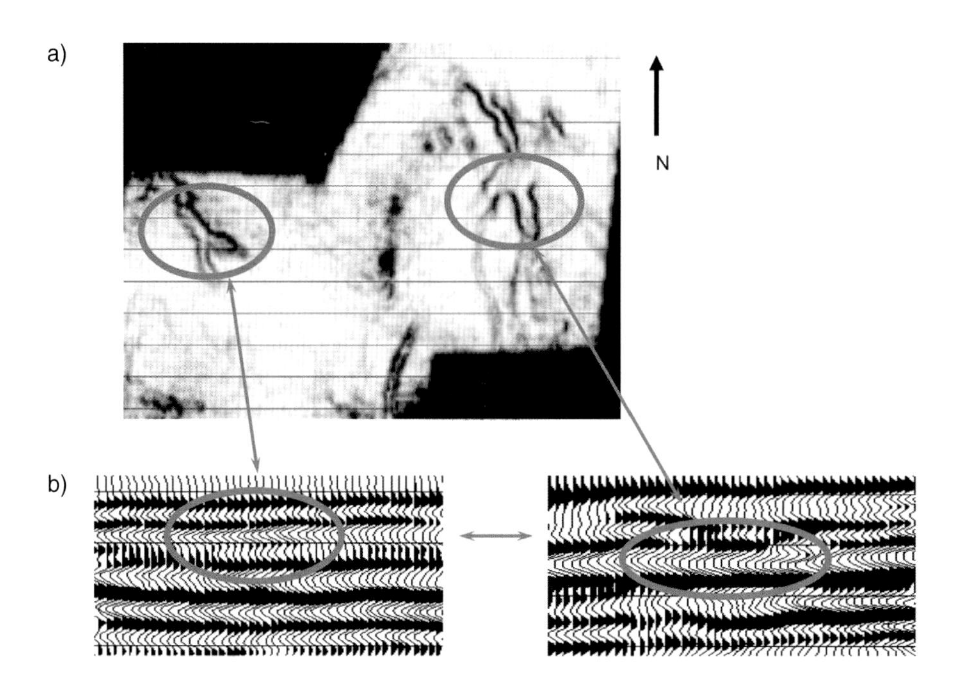

Figure 34. Braided channels. These channels are subtle in the (b) vertical seismic slices through the migrated data but are more clearly delineated on (a) the corresponding coherence time slice.

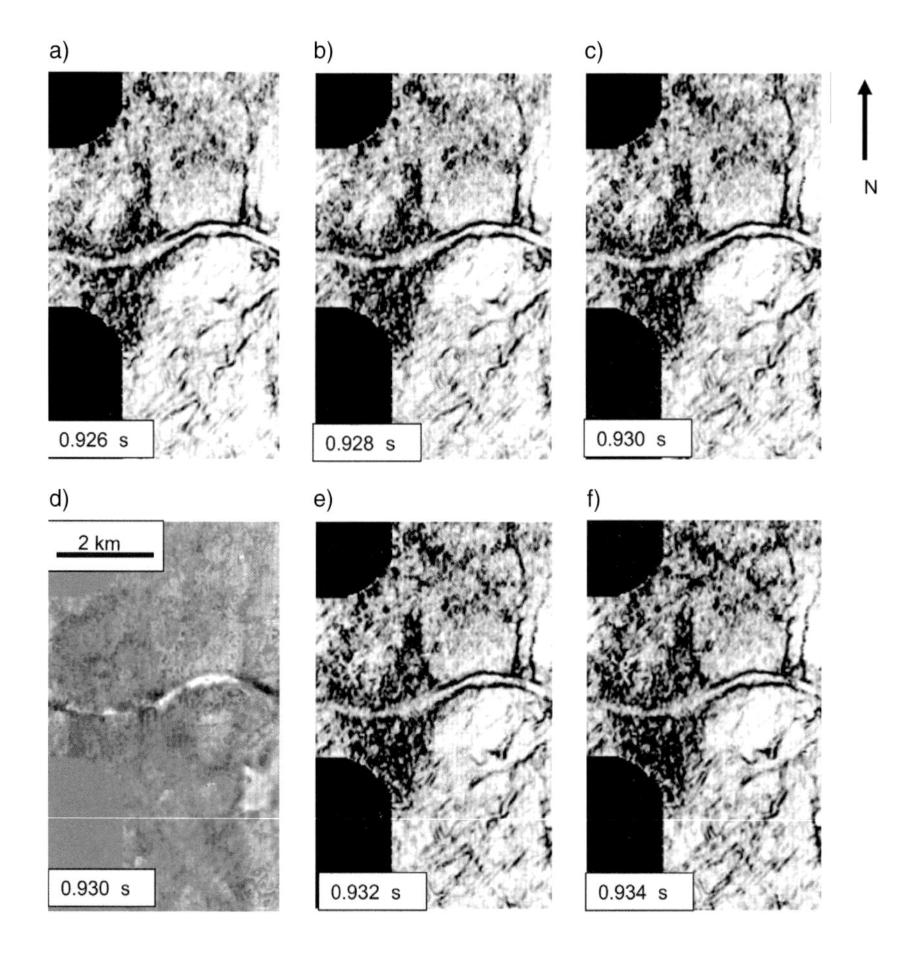

Figure 35. Time slices at t = (a) 0.926 s, (b) 0.928 s, (c) 0.930 s, (e) 0.932 a, and (f) 0.934 s through coherence volumes, and (d) at 0.930 s through a seismic data volume from a survey done in Alberta, Canada. An east-west Early Cretaceous channel filled by glauconitic sandstone is readily seen on the seismic time slice at t = 0.930 s in (d). However, coherence clearly illuminates a much more complex channel system. Note the marked stratigraphic changes at each 2 ms time slice increment, even though the seismic center frequency is 30 Hz. The vertical analysis window was ±2 ms.

clearly on the deeper coherence images (Figure 35c, e, and f). Yet a third oblique channel-like feature in the southwest is also indicated and again is clearest on the deeper coherence images. Animating through coherence slices above (Figure 35a and b) and below (Figure 35e and f) allows us to see which channels are higher and lower in the section.

In Figure 36a, we redisplay the time slice at $t = 0.930$ s from Figure 35, here with the vertical seismic section and using 3D visualization. In this manner we can directly relate the edge of the channel seen in coherence to the character of the seismic data. In Figure 36b, we redisplay a portion of the vertical slice from Figure 36a and indicate the coherence-revealed channel edge by black arrows.

Next we show horizon slices through a seismic data volume (Figure 37a) and a coherence volume (Figure 37b) corresponding to the horizon indicated by the gray arrows (Figure 37c) revealing a complex series of interrelated drainage channels in an estuary system. The horizon slice through the seismic data volume shows that a series of channels exists at this level, but the picture is ambiguous. The equivalent coherence horizon slice (Figure 37b) shows these channels in unquestionable detail, thereby providing the interpreter with a detailed map to be used directly to place wells.

Such channel features are three-dimensional bodies that an interpreter can map in 3D space by simply looking at a

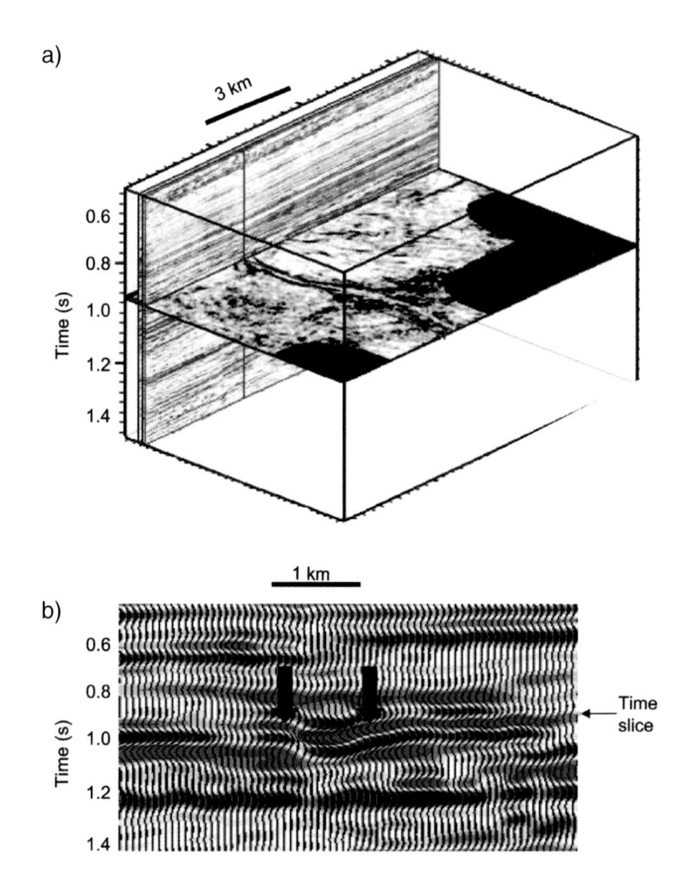

Figure 36. (a) A 3D visualization of the coherence time slice at $t = 0.930$ from Figure 35, shown here with a vertical seismic slice. (b) A zoom of the vertical seismic slice shown in (a). Arrows indicate the edges of channel revealed by coherence.

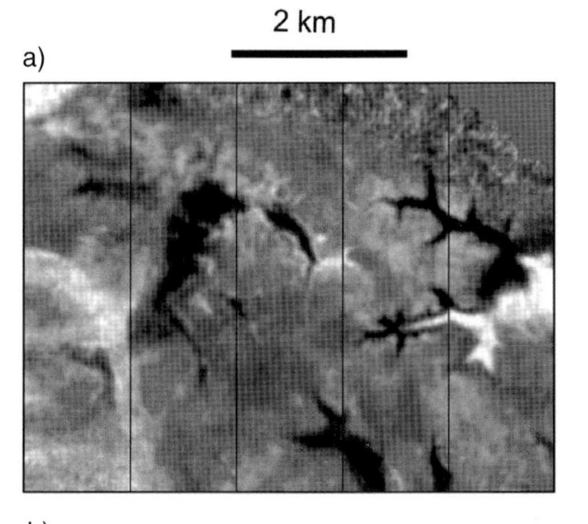

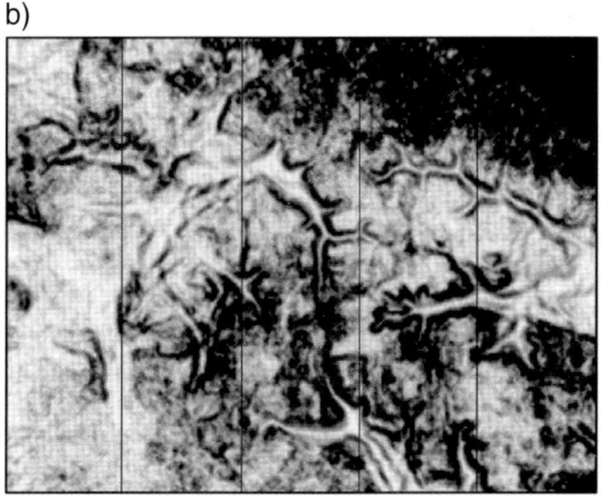

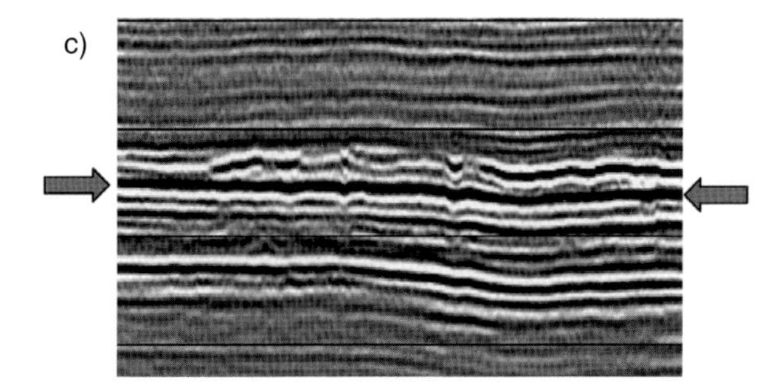

Figure 37. (a)-(b) Horizon slices through (a) a seismic data volume and (b) a coherence volume, illuminating a complex series of interrelated drainage channels in an estuary from Alberta. (c) Vertical seismic line AA′. Although the conventional seismic time slice is excellent, it does not show as complete an image as the coherence slice does.

series of parallel horizon or stratal slices over the time window encompassing the channel system. This particular channel system contains numerous production gas wells. By animating through horizon slices we can see how these features broaden or narrow with depth and thus we can better judge their interconnectivity (Figure 38). In general, channels edges appear sharpest in windows that are centered about them. Thus, we interpret the channel that is indicated by white arrows in the northwest corner of images (a) and (b) and that is best focused in image (a) to lie 12 ms below the picked horizon. In contrast, the major system on the east-central part of the images and indicated by gray arrows does not appear at this level. This system begins to appear 8 ms below the picked horizon (Figure 38b), is strongest at the picked horizon (Figure 38d), and continues to at least 8 ms above the picked horizon.

Maps of the edges of channel reservoirs are key to efficient production. In Figure 39, we display horizon slices through a seismic data volume (Figure 39a) and through the corresponding coherence volume (Figure 39b). Although the edges of the channel can be seen on the vertical seismic section (Figure 39c), they are very difficult to pick on the seismic horizon slice. In contrast, the areal extents of channels are clear on the coherence horizon slice.

In Figure 40, we show a sequence of time slices through a coherence volume. A system of channels is seen running north-south, although because of reflector dip no time slice captures the entire channel. In Figure 41, we redisplay the

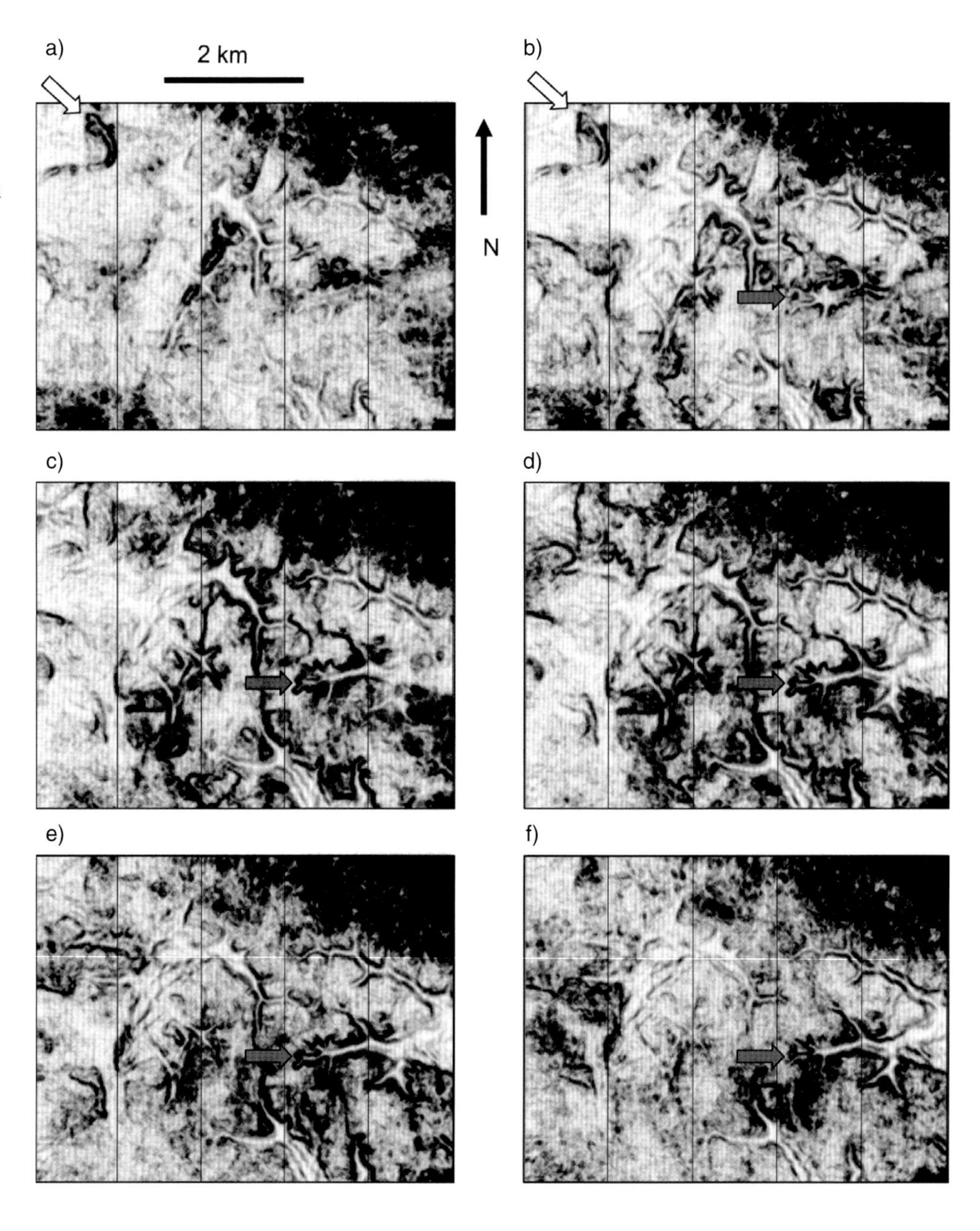

Figure 38. A suite of horizon slices, at (a) +12 ms, (b) +8 ms, (c) +4 ms, (d) 0 ms, (e) –4 ms, and (f) –8 ms below the time slice through the coherence volume shown in Figure 37b. These images give the areal disposition of the channel system and a qualitative estimate of the depth of channel sediments.

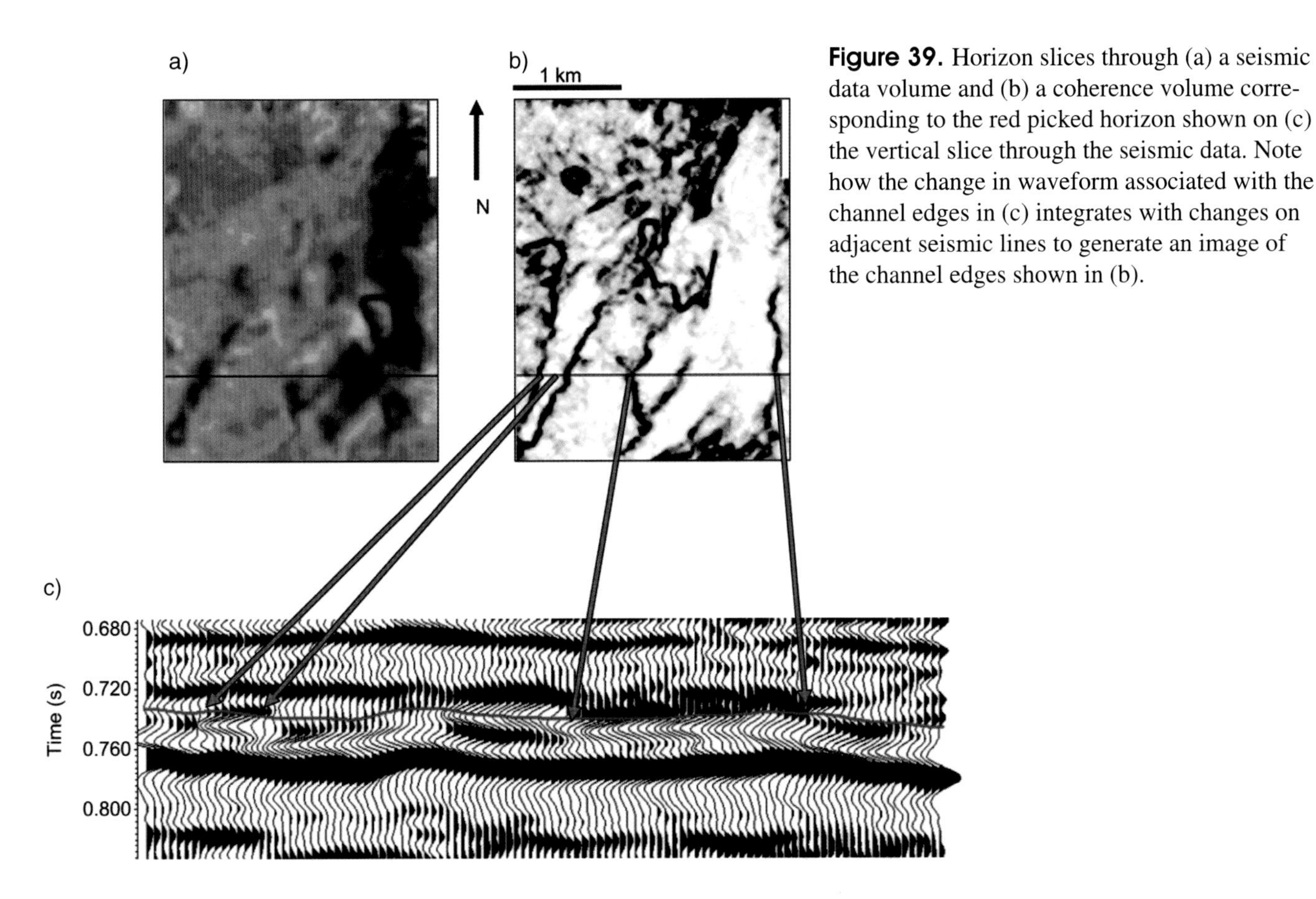

Figure 39. Horizon slices through (a) a seismic data volume and (b) a coherence volume corresponding to the red picked horizon shown on (c) the vertical slice through the seismic data. Note how the change in waveform associated with the channel edges in (c) integrates with changes on adjacent seismic lines to generate an image of the channel edges shown in (b).

coherence volume, this time flattened on an overlying marker horizon 100 ms above. Now we can see the channel system as a whole.

In Figure 42, we display successive slices through a flattened volume for another survey from Alberta, Canada. In addition to the main meander loop, several oxbows are seen on the 136-ms slice, in which the main loop and oxbows are focused best. Oxbows commonly are filled with different material from that in the main channel. Depending on the contrast of this fill with the surrounding rock matrix, an oxbow may appear more or less focused than the main channel. A second, narrower, east-west-trending channel lies beneath this main channel at 128 ms. The edges of both channels are preserved at different time levels at the spatial location where they cross, thereby suggesting that the shallower channel has not cut down into the deeper one.

Figure 43 shows a time slice through a coherence volume from British Columbia, Canada, showing faults in the lower half and channels in the upper half. Because of the dip in the data, the time slice cuts through the stratigraphy and only portions of the features are seen.

To avoid cutting through different strata, we examine two stratal slices approximating two different constant geologic times (Figure 44). In the shallower slice (Figure 44a), we see several faults clearly delineated and a channel running from left to right. The deeper stratal slice (Figure 44b) shows many more channels. Notice that on the vertical face of the slab the faults are through-going (white arrows), whereas the channel is confined to a single stratigraphic unit (black arrow). We redisplay this second deeper stratal-slice image from a different angle in Figure 45 and note that it exhibits some features more clearly.

Differential Compaction

When clayey sediments are deposited and by compaction converted to rock — shale — it typically contains much more porosity and water than sand does. Usually, shale compacts more than sandstone, and in so doing it can form a lateral change in horizon shape correlated with its lithology. Structures that originally are flat on the seafloor may change their shape during burial. If this change occurs over a short lateral distance or causes significant changes in vertical relief, it can induce weakness and faults in the overlying strata. Such compaction-induced faults can be quite misleading at first glance. Because we expect stratigraphic features to be confined to a given geologic horizon, we may be misled and assume that a channel feature seen on a horizon of interest is actually there, when instead what we are seeing is differential compaction resulting from a deeper channel. To avoid this pitfall, a careful interpreter should always animate through multiple attribute time slic-

Figure 40. A prominent channel seen on a suite of time slices through a coherence volume generated over a survey from northern Alberta. The original seismic data were courtesy of WesternGeco.

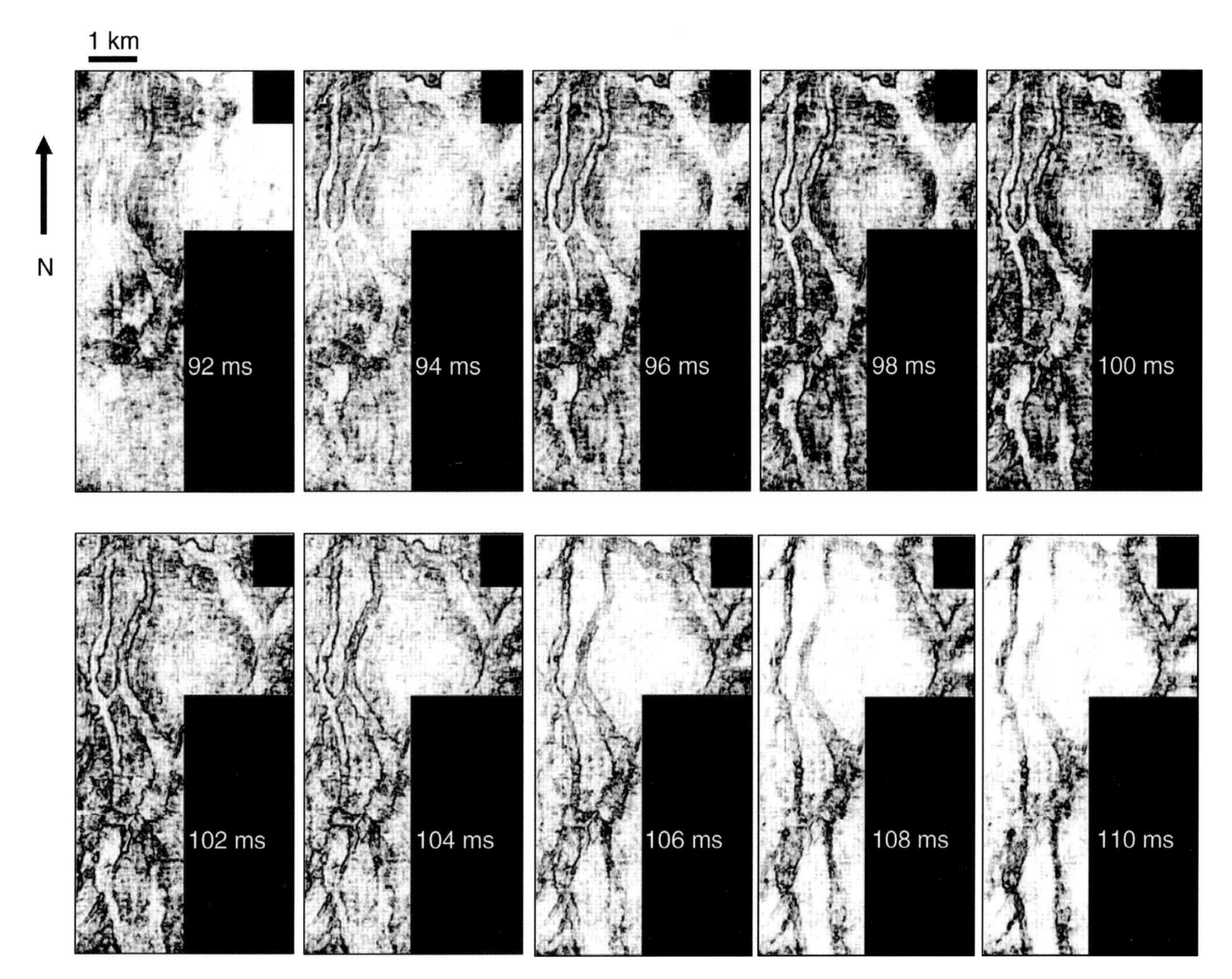

Figure 41. The same prominent channel shown in Figure 40, shown here flattened on an overlying marker horizon.

es and confirm the interpretation with vertical slices through the original seismic data.

We return now to Tertiary basins and recall an image from Deptuck (2003), presented here in Figure 46, that shows the amount of detail obtainable using high-quality 3D seismic data, seismic attributes (in this case coherence), and a geomorphology interpretation strategy (i.e., seismic geomorphology). This is an image of Hibernia Canyon, offshore the east coast of Canada. White arrows indicate erosional notches into the canyon. We see a channel meandering through the base of the canyon in Figure 46b. Haskell et al. (1998) mapped a similar canyon through the South Marsh Island area of the Gulf of Mexico using coherence and volumetric dip azimuth.

In Figure 47a, we display a shallower phantom horizon slice, 104 ms above the top of the Hibernia Canyon horizon shown in Figure 46a. The outline of the canyon is clearly seen (black arrows) as faults generated by differential compaction of the softer sediments within the canyon compared with compaction of firmer sediments outside the canyon. In Figure 47b and c, we also see a slump and other features of interest that we will investigate in more detail in Chapter 14.

In Figure 48a and b, we show a channel-like feature on both coherence and dip-azimuth time slices. While animating through the volume, Hughes et al. (1999) discovered that the real channel was actually 220 ms below these features, as shown in Figure 48c. The two shallower images of the channel are the result of faulting caused by differential compaction above this true channel.

We conclude our suite of images with one from the Green Canyon area of the deepwater Gulf of Mexico, U.S.A. Here we show vertical seismic slices cutting through a meander loop. This channel does not show up clearly on a coherence slice (Figure 49c), but because of differential compaction, it shows up well on a most-negative-curvature time slice (Figure 49b).

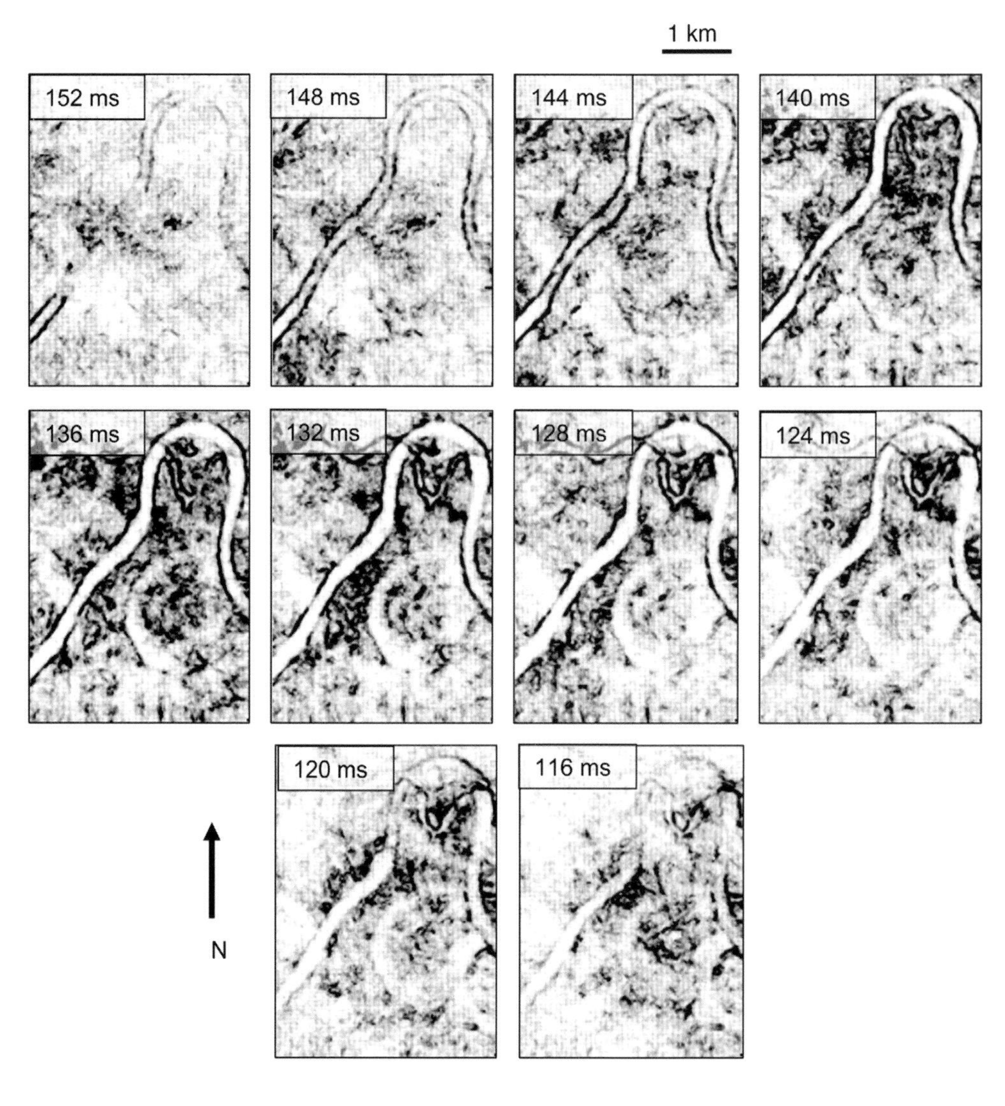

Figure 42. A channel seen on successive time slices through a coherence volume flattened on a marker horizon from a survey from southern Alberta. The time values indicate the slice's position above the flattened marker.

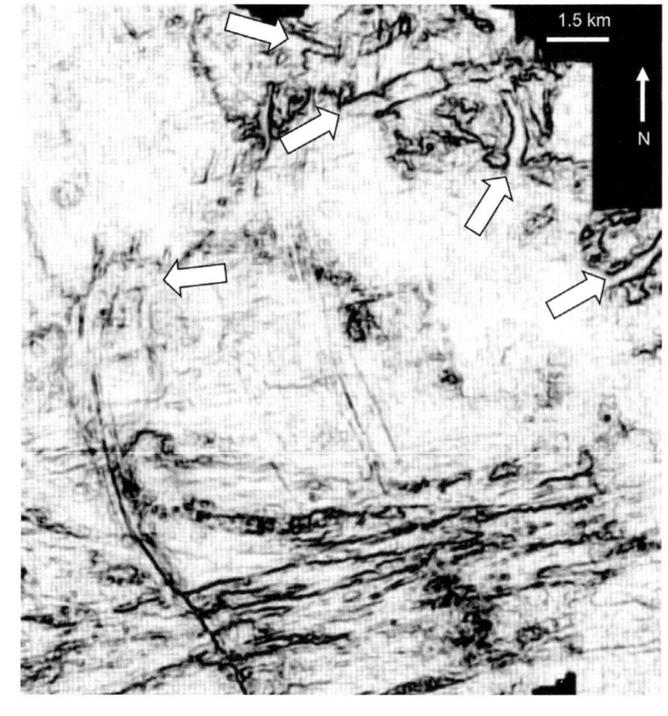

Figure 43. A time slice through a coherence volume from British Columbia, Canada, showing faults in the lower half and channels in the upper half. Because of the dip in the data, the time slice cuts across stratigraphy and only portions of the channels (arrows) are seen. Data are courtesy of Arcis Corporation, Calgary.

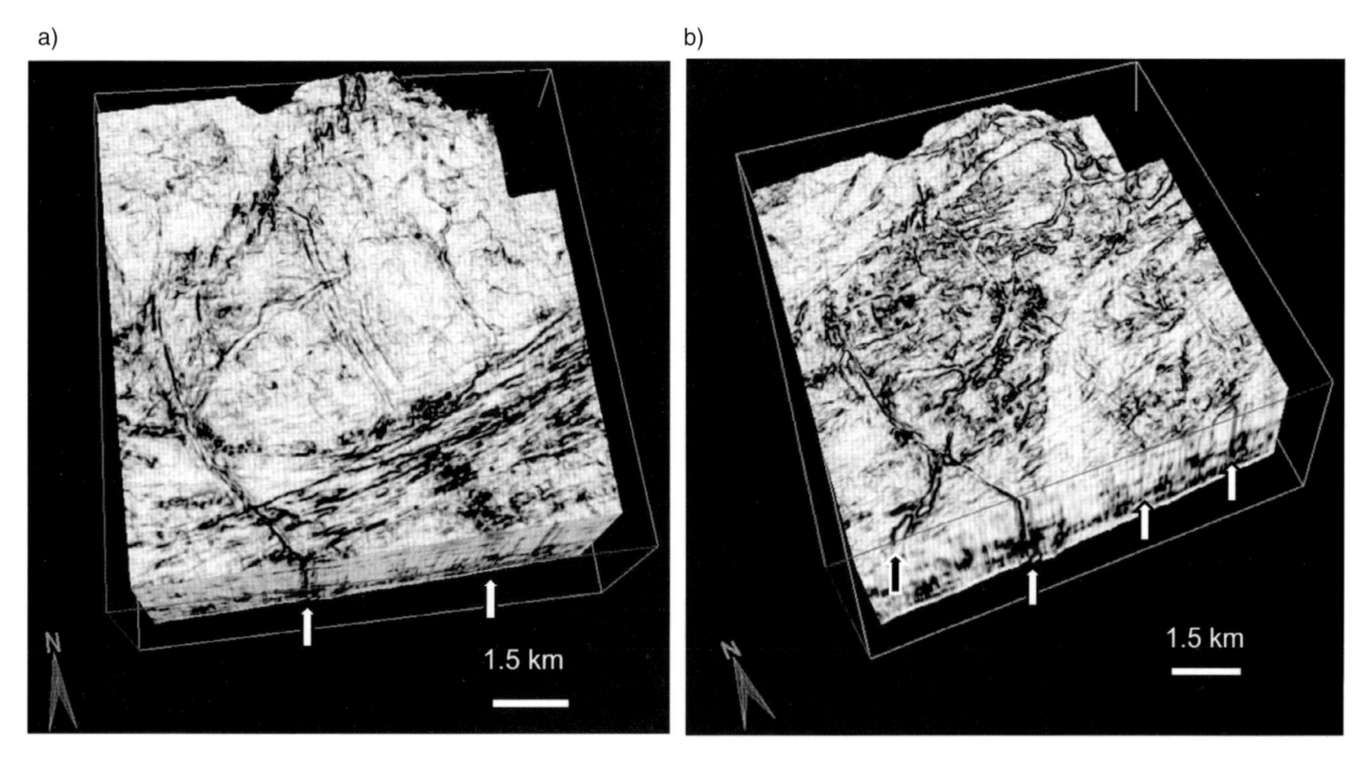

Figure 44. Two stratal slices through the same coherence volume shown in Figure 43. Slice (a) is shallower than (b) and exhibits faults, whereas slice (b) shows channels in more or less their complete disposition. Data are courtesy of Arcis Corporation, Calgary.

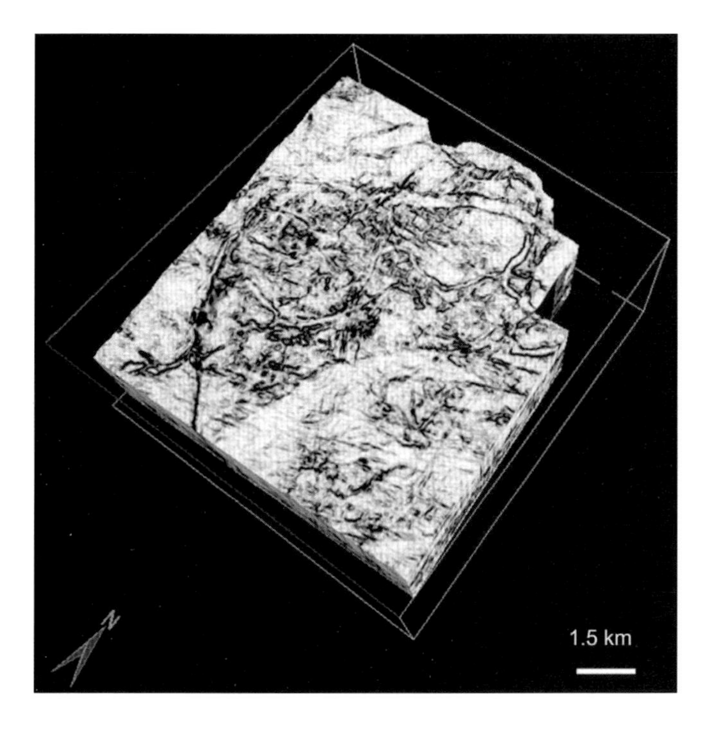

Figure 45. The stratal slice from Figure 44b through a coherence volume from British Columbia, Canada. Here, the stratal slice is viewed from a different angle than it was in Figure 44b, and we note that it exhibits some features more clearly. Data courtesy of Arcis Corporation, Calgary.

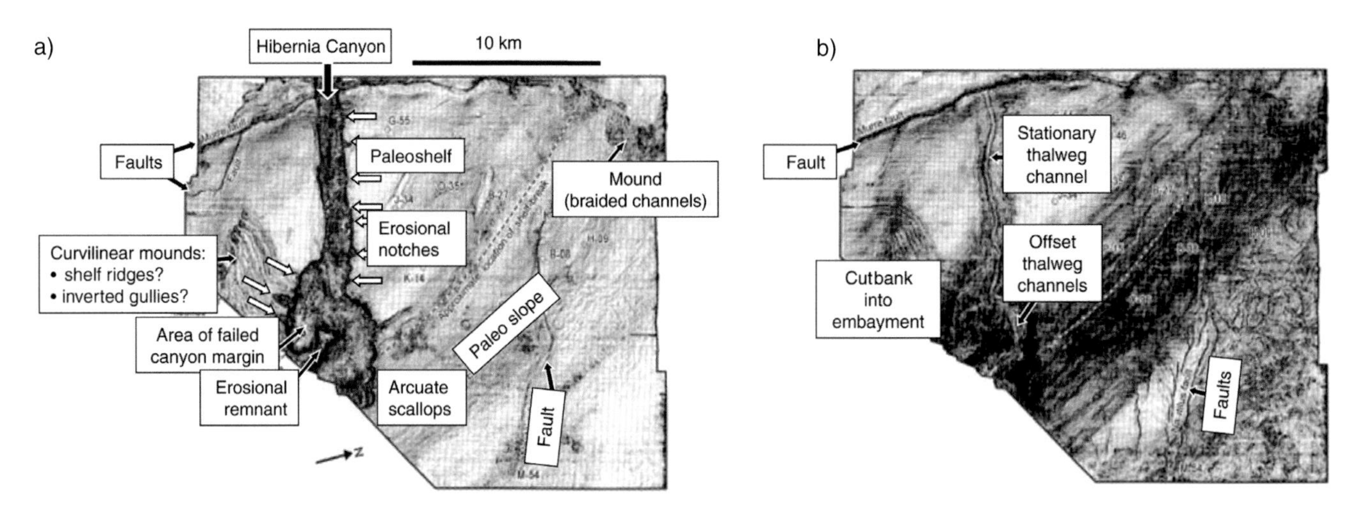

Figure 46. Horizon slices through a coherence volume (a) along the top of Hibernia Canyon. (b) A phantom-horizon slice 128 ms below that in (a) showing the erosive base of the canyon. After Deptuck (2003).

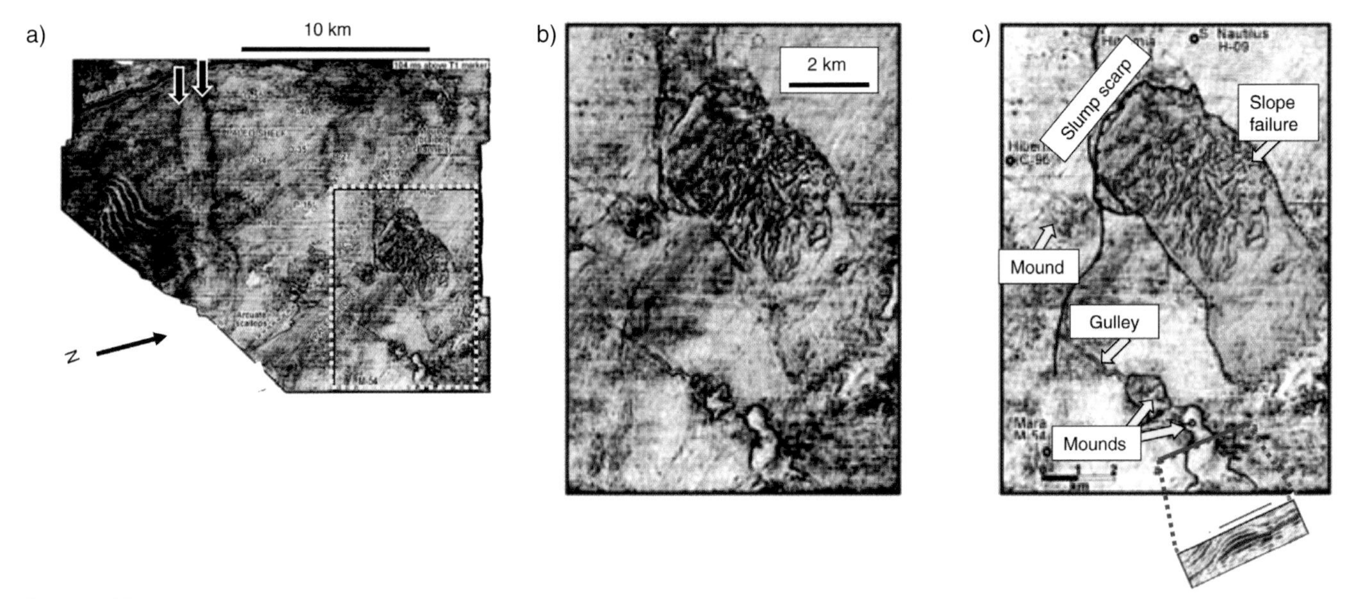

Figure 47. (a) A horizon slice 104 ms above that shown in Figure 46a. Note the differential compaction over the deeper canyon. Expanded view (b) without and (c) with interpretation of a small slope gulley (yellow) with mounds deposited at the canyon mouth. The areal extent of the Nautilus slope failure is shown in green. After Deptuck (2003).

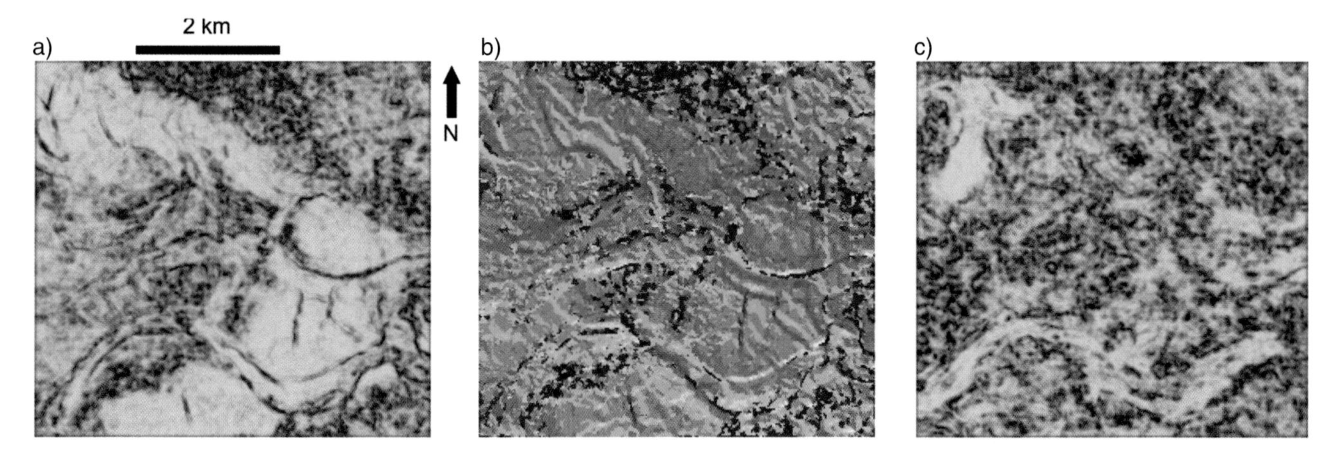

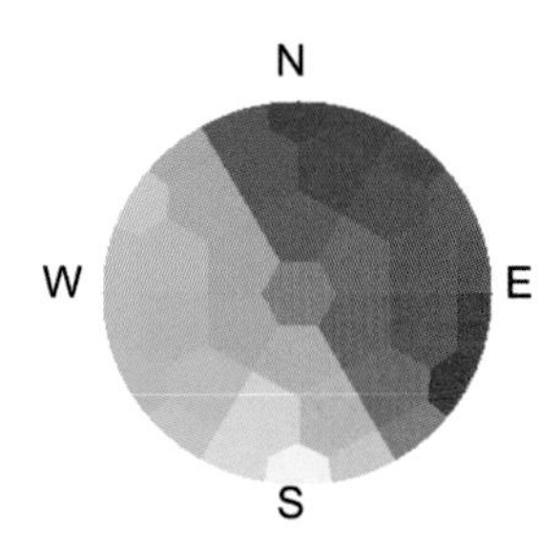

Figure 48. The appearance of differential compaction. (a)-(b) Time slices through (a) a coherence volume and (b) a dip-azimuth volume, at the suspected channel level. Note that on the south flank the apparent dip along the channel edges is inward, or toward the north-northeast (blue and magenta), and toward the south-southwest (yellow and green) on the north flank. (c) A time slice through the coherence volume 220 ms below that shown in (a). We now see that the true channel occurs at this deeper level and that faulting caused by differential compaction produced the congruent image of the channel on the shallow slice. After Hughes et al. (1999).

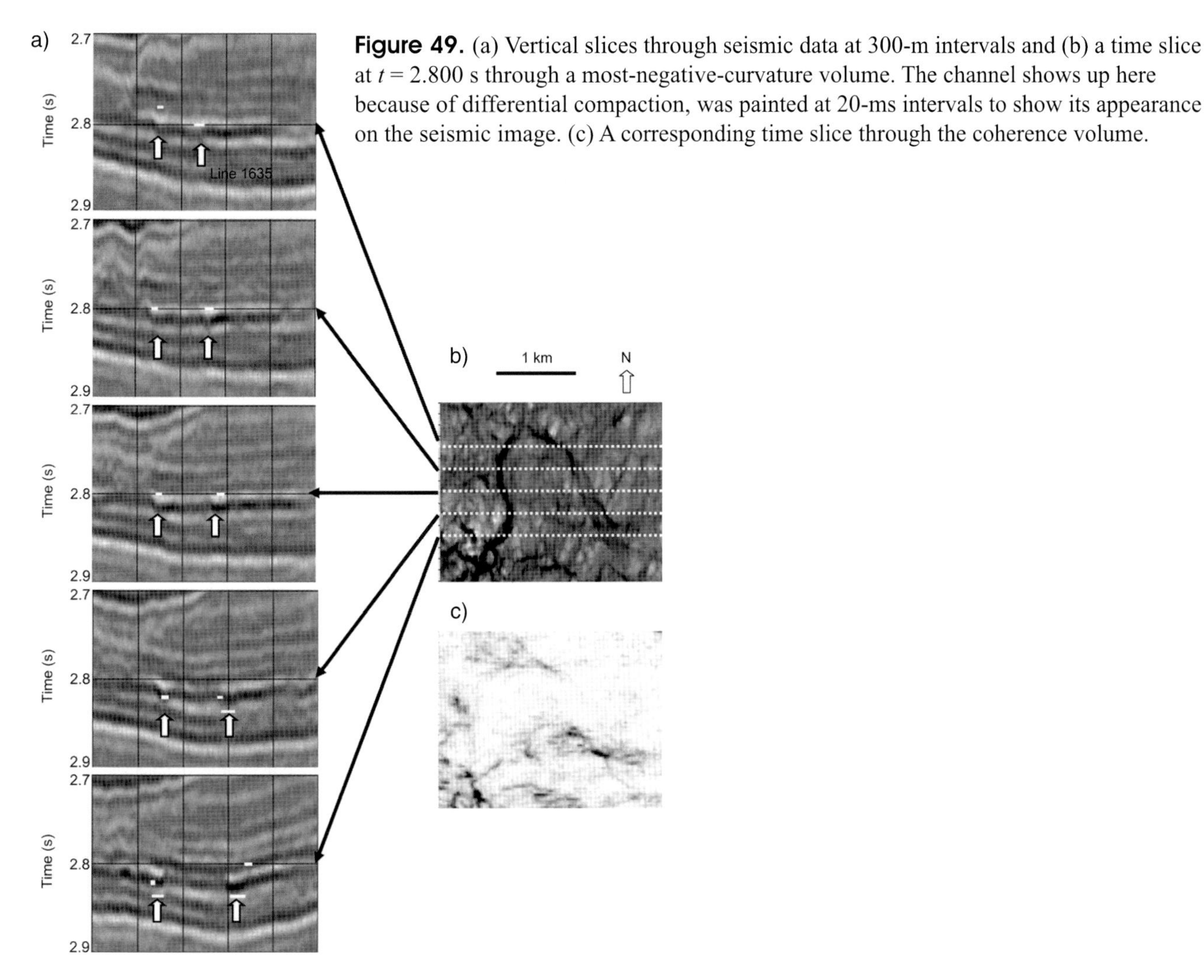

Figure 49. (a) Vertical slices through seismic data at 300-m intervals and (b) a time slice at $t = 2.800$ s through a most-negative-curvature volume. The channel shows up here because of differential compaction, was painted at 20-ms intervals to show its appearance on the seismic image. (c) A corresponding time slice through the coherence volume.

Chapter Summary

The current access to high-quality 3D seismic data has enabled the seismic stratigraphy of the 1970s to become incorporated into the seismic geomorphology of today. Ideally, a seismic-geomorphology interpretation of depositional features should be generated on a stratal slice corresponding to a single geologic age. Animation through such stratal slices allows an interpreter to visualize the depositional environment's evolution through geologic time. Seismic attributes significantly enhance one's ability to extract subtle features on stratal time slices, including individual channels, meander belts, levees, scarps, canyons, erosional notches, and slumps. In certain situations, one can avoid generating stratal or horizon slices and can paint large channels directly on attribute time slices to produce a map of the picked channel system in three dimensions. Because of their long, narrow, often meandering nature, channels are particularly easy to identify on seismic-attribute volumes. Other features of geologic interest, such as dunes, bars, and fans, are subtler and must be interpreted in the context of other features seen on a stratal slice and linked through models of depositional processes.

Channel-sand reservoirs, which frequently have excellent production characteristics, can be quite difficult to develop efficiently. The depositional mechanisms involved in channel fills create sand bodies whose thickness and quality can vary rapidly over short distances — perhaps as short as a few hundred meters. Because commonly channels are filled with a different material from that in the surrounding matrix, channels almost always generate a lateral change in amplitude. For that reason, energy-weighted coherent-amplitude gradients and spectral decomposition are particularly effective in mapping channels. If channels are thick enough to cause a lateral change in waveform, they can be detected by coherence. If they have led to differential compaction, they can be detected by curvature.

Finally, animation through adjacent slices (time, horizon, or stratal slices) is critical to an accurate interpretation of stratigraphy. Because stratigraphic features often are mixed by the seismic wavelet and attribute-analysis window, animation allows an interpreter to judge at which level a given feature is best focused and then to place it in the proper vertical position with other features seen on the same time slice. Equally important is the fact that animation through deeper time slices can help one avoid the pitfall of misinterpreting a shallow feature that looks stratigraphically reasonable but that is really the result of differential compaction over true stratigraphic features that lie deeper in the section.

References

Deptuck, M. E., 2003, Post-rift geology of the Jeanne d'Arc Basin, with a focus on the architecture and evolution of early Paleogene submarine fans, and insights from modern deep-water systems: Ph.D. thesis, Dalhousie University, Halifax, Nova Scotia, Canada.

Haskell, N. L., S. E. Nissen, J. A. Lopez, and M. S. Bahorich, 1995, 3-D seismic coherency and the imaging of sedimentological features: 65th Annual International Meeting, SEG, Expanded Abstracts, 1532–1534.

———, 1998, 3-D seismic coherency and the imaging of sedimentological features, *in* F. M. Gradstein, K. O. Sandvik, and N. J. Milton, eds., Sequence stratigraphy concepts and applications: Elsevier, 197–214.

Hughes, M. J., S. Dhanani, R. K. Frimpong, M. Gainski, N. L. Haskell, R. P. Heath, J. D. Kantorowicz, P. M. Maguire, and S. E. Nissen, 1999, Applications of the coherency cube in the UKCS, *in* A. J. Fleet and S. A. R. Bouldy, eds., Petroleum geology of northwest Europe: Proceedings of the 5th Conference: Geological Society of London, 1299–1305.

Jennette, D. C., 2005, Making sense of turbidite reservoirs: A multi-basin perspective on what drives architecture and rock properties: AAPG Distinguished Lecturer Series, Abstract, accessed June 22, 2005. http://www.aapg.org/education/dist_lect/index.cfm.

Liu, J., and K. J. Marfurt, 2005, Matching pursuit decomposition using Morlet wavelets: 75th Annual International Meeting, SEG, Expanded Abstracts, 786–789.

Peyton, L., R. Bottjer, and G. Partyka, 1998, Interpretation of incised valleys using new 3-D seismic techniques: A case history using spectral decomposition and coherency: The Leading Edge, **17**, 1294–1298.

Posamentier, H. W., and V. Kolla, 2003, Seismic geomorphology and stratigraphy of depositional elements in deep-water settings. Journal of Sedimentary Research, **73**, 367–388.

Prather, B. E., J. R. Booth, G. S. Steffens, and P. A. Craig, 1998, Classification, lithologic calibration, and stratigraphic succession of seismic facies of intraslope basins, deep-water Gulf of Mexico, AAPG Bulletin, **82**, 701–728.

Saller, A. H., I. A. T. Noah, A. P. Ruzuar, and R. Schneider, 2004, Linked lowstand delta to basin-floor fan deposition, offshore Indonesia: An analog for deep-water reservoir systems: AAPG Bulletin, **88**, 21–46.

Shirley, K., 2000, Understanding how basins fill: Stratigraphy concept morphing, AAPG Explorer interview with Henry Posamentier, accessed June 22, 2005. http://www.aapg.org/explorer/2000/08aug/geomorphology.cfm.

Smythe, J., A. Gersztenkorn, B. Radovich, C. F. Li, and C. Liner, 2004, SPICE: Layered Gulf of Mexico shelf framework from spectral imaging: The Leading Edge, **23**, 921–926.

Taner, M.T., F. Koehler, and R. E. Sheriff, 1979, Complex seismic trace analysis: Geophysics, **44**, 1041–1063.

Vail, P. R., R. M. Mitchum Jr., and S. Thompson III, 1977, Seismic stratigraphy and global changes of sea level, Part 4, Global cycles of relative changes of sea level: *in* C. E. Payton, ed., Seismic stratigraphy applications to hydrocarbon exploration: AAPG Memoir 26, 83–97.

Zeng, H., 2004, Seismic geomorphology-based facies classification: The Leading Edge, **23**, 644–645, 688.

Zeng, H., M. M. Backus, K. T. Barrow, and N. Tyler, 1998a, Stratal slicing, part I: Realistic 3-D seismic model: Geophysics, **63**, 502–513.

Zeng, H., S. C. Henry, and J. P. Riola, 1998b, Stratal slicing, part II: Real seismic data: Geophysics, **63**, 514–522.

Chapter 13

Attribute Expression of Carbonate Depositional Environments

Chapter Objectives

After reading this chapter, you will be able to

- build basin-specific workflows to identify reefs and other carbonate buildups using seismic-attribute volumes
- recognize karst and other diagenetic features
- use energy gradients and spectral decomposition to map carbonate reefs and channels below the tuning frequency
- correlate karst and other collapse features to underlying structure

Introduction

Even though carbonate reservoirs account for a very large percentage of the world's petroleum reserves, most geophysicists do not understand them as well as they understand siliciclastics. Recently, for economic and licensing reasons, large international oil companies have focused (and therefore dedicated manpower, research, and publications) primarily on understanding deepwater clastic depositional environments in the Gulf of Mexico and on both sides of the South Atlantic. Although much has been published about geophysical imaging of carbonate reservoirs on the Arabian Peninsula, little has been published in Western literature on applying such techniques to reservoirs in other parts of the Persian Gulf or in Central Asia.

Carbonate depositional environments differ in many ways from siliciclastic depositional environments, which we described in Chapter 12. Often, carbonates are generated in place through a mixture of chemical and biological processes. Sarg and Schuelke (2003, p. 640–641) summarize:

"The stratigraphic signatures of carbonate rocks result from the interaction of tectonic, eustatic, sedimentation, and climatic processes. Tectonic and eustatic processes combine to cause relative changes of sea level, which control the space available for sediments (accommodation space). Oceanographic and climatic conditions control the amount and types of sediments deposited (different carbonate facies and presence of evaporites or siliciclastics)."

They go on to say:

"Facies differentiation in carbonates is controlled by the geometry of the basin, water energy levels, and sediment type. Large, isolated platforms develop on horst blocks in rift settings, and around volcanoes and seamounts in oceanic settings. Platforms attached to continental or basin margins are long, linear features that face open seas. The depositional profile (i.e., ramp-to-rimmed or open shelves) in large measure depends on basin depth and subsidence rate at the time of deposition. Facies differentiation depends on the relationship of margin type (reefs, grain shoals, and unrestricted sand banks) and water circulation."

Carbonate deposition commonly requires warm water and shallow depths. In addition, organic generation of carbonates requires sunlight and clean water that is uncontaminated by siliciclastics. Carbonates often form stratigraphic traps that are associated with reefs, shoals, and ramps (Figure 1). If these carbonate features retain their porosity, and if they are buried by low-permeability rocks (such as micrite, shales, or anhydrite), they can form excellent reservoirs.

Carbonate terrains can be quite challenging for the seismic interpreter. First, the velocities of carbonates are, in general, significantly faster than the velocities of siliciclastics at comparable depths. For a given frequency, this implies that wavelength and therefore vertical and lateral resolutions are lower in carbonates than in siliciclastics. Carbonates also are denser than most siliciclastics. The combination of higher velocities and higher densities produces higher impedances

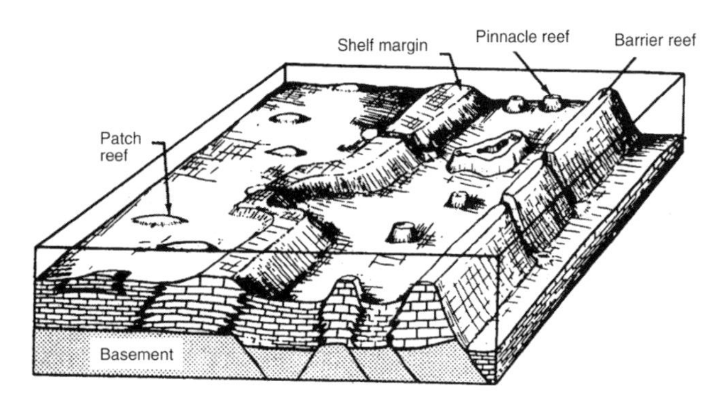

Figure 1. The typical environment for reef growth, and the types of reefs. After Sheriff and Geldart (1995), based on Bubb and Hatelid (1977). AAPG©1977. Reprinted by permission of the AAPG whose permission is required for further use.

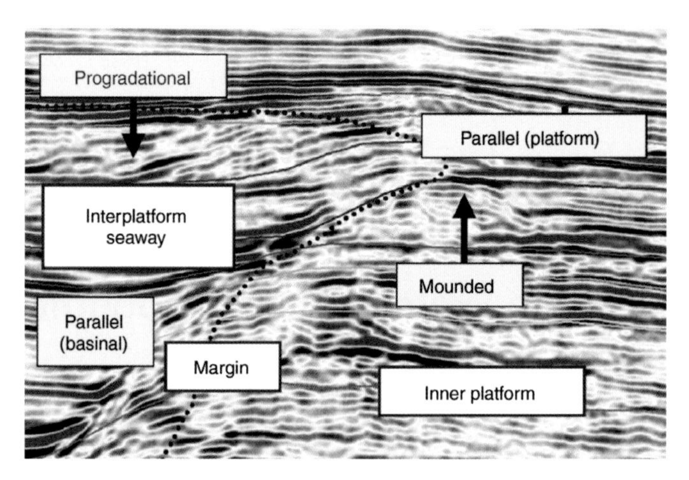

Figure 2. A seismic profile across the margin of a Neogene carbonate platform, showing different seismic facies. Platform margins are characterized by mounded to prograding geometries. Basin-center and platform interior-shelf areas have continuous to discontinuous parallel reflectivity. The platform margin's trajectory through time is shown by the dotted black line. The seismic line is approximately 5 km wide. After Sarg and Schuelke (2003).

for carbonates in contrast to those of surrounding siliciclastics, so carbonates produce higher reflection coefficients at bed boundaries. Thus, interbedded carbonates and siliciclastics generate strong interbed multiples.

In contrast, carbonate-on-carbonate reflections, such as those from the interface between a porous grainstone and a nonporous carbonate mudstone, generally are smaller than sand-shale reflection coefficients, thereby resulting not only in signals that have lower vertical and lateral resolution but also have lower amplitudes than sand-shale interfaces do. If carbonates are near the surface, they generate backscattered ground roll and reverberating refractions whose velocities may be indistinguishable from the reflections of interest. Low carbonate-on-carbonate reflectivity, backscattered noise, and interbed multiples create greater problems for interpreters than they encounter in most siliciclastic terrains.

The geometric relations for carbonates, although they are well understood (as illustrated by the caption for Figure 2), can be quite subtle on low-amplitude, low-frequency seismic data. Because carbonates are most often deposited in shallow water (only chalks generally are deposited in deep water), it is essential to interpret the data within a sequence stratigraphic framework. At the very least, it is important to know where the shore was, whether the carbonate was exposed subaerially, and if possible, the direction of wind and currents.

Because carbonates are composed primarily of calcium and magnesium carbonate, they undergo relatively rapid diagenetic alteration compared with sandstones. Dissolution and karstification can result in major, first-order modification of reflector geometries. Although carbonate plays often are structurally simple, they almost always benefit from careful 3D migration that properly focuses scattered energy from karsted surfaces (and irregular reefal buildups).

Less obvious, but equally important, is the effect that diagenesis has on internal reflectivity. Diagenesis can totally obliterate the original depositional geometries, leaving either the blank zones commonly seen in carbonate reefs and platforms, or replacing original geometries with diagenetic fronts (and reflections) that cut across the original depositional geometries.

Finally, carbonates often are associated with arid depositional environments, one of the most important of which is the sabkha. Prolonged evaporation of seawater can result in deposition of gypsum, anhydrite and, under some circumstances, large deposits of halite. At many places in the subsurface, vugs, fractures, and collapse features are filled with anhydrite. The result is the formation of excellent seals for hydrocarbon reservoirs. However, if exposed to water that is undersaturated in calcium sulfate, anhydrite may be altered to gypsum — or it may be dissolved. In the latter instance, significant amounts of secondary porosity and permeability may develop.

Although anhydrite can play a key role in determining a reservoir's viability, it is both faster and denser than the surrounding material and thus generates multiples. Also, local dissolution of anhydrite may create laterally varying velocity pull-ups, thereby exacerbating an already difficult seismic imaging problem.

In Figure 3, we reproduce well-established schematics (from Lines and Newrick, 2004; Sheriff and Geldart, 1995) of common carbonate geometries (originally published by Bubb and Hatfield, 1977). We note that the key to interpreting carbonate facies is reflector shape (including the absence of a lateral reflector), making these facies suitable candidates for geometric-attribute and seismic-texture analysis.

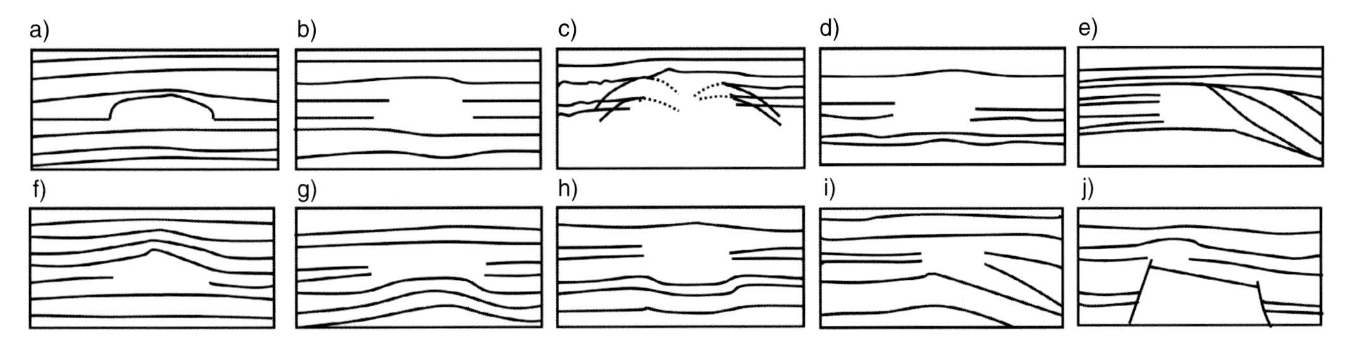

Figure 3. Seismic expression of reefs. Unless otherwise noted, all of the following figures represent the seismic expression of a reef in 3D migrated data. (a) Reefs often have a mound shape. (b) Porous reefs often display a reflection void, or dimming. The dimming is caused by a smaller velocity contrast between shale and porous carbonate rock than between shale and tight limestone. (c) Reef edges often create diffractions that can be observed in the unmigrated data. (d) In migrated data, reflections often terminate abruptly along the reef's flanks. (e) Reflection patterns differ on different sides of a reef. One side generally is in a basinal environment, whereas the other side is on the shelf. (f) Layers compact differentially, or "drape," over the top of a reef, because reefs tend to lithify early in their burial history. (g) Reflectors below a reef generally exhibit a velocity pull-up on a seismic time section so that subreef reflections arrive earlier. This occurs because seismic energy will have passed through high-velocity carbonate rocks rather than through the lower-seismic-velocity rocks that surround the reef. (h) Although it occurs less commonly, porous carbonates may be surrounded by higher-velocity rocks (such as anhydrite), in which case the rocks below the reef exhibit a velocity pushdown or delay on the time section. (i) Reefs often initiate on a hinge line or shelf edge. (j) Reefs may grow on a structural high caused by faulting. After Lines and Newrick (2004) and Sheriff and Geldart (1995), and based on Bubb and Hatelid (1977).

In addition to depositional and diagenetic differences, carbonates also often deform differently than surrounding clastics do. In the process of structural deformation, carbonate rocks are deformed in the manner of brittle substances (during lithification, but before lithification to chalk, calcium-carbonate muds are an exception). Brittle deformation leads to the "crackers and jelly" carbonate-in-shale deformation patterns described in Chapter 11.

Matrix porosity may be very effective if it is well connected. If matrix porosity has not been preserved, a carbonate reservoir needs fracture porosity (and fracture permeability) if it is to produce hydrocarbons. For that reason, many recent exploration techniques, such as azimuthal AVO, multiazimuth velocity analysis, and multicomponent acquisition, including shear-wave-splitting techniques, commonly are applied to carbonate reservoirs in an attempt to determine the degree and orientation of reservoir fracturing.

In this chapter, we begin by showing examples of reef identification using seismic attributes. We proceed with identification of carbonate slope and channel deposits and then progress to diagenetic alteration, with an emphasis on karst features. We conclude with examples of fracture identification.

Organic Buildups (Reefs and Bioherms)

Much of geophysical exploration has centered around determining locations and geometries of subsurface reefs and other carbonate accumulations that have unusual porosity and permeability. Although 3D seismic data can provide a good image of a reef's extent, internal details often are not clear. It is not uncommon for wells drilled in mature basins to miss the optimal part of a reef because of insufficient or inaccurate imaging of the reef's interior. Accurate definitions of a reef's margins and internal porosity distribution determine trap definition and economic reservoir limits, which can be critical risk factors in making a carbonate play viable. The use of 3D volumetric attributes, along with acoustic and elastic impedance inversion, helps us map these subtle heterogeneities.

Dolomitized or leached pinnacle reefs may form prolific hydrocarbon reservoirs. Overall reef geometry and pool dimensions can be interpreted accurately if the boundaries appear clearly, such we see in Figure 4. Coherence and other geometric attributes can provide valuable information with which we can form a comprehensive, three-dimensional model of the pinnacle reef.

The outer limits of a pinnacle reef can be drawn accurately on individual coherence slices and then merged as if the slices had piled up to form the pinnacle. Figure 5 shows time slices at every 20 ms from a coherence volume generated for a survey over a pinnacle reef from Alberta, Canada. Notice that we see a gradual broadening of the reef boundary as we go down in time, as we expect for a pinnacle reef. To understand reservoir variability within the reef, we use a geologic model of detailed growth patterns within the reef core surrounded by debris in the outer reefal limits. Such detailed information is very important when we draw

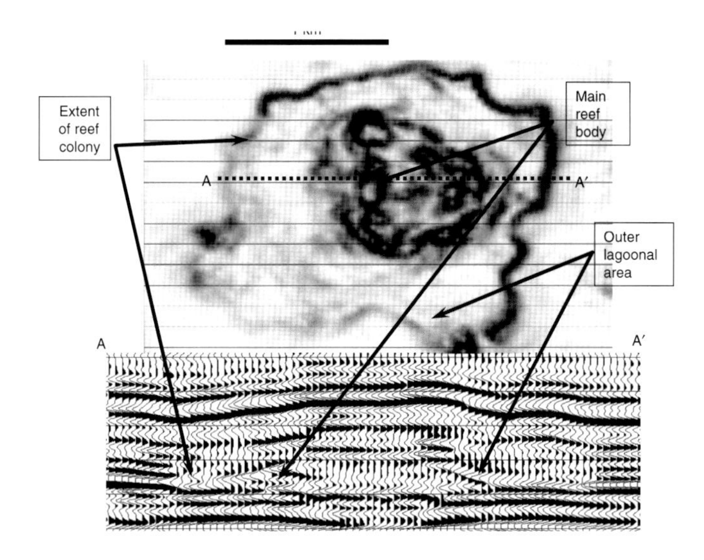

Figure 4. (a) A time slice at t = 1.200 s through a coherence volume and (b) a vertical slice AA′ through a seismic data volume, from a survey conducted over a pinnacle reef in Alberta, Canada.

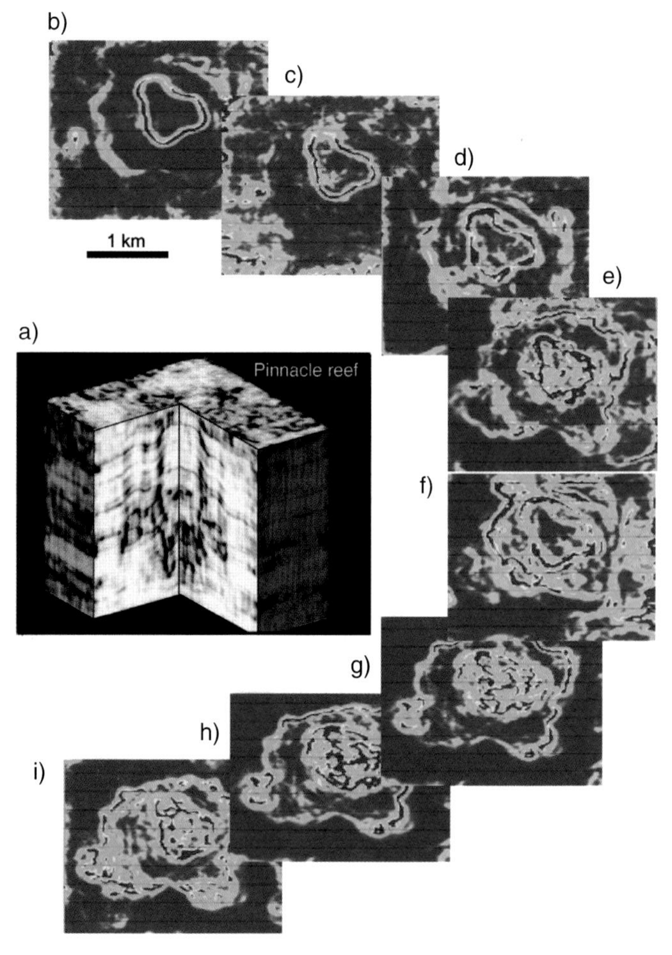

Figure 5. (a) A cutaway volume view and (b)-(i) time slices at 0.020 ms increments through a coherence volume generated from a survey over a pinnacle reef in Alberta, Canada. We see a gradual broadening of the reef boundary as we go down in time, which we would expect for a pinnacle reef. At the same time, the reef's inner structural details also become more apparent.

up plans for intersecting a hydrocarbon pool with vertical and horizontal boreholes. Also, we must be aware that reefs with good internal reflectors may be bedded and tight.

The area shown in Figure 6 depicts prominent reefs in the Zama Basin of northern Alberta, Canada. Because the area was adjacent to excellent source rocks, exploration was concentrated there. On average, these reefs consisted of 50- to 100-m-thick dolomite and held substantial quantities of oil in place.

The two wells marked A and B on the main reef are oil producers, whereas the one marked C is a waterflood injection well. Interpreters used 3D seismic data to evaluate the reef edges of the isolated buildups and to study porosity variation (not discussed here) in these bodies.

Time slices from the original seismic volume do not show the edges of the reefs clearly. However, the coherence displays in Figure 6 do indicate the boundaries of the two bigger reefs and also show a few small buildups located in between. Centered on t = 1.116 s, the coherence slices indicate a dimming (gray area) in the boundary of the reef (at D) that otherwise shows a continuous boundary. This dimming was suspected and later confirmed to result from a column of anhydrite that covered that part of the reef. Consequently, placement of the next production well was shifted from the gray shaded area to a location far into the pure-white area (high coherence) within the reef boundary (the result of the drilling is not known at this time).

The seismic signature corresponding to the edges of a smaller reef is shown in the top right of Figure 6. We can track the individual boundaries representing both the outer reefal limits and the inside reef core configuration and can study their three-dimensional geometry. Figure 7 shows part of a 3D reef-buildup display, depicted with the structure standing on a coherence slice.

Figure 8 displays time slices through a Winnepegosis reef from Alberta, Canada. We show the east-west component (Figure 8a) and north-south component (Figure 8b) of the energy-weighted coherent-amplitude gradient, as well as coherence (Figure 8c) and spectral decomposition (Figure 8d). We also display representative vertical slices through the seismic data (Figure 8e-g). Each of these images emphasizes subtle differences in the reef. The energy-weighted coherent-amplitude gradients show variations in reflection coefficient and thin-bed tuning, thereby emphasizing the thinning edges of the reef.

Although coherence is based on a measure of waveform similarity, in this example it produces an image that

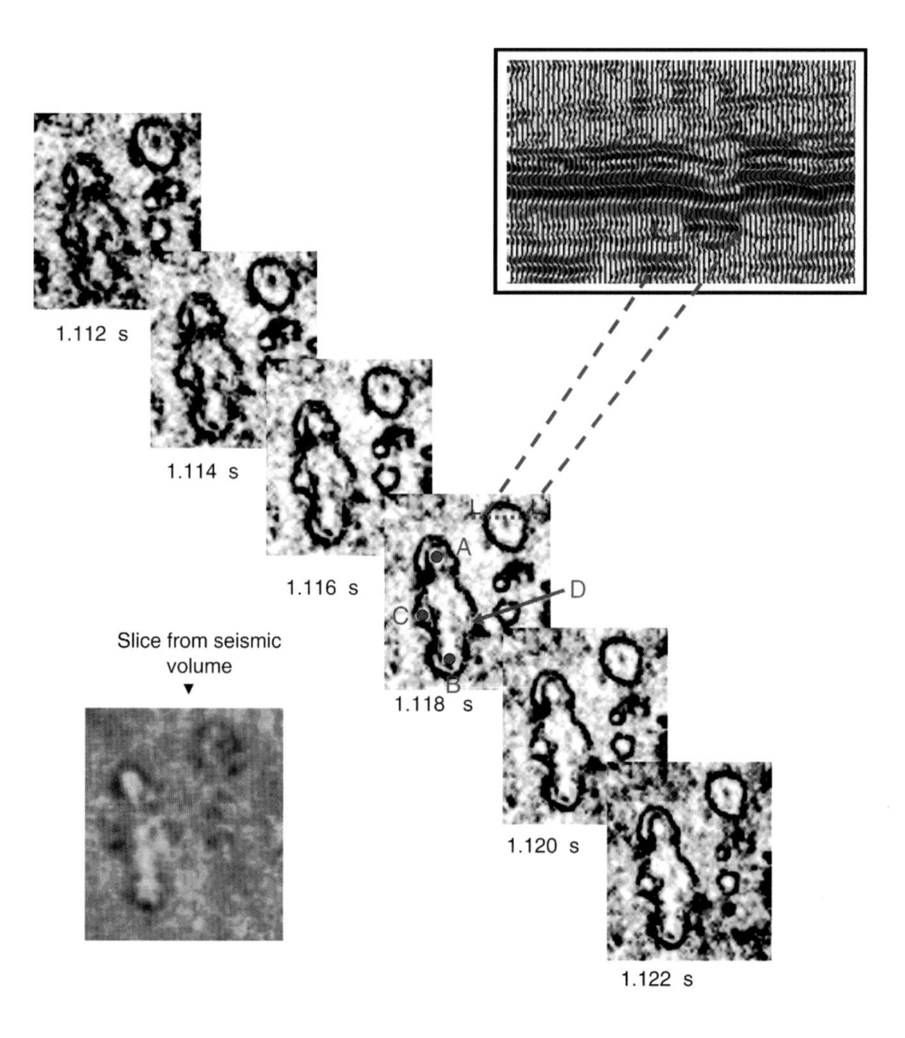

Figure 6. A representative slice through the seismic data and at 2-ms intervals through the coherence volume from a survey conducted in the Zama Basin, northern Alberta, Canada.

maps edges whose lateral placement is nearly identical to those revealed by the energy-weighted coherent-amplitude-gradient displays. Although the results of these two different algorithms are mathematically independent, they are connected through geology.

Spectral decomposition (Figure 8d) produces a significantly different image, showing different peak frequencies within the reef complex. The lateral discontinuities in peak frequency correspond to those in Figure 8a-c. These tuning frequencies are a function of the temporal reservoir thickness (in this case, it must be less than 0.100 s or 10 Hz) and, indirectly, porosity and true reservoir thickness.

Imaging reef edges and porosity in Devonian Slave Point carbonates, northwestern Alberta, Canada

Skirius et al. (1999, p. 390) described a 3D survey that was shot over a known producing gas field in Alberta, Canada. The target formation was an "aggradational to backstepping carbonate reef-shelf buildup averaging 50 m in thickness." Their goal was to map depositional facies in a limestone-dominated section so they could improve their porosity maps. They created attribute maps from the target horizon to identify features and then to calibrate those features with the existing well data, as shown in Figure 9a. A very vague partial outline of the southern isolated reef edge is visible on a time-structure map of the top of the target formation, derived from the processed 3D data (Figure 9b). The majority of the time-structure data related to the reef edge is the result of wavelet tuning rather than real structure. The south reef's edge is more completely defined on an amplitude map extracted at the top of the target formation (Figure 9c).

Also visible on the amplitude map in Figure 9c are the boundaries of the embayment (low amplitude, dark gray color) that define the northern edge of the isolated south reef and a (partial) southern edge of the north reefal buildup on the other side of the embayment. Little well control existed for establishing the north reef's areal extent. However, wells N1, N2, and N3 cored porous reefal material in a downdip (wet) position. Another embayment area indicated by low amplitudes defines the northern edge of the north reef. Logs and cores from wells E2 and N3 in this area also indicate embayment fill and slope facies, respectively.

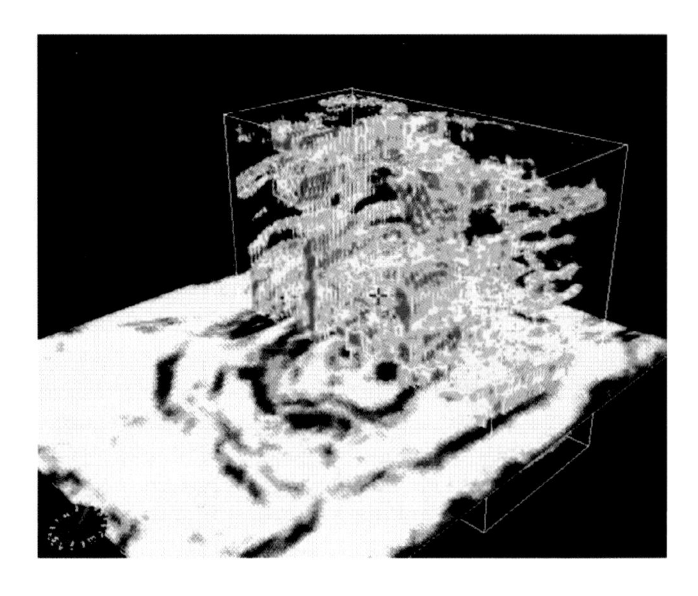

Figure 7. A voxel image of the envelope of the coherent energy corresponding to the images shown in Figure 5, corroborating the existence of multiple reefs and helping delineate their boundaries. The envelope of coherence was used in the connectivity analysis, using commercial voxel software.

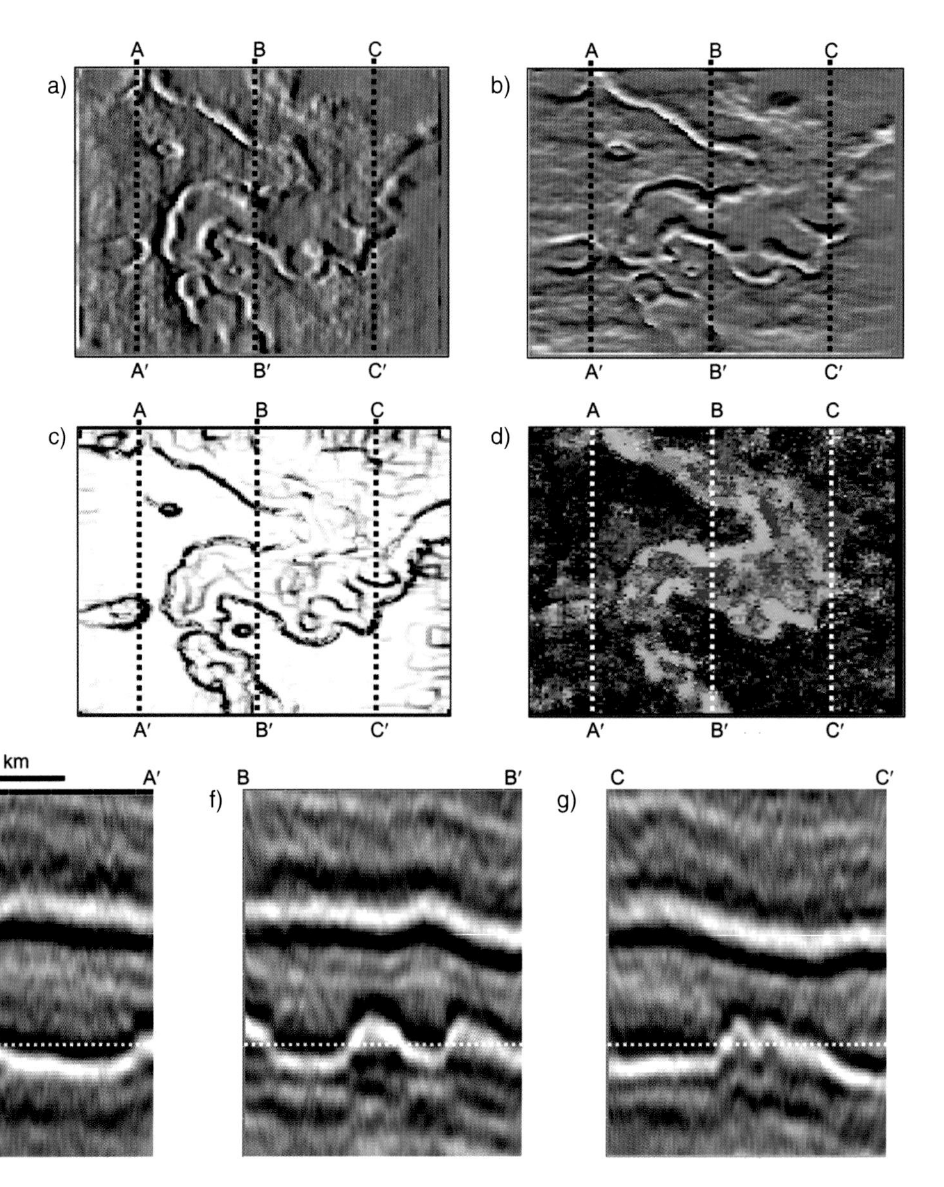

Figure 8. (a)-(d) Four time slices at t = 1.438 s through a Winnepegosas reef, from a survey acquired in Saskatchewan, Canada. (a) The east-west component and (b) the north-south component of a energy-weighted coherent-amplitude gradient, (c) a coherence volume, and (d) peak spectral frequency modulated by peak amplitude. (e)-(g) Vertical slices through the seismic data along lines (e) AA′ (f) BB′, and (g) CC′. The 2D color table for peak frequency versus amplitude of peak frequency is identical to the color table in Figure 30 of Chapter 12. Seismic data are courtesy of Talisman.

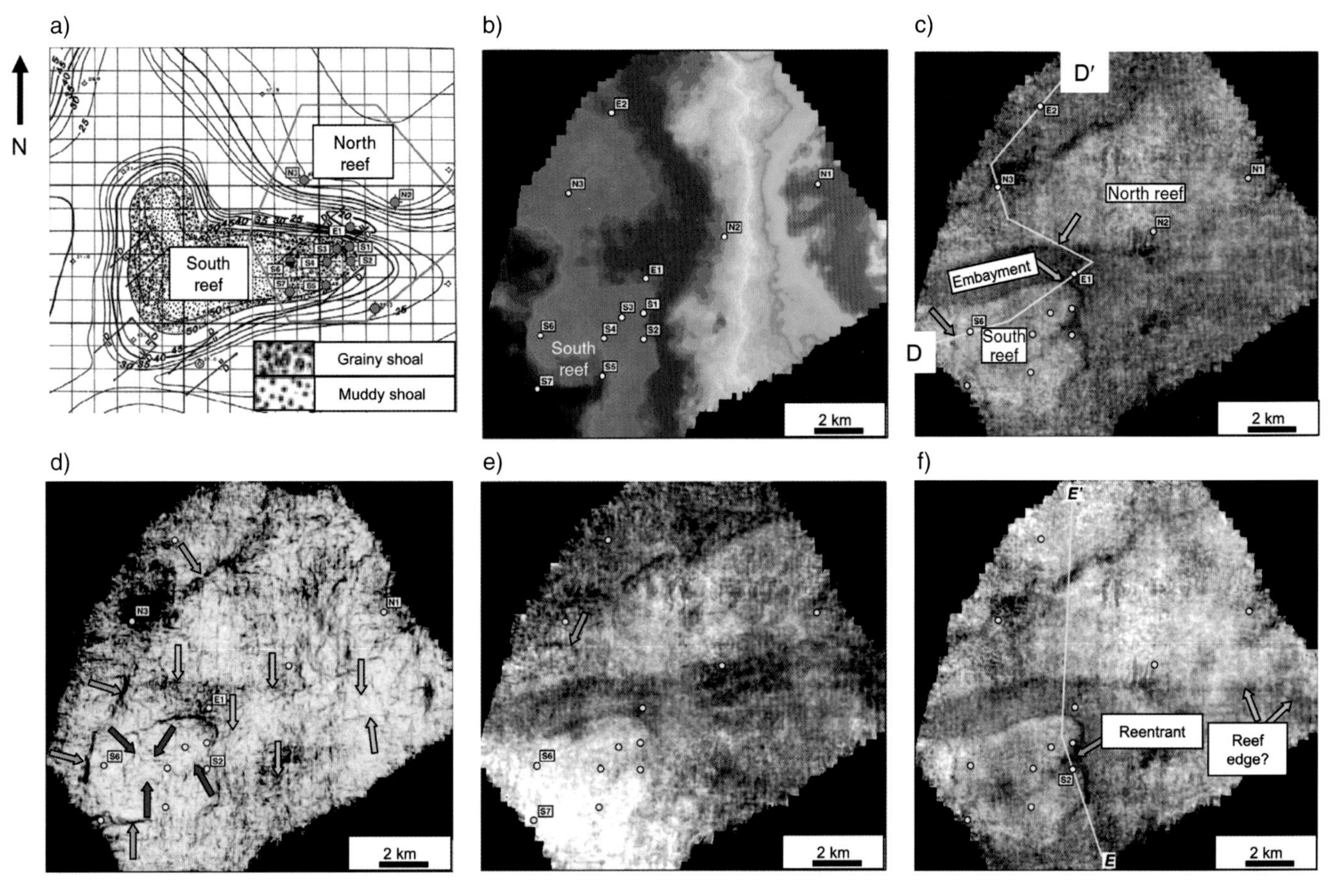

Figure 9. (a) A map of a producing gas field showing an approximate outline of isolated south reef and north reef margins. Isopach contours at 5-m intervals cover the top reservoir to datum. Mapped faults also are indicated. The area of the original 3D survey is outlined in orange. (b) A time-structure map of the target horizon. (c)-(f) Horizon slices along the top of the target formation through (c) a seismic-amplitude volume, (d) a coherence volume, (e) a 30-Hz component spectral-decomposition volume, and (f) a 60-Hz spectral-decomposition volume. After Skirius et al. (1999).

Coherence was run on the target formation and shows a segmented, approximate edge of the south reef, a vague indication of the southern edge of the north reef, and several probable faults that appear as dark, low-coherence lineaments (Figure 9d). Faint lineaments that outline an elliptical area in the central portion of the south reef (blue arrows, Figure 9d) are interpreted to be faults separating slightly upthrown and downthrown reefal blocks. These faults also separate a higher-amplitude area around well S6 from a lower-amplitude area in the central portion of the reef. The faulted blocks are expected to have influenced facies development during reef growth and/or subsequent porosity development.

Note that the faults just discussed separate the producing wells in the south reef from tight well S6. Subtle east-west to northeast-southwest indications of a possible reef edge or channels within the embayment are noted in the eastern part of the coherence image (green arrows, Figure 9d). A northeast-to-southwest low-coherence edge (orange arrows, Figure 9d) parallels the northwestern boundary of the survey and may indicate a northern reefal boundary. That boundary may have been influenced by an underlying basement fault that becomes more apparent as it crosses the embayment channel and extends into the south reef to the west of well S6.

Although the data were processed carefully, a subtle north-south, east-west acquisition footprint pattern is apparent in the coherence image (Figure 9d), as are a few areas of bad data around wells N3, E1, and to the east of wells N3, N1, and S2. Most of the coherence features, however, are at an angle to the direction of the acquisition footprint and therefore are distinguishable with more confidence.

A seismic profile across the south reef, embayment channel, and north reef (Figure 10a) shows the subtlety of the seismic expression of the reef (yellow horizon), the edge of which is identified by a small vertical jog to the left of the embayment (well E1). Flattening on a horizon within an overlying carbonate unit (dark blue) exaggerates the reef-edge profile (which is somewhat more apparent in the underlying formation; Figure 10b). The northern edge of the north reef in the vicinity of well N3 is less discernible in the coherence image and in the seismic profile, because the profile crosses near an area of bad data. The existence of the apparent north-south fault identified to the west of well S6 in the coherence image is confirmed by the offset at this location, which is visible in the seismic profile.

Spectral decomposition was run using 100-ms and 60-ms windows from the top of the target formation over the frequency range 1–80 Hz (Figure 9e and f). Individual frequency slices show different details, with brighter areas indicating higher amplitudes. The south reef's edge is poorly delineated at frequencies of 30 Hz (Figure 9e) and lower; however, an elliptical feature north of the embayment channel (see the orange arrow in Figure 9e) is only visible at frequencies near 30 Hz. The highest amplitudes on the 30-Hz slice are in the southern and western portions of the south reef and are coincident with tight, mainly muddy shoal or lagoonal facies penetrated by wells S6 and S7. A frequency slice at 60 Hz (Figure 9f) seems to show the most complete and clearly definable boundaries of the south reef and north reef. The dark, low-amplitude indentation in the south reef's edge just north of well S2 (and also apparent in most other frequency slices) may be a minor reentrant, perhaps influenced by the presence of an underlying fault.

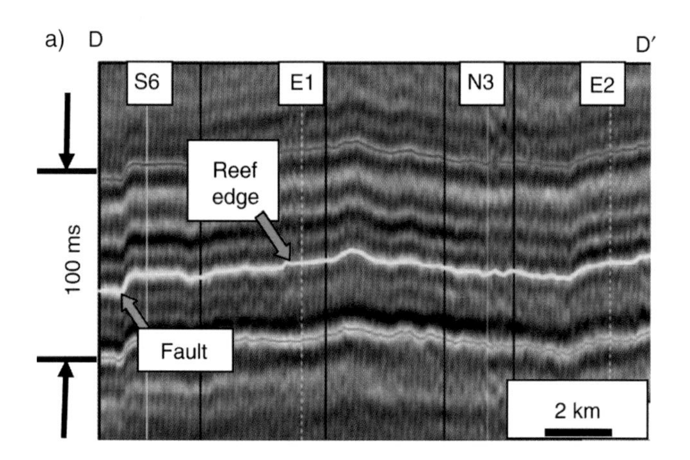

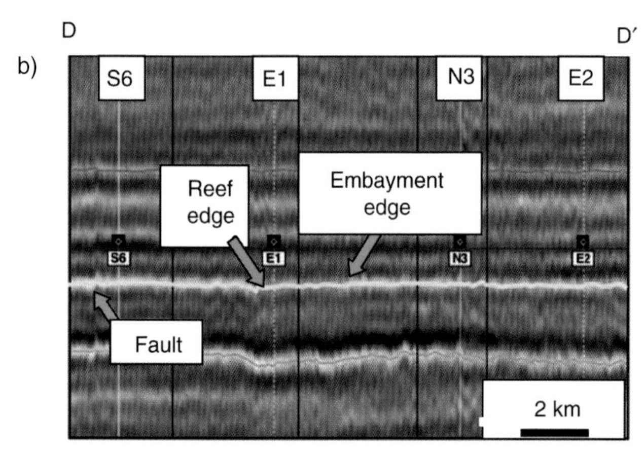

Figure 10. (a) A seismic profile over the south reef, embayment, and north reef from the previous figures. This profile shows an expression of the south reef's edge (green arrow) and a fault to west of well S6 (orange arrow). Light blue is an overlying carbonate unit; yellow is the reef (target formation); and green is an underlying carbonate unit. (b) Seismic profile flattened on horizon (dark blue marker) within the overlying carbonate unit. The red and green arrows correspond to the features highlighted in (a) and on the amplitude map in Figure 9c. After Skirius et al. (1999).

A flattened seismic profile that crosses this low-amplitude indentation feature supports the reentrant interpretation by a slight downwarp in the target formation and underlying unit reflections just to the right (north) of well S6 (Figure 10b). An underlying fault is not apparent from this profile. Higher-amplitude areas also are redistributed within the south reef, with a low-amplitude area in the center that is not penetrated by a well. Although the south reef's edge was known with some confidence from 2D seismic data and well control before the 3D seismic data were acquired, 3D-seismic-imaging techniques helped reinforce and refine the prior interpretation.

The edges of both the isolated south reef and the north reef can be imaged with greater confidence by using coherence and spectral decomposition than by using just an amplitude slice. This allows the areal extent of the reef to be mapped so that further infill-drilling locations can be considered. In areas with little well control, 3D coherence and spectral-decomposition images locate previously indistinguishable or poorly defined edges, especially for the undrilled north reef. In addition to helping interpreters better define reefal boundaries, the coherence image helps interpreters locate major and minor faults with more confidence. Fault locations are not always apparent in 2D seismic profiles but may have important implications relating to early reef establishment, reef growth, and later diagenetic influences.

Using curvature to map reefs

Because of limited vertical resolution and the accumulation of carbonate debris along the slope in front of a reef, carbonate reef edges often may appear to be gentle rather than abrupt. For this reason, they may not appear on images as distinct topographic highs (Figure 11a). Curvature maps generated using a seismic sampling grid may not sufficiently enhance the reef edges (Figure 11b). Hart (2003) showed that we can extract gentler, longer-wavelength features by first smoothing the horizon picks and then calculating curvature on a larger grid (Figure 11c).

Small-scale Michigan reefs

We conclude our discussion of reefs with images of small pinnacle reefs in the Michigan Basin, U.S.A. The known reefs indicated by green arrows in Figure 12c were found through conventional seismic interpretation. Note that the pattern is either that of Figure 3b or 3h. Figure 12d shows a vertical slice through the corresponding coherence volume. The A1 carbonate appears as a strong, coherent reflector.

In Figure 12a and b, we display horizon slices along the A1 carbonate horizon. The third (upper) green arrow indicates another productive reef. Two of the reefs are distinctively circular features that are smaller but have the same general shape as those we saw earlier for pinnacle reefs in Alberta, Canada. The third reef, to the northwest, has a more complex shape. Two of the reefs also have a local bowl shape, as indicated by negative (green) values of curvature amplitude. However, the third, most northwesterly reef has a positive curvature value, indicating that it is locally domal.

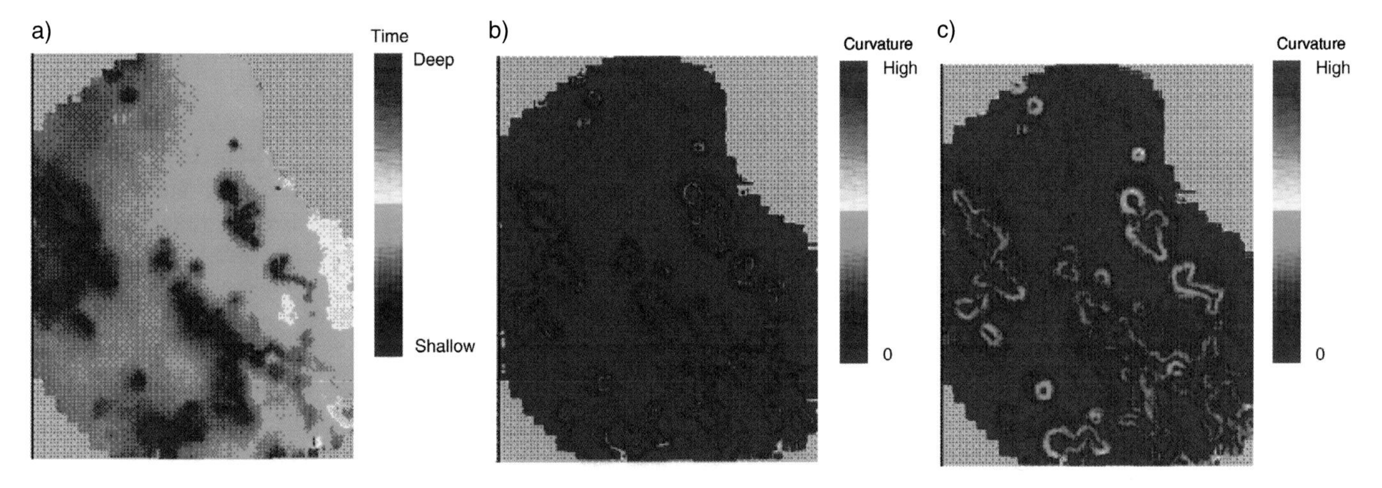

Figure 11. (a) A time-structure map. (b)-(c) Curvature maps for which dip magnitude was estimated using a (b) three-by-three-trace analysis window and a (c) seven-by-seven-trace analysis window over Devonian pinnacle buildups in the Williston Basin, U.S.A. Changing the aperture on the curvature calculations improves definition of the pinnacles. From Hart (2003).

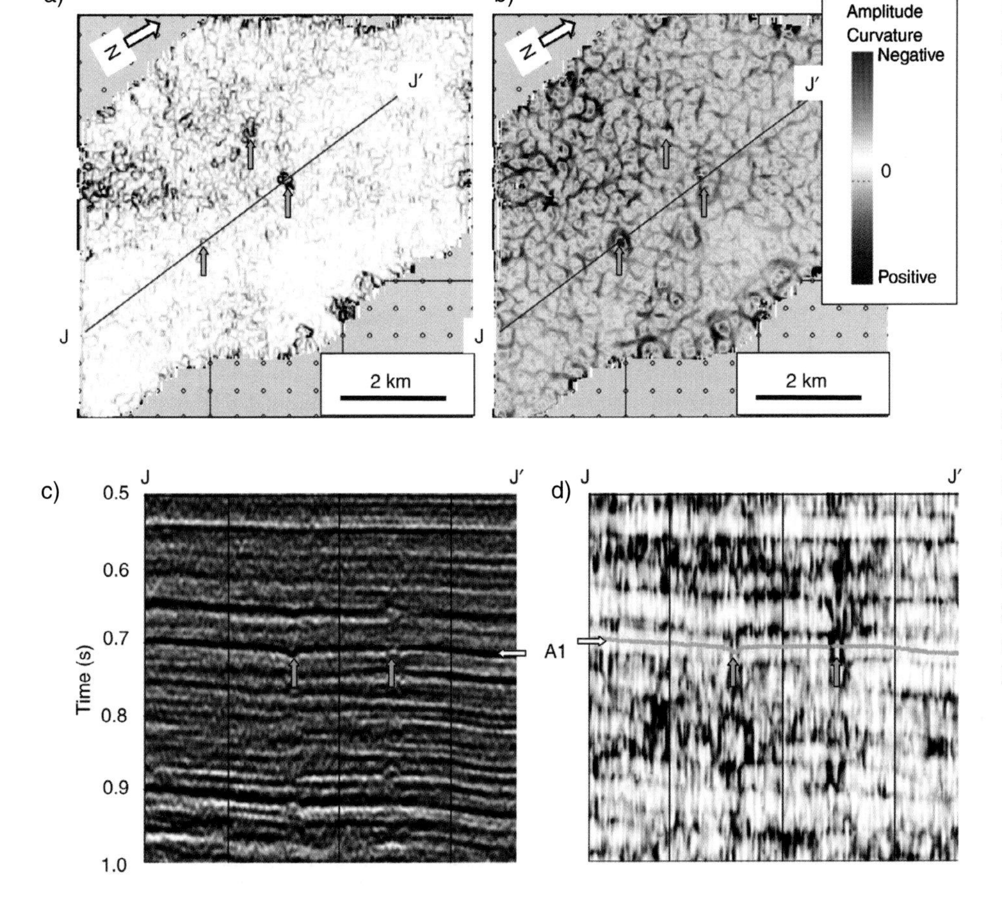

Figure 12. Attribute expressions of small Michigan reefs. Horizon slices through (a) a coherence volume and (b) a most-negative-curvature volume along the A1 carbonate horizon in the Michigan Basin, U.S.A. (b)-(c) Reefs expressed on vertical slices through (c) a seismic data volume and (d) a coherence volume. Green arrows indicate known reefs. The coherence slice provides a nice image of the extent of the known reefs and indicates several other candidate locations. The most-negative-curvature image (Figure 12b) is more ambiguous, with the reef to the south [toward the left in (c)] exhibiting a distinct bowl shape, whereas the reef farther north is somewhat flatter. Seismic data courtesy of Modroo Geophysical.

Platform Edges, Shoals, and Banks

In Figure 13, we display a coherence time slice and corresponding vertical seismic profiles through a platform edge, imaged from a survey acquired in Alberta, Canada. The platform edge is quite subtle on the vertical seismic slices but is obvious on the coherence slice. Mapping structural noses and reentrants often is key to high-grading areas that are likely to have porous carbonate shoals.

Figure 14a shows a horizon slice cutting through a seismic profile through a different 3D survey acquired in Alberta, Canada. The arrow indicates the edge of a reef seen to the right in Figure 14c. Figure 14b shows a coherence stratal volume intersecting a seismic profile different from the one in (a). A portion of a coherence horizon slice is shown in Figure 14c. As we see in these images, the reef's buildup is associated with high-amplitude coherent reflections and thus appears white on the coherence images.

In Figures 15 and 16, we show an example of shoaling along a platform edge from a survey acquired along the middle Permian shelf margin of the northern Midland Basin in west Texas, U.S.A. This example was released for publication originally in the paper by Skirius et al. (1999) but was omitted because the coherence and spectral-decomposition images, although of good quality, did not help the authors understand reservoir heterogeneity. We include the example here to illustrate that our understanding of textures seen in carbonate terrains is still in its infancy.

By 1999, this Midland Basin field had produced more than 800 MMBO from nine Permian Abo Formation wells. Generally, low production rates, poor waterflood communication, and variable decline rates suggest laterally discontinuous or compartmentalized reservoirs within the shelf-edge shoal complex. Variations in reservoir continuity, net porosity, and reservoir thickness in this field are related to changes in depositional facies. The Abo interval comprises progradational, upward-shoaling carbonates, with depositional facies arranged bathymetrically from a ramp-type to shelf depositional setting. Porous dolomite grainstone shoals grade updip into muddy dolomites, anhydrite, and shales.

Historically, the geophysical approach to exploring the Abo Formation has been to map amplitude values at the Abo level to try to distinguish different facies resulting from changes in lithology and/or porosity. This approach, as well as impedance inversion, generally was unsuccessful because amplitude values are similar for the shoaling facies (porous, clean dolomites) and for the lagoonal/tidal facies (shaly, microporous or anhydrite-plugged dolomites).

To better understand the lateral geometry of the porous shoal facies and the production variability within the Abo Formation in Sundown field, a 3D seismic survey over the area was acquired in 1995. The top and base of the Abo interval form discontinuous, poorly defined reflectors and therefore can be difficult to pick (Figure 15).

In Figure 16a, we display a horizon slice along the top of the Abo through a coherence volume; that image reveals features that may be related to shoal-body geometries and specific depositional environments. For example, the shelf margin is distinct as a linear edge running subparallel to the southern edge of the survey. To the south of the shelf edge is

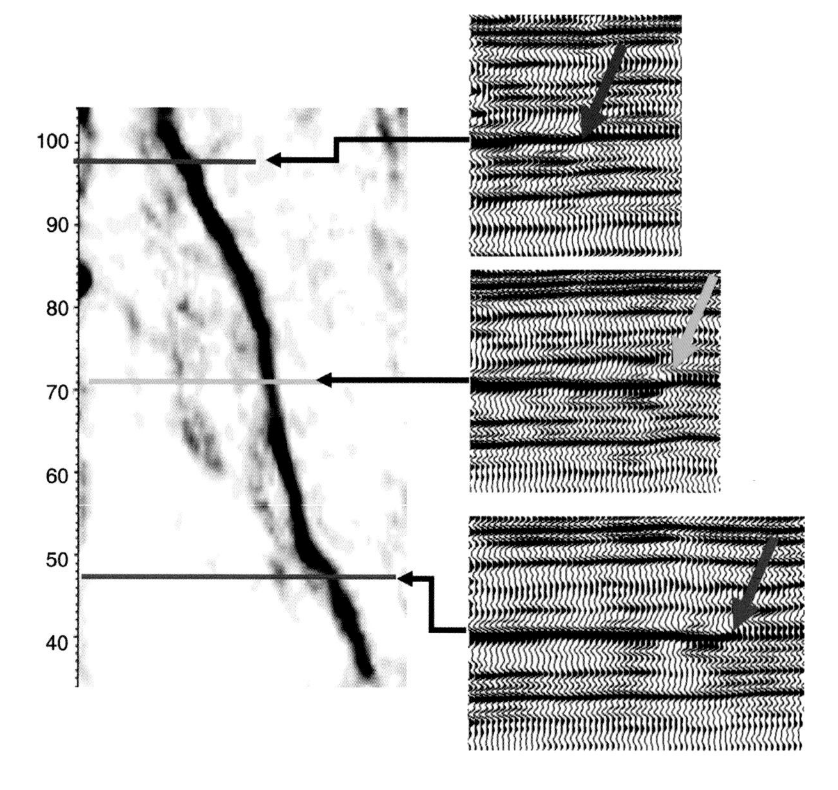

Figure 13. A platform edge seen on a coherence time slice at $t = 1.200$ s, and on three corresponding vertical seismic lines from a survey in Alberta, Canada. Note how the subtle changes in waveform on the vertical seismic slices are easily seen on the coherence slice.

a highly chaotic pattern, probably representing basinward-dipping foreslope deposits. The bright coherent zone to the north of and parallel to the shelf edge coincides with a large shoaling complex, which was defined by drilling. The best-producing Abo wells all appear to be located in a mottled area of generally low coherence (circled). However, this area also contains poor producers. Well B is in a mottled area and encountered lagoonal/tidal facies. The low-coherence linear feature in the northern part of the survey is probably a basement fault that runs parallel to a structural high immediately to the west of the fault.

Figure 16b is a spectral-decomposition slice at 40 Hz. The decomposition was run on the data in a 100-ms window that was ±50 ms around the picked top of the Abo horizon. Note that a low-spectral-component boundary cuts through the area and forms a northwest-southeast-trending lobate shape that is suggestive of a carbonate shoal. Good producing wells fall within this lobate feature and to the east of it, perhaps within adjacent or overlapping shoal bodies. The shelf edge that is visible in the coherence image appears as a linear low-amplitude feature in the spectral-decomposition image. Spectral decomposition also reveals the shelf edge in the northern part of the survey, but the coherence image does not.

Channels

The Devonian Thirtyone Formation has produced more than 750 MMBO from microporous chert reservoirs on the Central Basin Platform in west Texas, U.S.A. Chert is an unconventional reservoir rock that has been developed successfully in west Texas, Oklahoma, California, and Canada

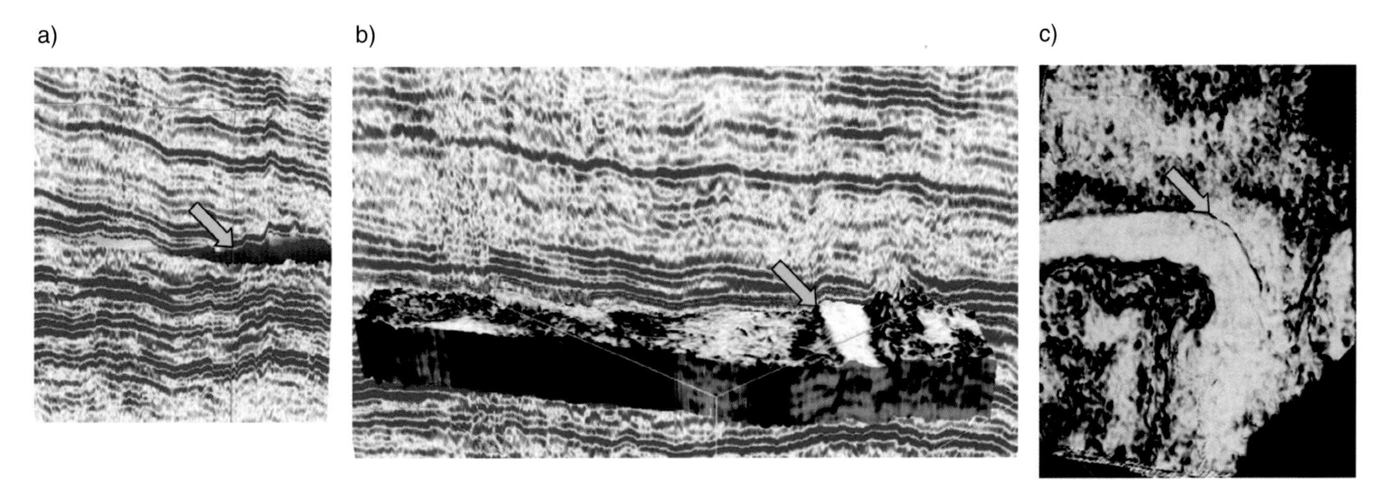

Figure 14. (a) A horizon slice cutting through a seismic profile from a 3D survey acquired in Alberta, Canada. The arrow indicates a reef edge. (b) A coherence stratal cube intersecting a seismic profile different from the one shown in (a); again, the arrow shows the reef's edge. (c) A portion of a coherence horizon slice with the arrow pointing to a reef edge. The reef buildup is associated with high-amplitude coherent reflections and so appears white on coherence images. Data are courtesy of Arcis Corporation, Calgary.

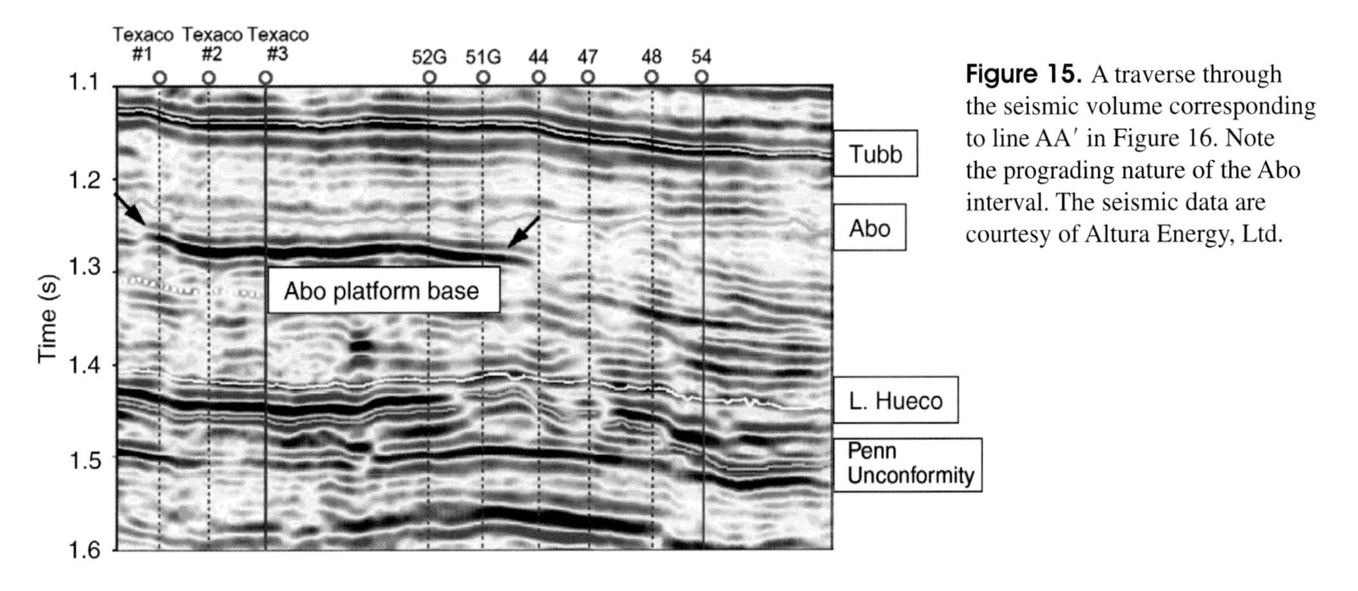

Figure 15. A traverse through the seismic volume corresponding to line AA′ in Figure 16. Note the prograding nature of the Abo interval. The seismic data are courtesy of Altura Energy, Ltd.

(Rogers and Longman, 2001). The Thirtyone Formation is a prolific reservoir rock that still plays an important role after more than one-half century of production.

Our study focused on the Devonian cherts on the south end of the Central Basin Platform, Crane County, Texas, U.S.A. The area's microporous chert originates from partial dissolution and alteration of redeposited beds of siliceous bioclastic carbonates, dominated by debris from sponges that outproduced the usually dominant carbonates during transgression or during times of temporary climate cooling.

These biogenic chert formations form two types of reservoirs in the Central Basin Platform: (1) relatively thick-bedded, continuous reservoir facies deposited proximally to platform/slope environments in the north and (2) thin, discontinuous, distal reservoir facies deposited as turbidites, along with interchannel laminated nonporous cherts, in a more basinal environment in the south (Ruppel and Barnaby, 2001). Many of the proximal reservoirs have undergone significant erosion and diagenesis and are represented by Dollarhide field, which we discuss in Chapter 15.

In this chapter, we show images from a survey acquired 100 km to the south of Dollarhide, in the distal part of the system, based on the work of Blumentritt et al. (2003). The model for the distal deposition consists of thin, sometimes stacked-channel and distributary-lobe deposits (Figure 17) that are below seismic resolution. Fu et al. (2006) have performed laboratory measurements demonstrating that seismic impedance can be used to differentiate between porous, reservoir-quality cherts, and nonreservoir cherts and tight bioclastic limestones.

Until recently, the primary means of mapping reservoir heterogeneity was through the drill bit. Delineation of channels and detection of lobes are beneficial to exploration and production, but their signatures generally are not visible on conventional amplitude-display seismic traces. Arrows in Figure 18a and b indicate Devonian channels that appear as local changes in thickness and/or amplitude after structure-oriented principal-component filtering. However, the channels are still difficult to track on horizon slices extracted parallel to the top of the Devonian A horizon (Figure 18c), even with structure-oriented filtering (Figure 18d).

In Figure 19, we display four horizon slices through the coherence volume that corresponds to the data in Figure 18. Although here we can recognize segments of channels, they appear to be quite discontinuous. Many of these channels have been cannibalized, resulting in short channel segments, and the coherence image is further complicated when channel thickness falls below seismic tuning thickness, thereby re-

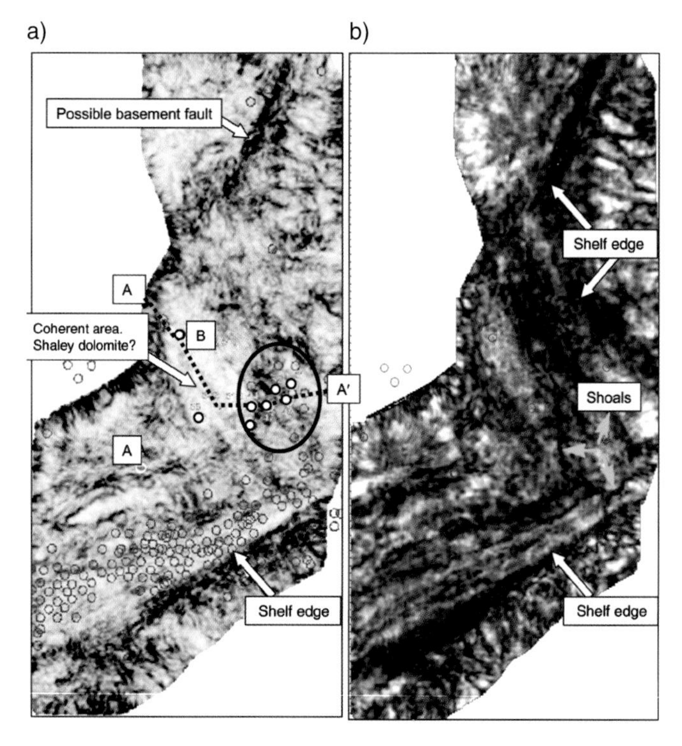

Figure 16. Horizon slices through (a) a coherence volume and (b) a 40-Hz spectral-decomposition volume along the Abo horizon from Figure 15. Production is localized landward of the shelf margin in shallow-water carbonate-sand shoals but is highly unpredictable. The seismic data are courtesy of Altura Energy Ltd.

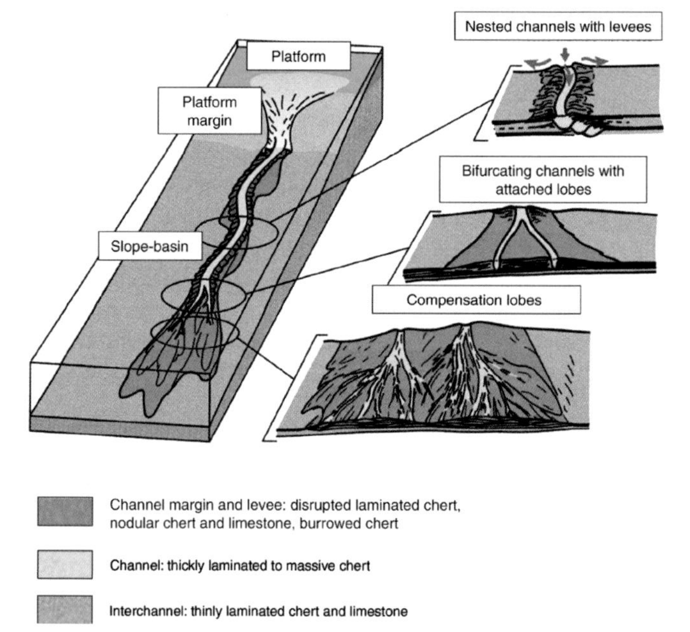

Figure 17. Depositional model for the Devonian Thirtyone Formation, Central Basin Platform, west Texas, U.S.A. Chert formed as sponge spicules originating on the platform to the north were carried downslope to the south as turbidite flows and formed channels, lobes, and fans of mixed chert and limestone. After Ruppel and Barnaby (2001). AAPG©2001. Reprinted by permission of the AAPG whose permission is required for further use.

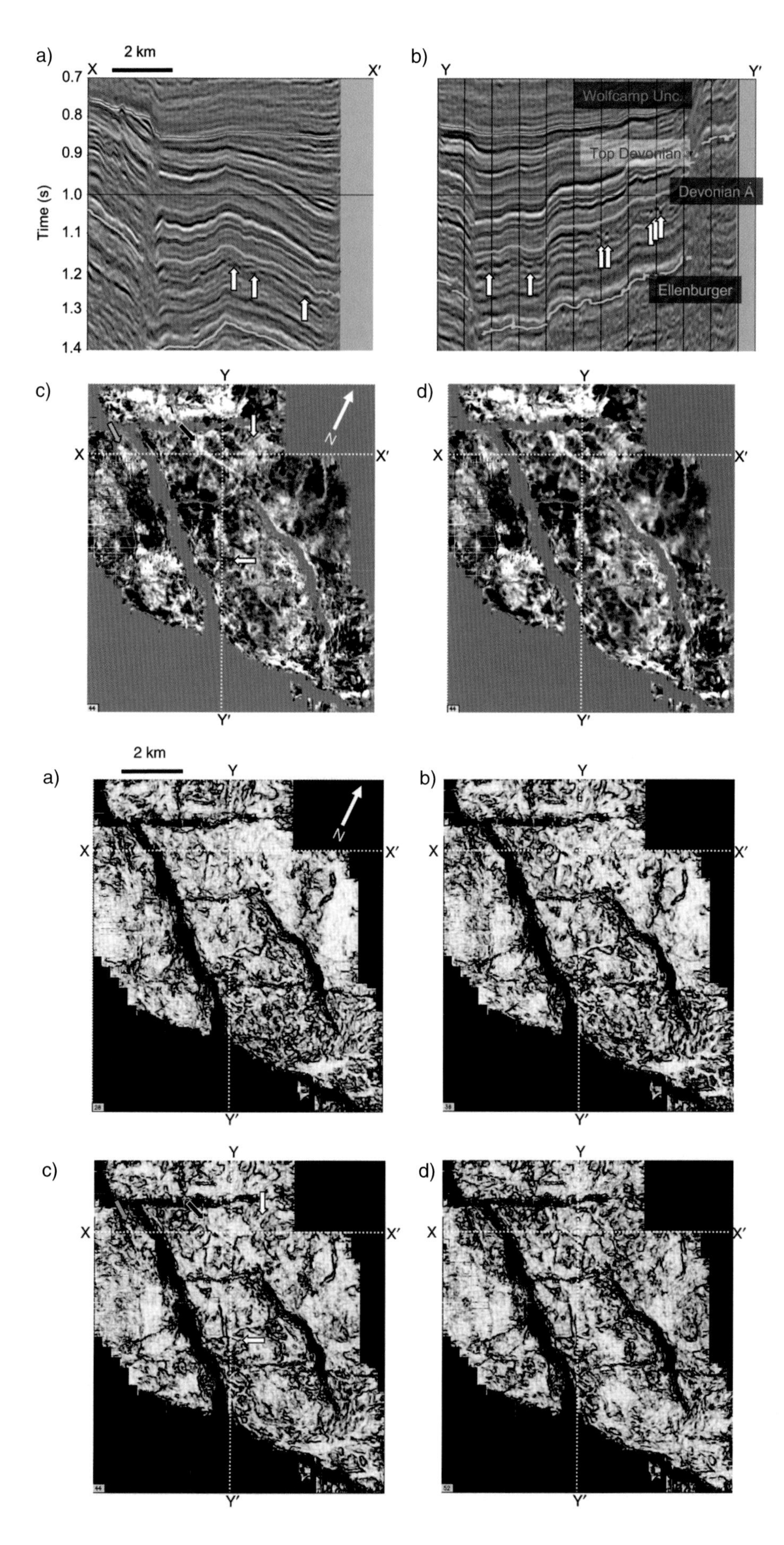

Figure 18. (a)-(b) Two representative lines, (a) XX′ and (b) YY′, from a survey acquired over the Central Basin Platform, Texas, U.S.A. Arrows indicate small channel features below the green Devonian A horizon. The data have undergone principal-component, structure-oriented filtering. (c)-(d) A horizon slice 44 ms below the green Devonian A horizon (c) without and (d) with structure-oriented filtering.

Figure 19. Horizon slices through the corresponding coherence volume at (a) 28 ms, (b) 36 ms, (c) 44 ms, and (d) 48 ms below the Devonian A horizon shown in Figure 18. In (c), the white arrow indicates channels, the black arrow points to a minor fault, and the gray arrow identifies a possible fault-controlled channel. After Blumentritt et al. (2003).

sulting in a laterally continuous waveform. The white arrow indicates channels, the black arrow (c) points to a minor fault, and gray arrow (c) indicates a possible fault-controlled channel.

For that reason, in Figures 20 and 21 we examine corresponding horizon slices through the inline (Figure 20) and crossline (Figure 21) components of the energy-weighted coherent-amplitude gradient. In Figures 20c and 21c, white arrows indicate channels, the black arrow points to a minor fault, and the gray arrow indicates a possible fault-controlled channel. The images on the energy-weighted coherent-amplitude-gradient components are consistent with, but more easily interpreted than, the coherence images in Figure 19. In Figures 20 and 21, note that here the channels can be traced into zones that are almost totally white (coherent) on the coherence images in Figure 19.

Blumentritt et al. (2003) observed that several of the channels (indicated by white arrows in Figure 21c appear to have a source to the southwest and bifurcate to the northeast. Other channels appear to be substantially longer and more consistent with the inferred northern source direction.

Paleotopography

Structural control of channels

We use the Pennsylvanian-age Caddo Limestone horizon mapped in a survey acquired in the Fort Worth Basin, Texas, U.S.A., to illustrate the basic concepts of both dip azimuth in Chapter 2 and curvature in Chapter 4. In Figure 22, we reexamine the channel feature in the northwestern part of that survey. This channel is both more consistent than and more curvilinear than the other two narrow features seen on this image — a strike-slip fault and a Riedel shear. Still, a clear correlation exists between the azimuth of this channel and the fabric of the long-wavelength undulations seen in this survey. For that reason, we examine three vertical seismic traverses perpendicular to the fault.

Not surprisingly, we note that the channel correlates laterally with deep, strong amplitude synclines. Moreover, other synclines at depth correlate with broad features at the Caddo level. Given well control data and our a priori knowledge that the adjacent Atoka Formation is most productive

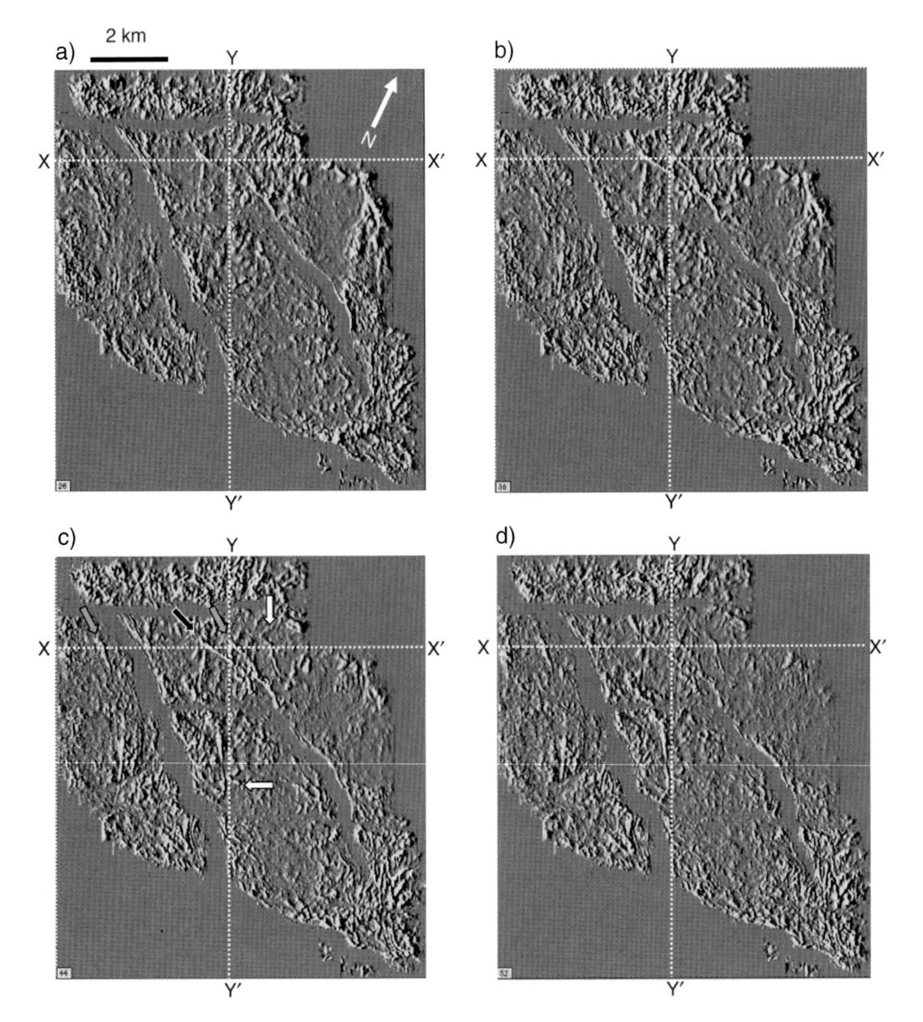

Figure 20. Horizon slices through the east-west component of the energy-weighted coherent-amplitude gradients at (a) 28 ms, (b) 36 ms, (c) 44 ms, and (d) 48 ms below the Devonian A horizon shown in Figure 18, and corresponding to the coherence slices shown in Figure 19. The positions of the arrows in (c) are identical to those shown in Figure 19c. After Blumentritt et al. (2003).

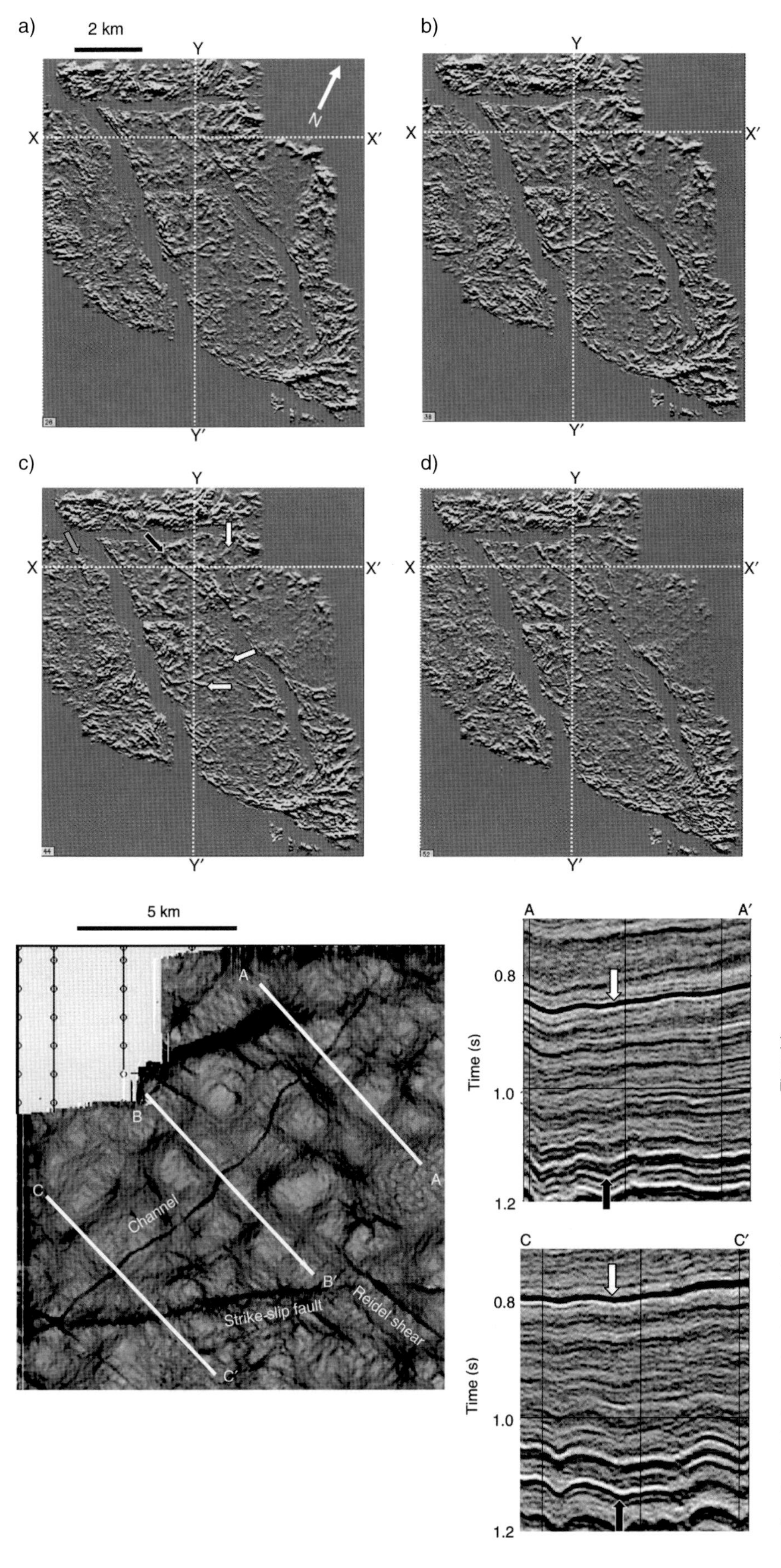

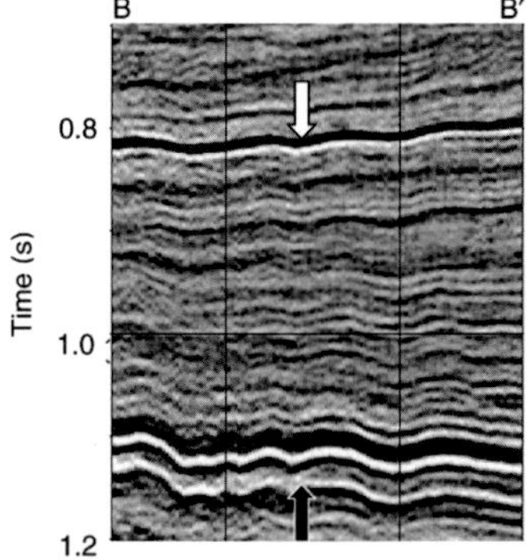

Figure 21. Horizon slices through the north-south component of the coherent energy gradient (a) 28 ms (b) 36 ms (c) 44 ms, and (d) 48 ms below the Devonian A horizon shown in Figure 18, and corresponding to the slices shown in Figures 19 and 20. Arrow locations in (c) are identical to those in Figure 19c. After Blumentritt et al. (2003).

Figure 22. A horizon slice along the Caddo horizon through a most-negative-curvature volume generated from a survey acquired over the Fort Worth Basin, Texas, U.S.A., and vertical slices through a conventional seismic volume along traverses AA′, BB′, and CC′. Note the narrow channel running from the northeast to the southwest. Vertical seismic slices show this channel to be structurally controlled from below. Seismic data are courtesy of Devon Energy.

in the lows where the reservoir sandstones are thicker locally, we interpret this channel to be controlled by deeper structure.

Incised valleys and scouring

Nissen et al. (2004; unpaginated) described the South Eubanks survey acquired over the Hugoton Embayment of the Anadarko Basin; the embayment lies within the Permian-producing giant Hugoton gas field. They described how "Chester reservoirs are best developed in fine-grained, well-sorted sandstones filling a narrow north-south trending incised paleovalley system (or scour)." Their 3D interpretation indicates a regional fault on the west side of the survey and a scour feature that runs the length of the survey (Figure 23a). Hugoton Energy Corporation drilled 14 successful wells in succession within this major erosional feature. Although many of the features that are visible on the 3D interpretation are small, the seismic data have allowed Hugoton Energy Corporation to identify targets and drill them with a high degree of success. The major scour feature is less than 300 m wide in most places. The 3D seismic data also indicate a series of karsted features that are visible in the Chester and other deeper horizons (see the coherence time slice in Figure 23b and the seismic profile in Figure 24). Sands that may be associated with the karst features have not been tested to date.

Karst

Lihua field, Pearl River Basin, China

One of the most stunning images of subaerial karst was presented by Story et al. (1999) in their analysis of the offshore Lihua field, Pearl River Basin, China. Miocene-age limestone developed on top of a deeper, older carbonate platform that had been exposed and deeply karsted prior to deposition of Miocene carbonates. Because the hydrocarbon objective is shallow and the water is relatively deep, the seismic data are of exceptionally high quality, containing frequencies as high as 200 kHz. Story et al. used coherence, impedance inversion, and AVO to define reservoir heterogeneity. In Figure 25a, we redisplay their coherence image along the top of the reservoir. We note several large karst features (black, with low coherence) to the southwest, indicated by white arrows. We also point to two large faults (yellow arrows). In Figure 25b, we redisplay Story et al.'s

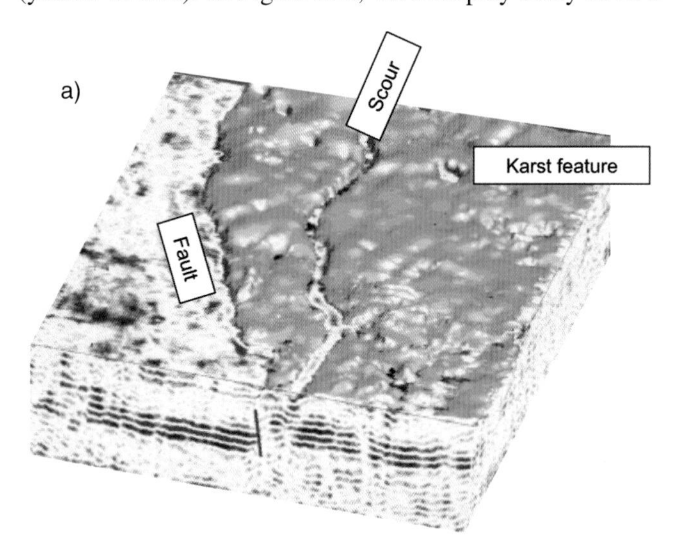

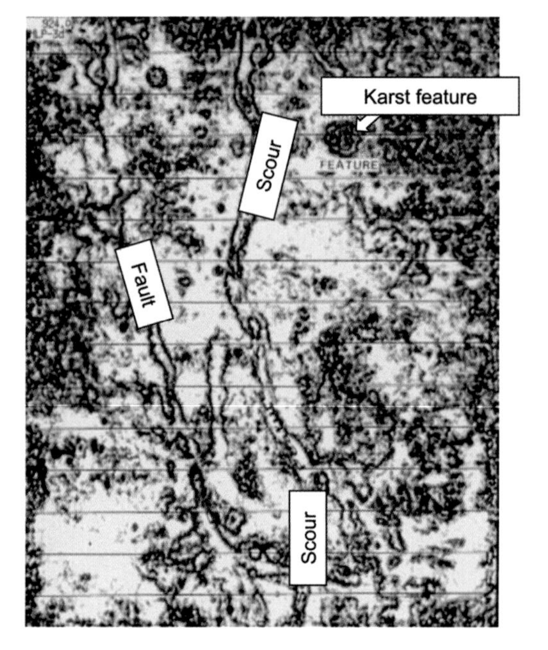

Figure 23. (a) A 3D seismic data volume from South Eubank field with the green Chester horizon surface superimposed, and (b) a corresponding coherence time slice at $t = 0.924$ s, showing a regional fault, the erosional Chester scour feature, and a karst sinkhole feature. After Nissen et al. (2004). The study area is located in the Hugoton Embayment of the Anadarko Basin and lies within the boundaries of the Permian producing Hugoton gas field. The Eubank field is on the north end of the study area and the Victory field is on the southeast end of the area. Data and figure are courtesy of Kirk Rundle, consulting geophysicist.

3D visualization of the mapped horizon, using the same arrows to indicate key features of interest.

In Figure 26, we reproduce Story et al.'s (1999) comparison of the size of one of their karst collapse features (Figure 26a) to the famed Great Blue Hole, offshore Belize (Figure 26b), which is one of the premier dive sites in the world. Karsting and subsequent cavern collapse form fractures and zones of weakness in overlying strata.

Story et al. (1999) illustrated that phenomenon by displaying vertical slices through a cube of instantaneous envelope (also called reflector strength) (Figure 27a and b). The karsted area in these images corresponds to that indicated by the gray arrow in Figure 25. Gas from the reservoir finds its way to the karsted area and from there upward toward the surface. Although we expect some differential compaction to result from cave collapse, the major contribution to the bowl-shaped feature above the karst in these images is velocity pull-down from gas in the overlying sediments. Indeed, the velocities are so poorly mapped that the data do not image in the lower part of what is commonly called a gas chimney, appearing here as a low-amplitude blue zone. We will discuss gas chimneys again in Chapter 14. Gas also appears to travel along the faults, as evidenced by the high-amplitude reflections indicated by the white arrows in Figure 27b.

Central Basin Platform, west Texas, U.S.A.

Figure 28a displays a vertical seismic section through a survey acquired over the Central Basin Platform, west Texas, U.S.A. We see two karst features in the Permian San Andres Limestone, which we highlight with white circles. In outcrop, at least three stratigraphic levels of karsting appear that are associated with sea-level drops during San Andres deposition (Kerans, 1994). In this seismic section, the karsting is pronounced both within the upper San Andres and below the Guadalupian 4 marker (red pick: regional Brushy Canyon sediment bypass unconformity). The larger karst feature to the east appears to be connected to the deeper faulting. In Figure 28b, we redisplay Kerans et al.'s (1994) schematic outcrop-based cross section.

In Figure 29, we display horizon slices at the approximate top of the San Andres Limestone, estimated by passing a phantom horizon 72 ms below the overlying, easier-to-pick Grayburg Formation. We used a phantom horizon because karsted horizons often are very challenging to pick and generate cycle skips and spurious artifacts in the resulting maps. In contrast, time or phantom-horizon slices through geometric-attribute volumes, such as coherence and curvature, provide an unbiased, artifact-free view of the karst features if the horizons are congruent (see Pennington, 2001). Although we are quite pleased with the results of structure-oriented filtering in clarifying faults and channels, such filtering can result in loss of critical details on intrinsically chaotic features (such as karst features in this chapter, slumps in Chapter 14, and hydrothermally altered dolomites in Chapter 15). We note that the incoherent zone indicated by arrows in Figure 29b (a horizon slice through a coherence volume without structure-

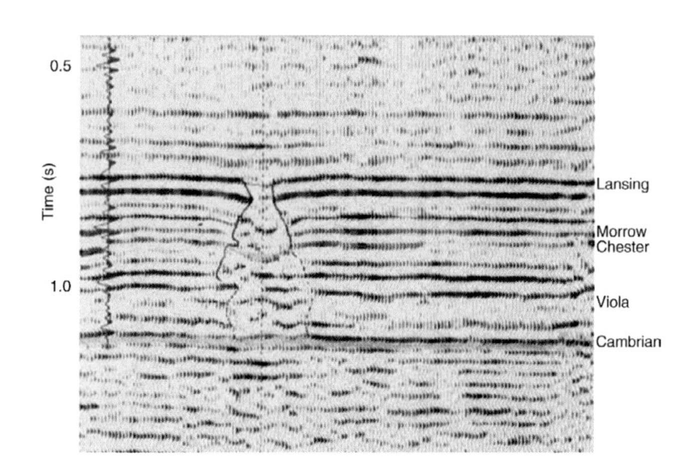

Figure 24. A seismic profile through the well-developed karst sinkhole feature located in the South Eubank field and identified by the 3D seismic survey shown in Figure 23. After Nissen et al. (2004). Data and figure are courtesy of Kirk Rundle, consulting geophysicist.

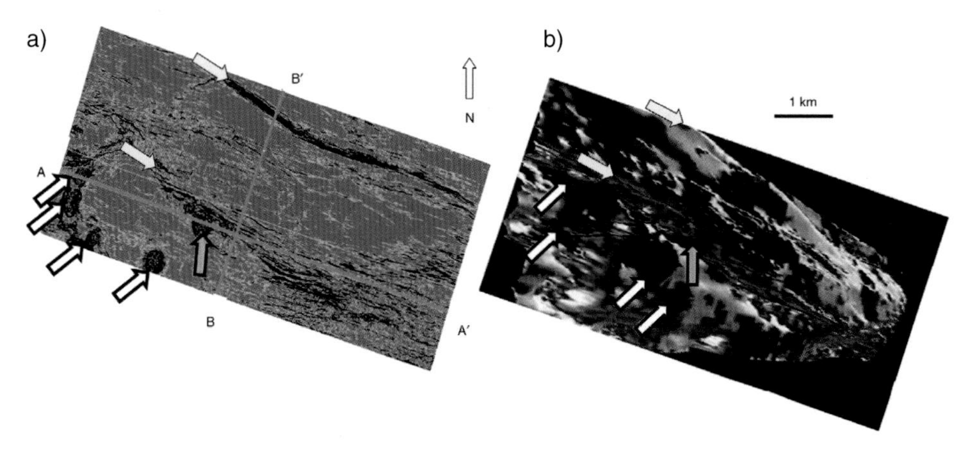

Figure 25. (a) Coherence horizon slice along the top of the Lihua field reservoir, Pearl River Basin, offshore China. The black circles indicated by the white and gray arrows correspond to karst features. Yellow arrows indicate faults. (b) A 3D illuminated surface showing karst geomorphology and faults. After Story et al. (1999).

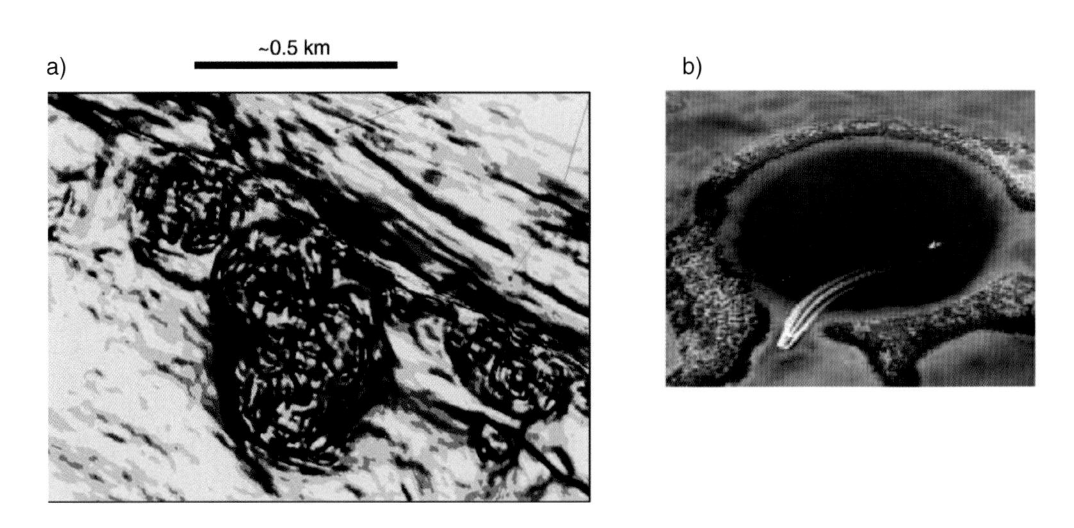

Figure 26. A modern-day analog of (a) a paleosinkhole in the Lihua field, offshore China, is seen in (b) the 400-m-diameter, 145-m-deep Great Blue Hole, Belize. Note the speedboat for scale. After Story et al. (1999) and http://www.bluedive.com.

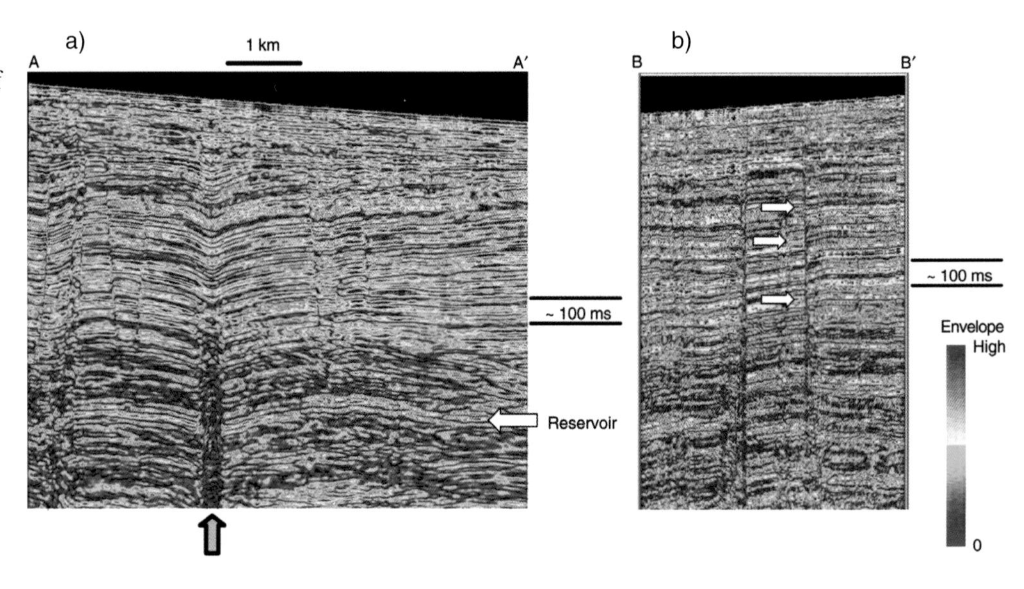

Figure 27. A vertical cross section through the envelope of the seismic data corresponding to lines (a) AA′ and (b) BB′ shown in Figure 25. The white arrow indicates the approximate reservoir level. The gray arrow indicates a gas chimney emanating from the sinkhole indicated by the gray arrow in Figure 25. Yellow arrows indicate faults. Note the gas sag resulting from slower velocities and decreased amplitude, probably caused by an incorrect stacking velocity. After Story et al. (1999).

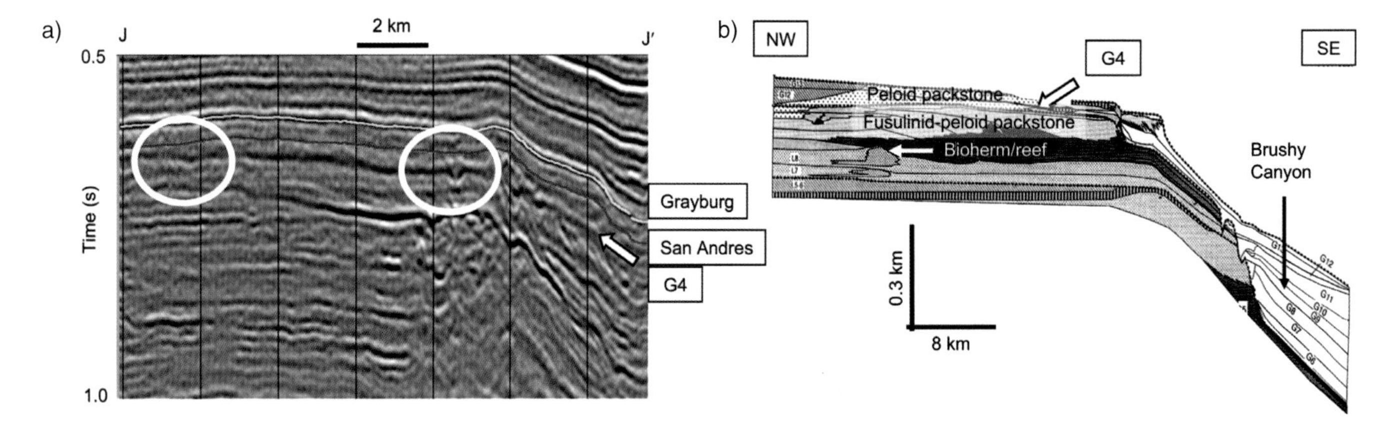

Figure 28. (a) Seismic data through a survey acquired over the Central Basin Platform, west Texas, U.S.A., and (b) Kerans et al.'s (1994) sequence stratigraphy for the same data volume, based on an outcrop study of the San Andres Limestone carbonates. The label G4 indicates the top of the Guadalupian 4 sequence, which is the regional bypass surface for the basinal lowstand deposits. The circles in (a) indicate karst features associated with subaerial exposure. Figure (a) is courtesy of Charlotte Sullivan, University of Houston. Data are courtesy of Burlington Resources. (b) AAPG©1994. Reprinted by permission of the AAPG whose permission is required for further use.

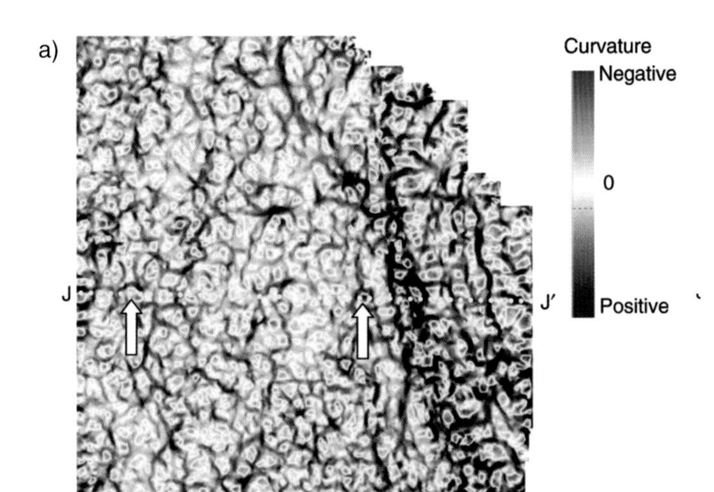

Figure 29. Horizon slices through (a) the most -positive-curvature volume, (b) a coherence volume without structure-oriented filtering, and (c) a coherence volume with structure-oriented filtering, along the base of the San Andres Limestone reservoir, which coincides with the Guadalupian 4 unconformity (approximately 72 ms below the top of the Grayburg, shown in Figure 28a). Arrows indicate the two karst features/sags shown in Figure 28a. The karst shows up as muddy areas on the coherence volume generated without structure-oriented filtering. The muddy areas do not show up well on the filtered version. The collapse features appear as green bowls in the most-positive-curvature volume.

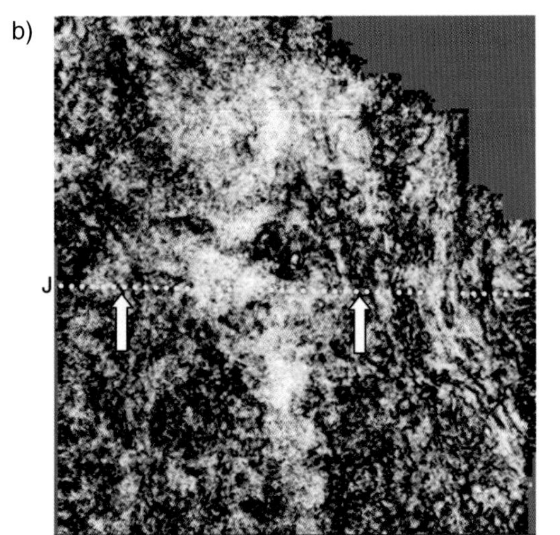

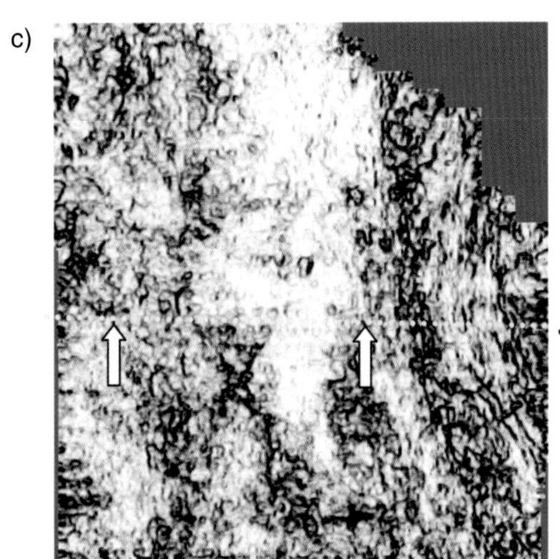

oriented filtering) has been cleaned up in Figure 29c (the corresponding coherence slice with filtering). Here, structure-oriented filtering removed the desired karst indicator. In Figure 29a (a horizon slice through a most-positive-curvature volume of the same data as in Figure 29b and c), the bowl appearance of these karst features shows up clearly as a (negative) green zone.

Because of the smudgy nature of karst on seismic-coherence data, calibration with wells is critical. In Figure 30a, we display an updip electrofacies log showing an abundance of anhydrite at the cycle tops. Figure 30b shows core sections from an updip well containing tidal-flat depositional facies with collapse breccias and vugs filled with anhydrite. Wherever open, natural fractures cut across the core, the anhydrite has been leached out and oil stain is present. Given our core control of the depositional/diagenetic environment, associating the two local collapse features with karst is quite reasonable.

Blumentritt et al. (2004) used core data along with production data to try to link oil and water production to attribute measures that in turn might be sensitive to karst or fractures. They examined coherence and curvature in horizon extracts and time slices. Figure 31 shows several wells that define two areas of high production (the highest single-well production was 18,000,000 bbl of fluid) surrounded by an area of poorer production. Anomalously high areas of various curvature measures are represented as plus signs and tend to occur along linear trends. These trends relate to joints or fractures, local brecciation, and collapse features. In the central area, the trend of pronounced curvature and broken reflectors diminishes significantly, which suggests that the bowl-shaped features (karst?) are less prevalent in that area.

Figure 32 illustrates a working hypothesis to explain the production data in Figure 31. In this model, subaerially karsted shallow-water carbonate facies have been completely plugged with anhydrite cement, and production is controlled by late-stage anhydrite dissolution, brecciation, and fractures. Some fractured and collapsed areas reach down to the oil-water contact and thus produce copious amounts of water.

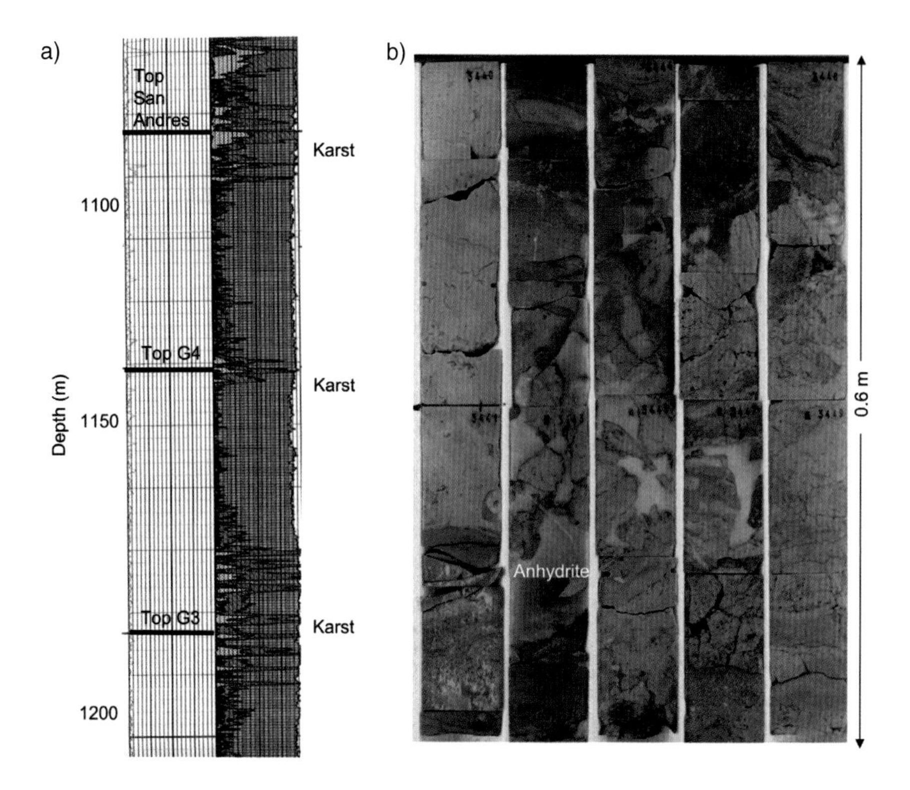

Figure 30. (a) Electrofacies through the San Andres Limestone, acquired from a well 20 km updip from the image shown in Figure 29. Karst features are associated with abundance of anhydrite (magenta) at sequence boundaries (G3, G4), and at the top of the San Andres Limestone. (b) Anhydrite-filled karst breccia in core sections from upper San Andres strata. After Sullivan et al. (2005).

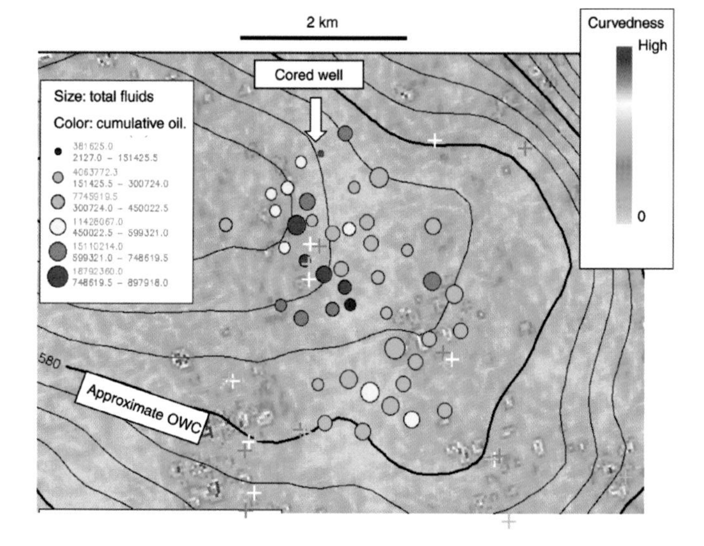

Figure 31. Correlation of oil and water production with curvature. Large red circles denote high oil production; large blue circles indicate high water production. Background map is curvedness, described in Chapter 4. White, orange, and violet crosses indicate anomalous values picked on curvedness, maximum curvature, and Gaussian curvature, respectively. After Blumentritt et al. (2004).

However, in other areas, fractures extend only into the reservoir, and the fractures leading down to the water table remain sealed by anhydrite.

Karst and collapse features in the Fort Worth Basin, Texas, U.S.A.

In Figure 33, we display time slices at $t = 1.200$ s at the Ellenburger Group level through coherence volumes derived from seismic data before (Figure 33a) and after (Figure 33b) structure-oriented filtering. As in the example from the Central Basin Platform, the effect here of such filtering may hinder identification of subtle karst features. We also note that many of these features are aligned (white arrows), implying that they are tectonically controlled.

To better understand the structural deformation in this survey, Figure 34 displays a suite of time slices through the combined dip-azimuth/coherence volume, using the technique described in Chapter 9. These images correspond exactly to coherence and curvature images contained in the case study on collapse features, which we include as Chapter 18. Note the northward dip (blue) on the fault that crosses center view. Note also that collapse features line up with bands of constant dip azimuth.

The filtered coherence shown in Figure 33b was one of three inputs used to generate Figure 34e, the time slice at t

= 1.200 s. Note in Figure 34e how the karst features line up with bands of constant dip azimuth. On each time slice, we note three and sometimes four strong color bands that interfere with each other. The width of these bands, or flexures, is rather wide, on the order of 0.5–2.0 km. The long-wavelength undulations of these flexures are amenable to generating long-wavelength estimates of curvature.

By animating through coherence, we can determine that many of these karst features are vertically localized, confined to either the Ellenburger or Marble Falls units. However, many other karstlike features are more accurately defined as collapse features associated with deeper tectonic pull-apart blocks in the basement. For this example, such relations are unraveled in Chapter 18.

In Chapter 15, we describe two other studies that address diagenesis of carbonate rocks. We discuss karsting and sealing versus conductive faults in limestones in Kansas, U.S.A., and also localized, hydrothermally altered do-

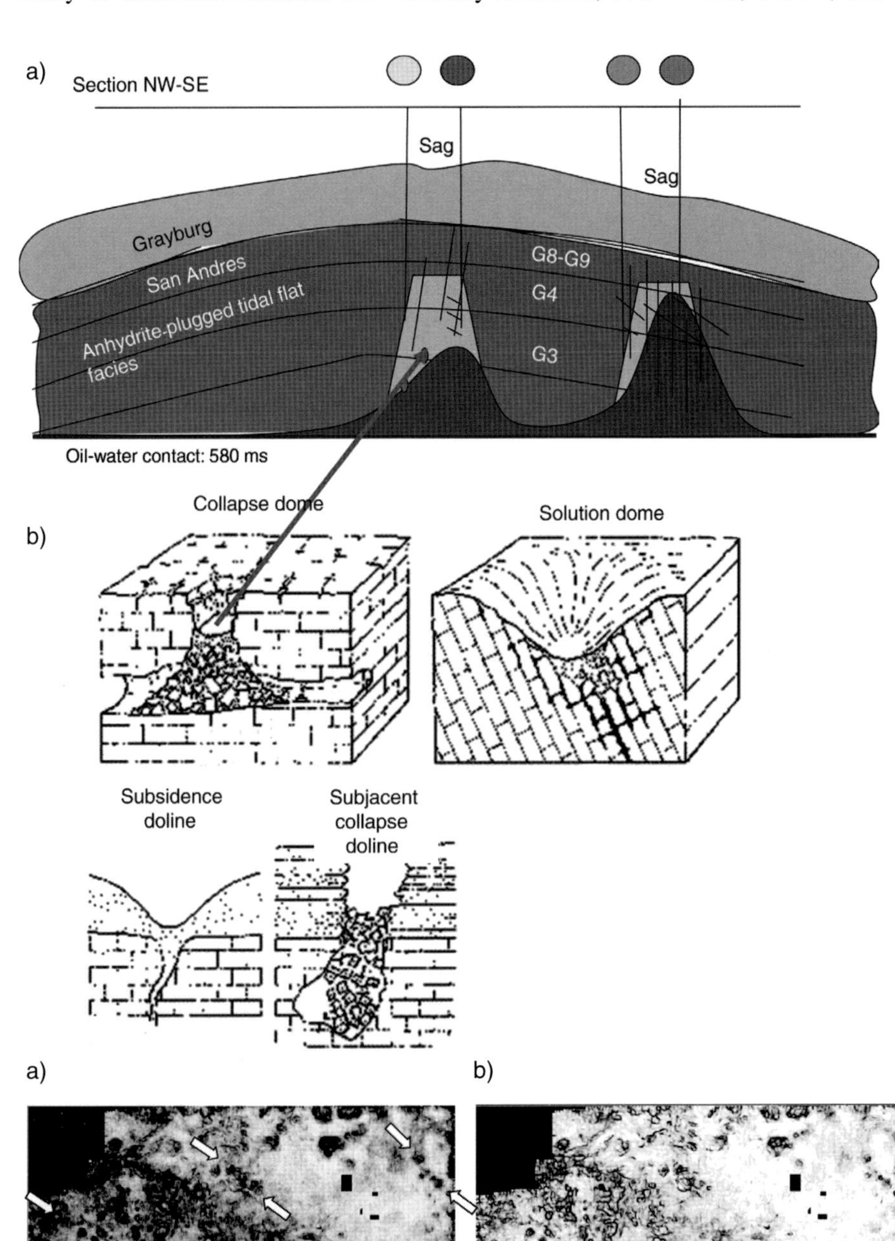

Figure 32. (a) Interpretation of the Grayburg Formation and the San Andres Limestone reservoir, as derived from seismic, attributes, well logs, and production data described in Figure 31 using (b) models of karst collapse features. Production is controlled by late-stage fractures and dissolution of anhydrite fill in karst breccias. The colors representing production correspond to those shown in Figure 31. Figure is courtesy of Charlotte Sullivan, University of Houston. Collapse feature diagrams are after Cansler and Carr (2001).

a) b)

Figure 33. Time slice at t = 1.200 s through seismic coherence volumes computed from a survey in the Fort Worth Basin, Texas, U.S.A. (a) before, and (b) after structure-oriented filtering. Although structure-oriented filtering produces images that generally are significantly sharper, some features of geologic interest, such as the aligned karst features indicated by arrows in (a), have an intrinsic, fuzzy character, and thus are attenuated in (b). Seismic data are courtesy of Devon Energy.

lomites in the Trenton Limestone in the Appalachian Basin, Ohio, U.S.A.

Slumps

Tor field, Norway (chalk)

Mineralogically, chalk is a carbonate. Typically, it forms in deep-sea environments. Skirius et al. (1999) reported that mobilization and redeposition of pelagic sediment prior to lithification have been recognized for many chalk sequences, including those described from Denmark, Sweden, and the North Sea. Redeposited (allochthonous) chalk also commonly shows substantially better reservoir qualities than does adjacent autochthonous chalk. Depending on proximity to the source area for sediment, and on travel distance and gradient, redeposition of chalk can result in slides and slumps, debris flows, mudflows, grainflows, and turbidites.

The degree of lithification and the mode of failure determine whether a chalk's mobilization results in grain transport, soft sediment deformation, or brittle deformation. Figure 35 is a coherence time slice through Tor field, in North Sea blocks 2/4 and 2/5. The yellow color indicates a horizon near the top of the chalk. A large fracture pattern is visible in the upper right of the display and is associated with massive slumping of the Tor and Ekofisk chalks in this area. The slump feature is approximately 8 to 10 km wide.

Skirius et al. (1999) stated that interpretation of paleontological data from well 2/05-07 (just to the west of the slump feature) and from other nearby wells indicates that the slump body is a series of reworked chalk slumps that were emplaced successively. Large-scale fracturing is interpreted from the coherence slice and suggests that the chalk was partially lithified or at least partially cohesive prior to mobilization, so that slumping movement caused brittle deformation and the observed en echelon fracturing.

The fracture pattern also suggests that the direction of movement, or the gradient, was downslope to the southwest. Because of the enhanced permeability and reservoir capacity provided by fractures in low-matrix-permeability chalks, detection of massively fractured chalks on a seismic scale could have important exploration potential. Fractured chalks become important targets because of their potential for enhanced production and also for providing routes for

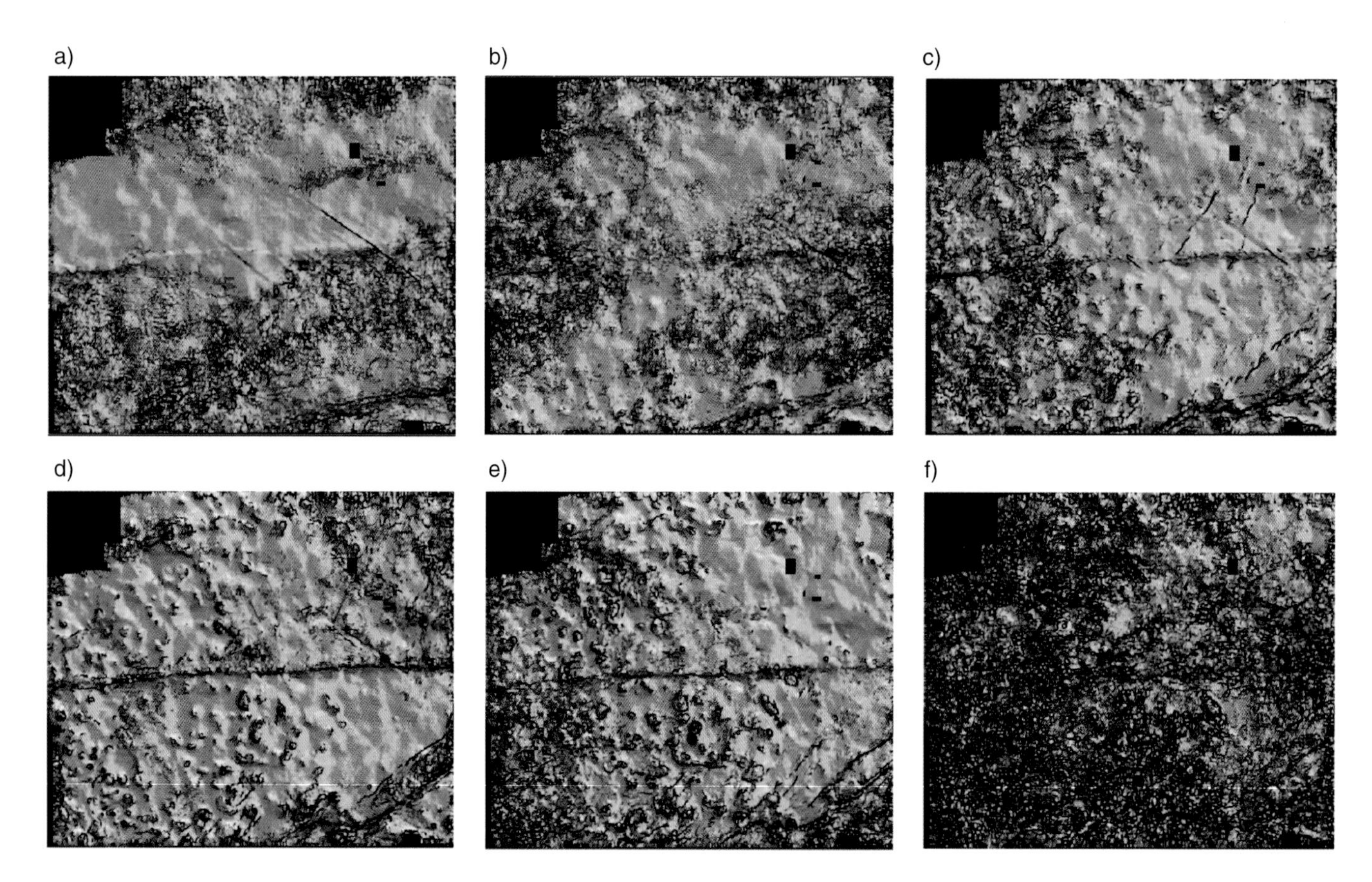

Figure 34. Time slices at t = (a) 0.800 s, (b) 0.900 s, (c) 1.000 s, (d) 1.100 s, (e) 1.200 s and (f) 1.300 s through the combined dip-azimuth/coherence volume (described in Chapter 9) for the survey shown in the previous figure. Note the northward dip (blue) on the fault that crosses center view. Note also that collapse features line up with bands of constant dip azimuth. Compare these images to those shown in Figures 13 and 14 of most negative and most positive curvature shown in Chapter 18.

hydrocarbon migration. Once chalk has lithified, it may undergo brittle rather than ductile deformation. In Chapter 15, we present an example of fracture identification from the Cretaceous Austin Chalk of central Texas, U.S.A. We present examples of slumping of siliciclastics (mass-transport complexes) in Chapter 14.

Vacuum field, New Mexico, U.S.A.

Vacuum field is located on the margin of a large carbonate platform at the northern end of the Delaware Basin, New Mexico, U.S.A. We used images from Vacuum field to illustrate the behavior of each of the attributes discussed in Chapters 2 through 5. In Chapter 12, we investigated the Brushy Canyon sandstones, which are windblown sands and silts that were dumped over the edge of the carbonate platform during sea-level lowstands. Here, we investigate the platform itself.

In Figure 36, we see a time slice through coherence data at $t = 1.064$ s. Note the slumps of the Brushy Canyon Formation in the southern part of the image. However, note also several crown faults along the edge of the carbonate platform (arrows). Lithified blocks of the carbonate platform likely form part of the debris slope to the south.

Figure 37a-c shows a sequence of time slices centered about the blue-picked Glorieta Sandstone horizon and cutting through a coherence volume. Again, we note the younger Brushy Canyon Formation in the southern part of the image. However, we also note a large, incoherent area in the center of each coherence time slice (arrows) that is well within the carbonate platform. Examining corresponding time slices through the energy-weighted coherent-amplitude gradient (Figure 37d-f), we note that this same area, although incoherent, also has relatively high amplitude. The north-south acquisition footprint contaminates the energy-weighted coherent–amplitude-gradient image. Although we do see some distinct channels cutting down across the platform (arrows), the likelier explanation for the incoherence and high amplitude is intense fracturing.

In Figure 38, we display the three vertical seismic lines indicated on the images in Figure 37. White arrows indicate possible karst. Black arrows indicate crown faults. The block to the right of the fault on line PP' (Figure 37b) had begun its descent into the basin before it was arrested. The blue pick is the Permian Glorieta Sandstone.

In Figure 39, we display a horizon slice 20 ms below the Glorieta Sandstone. This horizon does not continue out into the basin, beyond the platform margin, so it generates a somewhat smaller image. The white arrow indicates the same highly incoherent zone seen earlier in Figure 37. The black arrow indicates a crown fault. Gray arrows indicate a broad channel system that has cut across the platform in the western part of the survey.

Faults and Fractures

Because they are brittle, carbonates often fracture more easily than siliciclastics do. For that reason, mapping dip magnitude has been a very successful means of mapping fractures and fracture-enhanced porosity. We have already addressed the use of geometric attributes in mapping structural features in Chapter 11, and we address the more difficult task of mapping fractures in Chapter 15. Here, we simply present two examples — one dramatic, the second less so — showing where additional research needs to be done.

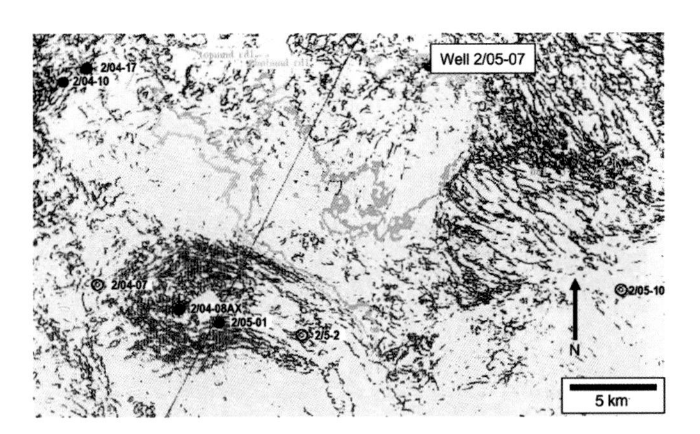

Figure 35. A time slice at $t = 3.356$ s, through Tor field, offshore Norway. Low-coherence (black) features correspond to massive chalk slumping that occurred soon after deposition, while the chalk was still plastic. These fractures were then locked into the formation after it lithified. After Skirius et al. (1999).

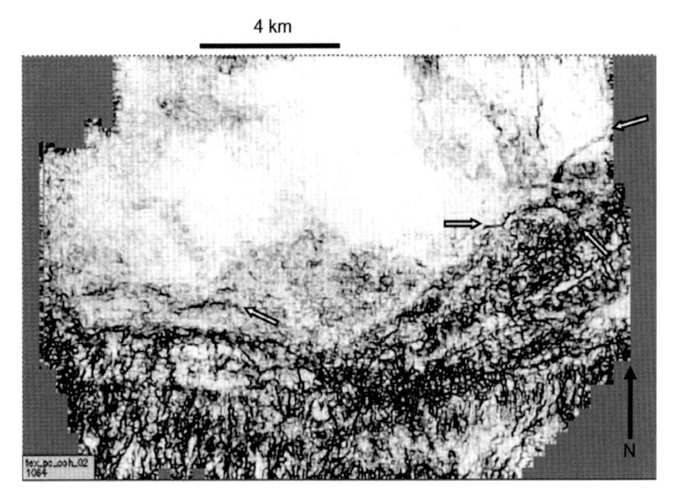

Figure 36. A time slice at $t = 1.064$ s through a survey in the Delaware Basin, New Mexico, U.S.A. Arrows indicate crown faults along the edge of the Permian carbonate platform. The time slice cuts through successively younger slumps to the south. Seismic data are courtesy of Marathon Oil Co.

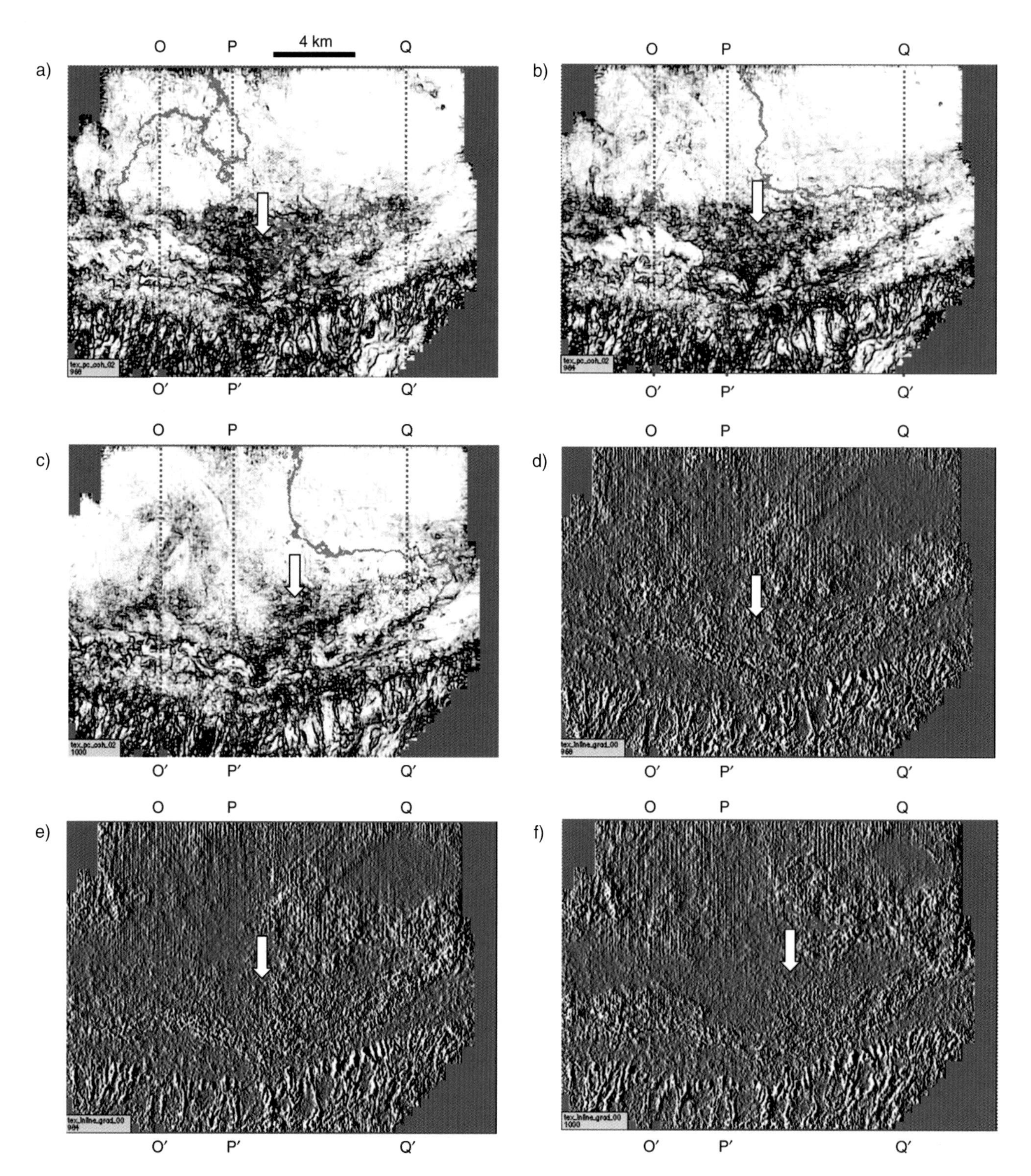

Figure 37. (a)-(c) Times slices at t = (a) 0.964 s, (b) 0.986 s, and (c) 1.000 s through a coherence volume generated for the Delaware Basin survey shown in Figure 38. (d)-(f) Corresponding time slices through the east-west component of the energy-weighted coherent-amplitude gradient at t = (d) 0.964 s, (e) 0.986 s, and (f) 1.000 s. The blue pick corresponds to the Permian Glorieta Sandstone horizon. Arrows indicate a low-coherence zone that narrows and moves to the east as we go deeper in the section. Seismic data are courtesy of Marathon Oil Co.

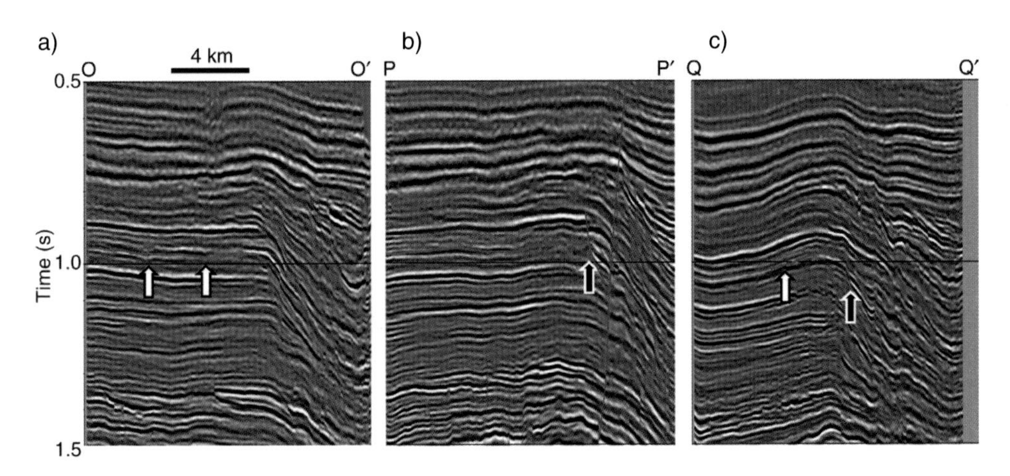

Figure 38. Vertical slices (a) AA′, (b) PP′, and (c) QQ′ through the seismic volume across the front of the Permian carbonate platform. Locations are indicated in Figure 37. White arrows indicate possible karst. Black arrows indicate crown faults along the front of the platform. The blue pick is the Glorieta horizon. Seismic data are courtesy of Marathon Oil Co.

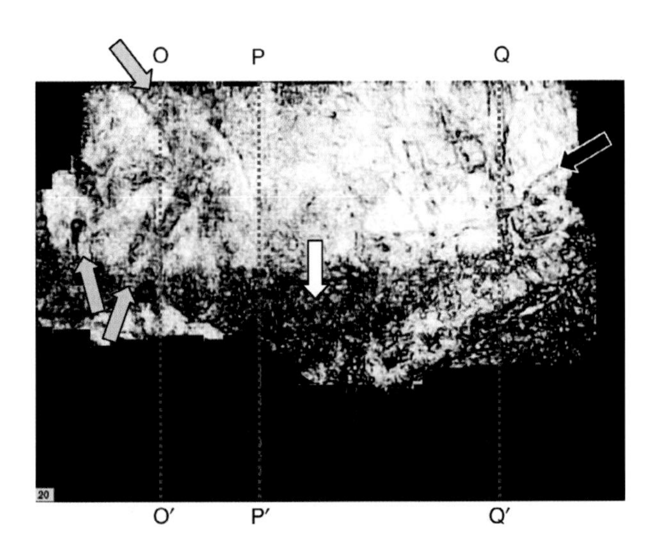

Figure 39. A horizon slice through the coherence volume 20 ms below the blue Glorieta pick shown in Figures 37 and 38. The white arrow indicates a low-coherence zone that may be fractured or karstified. The black arrow indicates a crown fault near the edge of the platform. Gray arrows indicate broad channel features that cut into the carbonate platform.

Figure 40 shows a vertical seismic section presented by Melville et al. (2004) over a giant carbonate reservoir in Abu Dhabi, U.A.E. This line is cut by a series of wrench faults.

Figure 41a, adapted from Melville et al. (2004), is a 3D visualization of a key horizon constructed from the dip azimuth. We note strong wrench-fault trends, which in turn caused strong antithetic faults at about 20°, all of which are linked to two different fold axes: one that appears to be trending at 40° to the wrench faults and another that is trending at about –40°. Both folds and faults are visible in the horizon-curvature image shown in Figure 41b, which forms a lattice of intersecting folds and faults.

In Figure 42, we return to the Central Basin Platform of west Texas, U.S.A. The figure displays a horizon slice through the most-positive curvature along the top of the Devonian Thirtyone Formation. Note the similarity here to the pattern seen in Figure 41b. The reason for these distinct patterns is a manifestation of the strain ellipsoid, which will be described in more detail in the case study given in Chapter 17. Figure 42 also displays an image log, which shows that the open natural fractures in the upper part of the Thirtyone Formation strike east-west at the well location. The challenge now is to develop a methodology for linking the curvature seen on the seismic attributes with the open fractures seen on the image log, via an appropriate model of structural deformation.

Future Trends: Computer-aided Facies Extraction, Malampaya Field, Philippines

A major geoscientific theme uses seismic geomorphology (the mapping and interpretation of reflector shapes using well-established geologic processes) as a means of predicting depositional environment, structural deformation, and diagenetic alteration, thereby constraining estimates of lithology and porosity. Typically, an experienced human interpreter identifies key morphological components (such as those shown in Figures 2 and 3) through the use of known patterns stored in his brain. The interpreter links those patterns to a possible geologic setting using either modern or ancient analogs such as those shown Figures 1, 28, or 32 (reef, shelf, or karst).

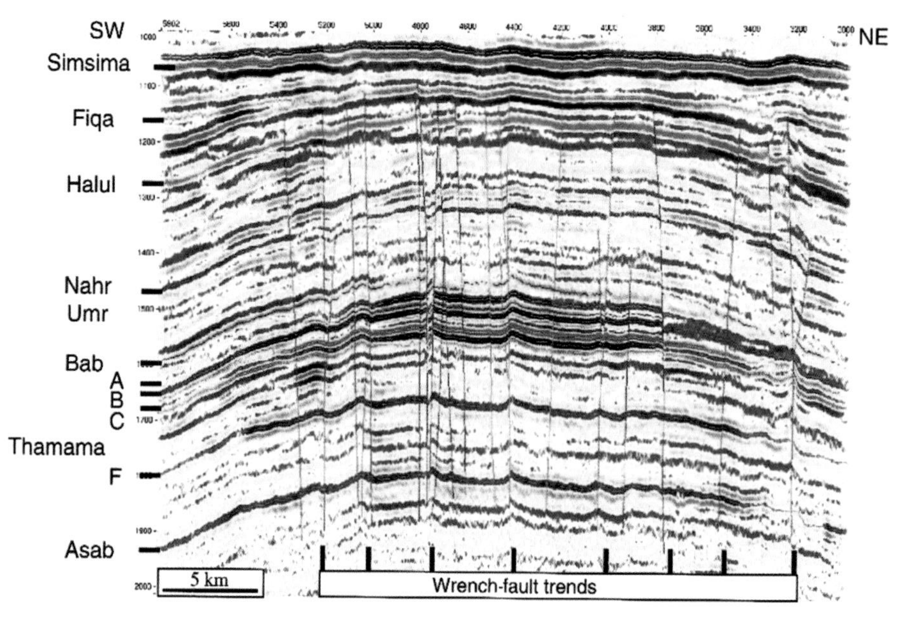

Figure 40. A seismic line from a giant carbonate reservoir in Abu Dhabi, U.A.E. This line is along the crest of the field's anticlinal axis and shows the Cretaceous section with interpreted horizons. The large anticline is cut by nearly vertical Late Cretaceous wrench faults. After Melville et al. (2004). AAPG©2004. Reprinted by permission of the AAPG whose permission is required for further use.

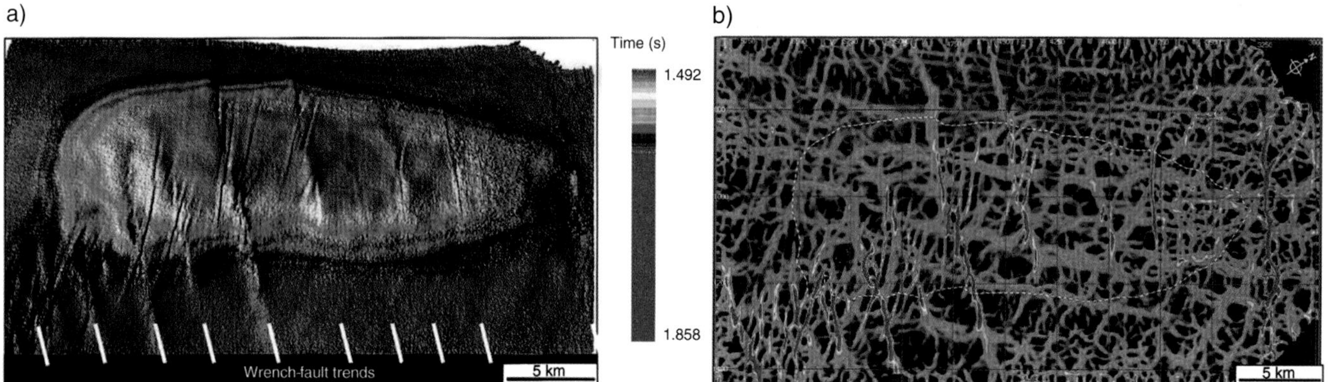

Figure 41. (a) A 3D visualization of the Top Thamama Zone B time horizon, from a survey acquired over the U.A.E. Colors correspond to two-way traveltime, and shading is from the south, showing the fault pattern in perspective. (b) Maximum curvature of the Top Thamama Zone B time surface. Larger faults appear as red, and smaller faults and flexures appear as green. After Melville et al. (2004). AAPG©2004. Reprinted by permission of the AAPG whose permission is required for further use.

Given the general success in using geostatistics and neural networks to predict porosity from seismic attributes (such as impedance inversion and spectral-decomposition components) in conjunction with available well control, several research teams have pushed that technology to automate the mapping of carbonate facies (e.g., Sarg and Schuelke, 2003; Masaferro et al., 2003). In the resulting workflow, the human interpreter manually identifies key seismic stratigraphic components and then trains the computer to replicate his or her actions.

Because carbonate facies are perhaps best identified by their reflection patterns, geometric attributes and seismic textures form the building blocks of this facies-mapping technique. As is the case in all geostatistical and neural-network-aided interpretation, it is essential to validate the results using data (in this case, manually interpreted sections) that are not included in the initial training set.

Masaferro et al. (2003) applied this technique to a reservoir in Malampaya field, Philippines. They manually interpreted two distinctive facies and used them as training data (Figure 43). The input attributes were dip azimuth, coherence, and co-occurrence matrix components (the last of which is discussed in Chapter 5). The first training set "represents the seismic character similar to the western part of the buildup (chaotic, steeply dipping discontinuous reflections). The second training set represents seismic facies from the interior of the buildup (high-amplitude, continuous, flat-lying reflections) (Masaferro et al., 2003, p. 23). We redisplay their results in Figure 44, which presents slices through their predicted facies. "Blue represents the cal-

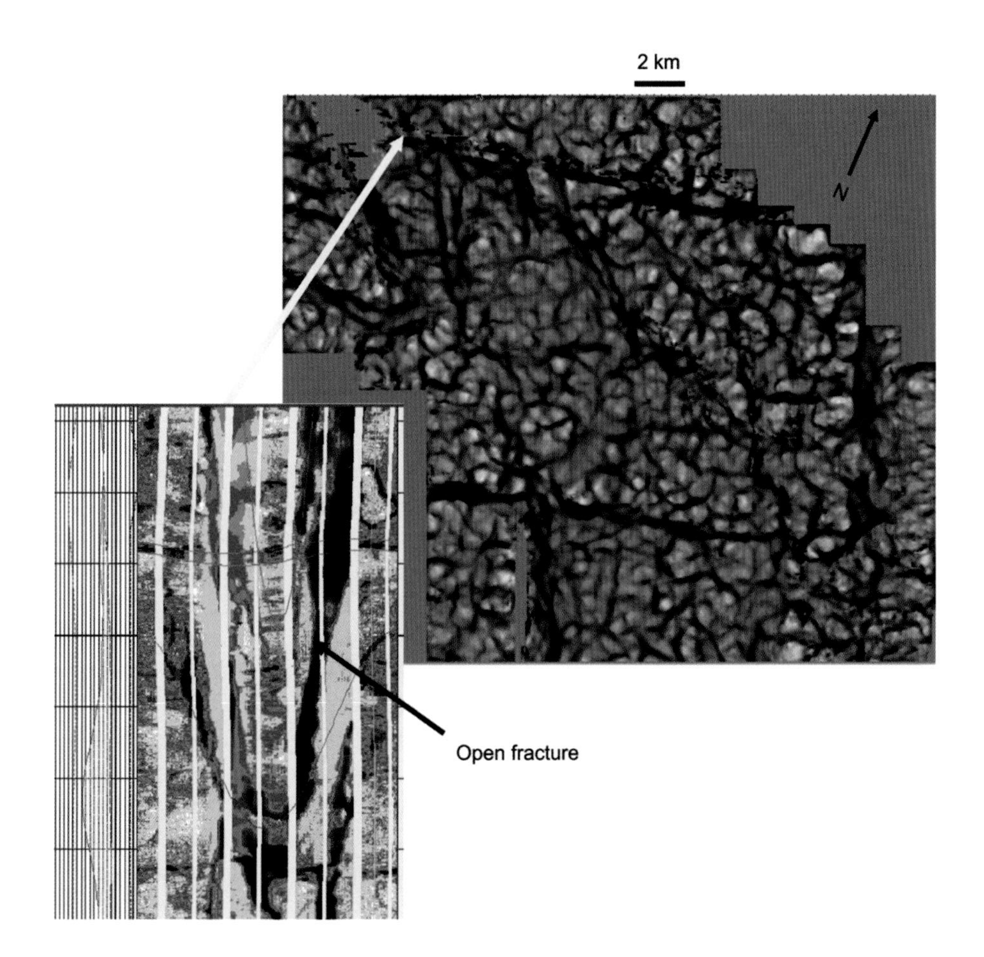

Figure 42. An example of calibration of most-positive curvature with image logs for a survey acquired over the Central Basin Platform, west Texas, U.S.A. The horizon slice is along the Devonian Thirtyone Formation. The image log shows that the Devonian open fractures strike east-west, and the log serves as ground truth for the attribute interpretation. Seismic data are courtesy of Burlington Resources. The image log is courtesy of Devon Energy. Interpretation is courtesy of Charlotte Sullivan, University of Houston.

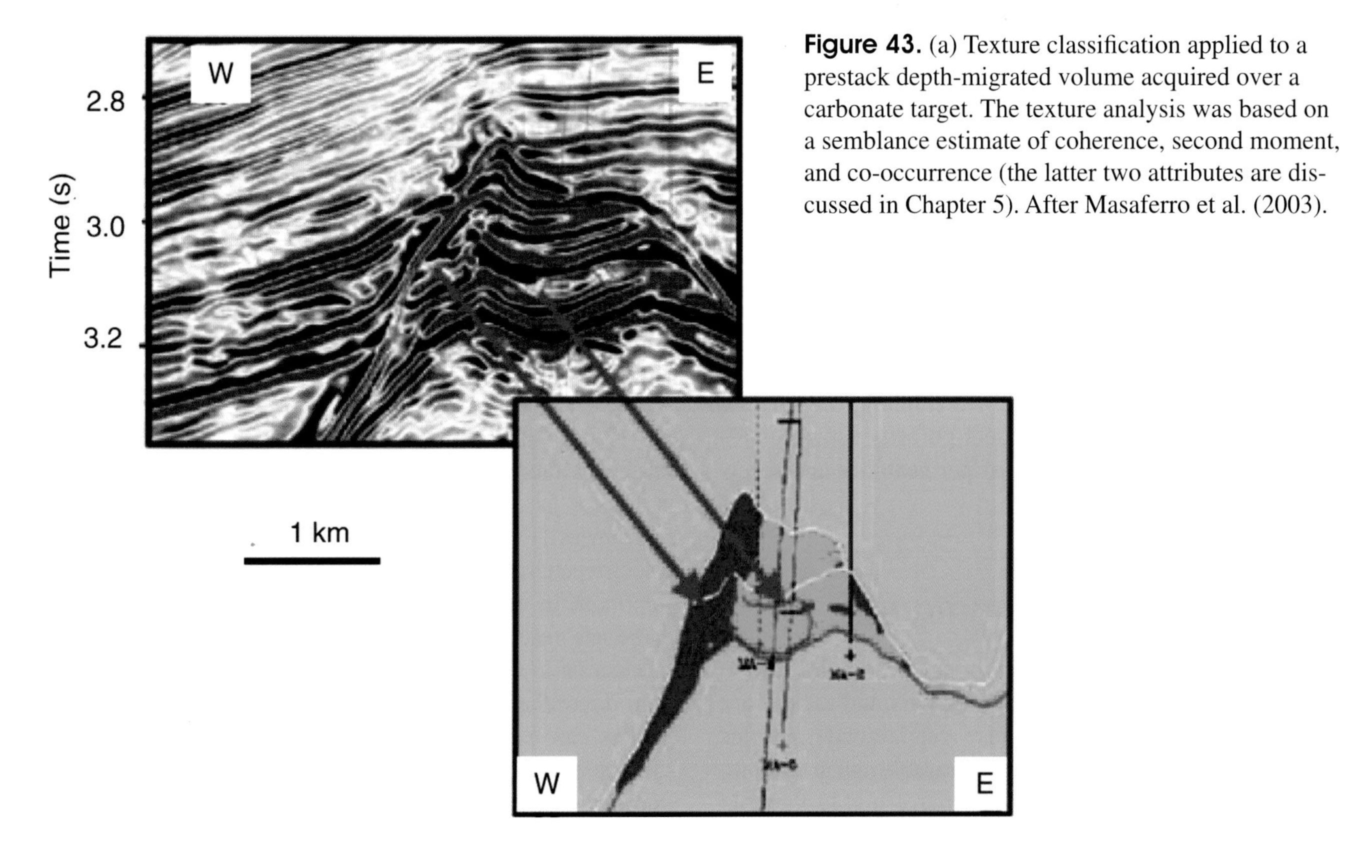

Figure 43. (a) Texture classification applied to a prestack depth-migrated volume acquired over a carbonate target. The texture analysis was based on a semblance estimate of coherence, second moment, and co-occurrence (the latter two attributes are discussed in Chapter 5). After Masaferro et al. (2003).

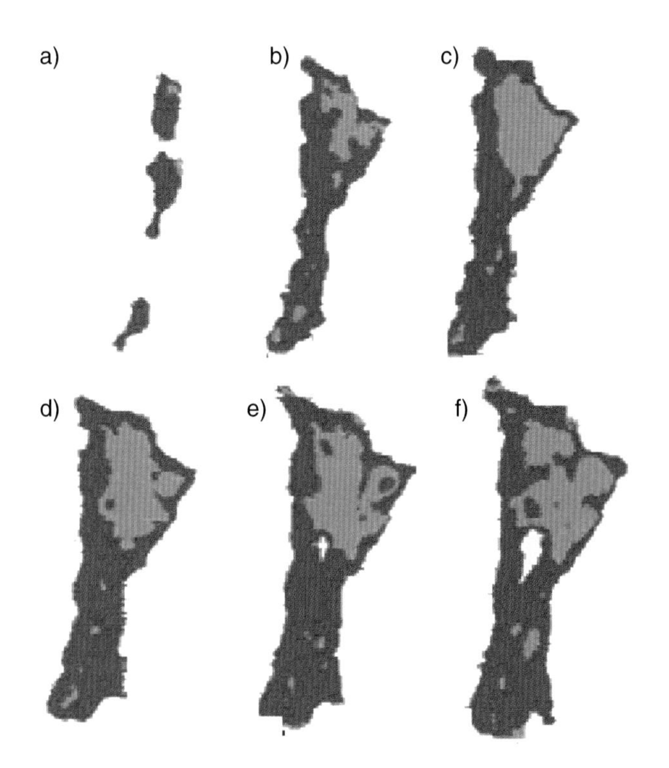

Figure 44. Results of texture classification performed on data shown in Figure 43 and displayed here on time slices at t = (a) 2.980 s, (b) 3.000 s, (c) 3.048 s, (d) 3.080 s, (e) 3.100 s, and (f) 3.124 s. Green represents continuous, high-amplitude reflections corresponding to the intrabuildup, lagoonal seismic facies. Blue represents chaotic, steeply dipping, discontinuous, reef-margin seismic facies. After Masaferro et al. (2003).

culated texture for the marginal reef-related seismic facies and light green the more internal seismic lagoonal facies" (Masaferro et al., 2003, p. 23). These authors then combined the results with impedance-inversion-derived estimates of porosity and used the combined data to constrain a reservoir simulation geomodel.

Dubrule (2003) discussed how combining the seismic facies information with independent porosity estimates results in more realistic estimates of permeability and reservoir performance.

Chapter Summary

Seismic data acquired over carbonate reservoirs tend to have lower resolution and lower reflectivity and to be more contaminated by backscattered noise and interbed multiples than do siliciclastic reservoirs of comparable age and depth. In addition, carbonate reservoirs can have highly variable porosity and permeability, both of which can be enhanced by natural fractures. Finally, carbonate reservoirs may have been subjected to one or more periods of diagenesis. Diagenetic fronts (which sometimes result in reflections) cut across and often obliterate previous stratigraphic reflectors. Gypsum is often deposited with carbonates, and when it is dewatered it forms anhydrite, which can infill vugs, pores, and fractures or be subjected to diagenesis. Laterally heterogeneous dissolution of overlying evaporites (gypsum, anhydrite, and salt) can cause severe data-quality problems when one is imaging carbonate reservoirs that are deeper with respect to the overlying evaporates.

The workflow for interpreting carbonate shoals, turbidites, and debris fans is similar to that used in siliciclastic environments. However, pinnacle reefs and karst features present a more challenging problem. Those features tend to have limited lateral extent and either to grow with (as in the case of pinnacle reefs) or to cut through (in the case of karst and collapse features) surrounding lithologies that may have radically different lithologic properties. Thus, conventional time-structure maps of pinnacle reefs and karst features are difficult to generate and provide only moderate value. In contrast, a sequence of attribute time slices (or of phantom-horizon slices from a nearby undisturbed stratigraphic horizon) through reef and karst features provides an unbiased image of the lateral extent of these features and their relationship to neighboring features in the survey, and also of their internal character. Three-dimensional visualization is particularly effective.

Karst can influence hydrocarbon production either positively or negatively, but often that influence is at a scale that cannot be resolved by conventional seismic data. We find that most-positive curvature (which has a negative value for bowl-like features) and shape index are particularly valuable in delineating karst.

Accurate identification and display of seismic textures is key to carbonate interpretation. Although structure-oriented filtering is a great aid in mapping faults, fractures, and channels in both siliciclastic and carbonate terrains, it often oversmooths the smudges and other subtle fingerprints associated with karst and hydrothermally altered dolomite.

Geometric attributes greatly augment our ability to map basement faults and reefal fault blocks that can influence carbonate facies development and subsequent porosity enhancement. Also, the ability to locate subtler features, such as fracture patterns and associated higher-permeability zones, is important in exploration and development of microporous carbonate reservoirs. During horizontal drilling to increase production in such cases, drillers can use coherence maps to help direct the wellbore to intersect fractures. Alternatively, drillers can use coherence and curvature attributes to help them avoid deep-seated open fracture systems that intersect underlying active aquifers. Reef margins, including boundaries of pinnacle reefs, low-relief isolated reef buildups, and shelf-margin buildups, also can be interpreted from coherence and spectral-decomposition images and then verified by additional well data.

References

Blumentritt, C. H., K. J. Marfurt, and E. C. Sullivan, 2004, Volume-based shape index attribute illuminates subtle (possibly subseismic) karst: 74th Annual International Meeting, SEG, Expanded Abstracts, 437–440.

Blumentritt, C., C. Sullivan, and K. Marfurt, 2003, Channel detection using seismic attributes on the Central Basin Platform, west Texas: 73rd Annual International Meeting, SEG, Expanded Abstracts, 466–469.

Bubb, J. N., and W. G. Hatfield, 1977, Seismic recognition of carbonate buildups in seismic stratigraphy, *in* C. E. Payton, ed., Applications to hydrocarbon exploration: AAPG Memoir **26**, 185–204.

Cansler, J. R., and T. R. Carr, 2001, Paleogeomorphology of the Sub-Pennsylvanian Unconformity of the Arbuckle Group (Cambrian-Lower Ordovician): Open-file Report 2001-55, http://www.kgs.ku.edu/PRS/publication/OFR2001-55/P2-02.html.

Dubrule, O., 2003, Geostatistics for seismic data integration in earth models: SEG Distinguished Instructor Short Course Series.

Fu, D., E. C. Sullivan, and K. J. Marfurt, 2006, Rock property and seismic attribute analysis of a chert reservoir in the Devonian Thirtyone Formation, west Texas, USA: Geophysics, **71**, B151–B158.

Kerans, C., F. J. Lucia, and R. K. Senger, 1994, Integrated characterization of carbonate ramp reservoirs using Permian San Andres formation outcrop analogs: AAPG Bulletin, **78,** 181–216.

Hart, B. J., 2003, Curvz: http://www.eps.mcgill.ca/~hart/CURVZ_website.htm, accessed June 22, 2005.

Lines, L. R., and R. T. Newrick, 2004, Fundamentals of geophysical interpretation: SEG Geophysical Monographs series.

Masaferro, J. L., R. Bourne, and J.-C. Jauffred, 2003, 3D visualization of carbonate reservoirs: The Leading Edge, **22**, 19–25.

Melville, P., O. al Jeelani, S. al Menhali, and J. Grotsch, 2004, Three–dimensional seismic analysis in the characterization of a giant carbonate field, onshore Abu Dhabi, United Arab Emirates, *in* G. P. Eberli, J. L. Masaferro, and J. F. Sarg, eds., Seismic imaging of carbonate reservoirs and systems: AAPG Memoir 81, 123–148.

Nissen, S., K. Rundle, R. Lockhart, and E. Morrison, 2004, 3–D seismic applications by independent operators in Kansas: Petroleum Technology Transfer Council, http://www.nmcpttc.org/Case_Studies/PTTCseismic_case/3d-seismic_appl.html.

Pennington, W. D., 2001, Calibration of seismic attributes for reservoir characterization: DOE Annual Report for DOE award DE-AC26-98BC15135.

Rogers, J. P., and M. W. Longman, 2001, An introduction to chert reservoirs in North America: AAPG Bulletin, **85**, 1–5.

Ruppel, S. C., and R. J. Barnaby, 2001, Contrasting styles of reservoir development in proximal and distal chert facies: Devonian Thirtyone Formation, Texas: AAPG Bulletin, **85**, 7–33.

Sarg, J. F., and J. S. Schuelke, 2003, Integrated seismic analysis of carbonate reservoirs: From the framework to the volume attributes: The Leading Edge, **22**, 640–645.

Sheriff, R. E., and L. Geldart, 1995, Exploration seismology: Cambridge University Press.

Skirius, C., S. Nissen, N. Haskell, K. Marfurt, S. Hadley, D. Ternes, K. Michel, I. Reglar, D. DíAmico, F. Deliencourt, T. Romero, R. DíAngelo, and B. Brown, 1999, 3-D seismic attributes applied to carbonates: The Leading Edge, **18**, 384–393.

Story, C., P. P. Peng, C. Heubeck, C. Sullivan, and L. J. Dong, 1999, An integrated study of the Liuhua 11-1 field using an ultra high resolution 3D seismic data-set: South China Sea: 69th Annual International Meeting, SEG, Expanded Abstracts, 905–908.

Sullivan, E. C., P. Elliott, K. J. Marfurt, and C. Blumentritt, 2005, Imaging inside fault zones: Integration of image logs and multitrace 3D seismic attributes: Presented at the West Texas Geological Society Fall Symposium.

Chapter 14

Attribute Expression of Deepwater Depositional Environments and Mapping of Potential Drilling Hazards

Chapter Objectives

After reading this chapter, you will be able to

- apply principles of geomorphology and volumetric attributes to reconstruct recent slope failures near the seafloor
- recognize mass-transport complexes by their pattern on time and phantom-horizon slices
- relate shallow gas pockmarks to flow along faults that originated tectonically or by differential compaction
- identify shale dewatering features preserved in deeper seismic sections
- use high-resolution images in shallow seismic sections as analogs to explain reservoir heterogeneity in lower-resolution deeper sections

Introduction

In hydrocarbon production, a geologic hazard is any natural phenomenon that can negatively impact drilling operations, subsurface installations, the environment, historical artifacts, and above all, human safety. Typical hazards include seafloor instability, the presence of shallow gas, strong turbidity currents, and sensitive biological communities on the seafloor. Movement along shallow faults or submarine slumps can damage the wellbore, platform moorings, and pipelines. Strong turbidity flows can scour sediment from underneath previously buried pipelines. Shallow gas is particularly dangerous, not only from the potential of a blowout before the well casing is set, but also from a sudden release of gas into the water column causing a decrease in the density of the water-gas mixture, which could collapse the platform or sink the drill ship.

Initially, most geologic-hazard surveys were conducted using high-resolution 2D single-channel seismic systems augmented by side-scan sonar of the water bottom. Later, single-channel surveys were supplanted by short-streamer surveys. Because short-streamer data are less sensitive to inaccurate estimates of velocity, they produce less smearing (and somewhat less noise rejection) than do long-streamer data. Hence, they generate improved vertical and lateral resolution.

Such short-streamer data work very well when the objectives are a shallow geologic section in a deepwater setting. In that environment, backscattered seismic noise is low, and multiples arrive at times that are beyond the depth of penetration.

However, velocity analysis is difficult with short streamers, so velocities must be borrowed from conventional longer-streamer surveys used in conventional seismic exploration or extrapolated from nearby well control, using a well-established compaction model.

Not surprisingly, conventional 3D seismic surveys in deep water generally are of very high quality and can be used in lieu of a hazard survey in many parts of the world. Seismic energy undergoes very little attenuation or geometric distortion in the water column, and because of the depth of the water, seismic energy provides high-frequency data with a significant number of traces contributing to the image. However, with the great cost of platforms and production facilities in deep and ultra-deep water, true 3D hazard surveys can be justified to accurately assess the shallow geologic section so that the safe locations for drilling and production facilities can be identified. In many areas of the world, 3D hazard surveys are required before drilling can proceed.

In this chapter, we show examples of a diverse range of geologic features that can become hazards under certain conditions. Because almost all of these data are extracted from within the top 1 s below the water bottom, and because most are from deep water (uncontaminated by free surface multiples), the data are of particularly good quality and have both vertical and lateral resolution greater than that of conventional 3D seismic data at exploration depths. Although variability in tectonic forces, basin subsidence, and sediment supply are important, deepwater depositional processes have changed little over geologic time. Thus, the shallow geologic features we see today on the seafloor provide a unique 3D laboratory that may help us understand reservoir heterogeneity, environments favorable to deposition and preservation of sands, and the processes that may rework those potential reservoirs.

Unlike modern-day analogs to fluvial and deltaic processes, carbonate buildups, and other sedimentary processes that we can observe directly on the earth's surface, the modern-day analogs of deepwater depositional environments can only be seen remotely through side-scan sonar, seismic surveys, and via bathysphere.

Geometric attributes behave particularly well in environments whose data have a good signal-to-noise ratio. Indeed, in this chapter the noise that we see generally is geologic rather than seismic noise. These noisy geologic features include mass-transport complexes (MTCs), dewatered shales, amalgamated channels, sand waves, and gas chimneys, which are features that do not have the parallel stratification that serves as the basis for interpreters to pick peaks and troughs. As seismic-processing geophysicists, we authors are confident that earlier in our careers we would have attributed such geologically chaotic data to some seismic cause and have been tempted to filter it out to provide a nice coherent seismic section that was amenable to autopicking.

We conclude this introduction by noting that most of the published literature, including this volume, shows excellent images of hazard-forming features in the shallow portions of the seismic sections. Few images are from deeper exploration depths. One reason for this dearth of examples is because of data access. Host governments and geophysical service companies are rather generous in releasing their shallow data for scientific study. Because of low pressures, shallow hydrocarbon accumulations usually are uneconomic, so that the disclosure of their existence has little impact on the economics of future lease sales or seismic data sales.

Mass-transport complexes, shale-dewatering features, contourites, and of course turbidite channels and fans are encountered and identified routinely in deeper seismic sections. Circular gas-charged pockmarks are also seen and often are the surface expression of active gas migration along deeper faults. As such deepwater basins become more mature, we anticipate that some of the associated data can be released to the scientific community for study and publication.

Mass-transport Complexes, Glide Tracks, and Outrunner Blocks

Mass-transport complexes — alternatively called debrites (for debris flows), underwater landslides, or simply slumps — are expressions of slope failure. Such failures are a function of slope morphology, sediment strength, sedimentation rate, water pressure, gas-hydrate pressure, and temperature, and can be triggered by earthquakes, volcanic tremors, storms, and tsunamis. The term *underwater landslide,* and its direct impact on subsea pipelines, drilling installations, and even its tsunamigenic potential, best captures the importance of mapping MTCs for hazard assessment. Mapping MTCs on or near the seafloor provides an indication of their frequency, size, scope, and location in recent geologic time. In the deeper geologic record, MTCs indicate the depositional environment during their time of emplacement. Also, MTCs may improve reservoir quality of chalky, microporous carbonates, as in Campanian reservoirs in Tunisia. They are thought to be the genesis of fractured reservoirs, such as the North Sea chalk reservoir shown in Figure 35 of Chapter 13.

Haskell et al. (1999) were perhaps the first to map MTCs using coherence images generated from high-quality conventional 3D exploration data from deepwater offshore Nigeria. In Figure 1, we display two vertical seismic slices and a horizon slice through a coherence volume 100 ms below the water bottom.

The seismic character on the vertical slice is best described as chaotic, as shown in Figure 1b and c. In contrast, the coherence slice has considerable organization, clearly showing a slump feature of about 5 km by 17 km (Figure 1a). Haskell et al. (1999) identified this feature as a rotational slump, characterized by extensional faulting, with relatively large rotated blocks in the updip direction and compressional structures downdip.

Nissen et al. (1999) applied this same analysis technique to a different 3D survey from offshore Nigeria. In Figures 2 and 3 (taken from their work), we display phantom-horizon slices 144 ms below the water bottom through a seismic data volume and a coherence volume, respectively. In the center of these images we notice slump scars bounding a channel-shaped submarine canyon. This canyon is a channelized debris flow formed by slumping, rather than a meandering submarine channel formed by fluid currents.

a)

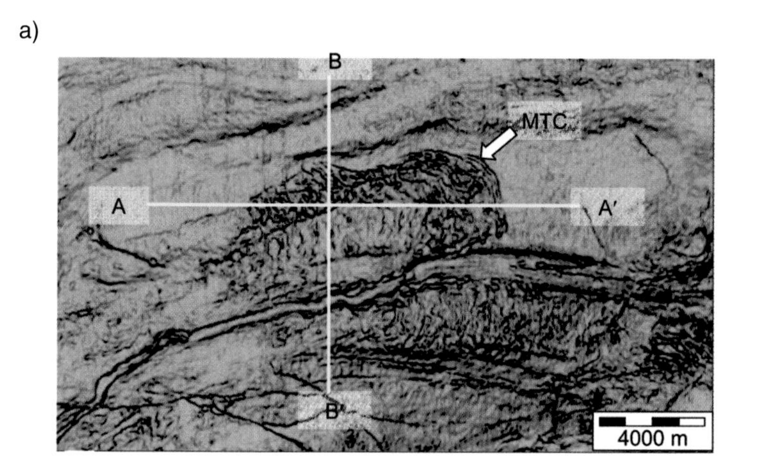

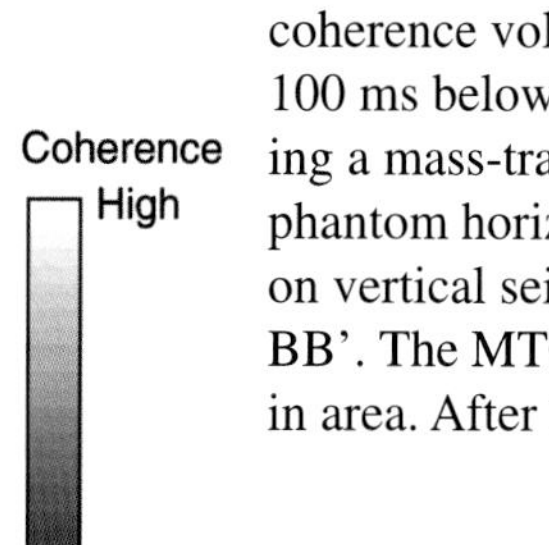

b)

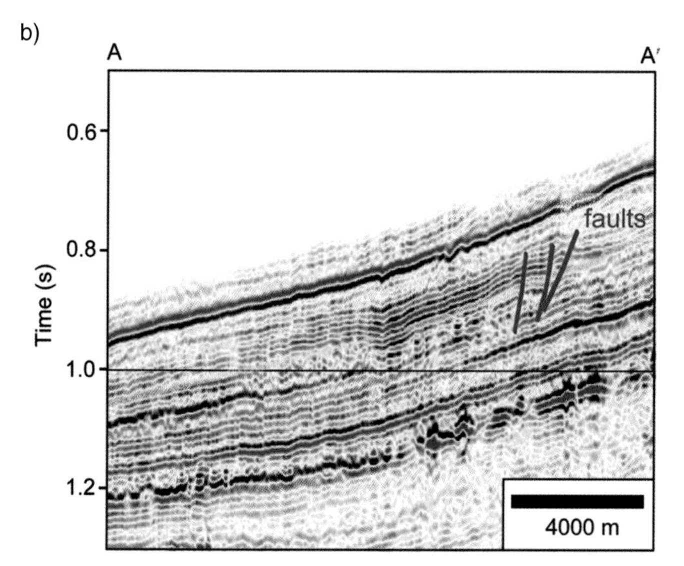

c)

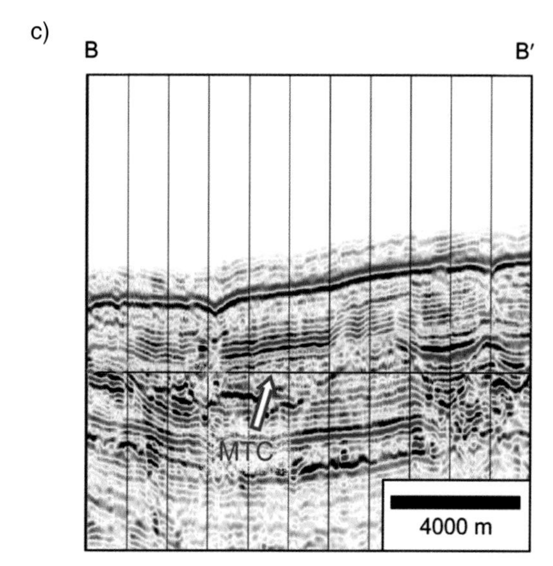

Figure 1. (a) A horizon slice through a coherence volume from offshore Nigeria 100 ms below the water bottom, showing a mass-transport complex (MTC); the phantom horizon is indicated in yellow on vertical seismic slices (b) AA′ and (c) BB'. The MTC measures 5 km × 17 km in area. After Haskell et al. (1999).

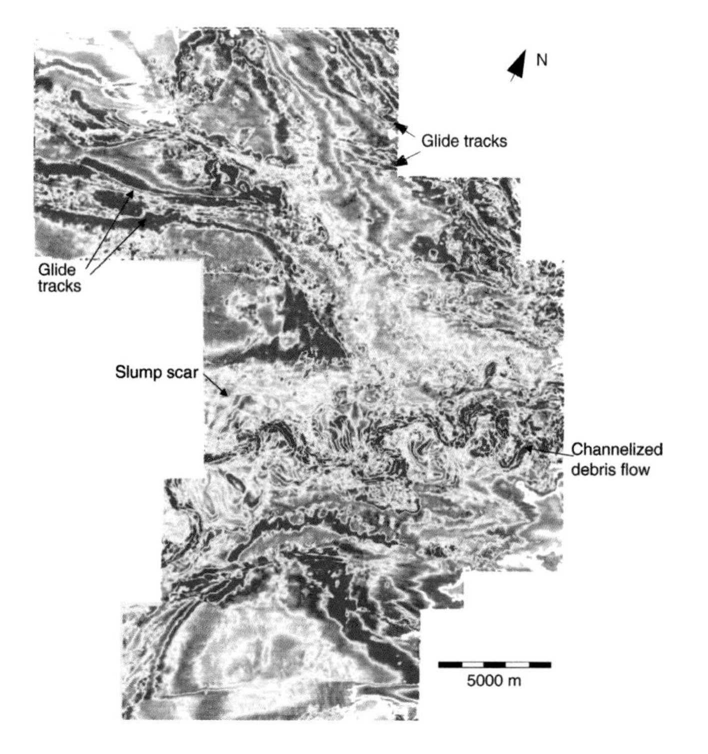

Figure 2. A phantom-horizon slice 144 ms below the seafloor, through a seismic data volume, offshore Nigeria. After Nissen et al. (1999).

To the north, we notice a suite of curvilinear features cutting from east to west. Originally, these curvilinear features were interpreted from the seismic data to be distributary channels. However, analysis of the coherence and dip-azimuth volumes led Nissen et al. (1999) to identify these features as glide tracks associated with a block of more competent sediment that had slid downslope over the soft water bottom, resulting in a local depression (Figure 4b) and terminating in the glide track itself (Figure 4a). The outrunner blocks are approximately 100 m wide by 250 m long by 10 m high. The more southerly glide track in Figure 4a and b is 12 km long.

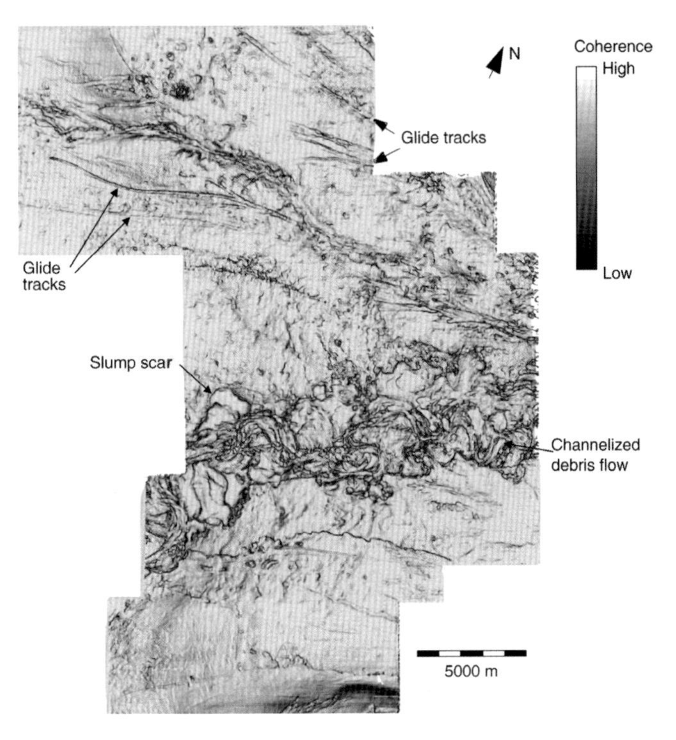

Figure 3. A phantom-horizon slice 144 ms below the seafloor, through the coherence volume corresponding to Figure 2. In addition to faults, we see a slump scar and channelized debris flow. We discuss the glide tracks in the next figure. After Nissen et al. (1999).

Each outrunner block terminates in a small depression (Figure 5a and b), and pushes up a pressure ridge in front of it. Such a pressure ridge should not be confused with pore pressure dealt with on a daily basis by exploration geoscientists. Rather, the pressure ridges associated with MTCs and these outrunner blocks are analogous to the ridges set up on a carpet if you try to move a heavy desk across it. Outrunner blocks and pressure ridges are morphologically similar to features associated with modern submarine landslides, such as an underwater landslide that occurred in Kitimat Fjord, British Columbia, Canada, in 1975. In Figures 5c and 6, we reproduce images provided by Dave Prior of Dalhousie University, who studied this MTC in Kitimat Fjord using side-scan sonar.

The 1975 Kitimat Fjord landslide generated 8-m waves that damaged dock facilities. Large slumps, such as the 750-m-long by 100-m-high slump (measured by a 2D seismic line) triggered by the Papua New Guinea Earthquake of 1998, are believed to be a major factor in generating tsunamis (Costas et al., 2002).

Nibbelink (1999) used a combination of coherence maps extracted from a 3D hazard survey acquired over the Sigsbee Escarpment, in the Green Canyon area of the Gulf of Mexico, U.S.A. He found that intervals just below the seafloor provide an effective tool for analyzing reservoir analogs in older depositional sequences.

More recently, Oyedele (2005) reexamined this data volume using a more complete set of attributes. In Figure 7, we display her time-structure map of the water bottom. Note that the Sigsbee Escarpment has 1 s (750 m) of relief. We also note indications of a major southwest-northeast fault on the platform and a slump scar toward the abyssal plain.

Figure 8 is a conventional dip-magnitude map of the time horizon shown in Figure 7. The faults are clearer and we note a major slump scarp and also lateral scars indicating the edges of the mass-transport pathway. In the southeastern

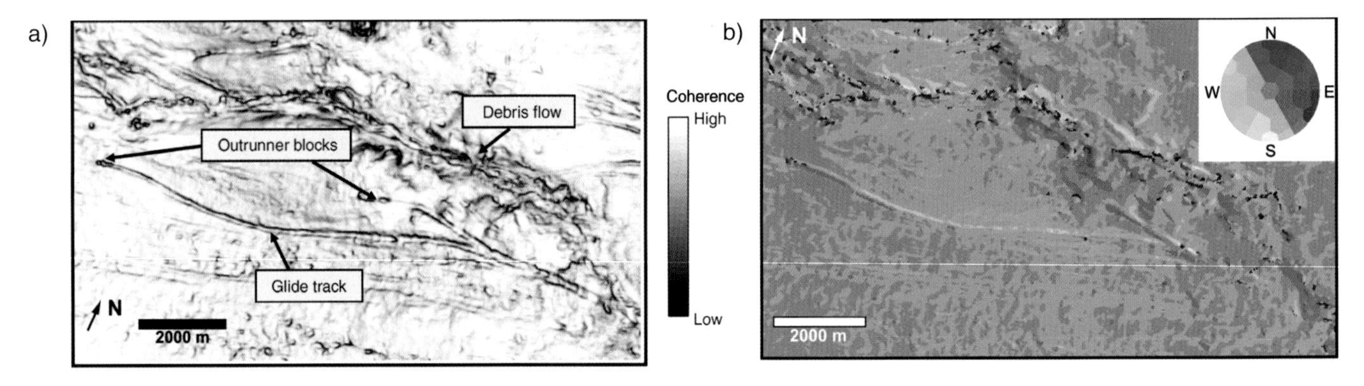

Figure 4. A phantom horizon slice 144 ms below the seafloor, through (a) a coherence volume and (b) a dip-azimuth volume, showing outrunner blocks, glide tracks, and other debris-flow features. Note how the northern flanks of the east-west-trending glide tracks dip to the south, whereas the southern flanks dip to the north. After Nissen et al. (1999).

corner of the survey we see a significant slump toward the base of the Sigsbee Escarpment; that slump was previously discussed by Orange et al. (2004). The survey does not extend far enough to observe where the plain flattens out.

In Figure 9, we display a horizon slice along the water bottom from Figure 7, shown here through the coherence volume. We note that the image is very similar to that of the dip-magnitude map and implies a smooth, mud-draped water bottom with most discontinuities resulting from faults and scarps that cut the water bottom. We also note that much of detail of the coherence image is lost because Oyedele was only able to plot every third inline and crossline to fit her computer screen and thereby lost many of the thinner fault zones.

In Figures 10 and 11, we display two horizon slices through the most-positive-curvature and most-negative-curvature volumes, respectively. Because these images are a long-wavelength estimate of curvature (α = 0.25), the display limitations do not overly compromise their quality.

In Figure 12a and b, we examine some of the prominent features parallel to the slump direction, by zooming in on the area denoted by the blue rectangle in Figures 9 through 11. Examination of Figure 12c shows these features to be a sequence of ridges (white arrows) and valleys (gray arrows). The reflectivity within the ridges seen in Figure 12c is chaotic and therefore probably does not represent erosional remnants. Rather, we postulate that the ridges are debris deposits in the shadow of a more competent updip obstacle, whereas the valleys are less well protected and more easily scoured. Brand et al. (2003) interpreted these valleys to be grooves carved into the escarpment by bottom-water currents. Neideroda et al. (2003) interpreted

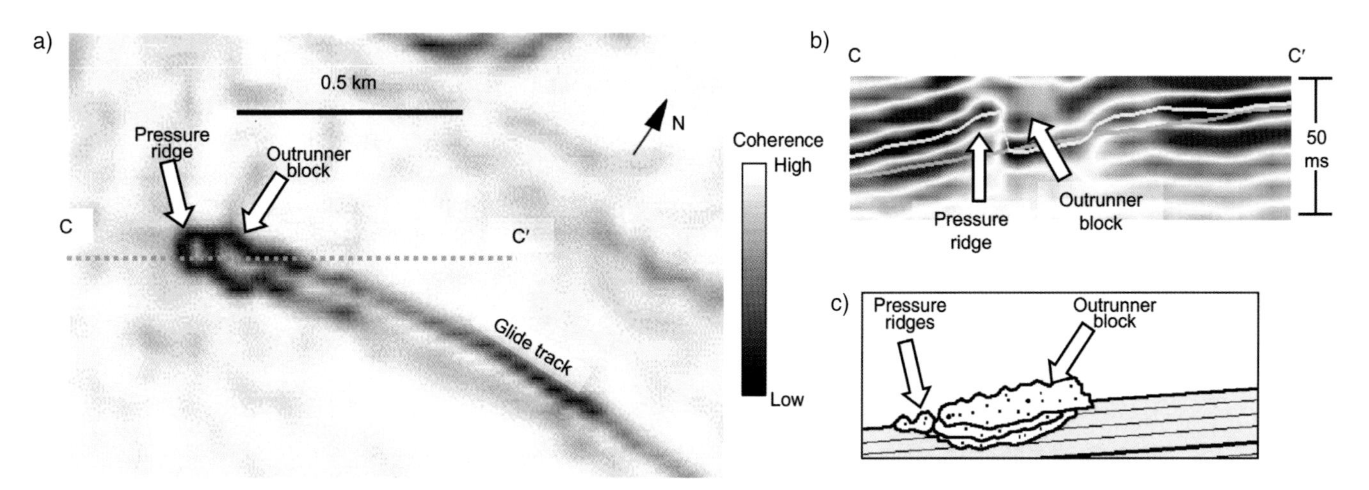

Figure 5. (a) An enlargement of some of the glide tracks shown in Figure 3. (b) A vertical seismic slice through the outrunner block. Yellow indicates a stratigraphic horizon, and green indicates a phantom horizon 144 ms below the seafloor. (c) A schematic diagram of an outrunner block in a modern mass-transport complex from Kitimat Fjord, British Columbia, Canada, courtesy of David Prior, Dalhousie University. After Nissen et al. (1999).

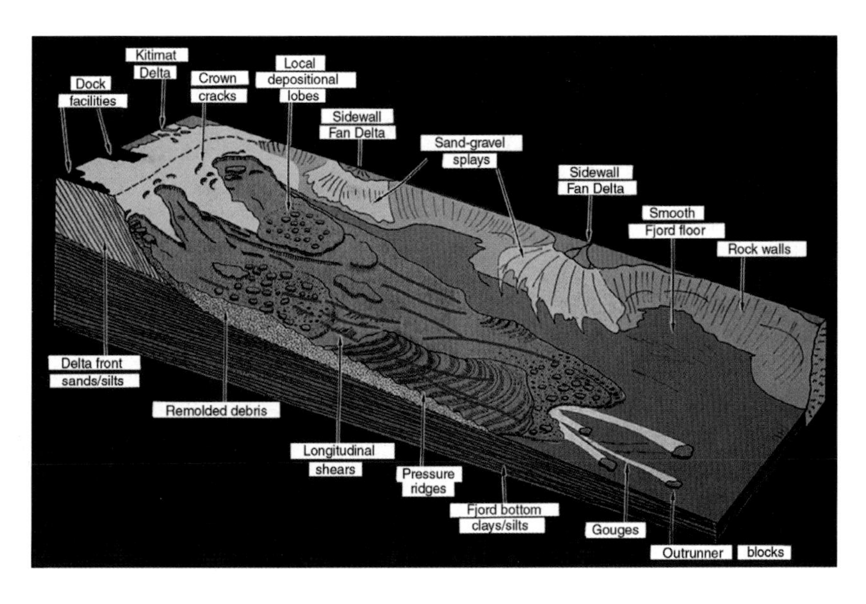

Figure 6. A modern analog of a mass-transport complex, from Kitimat Fjord, western British Columbia, Canada, showing the relationship among crown cracks, debris-flow lobes, pressure ridges, glide tracks (gouges), and outrunner blocks. A schematic section through an example of an outrunner block from Kitimat Fjord was shown in part (c) of the previous figure. This image was drawn from side-scan sonar data. After Prior and Coleman (1988). University of Chicago Press ©1984, whose permission is required for further use.

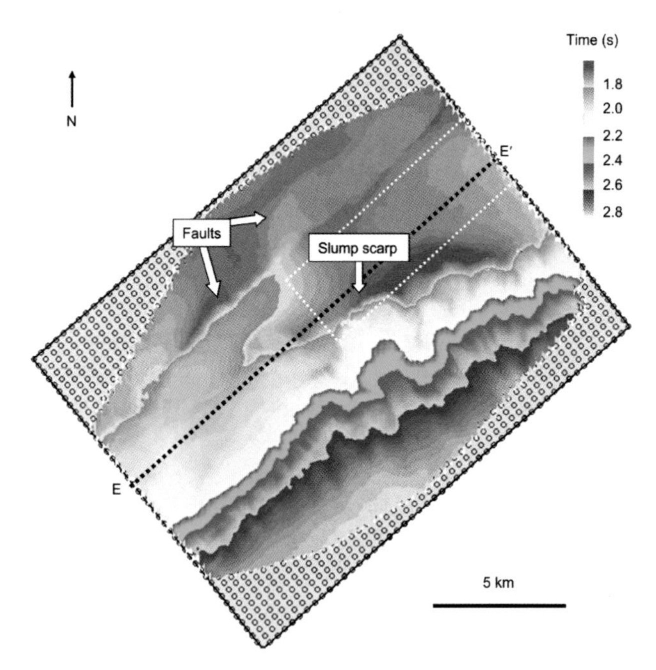

Figure 7. A time-structure map of the water bottom, generated from a 3D hazard survey acquired over the Sigsbee Escarpment, Green Canyon, Gulf of Mexico, U.S.A. The escarpment parallels the yellow contour. After Oyedele (2005).

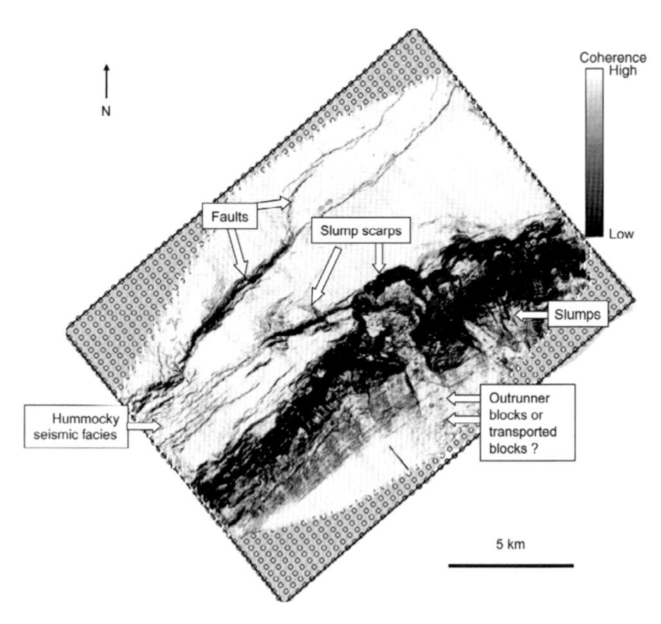

Figure 9. A horizon slice along the water bottom shown in Figure 7, through a coherence volume. Because coherence is calculated on the seismic volume before interpretation, it exhibits fewer picking errors than does the dip-magnitude map shown in the previous figure. Although the dip-magnitude and coherence images are quite similar, they measure different features of the seismic data, with coherence measuring lateral changes in waveform. After Oyedele (2005).

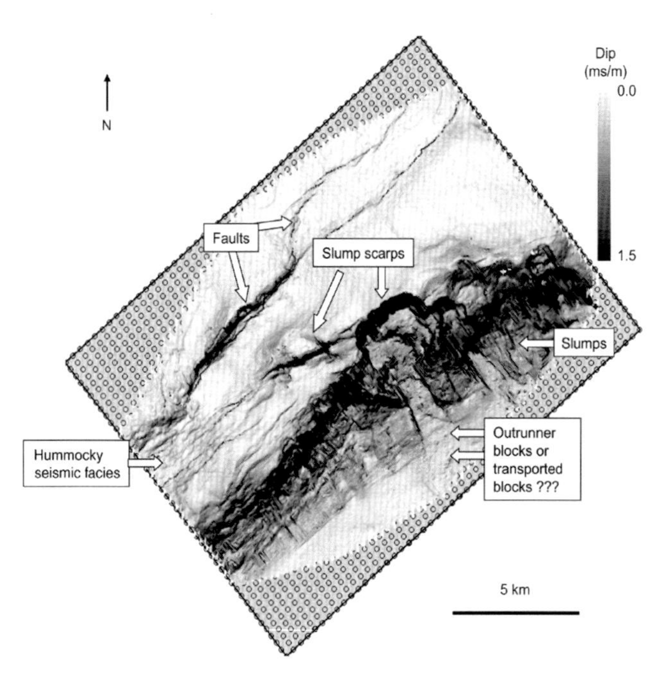

Figure 8. A conventional dip-magnitude map derived from a time-structure map of the water bottom shown in Figure 7. In addition to the Sigsbee Escarpment, we note several faults in the northwestern part of the figure on the continental shelf, several slump scarps near the escarpment, and slumps at the base of the escarpment. After Oyedele (2005).

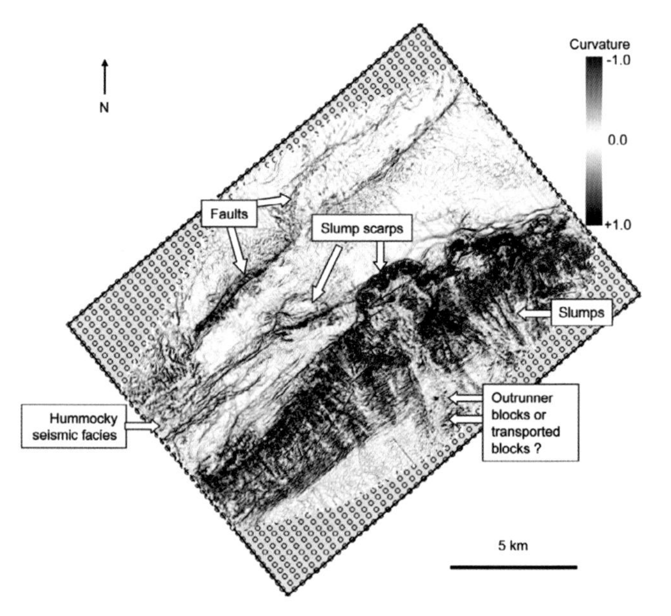

Figure 10. A horizon slice along the water bottom shown in Figure 7, through a most-positive-curvature volume. This image highlights in red the features that are anticlinal and provides significantly greater detail of the slump scarps and slumps at the base of the escarpment than do the previous three figures. After Oyedele (2005).

them as erosional channels for the transport of turbidite or debris flows to the upper continental rise.

Oyedele (2005) provided a detailed interpretation of the depositional environment behind the Sigsbee Escarpment, showing it to be populated by a sequence of MTCs, each of which later was draped by conformal sediments (Figure 13). She also noted a turbidite system in the lower part of the image, the top of which was identified by Nibbelink (1999). We reproduce Nibbelink's (1999) description of the evolution of the shape of the Sigsbee Escarpment as Figure 14. In this work, he described a "deepwater escarpment model where deep currents (the loop current in

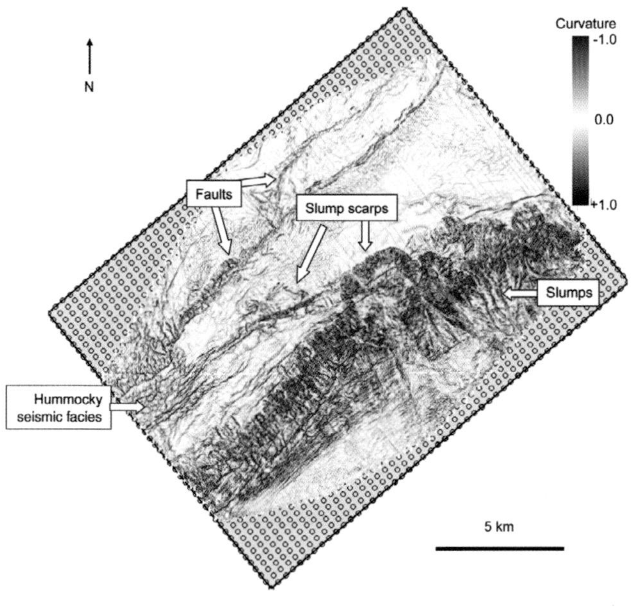

Figure 11. A horizon slice along the water bottom shown in Figure 7, through a most-negative-curvature volume. This image highlights in green the features that are synclinal and, like the most-positive curvature in the previous figure, provides significantly greater detail of the slump scarps and slumps at the base of the escarpment than do dip-magnitude or coherence horizon slices. After Oyedele (2005).

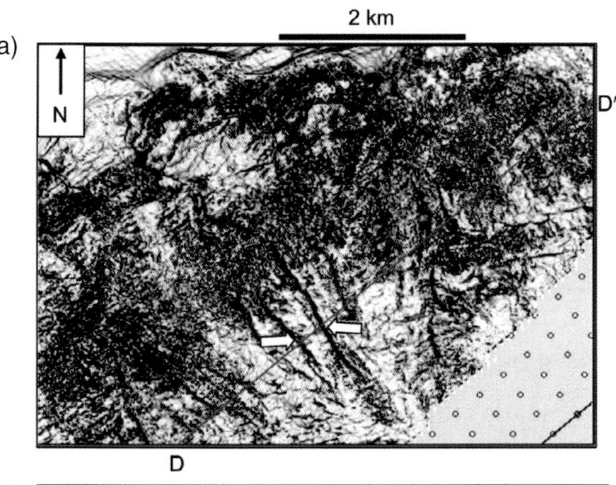

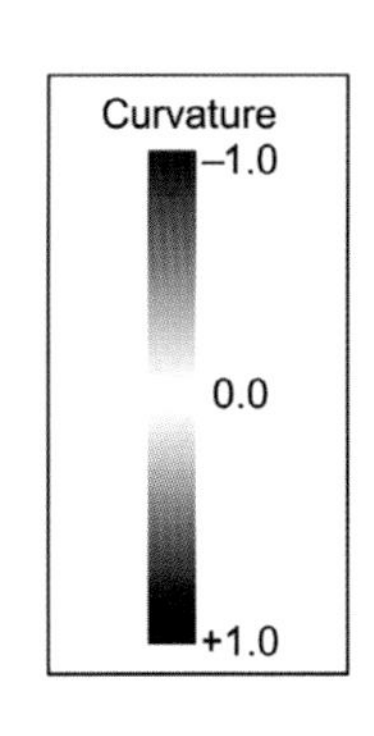

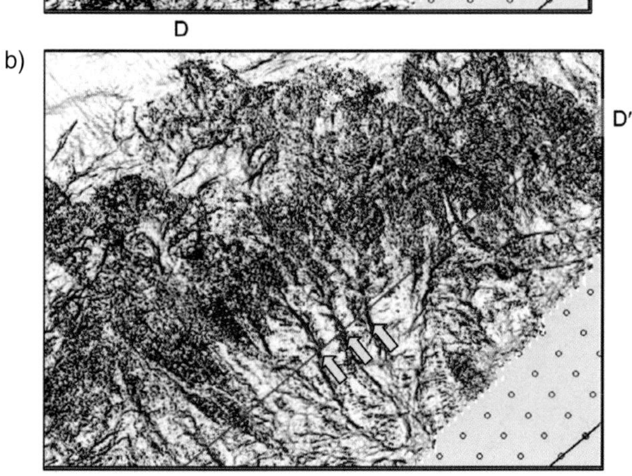

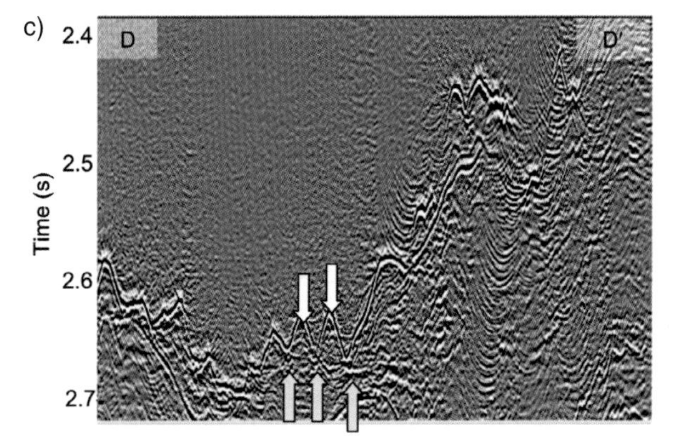

Figure 12. Details of (a) a most-positive-curvature and (b) a most-negative-curvature volume extracted along the water bottom in the area indicated by the blue rectangle in Figure 10. (c) Seismic line DD′. White arrows indicate long anticlinal features. Gray arrows indicate long synclinal features. After Oyedele (2005).

the Gulf of Mexico) erode the sediment overlying salt canopies, causing dissolution of salt at the seafloor and slumping of the section toward the abyssal plain" (Nibbelink, 1999, p. 552). Figure 14 includes (a) a rounded front, with a smooth, gentle slope; (b) a scalloped front, with a fault-slump escarpment; and (c) a truncated, flat front, with a fault slump escarpment and graben.

Nibbelink (1999, p. 552) also noted that "large slump blocks of sediment are not observed on the modern Sigsbee abyssal plain" and proposed that "the relatively unconsolidated material slumped off the front of the escarpment becomes disaggregated and ends up incorporated in the abyssal fan." He described the ponding of sediments behind the topographic rim created by an upwelling of salt.

Oyedele (2005) defined one of those ponded depocenters, and we show her work here in Figures 15 through 17. In Figure 15, we reproduce a seismic cross section through her lowermost mass-transport complex, MTC A, which was identified in Figure 13. Note that this complex is composed of at least two distinct slump events.

Figure 16 is the time-thickness map of MTC A. We note that MTC A has a narrow neck as it enters a minibasin,

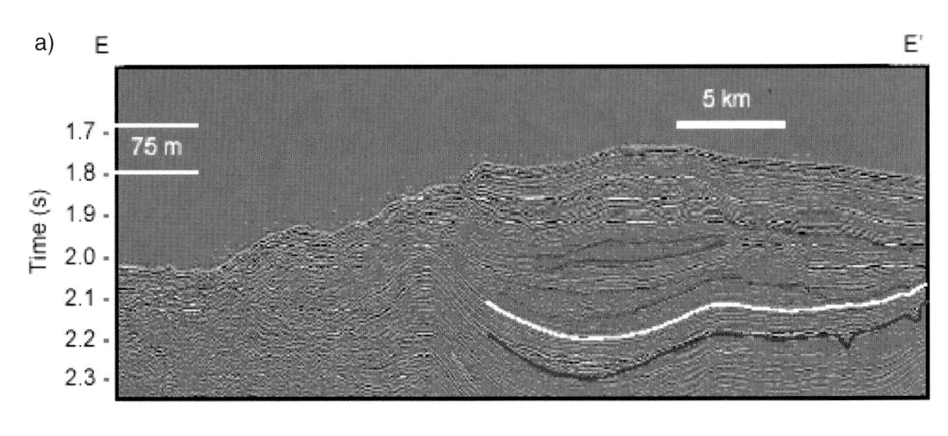

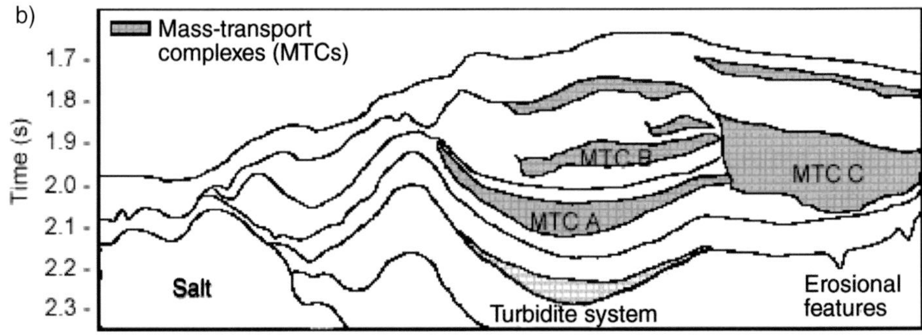

Figure 13. (a) Seismic line EE′ and (b) its corresponding interpretation, showing mapped seismic facies based on seismic reflectivity, event continuity, and external geometry. Observe the influence of salt withdrawal on deposition and the prevalence of MTC packages above the lobe complex. The location of line EE′ is shown in Figure 7. After Oyedele (2005).

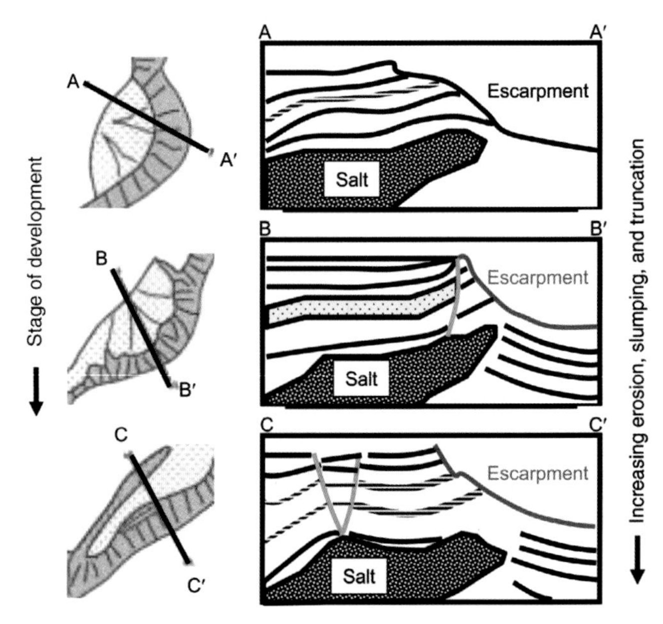

Figure 14. Nibbelink's (1999) model of the Sigsbee Escarpment, deepwater Gulf of Mexico, U.S.A. The model is a three-stage progressive one for scouring at the base and slumping off the front of salt canopies with overlying sediment along the eroded part of the Sigsbee Escarpment. It includes (a) a rounded front, with a smooth, gentle slope; (b) a scalloped front, with a fault-slump escarpment; and (c) a truncated, flat front, with a fault slump escarpment and graben. After Nibbelink (1999).

and then it broadens out to fill that basin. A small glide track cuts across the northeastern part of the image.

Figure 17a is a southwest-northeast seismic line through MTC A. Note in this figure the local ponding and the irregular interface between the two slump events. Blocks of sediment that produce high-amplitude reflections (HARs) are incorporated within the slump. Although the data are seemingly chaotic on the vertical seismic section, the coherence image in Figure 17b shows that the slump is actually quite organized. The limits of the slump are marked in blue. The most chaotic zones, which Oyedele (2005) calls high-energy debris flows, show up with very low coherence and appear as black zones. The HARs caught up in the debris flow show up as local coherent reflectors and appear as white. In addition, lineaments of high coherence cut from updip to downdip. These could indicate either later channels or glide blocks that have reworked the top of the debris flow and provide accommodation space for later more-organized sediments, or possibly for bands of sand that were part of the original debris flow itself and that since have been charged by gas.

Nibbelink (1999) described this ponding process in Figure 18. As the rim of the escarpment rises, it provides accommodation space for sediments behind it. Through a combination of slumps and turbidites, these minibasins fill and then overflow either into the next minibasin or over the edge of the Sigsbee Escarpment and onto the abyssal plain.

In Figure 19, we display Oyedele's (2005) MTC B. Figure 19a shows a phantom-horizon slice through a coherence volume 70 ms above the green horizon and cutting through

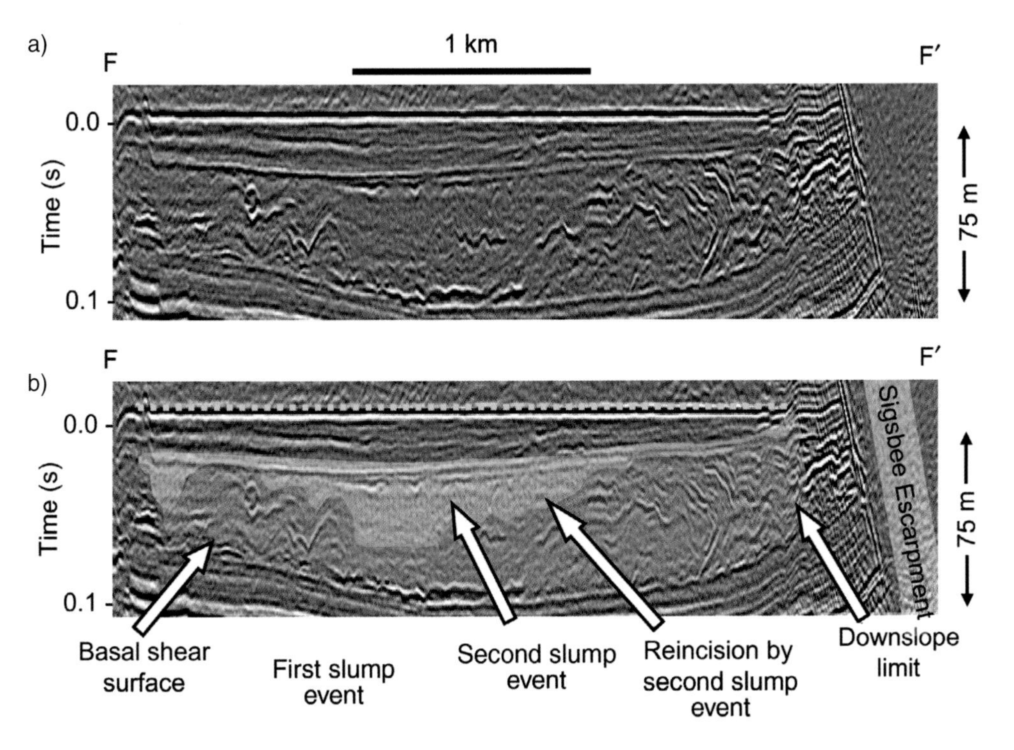

Figure 15. A northwest-southeast seismic section through MTC A, shown here (a) without interpretation and (b) with interpretation and mapped in Figure 16. Observe the differences in the internal fabric demarcated by a second scoured base. Data were flattened on the overlying green horizon. After Oyedele (2005).

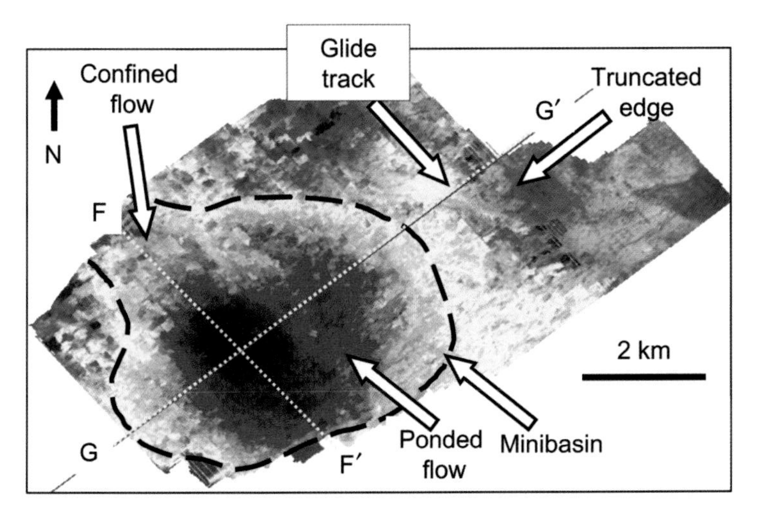

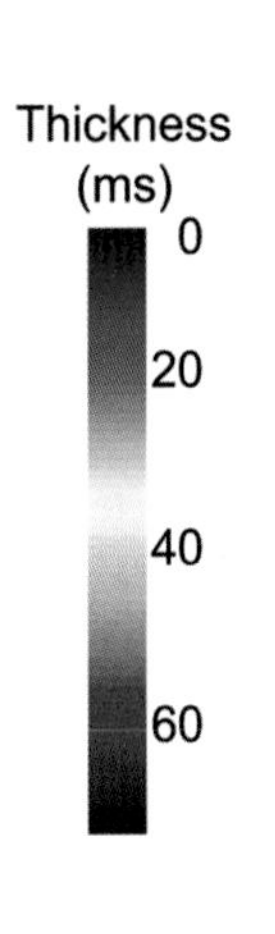

Figure 16. A time-thickness map between the top and base of the MTC A package shown in Figure 15. The lobate geometry imaged by the deposit reflects the influence of topography on deposition. Note the truncated edge of MTC A on its eastern flank. After Oyedele (2005).

MTC B. Like her MTC A, this slump also is composed of at least two separate units. The toe of the slump comes almost to the edge of the Sigsbee Escarpment, stopping at an earlier expression of this local high feature. In the western part of the images we see a wide glide track but do not identify any outrunner blocks, even though the seismic resolution is high. Figure 19b is a seismic section showing a depression approximately 8 m thick overlying MTC B.

In Figure 20, we examine Oyedele's (2005) MTC C, where three stages of a minibasin are seen at (a) 66 ms below, (b) along, and (c) 125 ms above the picked blue horizon shown in (d) line II'. In (a) deposition comes from the south, from the crest of the Sigsbee Escarpment. In (b) we see faulting around the edge of the basin, which shows that it continued to sag at a later time in response to salt withdrawal. In (c) we see MTCs derived from the north. A glide track within MTC Cm runs southeastward beyond the downslope limits of the three MTC slide lobes. This glide track appears as a small depression in (c).

As seen in Figure 20, this mass-transport complex is composed of at least three stages of slumping. Unlike MTC A and MTC B, it does not reach all the way to the Sigsbee Escarpment, but instead it peters out toward the south and ends with a fingering pattern. In this image, too, we can see

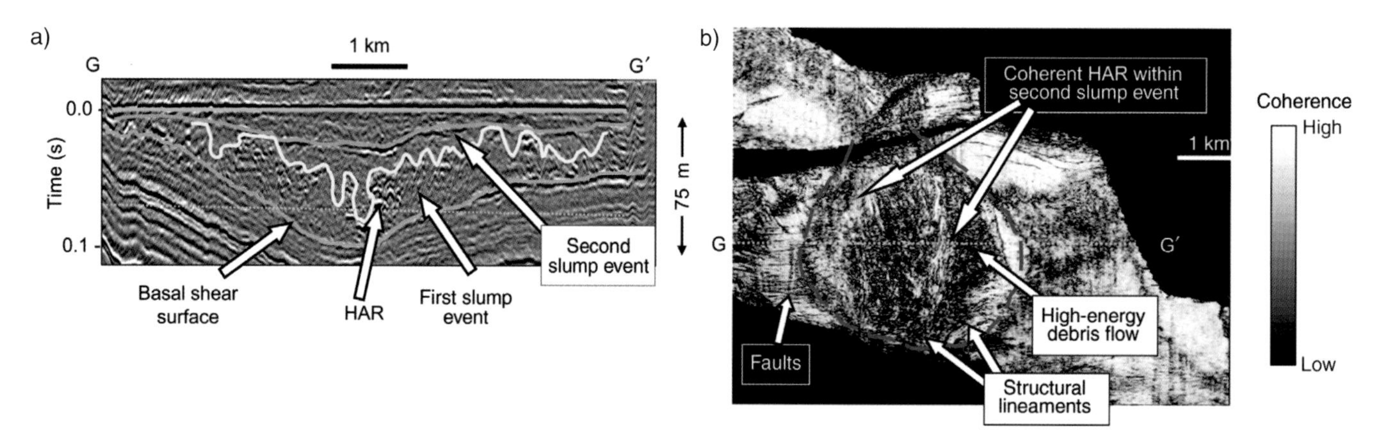

Figure 17. (a) A southwest-northeast seismic section showing an MTC. (b) A phantom-horizon slice 70 ms below the green horizon and through a coherence volume. In general, the lobate chaotic slump shows up as a region of low coherence. However, high-amplitude reflections (HARs) show up as coherent striations. After Oyedele (2005).

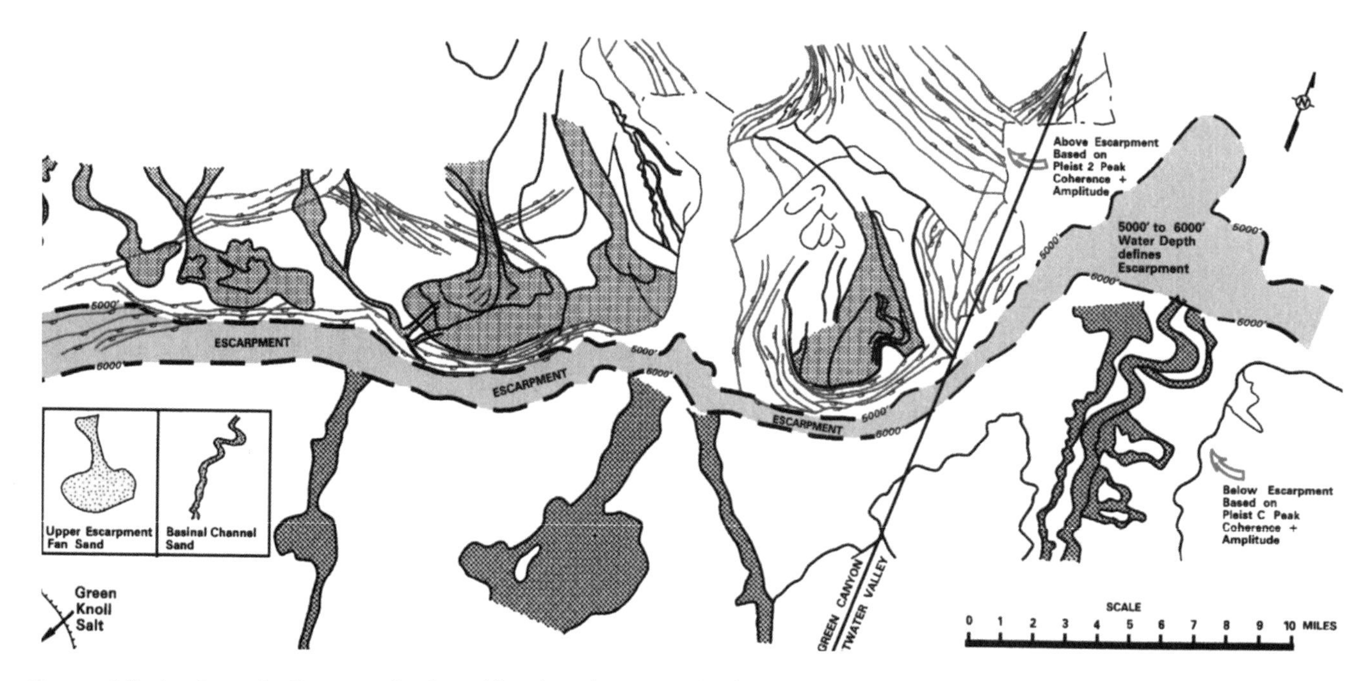

Figure 18. A schematic diagram of a depositional environment that is representative of the Sigsbee Escarpment, based on coherence and amplitude maps of a horizon approximately 500 ms below the seafloor. A series of upper escarpment fan sands appears above the escarpment, and several channel systems are developed on the abyssal plain. After Nibbelink (1999).

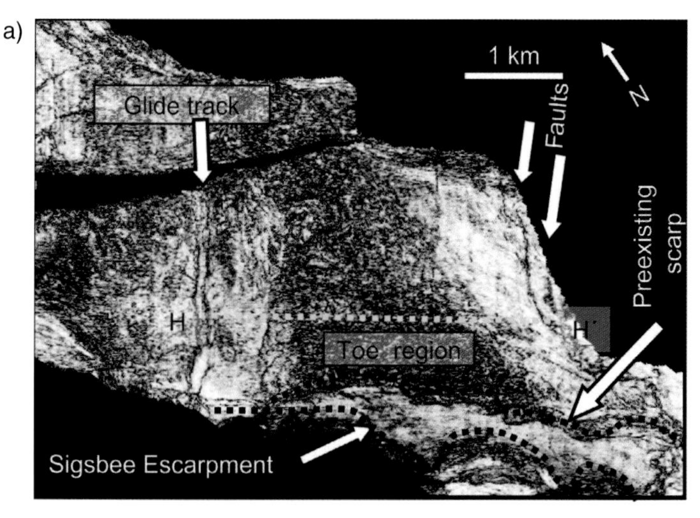

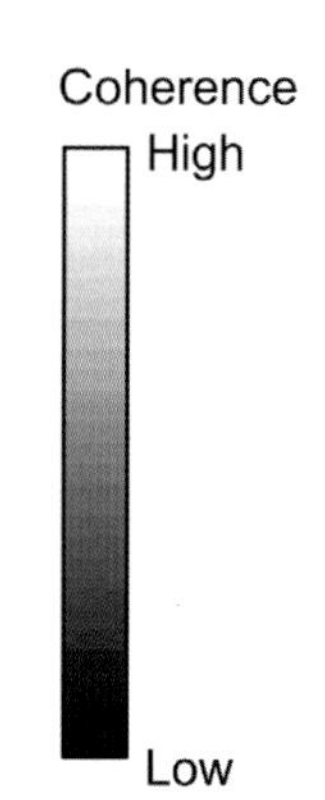

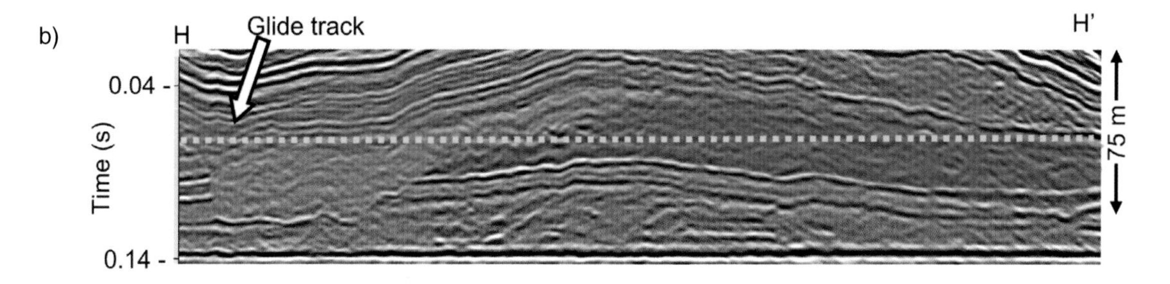

Figure 19. (a) A phantom-horizon slice through a coherence volume 70 ms above the green horizon and cutting through MTC B. Note the prominent glide track running parallel to the direction of transport. (b) A seismic section showing a depression approximately 8 m thick overlying MTC B. After Oyedele (2005).

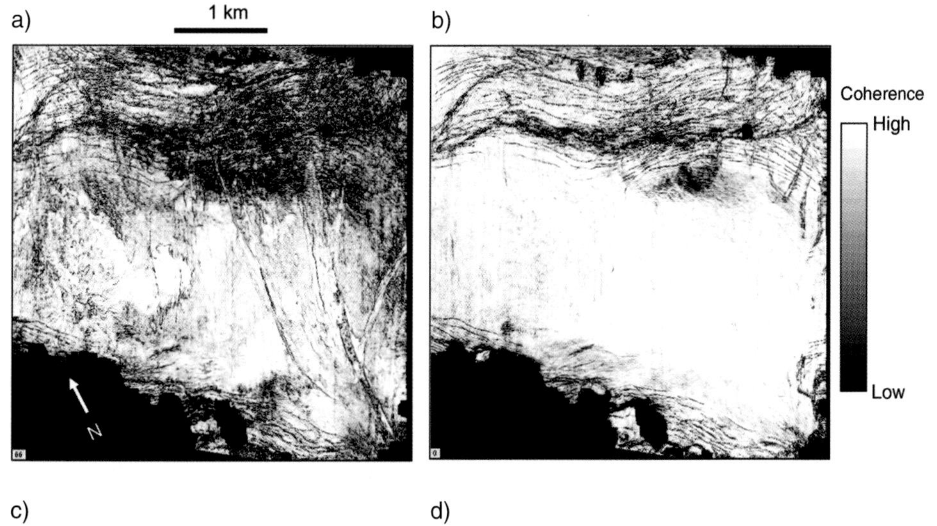

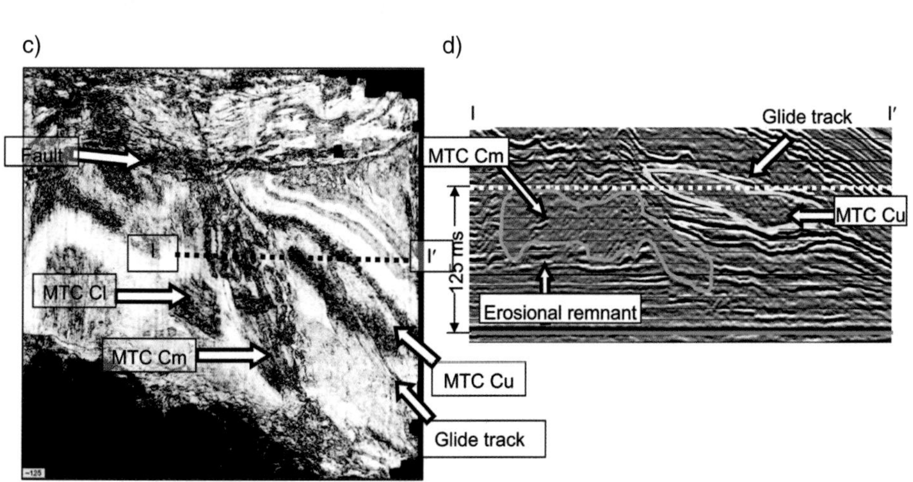

Figure 20. Three stages of a mini-basin, seen at (a) 66 ms below, (b) along, and (c) 125 ms above the picked blue horizon shown in (d) line II'. In (a) deposition comes from the south, from the crest of the Sigsbee Escarpment. In (b) we see faulting around the edge of the basin, which shows that it continued to sag at a later time in response to salt withdrawal. In (c) we see MTCs derived from the north. A glide track within MTC Cm runs southeastward beyond the downslope limits of the three MTC slide lobes. This glide track appears as a small depression in (c). After Oyedele (2005).

a clear glide track on both the seismic and the coherence image. Not all MTCs have a simple basal shear surface. Oyedele (2005) identified erosional remnants left intact after the slide passed. She also found that volumetric attributes allow an interpreter to animate through complex geologic features, such as MTCs, and thereby to reconstruct the depositional history. She noted that MTCs do not have a form amenable to autotracking, and the complex faulting would be extremely time-consuming to pick.

Gas-charged Channels

Shallow gas-charged channels also can be drilling hazards. Heggland (2004, p. 861) warns that "if faults and overlying sediments are impermeable, there is a potential for a pressure buildup in gas in the channel deposits." If there are no gas chimneys to provide a release, "drilling through the channel segments is therefore associated with a risk of encountering overpressured gas."

In Figure 21, we examine the erosional features identified earlier in Figure 13 and label them X, Y, and Z on an east-west seismic section cutting across three channel-like features. In Figure 21b, we see a root-mean-square (rms) amplitude map calculated over a 20-ms window centered about the green pick shown in (a). High amplitudes indicate levee complexes. At first, these features seem to be too straight to be interpreted as channels, and Oyedele (2005) postulated that they are glide tracks from outrunner blocks. However, the depth of scour of erosional features Y and Z appears to be too deep and too sharp to be associated with an outrunner block. The added frictional forces from the steep sides would prevent a block from sliding. In addition, a strong reflectivity is associated with flanks of these erosional features seen in Figure 21b and is consistent with either gas-charged levees or some other type of sheet-sand deposit. Figure 21c shows a time-thickness map between the green and yellow picks.

In Figure 22, we view these same erosional features using energy-weighted coherent-amplitude gradients (Figure 22a and b), coherence (Figure 22c), most-positive curvature (Figure 22e), and most-negative curvature (Figure 22d). The coherence and most-positive curvature images show the edges of the channel deposit. Coherence shows the channel edges because of waveform interference, and most-positive curvature shows the channel edges because the edges of the channels have an anticlinal form. The most-negative curvature maps the axis of the erosional features, or thalweg (if it is a channel), because it has a highly synclinal shape. Because the levees are thin, the waveform is nearly constant, so that the coherence images provide only moderate detail. In contrast, the energy-weighted coherent–amplitude gradients provide insight into the internal structure of the levee complex, with meanderlike features on the southern flank of channel Y.

Oyedele (2005) examined erosional feature Y in greater detail, as shown in Figure 23 in which a seismic profile is seen revealing a probable aggradational stacking pattern within channel complex Y from Figures 20 through 22. Clearly, the channel has been reoccupied more than once, as indicated by internal reflectivity. The coherence slice in Figure 23b shows correlation between a flank deposit and a

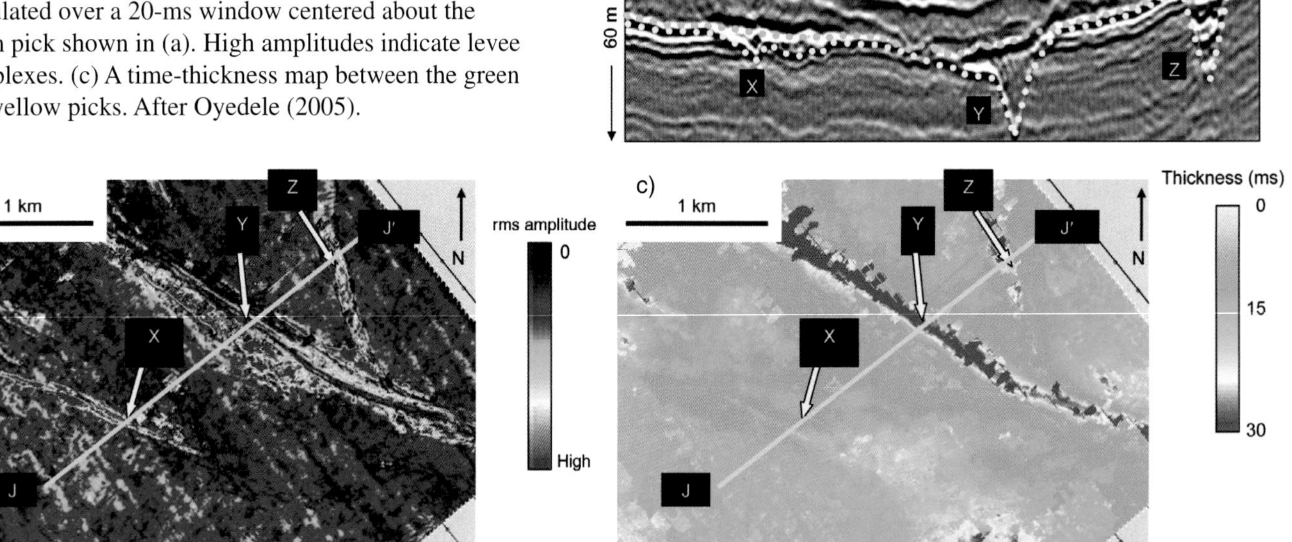

Figure 21. (a) An east-west seismic section cutting across three channel-like features, which are labeled X, Y, and Z. (b) A root-mean-square (rms) amplitude map calculated over a 20-ms window centered about the green pick shown in (a). High amplitudes indicate levee complexes. (c) A time-thickness map between the green and yellow picks. After Oyedele (2005).

sheet sand identified on the seismic profile. Although erosional feature Y is extraordinarily straight (not surprising, given the steep slopes that may have existed near the Sigsbee Escarpment during geologic time), Oyedele interprets it to be an amalgamated channel, flanked on the side by a high-amplitude (gas-charged?) sheet sand. Figure 23c shows an rms amplitude extraction that images the younger channel feature within channel complex Y. These features are quite deep in the seismic section and thus do not present a drilling hazard. For similar features very near the water bottom, we reproduce the work published by Rader and Medvin (2002) as a case study in our Chapter 20.

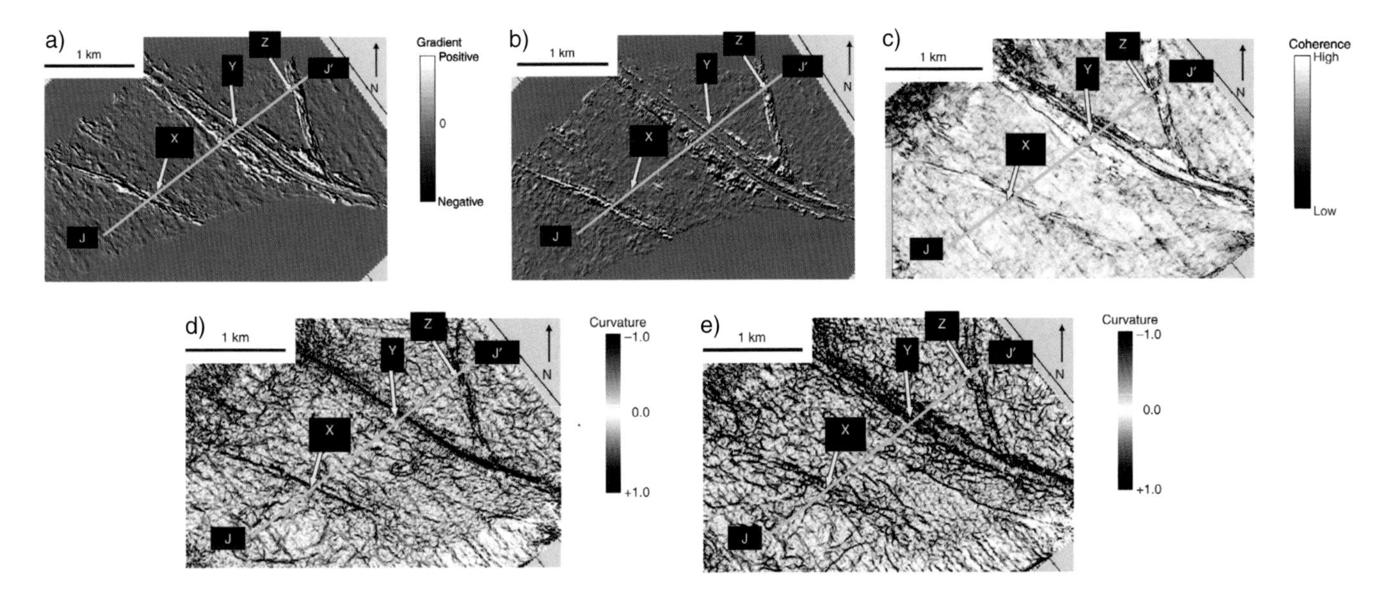

Figure 22. Horizon slices along the top of the channelized green pick from Figure 21: (a) an inline energy-weighted coherent-amplitude gradient, (b) a crossline energy-weighted coherent-amplitude gradient, (c) coherence, (d) most-negative curvature, and (e) most-positive curvature. The coherence and most-positive curvature show the edges of the channel complexes. The most-negative curvature shows the thalwegs, or axes of the channel complexes. The energy-weighted coherent-amplitude gradients show considerably more detail within the levee complex than does coherence where the thickness falls below thin-bed tuning. After Oyedele (2005).

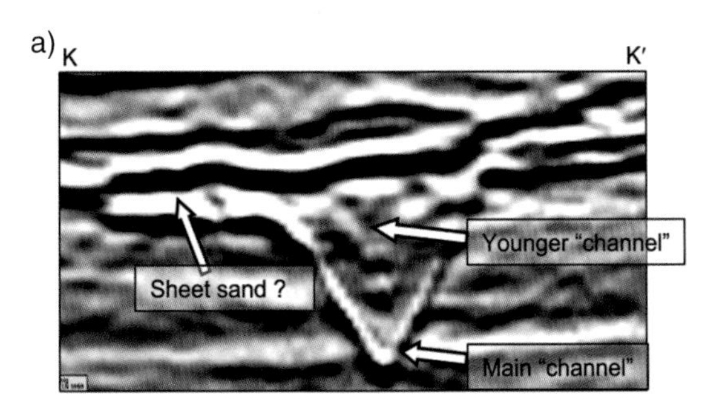

Figure 23. (a) A seismic profile showing a probable aggradational stacking pattern within channel complex Y from Figures 20 through 22. (b) Coherence, showing correlation between a flank deposit and a sheet sand identified on the seismic profile. (c) An rms amplitude extraction that images the younger channel feature within channel complex Y. After Oyedele (2005).

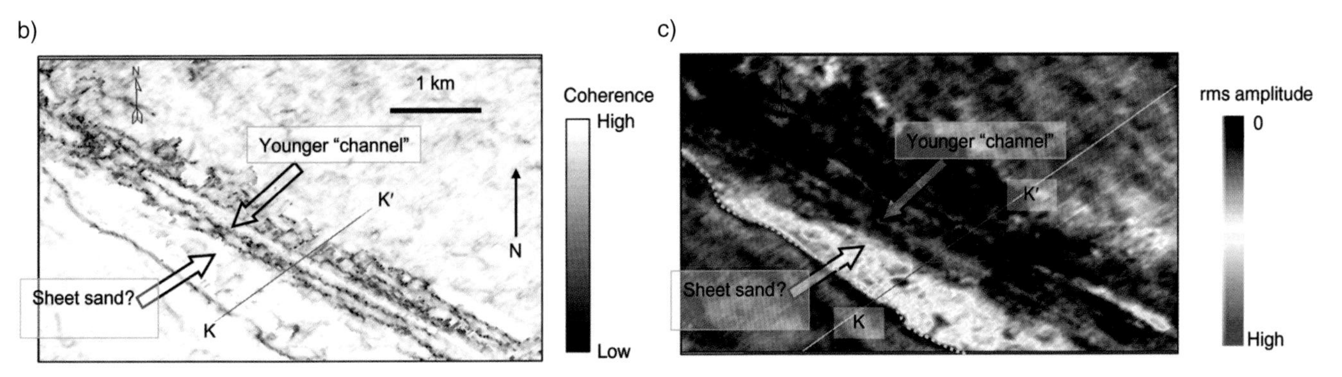

Circular Geologic Features

Various geologic processes can give rise to circular features that we encounter on 3D seismic data volumes. Figure 24 provides a summary of some key geologic mechanisms, scales, and geometric aspects of these features. Table 1 collates the key geometric and geologic criteria that lead to formation of different circular features and includes the mechanism of such features' formation and the nature of their spatial distribution. Those criteria facilitate identification of the circular features mentioned. We discuss circular diapirs in Chapter 11 and circular karsts in Chapter 13. In this chapter we discuss circular features in the context of seismic hazards. Most of these geologic features can be seen clearly on coherence displays, and their geometric configurations can be studied by proper 3D-data visualization on workstations.

Pockmarks

Because of buoyancy forces, gas generated at both great and shallow depths tries to escape to the surface. If possible, it reaches the surface through preexisting zones of weakness and forms a pockmark at the seafloor. Animating through coherence slices generated for a large survey acquired offshore Nigeria, Haskell et al. (1999) noted a strong organization of such features. In Figure 25, we display their phantom-horizon slices through the coherence volume at 0, 75, 150, and 225 ms below the seafloor. In the two deepest horizon slices, we note the presence of two meandering channels (magenta arrows) and a series of faults (yellow arrows). We also note that numerous circular features, which correspond to pockmarks at the seafloor and at 75 ms below the seafloor, correlate spatially with these deeper geologic features.

In Figure 26, we note that the pockmarks seen on vertical sections II′ and JJ′ are fault-controlled. Not only do we see the fault propagating all the way to the surface, we note that many of the layers adjacent to the fault suffer a velocity pushdown and have strong amplitudes, which implies that they are gas-charged. In contrast, the pockmarks seen on vertical section KK′ are associated with subtle faulting resulting from differential compaction over the channel indicated by the magenta arrows. Again, the gas follows these zones of weakness to the seafloor. Once an initial break toward the surface has been made, neighboring gas follows this new zone of weakness, thereby resulting in a string of circular pockmarks.

Pockmarks are found worldwide in a variety of depositional environments, including continental shelves, slopes, and ocean basins. Pockmarks generally form in soft, fine-grained sediments such as clays, muds, and silts. The finer the sediments are, the greater the size of the pockmark is. These pockmarks usually are less concentrated in fine-grained sediments. Although pockmarks can be controlled by faults and differential compaction, many pockmarks are uncorrelated to underlying stratigraphy or structure, implying that the fluids that formed them originated at shallow depths (e.g., vertical section LL′ in Figure 26).

In Figure 27, we display a time slice at 0.300 s through a migrated seismic data volume (Figure 27a) and its corresponding coherence volume (Figure 27b). The upper part of the slice shows the intersection of the seafloor with the time slice. Notice the scatter of pockmarks in the lower part of the slice.

In Figure 28a, we show a chair display of amplitudes from the same seismic data. Unfortunately, the positive and negative lobes of the seismic wavelet mask the details. In contrast, the coherence image shown in Figure 28b clearly shows the circular pockmarks at the seafloor and the vertical cut displays their roots as well as faults and a nearby shale diapir.

In Figure 29, we show a close-up of these same circular features. The radial patterns seen on some of the circular features approach 750 m in diameter. Concentric rings around some of the features suggest sediment collapse as the gas and fluids escape. More-coherent rings appear at a greater radius, where the sediments are flat, leading us to believe that these ring features are structural rather than artifacts of the computation wherever we encounter steep dip. Some of these pockmarks appear to be controlled by faults. The faults in turn appear to be controlled by the nearby shale diapirism.

Once the gas reaches the seafloor it expands, carrying shallow mud up into the water column where it can be carried away and dissipated by currents running along the seafloor. Such pockmarks often form the locus of unique chemosynthetic biological communities living on the dark ocean floor and may form small carbonate buildups. Because of their biological uniqueness, such communities are protected in many national waters.

Gas chimneys

Gas chimneys originate from regions of low-concentration gas escaping or migrating upward from a hydrocarbon accumulation or a reservoir. Chimneys are recognized on seismic data as zones of low-coherence reflection.

Three major conditions cause this poor data quality. First, there may be considerable absorption of compressional-wave energy if gas bubbles are present in the pores. One possible loss mechanism has water or other fluids viscously squirting from pore space to pore space as a compressional wave passes through.

A second condition for poor data quality results from very thin sand layers (less than 0.25 m thick) being charged by gas migrating toward the surface. The gas charge in these

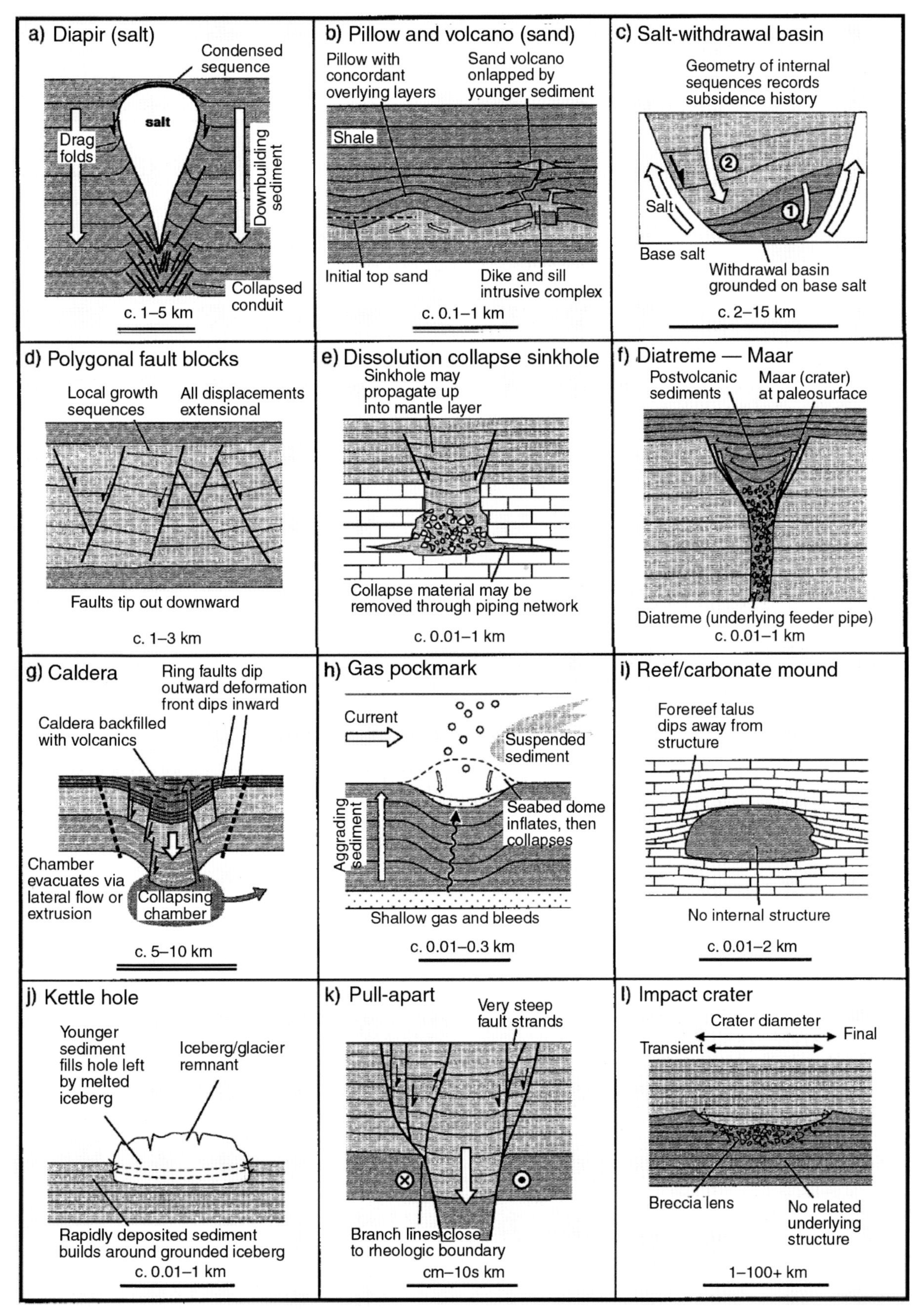

Figure 24. A schematic diagram showing the mechanism, scale, and geometric aspects of circular features. After Stewart (1999).

Table 1. Geologic and geometric criteria that can be used to identify circular features encountered on 3D seismic data. Modified from Stewart (1999).

	Geometric characteristics				Geologic relationships			
	Scale: typical diameter (km)	**Shape: typical max/min diameter ratio**	**Shape: typical depth/ width aspect ratio**	**Coherent internal structure/ fill?**	**Related to regional trends?**	**Characterize specific sedimentary environment?**	**Related to structure in under-lying strata?**	**Restricted strati-graphic occur-rence?**
Diapirs (salt, shale)	1–5	1	1–5	N	~	N	Y	N
Pillows (salt, sand, shale)	1–5	1+	0.01–5	N	~	Y	N	N
Withdrawal basin (salt)	2–15	1+	0.5–1	Y	~	N	N	N
Polygonal faults	0.3–2	1	0.5–3	Y	~	Y	N	N
Dissolution collapse	0.01–1	1	0–1	~	~	Y	N	N
Diatreme/maar	0.01–3	1	2+	~	~	N	~	N
Calderas	2–50	1	0.1–1	N	~	N	Y	N
Volcanoes (igneous)	1–50	1+	0.1–0.5	~	~	N	Y	N
Gas pockmarks	0.01–0.3	1	0.01–0.2	Y	~	Y	N	N
Reef/carbonate mounds	0.01–2	1+	0.1–0.5	N	~	Y	N	Y
Kettle holes	0.01–1	1+	0.01–0.1	Y	Y	Y	N	Y
Pull-aparts	0–40	2–5	0–1	Y	N	N	Y	N
Impact craters	1–100+	1	0.1–0.2	Y	N	N	N	N

thin layers may have only limited lateral extent, has very low impedances with respect to the surrounding shales, and may scatter energy incoherently.

The third and perhaps most important reason for poor data quality is the presence of gas that can result in a significant drop in compressional-wave velocity. In shallow sediments, this velocity may be less than that of the compressional-wave velocity in water. Consequently, seismic sections exhibit depressions in time, multipathing, and apparent faults. During acquisition, the sum of all of these phenomena produces wavefront perturbations that are very difficult for depth-migration algorithms to unravel. The result is an almost total loss of signal.

Gas chimneys occur throughout the world. If they are deeply seated, they are an excellent indicator of source rock. They can indicate either a breached or poor hydrocarbon seal, or more favorably, they may indicate a reservoir that is charged beyond its sealing capacity. We show one example of a chimney over the karsted area in Lihua field, Pearl River Basin, China, in Figures 25–27 of Chapter 13.

Because shear waves are relatively insensitive to the presence of gas in a chimney, they can be used to accurately image through a gas chimney. Much of the recent use of ocean-bottom multicomponent cable acquisition and converted-wave imaging has been driven by the need to image producing reservoirs that are masked by overlying gas chimneys.

In terms of hazards, Heggland (2004) noted that if chimneys or faults are present in a shallow seismic section, their associated gas-charged channels probably are not overpressured. To accurately map gas chimneys in a seismic volume acquired over a deepwater exploration area in the Green Canyon area, Gulf of Mexico, U.S.A., Heggland generated a meta-attribute (a combination of attributes) based on coherence, amplitude, and other measures that are sensitive to the texture of a chimney.

Heggland began by generating a suite of candidate attributes for the volume. Next he manually interpreted a coarse grid of data to identify the chimney texture. He also identified features that are not chimneys. Once a sufficient num-

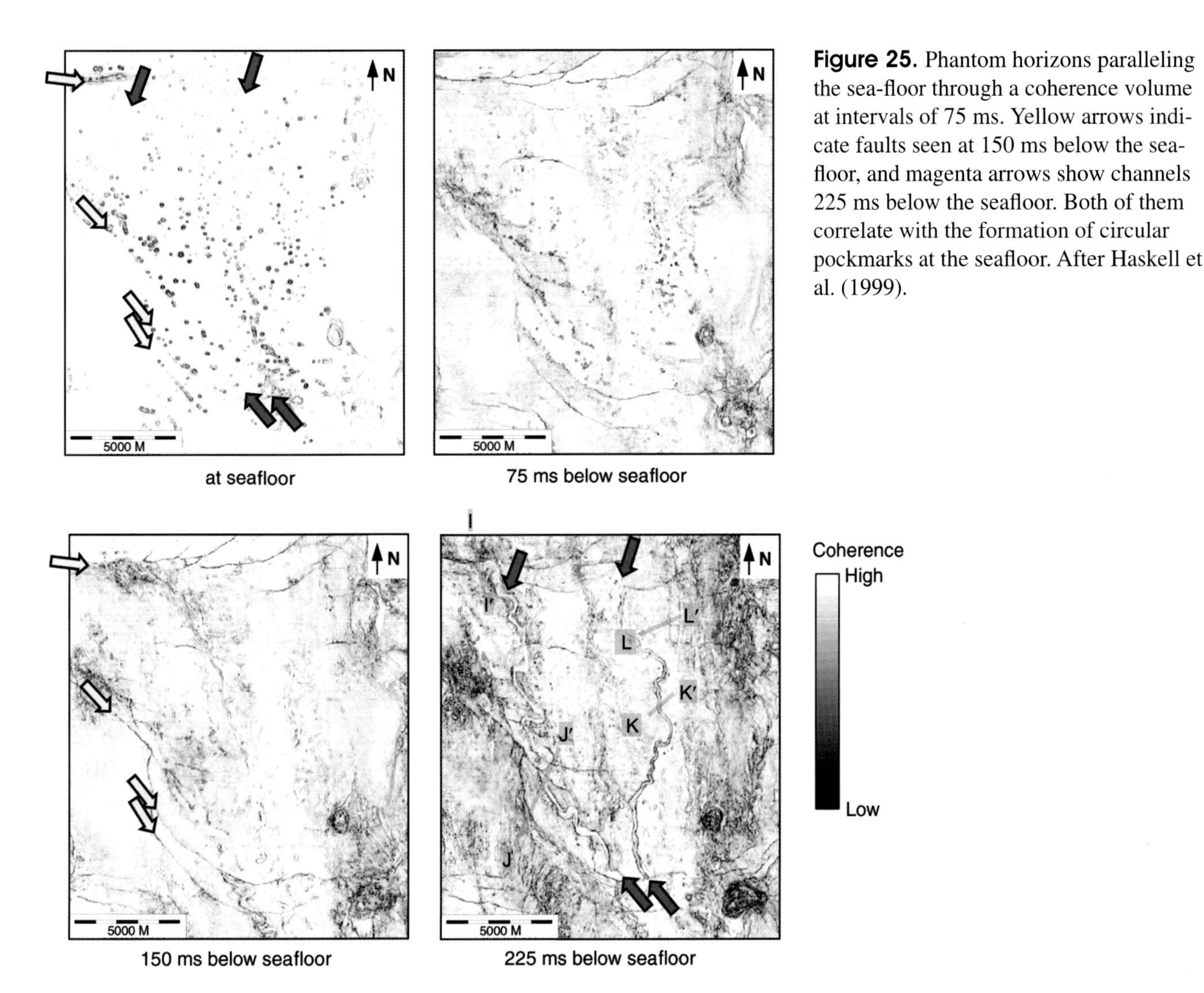

Figure 25. Phantom horizons paralleling the sea-floor through a coherence volume at intervals of 75 ms. Yellow arrows indicate faults seen at 150 ms below the seafloor, and magenta arrows show channels 225 ms below the seafloor. Both of them correlate with the formation of circular pockmarks at the seafloor. After Haskell et al. (1999).

ber of chimneys had been identified that represent the variation in appearance throughout the data, Heggland trained a neural network to construct a meta-attribute to predict the likelihood of a chimney being present. That neural network was validated on several chimneys that were not used in the training step. Once it had been trained and validated, this meta-attribute was computed for the entire volume.

In Figure 30, we redisplay Heggland's (2004) application of a meta-attribute to a deepwater survey from the Green Canyon area of the deepwater Gulf of Mexico, U.S.A. Figure 30a and b shows a representative line before and after detection of the chimney. The chimney appears to be associated with zones that are low amplitude and have a chaotic (low-coherence) character. Figure 30c and d shows 3D images of 40-ms rms amplitude extractions along horizons A and B overplotted with the chimney meta-attribute. Most convincingly, chimneys seem to correlate strongly with faults in the picked horizon. Heggland concluded that these faults are leaking, thereby reducing the risk of overpressure.

Shale-dewatering features

Haskell et al. (1999) produced perhaps the first coherence image of dewatering features, from a survey in the Valhall area of the North Sea (Figure 31). Time slices through the seismic data volume (Figure 31a) and a coherence volume (Figure 31b) for a survey from the Valhall area, North Sea, Norway, show salt and polygonal shale-dewatering features more accurately attributed to syneresis of clays. Since then, dewatering features have been identified offshore West Africa, Indonesia, Gulf of Mexico, offshore Brazil, and other areas. Cartwright (1994) originally attributed dewatering features to overpressure resulting from burial followed by hydrofracturing. This hypothesis was later modified in his work with Dewhurst et al. (1999, p. 794) in which they attributed the major cause as syneresis, "a process of spontaneous volumetric contraction and concomitant fluid expulsion that is (chemically and) not gravitationally driven." Syneresis occurs within 100 m of the water bottom and is controlled by

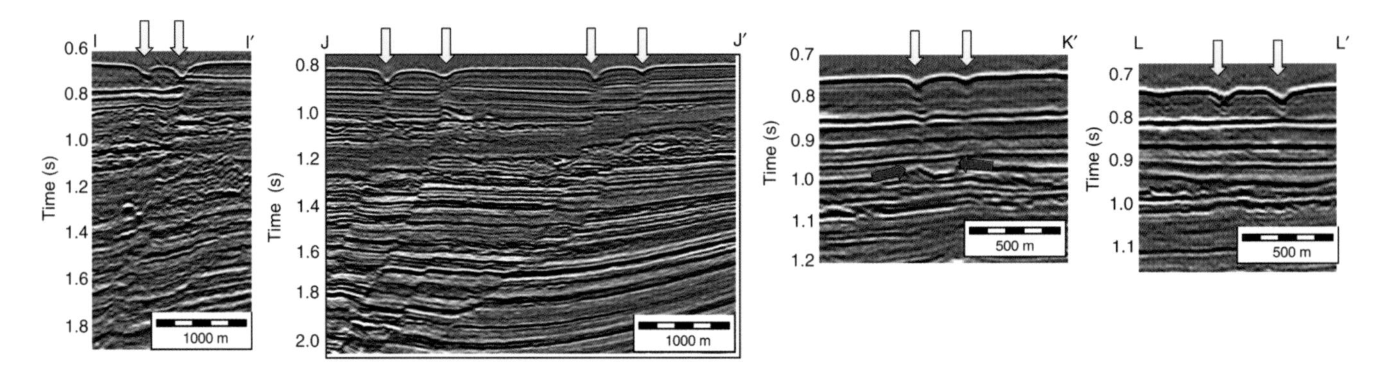

Figure 26. Arbitrary lines cut through the seismic data volume indicated by the orange lines on Figure 25. Yellow arrows indicate seafloor pockmarks. Pockmarks are fault-associated along lines II′ and JJ′, but are channel controlled along KK′. In this latter case, gas seeps up along unresolved faults caused by differential compaction. The channel on KK′ (magenta arrows) can clearly be seen on the vertical seismic section and on the coherence extraction 225 ms below the seafloor in Figure 25. Pockmarks on line LL′ have no apparent connection to underlying stratigraphy or structure, which suggests that the fluids that formed these pockmarks originated at shallow depths. After Marfurt and Nissen (1999).

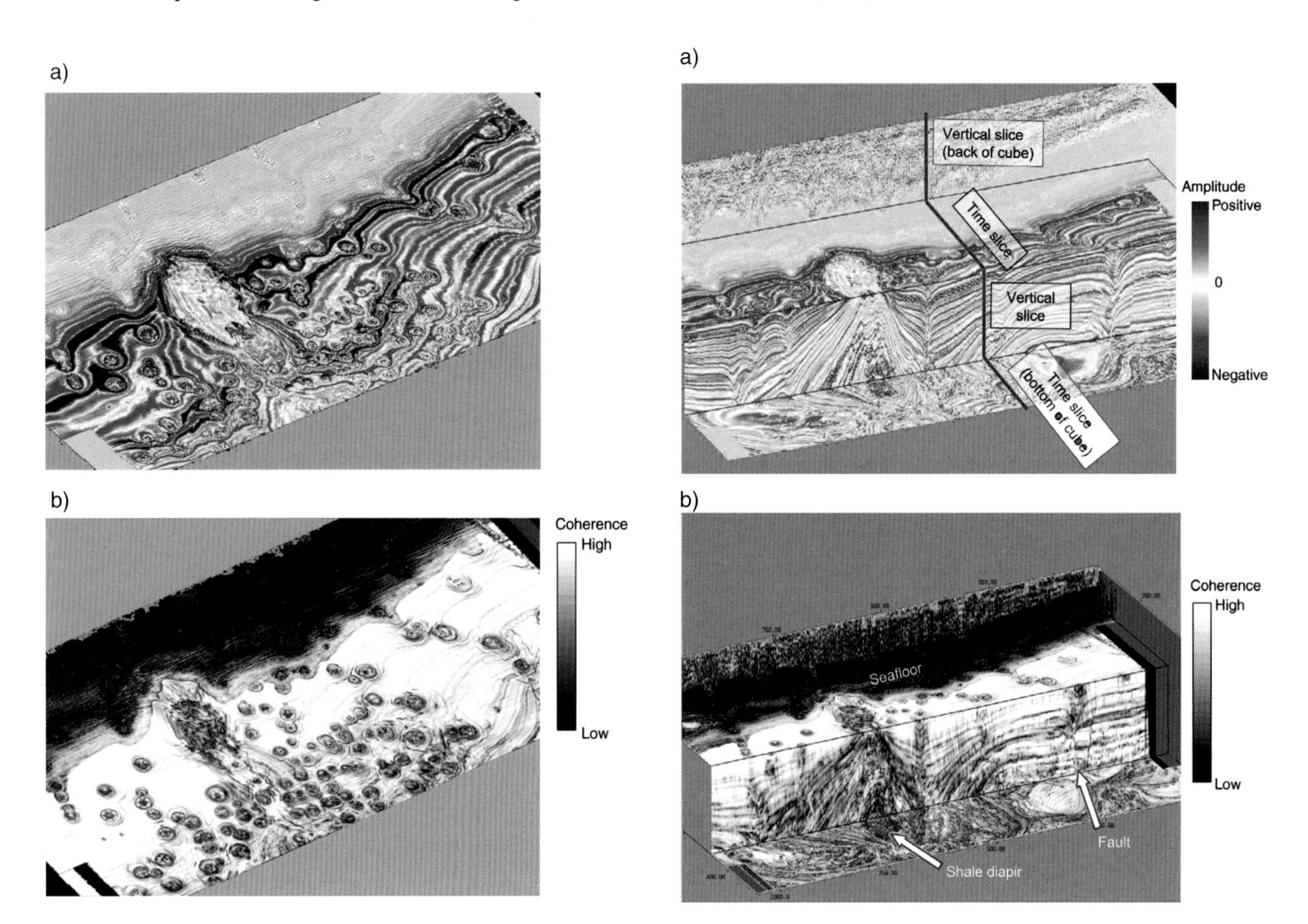

Figure 27. A time slice cutting the seafloor at $t = 0.300$ s, through (a) a seismic data volume and (b) a coherence volume, from a survey acquired offshore West Africa. Note the circular pockmarks associated with shallow flow of water and gas.

Figure 28. A chair diagram through a (a) seismic data volume and (b) a coherence volume from the survey shown in Figure 27. Note the velocity pushdowns below the pockmarks cut by the vertical slice, which indicate that the pockmarks are gas charged. Note the shale diapir indicated by the arrow.

clay particles, particularly smectite, that first flocculate and settle from the water column and then form larger agglomerates, which subsequently form a gel. If the amount of contraction in the gel from syneresis increases faster than the rate of vertical compaction, tensile stresses are set up and local normal faulting occurs. The resulting normal faults are not vertical but often have significant dip, so that coherence images generated over a 20- to 40-ms vertical-analysis win-

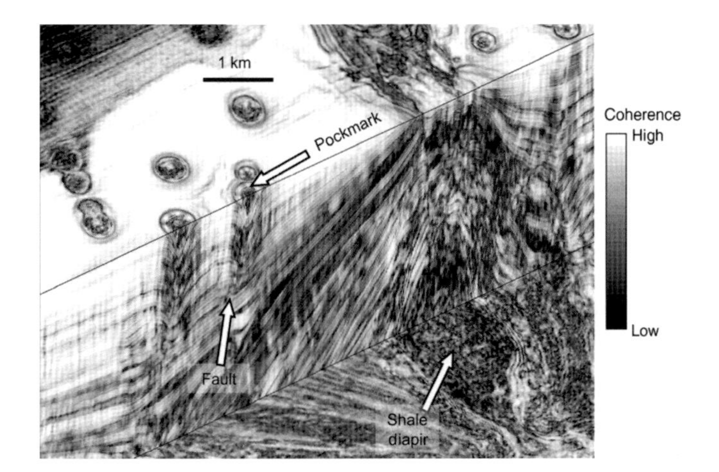

Figure 29. A chair diagram through a coherence volume from the survey shown in Figures 27 and 28. We now see that the pockmark denoted is controlled by a shallow fault associated with shale diapirism.

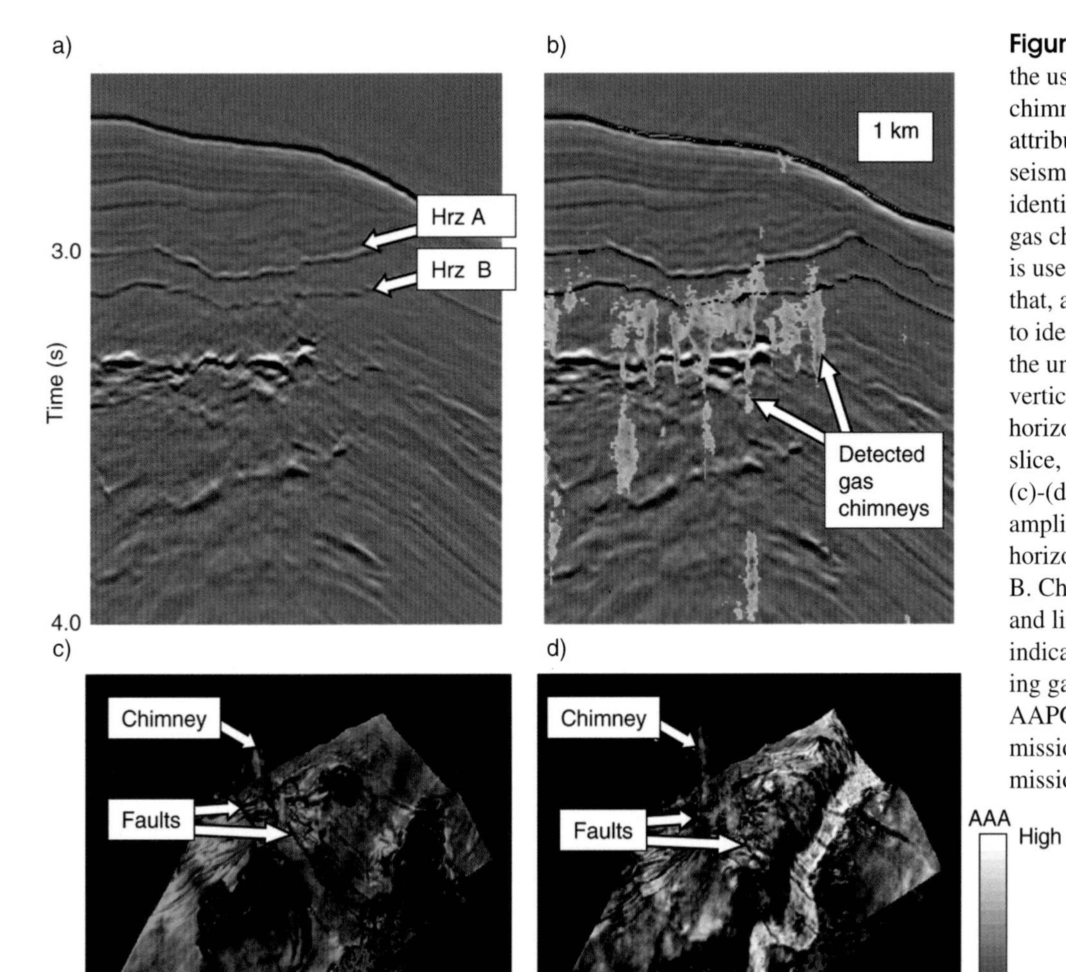

Figure 30. An example showing the use of a meta-attribute to map chimneys. First, a suite of texture attributes is generated from the seismic data. Next, an interpreter identifies zones with and without gas chimneys. This interpretation is used to train a neural network that, after validation, can be used to identify chimneys throughout the uninterpreted volume. (a) A vertical seismic slice showing horizons A and B. (b) The same slice, with predicted gas chimneys. (c)-(d) A 40-ms average absolute amplitude (AAA) map (c) along horizon A and (b) along horizon B. Chimneys are plotted in yellow and line up with the faults, which indicates that the faults are leaking gas. After Heggland (2004). AAPG©2004. Reprinted by permission of the AAPG whose permission is required for further use.

dow often show discontinuity at both the top and the bottom of the shale (formerly clay) layer. Those discontinuities give rise to the double faults seen in Figure 32a. An analogy of these features can be drawn to a dried riverbed in which the clay dries up, forming polygonal fault patterns (Figure 32b).

The geometries of shale-dewatering features cannot be recognized on vertical seismic sections (Figure 33a), but rather are best seen on seismic and coherence time slices (Figure 31a and b, Figure 33b and c). In Figure 33a we can see the nonvertical, confined nature of these faults. The example in Dewhurst et al. (1999) shows a stack of four dewatered shales, each separated by non-faulted lithologies, and each with its own unique polygonal pattern. The authors found that the presence of polygonal faults correlated with both the clay fraction and smectite content, with lateral changes in these fractions resulting in less faulting. If we were to use the original Cartwright (1994) model of overpressure and hydrofracturing, the presence of shale dewatering could be an indicator of deep drilling hazards. However, if we accept the more recent syneresis mechanism, the presence of shale-dewatering features is simply an indication of lithology.

Differential Compaction

In Figure 34, we display several slices through the shallow part of a coherence volume for a survey from the North Sea. In the deepest image, Figure 34d, 200 ms below the water bottom, we see a clear channel trending east-west (white arrow). Because of differential compaction, shal-

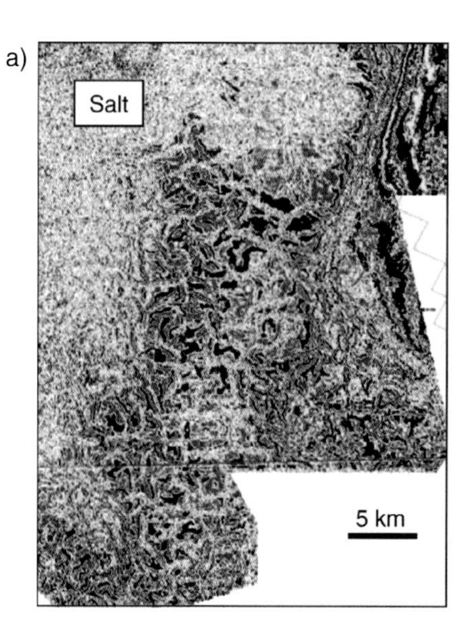

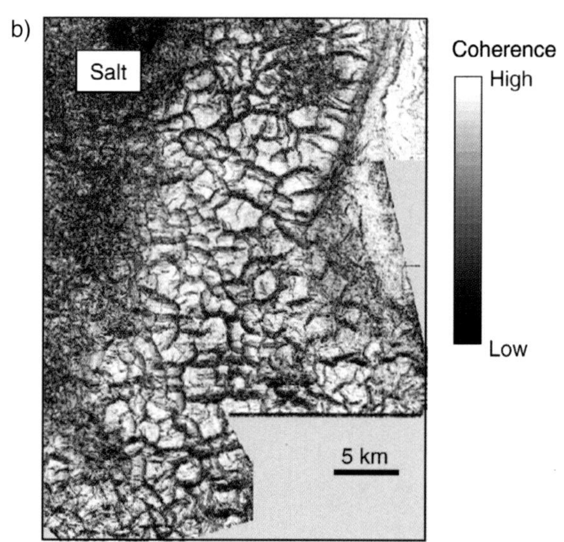

Figure 31. Time slices through (a) a seismic data volume and (b) a coherence volume for a survey from the Valhall area, North Sea, Norway, showing salt and polygonal shale-dewatering features more accurately attributed to syneresis of clays. After Haskell et al. (1999).

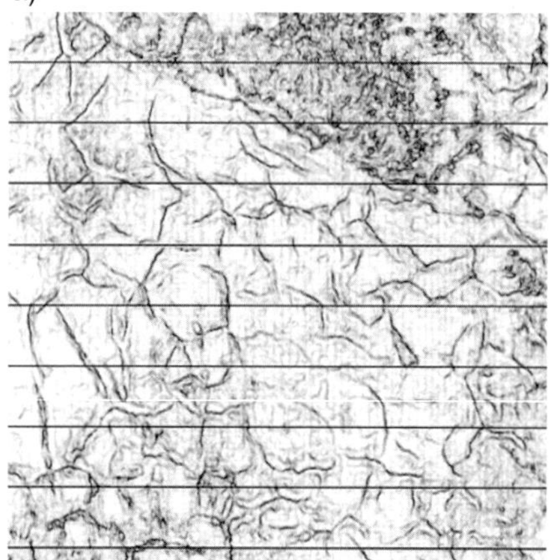

Figure 32. (a) Polygonal fault patterns resulting from shale dewatering in a survey from the North Sea and (b) a geologic analog of mud cracks seen in a dried streambed. The double-fault images result from a high dip rate on the vertically short and locally confined normal faults, which causes the coherence algorithm to see the discontinuity both at the top and at the laterally offset bottom of the fault.

lower images show faults associated with the channel. Careful examination shows that the morphology of many of these faults has a meandering character and thus probably is associated with differential compaction. In Figure 34c, we see another example of shale dewatering characterized by polygonal fractures. Interestingly, the alignment of these polygons is strongly controlled by the faults associated with differential compaction at deeper levels.

Iceberg Plow Marks

We conclude with a simple example of iceberg plow marks, originally shown by Gallagher and Heggland (1995). The theory of iceberg plow marks and their recognition on 3D seismic data is well documented in a recent paper by Rafaelsen et al. (2002). In summary, approximately 90% of an iceberg lies below sea level. Winds and currents push icebergs around at will, with the result that sometimes the keels (or bottoms) of icebergs drag across the soft seafloor and leave a depression.

In Alaska, plow marks reflect significant backscattered energy in the water column. Their treatment proved to be very problematic before 3D acquisition became common. As a drilling hazard, plow-mark depressions can fill with sand after a heavy storm. Later the plow marks are buried and sealed in shale, and subsequently they become charged with gas. Such plow marks have proven to be a significant drilling hazard in certain areas of the North Sea.

In Figure 35a, we show a time slice at 0.700 s through conventional seismic data (Gallagher and Heggland, 1995). We note that whether the plow marks show up as red (trough) or black (peak), amplitudes correspond to the way the time slice cuts across the plowed horizon, as indicated by arrows in Figure 35d. Clearly, the plow marks are strong in amplitude and show an image that is consistent with changing wind and current directions.

Figure 35b and c shows equivalent time slices through the coherence and dip-azimuth volumes generated by Amoco researchers in 1996. These images show that a coherence slice is not as effective as a conventional amplitude slice for visualizing plow marks; however, the volumetric dip-azimuth slice does provide additional information by showing that the plow marks are linear depressions.

Rafaelsen et al. (2002) noted that an intrinsic ambiguity exists on seismic amplitude regarding whether such plow-mark lineations are anticlinal or synclinal. Both types of features occur in the highly glaciated Barents Sea. The dip-azimuth image shown in Figure 35c resolves such an ambiguity (as would curvature images).

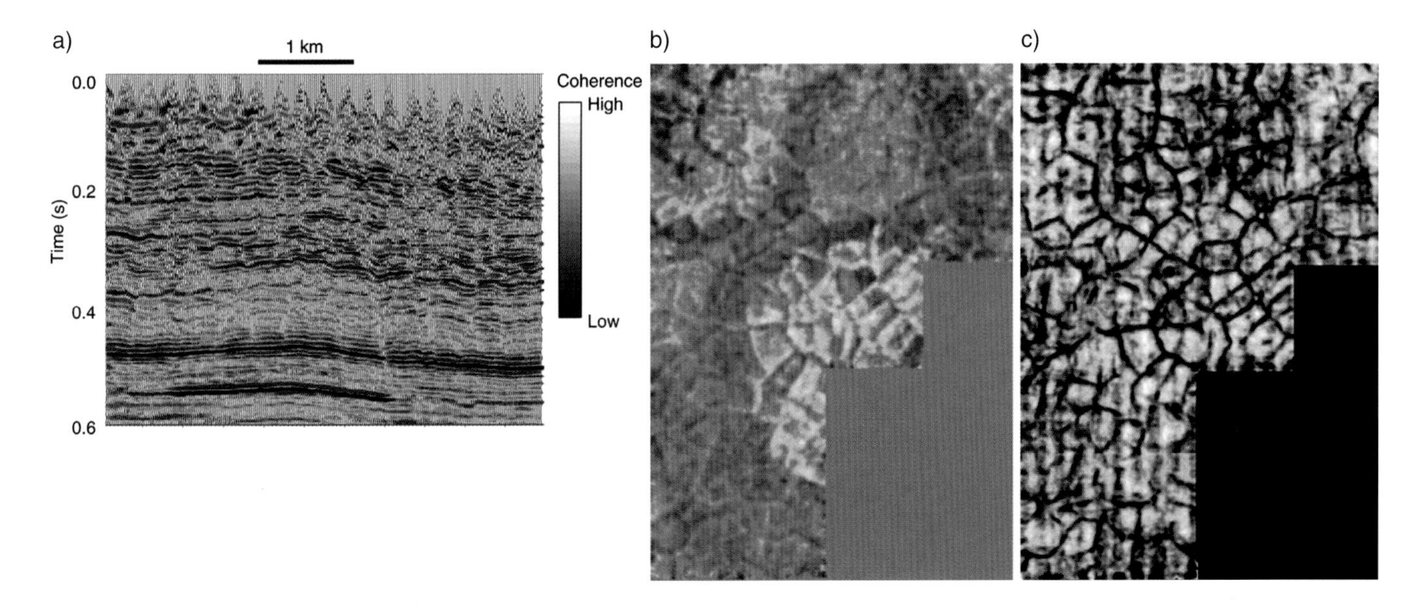

Figure 33. (a) A vertical slice through seismic data, and (b)-(c) time slices at t = 0.420 s, through (b) a seismic data volume and (c) a coherence volume, from a survey in Alberta, Canada. Polygonal fault patterns, delineating cells 1–5 km in diameter, are clearly seen on the coherence slice. Such faults are thought to have been caused by dewatering in overpressured shales. Their geometries cannot be recognized on vertical seismic sections and are extremely difficult to map on conventional 3D time slices. Because surfaces exhibiting polygonal fault patterns indicate areas with a potential for overpressure, recognition of these fault patterns on coherence slices can be important in planning wells.

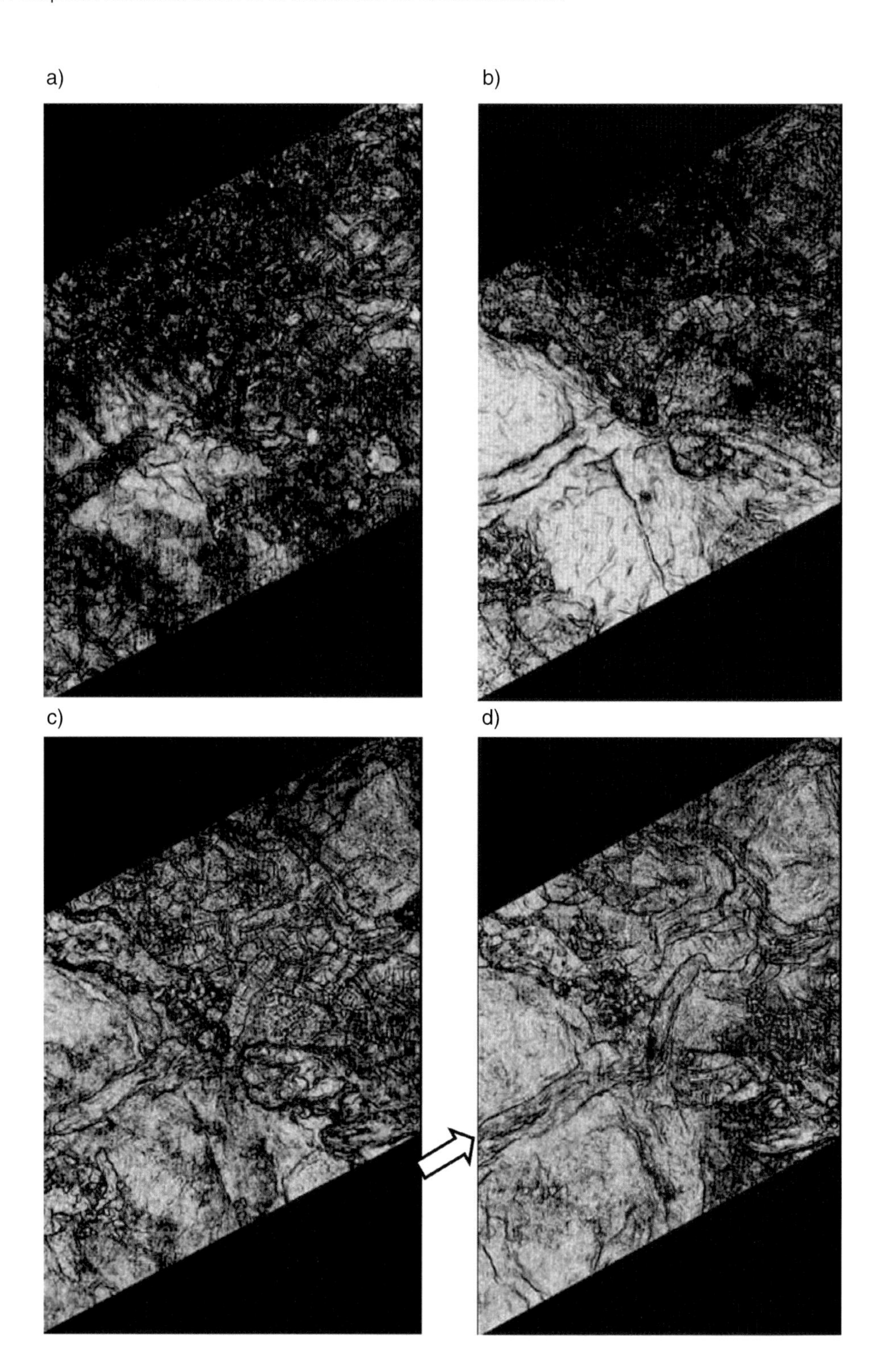

Figure 34. Rapid evolution of shallow faults in the North Sea as seen via time slices through coherence volumes obtained at (a) 0.032 s, (b) 0.124 s, (c) 0.164 s, and (d) 0.200 s below the water bottom. The larger faults apparently were caused by differential compaction across deeper channels (arrow), whereas the very complex polygonal pattern seen in (c) appears to be polygonal faulting associated with shale dewatering.

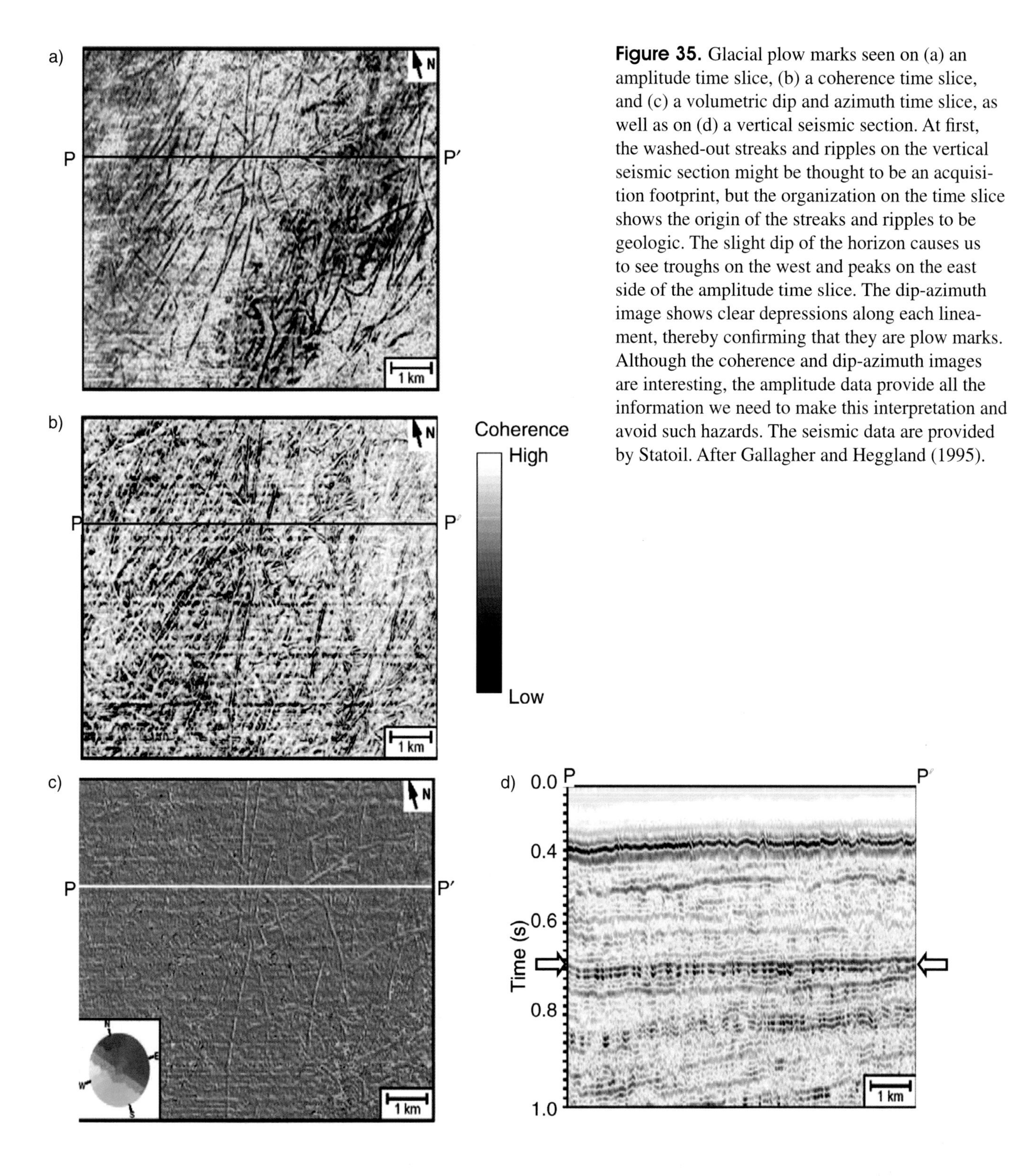

Figure 35. Glacial plow marks seen on (a) an amplitude time slice, (b) a coherence time slice, and (c) a volumetric dip and azimuth time slice, as well as on (d) a vertical seismic section. At first, the washed-out streaks and ripples on the vertical seismic section might be thought to be an acquisition footprint, but the organization on the time slice shows the origin of the streaks and ripples to be geologic. The slight dip of the horizon causes us to see troughs on the west and peaks on the east side of the amplitude time slice. The dip-azimuth image shows clear depressions along each lineament, thereby confirming that they are plow marks. Although the coherence and dip-azimuth images are interesting, the amplitude data provide all the information we need to make this interpretation and avoid such hazards. The seismic data are provided by Statoil. After Gallagher and Heggland (1995).

Chapter Summary

Many geologic hazards are seen more easily on attribute volumes than on conventional seismic volumes. Perhaps the most commonly used attribute in hazard delineation is the dip-magnitude map calculated along the seafloor. The extension of such dip-magnitude maps beyond the seafloor to deeper interpreted horizons and uninterpreted seismic volumes has given rise to the field of seismic geomorphology.

With the possible exception of faults, geologic hazards often are difficult to see using conventional seismic interpretation techniques. Three-dimensional volumetric attributes, coupled with 3D graphics tools, allow us to quickly visualize rather than manually pick features such as mass-transport complexes, amalgamating channels, plow marks, gas chimneys, and pockmarks. Coherence and other 3D texture attributes work well on conventional seismic data acquired in deep water. Such images can be used for the early detection and delineation of both stratigraphic and structural hazards prior to acquisition of high-resolution hazard surveys and can impact well planning and location development.

In addition to helping delineate hazards, an improved visibility of mass-transport complexes, including outrunner blocks, glide tracks, and pressure ridges, provides indicators of the paleodepositional setting, thereby allowing a skilled interpreter to put features in their proper context. In addition, high-resolution surveys allow us to generate 3D analogs from which we can better understand reservoir compartmentalization.

References

Brand, J. R., D. L. Lanier, M. M. Angell, K., Hanson, E. Lee, and R. A. George, 2003, Indirect methods of dating seafloor activity: Geology, regional stratigraphic markers, and seafloor current processes: Proceedings of the Offshore Technology Conference, Paper 15200.

Cartwright, J. A., 1994, Episodic basin-wide hydrofracturing of overpressured early Cenozoic mudrock sequences in the North Sea Basin: Marine and Petroleum Geology, **11**, 587–607.

Costas, E., Synolakis, Bardet, J. P. Borrero, J. C., Davies, H. L., Okal, E. A., Silver, E. A., Sweet, S., and Tappin, D. R., 2002, The slump origin of the 1998 Papua New Guinea Tsunami: Proceedings of the Royal Society of London, A, **458**, 763–789.

Dewhurst, D. N, J. A. Cartwright, and L. Lonergan, 1999, The development of polygonal fault systems by the syneresis of colloidal sediments: Marine and Petroleum Geology, **16**, 793–810.

Gallagher, J. W., and R. Heggland, 1995, Shallow gas evaluations based on conventional 3-D seismic data, 65th Annual International Meeting, SEG, Expanded Abstracts, 518–520.

Haskell, N. L., S. E. Nissen, M. Hughes, J. Grindhaug, S. Dhanani, R. Heath, J. Kantorowicz, L. Antrim, M. Cubanski, R. Nataraj, M. Schilly, and S. Wigger, 1999, Delineation of geological drilling hazards using 3-D seismic attributes: The Leading Edge, **18,** 373–382.

Heggland, R., 2004, Definition of geohazards in exploration 3-D seismic data using attributes and neural-network analysis: AAPG Bulletin, **88**, 857–868.

Marfurt, K. J., and S. E. Nissen, 1999, Interpretive aspects of seismic coherence and related multitrace attributes, *in* P. D. Anno, (ed.), Toolbox of advanced seismic interpretation techniques: Proceedings of the 1999 Spring Symposium of the Geophysical Society of Tulsa, 1–78.

Nibbelink, K., 1999, Modeling deepwater reservoir analogs through analysis of recent sediments using coherence, seismic amplitude, and bathymetry data, Sigsbee Escarpment, Green Canyon, Gulf of Mexico: The Leading Edge, **18**, 550–561.

Niederoda, A. W., C. W. Reed, L. Hatchett, A. Young, D. Lanier, V. Kasch, P. Jeanjean, D. Orange, and W. Bryant, 2003, Analysis of past and future debris flows and turbidity currents generated by slope failures along the Sigsbee Escarpment in the deep Gulf of Mexico: Proceedings of the Offshore Technology Conference, Houston, TX, Paper 15162.

Nissen, S. E., N. L. Haskell, J. A. Lopez, T. J. Donlon, and M. S. Bahorich, 1995, 3-D seismic coherency techniques applied to the identification and delineation of slump features: 65th Annual International Meeting, SEG, Expanded Abstracts, 1535–1536.

Nissen, S. E., N. L. Haskell, C. Steiner, and K. Coterill, 1999, Debris flow outrunner blocks on the Nigerian continental slope delineated by 3-D seismic coherency: The Leading Edge, **18**, 595–599.

Orange, D. L., M. Angell, J. R. Brand, J. Thomson, T. Buddin, M. Williams, W. Hart, and W. J. Berger III, 2004, Geologic and shallow salt tectonic setting of the Mad Dog and Atlantis fields: Relationship between salt, faults, and seafloor geomorphology: The Leading Edge, **23,** 354–365.

Oyedele, O., 2005, 3-D high resolution seismic imaging of deep water systems, SE Green Canyon, Sigsbee Escarpment, Gulf of Mexico: M.S. thesis, University of Houston.

Prior, D. B., and J. M. Coleman, 1988, Mass wasting on continental margins: Annual Review of Earth and Planetary Sciences, **16**, 101–119.

Rader, B., and E. Medvin, 2002, Shallow hazard detection in the near surface, a coherence cube processing application: The Leading Edge, **21**, 672–674.

Rafaelsen, B., K. Andreassen, L. W. Kuilman, E. Lebesbye, K. Hogstad, and M Midtbo, 2002, Geomorphology of buried glacigenic horizons in the Barents Sea from three-dimensional seismic data, *in* J. A. Dowdeswell, and C. O'Cofaigh, eds., Glacier-influenced sedimentation on high-latitude continental margins: Geological Society of London, Special Publication 203, 259–276.

Stewart, S. A., 1999, Seismic interpretation of circular geological structures: Petroleum Geoscience, **5**, 273–285.

Chapter 15

Mapping Reservoir Heterogeneity

Chapter Objectives

After reading this chapter, you will be able to

- choose appropriate attributes to map porosity and thickness and choose other attributes to map edges of reservoir compartments faults and fractures
- use geometric attributes to place traditional reservoir parameter estimation in the proper geologic context
- adapt existing reservoir-characterization workflows to use geometric attributes
- evaluate the use of production and tracer data with geometric attributes to better map reservoir plumbing

Introduction

Understanding and mapping reservoir heterogeneity, including porosity, permeability, layering and thickness of reservoir and seal, and barriers and conduits to fluid flow, are critical to successfully operating a hydrocarbon reservoir. Frontier opportunities are increasingly limited on this planet of fixed size. Because opportunities that do exist require increasing capital expenditure, we strive to develop additional reserves of petroleum in mature basins and to produce petroleum more efficiently. Therefore, more geoscientists are moving from exploration for new reserves to exploitation of proven reserves.

The key to and difficulty in reservoir characterization lie in data integration. Fortunately, the introduction of 3D seismic acquisition in the past 20 years provides reservoir managers with a fairly dense (say, 25 m × 25 m) seismic image of their reservoir. In contrast, wells are spaced considerably farther apart (500 m or more in the tracer example discussed in this chapter and shown in Figure 28). Although 3D seismic data provide superior lateral resolution compared with that from well data, vertical resolution from 3D data is on the order of tens of meters, depending on frequencies that penetrate into the reservoir and seismic velocities of the reservoir. In contrast, well logs provide high vertical resolution — typically 0.5 or 1 ft (0.15 to 0.30 m). Image logs provide higher resolution still, at the millimeter level.

Production measurements are on a different scale altogether and consist of pressure transients and chemical or radioactive tracers between wells in addition to the amount of oil, gas, and water throughout the lifetime of the reservoir.

Prediction of hydrocarbon (and water) production from a proposed well-development program is the motivation for reservoir characterization. Diverse geophysical, petrophysical, geological, and production data are integrated through models. First, we create a reservoir model that provides an initial estimate of lithology, porosity, permeability, and current fluid saturations. Next, we use this geologic model as input to a reservoir simulator, which predicts fluid flow through the reservoir as a function of time. History-matching the results of the model to past and present reservoir performance requires modifying the input reservoir model.

If we have good-quality seismic data, adequate well control, and a simple geologic setting, as an industry we are reasonably accurate at predicting porosity. However, we are much less accurate (some say not accurate at all) at predicting permeability. Permeability (and likewise porosity) can be divided into two categories: matrix permeability of the reservoir, and fracture permeability provided by faults, joints, or fractures (that are either natural or have been induced by engineers as part of the development process).

In this chapter, we show how the suite of attributes discussed in this book, coupled with an appropriate geologic working hypothesis, can aid us in mapping the reservoir plumbing (permeability) needed by reservoir simulators to produce a field economically.

Reservoir Characterization Workflows To Estimate Porosity and Thickness

Geometric attributes are sensitive to lateral changes in reflector impedance and morphology. The response of geometric attributes to a perfectly flat-layered earth would be zero. In contrast, impedance inversion (as commonly practiced in 2007), AVO, and spectral decomposition are sensitive to vertical variations in lithology, porosity, and fluid contents.

Our goal in this chapter is not to review the excellent work that has gone before us in reservoir characterization, but rather to illustrate how such workflows must be modified to use geometric attributes. From this discussion, some readers will realize that geometric attributes do not help them achieve their goal of estimating porosity or net-to-gross ratio. As we discussed in the introduction, the key to using attributes of any kind is in understanding their geophysical, petrophysical, and geological basis. Geometric attributes as point measurements do not correlate well with lithology or porosity. We illustrate this problem with the example shown in Figure 1.

In Figure 1a, we display a horizon slice through a coherence volume computed from a seismic survey acquired over southern Alberta. Although we can see the edges of an incised valley and other channels (arrows), we have little indication of what lithology lies inside the channel boundaries. In this case, the goal is to differentiate between porous glauconitic sands, tight sands, and shale within the channel boundaries. In terms of coherence, a shale-sand boundary would be identical to a sand-shale boundary. Although we can use a model of the depositional environment to argue in favor of sands lying inside rather than outside the channel boundary, we want to be more quantitative.

Figure 1b displays a corresponding horizon slice through a lambda-rho (λ-ρ) volume, which together with mu-rho (μ-ρ) is a powerful method for detecting anomalies (λ-ρ and μ-ρ attributes are derived from P- and S-impedance data; respectively, λ, μ, and ρ represent the incompressibility, rigidity, and density of rocks. Details are given in Chapters 1 and 10). We note here that a low λ-ρ anomaly (blue) occurs inside the major incised valley, which is associated with high μ-ρ values (in addition to some other small islands of blue). Because λ denotes the incompressibility and μ denotes the rigidity of a rock, for gas, λ is expected to be low, and μ, the measure of sand-rock matrix, is expected to be high. Consequently, low λ-ρ in conjunction with high μ-ρ is a good indicator for gas sand.

Well-log data would assist us in confirming this seismically derived conclusion. Understanding which attributes are sensitive to different types of geologic changes is key to intelligently interpreting attributes, whether one is a skilled geoscientist working with paper sections and colored pencils, or a skilled geoscientist using modern pattern-recognition and geostatistics software.

We strongly advise against what Bob Sheriff calls "mindless interpretation," whereby an interpreter generates dozens of attributes and looks for anomalies. To avoid the pitfall of false-positive correlations (Kalkomey, 1997) such as those discussed in Chapter 1, whether by a sometimes-overeager interpreter or an always-eager neural-network software application, one should always have an a priori or a posteriori (through subsequent modeling) reason to correlate a seismic attribute with a given well-log measurement.

We show such a correlation in Figure 1c, which is a correlation of gamma-ray values with acoustic impedance. We expect shales to differ from each other in both of these measures. Although shales almost always have higher gamma-ray values than sandstones have, their impedance values can be either higher or lower than those for sandstones, depending on depth of burial, porosity, and other basin-specific factors.

Once we have determined which attributes are sensitive to lithology, we can use them to train a neural network. The software constructs a transform between the attributes at a given suite of wells and the well-log measurements themselves. Ideally, this transform is tested or validated against a subset of wells that were not used in creating the transform (commonly called training the neural network). Once it is validated, this transform is used to predict the value of interest on a map, such as the map of gamma-ray values shown in Figure 1d. We refer the reader to an excellent overview of this and the related geostatistics workflow in the work of Russell et al. (2001), Hampson et al. (2001), Walls et al. (2002), and Dubrule (2003).

Hart (2002) broadened the validation process beyond these well-established workflows. He recommended that the prediction be validated using (1) a geologic model, (2) engineering data, and (3) forward modeling of the seismic data and corresponding attributes. He noted that AVO practitioners, who tie the AVO response to petrophysical properties and acquisition geometries, routinely use this third approach.

In Figure 2, we display Hart's (2002) analysis of a low-permeability Pennsylvanian carbonate from the Ute Dome Paradox field, New Mexico, U.S.A. In Figure 2a, we see "the peak gas production predicted from seismic attributes using an artificial neural network. The correlation coefficient of 0.96 between measured and predicted production represents a spurious correlation. The result

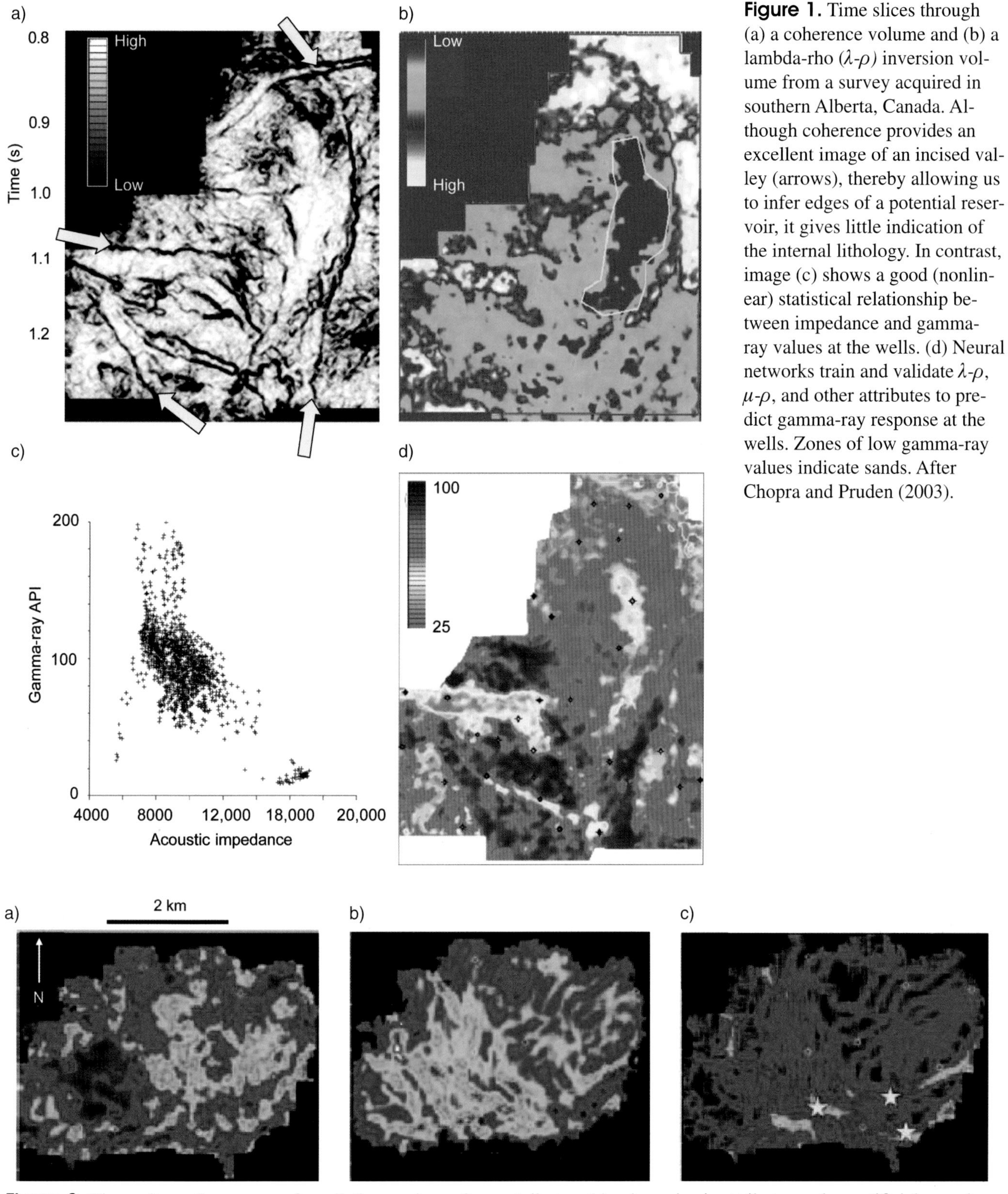

Figure 1. Time slices through (a) a coherence volume and (b) a lambda-rho (λ-ρ) inversion volume from a survey acquired in southern Alberta, Canada. Although coherence provides an excellent image of an incised valley (arrows), thereby allowing us to infer edges of a potential reservoir, it gives little indication of the internal lithology. In contrast, image (c) shows a good (nonlinear) statistical relationship between impedance and gamma-ray values at the wells. (d) Neural networks train and validate λ-ρ, μ-ρ, and other attributes to predict gamma-ray response at the wells. Zones of low gamma-ray values indicate sands. After Chopra and Pruden (2003).

Figure 2. Three alternative means of predicting peak gas from attributes: (a) using seismic attributes and an artificial neural network, (b) using multivariate linear regression with a correlation coefficient, and (c) using a simple dip-magnitude map. High dips are in hot colors (light blue to red). Stars indicate locations of wells drilled in 1999. The peak gas production correlates best with the dip map and is geologically reasonable because the reservoir consists of low-permeability limestones that are fracture-enhanced. The example is from Ute Dome, New Mexico, U.S.A. After Hart (2002).

was rejected because it did not conform to what is known about the controls on production from geologic and engineering analyses." In Figure 2b, we see "the peak gas production predicted from multivariate linear regression with correlation coefficient of 0.89 between measured and observed." In Figure 2c, we see the dip-magnitude map of the Paradox horizon. Hart notes, "Engineering and geologic analyses indicate that fractures, associated with high-dip areas, play an important role in enhancing gas production from these tight carbonates" (Hart, 2002, p. 1020). This third, qualitative prediction also fits the production data but is based on simpler, more reasonable assumptions about the geology.

Hart's Ute Dome case study discusses an important question about applying attributes to predict a particular property — in his case, peak production from wells. Interestingly, in such a case, in addition to geologic factors (e.g., fractures that relate to dip), other independent factors that may influence the correlation between peak production and attributes include completion technologies, thickness of perforation interval, and when a well was drilled. For instance, to elaborate on the last factor in the case at hand, the first well in the area was drilled in 1948 and the last one in 1979. We therefore hypothesize that wells drilled into reservoir pockets that have been partly depleted will not produce as much oil and gas as wells drilled into untapped compartments.

This leads us to the important question: Should there be a relationship between the attributes and the property to be determined or predicted? In the case of Ute Dome, the answer is yes. Hart et al. (2001) give a detailed description of this study.

Hart's example is an excellent use of geometric attributes to predict reservoir performance. In particular, changes in dip magnitude, and more properly, curvature, are closely linked to the presence of fractures [e.g., Lisle's (1994) image displayed as our Figure 5 in Chapter 4]. We review more of Hart's work (Sagan and Hart, 2004) later in this chapter, which discusses predicting production from a hydrothermally altered dolomite.

Use of Attributes To Understand Reservoir Compartmentalization: Dollarhide Field, Texas, U.S.A.

Dollarhide field is located on the Central Basin Platform in the Permian Basin of west Texas. This field has produced 70 million bbl of oil (MMBO) from cherts and dolomites of the Devonian Thirtyone Formation (Saller et al., 2001) and has an estimated oil in place of 175 million bbl. Optimizing recovery of remaining reserves depends greatly on understanding the reservoir and from that, on planning optimal secondary recovery.

Variability is related to differences in the thickness, quality, and continuity of the reservoirs (Saller et al., 2001). A complex interaction of faulting and fracturing, reservoir facies and diagenesis, and subcrop patterns determines the locations of the sweet spots within the main reservoirs (Ruppel and Hovorka, 1995; Ruppel and Barnaby, 2001). This poses a common problem with many fields in the area.

The objective of research carried out by Isabel Serrano and colleagues at the University of Houston has been to delineate stratigraphic and structural features at or below conventional seismic resolution in order to build a high-resolution geologic model. Understanding the fracture geometries and fault kinematics, and their impact on reservoir compartmentalization, is critical. A key part of the research was to test which 3D seismic attributes best image different features (faults, subcrops, and channels).

The Dollarhide structure formed during the late Paleozoic orogeny as the result of the North and South American plates colliding and the Central Basin Platform being uplifted. The structure is truncated at its crest by an unconformity at the base of Early Permian carbonates. Subcropping belts of carbonates, cherts, and shales show the configuration of the structure before Early Permian time. Reactivation of preexisting faults may have occurred during the early Tertiary Laramide orogeny.

The Dollarhide field is a north-south-trending asymmetric anticline bounded by major reverse faults on its eastern flank. The anticline is associated with a northeast-striking, right-lateral, strike-slip fault, and it is cut by an en echelon system of northeast-striking, right-lateral, synthetic Riedel shear faults. Conjugate, northwest-striking, antithetic shear faults have been identified on the downthrown block of the field. Some lineaments in the upthrown block have the same trend and may have the same origin.

Figure 3 displays a representative vertical slice through Dollarhide field's seismic data, showing well ties and the truncated top of the reservoir. The seismic data are generally good. However, the data are from one of the earliest 3D acquisitions, which took place in the early 1990s and were shot with a swath technique that resulted in somewhat lower north-south sampling and an increased east-west acquisition footprint.

In Figure 4a, we display a time slice at 1.060 s, which is below the major unconformity. Figure 4b, c, and d shows three vertical slices through the survey. Three large, high-angle reverse faults with right-lateral displacement are easily interpreted on the time slice and displayed in orange, red, and green. Reverse faults bound the field to the east and are shown in purple, yellow, and maroon on vertical sections AA′ and CC′.

Figure 5a and c displays images of the time-structure and porosity-thickness maps of the Devonian reservoir and originally were presented by Saller et al. (2001). To produce attribute extractions, we repacked the data and offer our time-structure map in Figure 5b, along with conventional dip-magnitude and dip-azimuth maps in Figure 5d and e, respectively. We note that the reservoir heterogeneity seen in Figure 5c is not indicated in any of the other maps.

Coherence and most-positive-curvature attribute volumes were generated to confirm the above observations and to gain more information for the formations under consideration. Figure 6 displays time slices through the coherence volumes (Figure 6a and c) and most-positive-curvature volumes (Figure 6b and d) corresponding to the time slice through the seismic data at t = 1.060 s in Figure 4a. These images exhibit considerably more detail than the dip-magnitude and dip-azimuth images displayed in Figure 5d and e. In addition to the southwest-northeast-trending faults discussed earlier, we observe here additional subparallel faults in green that were not readily seen on the seismic data. In addition, we note a second trend of northwest-southeast-trending antithetic faults in yellow. Taken together, this fabric is remarkably consistent with the contoured porosity-thickness map generated from well control alone and displayed in Figure 5c. Discussions with the operators confirm that water breakthrough occurs along the direction mapped by the green faults.

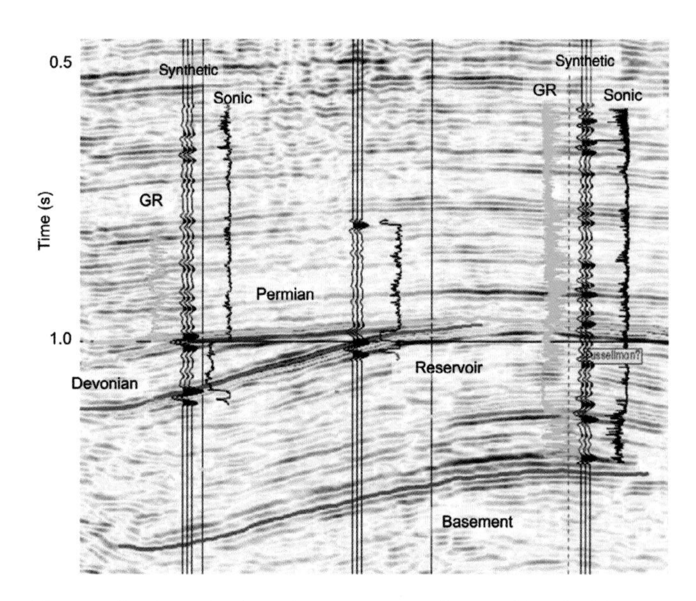

Figure 3. A vertical section corresponding to line AA' in Figure 4 and showing the Devonian Dollarhide reservoir and log ties, Central Basin Platform, Texas, U.S.A. Erosion has removed the upper part of the chert reservoir (blue pick) on the top of the upthrown block. Data courtesy of Pure Resources. After Serrano et al. (2003).

Geometric Attributes Correlated with Production from Hydrothermally Altered Dolomites, Appalachian Basin, Ohio, U.S.A.

Hydrothermally altered dolomites comprise important but difficult-to-predict reservoir targets in the Appalachian Basin of the U.S.A. and northern Alberta and British Columbia, Canada. Typically, hot fluids rise from depth and cause local changes in porosity, often with the original unaltered limestone forming a seal. We now review how Sagan and Hart (2004) used attributes to map a Trenton–Black River reservoir from a survey over Saybrook field in northeastern Ohio, U.S.A.

Figure 7 displays a conventional time-structure (Figure 7a), dip-magnitude (Figure 7b), and horizon slice through the seismic data (Figure 7c) from the top of the Trenton Limestone in this survey. The figure also displays the southwest-northeast component of the energy-weighted coherent-amplitude gradient (Figure 7d). The southeast-northwest component (not shown) is contaminated by acquisition footprint, as is the dip-magnitude map. The blue circles indicate producing wells, and the black circles indicate dry holes at the horizon. Note that all the production is associated with the strike-slip fault indicated by white arrows. Although there are hints of meandering channels and circular karst in Figure 7d, all of the wells outside the strike-slip fault zone found no porosity.

We obtained a copy of this survey from CGAS (although with a different processing flow from that used by Sagan and Hart) and generated the volumetric attributes shown in the following figures. In this manner, we used their careful horizon-based interpretation to calibrate a more expedient volumetric-attribute interpretation that augmented their interpretation.

Figure 8a and b displays lines AA′ and BB′, respectively, which correspond to lines 33 and 93 in their paper. Figure 8c and d display the composite images corresponding to the seismic data in Figure 8a and b, here overlaid with most-positive curvature. Black arrows indicate an anticlinal feature to the west of the strike-slip fault (indicated by the white arrows). The production correlates with the synclinal feature associated with the strike-slip fault. These anticlinal and synclinal features show up clearly in Figure 9c and d.

Figure 9 shows horizon slices through the coherence volume (Figure 9a), reflector rotation volume (Figure 9b), most-negative-curvature volume (Figure 9c), and most-positive-curvature volume (Figure 9d) corresponding to data from the top of the Trenton Limestone, shown in Figure 7. Wells that produce from the Trenton–Black River interval are displayed as blue, and wells that do not produce from this interval (some produce from other levels) are shown as black circles. The coherence image provides little additional information beyond that of the dip-magnitude image in the Figure 7b. However, the reflector rotation image (Figure 9b) shows that significant rotation about the major northwest-southeast fault has occurred.

Using wireline and production data, Sagan and Hart (2004, p. 1, poster 1) show that this fault was "probably reactivated during the Taconic Orogeny in Middle to Late Ordovician. The far-field stresses of this compressional activity caused strike-slip movement of the preexisting fault to create complex flower structures that branch 1350 ft (450 m) upward into the Trenton–Black River interval. Circular collapse structures within splays of the flower structure are the primary drilling targets."

Recalling that when the value of positive curvature is negative (green areas in Figure 9d) it displays a bowl-shaped structure, we note that each of the blue producer wells (indicated by the two blue arrows in Figure 9d) falls within the (green) collapse features bounded by the northwest-southeast-trending (red) anticlinal features. We also note that previous operators drilled a sequence of subtle anticlinal features that were tight, such as the one indicated by the yellow arrow in Figure 9d.

Sagan and Hart (2004) defined this deformation in terms of Riedel shears associated with strike-slip faulting in the basement (Figure 10). Figure 10a shows Mandl's (1988) block diagram of helicoidal deformation above a single base-

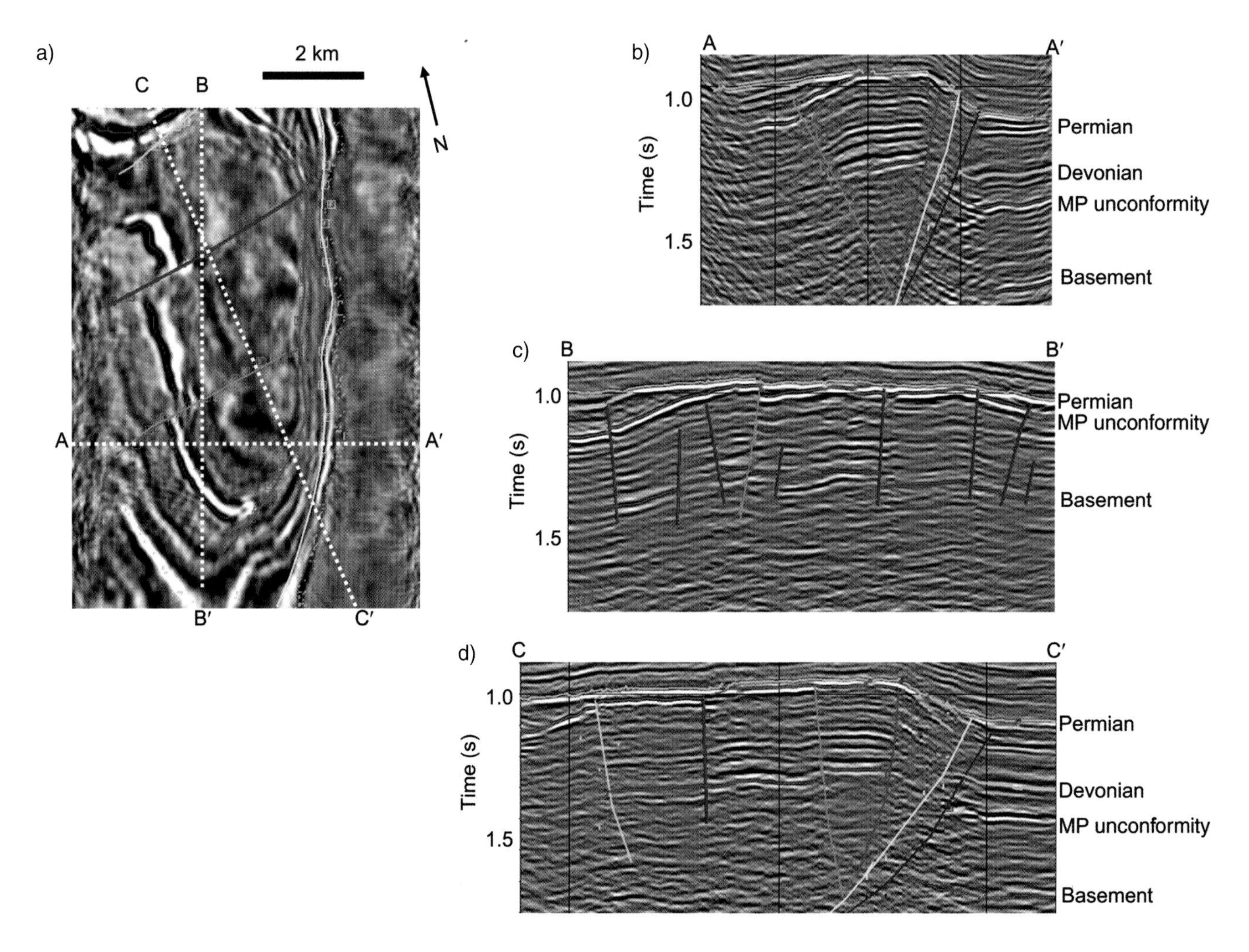

Figure 4. A time slice at t = 1.060 s, showing the locations of vertical seismic traverses (b) AA′, (c) BB′, and (d) CC′ at Dollarhide field. Reverse faults that bound the field to the east are shown in purple, yellow, and maroon on vertical sections AA′ and CC′. High-angle, northeast-striking reverse faults with right-lateral displacement are shown in orange, red, and green. The conjugate northwest-striking faults have not been interpreted on the upthrown block. The right-lateral strike-slip faults seen on the seismic time slice mask the presence of these lineaments. On the vertical seismic lines, the horizons are indicated by the following colors: cyan = the base of an Early Permian unconformity; blue = a Mississippian to Pennsylvanian (MP) unconformity; light green = the top of the Devonian Thirtyone Formation; and magenta = the top of Precambrian granite basement. After Serrano et al. (2003).

ment fault. The main Riedel shear, exhibiting a helicoidal nature, is shown in Figure 10b with the top of basement structure map. Figure 10c displays the main synthetic Riedel shear (light green) and less-developed Riedel shears (darker greens) with the shallower Trempealeau map. The en echelon nature of these faults is apparent from this angle.

To better illustrate the behavior of the fault with depth, we display a sequence of coherence slices (Figure 11) at 50-ms intervals, beginning at the Trenton level (Figure 11a) and ending at the basement (Figure 11d). As we go deeper in the section, the northwest-southeast-trending main fault is easier to trace toward the southeast. We also note perpendicular faults trending southwest-northeast at the basement level (yellow arrows in Figure 11d).

In Figure 12, we display a corresponding suite of time slices through composite dip-azimuth-coherence images generated using the color display technique described in Chapter 9. We note that at all levels significant scissorlike rotation occurs about the main fault, dipping to the northeast (magenta) north of the fault and dipping to the south (yellow) south of the fault. We also note that the colors are banded, which indicates a long-wavelength undulation and

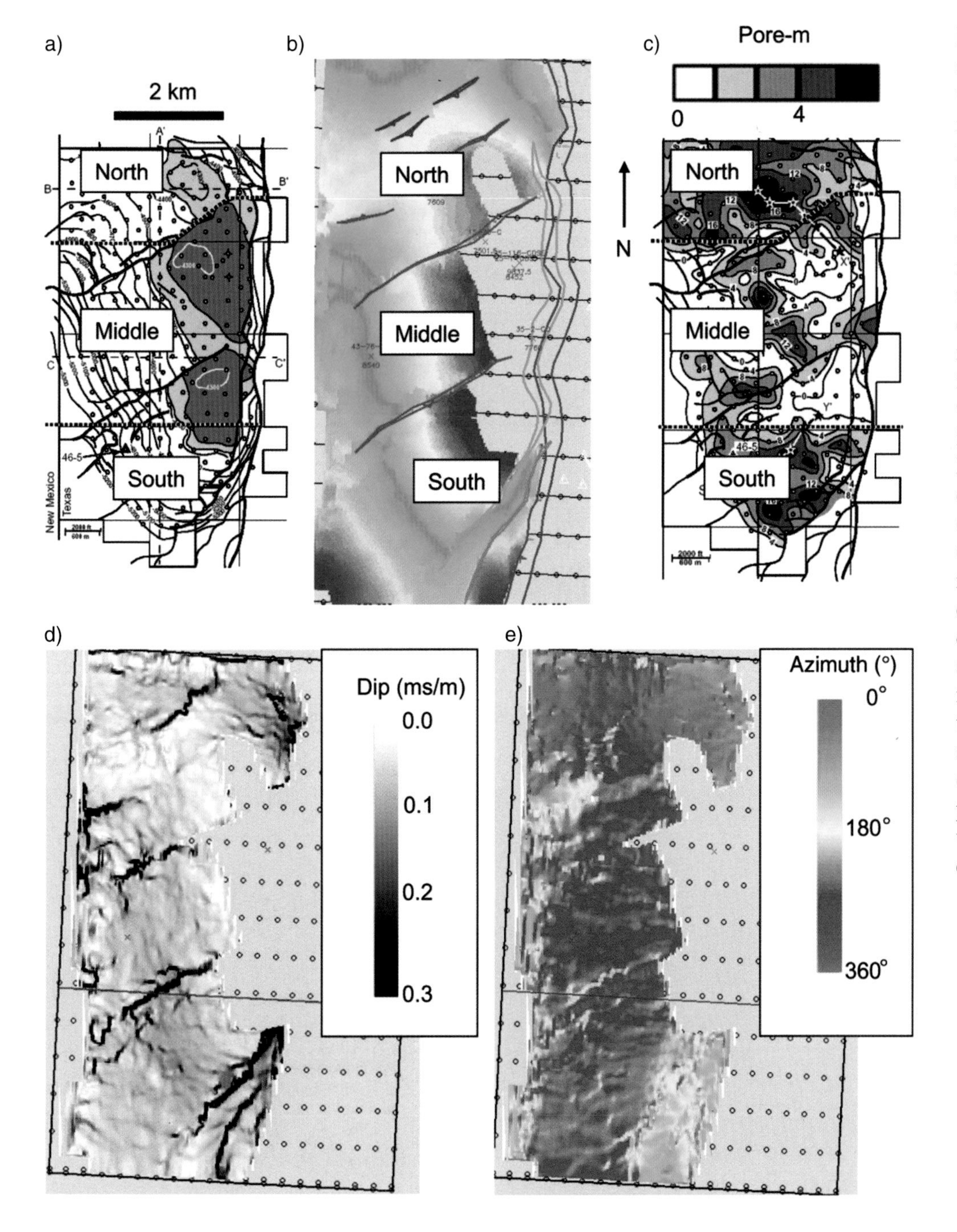

Figure 5. (a)-(b) Time-structure maps of the top of the Devonian in Dollarhide reservoir, Central Basin Platform, Texas, U.S.A., (a) after Saller et al. (2001) and (b) after Serrano et al. (2003). Dark-gray shading in (a) indicates the zone of truncation of the upper reservoir and part of the lower reservoir. Light-gray shading indicates the zone where the upper reservoir is partially truncated. (c) Porosity of the lower zone, obtained from well control (after Saller et al., 2001). (d) A conventional dip-magnitude map and (e) a dip-azimuth map, both derived from the time-structure map in (b) and neither of which indicates the lateral heterogeneity seen in (c). AAPG©2001. (a) and (c) reprinted by permission of the AAPG whose permission is required for further use.

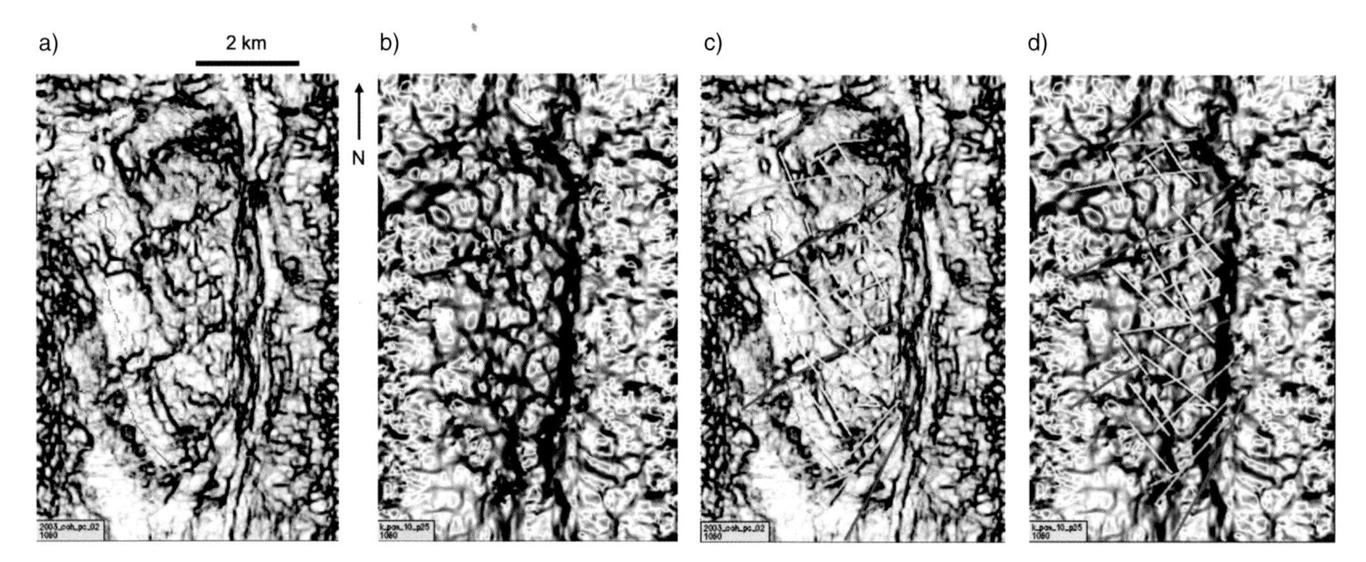

Figure 6. (a)-(b) Time slices at t = 1.060 s, through (a) a coherence volume and (b) a most-positive-curvature volume for the Dollarhide field. Figures (c) and (d) are the same images with interpretation. The northeast-southwest-trending green lineaments, interpreted to be smaller strike-slip faults, correlate positively with fluid flow in reservoir production. The magenta faults were picked directly from the migrated seismic image. The northwest-southeast yellow faults are antithetic to the strike-slip faults. Most of the east-west lineaments are the result of an acquisition footprint associated with the early 1990s 3D-swath seismic-acquisition program. The trends on these lineaments correlate well with porosity trends. After Serrano et al. (2003).

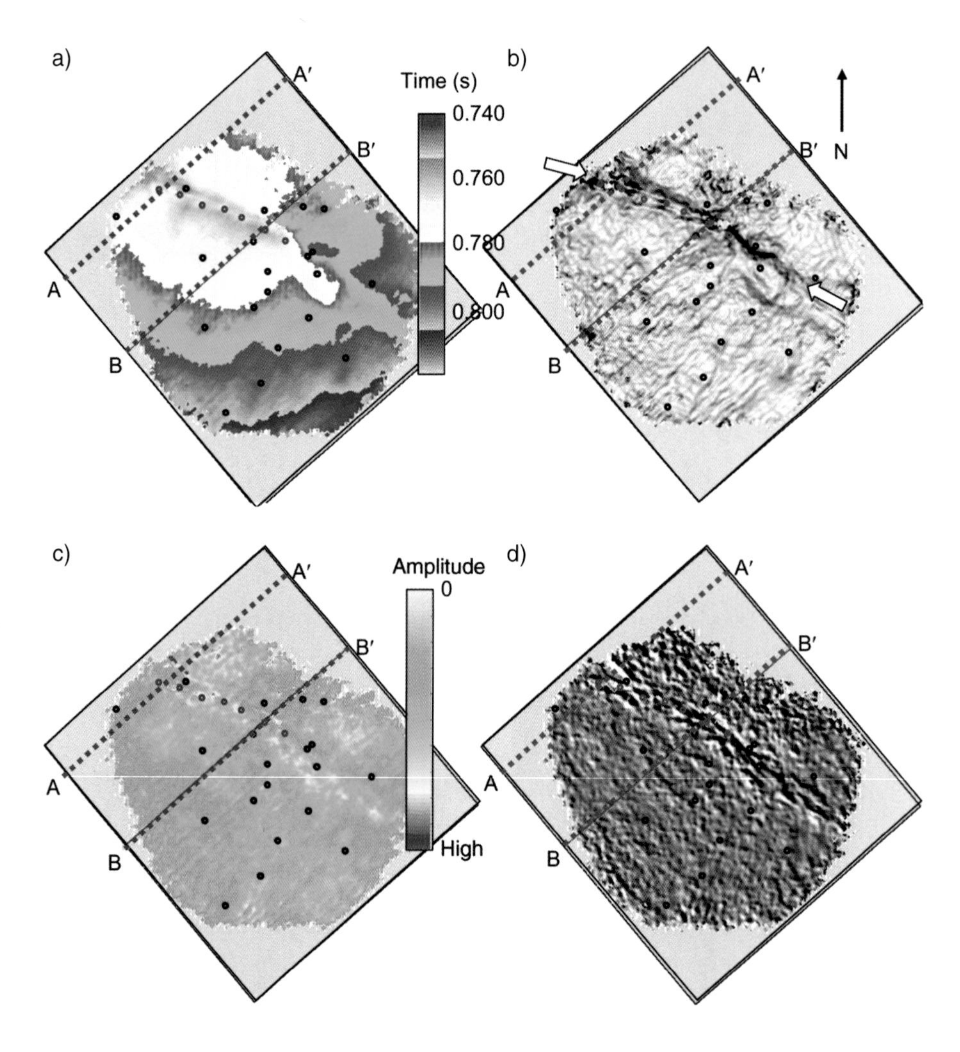

Figure 7. (a) A time-structure map of the top Trenton Limestone horizon from a survey acquired in Appalachian Basin, northeastern Ohio, U.S.A., and reported by Sagan and Hart (2004). (b) The corresponding dip-magnitude map and (c) the corresponding horizon slice through the seismic data. (d) A northeast-southwest energy-weighted coherent-amplitude-gradient map. An acquisition footprint contaminates the dip-magnitude map and the northwest-southeast energy-weighted coherent-amplitude-gradient map (not shown). Arrows on (b) indicate a fault. Seismic lines AA′ and BB′ are discussed by Sagan and Hart (2004) and are displayed in Figure 8. Data are courtesy of CGAS.

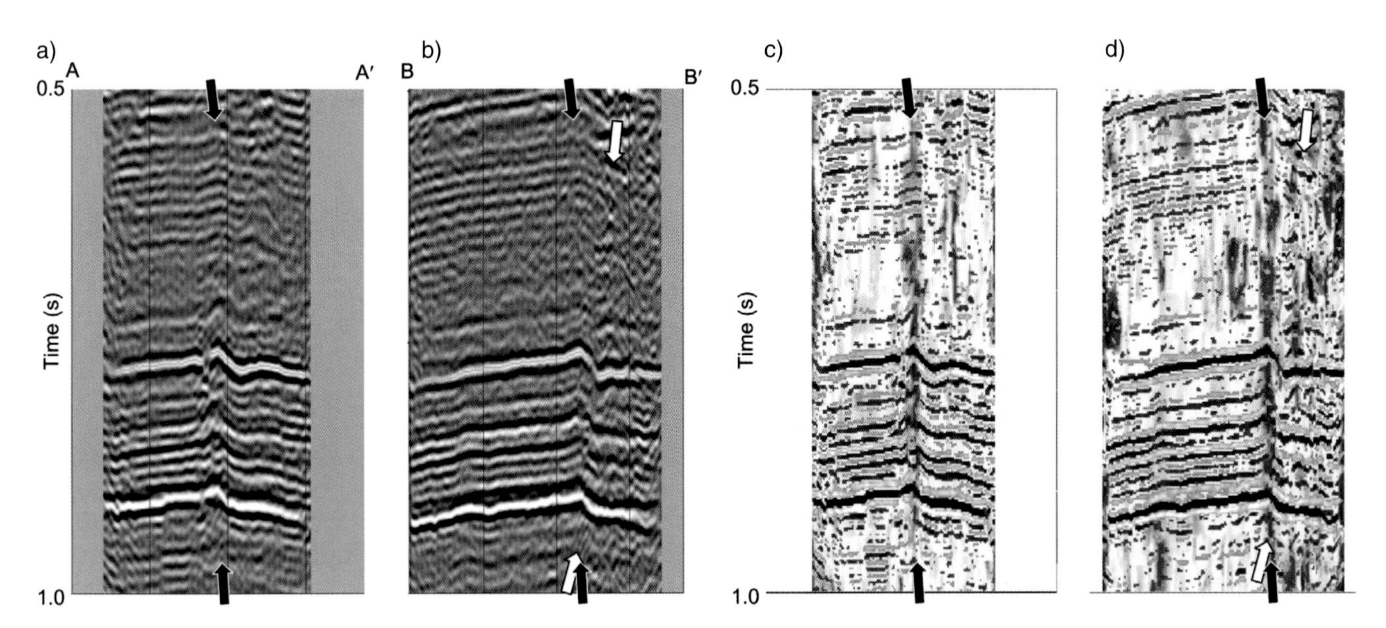

Figure 8. Seismic lines (a) AA′ and (b) BB′ [which correspond to lines 33 and 93, respectively, as discussed by Sagan and Hart (2004)], whose locations are shown in the previous figure. (c)-(d) The corresponding composite images of the seismic lines in (a) and (b), respectively, overlaid with most-positive curvature. Positive values are red, zero values are pale yellow (to distinguish them from the white troughs of the seismic), and negative values are green. Note that the fault indicated by white arrows in (b) lies in front of an anticlinal nose, which is indicated by black arrows in (d).

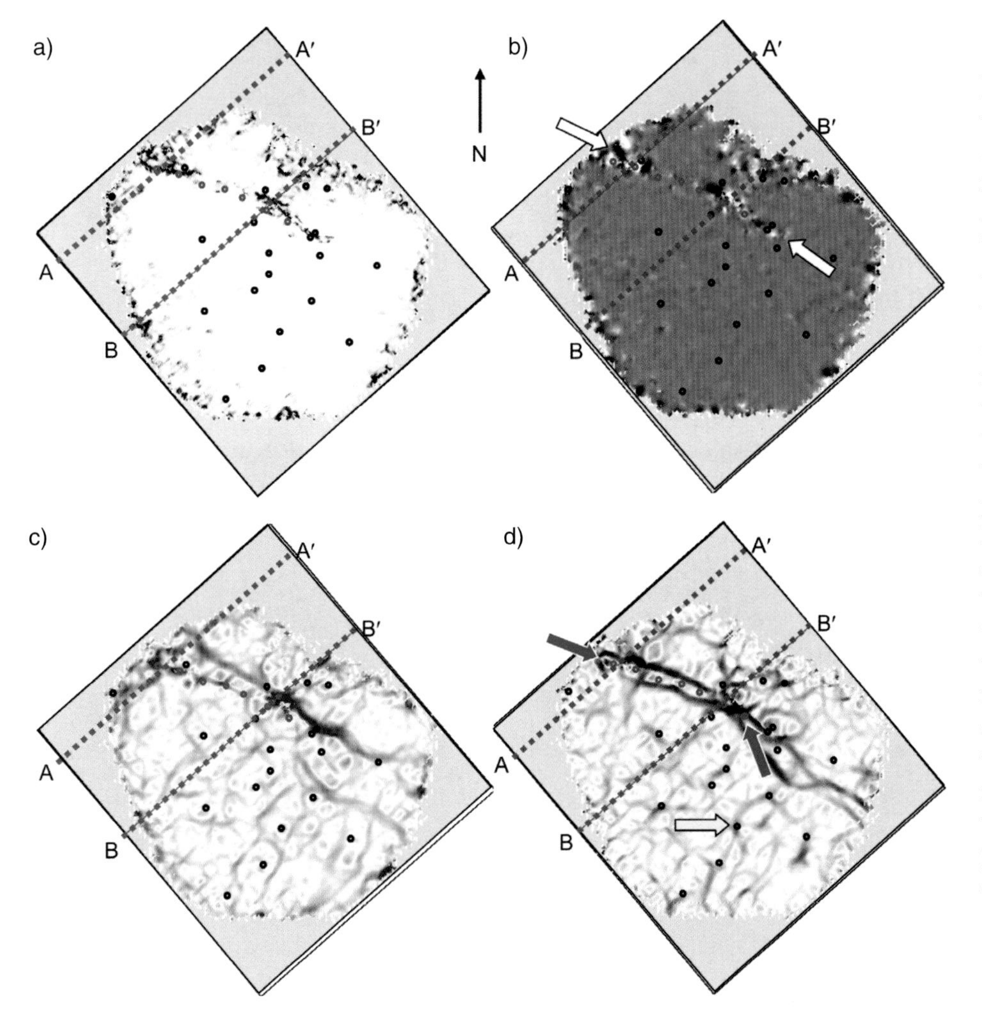

Figure 9. Horizon slices corresponding to the top of the Trenton Limestone shown in Figure 7a, through (a) a coherence volume, (b) a reflector-rotation map, (c) a most-negative-curvature volume, and (d) a most-positive-curvature volume. The coherence slice does not provide significant information beyond that seen in the dip-magnitude map shown in Figure 7b. The rotation map shows that the fault has rotational movement (white arrows), which allowed hydrothermal fluids to rise and to alter the limestone to porous dolomite at this horizon. Note how the producer wells (indicated by blue circles between the two arrows) correlate to negative values of the most-positive-curvature [green areas in (d)], which correspond to collapse features. The dry holes shown in (d) indicate that the operator drilled subtle anticlinal features (such as that indicated by the yellow arrow) but failed to find porous dolomite. Curvature was calculated using $\alpha = 0.25$.

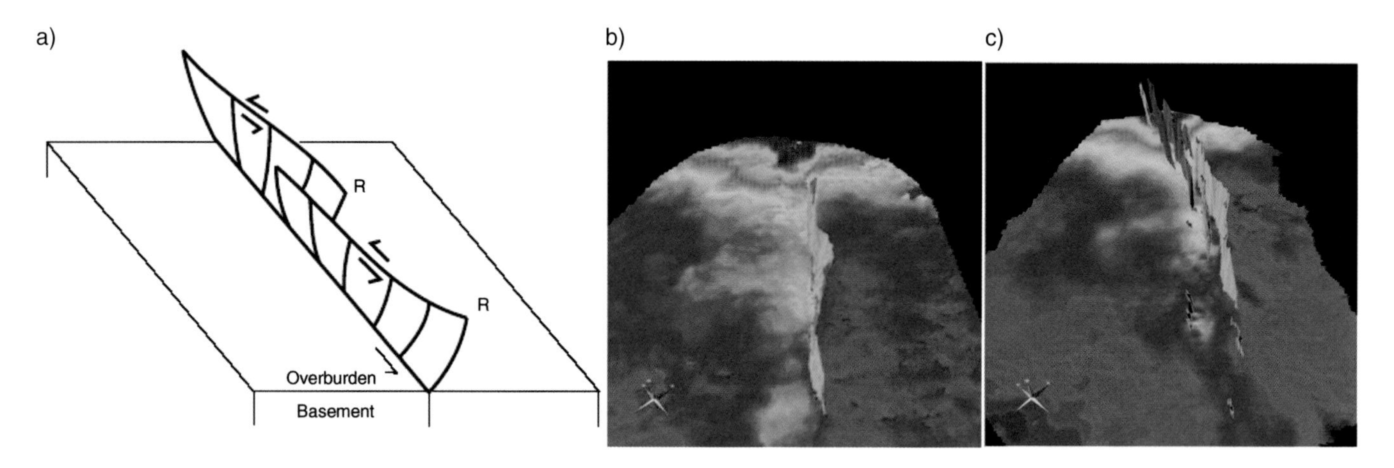

Figure 10. (a) Mandl's (1988) block diagram of helicoidal deformation above a single basement fault. (b) The main Riedel shear, exhibiting a helicoidal nature, shown here with the top of basement structure map. (c) The main synthetic Riedel shear (light green) and less-developed Riedel shears (in darker greens), shown with the shallower Trempealeau map. The en echelon nature of these faults is apparent from this angle. After Sagan and Hart (2004). AAPG©2004. Reprinted by permission of the AAPG whose permission is required for further use.

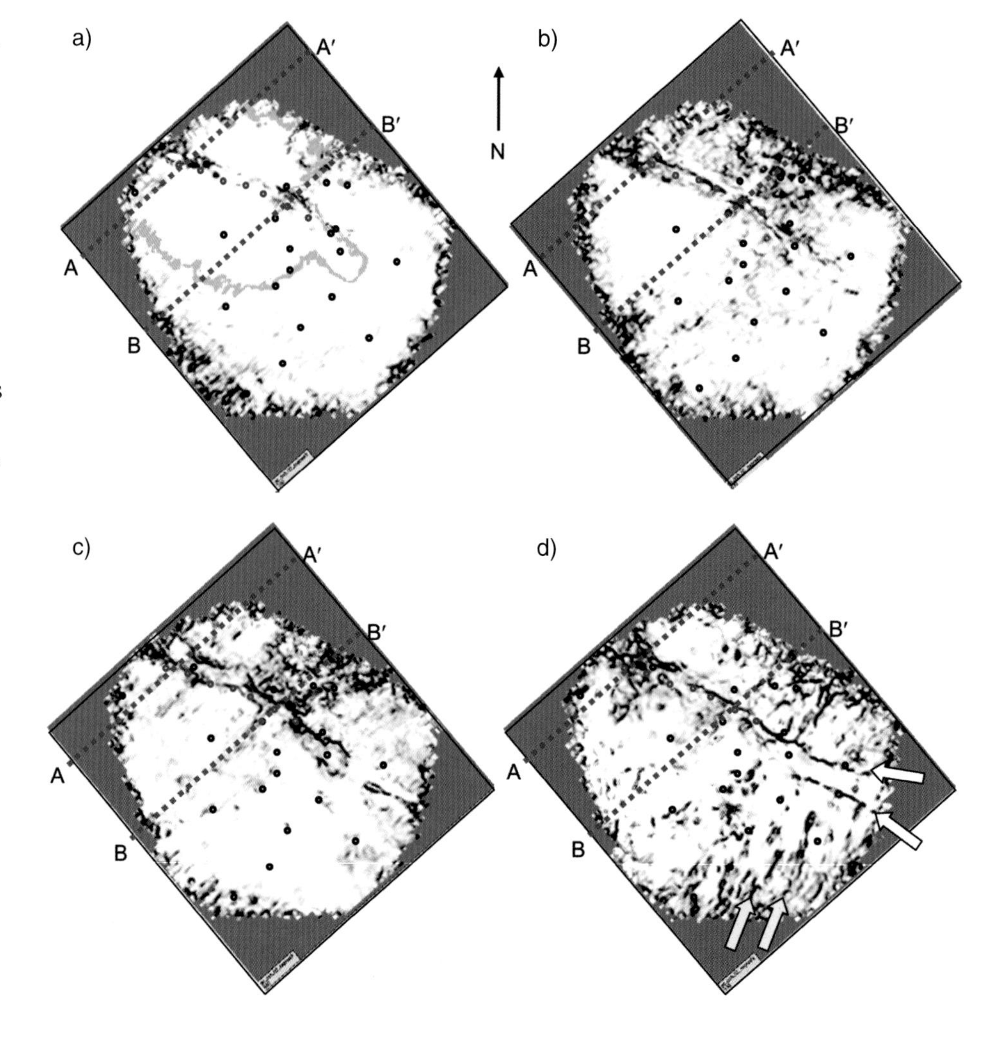

Figure 11. Time slices through the coherence volume at t = (a) 0.780 s, (b) 0.830 s, (c) 0.880 s, and (d) 0.930 s. The green horizon in (a) indicates the intersection of the Trenton limestone horizon with the time slice at 0.780 s, and (d) cuts the basement. Note how the fault becomes clearer toward the east as we go deeper in the section, giving rise to a graben at 0.930 s (white arrows). We also note antithetic faults in the basement, which Sagan and Hart (2004) interpreted to be Reidel shears.

implies that the southwest-northeast faults seen at the basement level (Figure 12d) also have a rotational component.

In Figure 13, we display corresponding time slices through the most-positive-curvature volume, computed with a value of $\alpha = 0.25$. We note that although the main northwest-southeast fault was difficult to trace in the shallow coherence image (Figure 11a), it is easy to trace in Figure 13a. The explanation is one of two possibilities: Either the displacement across the fault has been reduced to fall below seismic resolution, or the fault has died out geologically into a fold or flexure. (We discount an explanation of poor imaging, because we observe sharp discontinuities deeper in the section, where imaging generally is less accurate). We also note that the rightmost fold indicated by the gray arrow in Figure 13d is laterally displaced (and rotated) from the rightmost fault seen in Figure 11d. We interpret this image to be one of folds linking faults as we transfer from one Riedel shear surface to another.

We conclude our discussion of the Saybrook survey with another set of corresponding time slices, here through the reflector-rotation volume displayed in Figure 14. We discount the ring of anomalies associated with the edge of the survey, where our estimates of vector dip are erratic (because of low fold and migration artifacts). The plotting scale and wavelength ($\alpha = 0.25$) of the reflector-rotation attribute are equivalent to those of the most-positive-curvature image in Figure 13. We see little rotation in the shallow time slice away from the major northwest-southeast fault. However, in the deepest time slice, we note scissorlike rotation not only with this major fault, but also with the multiple northeast-southwest-trending faults seen in the southern part of the survey.

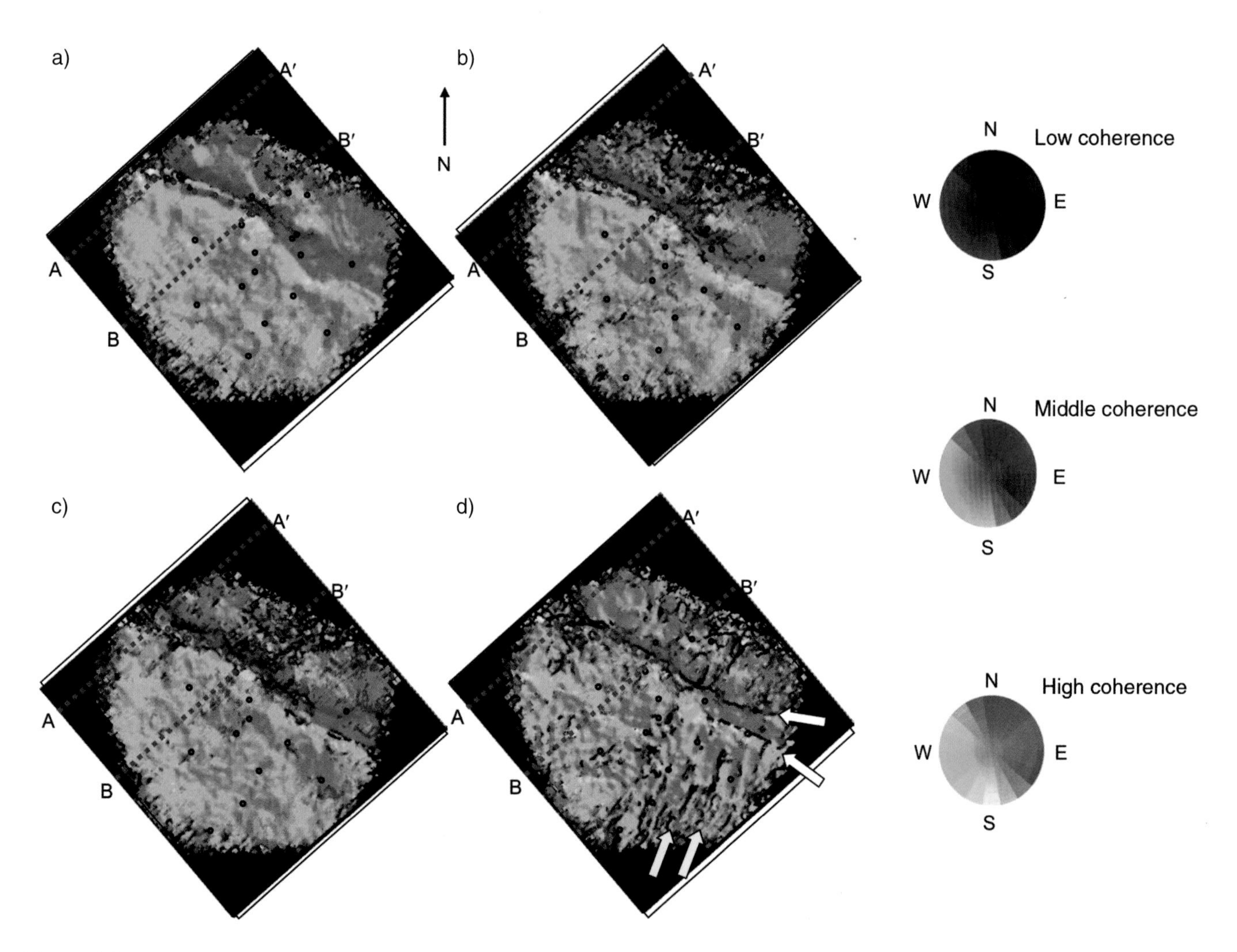

Figure 12. Time slices at t = (a) 0.780 s, (b) 0.830 s, (c) 0.880 s, and (d) 0.930 s through the corresponding composite dip-azimuth-coherence images, created using the display techniques described in Chapter 9. To the north of the major fault, reflectors are dipping to the northeast (magenta); to the south of the major fault, reflectors are dipping to the south and southwest (yellow and yellow-green). Note the rotation of the reflectors between the faults in (d) in the southern part of the survey.

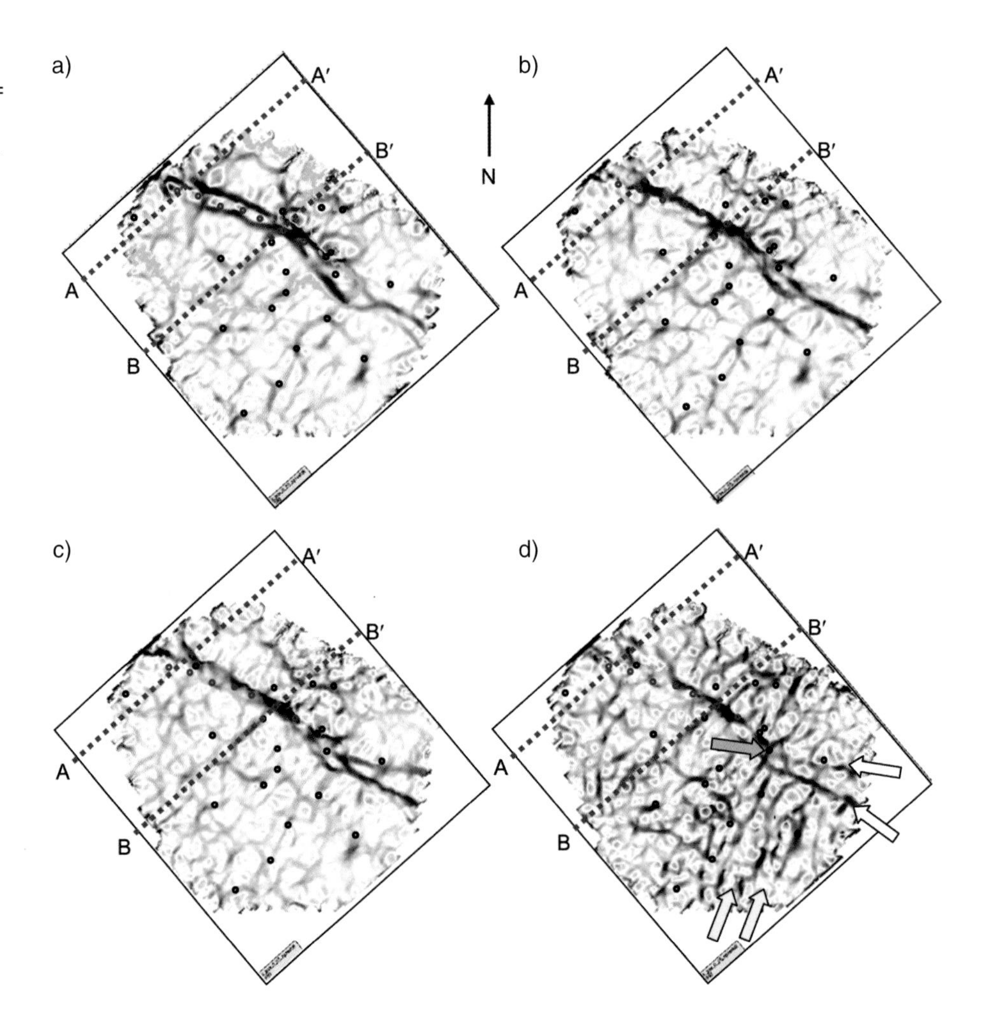

Figure 13. Time slices through the most-positive-curvature volume (α = 0.25) at (a) 0.780 s, (b) 0.830 s, (c) 0.880 s, and (d) 0.930 s, corresponding to Figures 11 and 12.

Use of Geometric Attributes To Map Fracture Location, Azimuth, and Localization: Austin Chalk, Central Texas, U.S.A.

The fractured Austin Chalk of central Texas, U.S.A., composes several mature oil fields that are known to retain significant oil in economic quantities. The Austin Chalk is a complex, layered reservoir that has only moderate structural deformation. An intermediate depth of the target results in good seismic-data quality. There is also a potential for deeper plays in the Buda Limestone, Glen Rose Limestone, and Georgetown Limestone formations. The operators selected the Piersall field as a good candidate for infill drilling, and after several attempts at multicomponent fracture imaging, acquired 3D conventional, P-wave seismic data with the goal of predicting fractures by mapping flexures in the interpreted horizons.

Figure 15 displays two simple models of the Austin Chalk. Fractures occur in swarms that strike northeast-southwest, with oil saturation approximately 50–60% inside and nearly zero outside the fracture zone. The matrix permeability is less than 0.01 to 10 md, but total permeability is enhanced by extensive swarms of microfractures. Within these swarms, microfracture density can be as high as three fractures per meter.

Shale volume controls fracture density within a given fracture swarm, and fracture-swarm density and lateral propagation are controlled by the local stress field. The local stress field and the presence of shales or volcanic ash also control vertical-fracture propagation.

Fracture porosity of 0.001 is supplemented by a matrix porosity of 0.020 to 0.050, giving rise to a dual-porosity reservoir. Finally, rate and pressure tests show the Austin Chalk to be a highly compartmentalized reservoir.

The Austin Chalk was one of the earliest successful targets for horizontal drilling. Horizontal wells increase the possibility of intersecting more fractures. However, not all fractures are created equal. The operators have found that very large through-going or megafractures can connect the chalk reservoir to either overlying or underlying water-filled aquifers, thereby ruining the well. Major fracture zones are often leaky whereas minor fracture zones result in isolated reservoirs. Thus the objective was to map these minor localized fractures, confined to the Austin Chalk formation. Volu-

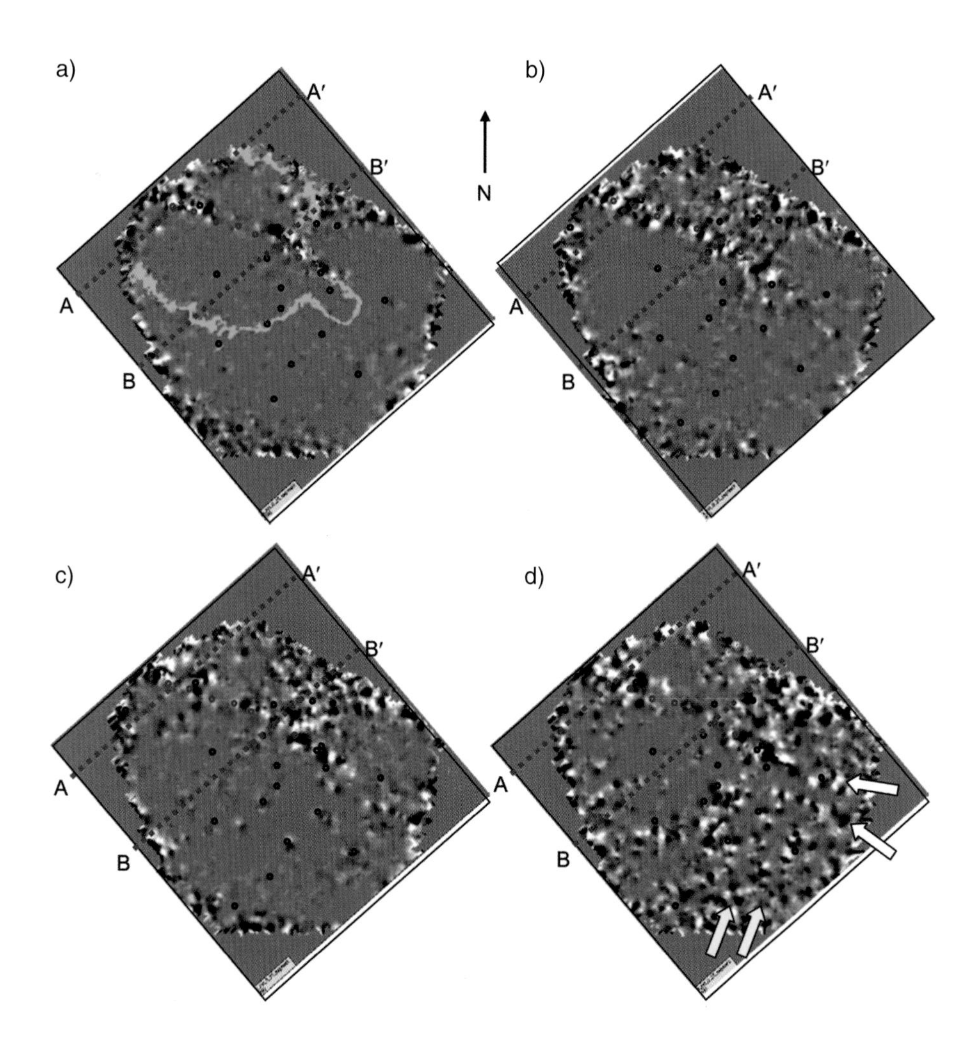

Figure 14. Times slices at t = (a) 0.780 s, (b) 0.830 s, (c) 0.880 s, and (d) 0.930 s through the reflector-rotation volume, corresponding to Figures 11 through 13. Note the significant rotation about both the main and antithetic faults in (d).

metric curvature provides a means of mapping such localized features that do not in general cut a picked horizon.

In Figure 16a, we display a representative seismic line through the Austin Chalk, and in Figure 16b, we have overlaid that seismic information on a vertical slice through the most-negative curvature volume. The black arrow indicates a local curvature anomaly that the operators interpreted to be associated with a minor fracture zone. On the vertical seismic section, that fracture zone appears to be confined vertically and hence to be an isolated reservoir. In contrast, the white arrows indicate a through-going flexure, which the operators associated with a likely megafracture that would produce water.

Prior to using volumetric curvature computations, operators picked multiple horizons, calculated the curvature on each horizon, and correlated those measurements with production. Although that workflow was successful, volumetric curvature provided more-robust images that extended the workflow into areas that were difficult to pick.

Figure 17a shows a vertical slice through seismic data along the Austin Chalk, and Figure 17b-d shows horizon slices through coherence, most-negative curvature, and maximum-curvature volumes, respectively (the last computed with a value of $\alpha = 0.25$). Red arrows indicate synclinal flexures and the black arrow indicates an anticlinal flexure.

Figure 18 displays production results from infill drilling through the fracture swarms. A 3D curvature analysis provided the opportunity to interpret mechanical units based on vertical-fracture terminations and fracture density.

Calibration of Geometric Attributes To Map Fracture Permeability: Kansas, U.S.A.

Geometric attributes are not amenable directly to established reservoir-characterization workflows developed to predict porosity and lithology for impedance and spectral decomposition. In such workflows, well-log measurements are crosscorrelated (or otherwise compared) with appropriate attribute values at or near the well.

Calibration of fluid flow through fractures requires a very different workflow. Nissen et al. (2005) developed a highly innovative workflow evaluating open versus shale-filled fractures in a naturally fractured, solution-enhanced Mississippian carbonate reservoir in Kansas, U.S.A. That

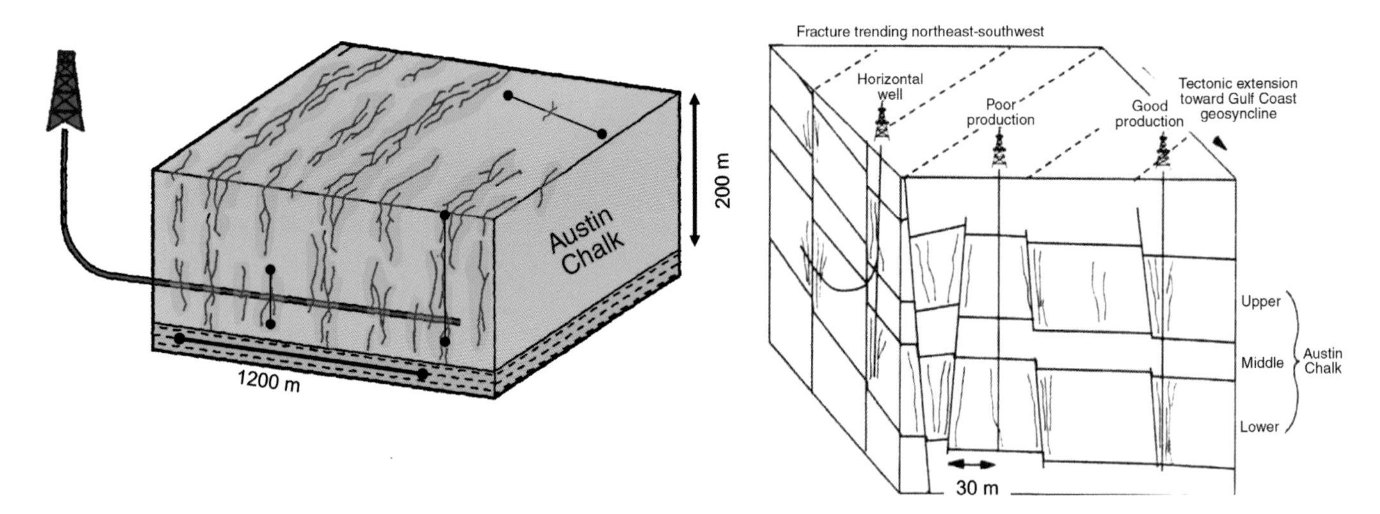

Figure 15. A geologic model of the Austin Chalk play, central Texas, U.S.A. The goal of such plays is to intersect as many fractures as possible, an objective aided by horizontal drilling. To avoid producing water, these fractures should be confined vertically to the chalk formations. From Schnerk and Madeen (2000).

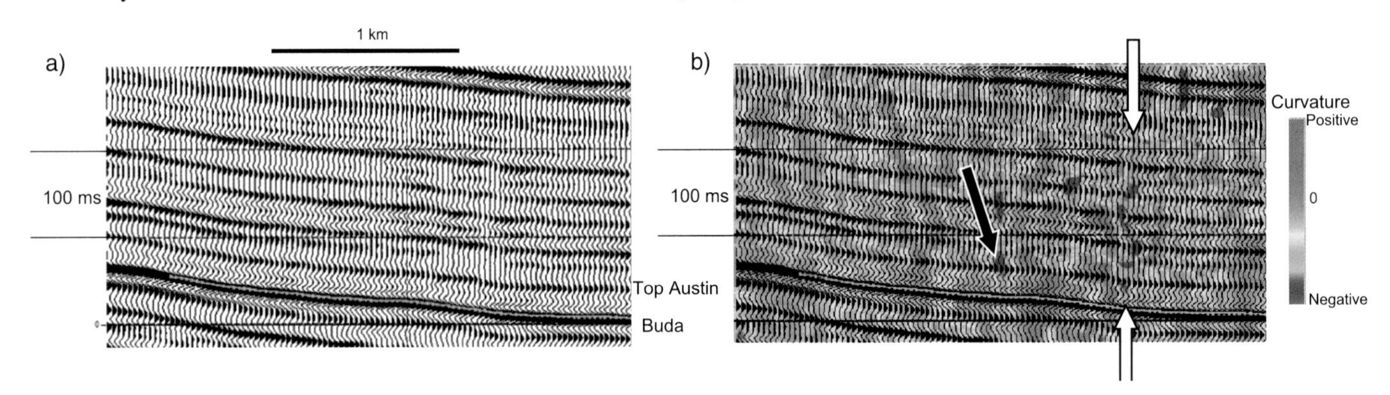

Figure 16. (a) A representative seismic section through a survey acquired over the Austin Chalk in Texas, U.S.A. Conventional interpretation required mapping the dip over multiple reflectors, some of which were difficult to pick. (b) The same seismic section plotted on top of a most-negative-curvature section. We can determine immediately whether the flexures are confined locally (black arrow) or are through-going (white arrow), thereby assigning risk that fractures may cut overlying or underlying water-filled formations. Figure courtesy of Geotexture.

workflow should be amenable to using attributes to assess permeability in general.

First, Nissen et al. recognized that the relevant measurement is not the value of an attribute at the well, but rather, the important measurement is the well's distance from an interpreted attribute lineament. Second, they recognized that in their study area such attribute lineaments are oriented predominantly along two orthogonal azimuths and that fractures related to lineaments with different azimuths are likely to have been open at different times, when the stress regime changed. For analysis, the workers therefore divided their interpreted lineaments into two families based on azimuth. Third, they noted that several of the wells are below the oil-water contact. Those wells test a different part of the formation and should be eliminated from certain statistical analyses.

That nonlinear behavior (to include or exclude a well in the calculation) is in principle one of the powers of neural networks. In our opinion, if one were to use neural networks to address this kind of problem, it would make sense to help the algorithm along by explicitly defining this parameter as part of the training process.

In Figure 19, we display Nissen et al.'s (2005) depth map of the top Mississippian horizon derived from a 3D seismic survey over the reservoir. The Mississippian reservoir is subjacent to a pre-Pennsylvanian unconformity and karst surface and has a strong bottom-water drive that is supported by an aquifer extending approximately 40–55 m (20–30 ms) below the reservoir.

In Figure 20, we display a representative seismic line through the Mississippian horizon from Figure 19. In Figure 21, we display the most-negative curvature along the

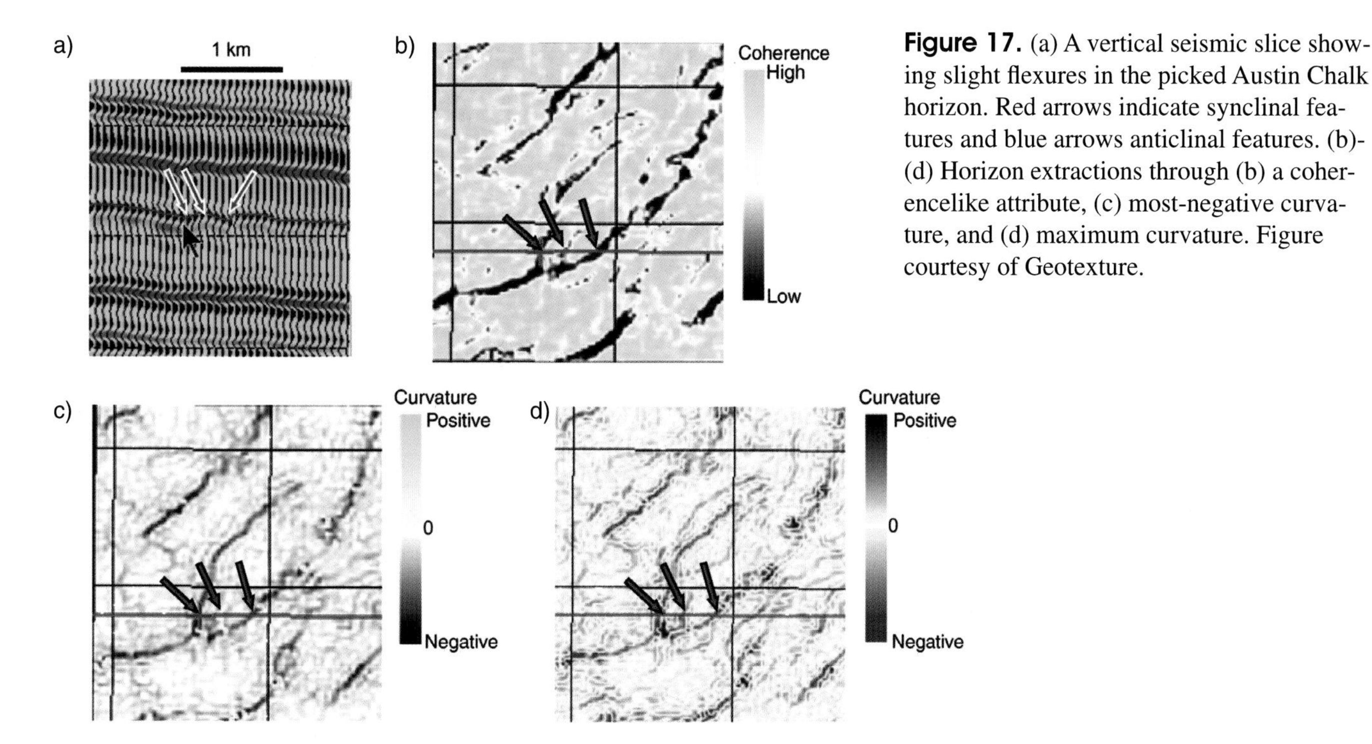

Figure 17. (a) A vertical seismic slice showing slight flexures in the picked Austin Chalk horizon. Red arrows indicate synclinal features and blue arrows anticlinal features. (b)-(d) Horizon extractions through (b) a coherencelike attribute, (c) most-negative curvature, and (d) maximum curvature. Figure courtesy of Geotexture.

top (in red) and base (in blue) of the Mississippian aquifer (see Figure 19), delineating a regular pattern of northeast-southwest- and northwest-southeast-trending lineaments, which represent faults, fractures, and flexures in the reservoir. These lineaments were picked (Figure 22a) and then displayed as rose diagrams of the number of lineaments versus azimuth (Figure 22b) and the total length of all lineaments versus azimuth (Figure 22c). The rose diagrams show that the number of lineaments interpreted with northeast-southwest and northwest-southeast azimuths is approximately equal; however, the northeast-southwest-trending lineaments have greater length and continuity than do the northwest-southeast-trending lineaments.

Mississippian carbonate reservoirs in Kansas typically contain fractures. These fractures may have been solution-enhanced by the pre-Pennsylvanian karst and subsequently filled with Pennsylvanian shale, thereby providing a barrier to fluid flow, or they may be open currently, thereby permitting water to channel from the underlying aquifer. Nissen et al. (2005) set out to evaluate whether a relationship exists between the most-negative-curvature lineaments and the presence of open versus shale-filled fractures, and in particular, whether the open and/or shale-filled fractures are related preferentially to lineaments with a given azimuth.

Shale-filled fractures can be identified directly in horizontal wells (Figure 23); however, in vertical wells, the presence of such fractures must be inferred using indirect evidence. Nissen et al. (2005) reasoned that fractures that were solution-enhanced by pre-Pennsylvanian karst are likely to have been filled by both Pennsylvanian shale and

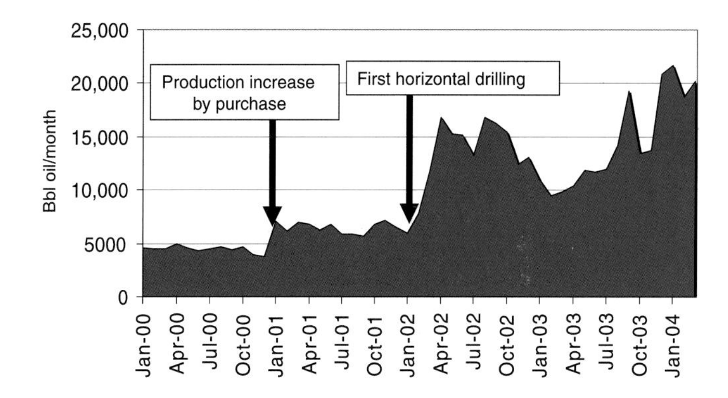

Figure 18. Austin Chalk oil production from Shiner Ranch field, Texas, U.S.A., after horizontal drilling through fractures mapped from seismic data. Figure courtesy of Geotexture.

weathered Mississippian debris; therefore, wells that penetrate such fractures should show evidence of a thicker karst zone (the section of weathered Mississippian material at the base of the Pennsylvanian).

Figure 24 shows crossplots of the thickness of the karst zone versus the distance to the nearest northeast-southwest-trending lineaments (Figure 24a) and to the northwest-southeast-trending lineaments (Figure 24b). These crossplots show that no apparent relationship exists between the thickness of the karst zone and the northwest-southeast-trending lineaments; but karst zone thickness increases the closer it is to the northeast-southwest-trending lineaments. Because several of the northeast-southwest-trending lineaments are interpreted to be longer than 0.5 km, these lineaments may provide significant barriers to fluid flow in the northwest-southeast direction.

Nissen et al. (2005) also correlated oil production (Figure 25) and water production (Figure 26) against distance from the nearest lineament in each azimuth family. Oil production is expected to be inhibited adjacent to lineaments representing fluid barriers, because (1) wells close to a compartment boundary have smaller drainage areas than do wells in the middle of a compartment, and (2) a higher concentration of shale-filled fractures can degrade reservoir quality. Water production may be enhanced adjacent to lineaments representing open fractures that extend into the underlying aquifer. The crossplots indicate that no relationship exists between oil production and the northwest-southeast-trending lineaments (Figure 25c), but an overall increase in oil production does appear to occur away from the northeast-southwest-trending lineaments (Figure 25b).

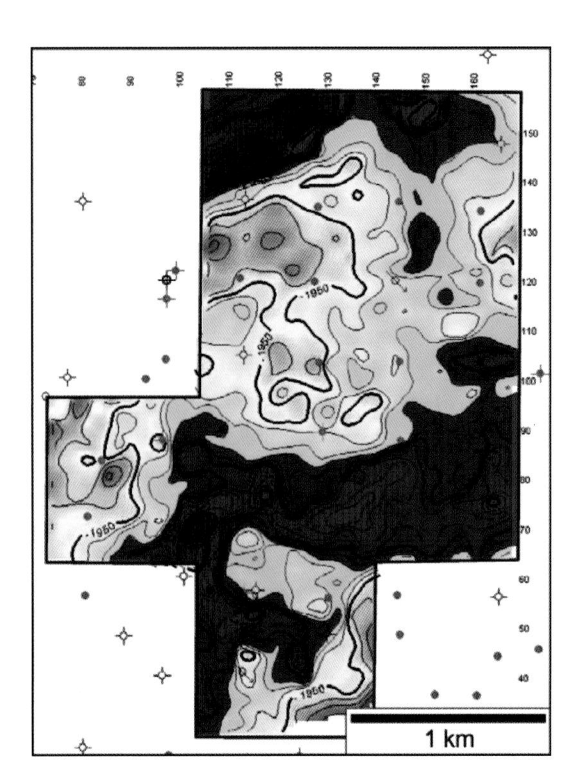

Figure 19. A depth map of the top of the Mississippian mapped from a survey over a Mississippian reservoir in Kansas, U.S.A. The contour interval is 10 ft (3 m). The blue-shaded overlay indicates areas where the top Mississippian is below the oil-water contact. After Nissen et al. (2005). AAPG©2005. Reprinted by permission of the AAPG whose permission is required for further use.

In contrast, a good correlation exists between water production and proximity to the northwest-southeast-trending lineaments (Figure 26c), but no relationship appears be-

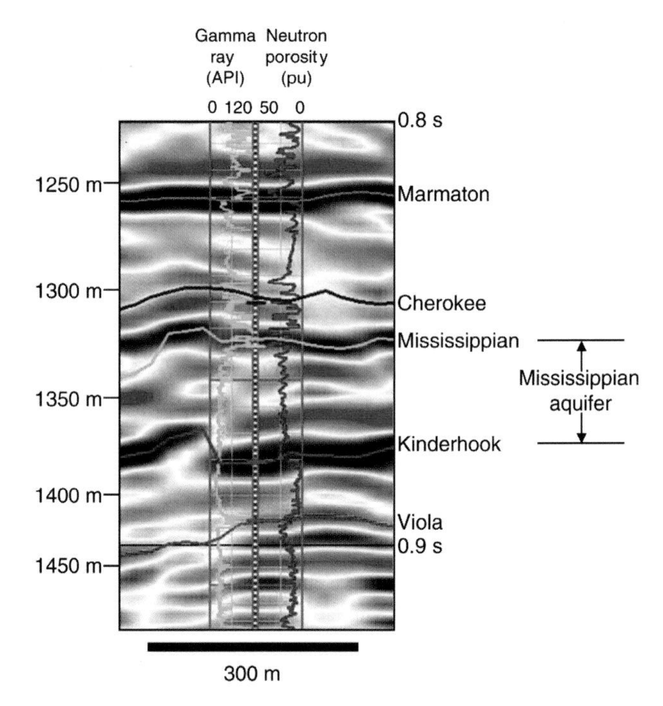

Figure 20. A vertical section through the Mississippian survey shown in Figure 19. After Nissen et al. (2004).

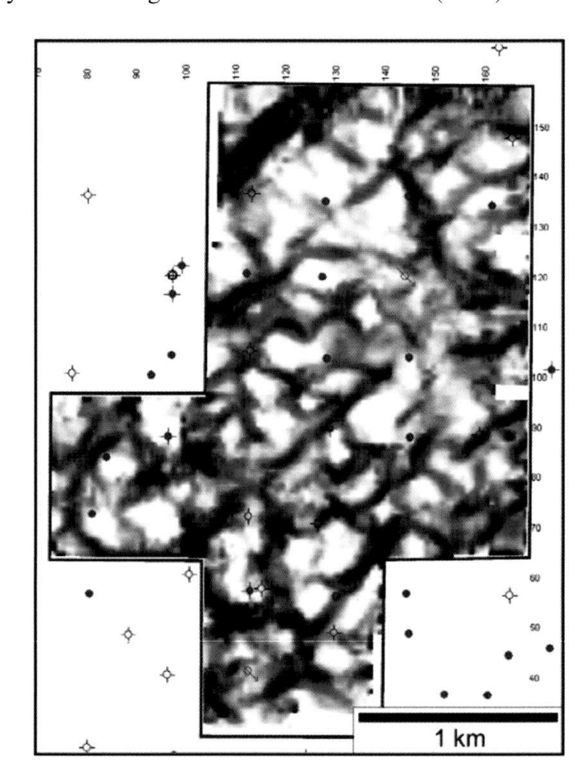

Figure 21. Most-negative curvature extracted from the top (in red) and base (in blue) of the Mississippian aquifer. After Nissen et al. (2004).

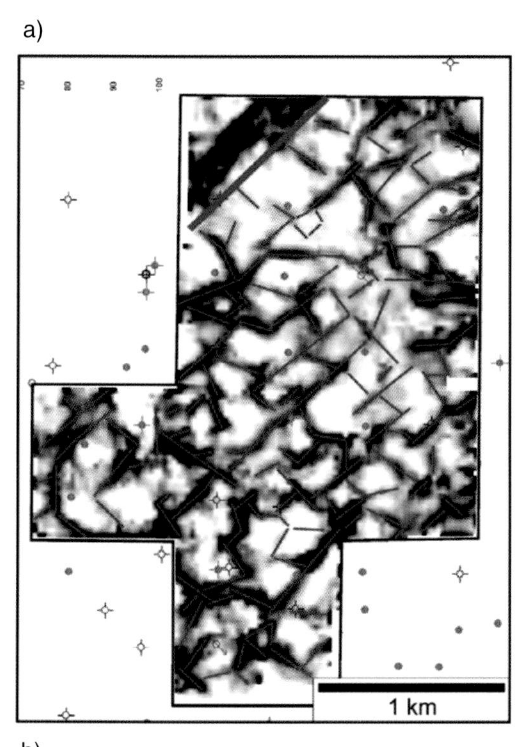

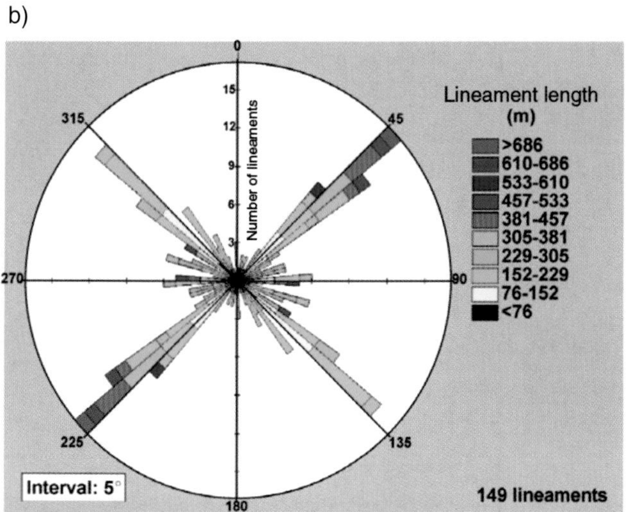

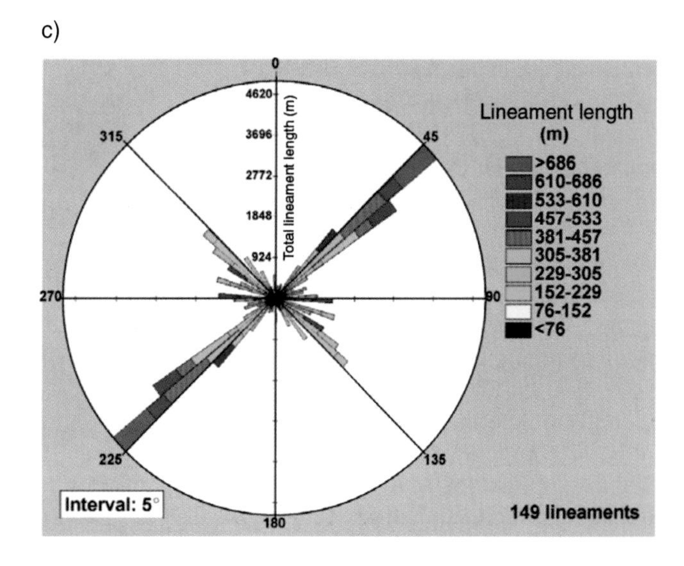

Figure 22. (a) An interpretation of lineaments seen on a most-negative-curvature volume along the base of the Mississippian aquifer. (b) A rose diagram of frequency (number of lineaments) versus azimuth. (c) A rose diagram of length (of all lineaments) versus azimuth. There are two preferred lineament directions, northeast-southwest and northwest-southeast. After Nissen et al. (2005). AAPG©2005. Reprinted by permission of the AAPG whose permission is required for further use.

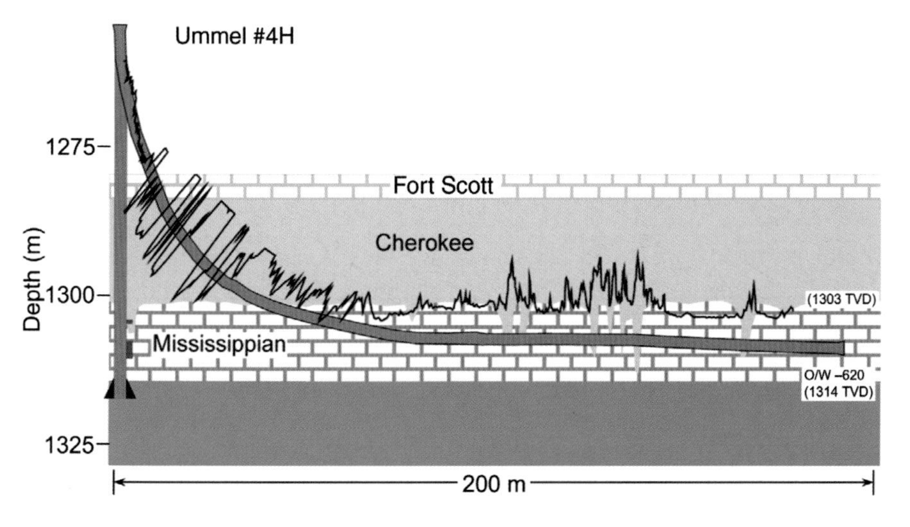

Figure 23. A cross section showing a horizontal well through a Mississippian reservoir, Ness County, Kansas, U.S.A. The gamma-ray log is in black. The upward-trending spikes on the near-horizontal reach of the log are evidence of fractures in the normally low-radioactivity carbonate rock. We interpret these fractures to contain higher-radioactive shales that were emplaced as mud during early stages of sedimentation of the overlying Cherokee Group. Data are courtesy of Mull Drilling Co. After Carr et al. (2000).

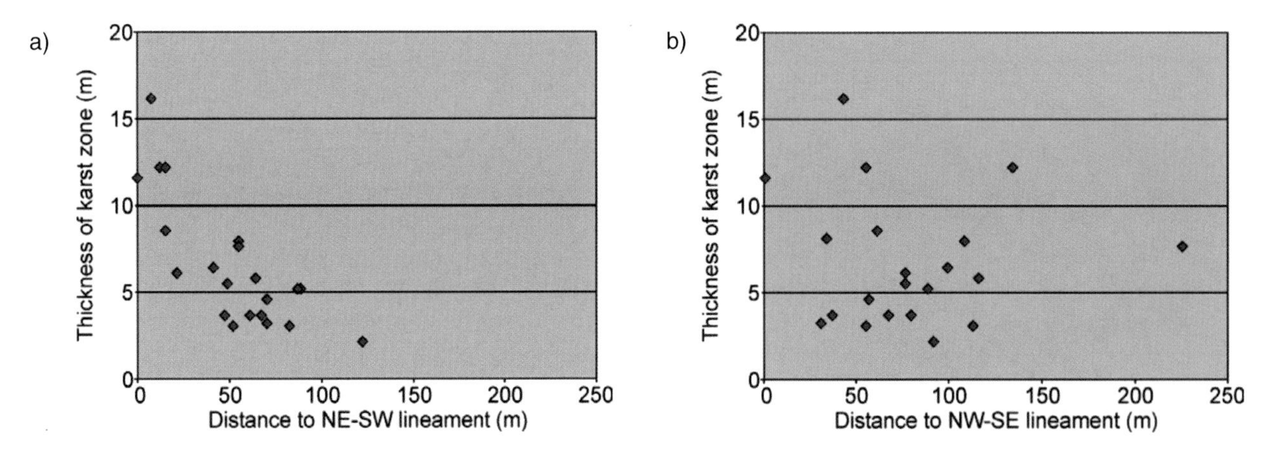

Figure 24. Correlation between thickness of the karst zone (thickness of weathered Mississippian material at the base of the Pennsylvanian, as identified from cuttings and core) and distance from the nearest (a) northeast-southwest lineaments and (b) northwest-southeast lineaments, showing that karst zone thickness increases with proximity to the northeast-southwest lineaments, particularly within 15 m of the northeast-southwest lineaments. After Nissen et al. (2005). AAPG©2005. Reprinted by permission of the AAPG whose permission is required for further use.

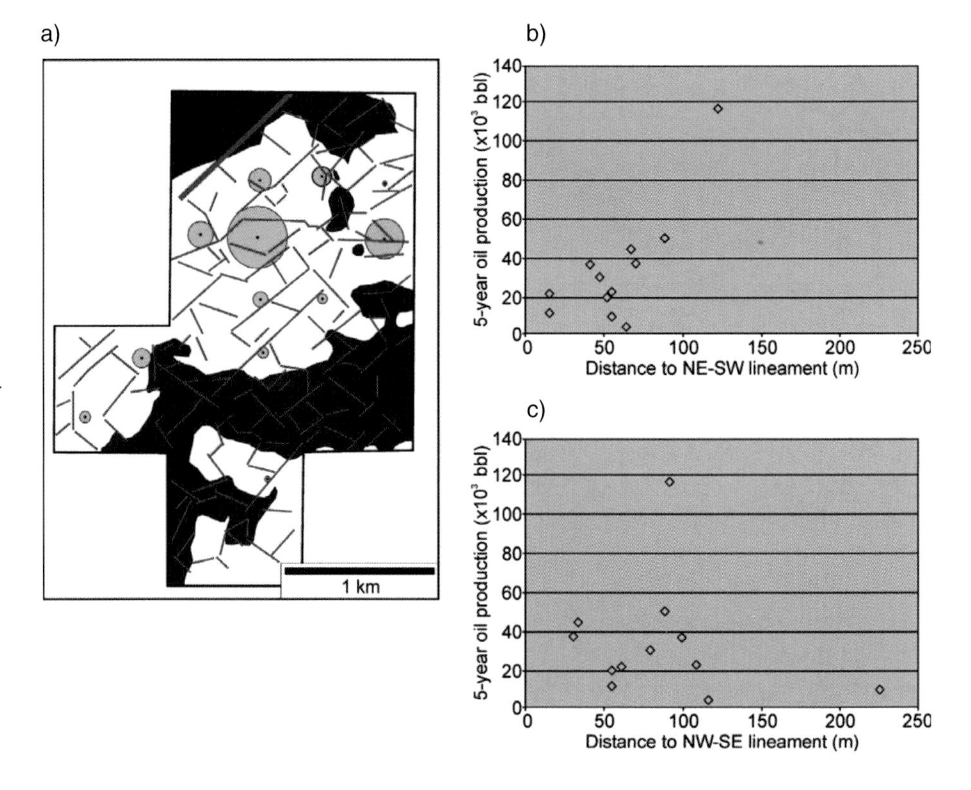

Figure 25. Correlation between (a) oil produced during the first five years of production (green circles, with the largest circle corresponding to approximately 117,600 bbl) and distance from the nearest (b) northeast-southwest and (c) northwest-southeast lineaments. Oil production increases with increasing distance from the northeast-southwest lineaments. No correlation exists between oil production and distance from northwest-southeast lineaments. After Nissen et al. (2005). AAPG©2005. Reprinted by permission of the AAPG whose permission is required for further use.

tween water production and the northeast-southwest-trending lineaments (Figure 26b). These results suggest that the northeast-southwest-trending lineaments are indeed barriers to fluid flow in the reservoir, whereas the northwest-southeast-trending lineaments appear to represent open fractures that serve as conduits into the underlying aquifer.

To our knowledge, this is one of the first attempts to correlate reservoir plumbing numerically with seismic attributes. In the next section, we discuss a more quantitative means of measuring well production and connectivity, but a more traditional (less quantitative) way of mapping fluid pathways.

Calibration of Fault-seal Capability Using Chemical Interwell Tracers, Alberta, Canada

Tracer technology has been used for several decades as a tool for characterizing geologic formations (Brigham and Dehghani, 1987; al Dolaimi et al., 1989). A tracer is a chemical or radioactive substance that allows fluid flow to be tracked through porous subsurface intervals. To qualify as a good tracer, a substance must

- not react with the formation, completion, or casing
- have an insignificant concentration in the reservoir fluids
- exhibit minimum hold-up in the reservoir (i.e., not lag behind the injected fluid)
- be stable under injection and production conditions
- be detected at extremely low concentrations
- be environmentally safe
- have an acceptable price tag

Mixed with the transporting fluid in the right concentration and quantity, a tracer is introduced into the formation of interest through an injector well. Once a tracer is in the formation, it travels laterally along with the reservoir fluid until some of it is produced by neighboring producer wells (Figure 27). The time needed for the tracer to traverse the distance from the injection point to the extraction or detection point is referred to as the transit or breakthrough time. Although permeable homogeneous formations allow a tracer to pass quickly, heterogeneities in formations often impede tracer flow. Consequently, breakthrough times can be used to characterize the plumbing of different formations in terms of fluid movement. Such characterization is important for enhancing oil production levels and obtaining higher ultimate recovery from oil fields.

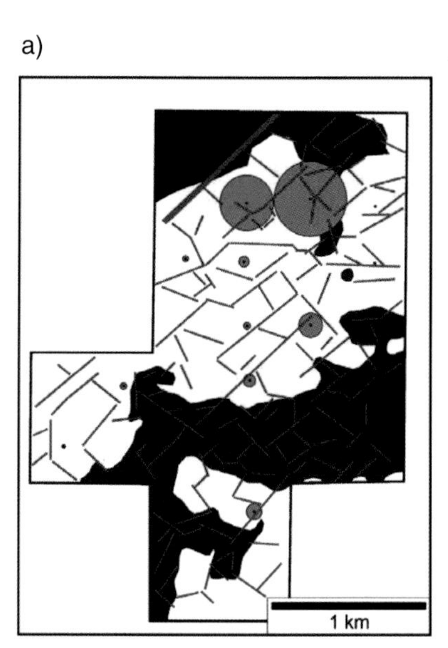

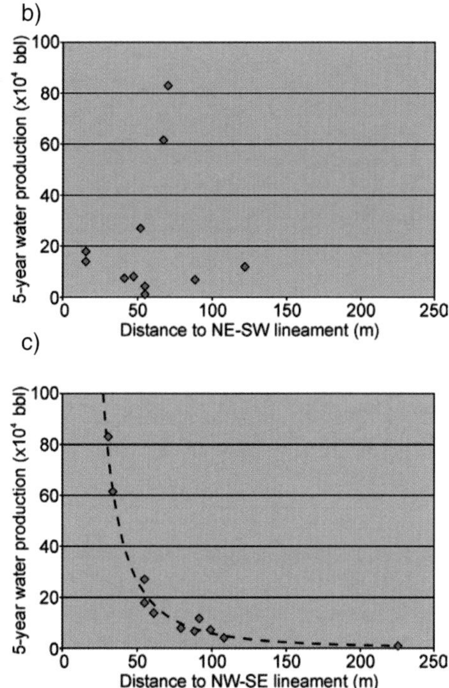

Figure 26. (a) Lineaments and the amount of water produced during the first five years of production (water production is indicated by blue circles, with the largest circle corresponding to approximately 830 500 bbl). (b)-(c) The correlation between water produced and the distance from (b) the nearest northeast-southwest lineament and (c) the nearest northwest-southeast lineament. Good correlation exists between water production and proximity to the northwest-southeast lineaments, with a power-law function [dashed line in (c)] providing a good fit to this relationship. No correlation exists between water production and the northeast-southwest lineaments. After Nissen et al. (2005). AAPG©2005. Reprinted by permission of the AAPG whose permission is required for further use.

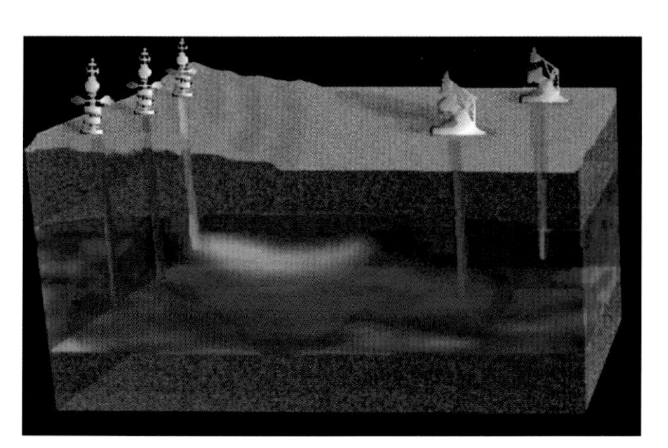

Figure 27. Chemical tracers track fluid movement. In this example, the purple tracer injected in the middle well (on the left) reaches the producing well to the right, whereas the yellow and orange injected tracers do not. Green indicates fluid untouched by the tracers. After Chopra and McConnell (2004). Reprinted by permission of *Oil & Gas Journal*.

Chemical interwell tracers provide a direct means of tracking fluid movement in a reservoir, thus generating an accurate measure of reservoir heterogeneity. Chemical tracers allow us to estimate the magnitude of any flow, whether it is radial or unidirectional, in a reservoir formation. Tracers map not only whether communication exists between injector and producer wells, but also the extent and speed of that communication.

Carefully designed and executed interwell tracer programs make it is possible to

- delineate flow barriers and boundaries
- identify directional flow paths and reservoir heterogeneity
- quantify the causes of early water breakthrough (allowing the operator to identify problem injectors and/or producers)
- identify dual or multiple porosity and permeability systems and their respective fractional volumes
- evaluate volumetric sweep efficiency and percentage of tracer recovered for each injector at each producer
- measure the relative in situ velocities of injected fluids
- improve the design and implementation of secondary and tertiary recovery projects

Tracer measurements are useful, but they provide information about point-to-point continuity. This information is not direct evidence of the actual pathways of fluids. Some formations contain flow barriers, low-permeability pockets, or significant intraformational lateral variations in porosity. In assessment of such formations, understanding the actual pathways is crucial to understanding the fluid flow.

Obviously, the areal images provided by seismic data, coupled with tracer measurements and a working hypothesis on what the major causes of heterogeneity might be (e.g., sealing faults), can aid us in mapping these fluid-flow pathways. Many if not most reservoirs are only a fraction of a wavelength thick. Thus, seismic peaks and troughs provide only limited insight into reservoir heterogeneity. In contrast, seismic attributes, such as coherence, spectral decomposition, and impedance inversion, allow interpreters to extract or enhance subtle details from the seismic data and present them in a manner that is useful to the reservoir engineer.

One field under study is located in southern Alberta (Chopra and McConnell, 2004). The discovery well was drilled in 1993, and that started the process of development drilling; the pool began producing in 1994. Presently, more than 20 wells have been drilled in the pool. Daily production, which peaked at 1200 m^3/day (7500 BOPD) in 1996, had dropped to 400 m^3/day (2500 BOPD) by 1999. The target reservoir is a Late Devonian lower Nisku Formation dolomite about 35 m thick. It was deposited as a widespread carbonate bank in a shallow, open-marine environment. Porosity is primarily vuggy within the oil reservoir but ranges to intergranular beyond.

Overlying the Nisku reservoir rock are dolostones and laminated impermeable anhydrites that formed in the subtidal to supratidal environment of a regressive, often hypersaline shelf. Below the Nisku are the Ireton and Leduc formations. The Ireton, an argillaceous dolomite, is very thin in that area. It is underlain by a thick, porous Leduc dolomite, which generally is regarded as a regional aquifer (Chopra and McConnell, 2004).

No waterflood pattern exists in this field because the five injector wells are in the western and central portions of the field and the majority of active producers are in the eastern and southern areas of the field (Figure 28a). Figure 28b shows a horizon slice below the reservoir through a seismic data volume, and a similar slice through a sharpened coherence volume is shown in Figure 28c. A northeast-southwest low-coherence trend can be seen in the upper-left corner, encompassing injectors INJ-1, INJ-2, and INJ–3, which do not communicate with any of the producers. This zone of low coherence is interpreted to be a flow barrier (graphically shown as a dashed line) that prevents fluids (tracers) from flowing away from these wells toward the right. The quick breakthrough to PRO-1 (teal arrow) in the south is explained by darker lines that depict the potential channel pathway for the tracer to arrive from INJ-4 in such a short time (the potential channel is highlighted by the yellow line).

Currently, the field has 24 actively producing wells. The entire field's water injection into the Nisku Formation currently is averaging 3200 m^3 water (20 134 BWIPD) from five injector wells.

Available 3D seismic data were reprocessed with the goal of increasing both the resolution and the signal-to-noise ratio at the target interval. Prestack migration and surface-consistent deconvolution helped interpreters to achieve this objective. The frequency bandwidth of the stacked data was enhanced by taking advantage of the higher resolution of the VSP data. The method, called high-frequency restoration (HFR), uses the frequency decay experienced at different VSP depth levels in a well (Chopra et al., 2002). After HFR, seismic data display an effect similar to that of a time-variant attenuation correction, resulting in compression of the embedded wavelet.

The frequency enhancement of the seismic data was evaluated by matching it with the VSP corridor stack before and after frequency enhancement, to ensure that the extra reflection cycles seen on the seismic data correlate with reflection events on the VSP stack. Coherence (Chopra, 2002) was applied both before and after frequency enhancement, to evaluate improvements in lateral resolution.

Figures 29 and 30, respectively, show the results of seismic data and corresponding coherence time slices before frequency enhancement (Figures 29a and 30a) and after it (Figures 29b and 30b). We note increased vertical resolution on the seismic data and increased lateral resolution (sharper discontinuities) on the coherence slices.

The east-west lineations (white arrows) in Figure 30 are associated with acquisition footprint (aligned with the receiver lines). This effect, however, is feeble and does not pose a problem. The northeast-southwest-trending lineaments (black arrows) are visible on the original coherence slice but are improved on the coherence slice by the frequency-enhanced data. More important, the frequency-enhanced coherence image shows a clear northwest-southeast trend in Figure 30b that is not as obvious in Figure 30a.

Chemical-tracer-analysis results

Wells INJ-1 through INJ-5 are the five injector wells seen in Figure 28a. Injector wells INJ-1, INJ-2, and INJ-3

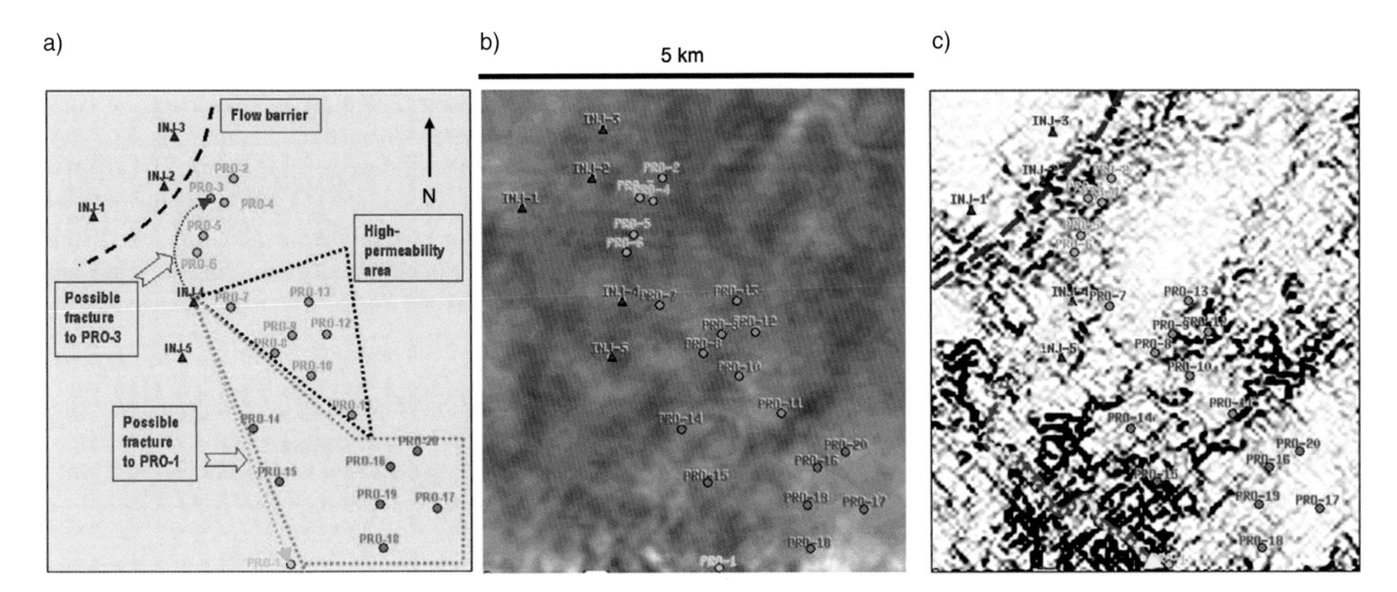

Figure 28. (a) A summary map of chemical-tracer responses, showing injectors in blue and delineating four zones of the reservoir that had different behaviors, indicated here by the green, yellow, magenta, and cyan producer wells. (b)-(c) Horizon slices below the reservoir through (b) a seismic data volume and (c) a sharpened coherence volume. We note a northeast-southwest low-coherence trend in the upper left corner, encompassing injectors INJ-1, INJ-2, and INJ–3, which do not communicate with any of the producers. We interpret this zone of low coherence to be a flow barrier (graphically shown as a dashed line) that prevents fluids (tracers) from flowing away from these wells toward the right. The quick breakthrough to PRO-1 (teal arrow) in the south is explained by darker lines that depict the potential channel pathway for the tracer to arrive from INJ-4 in such a short time (the potential channel is highlighted by the yellow line). After Chopra and McConnell (2004). Reprinted by permission of *Oil & Gas Journal.*

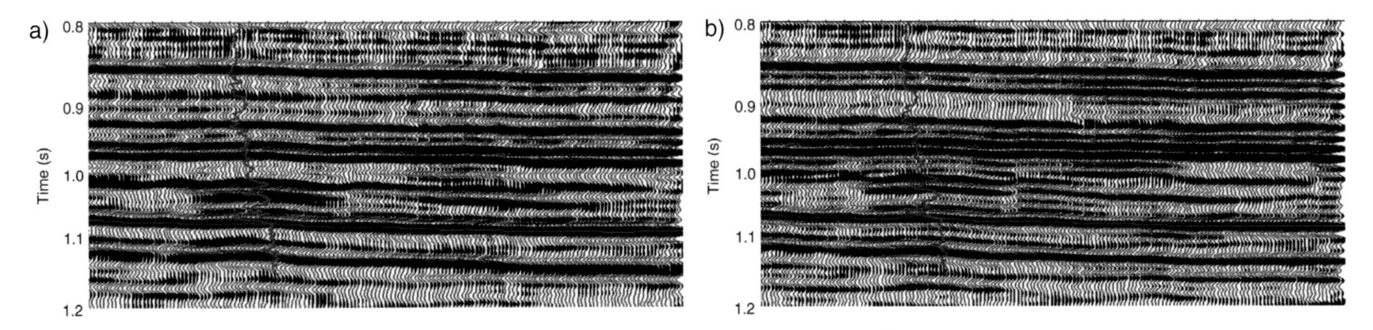

Figure 29. Segments of seismic sections with a seismic log overlaid (a) before and (b) after frequency enhancement. The blue pick indicates an anhydrite horizon. Enhanced resolution and better continuity of reflection events leads to confident interpretations. After Chopra and McConnell (2004). Reprinted by permission of *Oil & Gas Journal.*

in the northwestern portion of the field showed no pressure-maintenance support for the producers to the south. The chemical tracers injected into these three wells did not appear in any of the producer wells in the main producing pool to the south. This indicates some sort of flow boundary or barrier between these three injector wells and the producing area to the south.

The chemical tracer injected into vertical well INJ-5 showed a low, general response in the majority of the producers throughout the field. In contrast, the chemical tracer injected in horizontal well INJ-4 showed a high to medium, highly heterogeneous flow over the entire field, as summarized in Table 1. In summary, we observe that:

- The tracers injected in the northwestern part of the field (vertical wells INJ-1, INJ-2, and INJ-3, which are color-coded blue) have not been detected in any of the producers after a two-year period. This suggests that a flow barrier exists between the three injectors in the north end of the field and the producers to the south.
- Tracers injected in well INJ-4 (blue) reach well PRO-1 (light blue, to the south) in eight days, a distance of just over 2 km. Wells closer than PRO-1 and wells to the east (shown in pink) took 61 days to reach breakthrough.
- Tracers injected in well INJ-4 (blue) reach wells in the northeast. Tracer reached well PRO-3 (green) faster than it reached closer wells PRO-4 (green) or PRO-5 (green) and PRO-6 (green) wells.

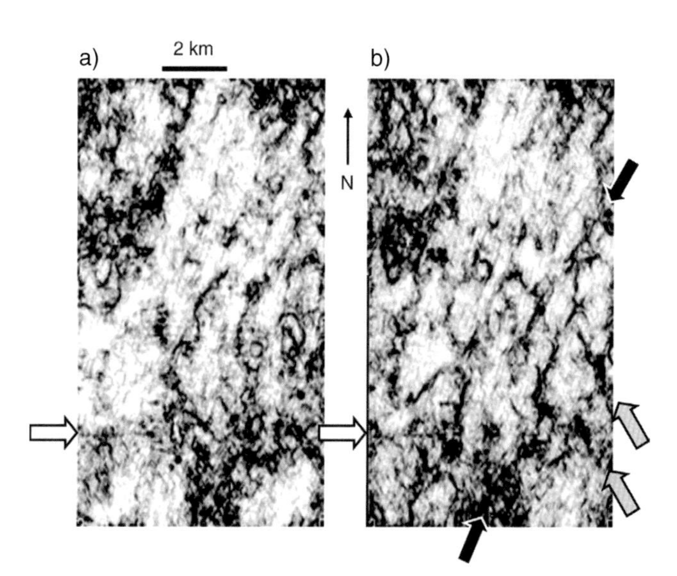

Figure 30. Time slices from the coherence volumes (a) before and (b) after frequency enhancement. The east-west-trending lineations (white arrows) seen in (a) are associated with acquisition footprint. The northeast-southwest-trending lineations (black arrows) are improved on the coherence slice after frequency enhancement. After Chopra and McConnell (2004). Reprinted by permission of *Oil & Gas Journal.*

- Tracers injected in well INJ-4 (blue) reached the wells in the cluster (orange) to its right (east) so fast (one day) that a high-permeability pathway seems to lead from this injector to the wells in that area.

Figure 28c indicates graphically the tracer's breakthrough response, seen from the most significant injector well INJ-4, and gives pressure support to the field. Significantly, 56% of the chemical tracer from this one injector was recovered. In contrast, a smaller amount of pressure support was seen from vertical well INJ-5, from which only 10% of the chemical tracer injected was recovered.

Integrated interpretation

Carbonate reservoirs often are characterized by complex depositional facies, diagenetic alteration, and fracturing, all of which make reservoir production a challenge. Whereas such factors affect hydrocarbon trapping and production, they also affect the reflectivity recorded by seismic data. Lateral changes in reflectivity result in frequency and phase changes on seismic traces, which are detected by the coherence attribute.

Table 1. Concentration of chemical tracer injected in well INJ-4, as seen from individual producing wells. An asterisk (*) indicates difficulty in obtaining water samples (e.g., samples are all oil), wherein breakthrough may have occurred earlier.

Producing wells	Time to initial breakthrough	Distance from INJ-4 to producer (km)
PRO-1	8 days	2.2
PRO-2	6 days	0.9
PRO-3	6 days	0.8
PRO-4	11 days	0.8
PRO-5	61 days	0.5
PRO-6	74 days*	0.4
PRO-7	34 days	0.2
PRO-8	1 day	0.6
PRO-9	1 day	0.7
PRO-10	1 day	0.95
PRO-11	1 day	1.30
PRO-12	1 day	0.9
PRO-13	1 day	0.75
PRO-14	61 days	1.0
PRO-15	61 days	1.45
PRO-16	61 days	1.75
PRO-17	61 days	2.2
PRO-18	61 days	2.2
PRO-19	61 days	1.9
PRO-20	61 days	1.85

The horizon corresponding to the anhydrite seal above the reservoir in the southern Alberta field was picked, and Figure 28b and c shows phantom-horizon slices through a seismic data volume and a sharpened coherence volume, respectively, just below the reservoir formation, on the expectation that we can image faults and fractures better in the base of the reservoir than in the reservoir itself.

The tracer injected in well INJ-4 reaches well PRO-1. Given the large distance traveled and the proximity of PRO-1 to the lineaments seen in the coherence image, it is geologically reasonable to explain (though not prove) this short tracer transit time by fluid flow along open faults and fractures, such as are indicated by the yellow path in Figure 28c.

In Figure 31a, we display a horizon slice 66 ms below the anhydrite top seal. We note from Table 1 that the tracer injected in INJ- 4 was detected in wells PRO-3 and PRO-2 after 3 days and in well PRO- 4 after 27 days. Upon examining the coherence slices in Figure 31a, one notices a low-coherence pathway for the tracer to follow, starting from well INJ-4 and traveling to wells PRO-3 and PRO-2. Well PRO-4 is located away from this low-coherence pathway and therefore takes a longer time to reach. The circular feature indicated by the yellow arrow is a sinkhole, caused either by dissolution of limestone at the surface or collapse of an underground cave. The fill material is different from the surrounding limestone or dolomite, thereby causing a lateral change in waveform and thus our coherence anomaly.

Figure 31b shows a horizon slice at 70 ms below the anhydrite seal. The tracer from well INJ-4 reaches the wells in the pocket marked in yellow in virtually no time (1 day). This observation is not surprising because the marked pocket has a mesh of crisscrossing low-coherence lineations, which may be fractures that could provide high-permeability pathways for fluid movement. Thus the sharpened coherence helps us understand fluid movement and permeability pathways in reservoirs.

Time-lapse Seismic Survey, East Schiehallion Field, West of Shetlands

We conclude our examples by citing work reported by Parr and Marsh (2000) on the results of a 3D time-lapse seismic project carried out by BP and partners (a time-lapse 3D survey commonly is called a 4D survey). Any 4D seismic survey requires not only consistent processing, but most importantly, consistent reoccupation of each source and receiver station. That can be difficult to achieve in a marine environment (Calvert, 2005).

Three surveys were conducted in a field east of Schiehallion. The first was a multisource preproduction survey, the second was a 3D development survey acquired in 1996, and the third was a similar time-lapse survey that was conducted in 1999 after several years of production.

In Figure 32a and b, we display the results of an amplitude extraction at the reservoir level. Magenta symbols indicate (horizontal) producers, whereas cyan symbols indicate (vertical) injectors. Note the large changes in amplitude around the producers and injectors. The reservoir lights up as a result of changes in pressure and gas liberated from solution.

Parr and Marsh (2000) computed coherence for both the 1996 and 1999 surveys, to help them better understand production. They provided an enlarged view over producers C and D (Figure 32c and d) and noted that the discontinuity between the two has disappeared in the zone indicated by the red oval. They showed in their paper how pressure data confirmed communication between these two wells. The yellow producer well (C) was drilled after the 1996 survey as a consequence of the 4D study. An additional injector well (N) was proposed at the time of publication.

Near producer F, Parr and Marsh (2000, unpaginated) noted "a slight amplitude increase at the base reservoir unit. This implies vertical connectivity, but it does not show any

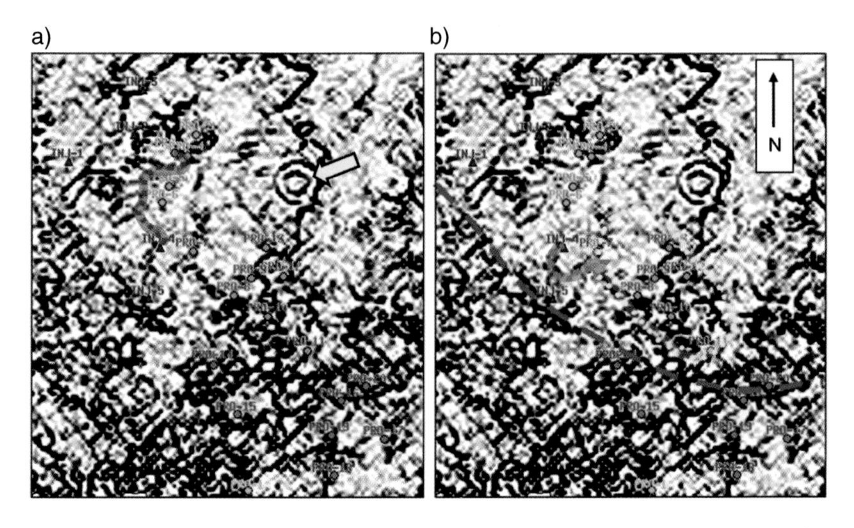

Figure 31. (a) Phantom-horizon slices at $t =$ (a) 66 ms and (b) 70 ms below the top of the reservoir, through the coherence volume. The red arrow in (a) depicts a potential pathway (of low coherence) for early breakthrough (six days), and bypasses two wells that are closer to the injector but have considerably longer breakthrough time (60 days) in an area of high coherence. Wells inside the yellow area in (b) had one day to break through, which we interpret to be a pocket of high permeability, with flow perhaps following the path of the blue arrow. After Chopra and McConnell (2004). Reprinted by permission of *Oil & Gas Journal*.

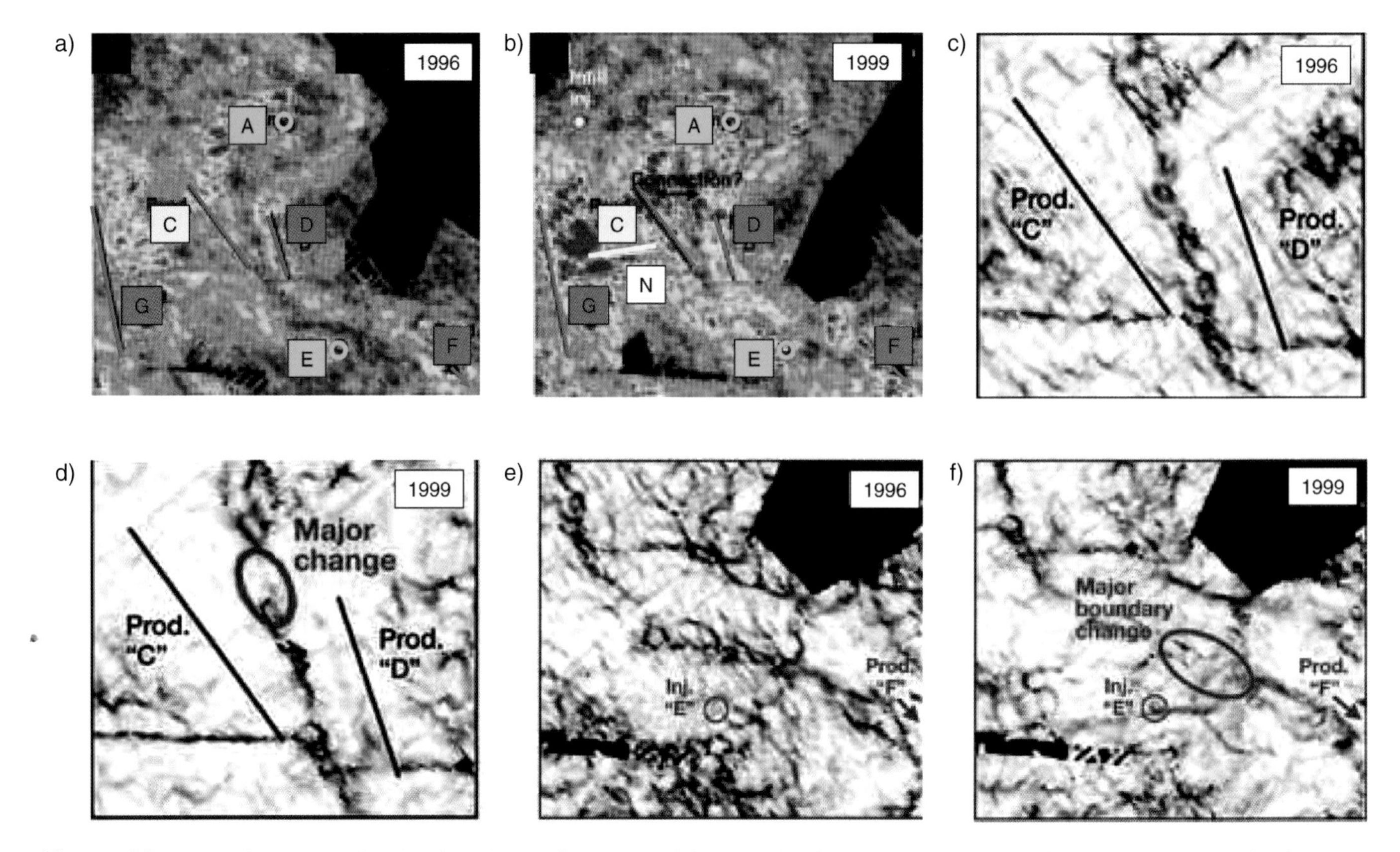

Figure 32. Time slices through seismic volumes from (a) 1996 preproduction survey and (b) a 1999 4D survey acquired east of Schiehallion, West of Shetlands, U. K. Note the large changes around the producers (magenta symbols) and injectors (cyan symbols). After Parr and Marsh (2000). (c)-(d) Zooms on corresponding coherence volumes about producers C and D over the (c) 1996 and (d) 1999 surveys. The 1999 survey suggests a connection (marked by a red circle) between these producers. (e)-(f) Additional zooms on the two coherence volumes show that the discontinuity seen on the (e) 1996 preproduction survey appears to have healed on the (f) 1999 4D survey. After Parr and Marsh (2000).

obvious sign of an elevated amplitude-gas signal at the top of the sand." They also noted that injector E and producer F were hydraulically connected. In a second zoom over injector E and producer F (Figure 32e and f), they noted that the discontinuity between the two appeared to have healed by the time of the 1999 survey.

Chapter Summary

Dense well logs coupled with 3D seismic information, including seismic attributes, help us map reservoir heterogeneity. In general, attributes that are sensitive to impedance and reservoir thickness, such as impedance inversion, AVO, and spectral decomposition, can be used to predict reservoir thickness, lithology, porosity, and fluid content. In contrast, geometric attributes such as coherence and curvature are more sensitive to lateral changes in impedance. Therefore, such attributes provide images of, or allow us to predict, the limits of reservoir compartments, faults, fracture swarms, and diagenetic changes.

All attribute predictions should be based on a sound geological or petrophysical model and should be validated by well control that is not used in the interpretation. Such analysis should be conducted either by a human being or by a geostatistical or neural-network software application.

Workflows and successful predictions of lithology and porosity from impedance- and thickness-sensitive attributes take considerable skill and care but are reasonably mature. In contrast, prediction of reservoir plumbing, including prediction of open or sealing faults and fractures and of intrinsic reservoir permeability, is in its infancy.

A reasonable (but expensive) workflow might be to use horizontal image logs to provide direct measurements of open and closed fractures as a function of azimuth, which then would be correlated against appropriate geometric attributes such as curvature or coherence. Once an interpreter has made such correlations, he can predict porosity by using the same workflow that is used in geostatistical and neural-net inversions, including the key validation step.

Less direct geologically (but more direct from a production point of view) is the use of production histories, pressure transient tests that provide data on pressure buildups in wells, tracer results, passive microseismic measurements of reservoir compaction, and time-lapse seismic data to predict flow pathways. Tracer results can depict flow boundaries, directional flow, problem injectors and producers, and heterogeneity of the field within the reservoir. However, tracer data do not show flow pathways and fluid movement. If the reservoir lights up as a result of gas coming out of solution, 4D seismic information can provide a snapshot of fluid fronts at a given instant in time. Ideally, one would couple such snapshots, tracer data, pressure transients, and flow histories with a reservoir simulator, whereby one can evaluate alternative geologic hypotheses (based on seismic-attribute images).

References

Al Dolaimi, A. M., D. Berta, M. J. Dempsey, and P. J. Smith, 1989, Evaluating tracer response of waterflood five-spot pilot: Dukhan field, Qatar: SPE Paper 17989.

Brigham, W. E., and M. A. Dehghani, 1987, Tracer testing for reservoir description: SPE Paper 14102.

Calvert, D., 2005, Insights and methods for 4-D reservoir monitoring and characterization: SEG Distinguished Instructor Short Course Series.

Carr, T. R., S. Bhattacharya, and R. Pancake, 2000, Horizontal drilling in Kansas: A case history: http://www.kgs.ku.edu/Workshops/Horz2000/R640/, accessed July 26, 2005.

Chopra, S., 2002, Coherence cube and beyond: First Break, **20**, 27–33.

Chopra, S., E. Blias, L. Chavina, V. Alexeev, and V. Sudhakar, 2002, High frequency restoration of surface seismic data: CSEG Recorder, **27**, no. 6, 5–12.

Chopra, S., and I. McConnell, 2004, Using interwell chemical tracers and the coherence cube to understand reservoir communication: Oil & Gas Journal, May 17, 37–42.

Chopra, S., and D. Pruden, 2003, Multiattribute seismic analysis on AVO-derived parameters — A case study: The Leading Edge, **22**, 998–1002.

Dubrule, O., 2003, Geostatistics for seismic data integration in earth models: SEG Distinguished Instructor Short Course Series.

Hampson, D. P., J. S. Schuelke, and J. A. Quirein, 2001, Use of multi-attribute transforms to predict log properties from seismic data: Geophysics, **66**, 220–236.

Hart, B., 2002, Validating seismic attributes: Beyond statistics: The Leading Edge, **21**, 1016–1021.

Hart, B. S., S. P. Cooper, S. Ralser, K. Nickolaissen, M. Herrin, and R. S, Balch, 2001, Ute Dome I: Multidisciplinary integration defines Dakota reservoir compartments, *in* D. Anderson, E. Coalson, J. Robinson and J. Estes-Jackson, eds., Gas in the Rockies: Rocky Mountain Association of Geologists Guidebook, 309–322.

Kalkomey, C. T., 1997, Potential risks when using seismic attributes as predictors of reservoir properties: The Leading Edge, **16,** 247–251.

Lisle, R. J., 1994, Detection of zones of abnormal strains in structures using Gaussian curvature analysis: AAPG Bulletin, **78**, 1811–1819.

Mandl, G., 1988, Mechanics of tectonic faulting: Models and basic concepts: Elsevier.

Nissen, S. E., T. R. Carr, and K. J. Marfurt, 2005, Using new 3D seismic attributes to identify subtle fracture trends in mid-continent Mississippian carbonate reservoirs: Dickman Field, Kansas: AAPG Search and Discovery article no. 40189 (2006), modified from the AAPG 2005 Annual Meeting extended abstract.

Nissen, S. E., K. J. Marfurt, and T. R. Carr, 2004, Identifying subtle fracture trends in the Mississippian saline aquifer using new 3D seismic attributes: Kansas Geological Survey Open-file Report 2004–56, accessed July 26, 2005, http://www.kgs.ku.edu/PRS/publication/2004/2004-56/.

Parr, R. S., and M. Marsh, 2000, Development of 4-D reservoir management West of Shetland: World Oil, **221,** No. 9, accessed June 22, 2005, http://awards.worldoil.com/magazine/MAGAZINE_DETAIL.asp?ART_ID=1154&MONTH_YEAR=Sep-2000.

Ruppel, S. C., and R. J. Barnaby, 2001, Contrasting styles of reservoir development in proximal and distal chert facies: Devonian Thirtyone Formation, Texas: AAPG Bulletin, **85**, 7–33.

Ruppel, S. C., and S. D. Hovorka, 1995, Controls on reservoir development in Devonian chert: Permian Basin, Texas: AAPG Bulletin, **79**, 1757–1785.

Russell, B., D. P. Hampson, and T. Todorov, 2001, Combining geostatistics and multiattribute transforms — A channel sand case study: 71st Annual International Meeting, SEG, Expanded Abstracts, 638–641.

Sagan, J., and B. Hart, 2004, Seismic and structural analysis of a Trenton–Black River hydrothermal dolomite reservoir: accessed June 22, 2005, Search and Discovery Article #40129, http://www.searchanddiscovery.com/documents/ 2004/ hart/index.htm.

Saller, A., B. Ball, S. Robertson, B. McPherson, C. Wene, R. Nims, and J. Gogas, 2001, Reservoir characteristics of Devonian cherts and their control on oil recovery: Dollarhide field, west Texas: AAPG Bulletin, **85**, 35–50.

Schnerk, G. C., and C. N. Madeen, 2000, The Austin Chalk: Simulation of horizontal wells in a heterogeneous formation: Society of Petroleum Engineers, SPE 20716.

Serrano, I., C. H. Blumentritt, E. C. Sullivan, K. J. Marfurt, and M. Murphy, 2003, Seismic attribute delineation of lineaments and reservoir compartmentalization: An example from the Devonian Dollarhide Field, Central Basin Platform, west Texas: 73rd Annual International Meeting, SEG, Expanded Abstracts, 1744–1747.

Walls, J. D., M. T. Taner, G. Taylor, M. Smith, M. Carr, N. Derzhi, J. Drummond, D. McGuire, S. Morris, J. Bregar, and Lakings, 2002, Seismic reservoir characterization of a U. S. Midcontinent fluvial system using rock physics, poststack seismic attributes, and neural networks: The Leading Edge, **21**, 428–436.

Section III

Case Histories

Chapter 16

INTERPRETER'S CORNER

Coordinated by Linda R. Sternbach

Discovery of ring faults associated with salt withdrawal basins, Early Cretaceous age, in the East Texas Basin

STEVEN J. MAIONE, Scott Pickford (A Core Laboratories Company), Houston, Texas, U.S.

The Jurassic Louann Salt has played a dominant role in influencing the structural and depositional history of the East Texas Basin, particularly during Jurassic and Cretaceous periods. Salt tectonics is closely associated with sandstone distribution, depositional facies, and reef growth, and consequently, with petroleum traps in the basin. The stratigraphic column includes several significant regional petroleum reservoirs—the Jurassic Cotton Valley Lime, Cretaceous Pettet, James, and Rodessa Limestones, and the Woodbine Sandstone.

Salt withdrawal basins, developed during the Early Cretaceous in response to salt movement and dissolution processes, are characterized by the presence of an expanded section of Lower Cretaceous marine and deltaic sedimentary rocks. Recognition of ring faults associated with the evolution of these salt-withdrawal basins has gone undetected until recent coherence cube processing of a spec 3-D seismic survey acquired in 1997 following oil industry interest in exploring for Jurassic Cotton Valley Lime reef production in Henderson and Anderson Counties, Texas. The interpretation in this paper focuses on the northern part of the survey in the vicinity of the La Rue salt dome. Coherence cube is a patented post-stack process that enhances visualization of faults and stratigraphic features embedded in the seismic wavelet data. The resultant seismic class can be loaded side by side with the original migrated amplitude seismic data in a 3-D workstation and used for interpretation of faults, stratigraphic discontinuities, and other seismic anomalies.

Discovery of Early Cretaceous-age ring faults brings new perspectives to development and exploration drilling in this mature petroleum province. The structural style of the high-angle ring faults creates a multitude of possible fault traps in a previously unattractive synclinal structural setting. The giant Fairway Field, which produces oil and gas from the Early Cretaceous James Limestone, is at the junction of two salt withdrawal basins that are densely populated with ring faults. The presence of Jurassic-type oil at Fairway indicates that ring faults are probably significant elements in evaluating petroleum migration patterns and traps in the basin. Future petroleum discoveries are expected to follow detailed mapping of ring faults in the East Texas Basin.

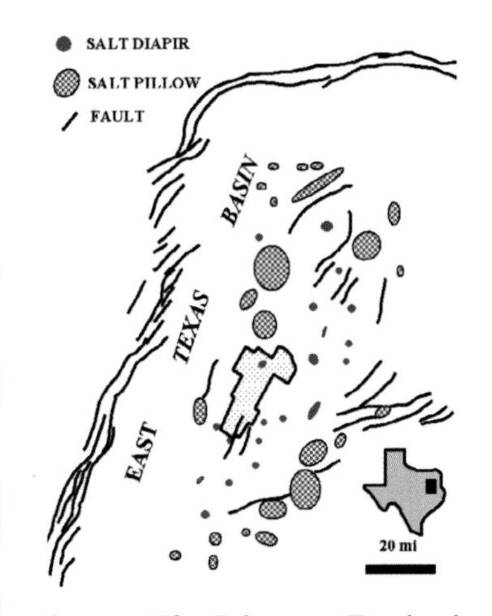

Figure 1. The Fairway 3-D seismic survey (stippled) in East Texas Basin, Texas.

		Production
U. CRET.	PECAN GAP CHALK	
	AUSTIN CHALK	
	EAGLE FORD SHALE	
	WOODBINE SAND - SHALE	✸
LOWER CRETACEOUS	BUDA LIMESTONE	
	GEORGETOWN LS. - SH.	
	KIAMICHI SHALE	
	GOODLAND LIMESTONE - SH.	
	PALUXY SAND - SHALE	✸
	GLEN ROSE GROUP: RUSK LS. - SH.	
	GLEN ROSE GROUP: FERRY LAKE ANHY.	
	GLEN ROSE GROUP: RODESSA LS. - SH.	✸
	BEXAR SHALE	
	JAMES LIMESTONE	✸
	PETTET LIMESTONE	✸
	TRAVIS PEAK (HOSSTON)	✸
JURASSIC	UPPER/LOWER COTTON VALLEY	
	BOSSIER SHALE - SAND	✧
	COTTON VALLEY LIME	✧
	BUCKNER ANHY - SH	
	SMACKOVER LS. - DOLO.	✧
	NORPHLET	
	LOUANN SALT	

Figure 2. Abbreviated stratigraphic column of principal production zones in East Texas Basin.

Geologic setting. The East Texas Basin, a mature, major hydrocarbon province in northeastern Texas (Figure 1) that formed during the Late Triassic-Early Jurassic, contains more than 20 000 ft of mostly Jurassic and Cretaceous rocks (Figure 2). The basin was originally floored by a thick layer of salt, the Louann Formation, which accumulated in a restricted marine environment during the Middle Jurassic. The salt may have reached a maximum thickness of 5000 ft in the center of the basin. Due to postdepositional halokinesis and dissolution, the present thickness of salt is highly variable and substantially less than originally deposited. In many places the salt is completely absent. A variety of salt pillows and diapirs populate the central part of the basin. Salt tectonics is closely associated with sandstone distribution, depositional facies, and reef growth and, consequently, with many major petroleum traps in the basin.

The northern part of the Fairway 3-D survey includes the La Rue salt dome, expressed as a detached teardrop-shaped salt diapir (Figure 3). Top of salt at La Rue is at 4450 ft below the surface. The La Rue diapir has a rim syncline of thickened Lower Cretaceous rocks and lies below a deformed roof of Upper Cretaceous formations. A remnant of the Louann Salt is identified in Figure 3, defined by strong top and base of salt reflectors. A single, strong reflector is present where salt is mostly absent (a salt weld), as seen in the right of the section. A strong Cotton Valley Lime reflector occurs about 600 ms above top of salt. This reflector was a main zone of interest throughout the oil industry during 1997, when the 3-D survey was first acquired. Although no Cotton Valley Lime production is known within the Fairway survey limits, coherence cube data did identify a prospective anomaly northeast of La Rue Dome. A small coherence cube amplitude image of a faulted carbonate reef prospect (shown in an insert in Figure 3) was captured from the coherence display of the Cotton

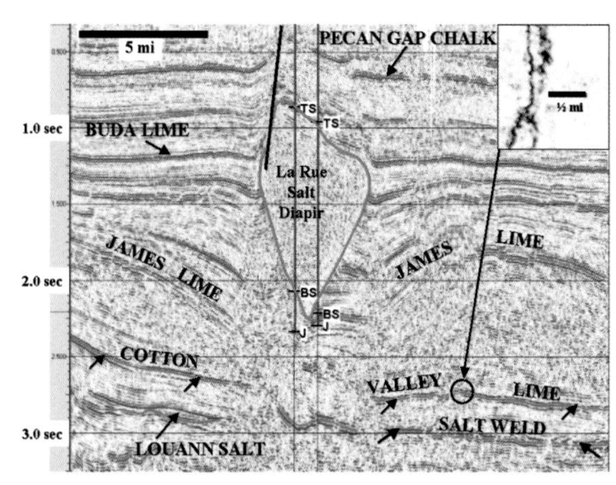

Figure 3. Seismic amplitude section through La Rue salt dome. Major reflectors are identified. Note the remnant of Louann Salt. Picks for top of salt (TS), base of salt (BS), and top of James Limestone (J) shown on two well tracts drilled through the salt dome. Insert shows coherence cube amplitude anomaly that is a possible reef structure discovered at the Cotton Valley Lime horizon.

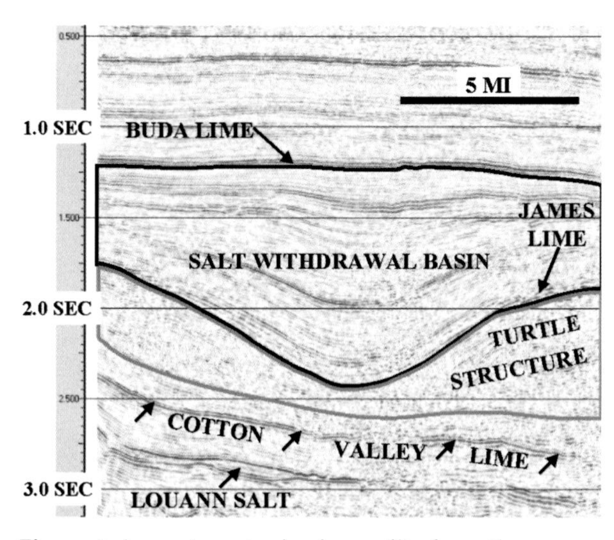

Figure 4. An east-west seismic amplitude section located immediately south of La Rue Dome showing the central salt-withdrawal basin and the western portion of a turtle structure. Note the remnant of the Louann Salt.

Valley Lime horizon at 2.75 s or about 18 500 ft.

Figure 4 shows an east-west seismic section a short distance south of the La Rue diapir. The seismic section has poor reflectivity between the Cotton Valley Lime and James Limestone. This interval is composed of deltaic/marine sandstone and shale of the Travis Peak, Hosston, and Bossier Formations. The two-way time (TWT) interval between the Cotton Valley Lime and James Limestone is displayed in Figure 5. The isochron thickness exceeds 1.0 s TWT in the eastern part of the survey and rapidly decreases to less than 400 ms TWT near the present site of the La Rue salt dome. Contours less than 600 ms form an oval-shaped closure oriented SSW-NNE. This contour pattern indicates a salt pillow of considerable relief once occupied the area, and its former extent is estimated on Figure 5. Uneven sediment loading mobilized the underlying salt during the Late Jurassic-Early Cretaceous and salt preferentially migrated into the salt pillow structure. Since the pillow structure acted as a paleogeographic high, only a thin veneer of sediments eventually accumulated across the crest of the La Rue pillow structure, while thick accumulations of Travis Peak and Bossier Formations formed off on the flanks of the pillow. Thick wedges of Travis Peak/Bossier form cores to turtle structures in the basin, one of which is partially imaged and labeled in Figure 4.

Following deposition of the Travis

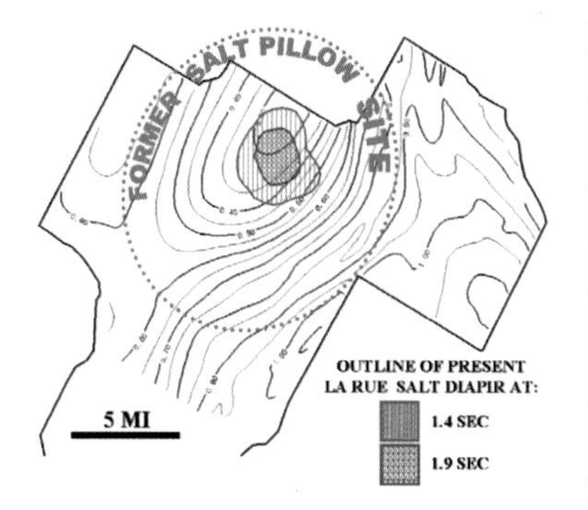

Figure 5. Isochron contour map of the Cotton Valley Lime to James Limestone interval. Contour interval is 0.05 s (50 ms). Estimated position of a salt pillow present at the time of deposition is shown by dotted line. The present extent of La Rue salt diapir is shown at two time depths.

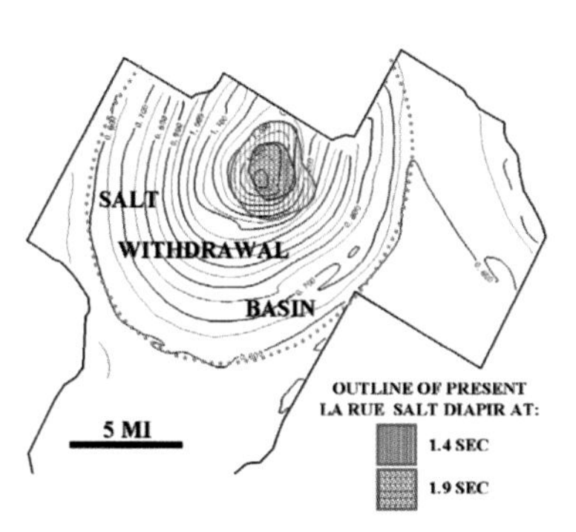

Figure 6. Isochron contour map of the James-Buda Limestone interval. Contour interval is 0.05 s (50 ms). Circumference of the salt-withdrawal basin is shown as a dotted line. The present extent of La Rue salt diapir is shown at two time depths.

Peak sequence, the depositional patterns at La Rue dramatically shifted. An isochron map of the seismic interval between the James and Buda Limestones is shown in Figure 6. The contours exhibit a near circular pattern indicative of a local subbasin that is nearly coincidental with the site of the earlier salt pillow. One consequence of growth of the salt pillow was increasing extensional strain in the more brittle Late Jurassic-Early Cretaceous rocks overlying the salt. Eventually these brittle rocks failed, and extensional normal faults developed at the crest of the pillow. Opening of the extensional faults triggered the movement of salt which progressively entered the extensional fault zone from below and eventually reached the paleosurface as an exposed salt diapir. The diapir was a very dynamic system that allowed large volumes of salt to leave the subsurface area. Salt eventually accumulated at or near the surface, dissolving by contact with ground or ocean waters. Migration of salt from the pillow structure through the diapir took place by slow, symmetric structural subsidence of the entire section above the deep salt pillow. This caused the paleosurface to sag and permitted thicker deposits of marine and deltaic sediments to accumulate, thus allowing a circular subbasin, or salt-withdrawal basin, to form.

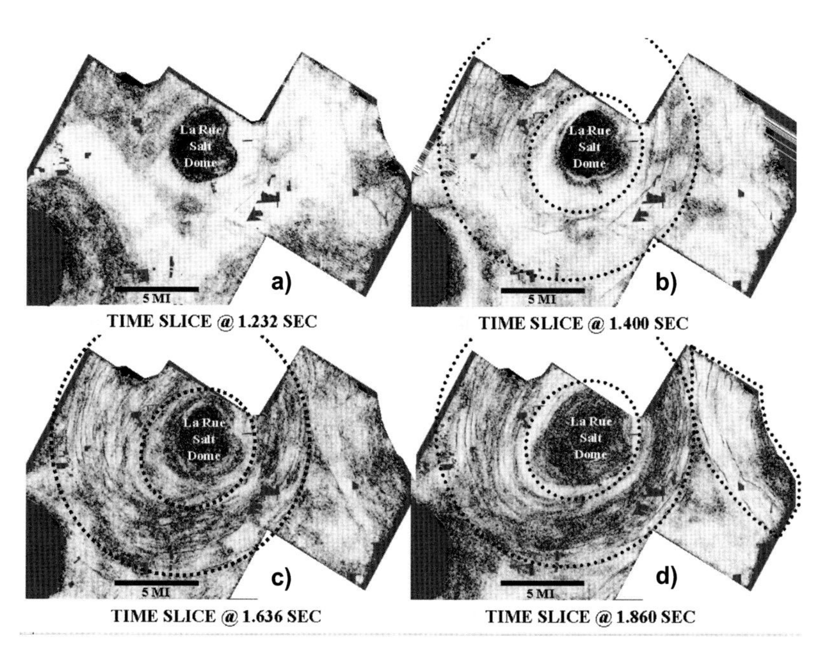

Figure 7. Four sequential coherence cube amplitude time slices through the La Rue salt-withdrawal basin structure. Note the appearance of ring faults concentric around the La Rue salt diapir beginning at 1.4 s between the dotted lines. Ring faults associated with the Brooks salt dome are outlined on the east side of image (d).

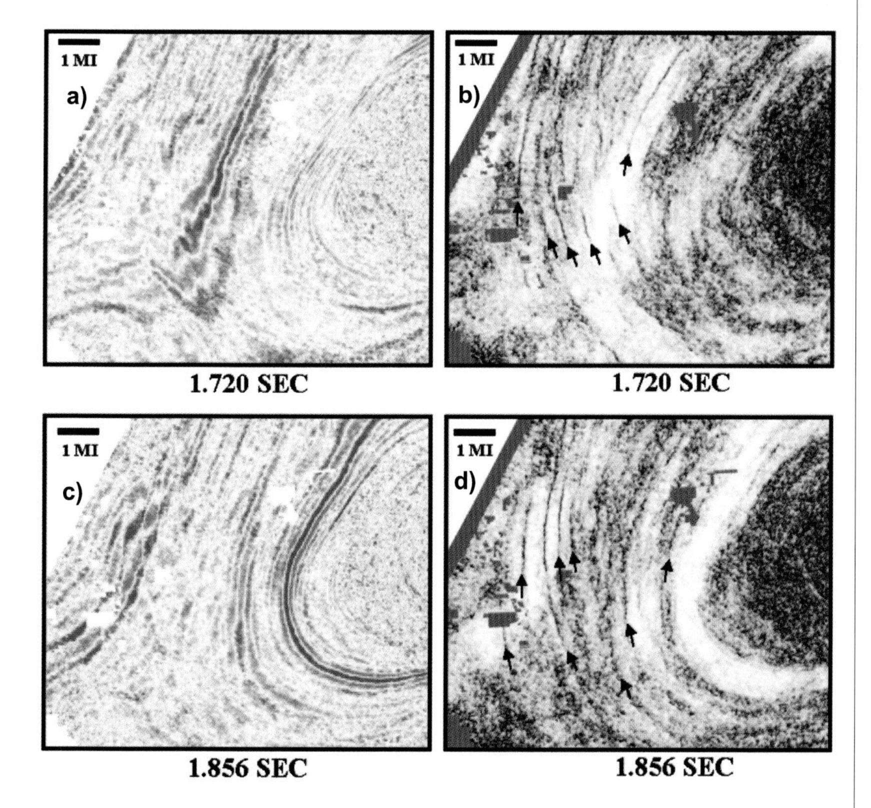

Figure 9. Two pairs of seismic (left) and coherence cube (right) amplitude time slices from west flank of the La Rue salt-withdrawal basin. Note the numerous ring faults (arrows) that are readily apparent on the coherence cube time slices but are difficult to recognize on the seismic amplitude time slices.

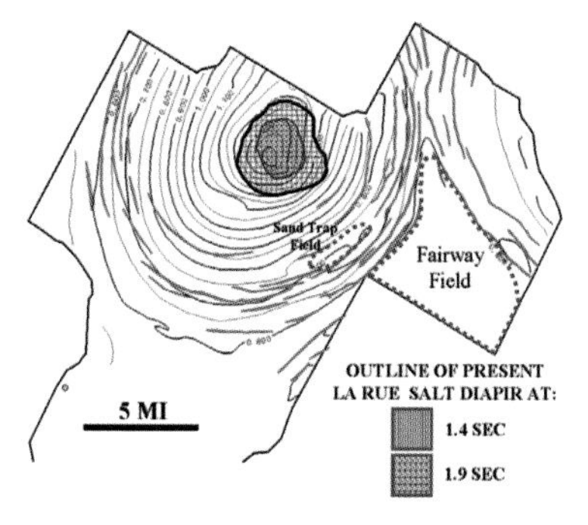

Figure 8. Mapped ring faults near James Limestone superimposed onto an isochron contour map of the interval between the James and Buda Limestones. The present extent of La Rue salt diapir is shown at two time depths. The locations of the Fairway and Sand Trap fields that produce from the James Limestone are shown.

Ring faults. Coherence images revealed that extraordinary sets of faults are present within the survey. Four sequential coherence time slices (Figure 7) at 1.232, 1.400, 1.636, and 1.860 s cut through the salt withdrawal basin. Few faults are visible at 1.232 s, but a set of en-echelon, arcuate faults appears at 1.400 s. These faults are present on all deeper images. These faults are more numerous in an annular belt 4-9 miles measured outward from the present center of the La Rue salt dome and appear most numerous due west and east of La Rue salt dome. Note on Figure 7d that arcuate faults near the eastern edge of the survey appear to define the presence of another salt withdrawal area because these faults are concave to the east. They appear associated with the Brooks salt dome several miles east. All these arcuate faults are best described as "ring" faults, defined as a series of concentric normal faults formed by the collapse of rock in response to deep salt withdrawal. The faults do not form a continuous ring, but displacement from one fault overlaps with the next, forming a circular pattern, hence the term *ring fault*.

Ring faults mapped on a reflector near the top of the James Limestone are shown in Figure 8. The correlation between the ring faults and the isochron map of the James to Buda Limestone interval is readily apparent, suggesting a case for simultaneous origin for both features. The locations of the Fairway and Sand Trap Fields that produce from the James Limestone also are shown.

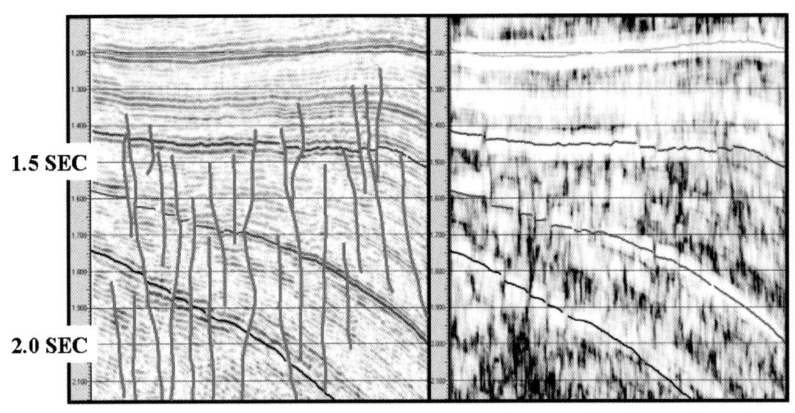

Figure 10. Seismic (left) and coherence cube (right) amplitude sections from west flank of the salt-withdrawal basin. The ring faults on the seismic section were first mapped using the coherence cube section (right) and then transferred onto the seismic amplitude display. Note the upward termination of the ring faults.

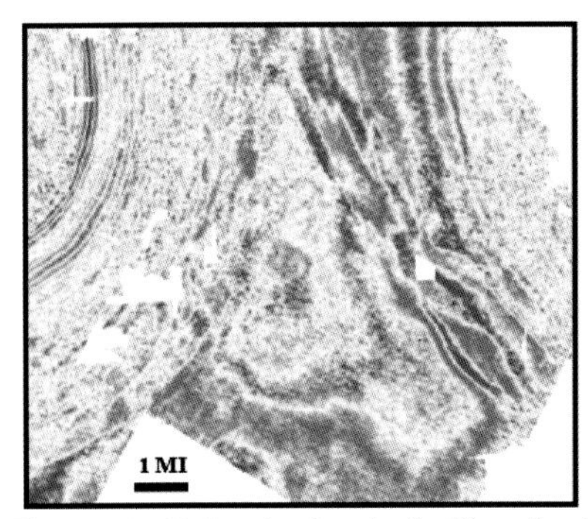

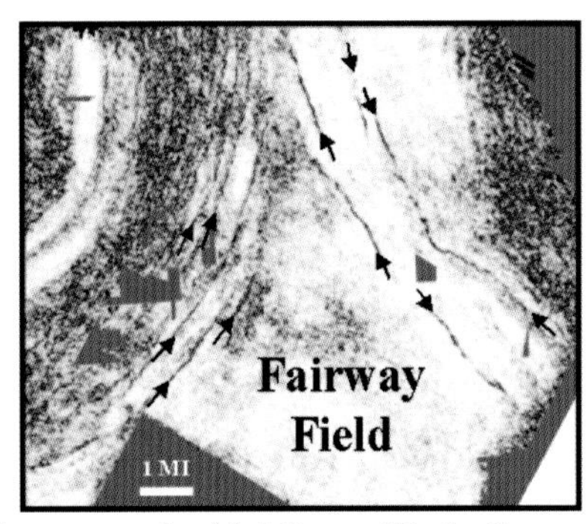

Figure 11. Pair of seismic (left) and coherence cube (right) amplitude time slices, both at 1.856 s, at the intersection of ring faults (arrows) associated with the La Rue (west) and Brooks (east) salt-withdrawal basins. Fairway Field occupies most of the triangular area between the two ring fault sets.

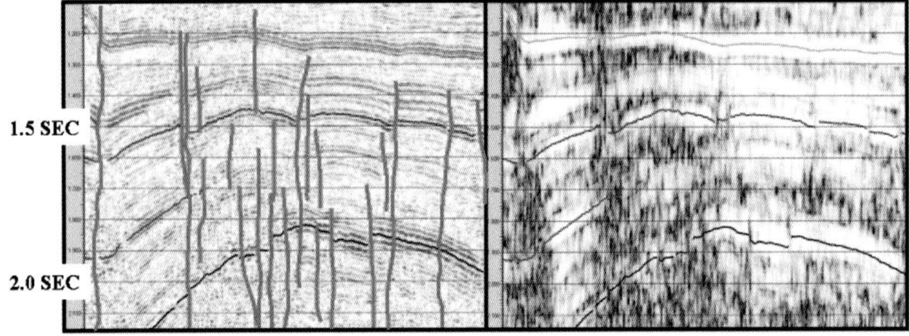

Figure 12. Pair of seismic (left) and coherence cube (right) amplitude sections along an east-west traverse near the northern limit of Fairway Field. The ring faults on the seismic section were first mapped using the coherence cube section view (right) and then transferred onto the seismic display. Note the upward termination of the ring faults.

Figure 9 contains two pairs of seismic and coherence time slices (A and B, C and D) from an area west of La Rue dome. Without coherence processing, identification and mapping of the ring fault system would be challenging. Notice that faults seen on the coherence images strike at an acute angle to the apparent strike of bedding on the seismic amplitude time slice. Note that the ring faults (Figure 10) terminate near 1.3 s. These ring faults can be classified as "blind faults" because they do not offset shallow formations. Vertical throw on each fault is 10-25 ms TWT (65-170 ft). Observations of these faults at greater depth indicate that they do not cut the Cotton Valley Lime but die out in the Bossier Shale and Travis Peak Formation.

A pair of seismic amplitude and coherence time slices (Figure 11) was examined in the vicinity of Fairway Field southeast of La Rue Dome. Fairway, discovered in 1960, has produced more than 209 million bls of oil and 790 billion ft^3 of gas from the James Limestone reservoir. The western limit of the field is well constrained by ring faults associated with the La Rue salt-withdrawal basin, while the eastern limit of the field is defined by ring faults associated with the Brooks Dome salt-withdrawal basin. A matched pair of seismic amplitude and coherence section views near the northern limit of the field is shown in Figure 12. Faults mapped on the coherence section are shown on the seismic amplitude section. Notice again that most faults die out vertically near 1.3 s.

Geologic evolution of a ring fault system. A series of diagrams (Figure 13) summarizes the geologic history of the La Rue salt dome and ring fault development. These diagrams incorporate the new geologic insights provided by coherence processing of the Fairway 3-D seismic survey.

At the time of Cotton Valley Lime deposition (Figure 13a), the Louann Salt beds responded to Late Jurassic sediment loading by forming small-amplitude salt swells. A salt swell at the La Rue site provided a positive paleogeographic feature on which Jurassic reef growth could flourish. The location of a reeflike seismic anomaly along the Cotton Valley Lime horizon suggests that reefs developed preferentially along the periphery of the salt swell.

By the time Travis Peak Formation was deposited (Figure 13b), a large amplitude salt pillow formed in response to uneven sediment loading brought about by the north-to-south prograding deltaic sandstone and shales of the Bossier and Travis Peak sequences. Pillow structures limited or prevented sedimentation atop the crest of the pillows and allowed thicker accumulations of sediments between salt pillows. Growth of the pillow structure at La Rue created strain in the brittle postsalt Jurassic formations and led to extensional faulting at the crest of the pillow. This faulting triggered vertical salt movement, allowing salt to flow into the base of the fault and form a diapiric mass that exploited the extensional fault zone to rise and reach the surface.

At James Limestone time (Figure

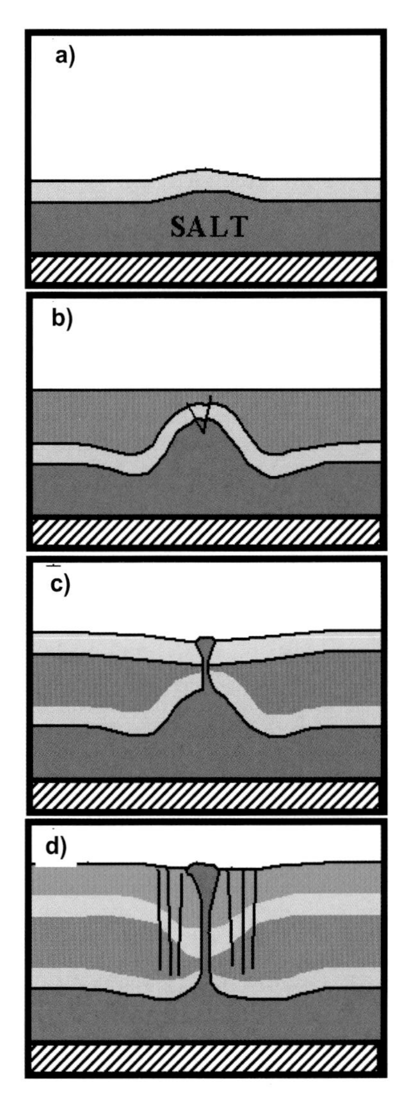

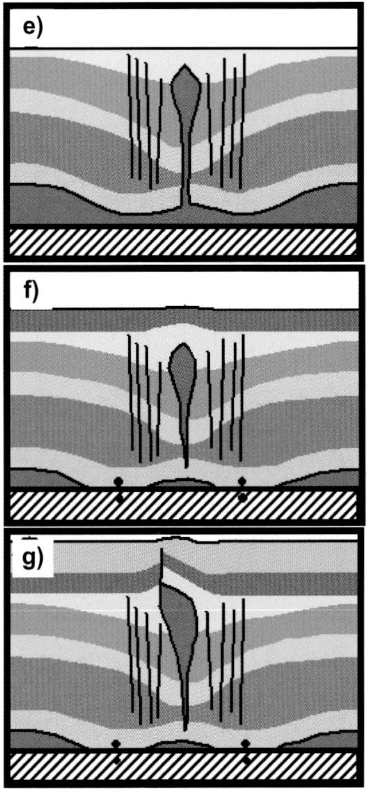

Figure 13. Schematic sequence of diagrams depicting the geologic history of the La Rue salt diapir at the following approximate times: (a) Cotton Valley Lime; (b) Travis Peak Formation; (c) James Limestone; (d) Paluxy Formation; (e) Buda Limestone; (f) Pecan Gap Chalk; and (g) Early Tertiary.

13c), the juvenile La Rue salt diapir entered its main period of growth, during which the net accumulation of salt at the surface exceeded the rate of sedimentation, allowing the dome to grow. Movement of large volumes of salt from the pillow and into the diapir triggered the growth of the salt-withdrawal basin. During periods of high carbonate production (e.g., James Limestone), paleohighs outside the salt-withdrawal sags provided ideal sites for more vigorous reef growth and accumulation of carbonate grainstones in higher-energy environments. The spectacularly productive James Limestone reservoir zone in Fairway Field is a result of these geologic conditions.

By Paluxy Formation time (Figure 13d), salt had continued to migrate through the diapir, forming a surface dome that reached 12 miles^2 in area. Continued migration of salt from the pillow structure and into the diapir allowed the overlying rocks to subside, forming a salt-withdrawal basin that expanded outward to include an area of about 170 miles^2. It is estimated that 55 km^3 of salt migrated from the pillow and mother salt areas via the diapir system. Salt that was not preserved in the expanding salt "deposit" at the seafloor was eventually lost to dissolution from either contact with ocean water or groundwater. About 10 km^3 of salt remains within the present diapir. It is estimated about 45 km^3 of salt that transited the diapiric system was lost to dissolution at or near the seafloor in Early Cretaceous.

The sets of ring faults that populate the withdrawal basin section are the results of extensional tectonics. Figure 14 depicts the sequence of events that led to the formation of ring faults. As the salt evacuated from the deep layer, horizontal strain increased in the upper levels of Travis Peak Formation in response to uneven subsidence rates. Strain was relieved by formation of ring faults, an extensional fault system. The ring faults formed principally within a zone of maximum bending. This explains why ring faults are preferentially distributed in an annular zone 4-9 miles from the present center of the La Rue diapir. Note the formation of a graben and the presence of some upthrown fault traps between the diapir and the graben (Figure 14c), an unexpected but prospective trap type.

Near the end of the Early Cretaceous, growth of the salt-withdrawal basin and accompanying ring faults slowed and gradually ceased development. The nearly complete evacuation of deep salt, characterized by "grounding" of the hanging wall onto the former base of salt and formation of salt weld, brought the development of ring faults to an end. Development of salt welds under the diapir assured the cutoff of any new salt supply to the diapir; consequently, with slowing rates of salt replenishment, the diapir decreased in size at the surface and was eventually overtaken and buried by early Late Cretaceous sediments. The 3-D data suggest that a palinspastic map depicting deposition of the Buda Limestone would exhibit very little surface relief associated with either the salt-withdrawal basin or diapir.

Cut off from any additional salt influx from the deep salt beds, the La Rue diapir responded isostatically to continual burial and possibly regional compression by arching the overlying rocks in Late Cretaceous time (Figure 13f). Thinning of the post-Buda sequences directly over the La Rue salt diapir indicates that the salt dome entered a postdiapir stage and became a persistent positive paleotopographic feature that redirected sedimentation away from the surface dome. In a well atop the diapir, the stratigraphic interval between the tops of the Buda Limestone and Pecan Gap Chalk is 1632 ft. The 3-D seismic and time-depth data indicate that the thickness of the same stratigraphic interval is more than 3100 ft—a short distance from the diapir.

In early Tertiary time (Figure 13g), more severe vertical salt movement ruptured the roof rocks of the diapir, forming a trapdoor fault, with its principal displacement on the west

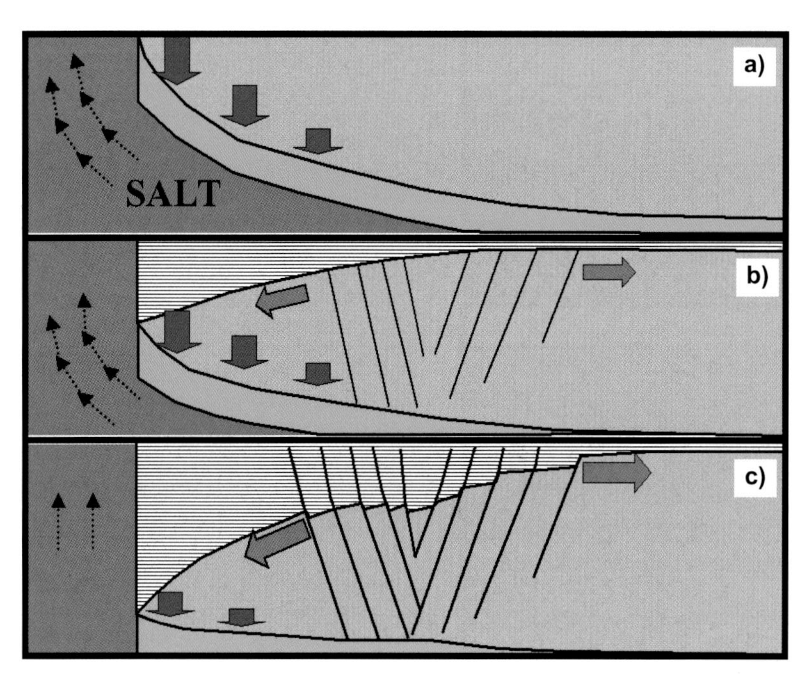

Figure 14. Generalized geologic model depicting the formation of ring faults at La Rue. (a) Lateral migration of deep salt is initiated following the formation of a diapir (left). Evacuation of deep salt initiates subsidence of the overlying formations. (b) Withdrawal basin (pattern) begins to form as subsidence occurs over the vacating salt. Varying rates of subsidence creates extensional strain in the upper part of the descending hanging wall (horizontal arrows). (c) Extensional faults develop in the hanging wall within the zone of maximum strain. Note the formation of a central graben, and the presence of fault traps between the diapir and the graben.

flank. The trapdoor structure involves principally Upper Cretaceous formations younger than the Georgetown Limestone. The roof (or "door") of the structure dips 5-7° to the east. On the west side of the diapir, the Buda Limestone exhibits vertical displacements in excess of 1600 ft along the trapdoor fault. Isostatically induced salt movement was unlikely to have formed the trapdoor structure without the contribution of compressional stress. The required compressional stress likely originated from the Mexia-Talco fault zone updip to the west (Figure 1). The Mexia-Talco fault zone contains an en-echelon array of grabens formed in response to basinward gravity gliding and spreading above the Louann Salt. Transfer downdip of the resultant compressional stress likely boosted diapirism of the La Rue Salt, uplifting and faulting the Upper Cretaceous overburden until the strain in the salt was relieved. Effects of the diapir on sediments younger than the Pecan Gap Chalk (less than 400 ms TWT) could not be determined from the 3-D data because these events are lost to the seismic mute zone.

Ring faults and the East Texas Basin petroleum system. Three major oil types have been identified in the East Texas Basin (Wescott and Hood, 1994) based on physical and geochemical characteristics of the basin: Jurassic, Lower Cretaceous, and Upper Cretaceous. Jurassic oils are not restricted to a particular stratigraphic interval but rather are found in reservoir rocks ranging in age from the Jurassic Smackover to the Upper Cretaceous Woodbine formations. Most oil fields in the East Texas Basin in which Jurassic-type oils have been identified are fault related, with faults either forming the trap or the trap being a highly faulted dome or anticline. Wescott and Wood (1994) observed a relationship between the amount of faulting and hydrocarbon production in the deep salt structures, and stated that those fields that are highly faulted have produced the largest amount of oil.

The ring faults that span the stratigraphic interval between the Upper Jurassic and Cretaceous formations could provide excellent vertical pathways for hydrocarbons to migrate from Upper Jurassic source rocks (Bossier shale) to Lower Cretaceous reservoir rocks. Development of ring faults during the Early Cretaceous could provide an early structural framework for the East Texas Basin petroleum system to flourish and provide hydrocarbon charge to the shallower reservoirs in faulted traps. Importantly, the blind fault character of the ring faults probably prevented any substantial loss of migrating hydrocarbons to the surface during peak periods of oil generation, estimated to have occurred between 88 million and 20 million years ago. An example of this fortuitous gathering of key petroleum system elements is demonstrated by oil from a Jurassic source rock found in the Lower Cretaceous James Limestone reservoir in Fairway Field. Ring faults border two of the three sides of the field and are well positioned to charge the James Limestone reservoir with Jurassic oils. Impressive rock quality and thickness of the James Limestone reservoir began with deposition of high-energy carbonate facies between two developing salt-withdrawal basins that developed a multitude of ring faults.

Discovery of ring faults associated with the La Rue salt-withdrawal basin adds to structures that contribute to the creation of petroleum traps in the East Texas Basin. Recognition and mapping of ring faults with 3-D data provide a basis for pursuing additional hydrocarbon exploration in this mature basin. A variety of structural traps can occur associated with ring faults, the most common being defined by two parallel ring faults where beds caught between the ring faults are accompanied by two- or three-way dip. Where complex relative ring-fault displacements are present, a horst block can occur between a pair of ring faults (Figure 14). This latter type of trap has been found productive in the Sand Trap gas field (cumulative production = 37 billion ft^3) immediately west of Fairway (Figure 8). A more speculative trap idea is the expectation that closely spaced ring faults may host fractured reservoir plays within Lower Cretaceous limestone and sandstone formations, even in areas of low porosity and permeability.

Ring-fault-style displacement at Fairway is duplicated at other salt withdrawal basin sites within the East Texas Basin, but mapping waits for additional coherence interpretation of other 3-D seismic surveys. Knowledge of the existence of ring faults associated with salt-withdrawal basins in east Texas is a key for effective exploration for traps located astride or adjacent to these principal migration pathways. Future petroleum discoveries are expected to follow detailed mapping of ring faults in the East Texas Basin.

Conclusions. Images derived from a 3-D coherence cube seismic volume in the East Texas Basin aptly exhibit extraordinary sets of closely spaced ring faults on the periphery of two salt-withdrawal basins, one associated with the La Rue Dome and part of a second associated with Brooks Dome. The giant Fairway Field is located at the junction of these two ring-fault sets.

The distribution and Early Cretaceous age of the ring faults establish that these faults are a significant element in petroleum migration patterns and traps in the basin. The ring faults span the stratigraphic interval between the Upper Jurassic and Cretaceous formations and could have provided vertical pathways for hydrocarbons to migrate from Upper Jurassic source rocks (Bossier Shale) and charge the shallower Lower Cretaceous reservoir rocks. Importantly, the blind fault character of the ring faults probably prevented any substantial loss of migrating hydrocarbons to the surface during peak periods of oil generation.

The structural style of high-angle ring faults creates a multitude of possible fault traps in a previously unattractive, synclinal, structural setting. Besides structural traps developed between ring faults, as found in Sand Trap Field, a more speculative trap idea is that closely spaced ring faults can be a fractured reservoir play within low porosity and permeability Lower Cretaceous limestone and sandstone formations. Description of Early Cretaceous ring faults in the East Texas Basin using coherence cube processing brings new perspectives to development and exploration drilling in this mature petroleum province. Future petroleum discoveries may follow detailed mapping of ring faults in the East Texas Basin.

Suggested reading. Coherence cube processing is described in "3-D seismic discontinuity for faults and stratigraphic features: The coherence cube" by Bahorich and Farmer (*TLE*, 1995); "3-D seismic attributes using a semblance-based coherency algorithm" by Marfurt et al. (GEOPHYSICS, 1998); "Eigenstructure-based coherence computation as an aid to 3-D structural and stratigraphic mapping" by Gersztenkorn and Marfurt (GEOPHYSICS, 1999); and "Revealing the geology of the Gulf of Mexico by 3-D seismic" by Maione (OTC paper 11055, 1999). East Texas geology is discussed in "Evolution of salt structures, East Texas diapir province: Sedimentary record of halokinesis, Parts 1 and 2," by Seni and Jackson (AAPG *Bulletin*, 1983); "Hydrocarbon generation and migration routes in the East Texas Basin" by Wescott and Hood (AAPG *Bulletin*, 1994); "Geology of Fairway Field, East Texas" by Terriere (AAPG Memoir 24, 1976); and "Upper Jurassic reef play, East Texas Basin: An updated overview. Part 1—background and outboard trend" by Montgomery et al. (AAPG *Bulletin*, 1999). E

Editor's note: Coherence cube is a registered trademark of Core Laboratories N.V.

Acknowledgements: Acknowledgement is given to Schlumberger for permission to publish images from the Fairway 3-D survey, and the assistance of Wayne C. Ackerman, formerly of Schlumberger, is gratefully acknowledged. Thanks to Bruno Vendeville, University of Texas at Austin, and Roger Sassen, Texas A&M University, for stimulating discussions on salt tectonics and salt dissolution processes. Appreciation is expressed to the staff at Scott Pickford (successor to Coherence Technology Company) and its parent organization Core Laboratories for encouragement and permission to publish the results of this study. An earlier version of this paper was published in the Transactions of the 50th Annual GCAGS/SEPM Convention, October 2000.

Corresponding author: smaione@corelab.com

Steven J. Maione, senior geophysicist for Scott Pickford, received a bachelor's degree in geological engineering and a master's in geology from the Colorado School of Mines. He joined Union Oil Company of California (now Unocal) in 1971. Between 1974 and 1992 he worked as an exploration geologist for the Unocal Geothermal Division and participated in geothermal exploration projects in North America, Philippines, Indonesia, and Japan. In 1998, he joined the seismic interpretation services group with Coherence Technology Company (CTC), and later with Core Laboratories Company following a merger of the two companies. He has interpreted numerous 3-D surveys, including offshore Nigeria, eastern Saudi Arabia, Anadarko Basin, East Texas Basin, Texas Gulf Coast, Colombia, and Mexico.

Chapter 17

GEOPHYSICS, VOL. 71, NO. 5 (SEPTEMBER-OCTOBER 2006); P. B159–B166, 13 FIGS.
10.1190/1.2335581

Volume-based curvature computations illuminate fracture orientations — Early to mid-Paleozoic, Central Basin Platform, west Texas

Charles H. Blumentritt[1], Kurt J. Marfurt[1], and E. Charlotte Sullivan[1]

ABSTRACT

Volumetric curvature analysis is a simple but computationally intensive procedure that provides insight into fracture orientation and regional stresses. Until recently, curvature analysis has been limited to computation along horizon surfaces that may be affected by unintentional bias and picking errors introduced during the interpretation process. Volumetric curvature is best estimated in a two-step process. In the first step, we use a moving-analysis subvolume to estimate volumetric reflector dip and azimuth for the best-fit tangent plane for each sample in the full volume. In the second step, we calculate curvature from adjacent measures of dip and azimuth. We use larger curvature analysis windows to estimate longer wavelength curvatures. Such a technique allows us to output full 3D volumes of curvature values for one or more scales of analysis. We apply these techniques to a data set from the Central Basin Platform of west Texas and find lineaments not observable with other seismic attributes. These lineaments indicate that, in the lower Paleozoic interval, a left-lateral shear couple oriented due east-west controls the local stress regime. Such a model predicts that extension faulting and fractures will be oriented northeast-southwest. The example demonstrates the potential of this new technology to determine stress regimes and predict azimuths of open fractures.

INTRODUCTION

This geologic curvature analysis is based on the principle that stresses applied to an area will result in predictable orientations of fractures, folds, and faults related to the orientations of the three principal stresses (Harding, 1974). The basic relation has been calibrated through surface studies from field mapping (e.g. Murray, 1968; Lisle, 1994) and air photo analysis (McQuillan, 1974). In the subsurface, stress analysis must be done by integrating surface trends with well and seismic data control (e.g., Ward and Beeson, 2004, personal communication). In this workflow, the interpreter generates a map of some identifiable geologic horizon and analyzes the map for areas of anomalous curvature. Then, using an appropriate geologic model, the interpreter relates curvature to regional or local stresses.

According to Roberts (2001), curvature at any point on a 2D section is the inverse of the radius of a circle whose circumference approximates the surface at that point (Figure 1). In the case of a 3D surface, curvature is calculated by passing a quadratic surface through a grid of nine or more data points. By successively low-pass-filtering such an interpreted map, Sigismondi and Soldo (2003) obtained longer wavelength curvature estimates. Bergbauer et al. (2003) calculated long wavelength estimates of curvature through a more direct Fourier (k_x, k_y) decomposition of an interpreted horizon. Al-Dossary and Marfurt (2006) extended these ideas to generate spectral estimates of curvature for an entire seismic volume by use of an (x, y) operator implementation of a (k_x, k_y) bandpass filter. Such an operator avoids the need to transpose the seismic dip and azimuth cubes and runs in parallel on an inexpensive computer cluster environment.

Geologists have been using curvature analysis in the petroleum industry for at least 35 years (e.g., Murray, 1968) to identify local areas of increased bending of rock units for the purpose of locating zones of increased fracturing and improved production. Lisle (1994) revisited the area studied by Murray (1968) and gave a more detailed analysis of the curvature of the structure, finding that areas of high magnitudes of Gaussian curvature correlate with areas of greater deformation and therefore greater density of fractures. He further indicated that faulting creates intense fracturing and thus may be identifiable by areas of high magnitudes of Gaussian curvature. More recently, Bergbauer et al. (2003) used maximum curvature to locate faults along a horizon in the North Sea. Massaferro et al. (2003) used maximum-curvature analysis on structures in Argentina to delineate structural trends and identify fracture zones. They found that the fractures observed on a vertical image log in one well were consis-

Manuscript received by the Editor July 13, 2004; revised manuscript received January 17, 2006; published online September 7, 2006.
[1]Allied Geophysical Laboratories, University of Houston Room 510 Science and Research Building 1, Cullen Road Entrance 14 Houston, Texas 77204. E-mail: cblumentritt@geo-texture.com; kmarfurt@uh.edu; charlotte.sullivan@pnl.gov.

tent in direction and intensity with the amount of fracturing predicted by the curvature technique. Sigismondi and Soldo (2003) showed examples of curvature analysis assisting in the interpretation of structures in Argentina. They found that maximum curvature highlights fault trends and sense of faulting and that most negative curvature delineates subtle lineaments within fault blocks. Hart et al. (2002) analyzed production data and showed that the intersection of curvature (change in dip) trends directly correlated with the better performing wells. In most cases, these workers limited their analyses to a single type of curvature.

In this paper, we begin with a review of the definition, calculation, and interpretation significance of the various curvature estimates. In the next section, we summarize the tectonic and depositional framework of the survey area, as well as the major features seen on the seismic data and attribute volumes, including volumetric curvature. Finally, we use these new attributes to predict the stress field at the time of structural deformation.

CURVATURE

Curvature of a surface at a particular point is the inverse of a circle's radius which is tangent to that surface at that point (Roberts, 2001). For our purposes, we will be concerned with circles in a plane normal to the surface and will consider positive curvature to be concave downward (Figure 1). Roberts (2001) gives a very readable discussion of the various types of curvature and other related attributes, based on work initially done by Gauss in the 1820s. He found that numerous types of curvature could be determined at every point on a gridded surface by fitting a quadratic surface to the data and using the coefficients of the quadratic equation. At any given point on a surface, there are an infinite number of circles in normal planes of different azimuths that may be tangent to the surface. For a quadratic surface, the curvature of the tangent circle with the smallest radius in a normal plane is called the maximum curvature, k_{max}. The curvature of the tangent circle in the normal plane perpendicular to this has the minimum curvature, k_{min}.

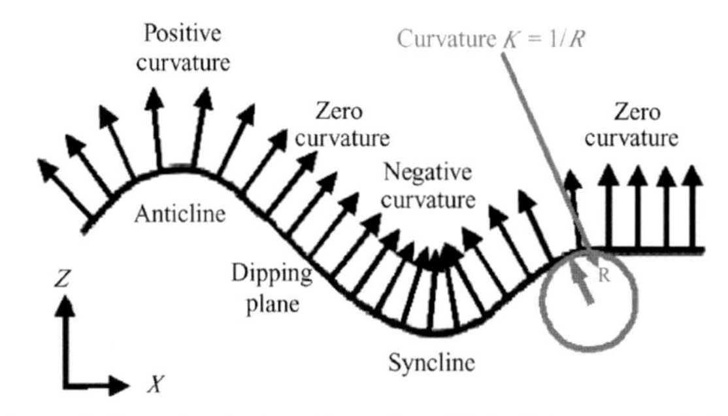

Figure 1. Curvature in two dimensions. Note that curvature is defined as the inverse of the radius of a circle that is tangent to the surface at any point and that, by convention, positive curvature is concave downward, and negative curvature is concave upward (after Roberts, 2001).

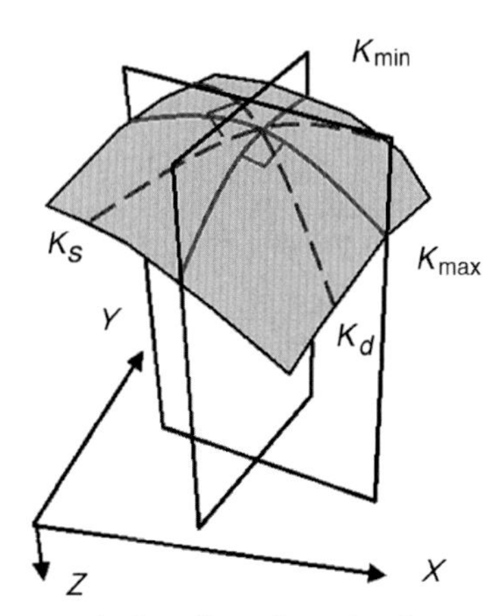

Figure 2. Curvature in three dimensions, showing maximum curvature k_{max}, minimum curvature k_{min}, dip curvature k_{dip}, and strike curvature k_{str}. Not shown are Gaussian curvature k_g, mean curvature k_{mean}, most positive curvature k_{pos}, and most negative curvature k_{neg} (from Roberts, 2001; after Sigismondi and Solda, 2003).

Together, these two curvatures are known as the principal curvatures and, along with the azimuth of k_{min}, completely define the quadratic surface. From k_{min} and k_{max}, we may compute the Gaussian curvature k_g as the product of the two principal curvatures and the mean curvature k_{mean} as their average. Other important curvatures are the most positive k_{pos}, most negative k_{neg}, dip k_{dip}, and strike k_{strike} curvatures. (See Figure 2 and Roberts, 2001, for more detailed descriptions of these.) Other attributes derivable in this analysis include curvedness, which is equal to $(k_{max}^2 + k_{min}^2)^{1/2}$; the shape index, which indicates the local morphological structure of the surface (dome, ridge, plane, valley, bowl, or saddle); and rotation, which measures scissors-like deformation not represented by our smooth quadratic surfaced model.

Several of these curvatures give information about the morphology of the surfaces from which they are extracted, as can be visualized by extending the curved line in Figure 1 infinitely into and out of the page. Such a structure is the result of folding an initially flat surface around axes perpendicular to the page (Lisle, 1994). It is intuitively evident that there is no deformation of the surface perpendicular to the page and varying amounts of deformation along the curved line. At every point along the curved line or any other line on the surface parallel to the line, the minimum curvature will be perpendicular to the page and will be zero. However, the maximum curvature will vary between a large positive value at the peak of the anticline through zero to a large negative value at the trough of the syncline. In this case, the Gaussian curvature, which is the product of the maximum and minimum curvatures, will be zero at all points on the surface. Maximum curvature, as noted above, will vary along the curved line but will be constant perpendicular to it.

Therefore, a color-coded map view of the maximum curvature of this surface will consist of a series of color bands perpendicular to the page, with bands representing the maximum positive value along the anticlinal axes and bands representing the maximum negative values along the synclinal axes. Faulting may be represented in the same manner by envisioning a break and offset in either a normal or reverse orientation between the anticline and the syncline and running perpendicular to the page. The anticline and syncline will then represent drag in the upthrown and downthrown blocks of the fault, respectively. The preceding descriptions will be true whenever the surface dips in a linear manner into and out of the page.

In the above visualization, if the extension of the curved line into and out of the page is not linear but rather curves downward in both directions, then the minimum curvature and the Gaussian curvature will no longer be zero. There will be deformation perpendicular to the page, and the surface cannot be formed by simple cylindrical folding of an initially flat surface but requires warping of that surface. Therefore, nonzero Gaussian curvature indicates that a surface has been warped. The greatest amount of total deformation is likely to be associated with areas of greatest absolute Gaussian curvature.

In the above discussions, the maximum curvature is the signed value of the largest absolute curvature at each point. Curvatures that are more sensitive to the sign are the most positive curvature and the most negative curvature. In the second case described above, in which the surface dips downward away from the page on each side of the page, the most negative curvature at the syncline will be parallel to the page, and the most positive curvature will be perpendicular. At the anticline, as illustrated in Figure 2, curvature at all azimuths is positive. The most positive curvature will be parallel to the page, and the most negative curvature, which in this case would be the least positive curvature, will be perpendicular to the page. Map views of color-coded most positive curvature, especially if values less than zero are omitted, will show anticlinal axes only, and map views of color-coded most negative curvature with the positive values omitted will show synclinal axes.

Roberts (2001), Massaferro et al. (2003), and Sigismondi and Soldo (2003) conducted their analyses on gridded surfaces interpreted from 3D seismic surveys. The use of such regularly sampled surfaces permits rapid calculation of curvatures for every point on such surfaces but introduces three problems. First, even the most optimally processed seismic data contain some noise that will affect the curvature computations. Second, such an interpretation by its very nature will have some influence or bias introduced by the interpreter. Finally, the grid spacing of the surface controls the scale at which the analysis is done.

Bergbauer et al. (2003) present the fractal nature of curvature from sand grains to continental bulges as well as the effects of noise on curvature calculations from a surface picked from a 3D seismic volume. Their solutions — as well as those of Roberts (2001) and other authors — to the first and third problems are to smooth or otherwise filter the surface being investigated to remove noise and to vary the grid spacing to precondition the surface to illuminate curvature at a particular wavelength. None of the authors discusses a solution for interpreter bias.

Al Dossary and Marfurt (2006) avoid the interpreter bias problem by calculating curvature at every point in the seismic volume. In their method, the moving subvolume used for computation provides sufficient averaging in the lateral and vertical directions to provide smoothly varying results on a local basis. We then display curvature extractions along rather than curvature calculations of a horizon. Such volumetric curvature calculations also are amenable to 3D visualization including animation, opacity analysis, and voxel picking. We address the problem of accurately determining local geologic dip without bias or noise effects through the use of a multiwindow estimation of dip and azimuth (Marfurt, 2006) that is based on a finite temporal window (containing 11 samples in this study) rather than the single-sample peak or trough estimates used in map analysis. We output the dip and azimuth from the analysis in the format of inline and crossline dip for each sample in the volume. Finally, we calculate curvature at each sample at various wavelengths using a fractional derivative of the dip vector (al Dossary and Marfurt, 2006) and the equations provided by Roberts (2001).

WEST TEXAS EXAMPLE

Geologic setting

The Permian Basin of west Texas and eastern New Mexico (Figure 3) is a world-class petroleum province that has been studied in detail for well over half a century (Galley, 1958; Frenzel et al., 1988). A key feature of this basin is the buried Central Basin Platform (CBP) that gives evidence the pre-Mesozoic may be divided into two gross intervals. First, the lower-to-middle Paleozoic interval records subsidence and deposition of shelfal to basinal deposits that ended with Mississippian to Pennsylvanian-age tectonism that uplifted the CBP. Second, the Permian interval records gentle subsidence with little large-scale deformation. Thus, the Pennsylvanian and older interval is effectively decoupled from the later section, has no surface expression, and can be studied only through well and seismic data (Figure 4).

The nature of the pre-Permian tectonics is enigmatic. The older part of the stratigraphic section, such as the Ordovician, has as much as 10,000 ft (3000 m) of vertical relief along the western side of the CBP (Frenzel, 1988), and the platform was initially interpreted to be the result of vertical tectonics. Harrington (1963) observed the orientations of the oilfield structures and the vertical nature of faulting and proposed that there is a component of right lateral faulting associated with the CBP. Gardiner (1990) divided the area into six

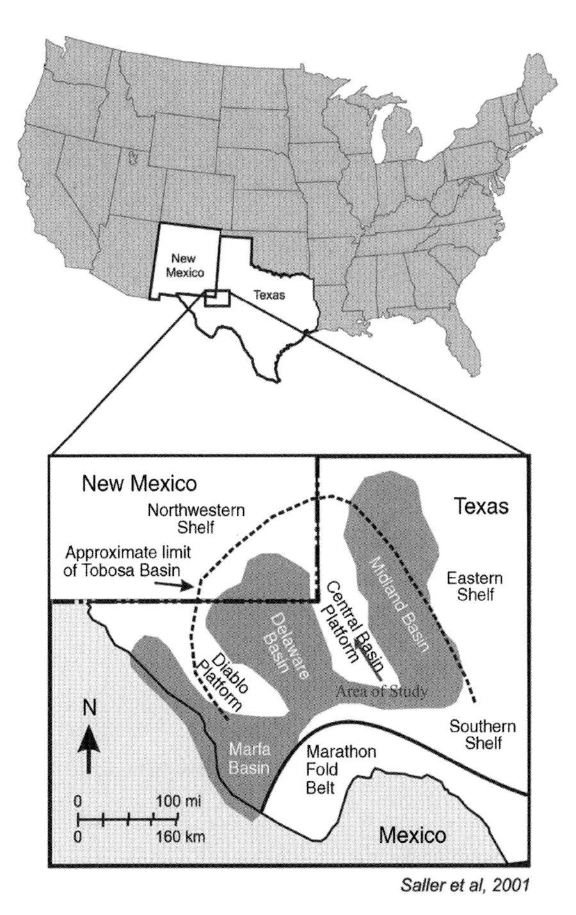

Figure 3. Location of the Permian Basin and Central Basin Platform of west Texas and eastern New Mexico (after Saller et al., 2001).

blocks, each with a different tectonic nature, with the southern part of the CBP affected by left lateral wrenching and the northern part by right lateral wrenching. Shumaker (1992) recognized the same six blocks and found them to be separated by trends of east-west left lateral faulting that cross the platform. He indicated that such movement and the clockwise rotation of the intervening blocks are the result of a basin-scale left-lateral shear couple applied to the entire platform. Yang and Dorobek (1995) commented that clockwise rotation of blocks would have to be created by right lateral faulting, and they related the formation of rotational blocks observed by Shumaker (1992) to right lateral movement along the roughly north-south-trending bounding faults along either side of the platform. They divided the platform into two blocks: the Fort Stockton Block of Gardiner (1990) and Shumaker (1992) in the southwest and the larger Andector Block in the north and east (Figure 5). They stated that their interpretation was regional in nature and did not describe any specific area in detail. The goal of this paper is to evaluate these hypotheses by applying our new suite of curvature attributes to a 3D seismic survey located along the Fort Stockton-Andector boundary.

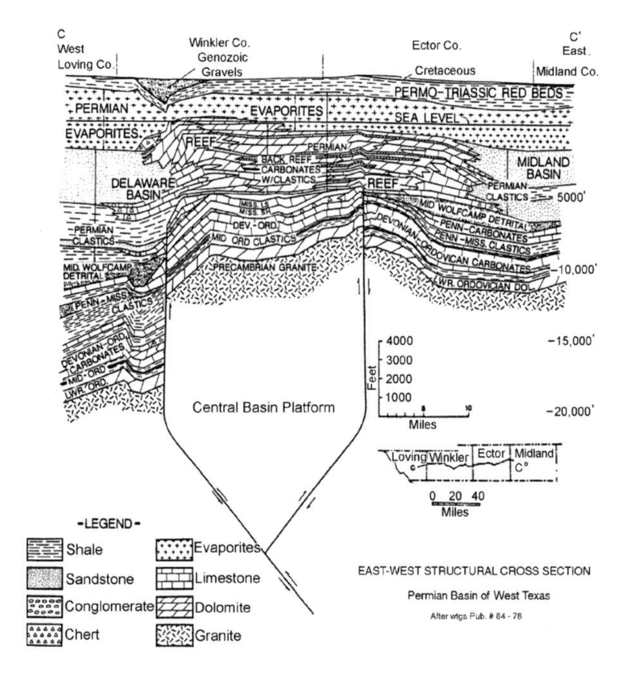

Figure 4. Cross section of Central Basin Platform, showing decoupling of pre-Permian and Permian sections (from Feldman, 1989).

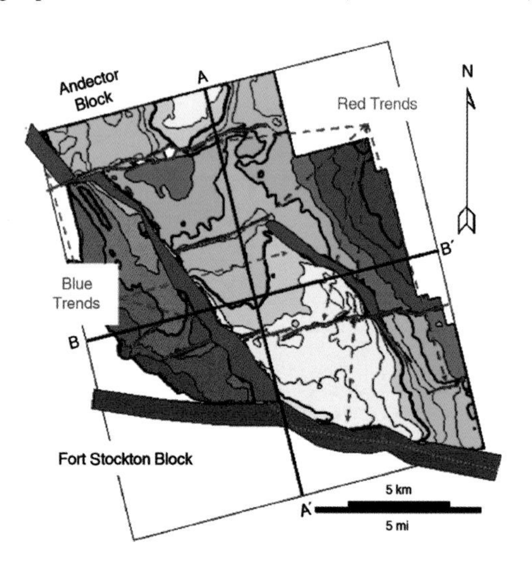

Figure 5. Devonian structure map from the study area. Note the east-northeast–west-southwest-trending red faults and the northwest-southeast-trending blue faults. The red faults show virtually no horizontal separation whereas the blue faults show substantial horizontal separation. Lines A and B are discussed in Figures 6 and 7, respectively.

Curvature analysis

Our data set was acquired over the southern part of the CBP along the boundary between the Fort Stockton and Andector blocks and covers an area of 18.8 by 17.6 km (11.7 by 10.9 miles) with an inline and crossline spacing of 33.5 m (110 ft). The subvolume size for the dip and azimuth computations was 3 × 3 seismic traces by 20 ms (11 samples) chosen from five laterally overlapping windows. The long wavelength estimates of curvature were calculated from these dip and azimuth estimates using a 21 × 21 seismic trace by one-sample analysis window. Al Dossary and Marfurt (2006) discuss this methodology in detail.

Figure 5 shows a time structure map at the top of the Devonian Thirty-one Formation. Two sets of nearly orthogonal faults are present in the data, with the east-northeast–west-southwest faults (the red faults) having a relatively narrow fault trace and the north-northwest–south-southeast faults having a much broader fault trace. The narrow and vertical fault traces of the ENE–WSW faults are evident on line AA′, running northwest-southeast, shown in Figure 6. This geometry, along with offsets of linear features across those faults, strongly suggests that these are left-lateral wrench faults. The broader fault trace and apparent repeat section of the northwest-southeast faults, which we call the blue faults, are evident on Figure 7, which runs west-southwest–east-northeast through the middle of the data set. These blue faults are actually zones of complex interaction because there is some evidence of reversal of direction of throw in the vertical direction and because the width of the disturbed zone is approximately three times the vertical separation across it.

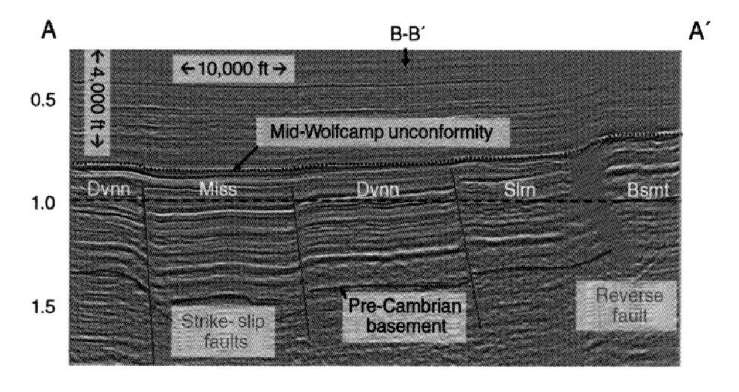

Figure 6. Seismic line AA′ showing tectonically active early-to-middle Paleozoic separated from tectonically quiescent Permian and younger. Note also the vertical nature and narrow trace of the strike slip faults (red faults). Time slices shown in Figures 8–10 are taken along the 1.000 s timing line. This section shows that the time slices cut across multiple stratigraphic levels, the various fault blocks are relatively flat, and the fault blocks step down from south to north. Vertical exaggeration is approximately 2.5:1.

In Figure 8, we display a time slice through the seismic data volume that shows the major trends, especially the broad zones of the blue faults and, to a lesser degree, the narrow faults traces of the red faults. The rocks represented by this slice and the other attribute slices (Figures 8–10) are all below the mid-Wolfcamp unconformity that separates the lower Paleozoic section from the Permian and younger section. Inspection of Figures 6 and 7 shows that within a fault block, the structure is relatively flat so that locally the time slices represent horizon slices. Immediately evident on these slices is the rhombic nature of the two central blocks, suggesting left lateral wrenching but not the block rotation of Shumaker (1992). However, these rhomboids do not indicate transtension because the blocks are not low areas; rather, they step down progressively from east to west and south to north.

Figure 9 shows a time slice of the coherence attribute at the same level seen in Figure 8. As might be expected, the coherence attribute shows better definition of the fault trends seen on the conventional data (Figure 8) and brings out additional information, such as faults not seen on the conventional data and potential stratigraphic features.

Figure 10 shows the Gaussian maximum, most positive, and most negative curvature attributes at the same time as the slices in Figures 8 and 9. Gaussian curvature (Figure 10a) has positive values, indicating maximum curvature and minimum curvature have the same sign (in red) and negative values (in green). Local anomalies occur within fault zones visible on other displays but do not show any alignments. Cylindrical folding, which would produce linear trends, has a minimum-curvature value of zero, thus causing the Gaussian curvature to be zero. The maximum curvature (Figure 10b) shows positive curvature, indicating anticlinal axes (in red) and negative curvature, indicating synclinal axes (in green). In many areas, axes of different polarity appear together, suggesting the anticline/syncline or upthrown/downthrown pairs described earlier. In other areas, isolated axes of one polarity or the other appear. The large number of such axes along with numerous parallel trends make it difficult to identify uniquely the features creating the patterns.

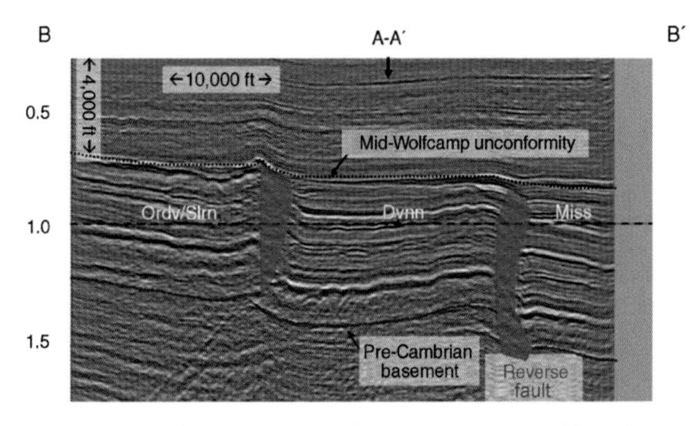

Figure 7. Seismic line BB′, showing reverse nature and broad trace of NW-SE trending reverse faults (blue faults). Time slices shown in Figures 8–10 are taken along the 1.000 s timing line. This section shows that the time slices cut across multiple stratigraphic levels, the various fault blocks are relatively flat, and the fault blocks step down from west to east. Vertical exaggeration is approximately 2.5:1

In contrast, the most positive curvature (Figure 10c) shows fewer lineaments and isolates each one from the others to permit easier identification and interpretation. Figure 10d shows that the most negative-curvature attribute is very similar to the most positive curvature, but close inspection shows that the locations of the lineaments have shifted, corresponding to the offset of the axes in an anticline/syncline pair. Interpretation of the most negative curvature

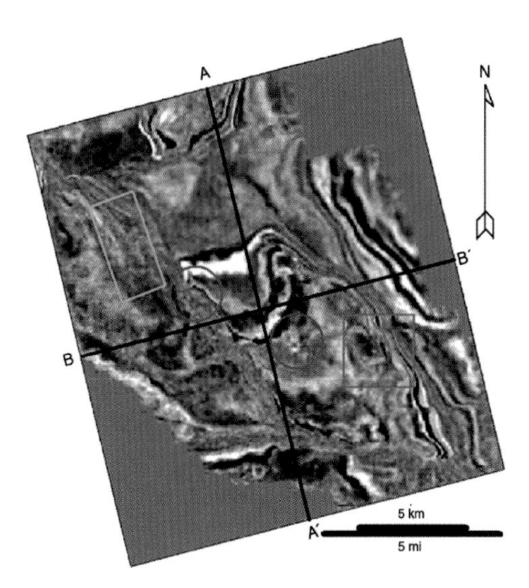

Figure 8. Time slice of conventional seismic data volume at 1.000 s. Significance of areas highlighted by geometric figures is discussed in Figure 9.

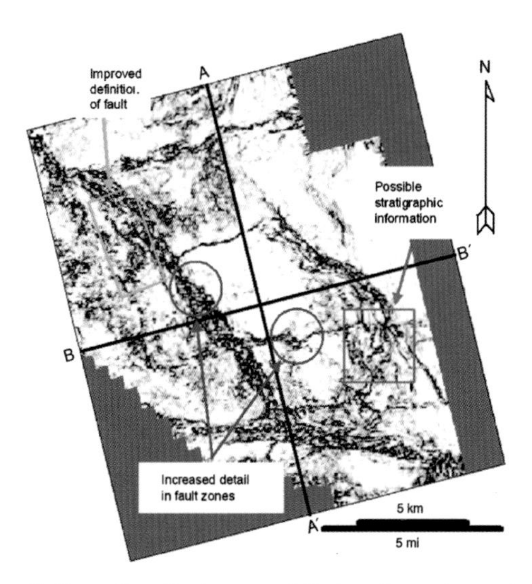

Figure 9. Time slice of coherence attribute volume at same traveltime as shown in Figure 8. Note that the broad zone of the northwest–southeast-trending faults shows up better and with increased detail on the coherence attribute. Note also the rhomboid character of the block in the center of the image. This is not a pullapart basin because the faults step down from south and west to north and east as indicated in Figures 6 and 7. Blue circles indicate areas of improved detail in fault trends versus conventional data; green rectangle indicates improved definition of fault, and orange square indicates area of illumination of possible stratigraphic features.

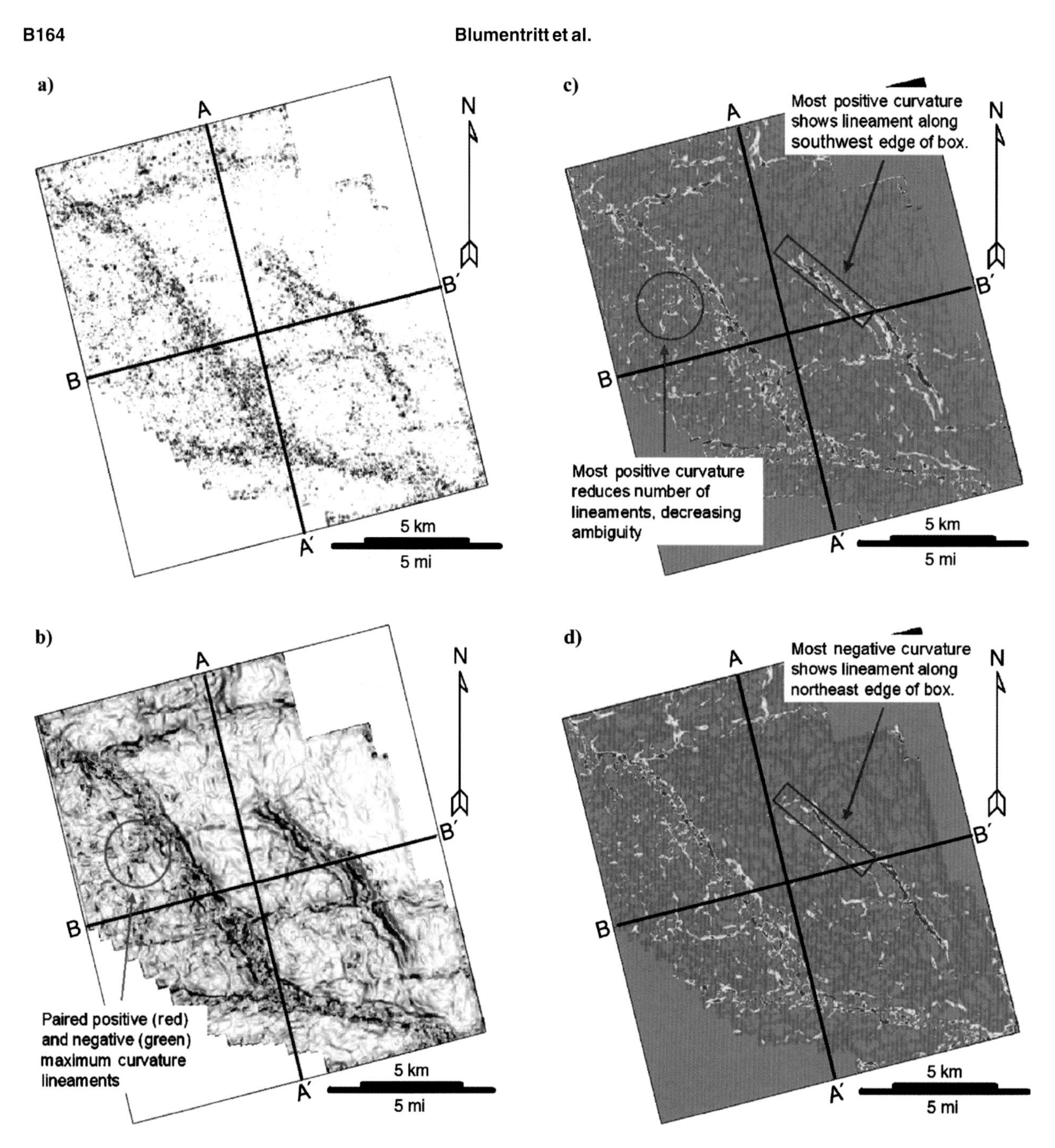

Figure 10. Comparison of curvature attributes. (a) Gaussian curvature; red indicates high positive values; green indicates high negative values. Plot shows detail in fault zones visible on amplitude and coherence data, but little detail within fault blocks. (b) Maximum curvature. Red indicates large positive values, and green indicates large negative values. Parallel trends of positive and negative (red circle) values indicate anticline/syncline pairs. Large numbers of trends increase complexity of interpretation. (c) Most positive curvature. Red indicates large positive values; gray indicates values less than or equal to zero. Parallel trends (red circle) replaced by positive trends only, decreasing number of lineaments and reducing ambiguity in interpretation. Purple box shows strong positive curvature trend, indicating drag in upthrown fault block. (d) Most-negative curvature. Red indicates large negative values; gray indicates values greater than or equal to zero. This is very similar to most positive curvature, except that trends are laterally displaced. Purple box shows strong negative curvature indicating drag in downthrown fault block. This trend is shifted northeast from the same trend shown in (c). Analyses of most-positive curvature and most-negative curvature should produce identical results. See text for additional discussion.

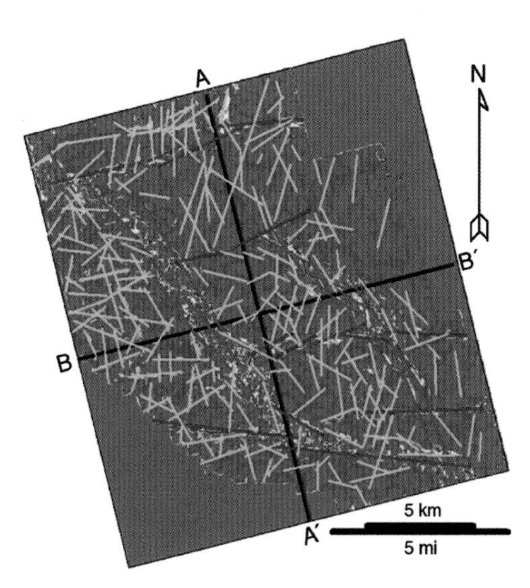

Figure 11. Time slice through most positive curvature volume with interpreted lineaments posted. This figure compares to Figure 10c. Red indicates high curvature; gray indicates low curvature. Note the improved delineation in the broad zones of the blue faults as well as the illumination of lineaments within the fault blocks on the most positive curvature attribute. Red and blue lineaments represent trends previously observed and discussed. Green lineaments represent trends visible only on curvature attribute.

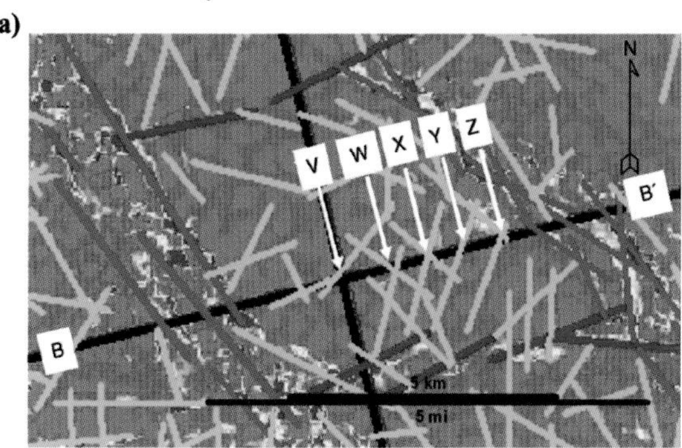

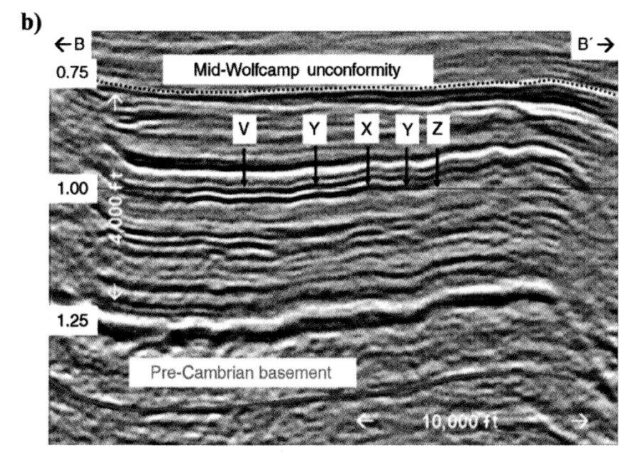

Figure 12. Enlarged views of (a) most positive curvature time slice and (b) line BB′ showing locations of five lineaments, indicated by arrows visible on the most positive curvature slice. Red indicates high curvature; gray indicates low curvature. Lineaments appear to be associated with undulations on seismic section but tie to different positions on different undulations.

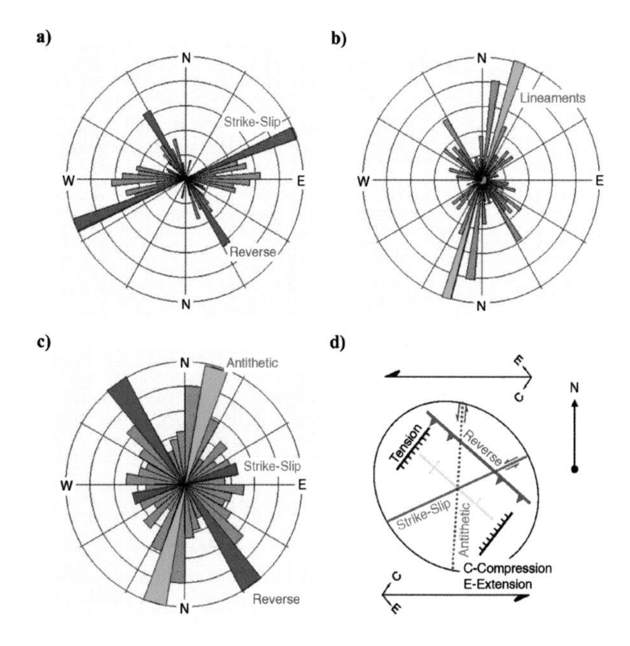

Figure 13. Rose diagrams of lineaments interpreted from most positive curvature attribute. (a) Red and blue trends that correspond to faults observable on all presentations of the seismic data; (b) green trends that correspond to lineaments that are observable only on most positive curvature attribute. The most frequently occurring azimuth does not correspond to any observed for the red and blue trends. The second most frequently occurring azimuth does align with the most often occurring azimuth for the blue trend. (c) All lineaments with the most frequently occurring azimuths for the primary trends highlighted; (d) a left lateral strain ellipsoid (modified from Harding, 1974) with the primary trends highlighted. In a–c, highlighted trends are color coded to match red, blue, and green trends discussed in text. This model suggests that tension fractures are oriented along a strike of N40–45°E.

should produce essentially identical results to interpretation of the most positive curvature, and the choice between them is arbitrary.

Figure 11 shows the most-positive curvature (K_{pos}) slice of Figure 10c with lineaments posted. The red and blue faults are still evident, with greater detail present in the broad zones of the blue faults, but a new level of lineaments — the green trend — is evident.

Figure 12 shows enlargements of the most positive curvature time slice (Figure 11a) and a portion of line B-B′ (Figure 11b) with five corresponding green trend lineaments indicated on each by arrows. Four of the lineaments, V, W, X, and Y, have a northeasterly strike and the fifth, Z, a northwesterly strike. Although all five seem to be related to an undulating reflection on the seismic section, they fall at different positions of individual waves along that horizon.

Next, we computed the azimuths and lengths of all of the lineaments picked on the most positive curvature time slice (Figure 11) and plotted them in rose diagrams. Figure 13a shows the rose diagram of just the red and blue trends because these are readily observable on all representations of the data. As expected, they show nearly orthogonal trends. Figure 13b shows the azimuths of the green lineaments, and these tend to be somewhat bimodal, with the main trend lying between those of the red and blue faults and a secondary trend lying along the same trend as the blue faults. Figure 13c shows a rose diagram of all lineaments, and Figure 13d shows Harding's (1974) strain ellipsoid for a left and right lateral shear couple.The observed faults fit the left lateral shear couple model with the shear couple aligned in a due east-west orientation. In that case, the expected primary shears correspond to the red faults and, as expected, the reverse fault trend corresponds to the blue faults. Using this model, the green lineaments correspond to the antithetic strike slip trend. This model (Harding, 1974) further predicts that extensional trends (mode 1, or open, fractures) will be oriented N40-45°E.

CONCLUSION

We have introduced a new volume-based method of evaluating stress regimes and predicting azimuths of open fractures. We build on a proven method of analyzing geologic structures by computing curvatures at each sample of a 3D seismic volume and outputting those curvatures as additional seismic volumes that may be sliced along time slices or interpreted horizons. Initial results of the application of this methodology to a data set from the CBP in west Texas indicate that analysis of these curvature volumes leads to structural interpretations that are consistent with the fault patterns but not the block rotation. These structural interpretations explain observed geologic features and predict stress regimes and directions of extensional fractures.

Most positive curvature (or most negative curvature) provides a more detailed and less ambiguous attribute for defining subtle lineaments related to regional or local stresses than the more commonly used Gaussian- and maximum-curvature attributes. This technique should be applicable in all terranes.

Our new method of calculating curvature provides a powerful tool for field- and basin-scale analysis of stress regimes and orientation of tension fractures. These findings have broad implications for exploration, development, and management of fractured reservoirs.

ACKNOWLEDGMENTS

The authors gratefully acknowledge Occidental Permian, Ltd., BP Americas, and Tobin for their data contributions and the state of Texas for funding through their Advanced Technology Program grant. We also acknowledge Core Laboratories for permission to display data processed with Coherence technology.

REFERENCES

al Dossary, S., and K. J. Marfurt, 2006, 3-D volumetric multispectral estimates of reflector curvature and rotation: Geophysics, this issue.

Bergbauer, S., T. Mukerji, and P. Hennings, 2003, Improving curvature analyses of deformed horizons using scale-dependent filtering techniques: AAPG Bulletin, **87**, 1255–1272.

Feldman, M. L., 1989, Paleozoic framework of the Gulf of Mexico, *in* J. E. Flis, R. C. Price, and J. F. Sarg, eds., Search for the subtle trap: Hydrocarbon exploration in mature basins: West Texas Geological Society Publication 89–85, 199–209.

Frenzel, H. H., R. R. Bloomer, R. B. Cline, J. M. Cys, J. E. Galley, W. R. Gibson, J. H. Hills, W. E. King, W. R. Seager, F. E. Kottlowski, S. Thompson, III, G. C. Luff, B. T. Pearson, and D. C. Van Siclen, 1988, The Permian Basin region, *in* L. L. Sloss, ed., Sedimentary cover — North American Craton: Geological Society of America, The Geology of North America, D-2, 261–306.

Galley, J. E., 1958, Oil and geology in the Permian Basin of Texas and New Mexico, *in* L. G. Weeks, ed., Habitat of oil: AAPG, 395–446.

Gardiner, W. B., 1990, Fault fabric and structural subprovinces of the Central Basin Platform: A model for strike-slip movement, *in* J. E. Flis and R. C. Price, eds., Permian Basin oil and gas fields: Innovative ideas in exploration and development: West Texas Geological Society Publication, 90-87, 15–27.

Harding, T. P., 1974, Petroleum traps associated with wrench faults: AAPG Bulletin, **58**, 1290–1304.

Harrington, J. W., 1963, Opinion of structural mechanics of Central Basin Platform area, west Texas: AAPG Bulletin, **47**, 2023–2038.

Hart, B. S., R. Pearson, and G. C. Rawling, 2002, 3-D seismic horizon-based approaches to fracture-swarm sweet spot definition in tight-gas reservoirs: The Leading Edge, **21**, 28–35.

Lisle, R. J., 1994, Detection of zones of abnormal strains in structures using Gaussian curvature analysis: AAPG Bulletin, **78**, 1811–1819.

Marfurt, K. J., 2006,Robust estimates of reflector dip and azimuth: Geophysics, **71**, this issue.

Masaferro, J. L., M. Bulnes, J. Poblet, and M. Casson, 2003, Kinematic evolution and fracture prediction of the Valle Morado structure inferred from 3-D seismic data, Salta Province, northwest Argentina: AAPG Bulletin, **87**, 1083–1104.

McQuillan, H., 1974, Fracture patterns on Kuh-e Asmari anticline, southwest Iran: AAPG Bulletin, **58**, 236–246.

Murray, Jr., G. H., 1968, Quantitative fracture study-Spanish Pool, McKenzie County, North Dakota: AAPG Bulletin, **52**, 57–65.

Roberts, A., 2001, Curvature attributes and their application to 3D interpreted horizons: First Break, **19**, 85–100.

Saller, A., B. Ball, S. Robertson, B. McPherson, C. Wene, R. Nims, and J. Gogas, 2001, Reservoir characteristics of Devonian cherts and their control on oil recovery; Dollarhide field, west Texas: AAPG Bulletin, **85**, 35–50.

Shumaker, R. C., 1992, Paleozoic structure of the Central Basin Uplift and adjacent Delaware Basin, West Texas: AAPG Bulletin, **76**, 1804–1824.

Sigismondi, M. E., and J. C. Soldo, 2003, Curvature attributes and seismic interpretation: Case studies from Argentina Basins: The Leading Edge, **23**, 1122–1126.

Yang, K.-M., and S. L. Dorobek, 1995, The Permian Basin of West Texas and New Mexico: Tectonic history of a "composite" foreland basin and its effects on stratigraphic development, *in* S. L. Dorobelt and G. M. Ross, eds., Stratigraphic evolution of foreland basins: SEPM Special Publication 52, 149–174.

Chapter 18

GEOPHYSICS, VOL. 71, NO. 4 (JULY-AUGUST 2006); P. B111–B119, 17 FIGS.
10.1190/1.2216189

Application of new seismic attributes to collapse chimneys in the Fort Worth Basin

E. Charlotte Sullivan[1], Kurt J. Marfurt[2], Alfred Lacazette[3], and Mike Ammerman[4]

ABSTRACT

Three-dimensional seismic volumes from the central Fort Worth Basin display roughly circular collapse chimneys that extend vertically about 800 m from the Ordovician Ellenburger Formation to the Atokan (middle Pennsylvanian) Caddo Limestone. Collapse chimneys in carbonates may be caused by subaerial karst, hydrothermal, or tectonic extensional processes. We use 3D multitrace geometric attributes including coherence, volumetric curvature, and energy-weighted, coherent amplitude gradients to investigate details of the origin of these structures. The Ordovician Ellenburger surface resembles a subaerial karst landscape of cockpits, dolines, and frying-pan valleys, while resistivity-based wireline image logs record 50 m of karst breccia facies. However, images from coherence and long-wavelength most-positive and most-negative-curvature volumes show many of the 800-m collapse features are associated with basement faults or with subtle Pennsylvanian and younger tectonic features, rather than with intra-Ellenburger collapse. We hypothesize that although the Ellenburger surface does contain a subaerial karst overprint, the first-order control on the formation of the vertically extensive collapse chimneys is bottoms-up tectonic-induced extensional collapse. Although these collapse chimneys have been affected by burial fluid diagenesis, the main consequence of burial fluid flow may be limited to the documented cementation of macrofractures. The apparent dominance of tectonic extension processes over subaerial karst and hydrothermal processes has basinwide implications for distribution of fractures, late-stage cements, and reservoir development and compartmentalization.

INTRODUCTION

Over one-third of the world's hydrocarbon reserves are in carbonate reservoirs, most of which are fractured, and many of which display collapse features that may vertically extend for 10s to 100s of meters. These collapse features can compartmentalize reservoirs (Bagdan and Pemberton, 2004) and, if they persist as topographic features, may influence the deposition and distribution of reservoir sands and carbonates in younger strata (Hardage et al., 1996). Rounded collapse features (collapse chimneys) in subsurface carbonates may result from subaerial karst processes and cavern collapse, from hydrothermal brecciation and dissolution, from tectonic extension associated with fault movement, or from some combination of these processes (Berger and Davies, 1999; Loucks et al., 2004; Sagan and Hart, 2004; McClay and Borora, 2001). Determining the relative contribution and sequence of each process generating collapse features is important for constructing reservoir models, understanding reservoir performance, and identifying potential for reservoir development related to suprastratal deformation. Data for determining the origin of collapse features include lithology and rock texture from well cuttings, cores and wireline image logs, and geochemical signatures of rock samples. When well data are not available, seismic data are the primary means of identifying the origin and evolution of collapse features. This paper demonstrates the use of multitrace seismic attributes to follow the evolution of vertically extensive collapse features in an area where borehole data are limited.

Volumetric seismic attributes, including coherence, reflector curvature, reflector rotation, and energy-weighted, coherent amplitude gradients provide improved means for imaging small scale and subtle features and tracking changes in these features. In particular, reflector curvature calculated from discrete interpreted horizons is well correlated to fracture intensity (Lisle, 1994; Roberts, 2001), while multispectral estimates of reflector curvature allow interpreters to view long and short wavelength geologic features. In contrast to conventional reflector curvature attributes, multitrace geometric

Manuscript received by the Editor January 6, 2005; revised manuscript received December 8, 2005; published online August 2, 2006.
[1]Pacific Northwest National Laboratories, P.O. Box 999, Richland, Washington 99352. E-mail: charlotte.sullivan@pnl.gov.
[2]502F S&R1, University of Houston, Allied Geophysical Laboratories Houston, Houston, Texas 77204. E-mail: kmarfurt@uh.edu.
[3]Natural Fractures.com LLC, 1302 Waugh Drive, Suite 637, Houston, Texas 77019. E-mail: alfred_lacazette@naturalfractures.com.
[4]Devon Energy Corporation, 20 North Broadway, Oklahoma City, Oklahoma 73102. Email: mike.ammerman@dvn.com.

attributes produce a 3D attribute volume and facilitate the recognition of irregular geologic features by avoiding the need to preinterpret horizons. Well-established coherence attributes measure the lateral changes in waveform, and, as such, are often sensitive to small faults and to lateral changes in stratigraphy such as channels and sinkholes. Estimates of reflector curvature, including most-negative, most-positive, Gaussian curvature, and related shape indices measure the lateral changes in reflector dip and azimuth and are mathematically independent of coherence measures. We have applied coherence and new volumetric, multitrace algorithms to a conventional 3D seismic volume from the Fort Worth Basin of north Texas to test hypotheses on the timing and origin of collapse chimneys that vertically extend from the Ordovician Ellenburger carbonates through Mississippian and Pennsylvanian siliciclastics and carbonates over a distance of almost 800 m.

The Fort Worth Basin is a Paleozoic foreland basin that formed along the advancing border of the Ouachita fold and thrust belt (Figure 1), associated with the oblique lithospheric convergence of the North American and South American plates (Walper, 1982). The lower Ordovician Ellenburger carbonates (Figure 2) were deposited in a shallow ramp setting and are unconformably overlain by upper Ordovician Viola Limestones (missing because of erosion in our area). The overlying organic-rich Barnett Shale records deposition in the developing deep-water foreland basin during the late Mississippian. Shallow-water siliciclastics and carbonates of the Marble Falls and Caddo record basin filling during the early to middle Pennsylvanian (Walper, 1982; Montgomery et al., 2005). The Ellenburger, in the area of seismic coverage, underwent at least two extensive episodes of subaerial weathering that may have produced karst landscape and cavern systems. The first episode occurred during the middle Ordovician and is associated with a cratonwide regional unconformity following the Ellenburger deposition (Kerans, 1990; Franseen et al., 2003). The second episode of exposure is less well constrained, but areally covered much of north-central Texas and occurred during the Mississippian development of the Fort Worth Basin. Silurian and Devonian strata are missing over the study area, along with any sedimentary record of possible additional times of exposure (Grayson and Merrill, 1991; Bowker, 2003).

In addition to being karsted, the Ellenburger underwent a number of postburial tectonic events, including compression and oblique slip associated with late Paleozoic continental collision and the westward advancing Ouachita orogen (Ball and Perry, 1996) and late extension related to the Mesozoic opening of the Gulf of Mexico and the later formation of the regional down-to-the-coast Miocene Balcones fault system (Hoskins, 1982). We anticipate that seismic attributes and conventional seismic volumes may reveal temporally different karst and tectonic overprints associated with these events.

Karst terrains contain geomorphic features such as sinkholes, cockpit landforms (Cansler and Carr, 2001), and round-ended frying-pan valleys. Cave and potential collapse systems most commonly develop at or above water tables, generally within the upper 100 m of an exposed carbonate surface (Kerans, 1990). Most of the buried Ellenburger cave systems of west Texas collapsed prior to the end of the Ordovician, as evidenced by the age of their fill. Associated cave fill deposits contain Ellenburger breccias and stratified deposits of the transgressive Upper Ordovician Simpson sandstones that regionally overlie the Ellenburger. Irregular Ellenburger topography often is filled completely by the first 20–50 m of Simpson

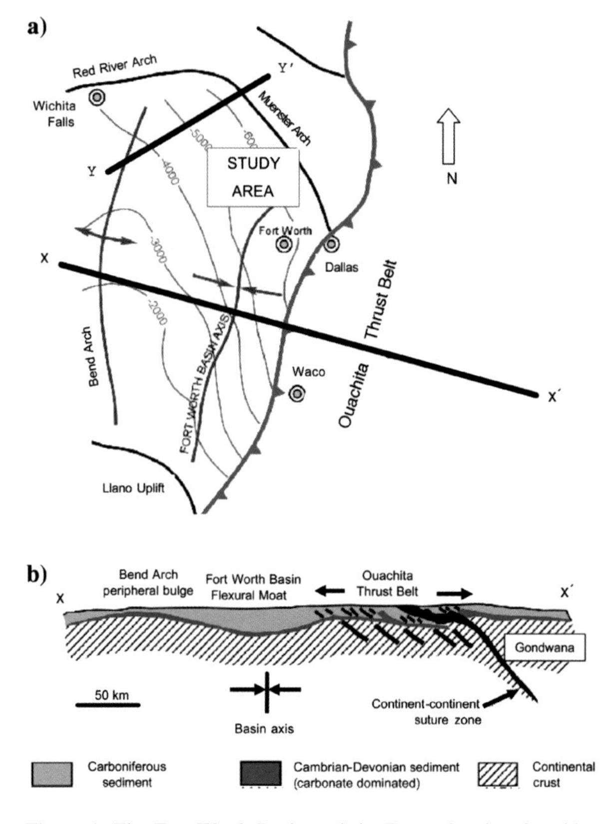

Figure 1. The Fort Worth Basin and the Pennsylvanian Ouachita thrust belt. The basin developed as a foredeep and underwent compression and strike-slip deformation during the Pennsylvanian, followed by Mesozoic and Cenozoic extension. Collapse breccias compartmentalize Pennsylvanian reservoirs in the shaded area (after Hardage et al., 1996).

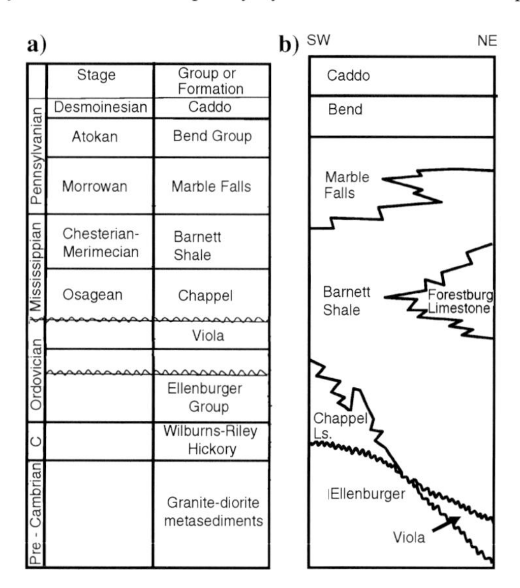

Figure 2. (a) Stratigraphic interval affected by collapse features and (b) southwest-northeast diagrammatic cross section from the Bend Arch to the Muenster Arch, along line Y-Y′ in Figure 1. The Forestburg carbonates appear to be shed from shallow water environments on the Muenster Arch (after Pollastro, et al., 2003).

deposition (Kerans, 1990). In contrast, the collapse chimneys in our data persist through about 800 meters of section. Collapse chimneys of similar vertical extent also are present above the Ellenburger to the west of our study area (Hardage et al., 1996).

The character of the vertical collapse features in the Fort Worth Basin may record a complex history, similar to the history interpreted by Lucia (1996) for outcrops at the McKelligon Sag, near El Paso, Texas. These outcrops record a vertical collapse system of 760 m that includes collapse of separate Ordovician, Silurian, and Devonian cave systems over a period of 100 million years. Once collapse ended, the surface topography quickly healed; only about 16 m of sediments was required to fill the irregular surface. Isotope data from saddle dolomite in fractures between the McKelligon collapse breccia blocks indicate cement precipitation from deep burial fluids during the Pennsylvanian (Kupecs and Land, 1991). They proposed that the source and migration of these deep burial fluids is related to the emplacement of the Ouachita thrust belt.

This paper sheds light on the possible causes and history of the collapse features in the Fort Worth Basin through the application of modern seismic attributes. We begin with a brief overview of the seismic data quality and geometric attributes. We then examine the geology in the survey area by integrating our new tools with more conventional time/structure and isochore maps. Finally, we use these new images to support our hypothesis that the collapse features are controlled more by tectonics than by subaerial karst or thermobaric processes. We propose that the collapse chimneys are extensional fault-related, polygonal depressions (rhombochasms), affecting basement and higher strata and, that these chimneys have been reactivated by multiple tectonic events.

METHODOLOGY

The seismic survey used in this study is a composite of three separate acquisition programs. The data were acquired and processed by a petroleum company through a commercial vendor using a workflow that consisted of elevation and static corrections, deconvolution, dip moveout, stack, and poststack time migration. This poststack data volume (Figure 3a) was then subjected to the attribute analysis described in this paper. First we applied edge-preserving principal-component filtering (Marfurt, 2006) to suppress random noise and enhance subtle discontinuities and offsets at minor faults (Figure 3b). We note that the impact on the waveform and amplitude is minimal but that the terminations are sharper.

Next we calculated a complete suite of geometric seismic attribute volumes on both the original and edge-enhanced seismic data, including coherence (Marfurt et al., 1999), multispectral curvature and energy-weighted, coherent amplitude gradients (Marfurt, 2006). We also tied wells and performed poststack impedance inversion and generated more conventional single-trace attributes. These attribute cubes were loaded into an interpretation workstation and interpreted along with the seismic data and well control. The coherence, dip/azimuth, and energy-weighted, coherent-amplitude gradient volumes were generated using nine overlapping nine-trace, ±10 ms analysis windows. The multispectral curvature and rotation volumes were calculated using circular analysis windows containing between 13 traces (for short wavelength calculations) and 78 traces (for long wavelength calculations). The principal-component filtered version of the data was more amenable to automatic picking. Of all the attributes calculated, we found the long wavelength most-positive and most-negative curvature, energy-weighed, coherent amplitude gradients, and principal-component estimate of coherence were the most valuable for our interpretation of faults, fractures, and karst features. However, we must emphasize that these high-tech attributes were only fully understood and are best communicated when integrated into the conventional interpretation work flow of tying wells, generating time/structure maps, generating isochores, and producing horizon extractions.

DATA ANALYSIS

In Figure 3b we indicate faults and some of the major horizons of interest in this study. Collapse features extend from within the Precambrian basement (yellow) through the Ordovician Ellenburger (green), early Pennsylvanian Marble Falls (magenta) and middle Pennsylvanian Caddo Limestone (cyan). The Atoka horizon marks the top of a sand/siltstone sequence that has been a prolific producer, enhanced by thicker sands filling in the collapse features. We plot faults that penetrate the deeper part of the section in orange and those that are limited to the shallower section in yellow. A regional wrench fault system crosses the survey near the white arrow, close to A. The

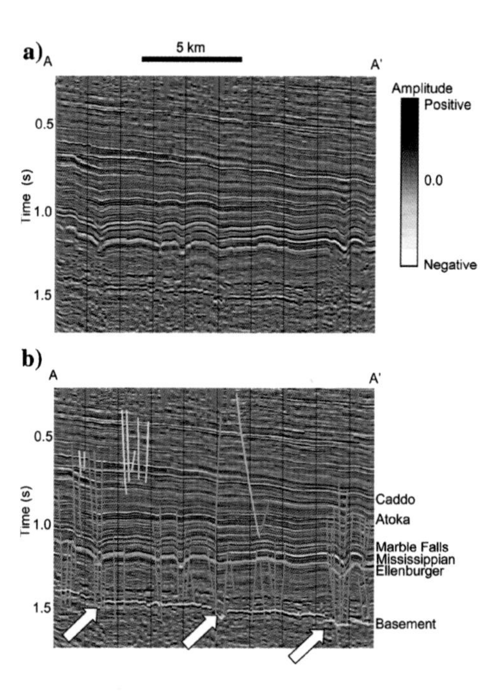

Figure 3. North-south line AA′ through the maps shown in Figures 4 and 5, (a) without and (b) with interpretation. We have applied edge-preserving principal component filtering to these data. The cyan horizon is the Pennsylvanian Caddo limestone; The green Ellenburger pick is Lower Ordovician. Note the vertical collapse features indicated by the white arrows. These collapse features are not filled in immediately above the Ellenburger but can be tracked from the basement to shallower events. Orange faults penetrate the basement; yellow faults are confined to strata above the basement. The magenta fault is the major fault crossing the center of the survey.

magenta fault is subtler but has components of dip, and perhaps, strike slip as well. The wrench fault, the magenta fault, and the collapse features are evident on the time structure maps of the Marble Falls (Figure 4a) and Ellenburger (Figure 4b). The time isochore between the Ellenburger and Marble Falls (Figure 5a) indicates a fairly uniform pattern, with thicker fill in the collapse feature and thickening north of the magenta fault. In contrast, the time isochore for the Marble Falls–Atoka interval (Figure 5b) displays a strong northeast-southeast and southwest-northeast blocky fabric. Time slices through the coherence volume (Marfurt et al., 1999) at the Marble Falls (Figure 6a) and Ellenburger (Figure 6b) levels show a complex system of lineaments and collapse features. Although horizon extractions of coherence are particularly valuable for mapping smooth stratigraphic features, time slices provide a less biased view of irregular or rugose surfaces. Although we do see the vertical trace of several faults, the most prominent features are the circular collapse features, which are more pronounced at the deeper Ellenburger level than at the Marble Falls level. These collapse features are aligned in conjugate northeast-southwest and northwest-southeast trends, and some are quite elongated, rather than circular. To understand these collapse patterns and their expression in the curvature attributes, we display a folded section (Figure 7) through the filtered vertical seismic cube corresponding to line AA′ in Figure 6, coupled with a time slice at 1.2 s through the original seismic volume. We then compare this image to time slices of 1.2 s through the most-negative and most-positive curvature attribute volumes.

To facilitate this comparison, we construct multiattribute displays (Figures 8 and 9), where the original seismic data are shown on the vertical face. Remember that although the value of the most-negative curvature is always less than the value of the (orthogonal) most-positive curvature at any analysis point, both attributes can have negative values (for a bowl), and both attributes can have positive values (for a dome). Examining Figures 8 and 9 confirms this relation. Features that are bowls (collapse features) will have a negative value of positive curvature, colored green in Figures 8a and 9a. Features that are domes will have a positive value of negative curvature and are red in Figures 8b and 9b. Lineaments in the most-negative curvature time slices can usually be interpreted as valleys, while lineaments on the most-positive curvature usually can be interpreted as ridges. We note in Figures 8 and 9 that our collapse features often are linked together, suggestive of cockpit karst and karst collapse features described in Figures 10 and 11. Although we expect there is a

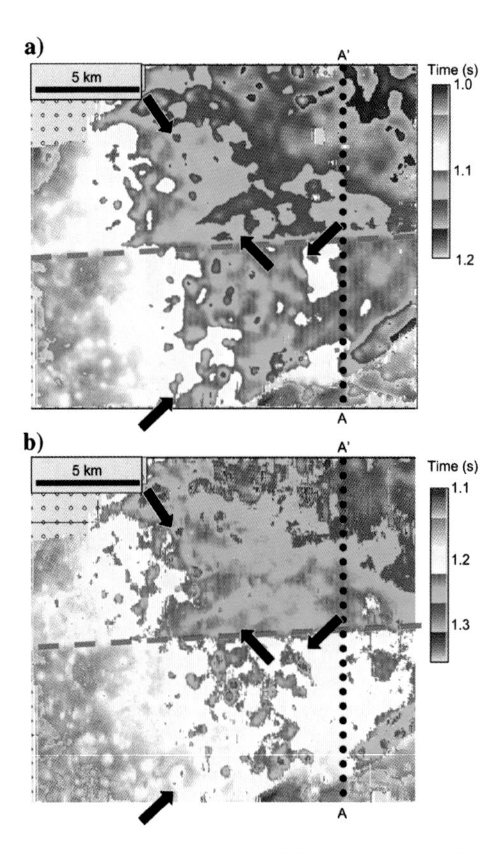

Figure 4. Time structure maps on the (a) Marble Falls and (b) Ellenburger horizons. Arrows are shown in Figure 5 for reference. Line AA′ is shown in Figure 3.

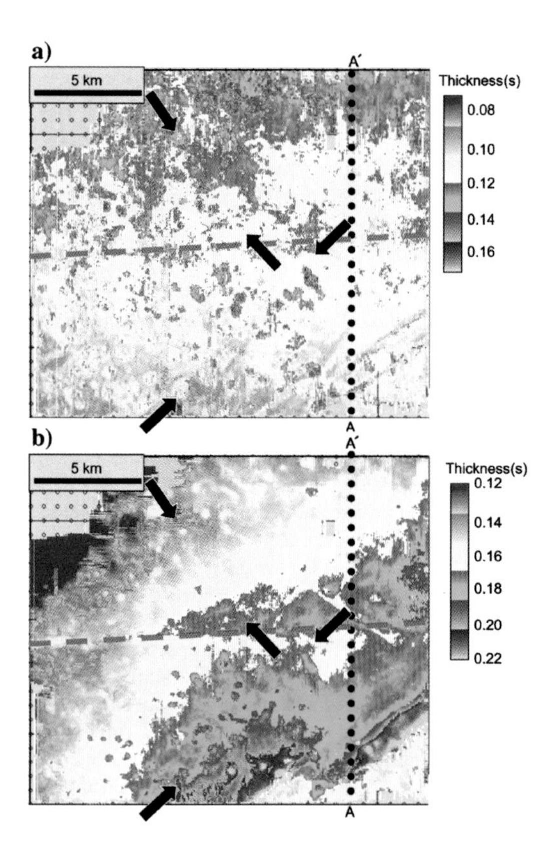

Figure 5. Isochore (time-thickness) maps between (a) the Ellenburger and Marble Falls horizons and (b) Marble Falls and Atoka horizons. Line AA′ is shown in Figure 3. Arrows are identical to those in Figures 3 and 4 showing collapse features. We note that we still observe differential thickness corresponding to continued collapse after Marble Falls deposition.

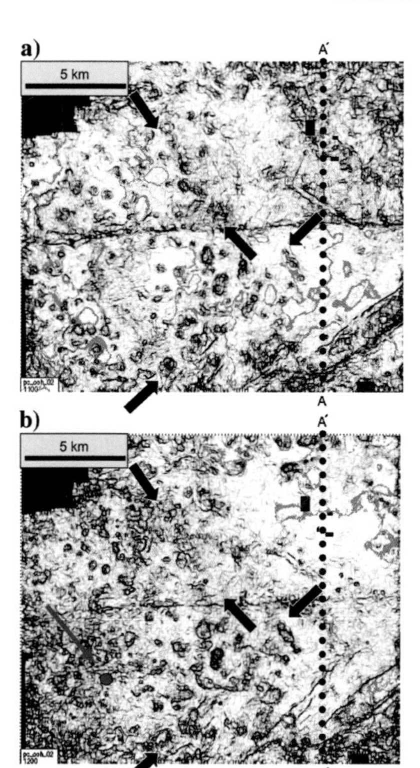

Figure 6. Time slices through the coherence volume at (a) 1.1 s and (b) 1.2 s. Note the Marble Falls (magenta), Mississippian shale (red) and Ellenburger (green) picks. Black arrows indicate collapse features shown in Figures 3–5. Red arrow locates a cored Ellenburger well.

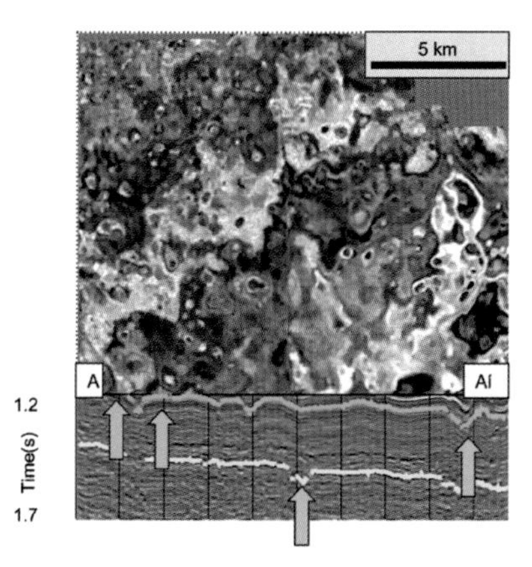

Figure 7. Foldaway view through the seismic data volume along line AA′ shown in Figures 3–6. Top slice is at 1.2 s. The green pick is the Ordovician Ellenburger. The yellow pick is approximate basement. Evidence of downthrown blocks continues into the basement (cyan arrows). Subaerial karst should originate within the Ellenburger, not in the crystalline basement. The seismic data shown here have been enhanced through the use of principal component, edge-preserving filtering.

subaerial karst component to the polygonal features observed in the seismic data, some of the collapse features extend into the Precambrian igneous basement, where karst processes cannot operate.

Time slices at 0.8 s (near top Caddo), 0.9 s, 1.0 s, 1.1 s (near top Marble Falls) 1.2 s (near top Ellenburger) and 1.3 s through the coherence volume (Figure 12), most-negative-curvature volume (Figure 13) and most-positive-curvature volume (Figure 14) provide unique views of the data. The most-negative- and most-positive-curvature attributes clearly image the fault crossing the center of the survey, the regional wrench fault in the southeast of the survey, and a complex system of northwest-southeast and northeast-southwest conjugate faults and joints. The coherence image illuminates the edges of the individual karst features but gives little direct indication of their linkage nor of the small offset faults that are clearly seen on Figures 3a and b. A dual gradational color bar is particularly effective for curvature analysis so that we see red domal features bounded

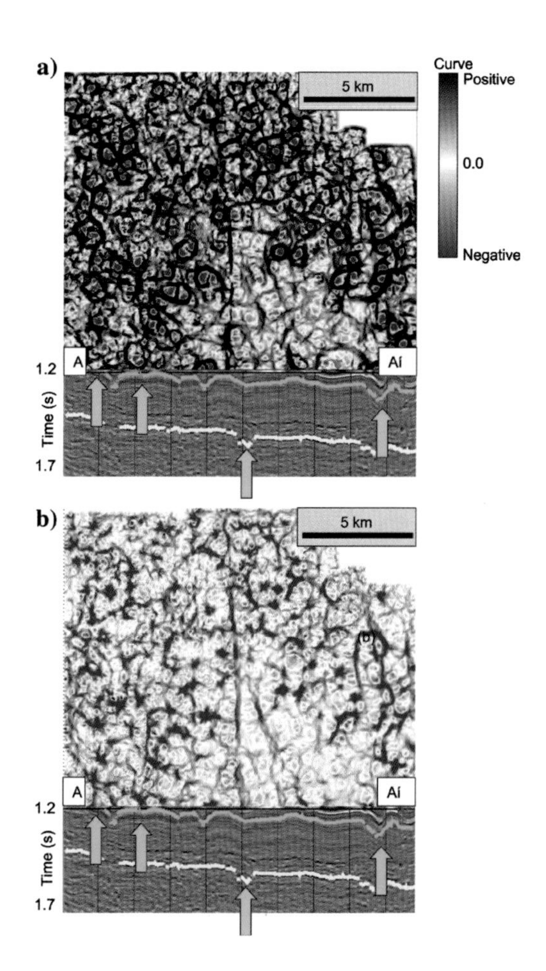

Figure 8. Foldaway combined attribute images corresponding to Figure 7. Seismic data are displayed on the vertical face. Long-wavelength (a) most-positive curvature and (b) most-negative curvature are shown on the time slices. Positive values (red) on the most-negative curvature slice correspond to domes, while negative values (green) on the most-positive curvature slice correspond to bowls. We interpret such bowls as tectonic collapse features, linked by a complex system of faults and joints.

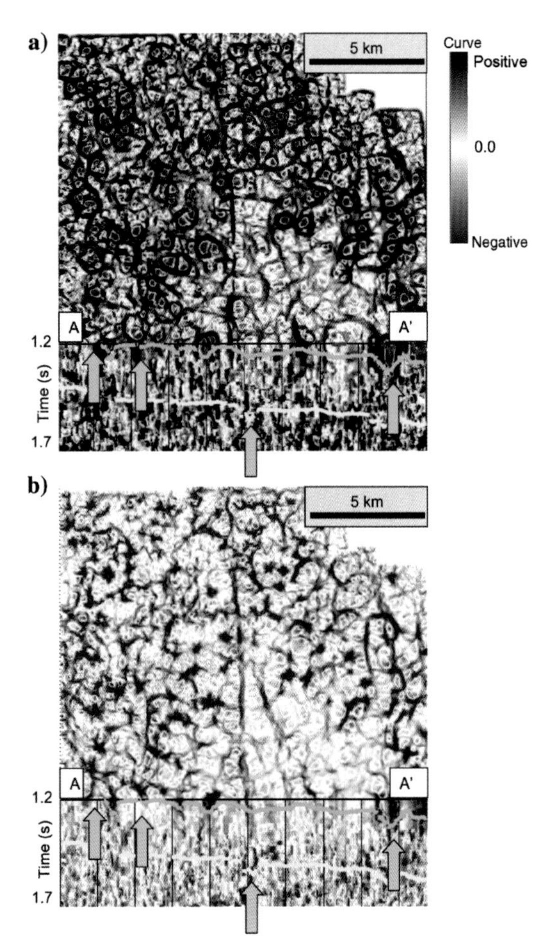

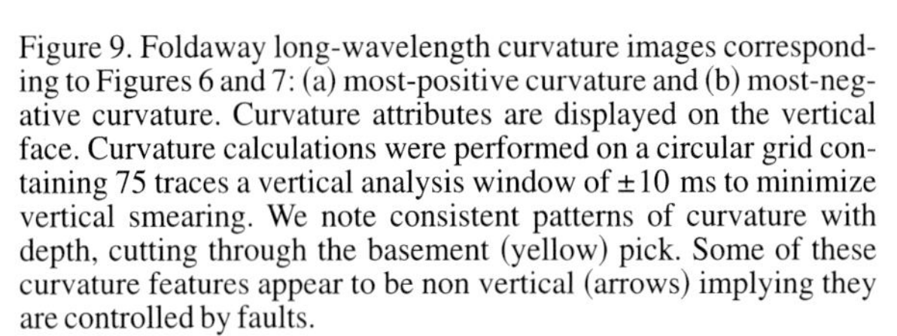
Figure 9. Foldaway long-wavelength curvature images corresponding to Figures 6 and 7: (a) most-positive curvature and (b) most-negative curvature. Curvature attributes are displayed on the vertical face. Curvature calculations were performed on a circular grid containing 75 traces a vertical analysis window of ±10 ms to minimize vertical smearing. We note consistent patterns of curvature with depth, cutting through the basement (yellow) pick. Some of these curvature features appear to be non vertical (arrows) implying they are controlled by faults.

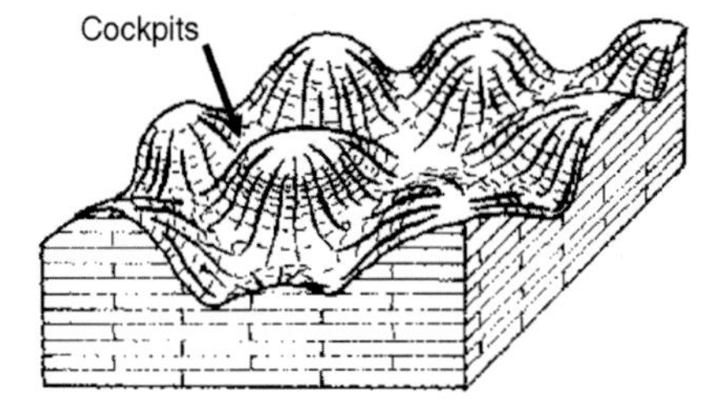

Figure 10. Mature cockpit karst topography results from a combination of dissolution and preburial collapse of cave systems. In this process, well cemented, low-porosity intercave areas persist as rounded knolls and hills (after Cansler and Carr, 2001).

Figure 11. Karst model of features associated with subaerial weathering and erosion of West Texas Ellenburger carbonates. Cave systems most commonly fill with collapse breccias and sediments associated with subsequent marine transgressions (after Kerans, 1990).

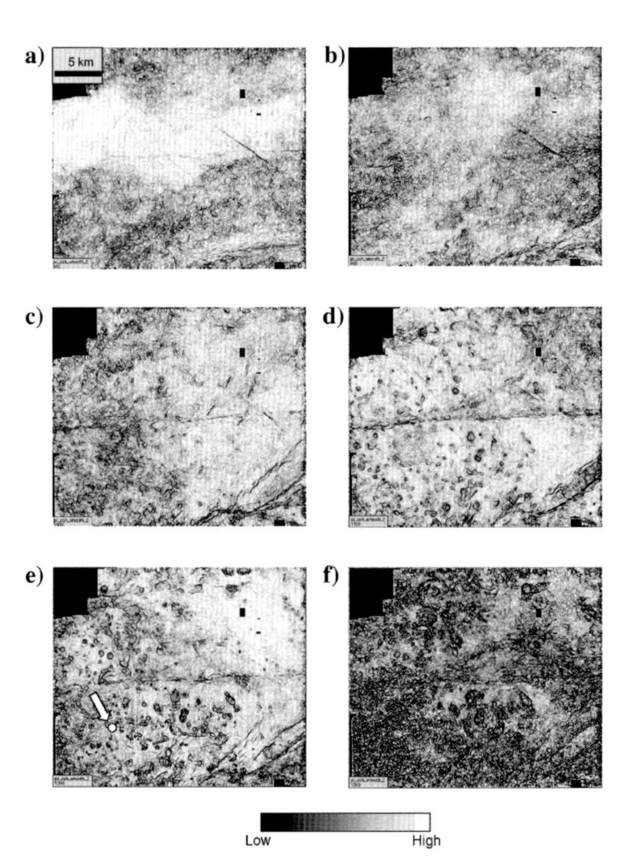

Figure 12. Slices through the coherence volume at (a) 0.8 s, (b) 0.9 s, (c) 1.0 s, (d) 1.1 s, (e) 1.2 s, and (f) 1.3 s. The analysis window is ±10 ms and 9 traces. White arrow in Figure 12e indicates location of image log shown in Figure 15.

by green valleys on the most-negative-curvature attribute (Figure 13) and green collapse features between red ridges on the most-positive-curvature attribute (Figure 14).

We also note that the collapse features appear to be most intense (sharpest) below the Ellenburger horizon in Figures 12e, 13e, and 14e and gradually broaden to the Caddo horizon in Figures 12a, 13a, and 14a. Although we feel confident that the Ellenburger has undergone subaerial karst generation, as evidenced by distinctive karst breccia facies in an image log (Figure 15) from the study area, we observe this is a pervasive background overprint. The location of the well in Figure 15 is marked in Figure 12e (white arrow), and is not associated with a large collapse feature. We note a marked change in the distribution of lineaments with age, which we show as rose diagrams in Figure 16. While the collapse features appear to be pervasive from basement to above the Caddo horizon, the tectonic stresses have changed direction over geologic time.

We have found in other surveys (Blumentritt et al., 2003) that the energy-weighed, coherent amplitude gradient can be effective in delineating lateral changes in rock thickness, which are often expressed in seismic data as changes in thin bed tuning. The energy-

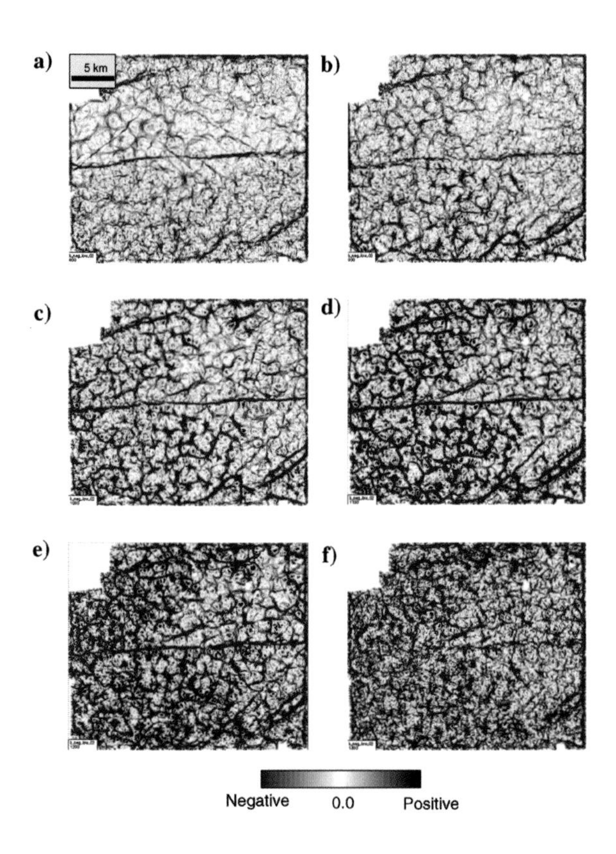

Figure 13. Slices through the most-negative-curvature volume at (a) 0.8 s, (b) 0.9 s, (c) 1.0 s, (d) 1.1 s, (e) 1.2 s, and (f) 1.3 s. We used a long-wavelength calculation with an analysis window of ±10 ms and 75 traces. Color bar is identical to those used in Figures 8 and 9. Domes appear brown. Bowls and valleys appear green. Note persistence of collapse features with depth and lack of lateral offset of features along post-Caddo east-west fault.

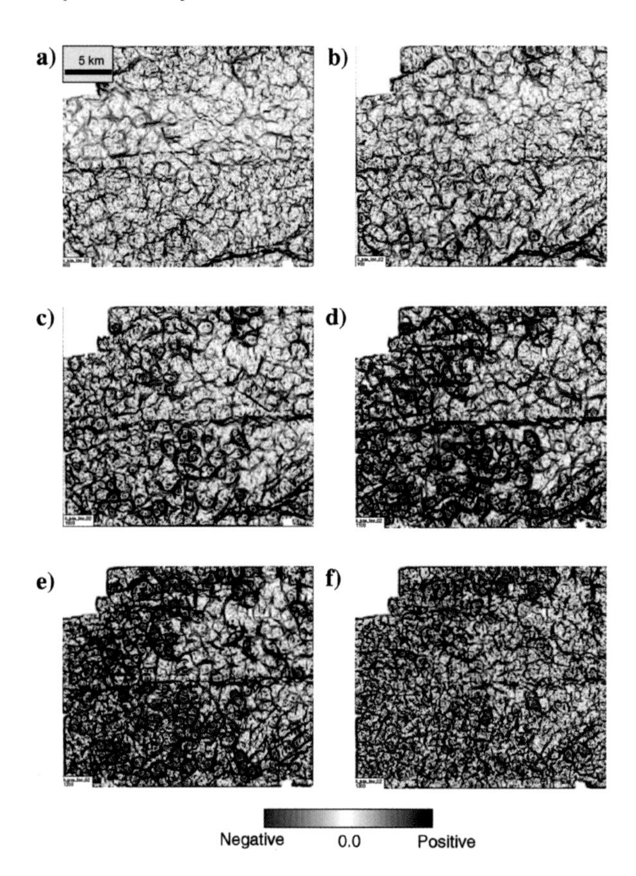

Figure 14. Slices through the most-positive-curvature volume at (a) 0.8 s, (b) 0.9 s, (c) 1.0 s, (d) 1.1 s, (e) 1.2 s, and (f) 1.3 s. We used a long-wavelength calculation with an analysis window of ±10 ms and 75 traces. Color bar is identical to those used in Figures 8 and 9. Bowls (collapse features) are green. Domes and ridges are brown.

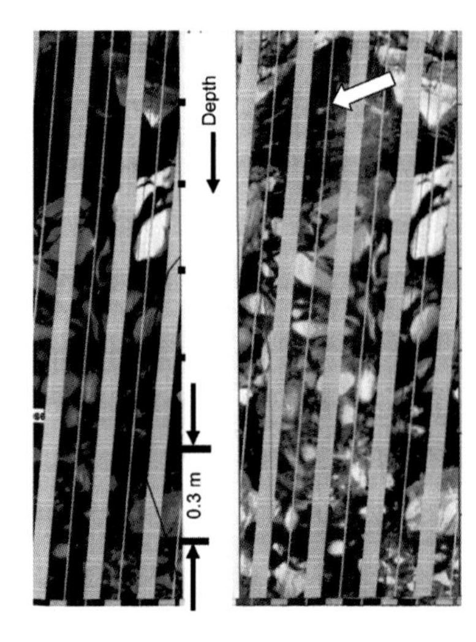

Figure 15. Resistivity-based image log showing karst breccia fabric, including rounded plus angular matrix-supported clasts and stratified fine sediment (white arrow). Location of well is indicated by arrow in Figure 12e; note that well location is not within a major collapse feature (data courtesy of Devon Energy).

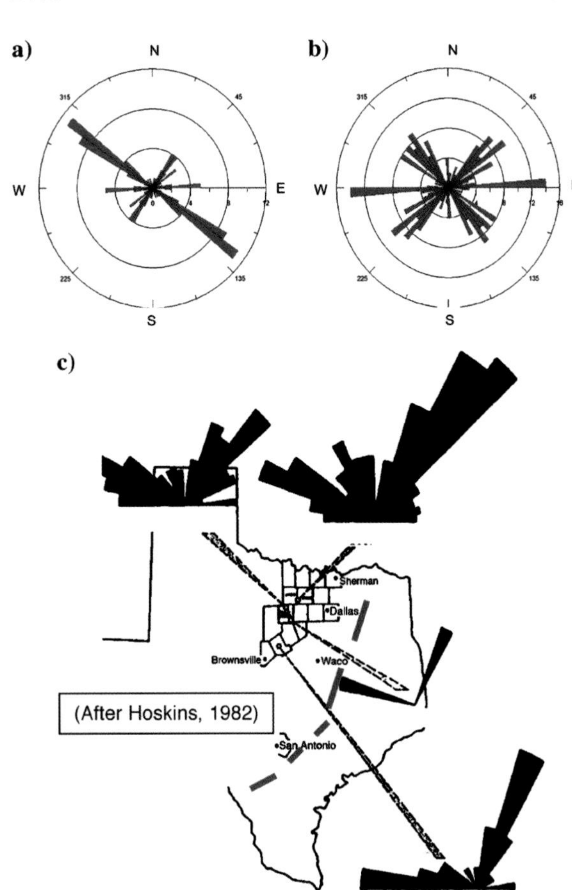

Figure 16. Rose diagrams of lineaments. Picked on time slices at (a) approximately top of the Caddo horizon at 0.8 s, as shown in Figures 12a, 13a, and 14a and (b) at approximately the top of the Ellenburger horizon as shown in Figures 12e, 13e, and 14e. Hoskins (1982) measured joints in surface outcrops (c) near the study area and related these to Miocene extension along the Balcones fault system (red lines). Present-day maximum stress σ_1 is vertical in the subsurface study area, and σ_2, the maximum horizontal stress, is N40–47°E (after Siebrits et al., 2000).

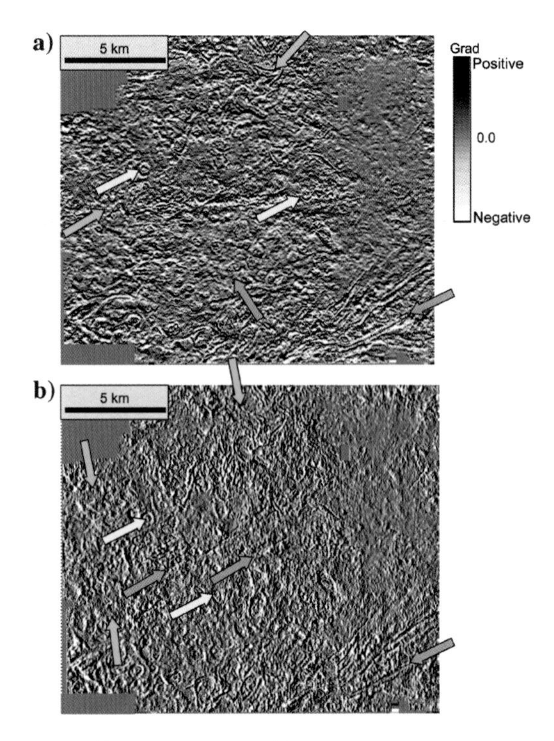

Figure 17. (a) North-south and (b) east-west energy-weighted, coherent amplitude gradient extracted along the Ellenburger horizon. Yellow arrows indicate representative circular collapse features; magenta arrows indicate lineations associated with faults and fractures, and green arrows indicate meandering channels and in-filled paleo topography. Subtle NS striations in (b) are attributable to acquisition footprint.

weighted, coherent amplitude gradients extracted along the Ellenburger horizon (Figure 17) show three types of features. The first type of feature, indicated by yellow arrows, has a craterlike appearance. These craters correspond to the location of collapse structures seen on the Ellenburger coherence volume (Figure 12e) and to local thickening on the Ellenburger-Marble Falls isochore map (Figure 5). We interpret these features as resulting from changes in sediment thickness within the collapse structures. The second type of feature, indicated by magenta arrows on the energy-weighted, coherent amplitude attribute image, are linear events that correlate well with faults and fractures seen in the other attribute volumes. The third type of feature, indicated by green arrows, is not apparent on any of the other attribute extractions or time slices. We interpret these features as thin meandering channels that appear to be controlled by the valleys and collapse features seen in Figure 13e. Other, more diffuse features we interpret as tuning effects associated with filling these valleys.

CONCLUSIONS

While the horizontal expression of the vertical collapse features in the Fort Worth Basin data is readily seen on traditional time/structure and isochore maps (Figures 4 and 5), their relationship to faulting is more clearly presented in time slices and horizon extractions through coherence and curvature attribute volumes (Figures 12–14). We note that the collapse features are intense at the Ellenburger time and cut into the basement in some areas but are greatly subdued at the Caddo Limestone level (Figures 12–14). Indeed, the expression at Caddo time (Figure 12a) shows no discontinuities, implying that the collapse seen on the curvature volumes (Figures 13a and 14a) is attributable to either continued compaction or dissolution from below, rather than to top-down, subaerial karst processes following deposition of the Caddo.

Isochrons of Marble Falls to Ellenburger (Figure 5a) and Caddo to Marble Falls (Figure 5b) show decreasing magnitude of the circular collapse features, demonstrating that collapse was episodic and decreasing by Atokan time. The alignment of collapse features at the deeper levels (Figures 12e–14e) with shallow lineaments suggests a post-Atokan reactivation of those joints. Current maximum stress in the subsurface Mississippian strata near the study area is vertical; in the area of seismic coverage, the stress σ_2 is N40-47E. Within the study area, open joint systems in surface outcrops of the Upper Pennsylvanian are dominated by NNE and NNW sets (Figure 16c), which Hoskins (1982) interprets as related to extension along the trans Texas Miocene-age, down-to-the-coast Balconies fault system (although we speculate there may be Mesozoic extension as well). We interpret the observed features in the seismic data as indicating that Ellenburger subaerial karst events were influenced by basement faults, and that these faults were reactivated during deposition of Atokan siliciclastics. Orientation of pinnate lineaments at the Ellenburger level and extensional joints at the Caddo level suggest possible reversal of stresses in the area related to the Ouachita orogeny and later Miocene or other extensional events.

We conclude that some of the collapse features originated as subaerial karst, as evidenced by channels cutting the top of the Ellenburger (Figure 17) and that karst formation was likely more intense below the Mississippian unconformity than below the middle Ordovician unconformity. We have observed that in other Fort Worth Basin 3D surveys that Lower Ordovician Ellenburger carbonates overlain by Upper Ordovician carbonates appear to contain a lower density of sinkholelike features than do Ellenburger carbonates overlain directly by Mississippian shales.

Although the Ellenburger carbonates were subaerially exposed at least twice, we propose that most of the extensive collapse chimneys observed in the seismic volume is the result of extensional faulting, enhanced, perhaps, by deep burial fluids moving along Pennsylvanian or younger fractures and seismic-scale faults. Calcite cement plugging of macrofractures observed within the Mississippian shales may represent a final stage of this process.

We anticipate that further improvements in the attributes that we have used will allow us to further separate subtle faults and collapse features that form under different conditions. For example, we expect that differences in timing and mode of karst formation have the potential to produce cave fill and plumbing systems with distinct patterns of porosity and permeability. The geomorphic expression of karst or tectonic collapse features is increasingly recognized as an important control on the deposition and fracturing of younger reservoirs for the Fort Worth Basin and for sandstones above karsted Mississippian carbonates in Kansas. We believe that the application of such new seismic attributes to 3D seismic volumes allows detection of normally subseismic features and provides a tool for determining timing and nature of features that may be related to karst, tectonic, or hydrothermal collapse and for improved mapping of reservoir bodies, permeability fairways, and various surfaces associated with weathered and fractured carbonates.

ACKNOWLEDGMENTS

We wish to thank the United States Department of Energy DE-FC26-04NT15504 and the sponsors of the Allied Geophysical Laboratory Consortium for financial support of research. We particularly thank Devon Energy for permission to use its data.

REFERENCES

Bagdan, C. A., and S. G. Pemberton, 2004, Karst breccia and bank collapse breccia: Implications for reservoir characterization of the McMurray Formation, Alberta, Canada: AAPG Bulletin, **88**, 13.

Ball, M. M., and W. J. Perry, 1996, Bend Arch-Fort Worth Basin Province: U. S. G. S. Report for Province 45.

Berger, Z., and G. Davies, 1999, The development of linear hydrothermal dolomite (HDT) reservoir facies along wrench or strike slip fault systems in the Western Canadian Sedimentary Basin: Canadian Society of Petroleum Geologists Reservoir, 34–38.

Blumentritt, C. H., K. J. Marfurt, and E. C. Sullivan, 2003, Limits to seismic resolution of stratigraphic features-Applications to the Devonian Thirty-one Formation, Central Basin Platform, in T. J. Hunt, and P. H. Lufholm, eds., The Permian Basin, back to the basics: West Texas Geologic Society Publication 03–112, 209–218.

Bowker, K. A., 2003, Recent developments of the Barnett Shale Play, Fort Worth Basin: West Texas Geological Society Bulletin, **42**, 4–11.

Cansler, J. R., and T. R. Carr, 2001, Paleogeomorphology of the sub-Pennsylvanian Unconformity of the Arbuckle Group (Cambrian-Lower Ordovician): Kansas Geological Survey, open file report 2001–55.

Franseen E. K., A. P. Byrnes, J. Cansler, D. M. Steinhauff, T. R. Carr, and M. K. Dubois, 2003, Geologic characteristics of Arbuckle reservoirs in Kansas: Proceedings of the 15th Oil Conference, Tertiary Oil Recovery Project, The University of Kansas, 28.

Grayson, R. C., and G. K. Merrill, 1991, Carboniferous geology and tectonic history of the Southern Fort Worth (foreland) Basin and Concho Platform, Texas: GSA Field Trip Guidebook: Dallas Geological Society, 67.

Hardage, B. A., D. L. Carr, D. E. Lancaster, J. L. Simmons, Jr., R. Y. Elphick, V. M. Pendelton, and R. A. Johns, 1996, 3-D Seismic evidence for the effects of carbonate karst breccia collapse on overlying clastic stratigraphy and reservoir compartmentalization: Geophysics, **61**, 1336–1350.

Hoskins, B. W., 1982, Fracture analysis of Pennsylvanian carbonate bank systems in the Graford Formation North Central Texas, *in* C. A. Martin, ed., Petroleum geology of the Fort Worth Basin and Bend Arch area: Dallas Geological Society, 179–192.

Kerans, C., 1990, Depositional systems and karst geology of the Ellenburger Group (Lower Ordovician), subsurface West Texas: The University of Texas at Austin, Bureau of Economic Geology Report of Investigations, 193, 63.

Kupecs, J. A., and L. S. Land, 1991, Late Stage dolomitization of the Lower Ordovician Ellenburger Group, west Texas: Journal of Sedimentary Petrology, **61**, 551–574.

Lisle, R. J., 1994, Detection of zones of abnormal strains in structures using Gaussian curvature analysis: AAPG Bulletin, **78**, 1811–1819.

Loucks, R. G., P. K. Mescher, and G. A. McMechan, 2004, Three-dimensional architecture of a coalesced, collapsed-paleocave system in the Lower Ordovician Ellenburger Group, central Texas: AAPG Bulletin, **88**, 545–564.

Lucia, F. J., 1996, Lower Paleozoic cavern development, collapse, and dolomitization, Franklin Mountains, El Paso, Texas *in* E. Stoudt, ed., Precambrian-Devonian geology of the Franklin mountains, west Texas- analogs for exploration and production in Ordovician and Silurian reservoirs in the Permian Basin: West Texas Geological Society 1996 Guidebook, 175–196.

McClay, K., and M. Borora, 2001, Analog models of restraining stepovers in strike-slip fault systems: AAPG Bulletin, **85**, 233–260.

Marfurt, K. J., 2006, Robust estimates of 3D reflector dip and azimuth: Geophysics, (this issue).

Marfurt, K. J., V. Sudhakar, A. Gersztenkorn, K. Crawford, and S. Nissen, 1999, Coherency calculations in the presence of structural dip: Geophysics, **64**, 104–111.

Montgomery, S. L., D. M. Jarvie, K. A. Bowker, and R. M. Pollastro, 2005, Mississippian Barnett Shale, Fort Worth basin, north-central Texas: Gas-shale play with multi-trillion cubic foot potential: AAPG Bulletin, **89**, 155–175.

Pollastro, R. M., R. J. Hill, D. M. Jarvie, and M. E. Henry, 2003, Assessing undiscovered resources of the Barnett-Paleozoic Total Petroleum System, Bend Arch-Fort Worth Basin Province, Texas: Transactions of the Southwest Section, AAPG Convention, AAPG/Datapages, CD-ROM 18.

Roberts, A., 2001, Curvature attributes and application to 3D interpreted horizons: First Break, **19**, 85–99.

Sagan, J., and B. Hart, 2004, Seismic and structural analysis of a Trenton-Black River hydrothermal dolomite reservoir: AAPG Search and Discovery Article #40129.

Siebrits, E., J. L. Elbel, R. S. Hoover, I. R. Diyashev, R. T. Holditch, L. G. Griffin, S. L. Demetrius, C. A. Wright, B. M. Davidson, N. P. Steinsberger, and D. G. Hill, 2000, Refracture reorientation enhances gas production in the Barnett Shale tight gas sand: SPE 2000 Annual Technical Conference and Exhibition, SPE paper 63030, 5.

Walper, J., 1982, Plate Tectonic evolution of the Fort Worth Basin, *in* C. A. Martin, ed., Petroleum geology of the Fort Worth Basin and Bend Arch area: Dallas Geological Society, 237–251.

Chapter 19

Applications of the coherency cube in the UKCS

M. J. HUGHES, S. DHANANI, R. K. FRIMPONG, M. GAINSKI, N. L. HASKELL, R. P. HEATH, J. D. KANTOROWICZ, P. M. MAGUIRE and S. E. NISSEN

Amoco (U.K.) Exploration Company, Amoco House, West Gate, Ealing, London, W5 1XL, UK

Abstract: Seismic coherency is a measure of the similarity between seismic traces. Coherency data play an important role in the delineation of structural and stratigraphic features by enhancing the images seen on conventional 3D seismic data. Through integration of coherency data with other technologies and calibration to well data, new applications are emerging. This paper discusses three examples from the UKCS.

Partial permeability barriers in the Leman Field were known to exist from well pressure data. A coherency cube revealed several lineations that separated the wells. These lineations can be correlated to a previously unmapped fault trend with very small throws on the vertical seismic lines. The coherency cube therefore provided additional information to improve confidence in the interpretation and enabled significant time-savings in the fault pattern interpretation.

Coherency data were used to assist in the well planning for the Arkwright Field development programme. Coherency slices through high pressure zones were characterized by polygonal faulting, whilst less faulting was observed in areas of lower pore pressure. These pressure zones were calibrated to pore pressures predicted from the original discovery well. The development trajectories were optimized with respect to the fault patterns interpreted from the coherency data. Model predictions were confirmed by drilling results.

A coherency cube was utilized to enable a quick interpretation of the structural framework of an area of the Central Graben. In particular the distribution of faulted Triassic rafts and Jurassic rifts is easily observed because the relatively coherent Jurassic reflectors contrast well with the relatively incoherent Triassic seismic reflectivity.

These three examples illustrate how coherency data can be used in production, development and exploration settings to improve the imaging of geological features ranging in scale from reservoir barriers to major faults.

Coherency is a measure of the similarity between a number of adjacent seismic traces. The degree of similarity between the traces can be measured by a variety of methods including cross correlation, semblance and eigenstructure (Bahorich & Farmer 1994; Marfurt *et al.* 1995; Gersztenkorn & Marfurt 1996). High coherency values represent areas where seismic traces are similar, whereas low coherency values occur where the adjacent seismic traces show more variation. Coherency algorithms are typically applied to 3D seismic data which have been loaded onto workstations creating a second volume of data called a coherency cube. Areas of discontinuity within the 3D seismic volume such as channel margins or faults appear greatly enhanced in the corresponding coherency cube data.

Over the last few years coherency data have been increasingly used in conjunction with conventional seismic data. Coherency is commonly generated at the start of a 3D interpretation project. This allows both faster interpretation and improved confidence in fault patterns (especially fault linkages) and large-scale stratigraphic features (Roberts *et al.* 1996). Coherency data has been of most benefit in complex geological settings and areas with poor quality seismic data.

Integration of coherency data with information from other technologies can provide additional insights. This paper discusses three case histories illustrating some innovative uses of coherency data.

Case history 1: partial permeability barriers in the Leman Field

The Leman Field is a giant gas field centred on UK Blocks 49/26 and 49/27 in the Southern North Sea (Fig. 1). The field is a faulted anticline that stretches for 50 km in an elongate NW–SE direction. Reservoir production is from Permian Rotliegend Group sandstones (Cameron *et al.* 1992) which are mainly aeolian in origin. These are vertically sealed by the overlying Zechstein Group which is predominantly carbonate

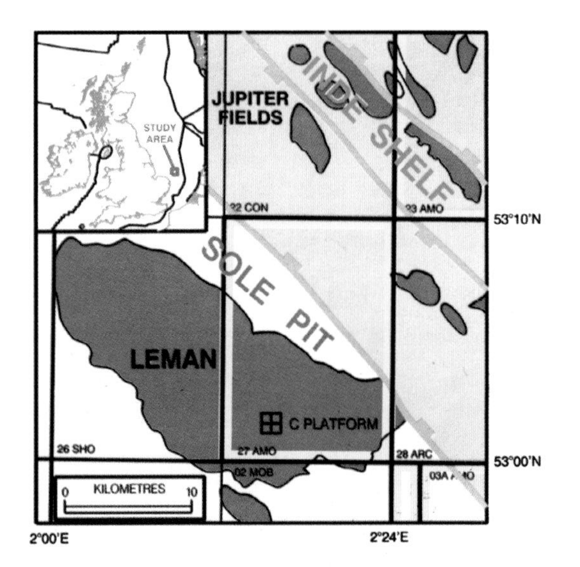

Fig. 1. Location map of the Leman Field.

HUGHES, M. J., DHANANI, S., FRIMPONG, R. K., GAINSKI, M., HASKELL, N. L., HEATH, R. P., KANTOROWICZ, J. D., MAGUIRE, P. M. & NISSEN, S. E. 1999. Applications of the coherency cube in the UKCS. *In*: FLEET, A. J. & BOLDY, S. A. R. (eds) *Petroleum Geology of Northwest Europe: Proceedings of the 5th Conference*, 1299–1305. © Petroleum Geology '86 Ltd. Published by the Geological Society, London.

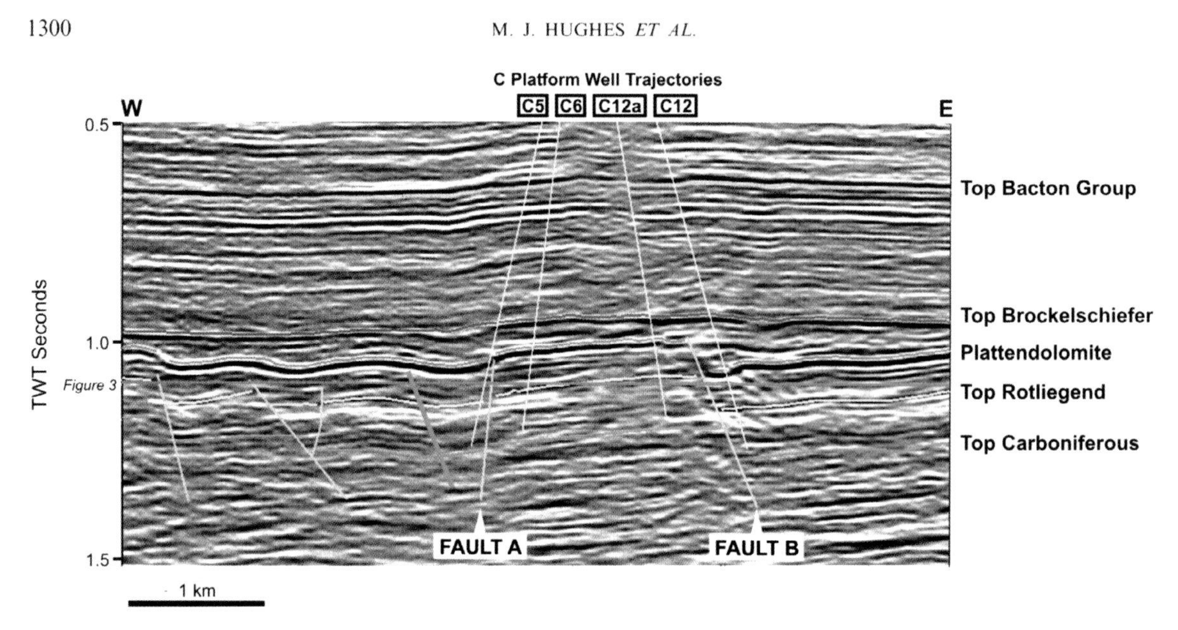

Fig. 2. Seismic line through the Leman C Platform area. (Location shown in Fig. 3.)

and anhydrite below the Plattendolomit whilst being halite rich above. The mobile salts have undergone plastic deformation to accommodate the underlying fault movement (Fig. 2). The Triassic sequence commences with a thin Brockelschiefer interval followed by the Bacton Group.

This case history focuses on the area around the C platform in the southern part of the Leman field (Fig. 1). Reservoir pressure data indicate that this area of the field contains several pressure regimes, interpreted as being the result of partial permeability barriers within the reservoir. The C8 and C12 wells were known to lie in a separate fault block which had been mapped using 2D seismic data. However, the cause of the pressure anomaly at the C5 well had not been identified.

Following the acquisition of a 3D seismic survey in 1995 a coherency cube was generated. A coherency slice at 1100 ms (through the Rotliegend and lower Zechstein intervals) is shown in Fig. 3. The encircled numbers on the figure indicate C platform well locations at Top Rotliegend. Immediately

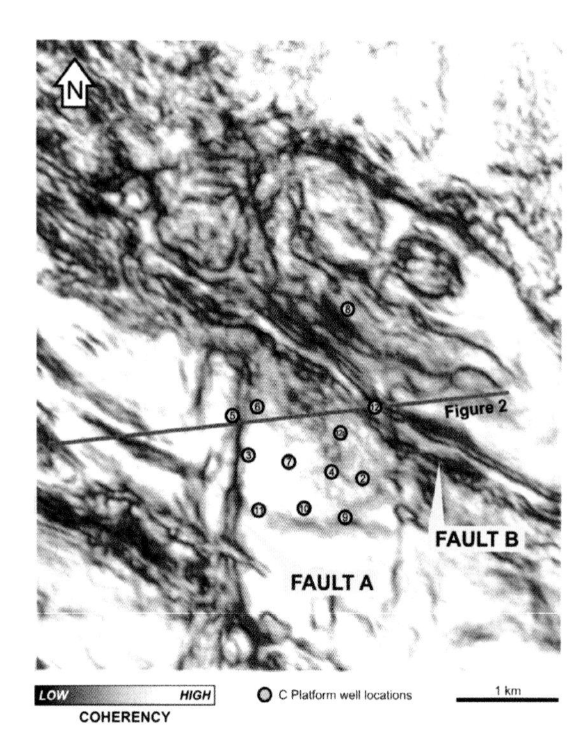

Fig. 3. Coherency slice at 1100 ms from the Leman C Platform area showing the position of a N–S low coherency lineation (Fault A) that isolates the C5 well.

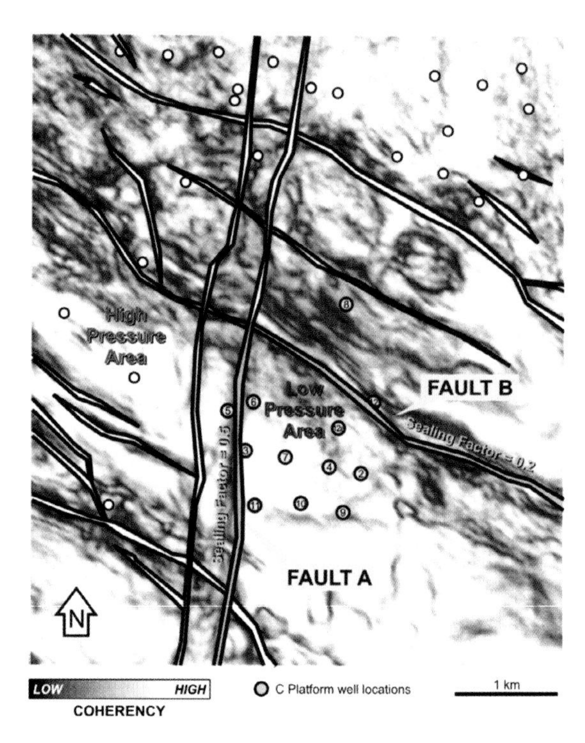

Fig. 4. Coherency slice at 1100 ms with fault interpretation at Top Rotliegend and fault seal data around the C platform from a reservoir simulation run.

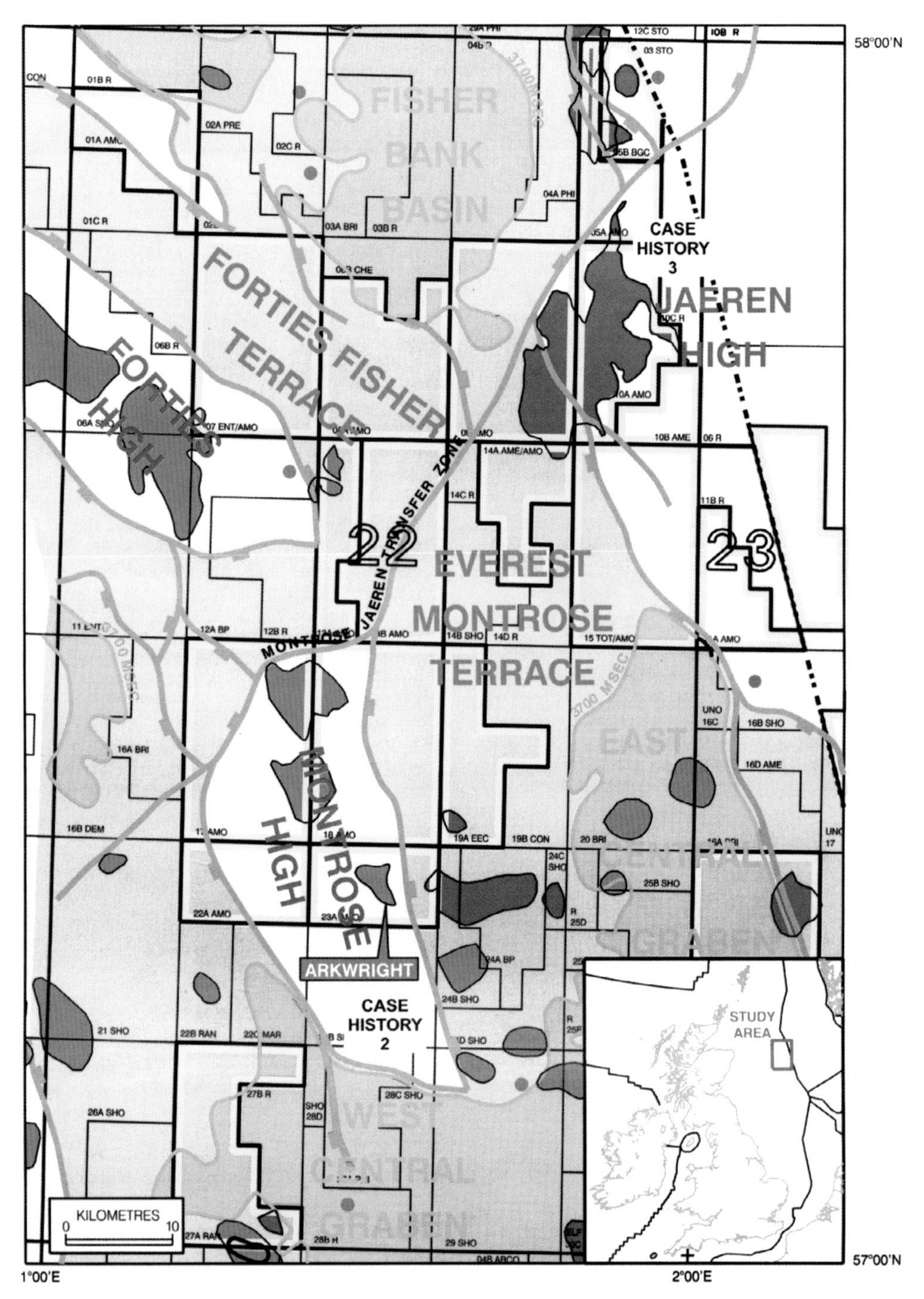

Fig. 5. Location map of the East Central Graben.

evident is a N–S trending low coherency lineation separating C5 from the remaining C platform wells (Fault A in Fig. 3). This lineation can be correlated to a fault with a small offset on the vertical seismic (Fault A in Fig. 2).

Reservoir simulation work has shown that a pressure barrier is required to separate the low reservoir pressure area around the C platform from a higher pressure area to the west. The faults identified were assigned a sealing factor between 0 (completely sealing) and 1 (no impact on reservoir flow). Fault A was assigned a sealing factor of 0.5 indicating that it forms a partially sealing reservoir barrier (Fig. 4).

Leveille *et al.* (1997) describe similar N–S trending faults in the Jupiter Fields area (25 km north) where, despite the small throws, the faults have a greater sealing potential when compared to other fault trends. This is explained by the high lateral continuity of these faults and their damage zones (when viewed regionally), the presence of halite and anhydrite in the fault rock cement and the fact that these faults represent a later phase of deformation (as they offset other faults).

The coherency slices through the strongly reflective package from the Top Rotliegend to the lower Zechstein often illuminate the fault patterns more clearly than slices lower in the Rotliegend Group where the reflectors are weaker (Fig. 2). The strong reflectors generate high coherency values except in faulted areas where the reflector terminations result in pronounced low coherency lineations. The deeper, less reflective data have a lower signal to noise ratio with less distinct terminations on the vertical seismic and less contrast between the faulted and unfaulted areas on coherency data. This effect is seen in the northern edge of Fig. 3 where the coherency slice cuts the base of the Rotliegend and the faults are less well defined.

Using coherency data at an early stage in the 3D interpretation project, the time spent interpreting faults was significantly decreased. In addition, as the coherency data were generated from an un-flattened seismic volume, it provided an image of the faulting that is not influenced by any interpretation. As a result the coherency data increased the confidence in the fault interpretation. In this case history a small-scale fault with important influence on reservoir properties was quickly mapped using the coherency data.

Case history 2: well planning in the Arkwright Field development programme

The Arkwright Field is situated in UK Block 22/23a on the Forties–Montrose High of the Central Graben (Fig. 5). The discovery well was drilled in 1990 into a low-relief, anticlinal closure with the reservoir in the turbidite sandstones of the Paleocene Forties Sandstone Member (of Knox & Holloway 1992). The structure is sealed by the overlying mudstones of the Sele Formation. The remainder of the overburden consists of a mudstone dominated sequence that exceeds 2500 m thick.

The field was mapped in detail following the acquisition of a 3D seismic survey over the area in 1993. Following approval for the field development in 1995, work began on planning for three production wells (for more information see Kantorowicz *et al.* 1999).

Seismic data over the field show that the overburden contains layers with numerous small-scale faults separated by relatively undeformed layers (Fig. 6). The faulting is similar to that described by Cartwright & Lonergan (1996) who attribute the deformation to volumetric contraction during compactional dewatering of overpressured shales. The condensed sequences that bound the faulted tiers are similar in age to those described by Cartwright (1994). The nature of the faulting is seen more clearly on coherency slices over the field (Fig. 7). A coherency slice through an unfaulted section is shown in Fig. 7A (952 ms). Figure 7B (1560 ms) shows the development of the polygonal fault trace geometry characteristic of this type of deformation. Below the Intra-Mid Oligocene marker there is a thin undeformed section that separates the two tiers of faulting (Fig. 6). Figure 7C (2100 ms) is through the lower faulted tier. This slice is less intensively faulted probably because of the increase in sand content observed in the wells which would increase horizontal permeability, providing an escape route for overpressured fluids. The faulting on the deepest slice (Fig. 7D, 2556 ms) is concentrated above the field margins where the dip is steepest as a result of the combined effects of the structural anticline and differential compaction in the underlying Forties Sandstone Member. It is suggested that this faulting has resulted from a combination of compactional dewatering and the effects of dip. As the overpressure in the shales neared fracture levels, the failure would have occurred first in the areas of steepest dip where the local stress field would be most intense.

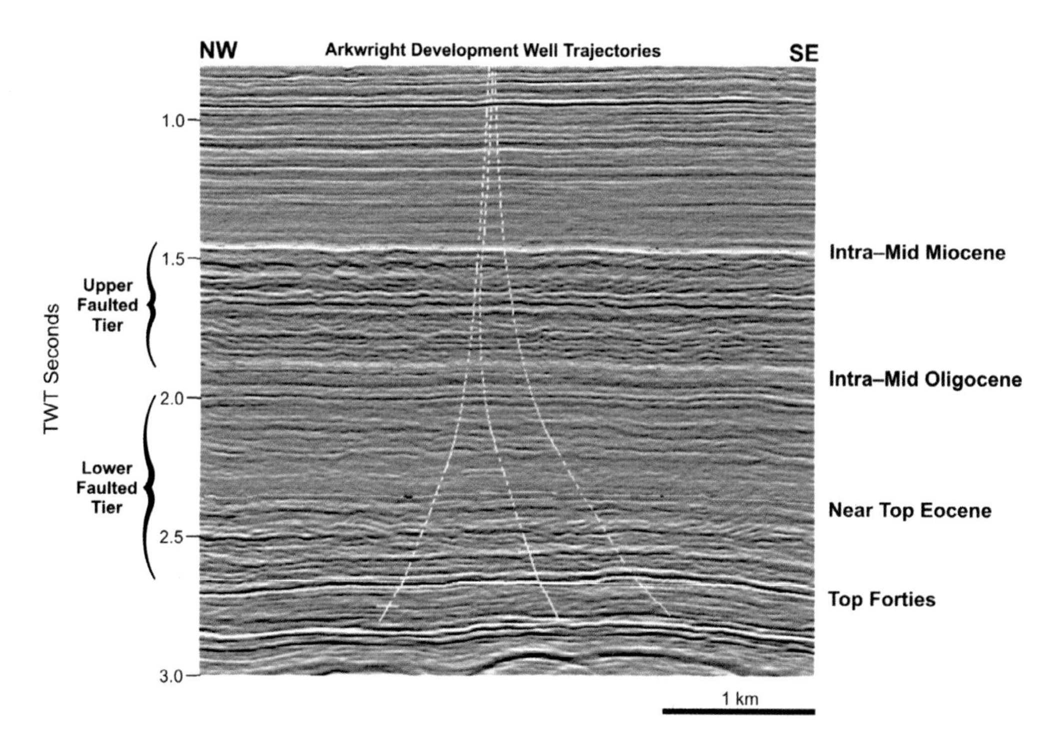

Fig. 6. Seismic line through the Arkwright Field (courtesy of PGS) showing proposed development well locations. Note the pervasive faulting in the upper and lower faulted tiers.

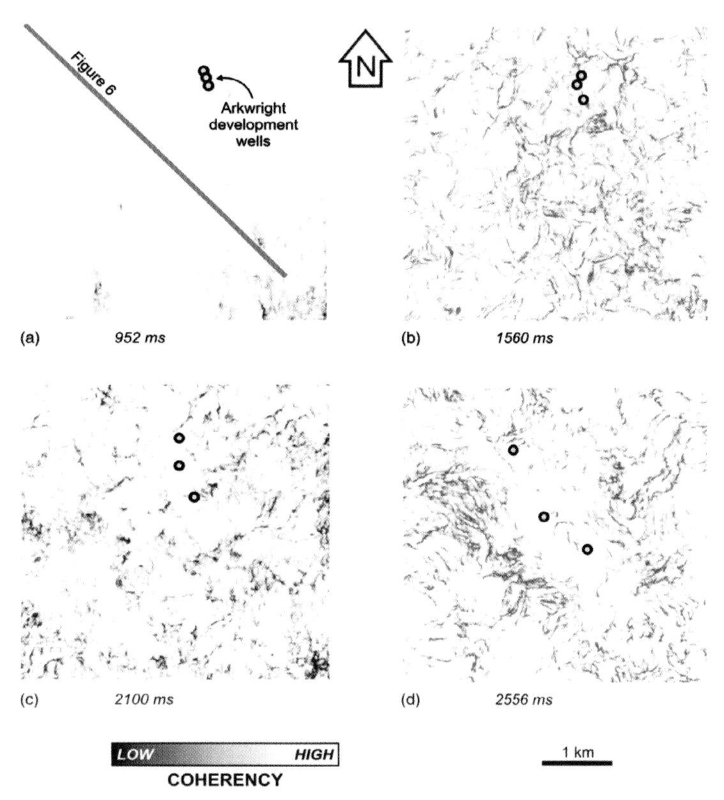

Fig. 7. Coherency slices above the Arkwright Field through undeformed and faulted levels.

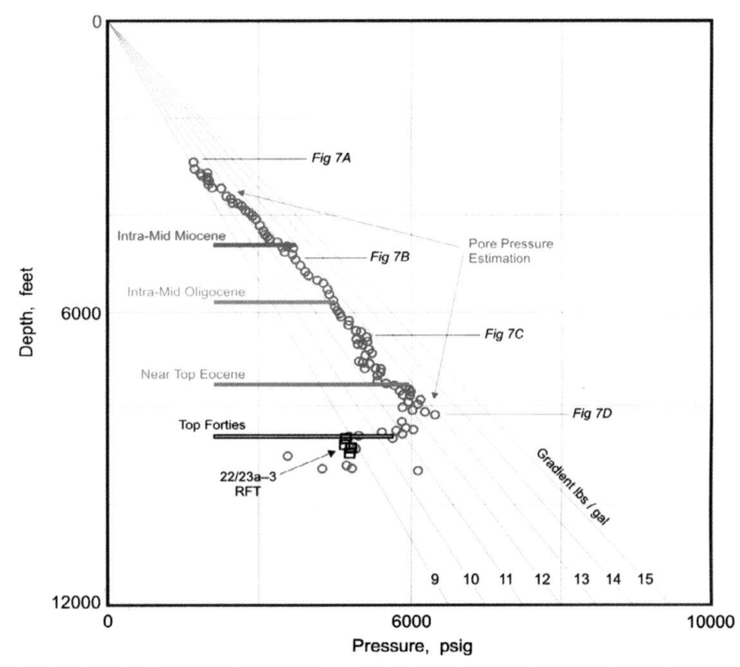

Fig. 8. Pore pressure estimation from the Arkwright discovery well. The seismic markers from Fig. 6 are shown along witn the positions of the slices from Fig. 7.

Figure 8 shows a plot of a pore pressure estimation based on the sonic log data of the discovery well. Normal (hydrostatic) pressure is approximated by the 9 lbs/gal^{-1} line. It can be seen that the faulted slices occur in areas of marked overpressure which are probably close to fracture pressure. The faults may be acting as bleed valves (as described by Sibson *et al.* 1975) whereby pore fluids which have become highly pressured during burial are intermittently released through the faults in such a manner that overpressure remains at depth.

From the earlier discussion, it can be seen that within these shales, areas with low coherency values (highly faulted) can be inferred as being of relatively high pressure whereas high coherency levels (unfaulted) have lower pressure. This information was used to impact the calculation of appropriate mud weights, and to facilitate the design of the casing scheme. Drilling through these faults with an excessive mud weight may cause the pore pressure to exceed the fracture gradient, with a consequent loss of drilling fluid into the fault. Casing was set above and below the faulted zone thus isolating the hydrostatically pressured Forties Sandstone Member.

A further use of the coherency cube was to ensure that the proposed well paths were designed to avoid drilling along faults planes. The progressively deeper positions of the well paths from a drilling centre offset to the northeast of the field are shown on Fig. 7. The intensely faulted areas were avoided in a potentially unstable zone above the reservoir (Fig. 7D). However, some of the small-scale faults are unavoidable, thus the strategy utilized was to anticipate the type of instability that might occur and plan the drilling mud weight response accordingly.

All three development wells were drilled through the overburden without significant drilling problems. However, difficulties in accurately setting casing above the reservoir in two wells created a number of minor problems which confirmed the instability of the overpressured zones when exposed to the lower mud weights needed for the reservoir section.

Case history 3: structural interpretation of the Jaeren High

The Jaeren High lies on the eastern margin of the Fisher Bank Basin and the East Central Graben (Fig. 5). The structural evolution of the area has been described by Penge *et al.* (1993, 1999). During the main period of regional extension (late Triassic to Early Cretaceous) large fault blocks of Triassic sediments were translated and rotated on the Permian Zechstein salt substrate forming relatively undeformed, discrete blocks called rafts. The rafts are separated by rifts that have been filled by the reactive and active rise of the Zechstein salt and the deposition of a thicker Jurassic/Cretaceous section.

Figure 9 shows a typical seismic line through a series of rifts and rafts. The structural highs at the Base Cretaceous event define the position of the rafts which consist of a thick, acoustically quiet, sequence of Triassic sediments overlying a thin Zechstein layer. The lows in the Base Cretaceous show the position of the rifts which contain a more reflective sediment infill above the chaotic seismic character of the Zechstein salt. The spatial distribution of the rifts (lows) and rafts (highs) can be seen in the 3D illumination of the Base Cretaceous TWT surface in Fig. 10A.

Coherency data can be used as a complimentary method of imaging the structural fabric. The rifts contain bright, continuous reflectors (above top Zechstein) that result in high coherency values whereas the rafts consist of a lower amplitude, more disordered sequence with lower coherency values. Figure 10B shows a 3D image of the Base Cretaceous coloured by coherency values at Base Cretaceous that clearly illustrate the position of the rifts. The coherency data also allow the detailed mapping of faults in both the rifted and rafted areas.

Figure 10C contains only the high coherency data in a window stretching 100 ms below Base Cretaceous. The low coherency data have been made transparent using voxel rendering software. The high coherency areas in the rifts are visible through the semi-transparent Base Cretaceous TWT surface.

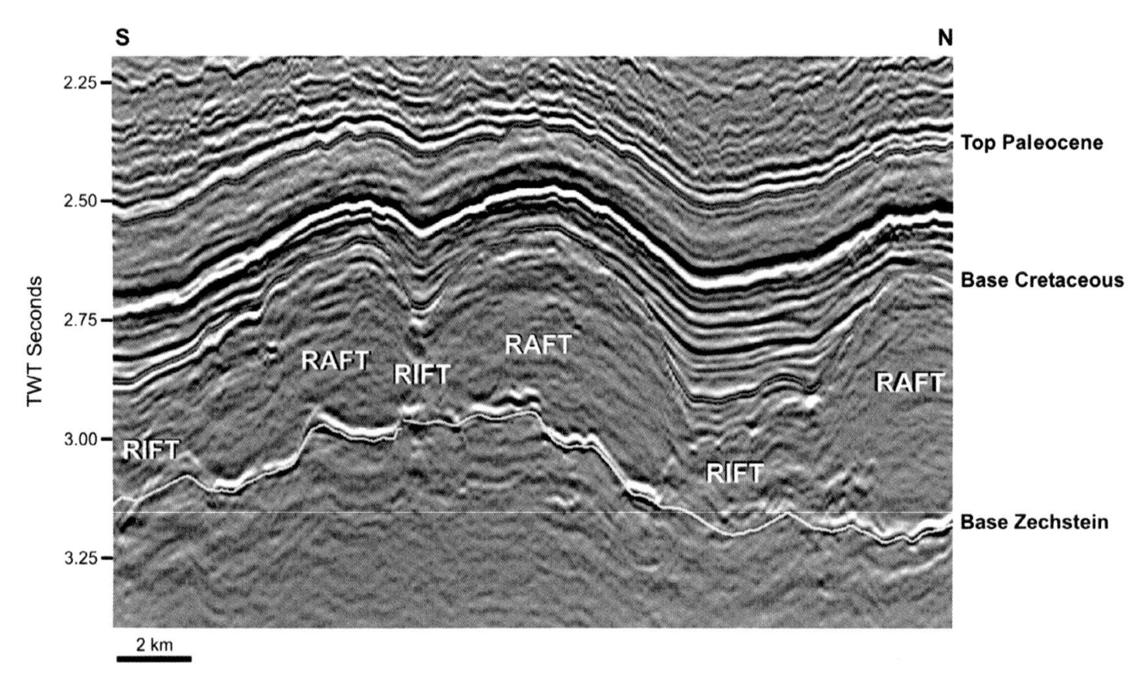

Fig. 9. Seismic line from the Jaeren High showing rift–raft tectonism (courtesy of PGS).

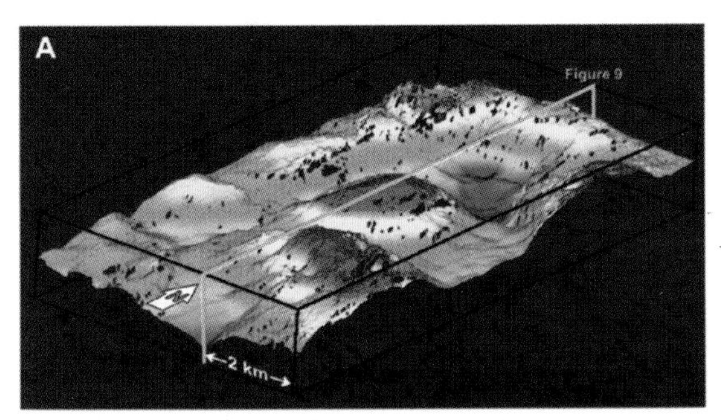

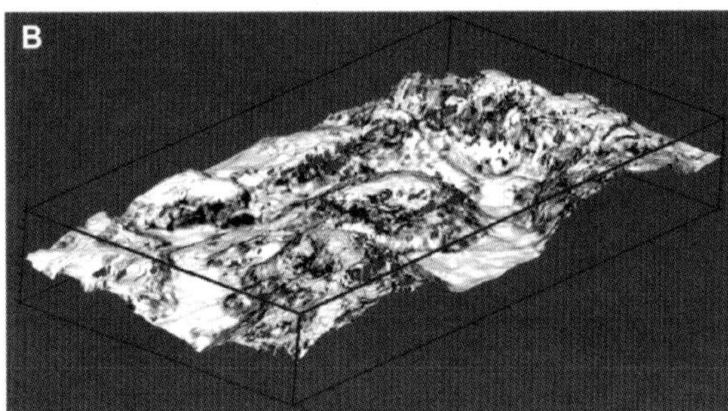

Fig. 10. 3D views of the Base Cretaceous horizon coloured by TWT (**A**), coherency (**B**), and partially transparent TWT (**C**). The high coherency values in a window stretching 100 ms below the Base Cretaceous are visible in Fig. 10C.

Analysis of coherency data has enabled the rapid interpretation of this structural fabric by clearly illuminating the positions of the rifts and rafts. The coherency data have been used to great effect in structurally complex areas where the rifts cannot be distinguished using Base Cretaceous topography alone and in areas deeper in the basin where seismic quality deteriorates.

Conclusions

Over the last few years coherency has played an increasingly important role in improving the cycle time and confidence of 3D seismic interpretations by improving the imaging of structural fabric and stratigraphic features. Coherency, being a relatively new application, is beginning to be integrated with other technologies to provide additional insights. Three examples have been discussed showing the integration of coherency data in production, development and exploration settings to improve the imaging of geological features ranging in scale from reservoir barriers to major faults, and to provide information for applications as diverse as calculating drilling mud weights to scoping the potential for infill well placement. As coherency technology matures it is likely that numerous other applications will emerge.

The authors would like to thank the following people at Amoco: P. Izienicki and J. Munns for reviewing the paper; C. McCrone for discussions on SNS stratigraphy; A. Cushing for drafting the diagrams; T. Walsgrove for work on the pressure prediction over the Arkwright Field; J. Penge for discussions on rift/raft tectonism. We are grateful to Dr J. Cosgrove of Imperial College for useful discussions on the relationship between overpressure and faulting. C. Hawkes of Texaco is thanked for work over Leman while employed at Amoco. We would like to thank the following partners for their co-operation in publishing this work: Amerada Hess Ltd, British Gas Exploration and Production Ltd and Enterprise Oil PLC. We are grateful to PGS for permission to show seismic data over the Arwright Field and the Jaeren High.

References

BAHORICH, M. S. & FARMER, S. L. 1994. 3-D Seismic discontinuity: the coherency cube for faults and stratigraphic features. *64th Annual International Meeting, Society Exploration Geophysics, Expanded Abstracts.*

CAMERON, T. D. J., CROSBY, A., BALSON, P. S., JEFFERY, D. H., LOTT, G. K., BULAT, J. & HARRISON, D. J. 1992. *United Kingdom offshore regional report: the geology of the southern North Sea.* London: HMSO for the British Geological Survey.

CARTWRIGHT, J. A. 1994. Episodic basin-wide hydrofracturing of overpressured Early Cenozoic mudrock sequences in the North Sea Basin. *Marine and Petroleum Geology*, **11**, 587–607.

—— & LONERGAN, L. 1996. Volumetric contraction during the compaction of mudrocks: a mechanism for the development of regional-scale polygonal fault systems. *Basin Research*, **8**, 183–193.

GERSZTENKORN, A. & MARFURT, K. J. 1996. Coherence computations with Eigenstructure. *58th EAGE Conference, Geophysical Division, Expanded Abstracts, X031.*

KANTOROWICZ, J. D., ANDREWS, I. J., DHANANI, S., GILLIS, M., JENNINGS, C., LUMSDEN, P. J., ORR, G., SIMM, R. W. & WILLIAMS, J. 1999. Innovation and risk management in a small subsea-tieback: Arkwright Field, Central North Sea, UK. *In*: FLEET, A. J. & BOLDY, S. A. R. (eds) *Petroleum Geology of Northwest Europe: Proceedings of the 5th Conference.* Geological Society, London, 1125–1134.

KNOX, R. W. O'B. & HOLLOWAY, S. 1992. Paleogene of the Central and Northern North Sea. *In*: KNOX, R. W. O'B. & CORDEY, W. G. (eds) *Lithostratigraphic Nomenclature of the UK North Sea.* British Geological Survey, Nottingham.

LEVEILLE, G. P., KNIPE, R., MORE, C., ELLIS, D., DUDLEY, G., JONES, G., FISHER, Q. J. & ALLINSON, G. 1997. Compartmentalisation of Rotliegendes gas reservoirs by sealing faults, Jupiter Fields area, Southern North Sea. *In*: ZIEGLER, K., TURNER, P. & DAINES, S. R. (eds) *Petroleum Geology of the Southern North Sea: Future Potential.* Geological Society, London, Special Publications, **123**, 87–104.

MARFURT, K. J., KIRLIN, R. L., FARMER, S. L. & BAHORICH, M. S. 1995. 3-D seismic attributes using a running window multitrace coherency algorithm. *65th Annual International Meeting, Society Exploration Geophysics, Expanded Abstracts.*

PENGE, J., TAYLOR, B., HUCKERBY, J. A., & MUNNS, J. W. 1993. *Extension and salt tectonics in the East Central Graben. In*: PARKER, J. R. (ed.) *Petroleum Geology of Northwest Europe: Proceedings of the 4th Conference.* Geological Society, London, 1197–1209.

——, ——, MUNNS, J. W. & WINDLE, T. M. F. 1999. Rift-raft tectonics: examples of gravitational tectonics from the Zechstein basins of Northwest Europe. *In*: FLEET, A. J. & BOLDY, S. A. R. (eds) *Petroleum Geology of Northwest Europe: Proceedings of the 5th Conference.* Geology Society, London, 201–214.

ROBERTS, G. A., ROBERTS, R. E., HUGHES, M. J. & MARFURT, K. J. 1996. Structural imaging using the Coherency Cube: A SNS Example. *PETEX 96 Conference Proceedings, A4.*

SIBSON, R. H., MOORE, M. C. M. & RANKIN, A. H. 1975. Seismic pumping – a hydrothermal fluid transport mechanism. *Journal of the Geolgical Society, London*, **131**, 653–659.

Chapter 20

Shallow hazard detection in the near surface, a coherence cube processing application

BRIAN RADER, Samedan Oil Corporation, Houston, Texas, U.S.
EVELYN MEDVIN, Core Laboratories, Houston, Texas, U.S.

Interpreting the depositional style of deepwater sediments requires high-resolution seismic data. Enhancement of the seismic volume through specialized processing and interpretation methods can greatly improve the usability of exploration and production 3D volumes for shallow drilling hazard detection. Coherence cube processing provides a highly innovative and accurate method for clearly imaging subsurface faults and stratigraphy recorded in 3D surveys. The application of this technology to traditional 3D seismic surveys is key to detecting shallow hazards in deepwater areas where traditional methods are costly or inadequate.

Shallow drilling hazards exist as shallow gas pockets, gas chimney features, pockmarks on the seafloor caused by fluid withdrawal, near-surface faults, and shallow-water flow sands (SWF). SWF are the most difficult to detect and most dangerous in the deepwater environment. Studies have shown that nearly 80% of deepwater wells in the Gulf of Mexico have encountered SWF. Brian Barley of BP commented: "Our failure to predict shallow flowing sands reliably is an expensive gap in the tool kit" (*TLE*, 1999).

Drilling hazards also affect the positioning of platform anchors, field development, processing facilities and the placement of pipelines. Focused geohazard surveys required by the U.S. Minerals Management Service (MMS) may be inadequate for assessing hazards that can negatively affect a deepwater discovery. Kerry Campbell analyzed this problem in a 1999 *TLE* article and concluded, "Clearly, the most reliable technical approach to minimize geohazards risk would be to use 3D exploration seismic data for a preliminary geohazard assessment...."

Applying specialized processing techniques to enhance conventional 3D seismic data is a logical approach to minimizing geohazard risks. We have found that coherence cube processing applied to conventional seismic data is particularly useful in identifying near-surface depositional patterns that can impact well placement without requiring acquisition of additional data.

Coherence cube processing is the measurement of local waveform similarities within a 3D seismic data set. Variations in waveform represent the lateral and vertical changes of geology in the rock volume imaged by 3D seismic data. These waveform variations are computed within a 3D global aperture that is defined in space and time. The dip and azimuth of a particular data set are important variables that are utilized in the definition of the processing parameters for each project.

By computing seismic wavelet variations, the coherence cube focuses on the subtle changes that have been recorded and preserved in traditional processing sequence. These subtle changes compare the relative waveform similarity rather than the amplitude variations traditionally mapped. By looking within and beyond the amplitude, the interpreter can define the structural and stratigraphic subtleties contained within the data more accurately and in less time.

Figure 1 shows two time windows of a relatively flat data set. The data in the upper part are characterized by a highly stable waveform that will produce a high coherence event on a time slice. Geologically, events such as this represent slow deposition, hiatus events, or possibly an onlapping sequence. Most time structure and amplitude maps are generated on these "good" seismic reflectors as interpreters can utilize autotracking techniques. However, most geophysicists, geologists, and reservoir engineers are more interested in seeing maps of the rapidly changing waveform events depicted in the lower image of Figure 1. Rapidly changing waveforms are characteristic of rapid sedimentation and lateral variations in the geology. These zones are more difficult to map, due to the highly varying nature of the seismic signal, and mapping them is quite tedious when using in-line and cross-line mapping techniques. Time slices from coherence cube volumes, however, will reveal the depositional nature of this type of seismic signal and provide the interpretation team with a paleogeomorphologic map of the depositional system (Figure 2).

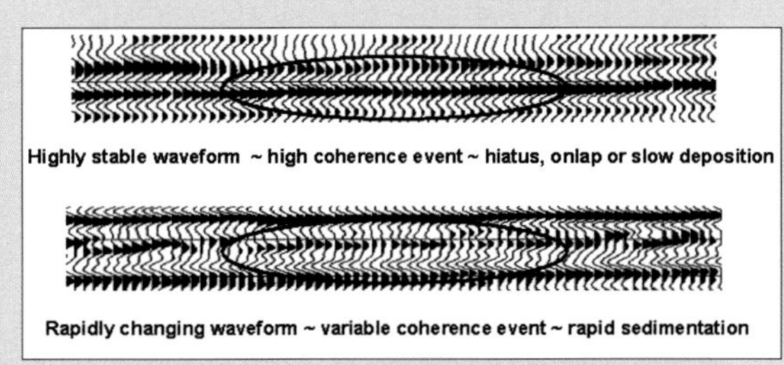

Figure 1. The top image shows a highly stable waveform that will result in high coherence values. The lower image shows a rapidly changing waveform that will result in highly varying coherence values (as shown in Figure 2).

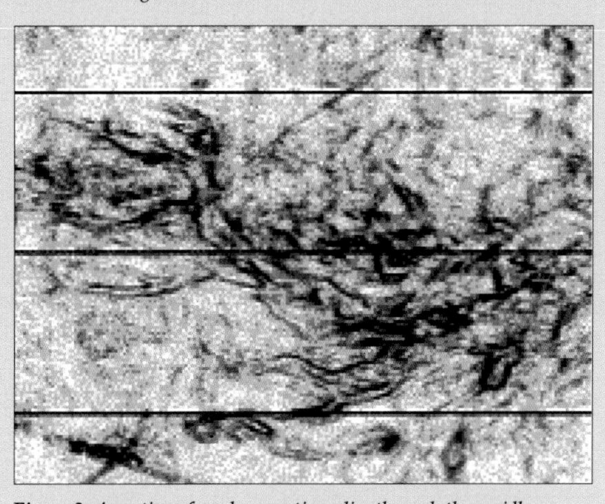

Figure 2. A portion of a coherence time slice through the rapidly changing waveform in the lower part of Figure 1. This is a dendritic channel system. White = areas of high coherence, homogeneous waveform. Black = low coherence values at channel edges where a sudden change in waveform occurs.

Examples. Coherence cube processing is typically done by oil and gas companies to evaluate the structural and strati-

Editor's note: Coherence Cube processing is protected under U.S. patents and is a mark of Core Laboratories.

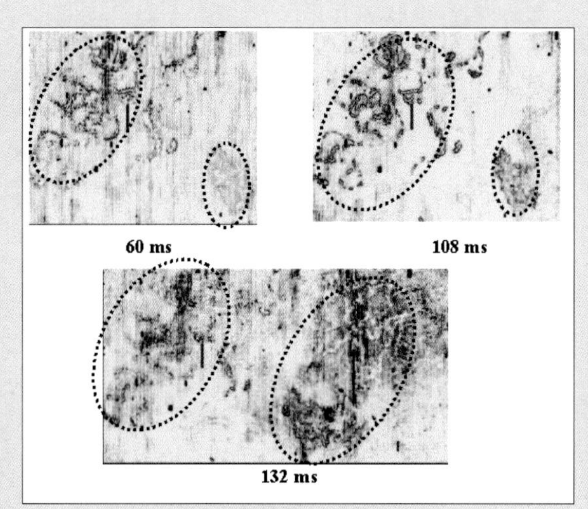

Figure 3. Evidence that multiple coherence cube time slices can reveal shallow channel features. Dark colors = low coherence edges of features where waveforms change suddenly. The ability to identify these channel features is a first step in the analysis of their potential as drilling hazards.

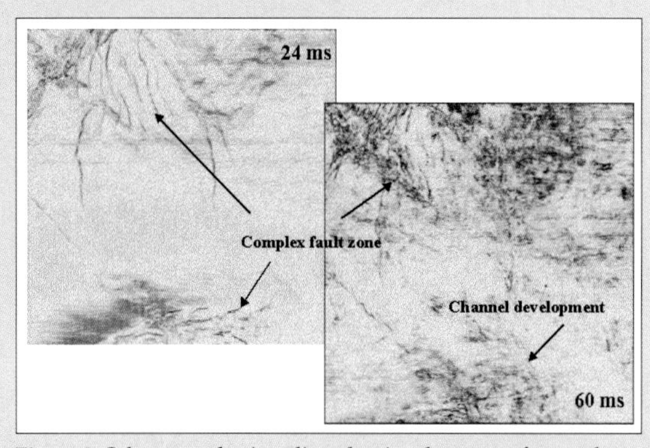

Figure 4. Coherence cube time slices showing the extent of a complex fault system at the seafloor. Black lineations = fault trace where the waveform changed rapidly from one side of the fault to the other. These faults indicate areas of instability and potential geohazards for drilling or deepwater operations. (Data courtesy of Geophysical Pursuit.)

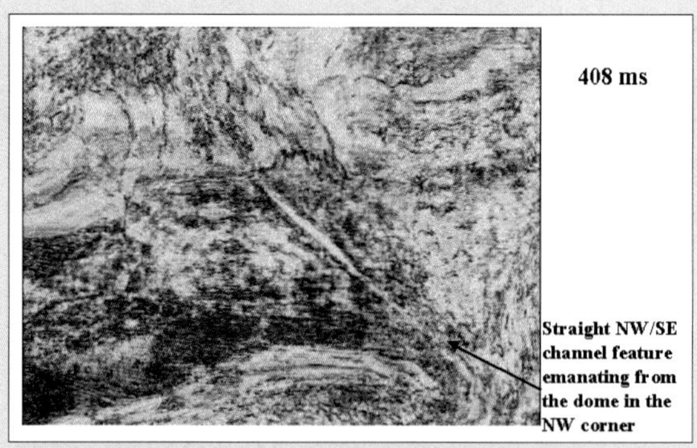

Figure 5. The scour feature in the center probably indicates SWF. The straight nature of the channel indicates that it was formed by high velocity event. Is it still an active conduit? (Data courtesy of Geophysical Pursuit.)

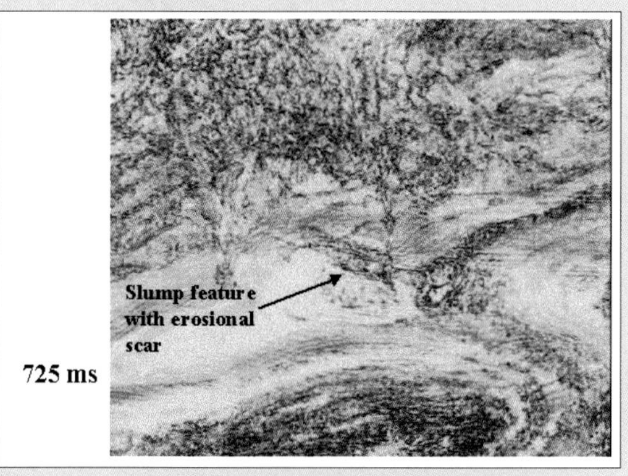

Figure 6. The channelized area with varying b/w pattern shows a slump feature. A fault or erosional escarpment emanating from the salt dome to the north subsequently cut the slump. (Data courtesy of Geophysical Pursuit.)

graphic details of their drilling objectives. As a standard practice the coherence volume is generated for the entire time or depth column, including the very shallow zone. Too often, interpreters do not analyze the shallow section of the data and the significant geohazard assessment value of the exploration data is unrecognized (Figure 3). Some companies have, however, utilized this valuable tool as part of their geohazard assessment program. In fact, movies of coherence cube time slices have been shown to the MMS as part of the site appraisal process.

Samedan Oil has successfully applied coherence cube processing for shallow hazard detection and gaining drill site approval from the MMS. The company found that the coherence cube processing on "spectrally whitened" 3D seismic data (1) provides finer resolution of channels, chaotic areas, and faults; (2) can be combined with amplitude values to show bright areas within coherent zones that could be indicative of shallow gas; and (3) assists in the fine-tuning of the final drilling location.

Viewing the time slices in a movie mode gives information about the stratigraphic layering and sediment deposition (Figure 3). Slow depositional rates produce a more continuous reflector shown as a high coherence zone. Rapid deposition typically produces a chaotic or low coherence pattern. Rapid deposition can pose a hazard because sand prone sections rapidly buried can exceed the ability of the sediments to dewater to normal hydrostatic pressures. These trapped overpressure zones can cause SWF problems when drilled through in the uphole section of the well. Several wells and even a platform location have been lost due to SWFs.

Coherence cube time or horizon slices can illustrate the depositional sequence patterns that can result in these overpressured zones. Channels and debris flows are resolved clearly by the coherence processing. SWF interpretation requires the identification of these sand-prone intervals that have been covered by a low permeability seal of clays and shales. The clay depositional sequence is sometimes represented as a condensed section with a high, continuous seismic reflector (high coherence response). The sand-prone to clay sequence can be seen on successive coherence cube time slices. If this sediment package is then buried too rapidly, the clay seal reduces the ability of the underlying sediments to dewater (to normal hydrostatic pressure) when loaded by this sediment overburden. This zone of overpressure, when penetrated, could enter the well bore and make the well difficult to control.

The coherence cube resolution can help identify uphole chaotic (low coherence) zones that represent sequences that may contain shallow flow hazards. Areas of potential SWF can vary in size and may require moving a drilling location away from the best location for the primary target. The well could be moved or drilled directionally at a higher cost, but both cases are preferred over losing a well to shallow hazards. Additional interpretation of coherence cube slices can help identify potential pressure-release mechanisms in the area of interest. Near-surface faults cutting through the suspected overpressure section and seafloor expression of expulsion features (mud mounds) may indicate that the overpressure may have been reduced through this venting mechanism.

In areas of undocumented shallow flow hazards, possible overpressure zones can be identified. The drilling engineer can then plan the well casing program and mud weights necessary to drill through this section. Geoscientists working in conjunction with the engineer can optimize the well location, target point, and well design to minimize costs.

The usefulness of the coherence cube does not end with the exploratory well. Following a discovery, the shallow information from the coherence cube can be used to determine any near-surface problems that would affect the installation of production facilities. Anchors or platform leg locations can be evaluated for subsurface features such as channels and faults that would impact the stability of the structure. Additionally, the pipeline route can also be evaluated to avoid any potential surface or near-surface features that might jeopardize the integrity of the pipeline. Any near-surface faults, active mud mounds, or potential slumps that could cause movement and damage the pipeline could be avoided and the flow line diverted around the shallow hazards.

Figures 4-6 show several coherence cube time slices extracted from a volume prepared for the Samedan MMS presentation. The data set was flattened on the water-bottom reflector to remove the dip effects in the shallow section. The first 800 ms of the data set was analyzed to understand where potential hazards exist, what changes to the surface well location were required, and what impact these changes would have on the primary objective. Additionally, the shallow zone was studied to investigate what drilling precautions were necessary to ensure that the well could be controlled during drilling. These data were also reviewed for potential pipeline routes in the event of a discovery.

Conclusions. Utilizing exploration 3D seismic data volumes enhanced with coherence cube processing can add value to existing seismic data and provide tools necessary for detecting shallow drilling hazards. As Samedan's Offshore Division discovered, coherence cube processing on the conventional seismic data has proved particularly useful in identifying near-surface depositional patterns that can impact well placement. Beyond fine-tuning specific well locations, this processing and interpretation methodology can positively impact development plans, safety, and commercialization efforts.

Suggested reading. "3-D seismic discontinuity for faults and stratigraphic features: The coherence cube" by Bahorich and Farmer (*TLE*, 1995). "Coherence cube reveals stratigraphic features more readily than traditional 3D time slice plots" by George (*Offshore*, 1996). "Interpretation of coherence cube processing in the 3D workspace" by Medvin et al. (GCAGS *Transactions*, 1999). "Revealing the geology of the Gulf of Mexico recorded by 3D seismic" by Maione (1999 OTC). "Deepwater problems around the world" by Barley (*TLE*, 1999). "'Deepwater geohazards: How significant are they?" by Campbell (*TLE*, 1999). "Application of coherence cube processing to shallow hazard detection in the near surface" by Medvin and Rader (*Geotechnical, Geological, and Geophysical Properties of Deepwater Sediments*, Proceeding of OTRC 2001 International Conference). TLE

Acknowledgments: We thank Geophysical Pursuit for permission to show seismic data and Kerry Campbell for numerous discussions on geohazards and seismic data. The authors thank Samedan Oil and Core Laboratories for support of this work.

Corresponding author: BRader@nobleenergyinc.com

Epilogue

Throughout the history of oil exploration and exploitation, no oil field is ever truly abandoned. Armed with new geologic-play concepts, production tools, and geophysical-imaging techniques, geoscientists and engineers continue to breathe new life into old oil fields. Although we would like to find an overlooked structural elephant to enrich our portfolio, many of us are looking for stratigraphic hydrocarbon traps in emerging or semimature basins, some in deepwater settings. Seismic attributes have a very significant role to play in that area.

Early humans lived contentedly without houses, without electric power, and without all the basic amenities we are used to today. But through the ages, there has been an ongoing evolution for the betterment of mankind, and we are sure many people questioned some of those advancements. Likewise, some older geoscientists, set in their ways of doing interpretation with a traditional mind-set, sometimes question the use of seismic attributes in modern seismic-data interpretation, thinking of them as mere colorful displays generated to convince management.

In truth, those older geoscientists are correct; a good attribute will attempt to reproduce what a seasoned interpreter would choose to map by using more traditional techniques. However, the time an interpreter would take to do specific tasks can be reduced drastically with the use of seismic attributes. Attributes can aid in the quantitative mapping of conventional features and can extract subtle but very important information not easily discerned in original data. Seismic attributes facilitate recognition of depositional environments, enhance recognition of seismic facies and, when calibrated by well control, help predict lithology, porosity, and fluid content.

Finally, with an understanding of the physical basis of attributes, coupled with the attribute expression of structural and stratigraphic features discussed in this book, we hope that younger, less experienced geoscientists can emulate the pattern-recognition interpretation techniques of those who have preceded them.

In this book, we have focused on attributes that are most useful in mapping lateral and vertical changes in structure and stratigraphy. From those, a good geoscientist armed with an appropriate geologic model can infer areas of potential hydrocarbon accumulation. We have made a sincere effort to compile current available information in terms of theory, practice, and experience on seismic attributes in a simple and concise way and to capture current interpretation workflows and best practices. This compilation should help the geophysicist to be aware of available seismic-attribute options, which definitely are going to increase in the coming years.

Once a reservoir-characterization problem is identified, we geoscientists should be able to select and combine attributes that can better delineate features of interest. Rather than applying "mindless interpretation," the interpreter will chose only attributes sensitive to the geologic hypothesis to be tested.

In contrast, we have not addressed attributes that are more sensitive to direct hydrocarbon detection and quantitative reservoir characterization such as AVO and impedance inversion. Since their introduction in the 1970s, seismic attributes have become popular analytic tools for lithology prediction and reservoir characterization — for example, a search of SEG's "Digital Cumulative Index" for the term *seismic attribute* furnishes several hundred publications on the subject. The quantitative use of those attributes requires an excellent understanding of petrophysics and can be facilitated greatly by modern tools of multivariate statistical analysis, geostatistics, and neural networks.

Other attributes useful in predicting pore pressure and anisotropy are under rapid development. Attributes based on time-lapse seismic and multicomponent surveys are in their infancy. A great deal of progress has been made since we completed our draft of this book in late 2005. If this book is accepted by the readership, we fully expect to revisit these areas in a second edition.

One often hears, "The larger the island of knowledge, the longer the shoreline of wonder." With the proliferation of seismic attributes that we have witnessed in the last two decades and their practical applications being reported in the last few years, it is quite evident that seismic attributes are on their way to a great future, enabling interpreters to continue to extract more and more information from seismic data.

Glossary of Technical Terms

Definitions are taken from references cited elsewhere in this book, in addition to Robert E. Sheriff's *Encyclopedic Dictionary of Applied Geophysics*, published by SEG.

analytic trace: A complex trace composed of the real trace, $d(t)$, and its Hilbert-transformed (or quadrature, imaginary) component, $d^H(t)$, given by the formula $a(t) = d(t) + id^H(t)$, where $i = \sqrt{-1}$.

angular unconformity: A change in reflector dip and azimuth across a horizon, typically associated with erosion.

antithetic faults: A secondary fault usually associated with a set of faults in an extensional regime whose sense of displacement is opposite to its associated major faults. In normal fault systems, most faults commonly dip in the same direction, but antithetic faults dip in the opposite direction.

apparent dip: The component of the dip vector projected along a given axis (in this book, typically along the inline and crossline axes of seismic acquisition).

artificial neural networks (ANN): An algorithm that can analyze and classify shapes using a discriminating and iterative process that replicates human brain mechanisms. Also known as *artificial intelligence.*

attributes: See *seismic attributes.*

bandwidth: The differences between half-power points, i.e., the frequencies at which the power drops to half the peak power (3 dB).

basis functions: Algorithms that form the basis for approximate methods used in numerical modeling for interpolating, approximating a function, or numerical integration. The functions may be polynomials, splines, trigonometric functions, sinc functions, etc.

binary image: The overall goal of image processing and analysis is the identification of features in data. This often results in a new data volume with voxels labeled in one of only two ways — feature or nonfeature. This kind of image data is referred to as *binary.*

body: The subarea of the image/volume identified as a region of interest. In exploration, commonly called a *geobody.*

breccia: A clastic sedimentary rock formed similarly to a conglomerate but with rock fragments that are sharp and angular, set in a fine-grained matrix formed from fine sand or silt and cemented by silica or calcite. The comprising rock fragments have not been transported long enough by water or wind to be rounded off.

bright spot: A zone in the seismic data that has anomalously strong amplitude. For gas plays in a Tertiary siliciclastic basin, bright spots typically have strong negative amplitudes.

chair diagram: A visualization display technique that combines a time slice through the data (forming the seat of the chair) with two vertical slices (forming the front and back of the chair). Chair diagrams allow us to follow a vertical discontinuity such as a fault from one seismic line to another via the seismic time slice.

chimney: A region of low-concentration gas escaping and migrating upward from a hydrocarbon accumulation. Gas chimneys appear as low-amplitude, chaotic zones on conventionally imaged seismic data.

classification: The organization of data into groups that represent a specific property.

clustering: Organization of seismic attributes into a discrete number of groups that have similar properties. Synonymous with *segmentation.*

CMYK: A color model defined in terms of cyan, magenta, yellow, and black, generally used in generating hard-copy images.

coherence: A measure of seismic waveform similarity, most commonly through crosscorrelation, semblance, and principal component algorithms.

compaction: See *differential compaction.*

complex trace: See *analytic trace.*

complex-trace attributes: Time/frequency attributes obtained from the complex or analytic seismic trace (the original data and its Hilbert transform).

composite image: A seismic image created from two separate input images using simple Boolean logic. For example, we might choose to plot amplitude against a color scale if the value falls within a given user-defined range, and we might plot coherence using grayscale if they do not.

connectivity: The rule applied to decide whether two voxels are touching. A voxel is considered to be a cube, with six faces, 12 edges, and eight corners. The two rules implemented are commonly either six-way, in which a voxel is connected to another if they share a face, or 26-way, in which a voxel is connected to another if they share a face, edge, or corner. See *geobody.*

continuous wavelet transform (CWT): The result of running-window crosscorrelation of a suite of wavelet-basis functions against a seismic signal. See *Morlet wavelets.*

contourites: Depositional features typically contoured by deepwater currents, ranging from those that build up individually distinct bodies (mounded drifts) to those that occur closely interbedded with other deepwater facies.

contrast: A gray-level co-occurrence matrix measure given by $\sum_i \sum_j (i-j)^2 P_{ij}$, where P_{ij} are the components of the gray-level co-occurrence matrix. Contrast is a measure of local variation in an image.

covariance matrix: A statistical measure of data or attribute variability between separate vectors (measures between different populations or between a suite of attributes at different spatial locations) about their means. The *ij*th component of the sample covariance matrix containing K samples is $C_{ij} = (1/K)\sum_k [(a^i_k - a^i_{mean})(a^j_k - a^j_{mean})]$.

crossline: The axis perpendicular to the inline direction of shooting. Sometimes the inline direction may be assigned arbitrarily.

crossline dip: The component of dip along the azimuth, ψ, of the crossline axis measured clockwise from north. If $|s|$ is the dip magnitude, then $s_{crossline} = |s| cos(X)$.

crossplot: A plot of attribute value pairs (triplets, quartets, etc.), with the range of each attribute plotted against a different axis.

curvedness: A measure of the total deformation of a horizon given by $c = \frac{1}{2}(k_{min}^2 + k_{max}^2)^{1/2}$, where k_{min} and k_{max} are the minimum and maximum curvatures.

CWT: See *continuous wavelet transform.*

debrite: See *mass-transport complex.*

depositional facies: A general descriptive terminology that is a function of lithologic and morphological texture formed in a specific depositional environment, at a specific location, in a specific time as a depositional system evolves.

depth slice: Extraction of values from a seismic or attribute volume corresponding to a constant depth value, z.

dewatering: The process of driving water out of muds and shales. See *syneresis.*

DFT: See *discrete Fourier transform.*

diapirism: A process in which a relatively mobile rock mass intrudes into preexisting overlying strata. Driving forces include density differences and differential loading of shallower sediments. Shales, evaporitic salt deposits, and gas-charged muds often form diapirs. Intrusion of diapirs usually takes place vertically upward.

differential compaction: A geologic process whereby laterally varying lithology undergoes different mechanical compaction, dewatering, or diagenesis, giving rise to a structural shape or thickness not seen when the sediments originally were deposited. Zones of weakness may occur near those transition zones, giving rise to faults and gas-charged chimneys. Differential compaction is common above channels and carbonate buildups.

diffraction: Seismic energy scattered from a laterally variable discontinuity in impedance and/or thickness, such as a fault, channel edge, or karst.

diffractor: A geologic feature giving rise to a diffraction.

dip azimuth: The azimuth of the dip vector, $\theta = tan^{-1}(s_y/s_x)$, where s_x and s_y are the *x*- and *y*- (east and north) components of dip.

dip curvature: The component of curvature projected along the direction of reflector dip azimuth.

dip magnitude: The magnitude of the dip vector, $|s| = (s_x^2+s_y^2)^{1/2}$, where s_x and s_y are the *x*- and *y*- (east and north) components of dip.

discrete Fourier transform (DFT): The result of crosscorrelating sines and cosines with a seismic wavelet.

edge-preserving filtering: A process that minimizes noise along a seismic reflector but preserves discrete reflector discontinuities. Edge-preserving smoothing, in which a mean filter is used away from discontinuities, is one type of edge-preserving filtering. If the smoothing follows reflector strike and dip, we obtain a structure-oriented, edge-preserving filter.

eigenstructure: The process by which a matrix is broken into eigenvalue-eigenvector pairs. Eigenstructure coherence is determined by computing all eigenvalues of a covariance matrix computed by crosscorrelating adjacent traces and then taking the ratio of the largest eigenvalue to the sum of all other eigenvalues. Also called *principal-component analysis.*

en echelon faults: Subparallel offset faults.

energy: A gray-level co-occurrence matrix measure given by $\sum_i \sum_j P_{ij}^2$, where P_{ij} are the components of the gray-level co-occurrence matrix. Energy is a measure of textural uniformity of an image.

entropy: A gray-level co-occurrence matrix measure given by $\sum_i \sum_j P_{ij} \log P_{ij}$, where P_{ij} are the components of the gray-level co-occurrence matrix. Entropy represents the degree of disorder of a system and thus is a measure of complexity of any image.

envelope: The magnitude of the complex (or analytic) trace. Also called *reflection strength.*

facies: See *depositional facies* or *seismic facies.*

fast Fourier transform (FFT): A minimally sampled, orthogonal, discrete Fourier transform that exploits common terms to provide computation speeds on the order of $N\log_r N$ rather than N^2 for a conventional DFT when applied to a seismic signal of length *N.*

FFT: See *fast Fourier transform.*

flexure: A term that defines a simple lateral change in dip magnitude and/or dip azimuth of a horizon.

folds: A term that refers to the original rock formation surfaces which have become bent or curved through either elastic or plastic deformation.

formation attributes: Seismic properties or attributes that represent information between two horizons. Internal velocity and attenuation also can be considered formation attributes.

frequency: Number of cycles per second (Hz).

Fresnel zone: Zone illuminated by the same positive or negative lobe of a seismic wavelet along a reflector.

gas chimney: A region of low-concentration gas escaping and migrating upward from a hydrocarbon accumulation. The presence of gas causes seismic scattering, attenuation, and decrease in velocity, all of which contribute to a vertical zone of incoherent seismic energy.

Gaussian curvature: The product of the principal curvatures $k_{\text{Gauss}}=k_1 k_2$.

general attributes: Attributes that have a direct correlation to physics and/or geometry of the subsurface. For example, the magnitude of the trace envelope is proportional to acoustic impedance contrast, and frequencies relate to bed thickness, wave scattering, and absorption. Instantaneous and average velocities relate directly to rock properties. Dip/azimuth measures the attitude of a reflector in 3D space. In contrast to specific attributes, general attributes have wide application and can be calibrated to geology through an understanding of the underlying physics.

geobody: A collection of connected voxels that have similar attributes, such as an acoustic impedance that falls between a user-defined minimum and maximum. Geobodies can be used to compute volumetrics directly.

geologic hazard: Any natural phenomena that can negatively impact drilling operations, subsurface installations, environment, historical artifacts, and above all, human safety.

geometric attributes: Multitrace attributes that measure changes in reflector shape or morphology. Examples include coherence, dip/azimuth, energy gradients, and curvature.

geomorphology: See *seismic geomorphology.*

GLCM: See *gray-level co-occurrence matrix.*

glide track: The depression formed by an outrunner block as it moves downslope over soft sediment.

gradient structure tensor (GST): A statistical (spatially and temporally averaged) measure of lateral and vertical change in seismic amplitude (or other attribute) that is amenable to subsequent eigenstructure analysis to determine the values and axes of data similarity. Specifically, the GST can be used to estimate reflector dip/azimuth, coherence, lineations, and (when applied to coherence or other edge detectors) fault-plane dip/azimuth.

gray-level co-occurrence matrix (GLCM): A method of evaluating intertrace and intratrace amplitude variation. First, each neighboring voxel is compared to the voxel at the center of an analysis window. A robust estimate of the GLCM is obtained by averaging those changes over a suite of analysis windows that represents the same texture. Sometimes called *voxel co-occurrence matrix* (VCM). See *energy, entropy, homogeneity,* and *contrast.*

halokinesis: The process of salt deformation in sedimentary basins.

HAR: High-amplitude reflection. This descriptive term is used by the seismic-geomorphology community to define strong reflections that may arise because of gas charge, hydrates, or sands.

heliocoidal deformation: A term used to describe the helical rotation of faults in a weaker sedimentary layer that often are associated with strike-slip faults in the more rigid basement.

Hilbert transform: A process that creates a new quadrature, or imaginary, trace by rotating each frequency component of the input (real) seismic trace by 90°. Along with the real trace, the Hilbert-transformed trace forms the basis of complex-trace analysis.

HLS: An abstract color model defined in terms of hue, lightness, and saturation. Although more directly tied to human perception and attributes, HLS colors must be converted to RGB (generally for screen images) or to CMYK (generally for hard-copy images). See also *RGB, CMYK, hue, lightness,* and *saturation.*

Holder exponent: A measure of seismic amplitudes as a function of wavelet scale, used to measure discontinuities in spectra.

homogeneity: A gray-level co-occurrence matrix measure given by $\sum_i \sum_j \frac{1}{1+(i-j)^2} P_{ij}$, where P_{ij} are the components of the gray-level co-occurrence matrix. Homogeneity is a measure of the overall smoothness of an image.

horizon slice: Extraction of values from a seismic or attribute volume corresponding to an interpreter-provided horizon.

Hough transform: An image-processing technique that expresses linear features seen in x-y Cartesian coordinates as intensity images in ρ-θ polar coordinates.

hue: A measure of color wavelength. Hue always is defined in a cyclical pattern measured in degrees. In this book, blue = 0°, magenta = 60°, red = 120°, yellow = 180°, green = 240°, cyan = 300°, and blue (once again) = 360°.

image analysis: Extracting either quantitative or qualitative information from an image/volume; for example, making measurements on bodies.

image processing: Operations on an image/volume which result in another image/volume. For example, image-processing operations might include defect correction (noise removal); image enhancement, including data rescaling or highlighting; segmentation (identifying a range of voxel values that separate features of interest); and binary image manipulation.

incised valley: A feature that has been downcut or entrenched into the surface during rejuvenation of channel flow or relative uplift of the surface.

inline: For marine streamer data, the axis parallel to the direction of shooting. For land data and ocean-bottom seismometer or cable data, the inline direction might be assigned arbitrarily and is used mainly as a means of referencing the data grid.

inline dip: The component of dip along the azimuth, ψ, measured from north of the inline axis, $s_{inline} = |s|cos(\psi)$.

instantaneous attributes: Time-frequency attributes based on the real and quadrature components of the complex trace at each instant in time.

instantaneous frequency: The rate of change of instantaneous phase from one time sample to the next (first derivative of the phase).

instantaneous phase: The angle between the imaginary and real parts of the analytic trace when plotted in polar coordinates. Instantaneous phase enhances the continuity of events by ignoring the amplitude information in time samples. Instantaneous phase is expressed in degrees, usually from –180° (trough) through 0° (peak) to +180° (trough).

instantaneous spectral attributes (ISA): Spectral decomposition that fits a wavelet-basis function to the original seismic data using a matched-pursuit technique. Spectral decomposition then is obtained by summing the complex spectra of the fit wavelets.

ISA: See *instantaneous spectral attributes.*

karst: A geologic process wherein the dissolving action of water on limestone, dolomite, or marble formations results in different surface or subsurface features such as sinkholes, vertical shafts, complex underground drainage patterns, or caves.

keel marks: Deformation of the marine subsurface caused by scraping by the keel of current- or wind-driven icebergs. Also called *plow marks.*

k-means clustering: A clustering (segmentation) algorithm that divides an N-dimensional attribute space into k-user-defined clusters. Each cluster has a mean and standard deviation which can be used in subsequent Bayes' classification. A given attribute vector is assigned to the cluster whose mean is the minimum Mahalanobis distance away.

kriging: A gridding algorithm that estimates grid node values of a parameter of interest so that the squared difference between estimated values and control-point values fits the variogram model in a least-squares sense.

kriging with external drift (KED): Kriging that estimates grid values as the weighted average of control points (e.g., log data at a well) using guide data (e.g., seismic data).

Kuwahara filter: An image-processing technique whereby smoothed data is approximated by the mean of one of several windows that overlaps the analysis point — the window that has the minimum variance.

least-squares: A means of fitting a mathematical function or surface to data measurement points so that the squared distance from each point to the surface is minimized.

lightness: The level of color intensity, typically measured from 0.00 (black) through 0.25 (midnight colors), 0.50 (pure colors), and 0.75 (pastel colors), ending at 1.00 (white).

lineament: A broad term used to describe any curvilinear feature seen in outcrop or seismic data.

low-frequency shadow: A phenomenon in which spectral content of reflectors lying below a reservoir appears to have ananomously lower-frequency content.

Mahalanobis distance: A distance between a vector **x** and a cluster mean, m, given by $r^2 = (\mathbf{x} - m)\mathbf{C}^{-1}(\mathbf{x} - m)$, where **C** is the covariance matrix obtained by crosscorrelating each attribute with all other attributes and itself.

mass-transport complex (MTC): A term generally used to refer to mass-failure events, wherein sediments on the slopes and floors of deepwater basins give way, followed by their downdip deposition. MTCs comprise slides, slumps, and debris flows and are caused by sediment instability. Also called *debrites.*

matched pursuit: An algorithm designed to fit a seismic trace with a suite of basis functions using a user-defined criterion. A greedy matched-pursuit wavelet-decomposition algorithm is an iterative scheme that decomposes an input seismic trace by successively subtracting the wavelet that removes the most energy from the input trace.

maximum curvature: The signed value of the principal curvature, k_1 or k_2, that has the larger absolute value.

mean curvature: The mean of the principal curvatures, $k_{mean} = (k_1 + k_2)/2$.

meta-attribute: A linear or nonlinear combination of attributes, sometimes generated when fitting a suite of seismic attributes to a geologic measure of interest using numerical techniques such as artificial neural networks.

minimum curvature: The signed value of the principal curvature, k_1 or k_2, that has the smaller absolute value.

Morlet wavelets: Basis functions that consist of sines and cosines modulated by a Gaussian taper.

most-negative curvature: The minimum-signed curvature at any given point on a quadratic surface. Because $k_{neg} \leq k_{pos}$, a positive value for most-negative curvature, k_{neg}, indicates a dome shape. Unlike principal curvatures, most-positive and most-negative curvatures do not depend on vector dip.

most-positive curvature: The maximum-signed curvature at any given point on a quadratic surface. Because $k_{neg} \leq k_{pos}$, a negative value for most-positive curvature, k_{pos}, indicates a bowl shape. Unlike principal curvatures, most-positive and most-negative curvatures do not depend on vector dip.

MTC: See *mass-transport complex.*

multiattribute analysis: Using several seismic attributes for mapping reservoir rock properties, including distribution of lithofacies in subsurface reservoirs.

multispectral analysis: The process of examining more than one frequency- or wavenumber-filtered version of data.

offlap: The geometry of seismic reflections corresponding to a sequence of layers of sedimentary rock formed during an oceanward migration of the shoreline. Gently dipping younger strata terminate oceanward against more steeply dipping older strata.

onlap: The geometry of seismic reflections corresponding to a sequence of layers of sedimentary rock formed during a landward migration of the shoreline. Shallow-dipping younger strata terminate against more steeply dipping older strata.

outrunner block: A block of competent material that detaches from a scarp or slump and moves downdip, often leaving a glide track in its wake. Outrunner blocks may vary in size from tens of meters to a kilometer or more.

parasequence: A relatively conformable succession of genetically related beds bounded by flooding surfaces. One results from a small-scale relative sea-level rise and still-stand with little intervening fall, often with cyclicity of 100–150, 40, or 20 ka. A parasequence is terminated by another rise in sea level.

pattern recognition: Analysis of data to discover the combinations of different kinds of measurements or features that are distinctive of specific patterns or classes. Sometimes called *automatic identification of shapes and forms*.

peak amplitude: The maximum-seismic amplitude seen in a seismic-frequency spectrum.

peak frequency: The temporal frequency at which the seismic response is maximum.

peak phase: The phase of the peak-frequency component.

phantom horizon: A horizon that has not been picked physically but has been generated by mathematically manipulating one or two nearby more easily picked horizons. Because they do no contain independent time/structure information, phantom horizons usually are used in amplitude or attribute extractions. For example, we may find an easy-to-pick flooding surface or volcanic deposit that covers the area above a deeper-lying complicated fluvial deltaic system. Extractions made along a phantom horizon 50 ms below the picked flooding surface would exhibit lateral changes in channel reflectivity while removing most structural complexity.

pixel: The smallest discrete component of a 2D digital image.

plow marks: The gouges or ruts made in the seafloor by the keel (bottom) of an iceberg pushed by wind or currents. Also called *keel marks*.

pockmarks: Shallow circular indentations formed in the seafloor by fluid (usually gas) escaping from below.

principal components: For a suite of J sample vectors composed of N values each (such as a window of seismic traces or a list of attributes), the first principal component is the eigenvector that best represents all members of the suite in a least-squared sense. The percentage of the energy of the sample vectors represented by this vector is called the first eigenvalue. If we subtract the predicted data and form a residual, we can repeat the process and thereby determine the second principal component (eigenvector) and corresponding eigenvalue. Mathematically, the eigenvectors and eigenvalues can be calculated by forming a covariance matrix by crosscorrelating each data vector with itself and all the others.

principal curvatures: The minimum- (k_1) and maximum- (k_2) signed curvatures of a quadratic surface that have dip; k_1 and k_2 are always perpendicular to each other.

quadratic surface: A 3D surface that can be defined by the formula $z(x,y) = ax^2 + bxy + cy^2 + dx + ey + f$. In the limit, the quadratic surface can define domes, anticlines, saddles, synclines, and bowls as well as planar surfaces.

quadrature component: The Hilbert transform of the original seismic data (real) trace. Also called *imaginary component of the analytic (complex) trace*.

real component: The original seismic data itself, in contrast to the quadrature (or imaginary, Hilbert-transformed) component of the analytic (complex) trace.

reflection strength (envelope): A measure of reflection amplitude that is insensitive to phase.

reservoir characterization: Quantitative analysis of seismic data, well logs, and production data to produce a 3D understanding of porosity, thickness, permeability, lithology, fractures, and compartmentalization.

reservoir heterogeneities: Spatial variability in rock properties in a reservoir. These may be produced by geologic processes such as sedimentation, diagenesis, erosion, faulting, etc. Multiattribute analysis and geostatistical techniques usually are used to estimate heterogeneities by using well control, with seismic data guiding the analysis.

response attributes: Time-frequency attributes corresponding to the instantaneous attribute at the peak of the envelope in which each sample falls. Synonymous with *wavelet attributes*.

RGB: A color model defined in terms of red, green, and blue, generally used in generating screen images.

running window: A seismic-data analysis or filtering technique that produces an output sample value from a window of three or more input values centered about the output sample. The running window can be one dimensional, which is used in a 500-ms automatic gain control; two dimensional, which is used in smoothing a time-structure map; or three dimensional, which is used in estimation of coherence and dip/azimuth volumes.

saturation: The degree of tint applied to a color. Saturation ranges from 0.0 (gray) through 0.5 (dirty colors) to 1.0 (pure colors).

scan: A process of successively evaluating the likelihood of a given behavior of seismic data. In this book, the scan can be a velocity scan or a 2D-dip scan (dip and azimuth).

sediment waves and ridges: Geologic structures formed by submarine fluid flow, often associated with turbidites and contourites.

segmentation: Organization of data into clusters that have similar properties.

seismic attributes: A measurement derived from seismic data, usually based on measurements of time, amplitude, frequency, and/or attenuation. Lateral changes in those properties give rise to geometric attributes. Attributes are useful to the extent that they correlate with some physical property of interest. The primary usefulness of attributes is that they sometimes help one to see features, relationships, and patterns that otherwise might not be noticed.

seismic facies: The character of a group of reflections involving amplitudes, abundance, continuity, and configuration of reflections. A seismic feature or wiggle-trace pattern characterized by amplitude and intertrace and intratrace amplitude relationships at a specific location in seismic image space.

seismic facies map: A map representing the similarity of seismic traces or attributes within an analysis window to previously defined model traces or attributes that represent distinct waveform shapes or patterns.

seismic geomorphology: The use of seismic data to study subsurface sedimentary strata, including their origin, evolution, and the processes that shaped them. Good-quality 3D seismic data help in understanding the internal and external architecture of reservoirs and their depositional process features.

self-organized maps: An unsupervised computational method for visualization and analysis of high-dimensional data that produces maps of seismic traces and/or attributes that exhibit similar patterns.

semblance: A statistical measure of waveform similarity given by the ratio of the energy of the average data trace to the average energy of each data trace. Semblance is a workhorse of seismic data processing, used routinely in velocity estimation and filtering and in a semblance estimate of reflector discontinuities on migrated data volumes.

shaded relief: Seismic reflections represented as apparent topography. Such displays help in the geologic understanding of structural and stratigraphic details that otherwise are not obvious in seismic data.

shale-dewatering features: Vertically confined fractures seen in shales, caused by expulsion of water or by clay syneresis.

shape components: The probability of any point in a seismic data volume being a dome, ridge, saddle, valley, or bowl.

shape index: A measure between –1.0 and +1.0 that defines the likelihood of the quadratic surface being a dome, ridge, saddle, valley, or bowl.

sharpening filter: An image-processing technique that replaces the value of a 2D pixel (or 3D voxel) by the second-derivative Laplacian operator applied to neighboring pixels (or voxels).

short-window discrete Fourier transform (SWDFT): A discrete Fourier transform achieved by crosscorrelating the seismic data with sines and cosines within a tapered-analysis window. Typically, windows are moved incrementally to be sampled at every desired sample in the seismic data, so that adjacent windows overlap. In general, the SWDFT is a nonorthogonal transform.

special attributes: Attributes that have only a statistical correlation to properties and geometries of the subsurface. Although useful, special attributes require calibration for each formation and basin.

spectral decomposition: Decomposition of a temporal window of data into its Fourier magnitude and phase components.

specular reflection: Seismic scattering from a smoothly deformed surface, in contrast to diffractions, which consist of seismic scattering from lateral discontinuities.

SPICE (spectral analysis of correlative events): A commercial algorithm that maps vertical discontinuities in seismic waveforms by estimating the Holder exponent from spectral components.

stratal (strat) slice: A means of displaying seismic data along a surface that is proportionally equal between an upper- and lower-interpreted surface, mimicking surfaces that display a fixed geologic time.

strike curvature: Curvature projected along the direction of reflector strike.

structure-oriented filtering: Filters applied along an estimate of reflector dip and azimuth.

supervised segmentation (classification or **learning):** Classification based on controlled-input data (real or interpreter hypotheses).

SWDFT: See *short-window discrete Fourier transform*.

syneresis: Spontaneous volumetric contraction and concomitant fluid expulsion, giving rise to polygonal fractures in mud rocks.

texture: The repetitive pattern of local variations in image intensity, a feature used to partition images into regions of interest and to classify them. Commonly statistical measures such as co-occurrence matrices are used in 3D seismic data to compute different types of textures.

time slice: Extraction of values from a seismic or attribute volume corresponding to a constant time value, t.

time-lapse seismic: An experiment in which a seismic survey is reacquired over the same geographic area with the intent of mapping changes associated with fluid injection and/or production.

tracer: A chemical or radioactive substance that allows tracking of fluid flow through porous subsurface intervals. Substances that qualify as good tracers do not react with the formation, completion, or tubulars; have an insignificant concentration in reservoir fluids; exhibit minimum holdup in the reservoir; are stable under injection and production conditions; can be detected at extremely low concentrations; are environmentally safe; and have an acceptable price tag.

trace-shape classification: Assigning windows of seismic traces along an interpreted horizon to a small number of preselected waveforms that might come from a numerical or geologic model (such as sines and cosine, Chebyshev polynomials, or synthetics modeled from impedance logs) or from the data itself, most often based on preprocessing using self-organized maps (SOM).

unsupervised segmentation (classification or **learning):** Uncontrolled data clustering into groups that have similar properties.

variance: A statistical measure of data or attribute variability about the mean. The sample variance from K samples is $\sigma = (1/K)\sum_k (a_k - a_{mean})^2$. The variance cube is a coherence attribute which is mathematically equivalent to 1D semblance.

variograms: A mathematical tool used to quantify spatial correlation or continuity.

voxel: The smallest discrete spatial component of a 3D digital volume.

voxel filters: Image-processing operations applied over a neighborhood to produce an output value.

wavelet attributes: Time-frequency attributes corresponding to the instantaneous attribute at the peak of the envelope in which each sample falls. Synonymous with *response attributes*.

wavelet decomposition: Decomposition of a seismic trace into components by projecting it onto a suite of wavelet-basis functions. Common basis functions include Morlet and Ricker wavelets. A least-squares decomposition will allow reconstruction of the original seismic trace from the wavelet components.

wavelet-basis function: A suite of precomputed waveforms crosscorrelated with a seismic signal with the goal of filtering, spectral analysis, or data compression. Morlet and Ricker wavelets are commonly used wavelet-basis functions.

wavenumber: The number of cycles per meter (or foot), in contrast to temporal frequency, which measures the number of cycles per second (Hz).

Index

D

E